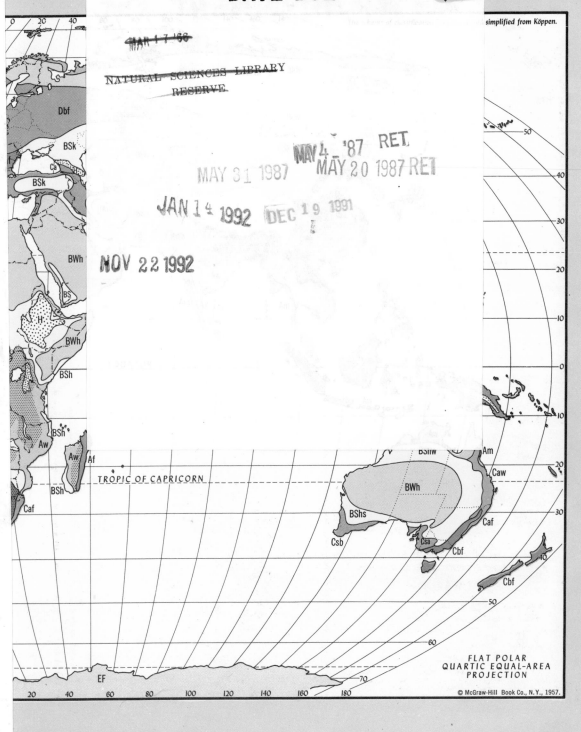

simplified from Köppen.

TROPIC OF CAPRICORN

FLAT POLAR
QUARTIC EQUAL-AREA
PROJECTION

© McGraw-Hill Book Co., N.Y., 1957.

Elements of Geography

McGRAW-HILL SERIES IN GEOGRAPHY

JOHN C. WEAVER, *Consulting Editor*

VERNOR C. FINCH was Consulting Editor of this series from its inception in 1934 to 1951.

Elements of Geography

PHYSICAL AND CULTURAL

VERNOR C. FINCH, *Professor Emeritus of Geography, University of Wisconsin*

GLENN T. TREWARTHA, *Professor of Geography, University of Wisconsin*

ARTHUR H. ROBINSON, *Professor of Geography, University of Wisconsin*

EDWIN H. HAMMOND, *Associate Professor of Geography, University of Wisconsin*

FOURTH EDITION

McGRAW-HILL BOOK COMPANY, INC.

NEW YORK   TORONTO   LONDON   1957

ELEMENTS OF GEOGRAPHY

Introductory Statement

Part 1. For the Instructor

The fourth edition of this book, like its predecessors, is designed to cover the major elements of geography in a form suitable for beginning courses in college geography. For those students who will have no further contact with formal geography the materials have been selected and organized so as to introduce them to the principal facts of geography and to show how these facts may be used to gain an understanding of the great variety that characterizes the earth's surface. The emphasis on geography's contribution to a general education is kept paramount. For the smaller group of students who will continue the study of geography, the book is planned to provide a substantial foundation upon which a more comprehensive superstructure may be built. It is intended to give to all students an intelligent understanding of the physical earth as the home of man, as well as the broad outlines of how the human animal has spread himself over the earth and utilized its natural resources and equipment. Needless to say, the authors have the conviction that the materials presented are of genuine value to the intelligent citizen endeavoring to exist in the modern world.

The selection of material has been made with a single objective: to describe and depict the major elements of geography and to interpret their distribution over the earth so that the student will come to have an understanding of the nature and origin of the larger world geographic patterns and their areal associations. The emphasis is upon *world* patterns rather than upon the unique characteristics of specific regions.

The book's plan is systematic or analytical in character, the individual geographic elements being treated separately. But although the elements are discussed individually, their regional associations and interrelationships are not neglected. The organization of the book is considered an essential part of the presentation. Following this Introduction, which is divided into two parts, one intended primarily for instructors and the other for students, there is a preliminary chapter which discusses the earth as a planet and the general nature and use of maps. The main body of the book has three principal parts: Part One analyzes the nature, origin, and distribution of the important elements of the physical or natural earth which comprise the human habitat. Part Two describes the distribution of mankind, or population, the principal utilizer of the earth resources treated in Part One and the agent responsible for the cultural elements described in Part Three. The cultural earth as treated in Part Three is thus the product of man's creation from the natural stuff. The book ends with a short Retrospect and Conclusion, followed by appendices which give additional climatic data, a treatment of map projections, a brief description of the systems of American land survey, and a selected list of United States topographic quadrangles. At the end of individual chapters or sections are suggested references which provide the instructor and student with supplementary reading materials. Chapter outlines and questions have been intentionally omitted, the authors feeling that, at the college level, these intended aids actually operate to weaken the learning and teaching processes.

The fourth edition of "Elements of Geography" is prompted by four considerations: the addition of two new authors, the rapid advancement of knowledge in some geographical subdivisions, the practical test of additional years of classroom use, and the kindly criticism of professional colleagues. Those sections which, in the earlier editions, were the work of Professor Finch have in this edition received the combined attention of Professors Robinson and Hammond, with the consequent revision in content and organization which new authorship naturally entails.

Section A1 of Part One, which covers the elements of climate, has undergone extensive revision in order to utilize the flood of new materials which has accompanied the rapid growth of atmospheric science during the postwar period. Section A2, dealing with types of climate, has been somewhat shortened and simplified, while at the same time greater emphasis has been given to explanations.

Section B, "Landforms and the Seas," has been modernized, shortened, and rearranged. A revised classification of terrain types provides the framework for the reorganization. Three new chapters have been added, *viz.*, "The Elements and Types of Terrain," "The Continental Margins and the Sea Floor," and "The Seas." The information which was formerly included in four chapters on "Plains" has been shortened and combined into a single chapter. The material on "Plateaus" has been replaced by a chapter entitled "Tablelands, and Plains with Hills and Mountains," in line with the revised classification of landforms. "Hills" and "Mountains," because of their basic similarity, have been combined into a single chapter.

Various degrees of revision have been applied to the chapters included in Section C, "Earth Resources." The material on "Water Resources" has been brought up to date and revised in accordance with the modern viewpoint on this topic. In the chapter on "The Biotic Resource" the classification of natural vegetation has been simplified, and much of the text on the earth's grasslands has been rewritten. There has been a general modernization and rearrangement of the material on "Soils," which has resulted in a thorough revision of those two chapters. A similar but less extensive procedure has been applied to the chapters dealing with mineral resources.

In the previous edition "Population" was included as a single chapter in Part Two, "The Cultural Elements of Geography." Actually, population is not a cultural element but is rather the originator of culture. Moreover, the deserved eminence of population in geography is not properly recognized by including it as merely one of several cultural elements. Since the authors believe that population has a unique and distinctive position which sets it apart from both the physical and the cultural elements, the present revision makes a threefold grouping of the geographic elements, *viz.*, (*a*) physical, (*b*) population, and (*c*) cultural. Under this new organization the treatment of population has been greatly expanded.

While all chapters in Part Three, "The Cultural Elements," have undergone modernization and revision, the rewriting has been less extensive than that which has been required in many other parts of the book.

The illustrations have received special attention in this revision. Many of the old illustrations have been redrawn to improve their clarity and accuracy. The inclusion of much new textual material has required the elimination of numerous old illustrations and the substitution of others which are more applicable. A completely new world base map, on a new interrupted equal-area projection, has been prepared and used for all the folded plates and for many of the world maps included in the text. All the color plates have been revised and redrawn.

The indebtedness of the authors for valuable suggestions, illustrations, and other kinds of aid extends in many directions and to many individuals. Their cordial cooperation is much appreciated. The sense of obligation for assistance received is particularly strong as it applies to the members of the geography staff at the University of Wisconsin.

Part 2. For the Student

The Content of Geography. It is not easy to formulate a short, simple, yet accurate definition of a field of knowledge. Still, a student who is about to begin a study of geography should inquire what he may look forward to, and what contribution such a study can make to his education. Geography focuses its attention upon the surface of the earth, a thin zone where the atmosphere meets the solid and liquid earth. Within this thin surficial zone life in its various forms exists. Here the organic and inorganic elements intermingle and interrelate, and from their combined patterns of distribution emerges the variety of the earth's surface.

Because of this variety a science of geography exists. If uniformity prevailed over the earth there would be no basis for geographic study. The face of the earth has its present character because its different features are variously arranged or distributed, and because the combinations of these features contrast from place to place. One thinks geographically, therefore, when he is concerned with the location of specific classes of earth features or with the associations of features which characterize particular parts of the earth's surface. How the various places on the face of the earth resemble or differ from one another is the very core of geography.

Because the distinctive character of any earth area is a composite of its various elements, geographical analysis normally proceeds through a systematic study of each of the individual elements. In summary, it may be said that location, distribution, arrangement, and association are concepts which, when applied to the things on the earth's surface, are at the heart of geographical study.

The Geographic Elements. It may be asked, "What, specifically, are the things on the face of the earth that a geographer studies?" To this, too, it is difficult to give an answer which is brief yet comprehensive, for it is true that regional similarities and differences arise from combinations of an almost unlimited number of features or elements. Some of these, such as terrain, mineral resources, factories, and fields, are material in nature and visually observable. Others, such as social traits and political institutions, are more abstract in character. Theoretically the things that vary from place to place over the surface of the earth are almost limitless. Actually, however, most geographers focus

their attention upon three great classes of interrelated earth features: (*a*) those provided by nature (among them climate, terrain features, surface and underground water, soils, economic minerals, and native plants and animals); (*b*) man or population, including numbers and characteristics; and (*c*) those features which man has added through living on the natural earth and using its resources (including settlements, farms, factories, mines, domesticated plants and animals, and transportation facilities).

To be sure, other fields of learning also deal with one or more of these same features, so that the distinctive nature of geography lies not so much in the particular features or elements studied, but rather in the way they are treated. Geographical method is exhibited in the analysis of the distributional aspects of the features on the face of the earth and the study of the combinations of these features within particular regions.

Since the earth's surface which is the focus of a geographer's attention is composed of interrelated features, some of natural origin and others associated with population and with the use of natural resources by man, it follows that geography belongs exclusively neither to the natural sciences nor to the social sciences. It has features of both, while still remaining a unified field of knowledge.

How the Materials Are Handled. Geography is a very old field of learning, for even the ancients were keenly aware of the differences between the parts of the then-known world. The early geographers were mainly concerned with describing what they could see of both natural and man-made features as these varied from region to region. Their descriptions were often accompanied by attempts to measure the extensiveness and boundaries of things and to record these measurements on maps. Inquisitiveness about the causes or origins of the surface phenomena and regional differences was not lacking in ancient and medieval man, and some of his speculations and hypotheses showed keen insight into causative processes. Nevertheless, the systematic study of the surface of the earth in terms of both its physical processes and the features resulting from these processes has been chiefly a development of the modern period. The modern geographer recognizes that while description and classification are an essential part of his work, an understanding of the basic processes underlying the irregular but patternful distribution of earth features is also fundamental to an explanation of the arrangement and association of things as they are.

An understanding of these processes emphasizes the fact that the earth's surface is constantly changing. Most of the processes have occurred in the past and will continue into the future, so that the geography of the present has evolved out of the past and is closely linked to that to come. We are observing the earth in only one instant of a very long time scale. Geography, then, is both *descriptive* and *explanatory* as it analyzes the face of the earth, and it views its subject matter as changing and dynamic rather than static and fixed.

The Map. The geographer, in his study of the distribution of a single element over the earth as a whole, or of several associated elements within a particular region, has the problem of trying to understand something which is far more extensive than his actual range of vision. This problem is exactly opposite to that commonly confronting the biologist, bacteriologist, or mineralogist, whose objects of analysis may be so tiny that the microscope is necessary in order to *enlarge* what the human eye desires to observe. On the other hand, the geographer usually needs to *reduce* in scale earth features which are of great areal extent and widespread in their distribution, so that their arrangements and combinations can be encompassed by the human eye. The geographer's method of reducing in size the whole or parts of the earth's surface is to represent the things to be studied on maps, from which may be discovered their areal, linear, and directional relationships. Maps, then,

with their variety of symbols, become a part of the technical language of geographers. Admittedly maps are used by workers in other fields of learning, social and natural, but not to the same extent or in the same variety as they are employed by geographers. They are literally the badge of the geographer's craft and when others use them they are, consciously or not, employing a geographic method. In using this book the student will become keenly aware of the extent to which, and the variety of ways in which, maps are used to study and portray the earth's features and regions.

The Present Book: Title, Content, and Organization. If the position is taken that geography is primarily concerned with a study of the earth's surface, it remains to be pointed out what particular contribution to that study this book is intended to make. It is an introduction to geography through a systematic study of the more important individual elements or features that together comprise the face of the earth. The title of the book suggests the content. It is not intended to be a general summary of geographic knowledge. On the contrary, the purpose is to acquaint the beginning student with the fundamentals of geography and to offer suggestions as to how they may be used in understanding the earth's surface. It is more in the nature of an outline of geography, whose content provides organization and factual material on the three great groups of surface features: (*a*) natural, (*b*) population, and (*c*) cultural. Its scope is extensive, for essentially it is the *world* patterns of the individual elements which are emphasized, rather than those of particular countries or regions.

Vernor C. Finch
Glenn T. Trewartha
Arthur H. Robinson
Edwin H. Hammond

Contents

Contents

Part Three: The Cultural Elements of Geography

FEATURES RESULTING FROM MAN'S USE OF THE LAND

Part Four: Appendices

Plates

(All plates are to be found in a special section following page 374. Plate 2 is shown as the front end paper.)

1. Average Annual Precipitation.
2. Climates of the Earth.
3. Terrain of the Earth.
4. Lithic Regions.
5. Natural Vegetation.
6. Distribution of Soils.
7. Distribution of Population.
8. Agricultural Types and Regions.
9. Surface Temperature Regions of the Continents.

1

The Form of the Earth, Its Planetary Relations, and Its Representation on Maps

1.1 The Size and Shape of the Earth. The number of important consequences resulting from the shape and size of the earth and its relation to other heavenly bodies, especially the sun, is more than most people realize. Such earthly concepts as distance, area, direction, time, and weight are usually accepted without question, but they all are dependent upon these primary conditions. Even such familiar phenomena as day and night, the seasons, and even the tides of the oceans are also dependent upon them. Consequently, it is necessary initially to review some of the more important of these primary facts, and some of their consequences, before proceeding to a more detailed consideration of the nature of the earth environment and man's occupancy of it.

The earth is almost a true sphere, the radius of which is a little less than 4,000 miles. The greatest departure from sphericity is a slight flattening in the polar regions and a slight bulging in the equatorial regions. Because of this, the polar radius is about 13.5 miles shorter than the equatorial radius. Relative to the size of the earth this spherical discrepancy is small; it would amount to less than $\frac{1}{10}$ in. on a ball 5 ft. in diameter. None of the other departures from sphericity (ocean depths or mountain peaks) is as great as the polar flattening, for the highest mountain is only about 5.5 miles above sea level and the greatest depth of the ocean is less than 7 miles. The relative smoothness of the earth's surface may be appreciated from the fact that, if the earth were reduced to

the size of an ordinary desk globe 1 ft. in diameter, one could hardly feel the roughness of the earth's surface. On such a globe the peak of Mount Everest (29,141 ft. above sea level) would be less than $\frac{1}{100}$ in. above the general surface of the globe.

1.2 Earth Features and the Earth Interior. The relatively small departures of the earth's surface from a truly smooth spheroidal form have a meaning of wider interest than their mere size. It seems surprising that some of the great mountains of the earth are not higher and that the great ocean depths are not deeper than they are. Forces of crustal distortion are constantly at work bending, breaking, and warping the crust, and, at first thought, these forces would appear capable of producing irregularities much greater than those which exist. That they are not greater seems due to a natural limit upon the size to which they may grow. This limit is set by the plastic nature of the earth and the consequent inability of the interior to support the weight of projections upon its exterior of a greater order of height than that of the existing continental masses. If the earth's crust be thought of as composed of a mosaic of segments or blocks, then those which include the continents are slightly taller, measured from the center of the earth, than are those which include the ocean basins. It is believed that the higher segments are composed of rocks sufficiently lighter than the average so that they are nearly in balance with the lower but heavier segments. This state of balance is constantly

1

being disturbed by various other processes, such as the removal of earth from the continents by streams and its deposition in the oceans. This disturbance is in turn constantly being counteracted by the slow movement of plastic material beneath the earth's crust.

The polar flattening and equatorial bulging are also evidence of a plastic earth interior, since that is the deformation which would occur in a plastic sphere as a result of gravitation and the centrifugal force due to rotation. The concept that the earth is plastic will be useful later in connection with studies of the molding of the surface forms of the land.

1.3   Land, Water, and Air. The home of man is upon the 197 million square miles of the exterior of the earth, but the earth's surface differs markedly in terms of its human utility. The solid mass of the earth (the lithosphere) is covered in part by water (the hydrosphere), and both are surrounded by a thin gaseous film (the atmosphere). Each of these "spheres" touches upon the life of man in many ways.

Their many different features or phases combine and recombine in hundreds of ways to make up the sets of physical conditions that exist in parts of the world. Some of the combinations are eminently suited to the habitation of man and to intensive use by modern human society; others form regions that are very unsuited. In the latter group are the depressed segments of the earth crust which are filled by the oceans and the great seas, and these together occupy about 71 per cent of the surface of the sphere. The remainder, about 29 per cent, are the exposed continental surfaces and only these are in any degree suited to permanent human abode.

The total area of the land and ice-covered surface of the continents is about 57 million square miles, equal to about nineteen times the area of the United States. Upon this rather restricted surface the entire human population of the earth resides and endeavors to secure a living. There are large parts of this land area, however, which, for one reason or another, are ill-suited to intensive human occupation or use.

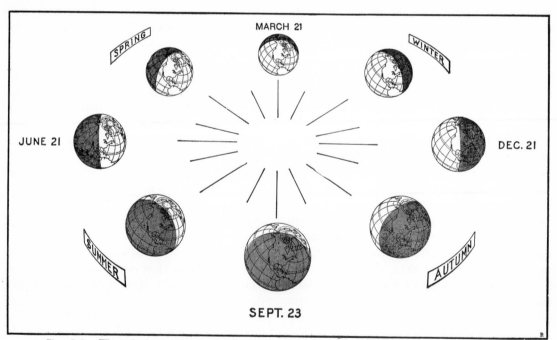

Fig. 1.1   The relation of the inclination and parallelism of the earth's axis to the change of the seasons. For this drawing the observer is far outside the earth's orbit and slightly above the plane of the ecliptic. Compare with Fig. 1.4 which shows equatorial views of the earth at the time of the summer and winter solstices.

1.4 Earth Rotation and Its Consequences. The earth is held in space by the combined gravitational attraction of the heavenly bodies and it has certain regular movements relative to the others. The two principal earth motions are *rotation* and *revolution*. The earth rotates about an axis which, owing to the polar flattening, is its shortest diameter. The ends of the axis of rotation are at the earth poles. The time required for the earth to rotate once with respect to the sun is about 24 hr., or 1 day, although it varies a bit from one part of a year to another. During that 24-hr. period most places on the sphere turn alternately toward and away from the sun, thus experiencing a period of energy and light receipt and a period of darkness, and are twice passed through the boundary between light and dark, the circle of illumination, once at dawn and again at twilight. The earth rotates toward the east, and this fact has broad significance. Not only does it determine the direction in which the sun, moon, and stars appear to move across the sky, but it is related to other earth phenomena of far-reaching consequence, such as the general circulation of the atmosphere and oceans, which will be studied later.

1.5 Earth Revolution. The rotating earth revolves in a slightly elliptical orbit about the sun, from which it keeps an average distance of about 93 million miles. The average time required for the earth to pass once completely around its orbit fixes the length of the year. During the time of one revolution around the sun the earth rotates relative to the sun approximately $365\frac{1}{4}$ times, thus determining the number of days in the year. All points in the earth's orbit lie in an imaginary plane which also passes through the sun. This plane is called the *plane of the ecliptic,* and the axis of the earth's rotation has an inclination of about $66\frac{1}{2}°$ from this plane (or $23\frac{1}{2}°$ from vertical to it). This position is constant, and therefore the axis at any time during the yearly revolution is parallel to the position that it occupied at any previous time (Fig. 1.1). This is called the *parallelism* of the axis.

The degree of *inclination* of the earth's axis

and its *parallelism,* together with the earth's shape, its *rotation* on its axis, and its *revolution* about the sun, combine to produce several earth phenomena which are of vital importance among the conditions that surround earth inhabitants. Some of these are (*a*) the primary distribution of solar energy over the earth, (*b*) the changing of the seasons, and (*c*) the changing lengths of day and night. These matters, and others related to them, will be discussed more fully in their connection with climate.

Location on the Earth

1.6 The Earth Grid. The conditions described above also are matters of great importance in another way. They constitute the bases upon which has been developed a means of determining and describing the position or relative location of any place on the earth's surface. On a sphere there is neither beginning nor ending, no natural point or line of reference from which to begin to measure the relative positions of other points. If it were not for its motions and other planetary relations, the earth also would have no natural point or line from which to measure distance or direction. Since the fact of rotation establishes the geographic poles of the earth, these serve as reference points upon which is based a coordinate system, called the earth grid, by means of which directions and locations are determined.

The coordinate system on the earth is similar to the familiar rectangular coordinate system on cross-section paper, except for modifications necessary to fit the spherical earth. A line around the earth lying everywhere midway between the poles is called the *equator.* Any number of other lines parallel to the equator may be placed on the earth, as is illustrated in Fig. 1.2. These lines, together with the equator, are called *parallels,* and the earth directions *east* and *west* are determined by their orientation. Since each of these parallels is parallel with the equator it follows that every point on a given parallel will be the same distance to the north or to the south of the equator. The concept of the distance north or south on the earth coordinate system is called *latitude* and is expressed by identifying the appropriate parallel.

Needless to say a statement of latitude is

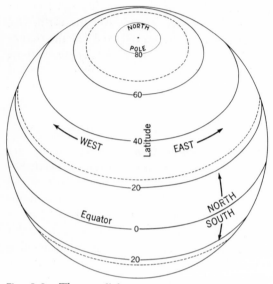

Fig. 1.2   The parallel system of the earth's coordinate net. It establishes the directions east and west, and it provides a method for designating position north and south.

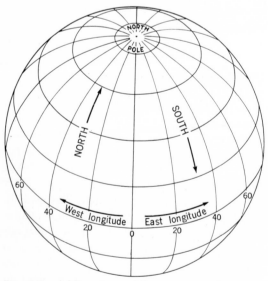

Fig. 1.3   Adding the meridian system of the earth's coordinate net to the parallel system establishes the directions of north and south, and it provides a method for designating position east and west.

not enough to locate a position since a parallel is a continuous line. Distance east and west, called *longitude*, is expressed by the second set of lines at right angles to parallels. In the normal flat coordinate system these lines are also parallel with one another, but on a sphere they must converge and meet at the poles. They are, however, equally spaced on any parallel. These lines, called *meridians*, determine the directions *north* and *south* and are shown in Fig. 1.3. They are all the same length and each bisects the equator and all other parallels. They are the largest circles one can draw on a sphere and are called *great circles*. The equator is also a great circle. In practice each meridian great circle is divided at the poles and forms a pair, one meridian being a semicircle extending from one pole to the other.

The great circle, of which the meridians and the equator are some examples, is the path of the shortest distance over the earth's surface between two points. All great circles bisect one another, which fact is significant in a number of ways; especially is this so with respect to the length of day at various places on the earth, as will be seen later.

1.7   Latitude.   In the system of numbering used on the earth's coordinate net it is customary to divide the circle formed by each pair of meridians into quadrants, the points of division being the poles and the two intersections with the equator. Each quadrant is divided into 90 parts, called degrees (°) of latitude, the sum of the number of degrees in the four parts being the 360 degrees of the meridian circle. The numbering of the degrees proceeds from the equator to either pole, and positions on the meridian are marked by the east-west cross lines of the parallels. By means of the parallels, latitude is reckoned from the equator (0°Lat.) northward to the North Pole (90°N.Lat.) on any meridian and, in the same way, from the equator to the South Pole (90°S.Lat.).

1.8   The Lengths of Degrees of Latitude.   On a sphere each degree of a great circle (*i.e.*, circumference), measured in any direction, has the same length, but this is not quite true on the earth. Latitude is determined by observ-

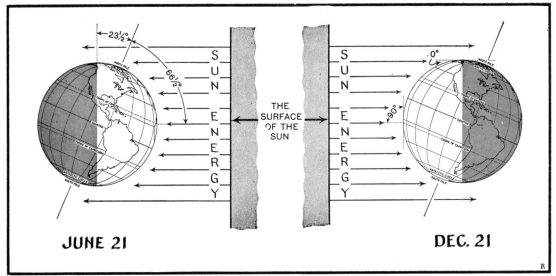

Fig. 1.4 The angular relationship between the direction of the sun's energy (the sun's position in the heavens) and the earth's surface changes during the year. For example, on Dec. 21 a person on the Tropic of Capricorn would see the sun directly overhead (90°) at noon, while on the Arctic Circle the sun would appear on the horizon, *i.e.* the rays would be tangent (0°) to the earth's surface. The segments of the sun's surface shown here to scale with the earth represent only about $\frac{1}{200}$ part of its circumference. Consequently, for practical purposes they have almost no curvature.

ing the angle formed by the horizon and some celestial body, such as the sun or Polaris (the North Star). A degree of latitude is the distance north or south one must travel in order to observe 1° change in this angle. Because of the flattening in the polar regions the earth's surface does not curve so rapidly. Consequently, one must travel farther in these areas to obtain a change of 1°. The opposite is true in the equatorial regions where the curvature is greater. This results in the degrees of latitude near the poles being slightly longer than those near the equator. The first degree of latitude from the equator has a length of 68.69 miles, while the first degree from the pole is 69.39 miles long. Each degree of latitude is divided into 60 minutes (′), and each minute into 60 seconds (″). One minute of latitude has an average length of 6,080 ft. (1 nautical mile) or about 1.15 statute miles, and one second of latitude is about 101 ft. The length of the meter, standard of measurement in the metric system, is, in theory, exactly one ten-millionth of the meridian distance from the equator to the pole.

1.9 A parallel of latitude, drawn through points equally distant from the equator on all meridians, may be constructed for any degree, minute, or second of latitude. Commonly only a few of the many possible parallels are shown, for example, those of the multiples of 5 or 10°. Almost always, however, four fractional parallels are shown in addition to the others, because they have special significance. These are the parallels of approximately $23\frac{1}{2}$°N. and S. latitude and of $66\frac{1}{2}$°N. and S. latitude. Their importance is derived from the fact that the sun, at various places and times, appears at different elevations above the earth's surface, as a consequence of that surface being curved combined with the inclination and parallelism of the earth's axis. The parallels of $23\frac{1}{2}$°N. and S. are called the Tropics of Cancer and Capricorn, respectively. They mark the limits north and south of the equator of that portion of the earth within which the sun ever appears directly overhead (Fig. 1.4). The parallels of $66\frac{1}{2}$°N. and S. are called the Arctic and Antarctic Circles, respectively. They mark the limits of the polar area in each hemisphere within which the sun ever appears above the horizon continuously for one day or more, or, at the same time in the opposite hemisphere, remains below the horizon for one day or more (Fig. 1.4.).

1.10 Longitude is reckoned east or west, *i.e.,* along the parallels of latitude. It is necessary to start counting at a particular meridian, but among the meridians there is no particular one marked by nature (as is the equator for counting latitude) from which numbering may begin. All are exactly alike, and it is possible to begin to count from any one of them as 0°Long. This was in fact done for several centuries, each important country beginning with a meridian drawn through a spot within its own borders. So much confusion resulted that, in the year 1884, the meridian passing through the Royal Astronomical Observatory at Greenwich, near London, was chosen by international agreement as the zero meridian. It is called the *prime meridian.* It intersects the equator in the Gulf of Guinea at a point which has the distinction of having 0°00′00″Long. and 0°00′00″Lat. This point is, then, the "point of origin" of the earth's coordinate grid. The degrees of longitude in the equator and each parallel are numbered to 180°E. and 180°W. of the prime meridian on the opposite side of the earth.

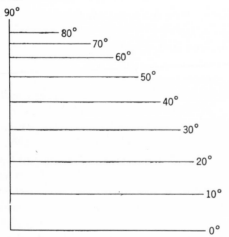

Fig. 1.5 The comparative lengths of the radii of the parallels.

1.11 Degrees of Longitude Vary in Length. All the parallels of latitude, except the equator, are less than great circles, the lengths of those near the poles being much less than that of the equator or of the other parallels near to it (Fig. 1.5). Since each parallel circle, regardless of its length, is divided into 360°, it follows that the length of 1° of longitude must be a decreasing distance with higher latitude. One degree of longitude on the equator, a great circle, has about the same length as an average degree of latitude (69.15 miles). At latitude 30°N. or S. the length of a degree of longitude is 59.94 miles; at 60° it is 34.60 miles; at 80° it is 12.05 miles; and at the poles it is, of course, zero.

1.12 Determination of Position. The intersection of any two lines is a point; consequently, any point on the earth's surface may be located by determining that it lies at the intersection of a certain meridian with a certain parallel. Therefore, by exact determination of its latitude and longitude the location of any place may be expressed briefly and with great accuracy. Thus if one were to say that the dome of the National Capitol at Washington was located at 38°53′23″N.Lat and 77°00′33″Long. west of Greenwich, one would state its position on the earth to within 10 paces.

The latitude of a place is determined by instrumental observation of the angle between the horizon and a celestial body. The earth is so relatively small compared to its distance from the stars and the sun that for all practical purposes the rays of light from a celestial body intercepted by the earth are parallel. Since the quadrant of latitude is divided into 90° and its curvature also covers 90°, it follows that the change in curvature will exactly match the change in angular height of a celestial body. For example, at the North Pole, Polaris (or the North Star) will be directly overhead; therefore its angular height above the horizon will be 90°, and the latitude of the North Pole will be 90°. Similarly, if it could be seen from the equator it would be on the horizon (*i.e.,* tangent to it) at an angular elevation of 0°; and at 45°N.Lat. it would appear halfway between the

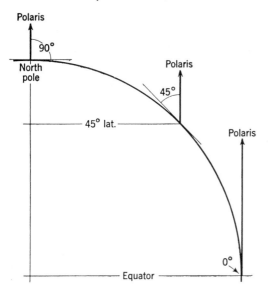

Fig. 1.6 The relation between the north-south curvature of the earth and the angular height of Polaris above the horizon.

zenith and the horizon. Figure 1.6 illustrates these relationships. They may be summarized simply by stating that the difference in latitude in degrees between two points on the earth is the angular difference in the heights above the horizon of a given celestial body as observed at the two points.

The use of celestial bodies other than Polaris to determine latitude is somewhat more complicated since a correction must be introduced to take into account the fact that they are directly overhead at some latitude other than the Pole. For example, the sun's vertical rays fall on a different latitude in the tropics every day, but tables are available to provide this information.

Distance east-west is determined by observing the difference in sun time between the two points. Since the earth rotates through approximately 360° in 24 hr. it turns through about 15° in 1 hr. Consequently, if it is noon at one place and 10:00 A.M. at another, then 30° of longitude separates them. The longitude of an unmapped place east or west of the prime meridian, or of a ship at sea, can be determined only by finding the difference in time between that place and the prime meridian. This was

first accomplished by means of accurate timepieces (chronometers) carried on shipboard and set at Greenwich, or prime-meridian, time. Observation of the sun at the instant when it reached the highest point (zenith) in its daily course across the sky gave local noontime, which could then be compared directly with the chronometer, and the difference in time translated into degrees and minutes of longitude. Now, instantaneous communication by telegraph and radio makes accurate time comparison possible almost everywhere and, therefore, makes possible greatly improved determinations of longitude. This is of particular aid in geographical exploration.

1.13 Longitude and Time. Solar time is the time determined by the instant when the sun reaches its zenith and it changes from longitude to longitude. When noon arrives at any meridian, it is already 1 hr. later (1:00 P.M.) on the meridian 15° east of that one, and it lacks 1 hr. of noon (11:00 A.M.) on the meridian 15° to the west of it. For the instant, it is noon on the one meridian only, but it is noon on that meridian from North Pole to South Pole. Four minutes later it is noon on the meridian 1° farther west.

In generations past, each town kept the time of its own meridian, which was called apparent solar time or, in common American parlance, "sun time." When rail transportation permitted rapid travel, it became awkward or impossible to change one's time a few minutes with every village passed. To avoid this necessity, each railroad adopted an arbitrary time scheme which differed from that of most of the places that it passed through but was the same for considerable distances on the rail line. Unfortunately, several railroads in a region often adopted different times for their own use. Consequently, it sometimes happened that a town reached by different railroads found itself required to use, or distinguish between, several different kinds of time: its own solar time and one for each of its railways. The awkwardness and confusion of this situation led to the adoption by American railways, in 1883, of a system of *standard time.*

The standard-time system, in theory, supposes that all parts of a north-south zone 15° of longitude in width adopt the solar time of the central meridian of that zone. Places within the zone that are east or west of the central meridian, instead of differing in time by a few minutes from it and from each other, all have the same time. Changes of time are then necessary only in crossing the boundary of the zone, and each change is exactly 1 hr. The timepiece is set forward (*i.e.,* later, as from 12:00 to 1:00) in traveling east and back (*i.e.,* earlier, as from 12:00 to 11:00) in traveling west. In practice, these zones are not bounded by meridians but by irregular lines, the locations of which are subject to change and are dictated by local convenience. Figure 1.7 shows the present standard-time zones of the United States.

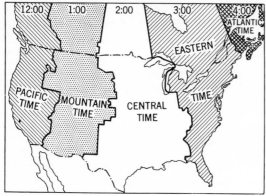

Fig. 1.7   The standard-time belts of the United States.

On the whole earth there should be 24 standard-time zones, each extending from pole to pole and each differing from Greenwich time by an integral number of hours. In practice the arrangement is not quite so simple, for, although most countries follow the plan, certain isolated ones have not yet adopted standard time at all, and a few countries employ standard meridians that are not multiples of 15 and therefore do not differ from Greenwich time by exact hours.

1.14   The International Date Line. The quickness with which the earth may be circumnavigated has introduced a similar problem of calendar correction. The nature of this problem may be visualized if one imagines an airplane sufficiently fast to fly around the earth in the latitude of Chicago in exactly 24 hr. If the flyer left Chicago, *going westward,* at noon on Monday the tenth of the month, his speed would exactly match the rotation of the earth in the opposite direction. Consequently, the sun would have no apparent motion, *i.e.,* he would see it in the same position all the way, and he would return to Chicago the same (to him) noon. In other words he has not experienced a solar day of light and dark. To persons in Chicago a night would have intervened, and it would be noon of Tuesday the eleventh. The flyer would have "lost" a calendar day. If, on the other hand, he had flown eastward, he would have experienced midnight over Spain, noon of another day over Central Asia, a second midnight over the Pacific Ocean, and would have returned to Chicago at noon of the second day, though he had been gone only 24 hr. On his calendar it would be noon of Wednesday the twelfth, while to those who remained it is, as before, Tuesday the eleventh. The flyer has "gained" a day. The fact that one who travels slowly by train and boat loses or gains this time by 24 time corrections of 1 hr. each does not alter the case in the least. Unless he sets his *calendar* ahead one day when traveling around the earth westward and sets it back when traveling eastward, it will be out of adjustment on his return. To avoid confusion that would result from individual choice as to place of change, an *international date line* has been established at the 180th meridian. There, correction may be made uniformly, and no correction of date is necessary unless that line is crossed. Certain deviations of the date line from the 180th meridian are agreed upon to prevent confusion of day and date in certain island groups or land areas that are divided by the meridian.

1.15   Direction. The location of places with respect to each other may be expressed in terms of direction and distance as well as by relative location in latitude and longitude. Direction usually is stated in terms that signify an angular

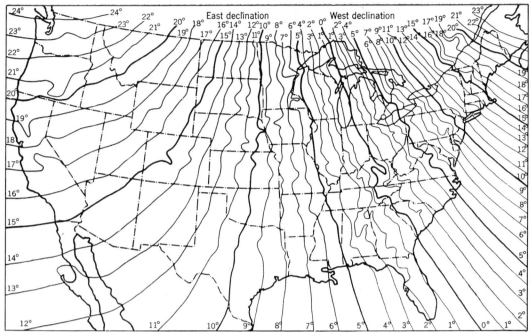

Fig. 1.8 Lines of equal magnetic declination (isogonic lines) in the United States. Only at points on the agonic line (0° declination) does the magnetic compass point true north. (*Generalized from a map by U.S. Coast and Geodetic Survey.*)

relation (azimuth) to the meridian, or geographical north. Although, in recent years, the gyroscopic compass and other devices have made it possible to maintain direction by immediate reference to true north, yet much direction finding, especially in land surveys, still is accomplished by means of the magnetic compass. The needle of this instrument aligns itself with the lines of magnetic force emanating from that great magnet, the earth. However, the positions of the *magnetic* north and south poles are neither opposite one another nor do they coincide with the geographic poles. They are even subject to slight changes of position. In consequence, there are few places on the earth where the magnetic needle points toward true geographical north. At all other places the compass reads at an angle with true north. These angles vary considerably in size from place to place, and their amount is called the compass declination. Figure 1.8 shows the lines of equal compass declination in the United States. East of the line of zero declination the compass has a west declination. In parts of the frequented oceans the compass declination is as

much as 30 to 40° from true north. It is obvious that true direction cannot be found by the magnetic compass alone, and that true maps cannot be made without a knowledge of the degree and direction of compass declination. This may be obtained by an observation on Polaris.

The Nature and Uses of Maps

1.16 Maps Are Essential Tools. Maps are graphic representations of the surface of the earth. They are used in many fields of learning but especially in earth sciences. For the student of geography *the map is an essential tool;* it is a device on which facts may be recorded, and it is also a means of presenting information. Maps are almost infinite in number, size, form, and meaning, and they constitute almost a language in themselves. For their ready interpretation it is necessary that their important types and qualities be understood. To that end it is desirable that the student have a quick appreciation of at least three fundamental matters concerning all maps. These are (*a*) the size of the map representation compared

9

with that part of the earth which it represents; (b) the nature of the plan, scheme, or "projection" employed in making the representation; and (c) the types of things represented on the map and the meanings of the various symbols or devices used to show them.

1.17   The Map Scale. A simple globe is the form of earth representation requiring the least interpretation. The dimensions of the globe may be measured, and the relation of its size to that of the earth, indicated in like units, may be expressed as a ratio. The ratio is called the *scale* of the globe. The earth has a diameter of about 500,000,000 in. and if, for example, a large globe has a diameter of 50 in., then the ratio of the distance between any two places on the globe, measured in inches, to that between the same two places on the earth, measured also in inches, will be as 50 is to 500,000,000. That ratio is as 1 is to 10,-000,000, and it is often written as a fractional scale, thus: $\dfrac{1}{10,000,000}$ or 1:10,000,000—and is called the *representative fraction,* or RF for short.

Maps, like globes, bear proportional relations to the parts of the earth that they represent. The statement of the proportion is printed on many maps in the form of the representative fraction. It is called the *map scale.* Frequently the scale is expressed verbally also, or, more often, by means of a measured line. Maps may have large scales or small. A ratio of 1:10,000,-000 indicates a small scale because one unit of map distance represents 10,000,000 units of earth distance, and the map is, by comparison, extremely small. A ratio of 1:100,000 indicates a map of much larger scale, and a ratio of 1:1 would indicate a map as large as the area mapped. Reference to a student's atlas will serve to illustrate the range of map scales ordinarily employed in such publications. There is one essential difference between the application of scales to globes and to maps. The scale of a globe, no matter how small, may properly be applied to it in any part and in any direction. On small-scale maps of large areas, especially of the entire earth, the indicated scale seldom is equally applicable to all parts of the map. A reason for this will appear below.

1.18   The Nature of a Map. A map differs from a globe in that it is a representation of some part or all of the earth's *spherical* surface on a *plane.* A map may be made on a flat sheet of paper which will show a farm or the area of a village without distortion of shape or of relative area, because the part of the earth's spherical surface included in either of them is so small as to be itself practically flat. To make a map of the entire earth, a hemisphere, a continent, or even a state without some degree of distortion is not possible, because a spherical surface cannot be transformed into a plane surface without introducing some distortion. The greater convenience of maps as compared with globes has led, however, to the invention of many systems of transformation of the sphere to the plane, designed in such a way that what at first may appear to be an unavoidable liability actually sometimes turns out to be an asset. In each system the distortion follows a specific pattern. Such a systematic transformation is called a *map projection.*

1.19   Map Projections. The distortion of the earth's surface inherent in map projections may be controlled in such a way that one or more of several objectives may be attained. The map may (a) represent the angles around each point correctly, (b) represent sizes of *areas* truly so that all parts of the map are in proper areal relation to one another, or (c) show *direction* correctly from some point selected by the map maker. However, for advantages gained in one quality, by the mode of construction of the map projection, some other quality must be sacrificed. *It is impossible for any map that shows a considerable part of the earth's surface to accomplish all these objectives at the same time,* and some accomplish none of them.

For a more extended discussion of the nature of map projections and the appearance and properties of a few of their many forms the student is referred to Appendix B.

1.20   Representations on Maps. Maps are employed to show the areal distribution of many kinds of things. The devices used on the map to show distribution also are many. However, in a general way, they may be arranged in four groups which are neither all-inclusive nor even quite mutually exclusive. The groups are (*a*) devices employed to show areal extent, shape, or outline; (*b*) devices for showing patterns of arrangement; (*c*) devices intended to convey an impression of relative land elevation or surface relief; and (*d*) devices employed to show the areal distribution of statistical values of actual or relative quantity.

In the first group may be included all those familiar devices of line and color which characterize the many kinds of regional maps that show the extent or the boundaries of areas classified upon the basis of some kind of unity. These may be countries or other political divisions, areas of unity in geological formation, climatic type, landscape composition, or of any other nature. In the second group may be found maps of drainage patterns, city-street and road patterns, the patterns of other means of transportation and communication, and patterns of the distribution of towns and cities with respect to each other. In the third group are devices such as shadings and hachures (Fig. 1.15) arranged to produce the effect of light and shadow, simulating modeled relief on the earth. Some of these are of great intricacy and beauty and are the supreme examples of the map maker's skill. In this group also is that useful device, the contour line, which is discussed more fully below.

The fourth group includes many devices, prominent among them being such things as dots or squares, denoting area, or representations of cubes or spheres, indicating volume. Each of these is intended to convey the idea of the existence of a unit of number or value in a specific locality on the earth's surface. Maps having devices of this class are sometimes called cartograms. Their effectiveness as geographic tools is generally in inverse proportion to the size of the areal units for which the values are shown. Thus a few dots or squares, each representing a large unit of value and covering a large area, show generalities. Many of them, each representing a small unit of

value and distributed properly within small units of area, show valuable details of distribution. They may be used to show in an effective way the areal arrangement of many kinds of things, especially such as have large space requirement but do not occupy the entire area. Such are agricultural crops, the distribution of livestock, or the distribution of rural population. For such uses the dot map is unexcelled because, when the pattern of distribution, and not the quantity distributed, is the thing desired to be shown, a proper arrangement of the dots most nearly reproduces the actual distribution of the thing represented. The dot map is properly effective only when shown on a nearly equal-area projection, where the relative area covered by a dot remains almost constant over the entire map. The dot map is not suited to the effective representation of the distribution of things that have no definite relation between area and quantity, such as urban population, volume of manufactures, or value of mineral output. For such uses other devices are indicated, particularly such as show concentration within a local area rather than general distribution. Graduated circles, spherical representations, or drawings of block piles, whose component blocks may actually be counted, are particularly effective in cartograms of that type.

Most of these cartographic devices are self-explanatory to a college student or, if not, their specific quality may be determined by reference to the *legend* which usually accompanies a map. Care must be exercised, however, by the map reader so that he does not "read into" the map symbols a greater degree of accuracy or precision than is warranted by the nature of the symbols or the scale of the map. Except for very large-scale maps all information presented on a map must be *generalized, i.e.* simplified in some way. For example, many of the maps in this book show distribution of things by coloring areas differently or by separating areas by lines; yet such color changes or boundaries frequently represent only *average* conditions. Similarly, coastlines, boundaries, roads, wind-direction lines, average rainfall amounts, and other such information must be greatly simplified. This is necessary for two reasons: first the details cannot be represented at small scales, and, second, basic facts and patterns would not be so apparent were more detail shown.

1.21 Isarithms and Isopleths. One of the frequently used, but not self-explanatory, devices employed to show distributions of quantity on maps are the successive lines on a map, each of which is drawn through all points that have a particular numerical value. Such lines are called *isograms* or *isolines* from the Greek *isos* meaning equal. When the values represented are actual measures such as the atmospheric pressure, depth of rainfall, or actual temperatures the lines are called *isarithms* (Gr. *isos*, equal, + *arithmos*, number); when they represent relative values expressed as ratios, such as the number of persons per square mile or the per cent of land in crops, the lines are called *isopleths* (Gr. *isos*, equal, + *plethos*, amount). The major distinction between the two is one of relative precision, isarithms generally being the more precise.

Isarithms and isopleths are of many kinds and commonly are used to present elements of geography. Isarithms employed to present a particular class of natural phenomena are sometimes named by combining the prefix *iso* with a term derived from the type of data. Hence one speaks of isotherms (temperature), isobars (air pressure), isobaths (water depth), and many others. Isarithmic maps may also show the distribution of relative values, such as the percentage departures from the normal rainfall, or rainfall variability, in the different parts of the world.

1.22 The contour map is an isarithmic map the purpose of which is to show the surface irregularities of the land. So useful is this kind of map that it is more widely employed than any other for the purpose of depicting the comparative elevations of the land-surface features above sea level, *i.e.*, land-relief representation. These kinds of isarithms are isohypses (Gr. *hypsos*, elevation) but are commonly called *contour lines*. A contour is drawn on the map so that it passes only through those points

which, on the surface of the earth, have the same elevation above sea level. The idea of contour lines, their spacing, and their irregularities may be made clear by a simple illustration.

In an open tank one may mold an oval mound of wax $6\frac{1}{2}$ in. high, steeply sloping at one end and gently sloping at the other. If 6

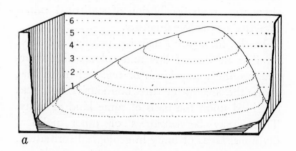

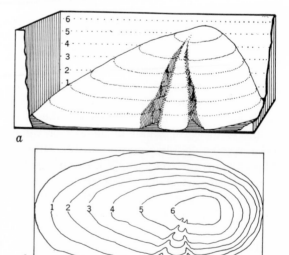

Fig. 1.9 Compare this diagram with a photograph of one of the United States topographic maps shown in Fig. 1.15.

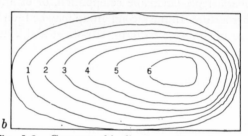

Fig. 1.10

Fig. 1.11   Nature's contours on an emerging shore. Wave-cut lines on a hilly slope, resulting from the intermittent withdrawal of water from an irrigation reservoir. (*Courtesy of Taylor-Rochester.*)

in. of water is permitted to flow into the tank, only $\frac{1}{2}$ in. of the mound will protrude. With a sharp point the position of the edge of the water upon the wax may be marked, and then the water level may be lowered by 1-in. stages and the position of each stage marked on the surface of the wax. The marks made will now appear as contour lines on the wax mound, the lowest being everywhere 1 in. above the bottom of the tank, the next 2 in., and so on to the sixth, as in Fig. 1.9a. If the mound is viewed from directly above, the arrangement of the lines will be that of Fig. 1.9b. From this pattern of arrangement certain things may be learned which will help in the general interpretation of contour maps. Most important of these is the fact that where the slope of the mound is steep the contour lines are close together and that they are more widely spaced as the slope becomes more gentle.

On this little model the water levels, and therefore the contour lines, have a vertical separation of 1 in. This may be called the *contour interval*. If the pattern of the lines,

as seen from above, is reproduced upon a sheet of paper, the result may be called a contour map, which, in this case, has a contour interval of 1 in. The lines may be numbered accordingly.

Few hills in nature are so smooth as this mound, and the example may be made more real by introducing a pair of gullies in its side (Fig. 1.10a). If the submergence is repeated, and the lines redrawn in the wax, it will be seen that in each gully the lines now follow along the gully side, cross its bottom, and return along its other side. If, now, the pattern of the lines, as viewed from above, is transferred to a map, it will look like Fig. 1.10b. From the arrangement of these lines other general facts become apparent. One is that when a contour line crosses a valley it does so by a bend such that the closed end of its loop points in the upslope direction. Between the two gullies is a ridge. On the contour map of this hill the contour lines that emerge from the gullies and pass over the ridge appear to loop so that their bends point in the downslope direction. Thus, contour lines bent sharply toward the down-

13

slope direction always indicate ridges. An illustration of this principle is seen in Fig. 1.11, where natural contour lines are marked on a hill slope as a result of wave work performed in a reservoir at different stages in the lowering of the water level.

1.23 Air Photographs and Topographic Maps. The air photograph is another kind of device whereby the relationships of geography may be studied. It is not the same as a map since it records everything a camera "sees," whereas the map is a result of a process of selection and interpretation. By the recognition of different tones of dark and light and various kinds of patterns one is able to identify many of the physical and cultural elements of geography. With the aid of a stereoscope the overlapping air photographs may be studied in three dimensions. The ungeneralized and realistic appearance of the earth's surface as seen in air photographs makes them a useful aid in revealing and understanding the complexities of geography.

Many of the world's topographic maps are made from air photographs by analyzing their geometric properties and by interpreting the earth's image on them. The air photograph has thus become an aid to, as well as a companion of, the topographic map. The detailed knowledge of any part of the earth is gained, in part, from its maps and its air photographs and thus a knowledge of how well the earth has been mapped and photographed aids in understanding how much is known about its various parts. Figures 1.12 and 1.13 show the extent of world coverage. It should be remembered that maps and photographs of some areas are old, or of poor quality, or difficult to obtain, so that generalizations about man's knowledge of the earth must be made with care.

Almost all of the United States has been photographed at least once and many parts of it have been photographed several times. Most of the photographs are at a scale of about 3 in. to 1 mile (1:20,000) and since the photographs overlap one another a tremendous number is involved. Topographic maps made by the U.S. Geological Survey and other governmental

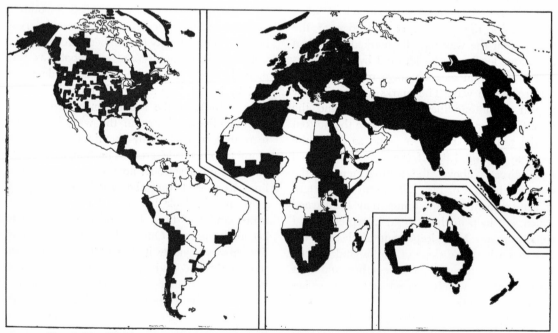

Fig. 1.12 Highly generalized map of topographically mapped areas of the world. The black areas show regions generally covered by medium and large-scale topographic maps.

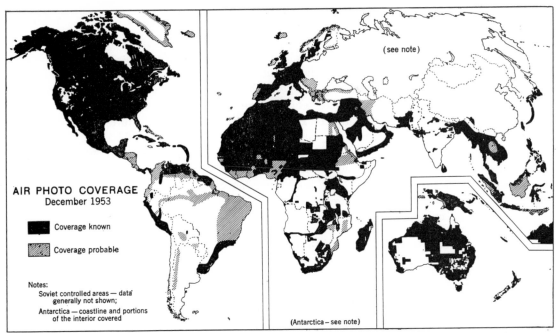

Fig. 1.13 World air photo coverage. (*Map by Kirk H. Stone, courtesy of Photogrammetric Engineering, published by American Society of Photogrammetry.*)

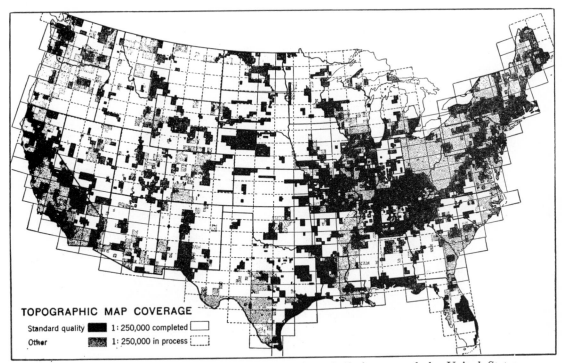

Fig. 1.14 Large-scale topographic maps for about half the area of the United States were available in 1956. (*Courtesy of U.S. Geological Survey.*)

15

agencies are now available for more than half the area of the United States (Fig. 1.14). The standard United States topographic map includes a quadrangle of 0°15′ of latitude and longitude. It is printed either at a scale of 1:62,500 (approximately 1 in. to 1 mile) or at a scale of 1:24,000 (approximately $2\frac{1}{2}$ in. to 1 mile). Some maps are printed at other scales.[1]

The maps are printed in three or four colors, each having a restricted meaning. In *black* are shown those features in the surveyed area that may be classed as culture, *i.e.,* have human

[1] The Map Information Section of the U.S. Geological Survey, Washington 25, D.C., publishes regularly up-to-date indexes showing the status of topographic mapping and air photography and the agencies from which they are available.

origin. In this color are roads, houses, towns, place names, boundary lines, and parallels and meridians. In *blue* are printed all water features, both natural and man-made, such as canals, streams, marshes, millponds, lakes, or seas. The various classes of such features are distinguished by appropriate symbols in blue. In *green,* if that color is shown, are areas covered by timber or woodland. This feature is shown on a small number of the published maps only. The contour lines and other symbols relating to the relative elevation of the land surface are shown in *brown.*

Each map is provided with a place title and with parallels and meridians that indicate its exact location and extent. Each is provided also with a scale and with a statement of the contour

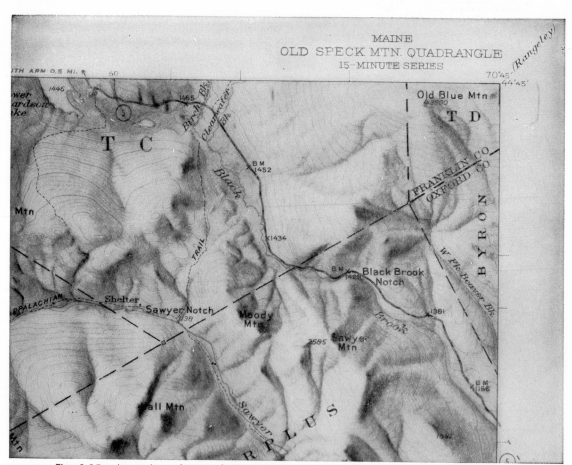

Fig. 1.15 A portion of one of the modern topographic maps of the U.S. Geological Survey with terrain shading. These are among the best topographic maps made anywhere.

interval used on that map. The contour intervals employed usually are 10, 20, 50, or 100 ft. On the maps of extremely flat land, intervals as small as 5 ft., or even 1 ft., are used; but on maps of rugged mountains, intervals are sometimes as much as 250 ft. Both the map scale and the contour interval of each map must be read and considered before the true meaning of the map can be interpreted. In recent years shading has been applied to U.S. Geological Survey topographic maps in order to enhance the visual impression of the terrain. A portion of such a map is shown in Fig. 1.15.

Facility in the interpretation of maps and air photographs comes only with experience. In chapters to follow, the nature and arrangement of many of the landforms to be described can be made much more clear and real if the text is supplemented by selected topographic maps and air photos. Specific topographic quadrangles which illustrate the various features discussed in the text are indicated in Appendix D. It is hoped that some of these at least may be made available and that the student will acquire sufficient ability to read them so that they may make their full contribution to his understanding of the element of landforms in the natural environment.

References for Chapter 1

Birch, T. W. "Maps, Topographical and Statistical." Oxford University Press, London and New York, 1949.

Chamberlin, Wellman. "The Round Earth on Flat Paper." The National Geographic Society, Washington, D.C., 1947.

Fisher, Irving, and O. M. Miller. "World Maps and Globes." Essential Books, New York, 1944.

Greenhood, David. "Down to Earth." 2d ed. Holiday House, Inc., New York, 1951.

Johnson, Willis E. "Mathematical Geography." American Book Company, New York, 1907.

Monkhouse, F. J., and H. R. Wilkinson. "Maps and Diagrams." Methuen & Co., Ltd., London, 1952.

Raisz, Erwin. "General Cartography." 2d ed. McGraw-Hill Book Company, Inc., New York, 1948.

Robinson, Arthur H. "Elements of Cartography." John Wiley & Sons, Inc., New York, 1953.

Steers, J. A. "An Introduction to the Study of Map Projections." 7th ed. University of London Press, Ltd., London, 1949.

PART ONE

Physical Elements of Geography

THE RESOURCE BASE

Section A1 THE ELEMENTS OF CLIMATE

General Considerations. Weather and climate have reference to the earth's atmosphere, which, like a gaseous shell or hull several hundred miles thick, completely surrounds the solid-liquid earth. The atmosphere is not to be thought of as above or beyond the earth proper; it is just as integral a part of the planet as land and water, and is equally important as they are in comprising the human habitat. It is at the narrow zone of contact, some 16 miles in thickness, between the atmosphere on one hand and the solid and liquid earth on the other that life in its various forms exists.

To be sure, man lives on the solid portion of the earth's surface but in, and at the bottom of, this sea of air. He is, as a consequence, much affected by changes that take place in the gaseous medium that surrounds him. In fact, among the several elements that comprise the natural equipment of a region (climate, native vegetation, landforms, minerals, soils, etc.) for human occupance and use, climate is the single most important one causing variations in the productive potentialities between the earth's regional subdivisions of the first order of magnitude. This results from the fact that not only is climate in and by itself a major element of a region's natural equipment, but also it directly affects vegetation, soil, and drainage characteristics and, to a degree, the nature of the landforms as well. Thus large areas with similar climates are likely to have strong resemblances in vegetation and soil also.

What is the Atmosphere? The earth's atmosphere is a mechanical mixture of a number of gases, but nitrogen and oxygen comprise about 98 per cent of its total volume. In addition there are smaller amounts of carbon dioxide, argon, ozone, hydrogen, and a number of other gases. Ordinary surface air differs somewhat

from the above description, for it is in the lower atmosphere that water vapor and numerous organic and inorganic impurities (called dust) are concentrated. The content of water vapor varies considerably both areally and temporally, and on very hot humid days it may comprise as much as 4 or 5 per cent of the volume of surface air.

But although water vapor is a minor gas in terms of total atmospheric volume, it is, nevertheless, by far the most important one in terms of weather and climate. Thus water vapor is the source of all forms of condensation and precipitation (clouds, dew, white frost, sleet, hail, rain, and snow), is the principal absorber of solar energy and of radiated earth energy as well, thereby greatly influencing temperature distribution over the earth, and is one of the main energy sources for the development and growth of storms. Since water vapor is much more transparent to the sun's rays than to the energy radiated from the earth's surface, it acts as a regulator of earth temperatures with the effect of reducing the extremes between day and night.

Some of the air's microscopic dust particles which have hygroscopic, or water-absorbing, properties provide the nuclei around which atmospheric condensation takes place. Over large cities smoke and dust act as an effective screen against incoming sunlight.

The Elements of Weather and Climate. The condition of the atmosphere at any time or place, *i.e.,* the weather, is expressed by a combination of several elements, primarily (*a*) *temperature* and (*b*) *precipitation* and *humidity,* but to a lesser degree by (*c*) *winds* and (*d*) *air pressure* as well. These four are called the *elements of weather and climate* because they are the ingredients out of which various weather and climatic types are compounded. The *weather* of any place is the sum total of its atmospheric conditions (temperature, pressure, winds, moisture, and precipitation) for a *short* period of time. It is the momentary state of the atmosphere. Thus we speak of the weather, not the climate, for today or of last week. *Climate,* on the other hand, is a composite or generalization of the variety of day-to-day weather conditions. It is not just "average weather," for the variations from the mean, or average, are as important as the mean itself. "Certainly no picture of climate is at all true unless it is painted in all the colors of the constant variation of weather and the change of season which are the really prominent features." (Kendrew.)

The composite atmospheric condition, called climate, varying regionally over the earth and also with time, is of the highest importance in affecting man's use of the land. Most portrayals of the climatic picture result from the use of data representing the averages of the climatic elements, particularly those of temperature, rainfall, and winds. Still another method of representing climate is through the use of the variety of day-to-day weather types, as shown on the synoptic chart, which taken together comprise the climate. Without doubt climate can best be represented through combining the two methods suggested and therefore making use both of weather types and of statistical averages of the climatic elements.

The Controls of Weather and Climate. Weather varies from day to day, and climate differs from place to place, because of varia-tions in the amount, intensity, and areal distribution of these several weather and climatic elements, more particularly temperature and precipitation. One may naturally inquire what it is that causes these several climatic elements to vary from place to place and season to season on the earth, resulting in some places and some seasons being hot and others cold, some wet and others dry. The answer is to be found in the *climatic controls.* These are (*a*) latitude or sun, (*b*) distribution of land and water, (*c*) winds and air masses, (*d*) altitude, (*e*) mountain barriers, (*f*) the great semipermanent high- and low-pressure centers, (*g*) ocean currents, (*h*) storms of various kinds, and a number of other minor ones. It is these controls, acting with various intensities and in different combinations, that produce the changes in temperature and precipitation, which in turn give rise to varieties of weather and climate. The diagram below may help to clarify the relationship among (*a*) *elements,* (*b*) *controls,* and (*c*) the resulting weather and climate.

Although it is the composite of atmospheric conditions, called climates, and their world distribution that are of principal interest to geographers, a description of climatic types will be more intelligible if preceded by an analysis of the characteristics, origins, and distributions of the individual elements which comprise the climatic complex. The next few chapters, dealing with air temperature, pressure and winds, moisture and precipitation, and storms, provide this background, which is desirable for understanding the origin of various types of climate and their distribution over the earth.

Climatic Controls	Climatic Elements	
1. Sun or latitude		
2. Land and water distribution		
3. Semipermanent low- and high-pressure cells		
4. Winds and air masses	1. Temperature	
5. Altitude	2. Precipitation	Types and varieties
6. Mountain barriers	and humidity	of weather and
7. Ocean currents	3. Winds and	climate
8. Storms	air pressure	

acting upon → ... produce →

General References for Section A

Blair, Thomas A. "Weather Elements." 3d ed. Prentice-Hall, Inc., New York, 1948. An elementary, nontechnical meteorology.

Brooks, Charles Franklin. "Why the Weather?" Harcourt, Brace and Company, Inc., New York, 1935. A popularly written but scientific analysis of weather.

Byers, Horace Robert. "General Meteorology." McGraw-Hill Book Company, Inc., New York, 1944. Appropriate for relatively mature students.

"Climate and Man." Yearbook of Agriculture, 1941. U.S. Department of Agriculture, Washington, D.C. See particularly Parts 1 and 4.

"Compendium of Meteorology." American Meteorological Society, 1951. The best source summarizing the recent developments in meteorological science written by specialists in their fields.

Conrad, V. "Fundamentals of Physical Climatology." Harvard University, Blue Hill Meterological Observatory, Milton, Mass., 1942.

Garbell, Maurice A. "Tropical and Equatorial Meteorology." Pitman Publishing Corporation, New York, 1947. Both regional and topical.

Haurwitz, Bernhard, and James M. Austin. "Climatology." McGraw-Hill Book Company, Inc., New York, 1944. Regional as well as topical.

Kendrew, W. G. "Climatology." 3d ed. "Climate." Oxford University Press, New York, 1949.

Landsberg, Helmut. "Physical Climatology." State College, Pennsylvania, 1941.

Miller, A. Austin. "Climatology." 3d ed. E. P. Dutton & Co., Inc., New York, 1953.

Petterssen, Sverre. "Introduction to Meteorology." McGraw-Hill Book Company, Inc., New York, 1941. An abbreviation and simplification of the author's "Weather Analysis and Forecasting."

Riehl, Herbert. "Tropical Meteorology." McGraw-Hill Book Company, Inc., New York, 1954. Incorporates the recent advances in tropical meteorology.

Taylor, George F. "Elementary Meteorology." Prentice-Hall Inc., New York, 1954.

2

Air Temperature (Including Insolation)

Sun Energy or Insolation

2.1 Source of Atmospheric Heat. The sun, which is one of the smallest stars of the universe, is the only significant source of heat for the earth's atmosphere. Out into space from this gigantic body, whose diameter is more than one hundred times the earth's and whose surface is estimated to have a temperature of about 10,300°F., streams a tremendous mass of energy. The earth, nearly 93 million miles distant, intercepts less than 1/2,000,000,000 part of the solar output. Yet to this small percentage of the sun's total energy many of the physical, and all of the biotic, phenomena of the earth owe their existence. The radiant energy received from the sun, transmitted in the form of short waves (1/10,000 to 1/100,000 in. in length) and traveling at the rate of about 186,000 miles a second, is called *solar radiation,* or *insolation.* A part of the solar-radiation spectrum can be perceived as light. But there are other waves, some shorter (ultraviolet) and others longer (infrared), which cannot be seen. Since solar radiation is the single important source of atmospheric heat, its distribution over the earth is fundamental to an understanding of weather and climatic phenomena. In solar energy is to be found the *ultimate* cause of most of the features of atmospheric circulation.

2.2 Major Factors Determining the Distribution of Solar Radiation. Omitting for the moment the effects of an atmosphere, the amount of solar energy, *i.e.,* climatic energy, that any latitude on the earth's surface receives will depend primarily upon two factors: (*a*) the *intensity* of solar radiation, or the angle

at which the rays of sunlight reach the earth, and (*b*) the *duration* of solar radiation, or length of day. Because an oblique solar ray is spread out over a larger surface than a vertical one, it delivers less energy per unit area (Fig. 2.1). Moreover, although for the moment the effects of an atmosphere are being omitted, it may be added that an oblique ray also passes through a considerably thicker layer of scattering, absorbing, and reflecting air. Outside the tropics, therefore, winter sunlight is much weaker than that of summer. For example, in late December the noon sun at Madison, Wis., located at 43°N., is only 23½° above the horizon, whereas in late June it has an elevation of 70½°. For the same reasons, the daily period is characterized by a much more potent

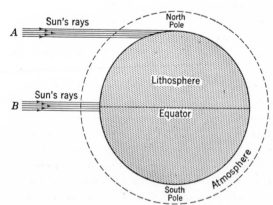

Fig. 2.1 The oblique ray, *A*, delivers less energy at the earth's surface than the vertical ray, *B*, because its energy is spread over a larger surface and likewise because it passes through a thicker layer of absorbing and reflecting atmosphere which diminishes its energy.

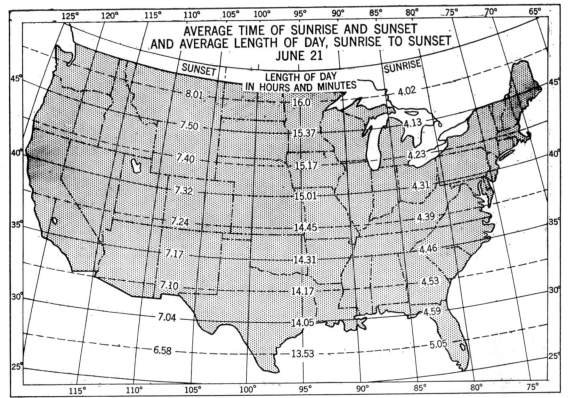

Fig. 2.2 At the time of the summer solstice days are about 2 hr. longer in northernmost United States than in the extreme south. This greater length of time the sun shines in the north somewhat compensates for the more oblique rays of the sun.

noon sun than is true of that in the early morning or late afternoon hours.

As regards the second item, *viz.*, duration of solar radiation, it would seem to require no further explanation of the fact that the longer the sun shines (length of day), the greater the amount of solar energy received, all other conditions being equal. Thus the longest summer days (15 + hr.) in the latitude of southern Wisconsin, which have 6+ hr. more of daylight than the shortest winter days (9— hr.), allow for much greater receipts of solar energy (Figs. 2.2 and 2.3). It is quite understandable, then, why in these latitudes summer temperatures are so much higher than winter temperatures, since (*a*) sun's rays are less oblique, and (*b*) days are much longer in summer.

Since along any parallel the length of day and the angle of the sun's rays are equal, it follows that all parts of a parallel (except for differences in the transparency of the atmosphere) receive identical amounts of insolation. Similarly, different parallels or latitudes receive unlike amounts of solar radiation, the annual amount decreasing from equator to poles. If solar energy were the only control of weather and climate, all places in the same latitude should have identical climates. Although certainly not identical throughout, the strong climatic resemblances within latitude belts testify to the dominant, although not exclusive, rank of sun control.

2.3 Earth and Sun Relations. The rotation and revolution of the earth and the inclination

Length of the Longest Day (Hence Also of the Longest Night) at Certain Latitudes

Latitude	0°	17°	41°	49°	63°	66½°	67°21′	69°51′	78°11′	90°
Duration	12 hr.	13 hr.	15 hr.	16 hr.	20 hr.	24 hr.	1 mo.	2 mo.	4 mo.	6 mo.

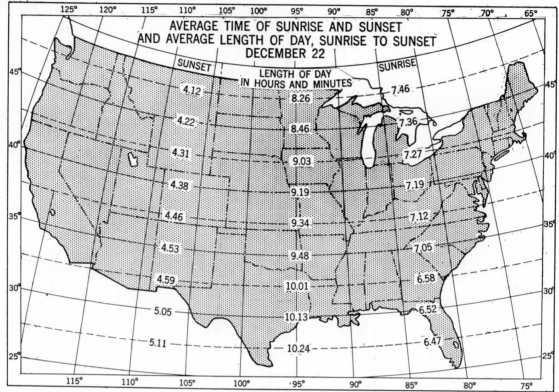

Fig. 2.3 At the time of the winter solstice days are about 2 hr. shorter in northernmost United States than they are in the extreme south. This, together with the more oblique sun's rays, cause the north to be much colder than the south in winter.

and parallelism of its axis have been discussed in an earlier chapter (1). It remains to be analyzed, then, how these earth motions and positions act to produce the changing lengths of day and varying angles of the sun's rays, which in turn are the causes of the seasons.

2.4 *The Equinoxes; Spring and Fall.* Twice during the yearly period of revolution, on Mar. 21 and Sept. 23, the sun's noon rays are directly overhead or vertical at the equator (Fig. 2.4). At these times, therefore, the circle of illumination, marking the position of the tangent rays, passes through both poles and consequently cuts all the earth's parallels exactly in half. One half of each parallel (180°) consequently is in light, and the other half in darkness. For this reason, since the path described by any point on the earth's surface during the period of rotation is coincident with its parallel of latitude, days and nights are equal (12 hr. each) over the entire earth. From this fact the two dates Mar.

21 and Sept. 23 get their names, the *equinoxes* (spring equinox Mar. 21, autumn equinox Sept. 23—Northern Hemisphere). At these seasons the maximum solar energy is being received at the equator, from which latitude it diminishes regularly toward either pole, where it becomes zero.

2.5 *The Solstices; Summer and Winter.* On June 22 the earth is approximately midway in its orbit between the equinoctial positions, and the North Pole is inclined $23\frac{1}{2}°$ *toward* the sun (Fig. 2.4). As a result of the axial inclination, the sun's rays are shifted northward by that same amount ($23\frac{1}{2}°$), so that the noon rays are vertical at the Tropic of Cancer ($23\frac{1}{2}°$N.), and the tangent rays in the Northern Hemisphere pass over the pole and reach the Arctic Circle ($66\frac{1}{2}°$N.), $23\frac{1}{2}°$ on the opposite side of it. In the Southern Hemisphere the tangent rays do not reach the pole but terminate at the Antarctic Circle, $23\frac{1}{2}°$ short of it. Thus while all parts of the earth north of the Arctic Circle are experiencing constant daylight, similar latitudes in the Southern Hemisphere (poleward from the Antarctic Circle) are entirely without sunlight. At this time, June 22, or the *summer solstice,* all

parallels, except the equator, are cut unequally by the circle of illumination, those in the Northern Hemisphere having the larger segments of their circumferences toward the sun so that days are longer than nights. Longer days, plus a greater angle of the sun's rays, result in

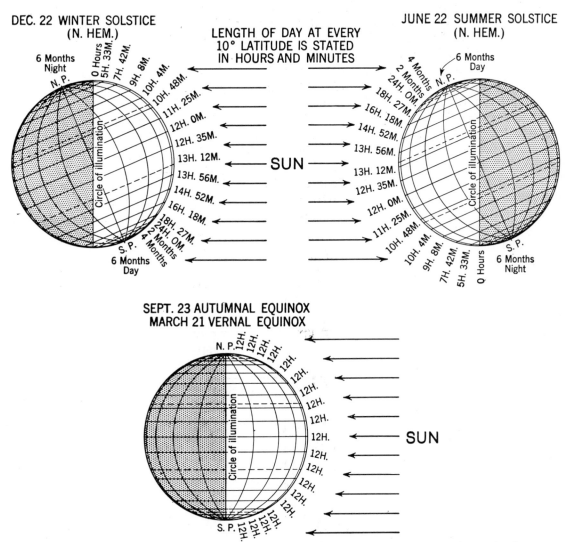

Fig. 2.4 On the equinoxes, when the sun's vertical rays are at the equator, the circle of illumination cuts all the parallels in half, and days and nights are equal in length over the entire earth. At this time insolation decreases regularly from equator to poles. See Fig. 2.6 for distribution of insolation from pole to pole at the time of the equinoxes. At the times of the solstices the sun's vertical rays have reached their greatest poleward migration. The circle of illumination cuts all the parallels (except the equator) unequally so that days and nights are unequal in length except at latitude 0°. See Fig. 2.7 for distribution of isolation from pole to pole at the time of the solstices.

a maximum receipt of solar energy in the Northern Hemisphere at this time. Summer, with its associated high temperatures, is the result, and north of the equator June 22 is known as the summer solstice. In the Southern Hemisphere at this same time, all of these conditions are reversed, nights being longer than days and the sun's rays relatively oblique, so that solar radiation is at a minimum and winter conditions prevail.

On Dec. 22, when the earth is in the opposite position in its orbit from what it was on June 22, it is the South Pole that is inclined $23\frac{1}{2}°$ *toward* the sun (Fig. 2.4). The latter's noon rays are then vertical over the Tropic of Capricorn ($23\frac{1}{2}°$S.), and the tangent rays pass $23\frac{1}{2}°$ over the South Pole to the Antarctic Circle ($66\frac{1}{2}°$S.). Consequently, south of $66\frac{1}{2}°$S. there is constant light, while north of $66\frac{1}{2}°$N. there is a continuous absence of sunlight. All parallels of the earth, except the equator, are cut unequally by the circle of illumination, with days longer and sun's rays more nearly vertical in the Southern Hemisphere. This, therefore, is summer south of the equator but winter in the Northern Hemisphere (winter solstice), where opposite conditions prevail.

2.6 Effects of the Atmosphere upon Incoming Insolation. The total effect of the atmosphere upon a beam of sunlight passing through it is to reduce its intensity (Fig. 2.5). As a result of this weakening effect of the atmosphere upon incoming insolation the sunlight reaching the earth is, on the *average,* only 50 to 60 per cent as strong at it was at the outer limits of the earth's atmosphere. To be sure the above figure varies with latitude, with the seasons, and with the amount of cloudiness. The processes by which the atmosphere weakens solar energy are: (*a*) *selective scattering* chiefly of the short waves of blue light by very small obscuring particles; (*b*) *diffuse reflection* of all wave lengths by larger particles, such as cloud droplets; and (*c*) *absorption* of selected wave lengths, chiefly by water vapor which is concentrated in the lower strata of the atmosphere. The scattering and reflecting processes operate to send some of the insolation back to space but some of it also reaches the earth's surface as diffuse daylight.

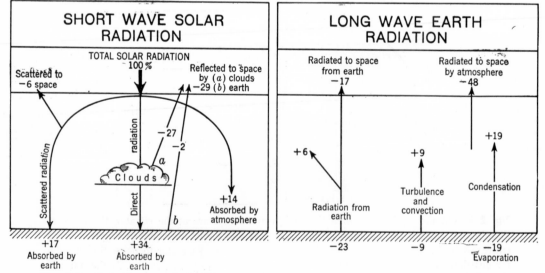

Fig. 2.5 Only about one-half (51 per cent) of the incoming solar radiation passes through the atmosphere and heats the earth's surface. Another 14 per cent is absorbed by the atmosphere. Some 35 per cent of the solar energy is scattered and reflected back to space and thus has no effect on heating either the earth's surface or its atmosphere.

It is estimated that 35 per cent of the total insolation reaching the outer limits of the air layer is returned as solar energy to space by scattering and reflection from clouds, small dust particles, molecules of air, and the earth's surface. This has no part in heating either the earth or its atmosphere. Fourteen per cent of the solar radiation may be absorbed directly by the atmosphere, most of it by water vapor. The remaining 51 per cent reaches the earth's surface either as direct sunlight or as diffuse daylight, is absorbed by it, heats it, and eventually heats the atmosphere as well.

From the preceding analysis it is obvious that only some 65 per cent of the solar radiation (14 per cent absorbed by the atmosphere directly and 51 per cent absorbed by the earth's surface) is available for heating the atmosphere. Equally significant is the fact that the atmosphere receives eight to ten times as much energy from the heated earth's surface as it does from its own direct absorption of solar radiation.

2.7 Distribution of Solar Radiation over the Earth's Surface. It is clear from the previous discussion that the belt of maximum insolation swings back and forth across the equator during the course of a year, following the shifting rays of the sun, with two variables, (a) angle of sun's rays and (b) length of day, largely determining the amount of solar energy received at any time or place.

2.8 *Distribution from Pole to Pole along a Meridian. For the year as a whole* insolation is highest at the equator and diminishes with regularity toward the poles. The Northern and Southern Hemispheres share equally in the annual amounts of solar energy received (Fig. 2.6a).

Fig. 2.6 Latitudinal distribution of solar energy at the earth's surface. For the year as a whole and at the two equinoxes solar energy is symmetrically distributed in the Northern and Southern Hemispheres. There is a maximum in equatorial latitudes and minima at the North and South Poles. At the solstices solar energy is very unequally distributed, with the summer hemisphere receiving two to three times the amount that the winter hemisphere does.

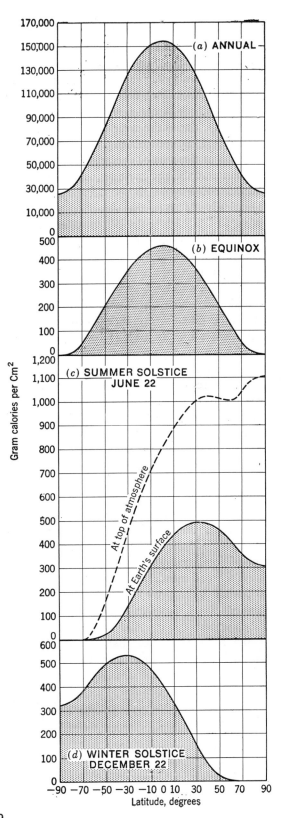

29

The distribution is similar at the time of the two *equinoxes,* there being one equatorial maximum and two polar minima, except that at these two dates insolation declines to zero at the poles which is not true, of course, for the average of the entire year (Fig. 2.6*b*). This symmetrical latitudinal distribution of solar radiation at the time of equinoxes, with a single maximum at the equator and a regular decline toward either pole, is of great importance climatically. It is in the transition seasons of spring and fall when the Northern and Southern Hemispheres are receiving approximately equal amounts of insolation that temperature conditions in the two hemispheres are most nearly alike. Similarly, pressure, wind, and precipitation conditions, and as a result the overall weather situation, are more in balance to the north and south of the equator. Significantly, world temperature, pressure, wind, and precipitation-distribution patterns for spring and fall bear close resemblances to the average annual patterns for these same climatic elements.

At the time of the *two solstices* (June 22 and Dec. 22), when the sun's noon rays are vertical $23\frac{1}{2}°$ poleward from the equator and the length of day increases toward the pole where it reaches a maximum, the latitudinal distribution of insolation is very asymmetrically developed, with the summer hemisphere receiving two to three times the amount of the winter hemisphere (Fig. 2.6*c*, 2.6*d*).[1] Latitudinal distribution of insolation at the surface of the earth shows a broad maximum at about latitude 35°–40°, while latitude 60° receives more than the equator. Even the pole in the summer hemisphere receives more solar energy at the time of the summer solstice than do the tropical latitudes poleward from 10° to 15° in the winter hemisphere. It is not unusual, therefore, that the maximum surface air temperatures should occur over the land masses of the lower middle latitudes and not at the equator. During

the course of a year the zone of maximum insolation shows a total latitudinal displacement of 70° to 80°, a fact that must have important effects upon seasonal temperatures, rainfall, pressure, and winds. It is climatically significant also that the insolation *gradient* in the winter hemisphere is much steeper than that in the summer hemisphere. The above described characteristics of solar-radiation distribution at the times of the solstices, which times represent the extreme seasons of summer and winter, provide the basic explanations for many of the earth's larger features of weather and climate. Some of the latter are (*a*) the marked north-south migration of the temperature, wind, and precipitation belts following a similar migration of insolation belts; (*b*) the warm-to-hot summers of the lower middle latitudes where insolation reaches a maximum for the summer hemisphere; (*c*) the much steeper temperature gradients in the winter hemisphere (paralleling insolation distribution) as compared with the summer hemisphere; and (*d*) the greater storminess and weather variability in the winter hemisphere.

2.9 Annual Distribution of Insolation for Representative Latitudes. The yearly insolation curves for the several latitudes can be arranged in three general groups: low, middle, and high latitudes (Fig. 2.7). (*a*) In the tropical or low-latitude type, which prevails in those regions between the Tropics of Cancer and Capricorn, insolation is constantly high and varies little throughout the year. This feature accounts for the constant heat of the tropics. Since during the course of a year all regions between the two tropics are passed over twice by the vertical rays of the sun, the insolation curve for low latitudes contains two weak maxima and two slight minima. (*b*) The middle-latitude type, on the other hand, has a single maximum, and as in the tropics, insolation at no time declines to zero. The great seasonal contrasts in insolation are reflected in similar seasonal contrasts in temperature. (*c*) The polar type, *i.e.,* poleward from the Arctic and Antarctic Circles, also has but one maximum and one minimum period of insolation, but unlike the other lati-

---

[1] By "summer hemisphere" is meant the hemisphere that has summer. Thus the Northern Hemisphere would be the summer hemisphere in July and the Southern Hemisphere would be the summer hemisphere in January.

tudes there is a portion of the year when direct sunlight is completely absent. For this reason, the insolation curve for the high latitudes declines to zero. Here also seasonal contrasts in insolation are marked and temperature contrasts are also marked.

ABSORPTION OF INSOLATION AT THE EARTH'S SURFACE; PROCESSES ASSOCIATED WITH THE HEATING AND COOLING OF THE EARTH'S SURFACE AND ATMOSPHERE

Heating and Cooling of Land and Water Surfaces

2.10 Land and Water Contrasts. Thus far the discussion has been concerned largely with the latitudinal distribution of solar energy, the single important source of atmospheric heat. But sun energy is of such short wave lengths that only relatively small amounts (14 per cent) of it can be absorbed directly by the earth's atmosphere. Perhaps, on the average, a little more than one-half of the solar energy slips through the atmosphere and reaches the surface of the earth, although to be sure, a small part of this is reflected back again, leaving only about 51 per cent as effective in heating the earth's surface.

All bodies whatever their temperature give off energy or radiation which is transmitted in a form that resembles waves. The hotter the body, the more intense the radiation and the shorter the wave lengths. Low-temperature long-wave radiation like that of the earth is invisible, whereas a part of the sun's high-temperature short-wave radiation is visible. In order to be readily absorbed by the air, sun energy first must be converted into terrestrial energy, which is composed of longer wave lengths. (Ratio of wave lengths of solar and terrestrial energy is roughly 1:25.) This conversion from short-wave solar to long-wave terrestrial energy takes place principally at the earth's surface, by which insolation is much more readily absorbed than it is by the relatively transparent atmosphere. Absorbed at the earth's surface, the solar energy is there converted into heat, after which the earth itself becomes a radiating body. Thus the atmosphere receives most of its heat only *indirectly* from the sun but *directly* from the earth's surface, which in turn had previously absorbed and consequently been warmed by solar energy. It is obvious, therefore, that preliminary to a discussion of heating and cooling the atmosphere,

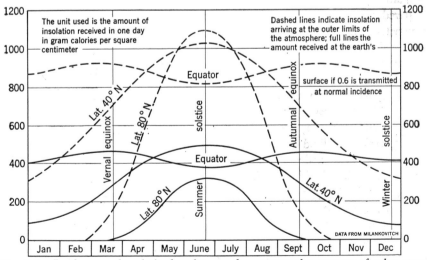

Fig. 2.7 In the very low latitudes close to the equator the amount of solar energy received is large and it varies little throughout the year. In the middle and higher latitudes there are large seasonal differences in the receipts of solar energy.

it is necessary to understand the comparative reactions to solar energy (in terms of reflection, absorption, transmission) of the various kinds of terrestrial surfaces. Here the greatest contrasts are between land and water surfaces, although to be sure, there are no fixed values even for all land areas, because of such variables as snow cover, soil color, and vegetation color, all of which react differently to incident solar radiation.

Land and water surfaces with identical amounts of insolation falling upon them do not acquire similar temperatures, nor do they cool at the same rate. The primary reason for this contrast is related to the fluid character of water. Vertical convection currents, together with waves, drifts, surface currents, and tides, tend to distribute the absorbed solar energy throughout a large mass of water. As a consequence the surface temperatures of the water do not rise rapidly. Land, on the other hand, is unable to distribute the absorbed solar energy throughout a large volume, with the result that the land surface acquires a higher temperature. It is this ability of water to distribute heat gains and losses at the surface throughout a large volume that accounts for its greater conservativeness in temperature changes as compared with land.

A supplementary, although less important, factor is the relatively greater transparency of water as compared with land. The sun's rays are able to penetrate a water body to considerable depths, with the result that energy is distributed throughout a somewhat larger mass. On the other hand, the opaque land concentrates the sun energy close to the surface, which results in more rapid and intense heating. This same concentration of the energy close to the surface likewise permits the land area to cool more rapidly than is true of a deeply warmed water body. Also of some significance is the fact that the *specific heat* of water is higher than that of land. In other words, it requires only one-third to one-half as much energy to raise a given volume of dry earth by one degree as it does an equal volume of water. For the earth as a whole, the losses of solar energy by reflection from land and water surfaces are not greatly different, so that reflection is not a significant item in the heating and cooling contrasts of land and water surfaces. It is of considerable importance, however, in determining the surface temperatures of land surfaces with contrasting reflecting powers.

From the above comparisons of land and water as regards their reactions to insolation, it becomes evident that land-controlled, or continental, climates should be characterized by large daily and seasonal extremes of temperature, becoming alternately hot and cold, whereas ocean-controlled, or marine, climates should be more moderate with only small seasonal and daily temperature changes. The ocean surface probably changes temperature not more than 1° between day and night, and seasonal changes also are very small. The relatively slower heating and cooling of water bodies quite naturally lead to a lag in the seasonal temperatures of marine climates.

HEATING AND COOLING THE ATMOSPHERE

2.11 Being acquainted now, as a result of the previous discussion, with (a) the distribution of solar energy over the earth and (b) the contrasting reactions of land and water surfaces to this solar energy, and (c) being aware that the air receives most of its energy *directly* from the surface upon which it rests and only *indirectly* from the sun, the background is sufficient to proceed with an analysis of the processes involved in heating and cooling the atmosphere.

2.12 Absorption of Direct and Reflected Insolation. The earth's atmosphere is relatively transparent to direct and reflected solar radiation, which is short-wave energy, only about 14 per cent being absorbed, and that chiefly by small amounts of water vapor. About one-half of this absorption takes place in the lower two kilometers of air, but this is a large mass of air through which to spread 7 per cent of the solar radiation. The process is not very effective therefore in producing the normal daytime rise in air temperature close to the earth's surface, or of the seasonal changes in middle and high latitudes. Evidence of this is suggested by the fact that often on a clear winter day, when the land surface is blanketed by a reflecting snow cover, air temperatures may remain extremely low in spite of a bright sun. At the same time, on the south side of an absorbing brick wall or building, where short-wave sun energy is being converted into long-wave terrestrial energy, it may be comfortably warm.

2.13 Conduction. When two bodies of unequal temperature are in *contact* with one another, energy in the form of heat passes from the warmer to the colder object until they both attain the same temperature. Thus, during the daylight hours, the solid earth (without a snow cover), being a much better absorber of insolation than air, attains a higher temperature. By conduction, therefore, the layer of air resting upon the warmer earth becomes heated. But air is a poor conductor, so that heat from the warmed layer in contact with the earth's surface is transferred very slowly to those above. Unless there is, through movement, a constant replacement of the warmed layer in contact with the earth, only the lower few feet will be heated by this process during the course of a day. Through air currents and winds, however, more air is brought into contact with the heated earth's surface and consequently is warmed. Heating by conduction is primarily a daytime and a summer process.

Just as a warm earth on a summer day heats the air layer next to it by conduction, so a cold earth, chilled through energy losses to space by terrestrial radiation on a winter night, has exactly the opposite effect. The earth cools more rapidly than the atmosphere because it is a more efficient radiator of energy. It not infrequently happens that, during clear, calm winter nights, as a result of radiation and conduction, the atmospheric strata adjacent to the earth become colder than those at some distance above its surface. In general, heat transfer by conduction in the atmosphere is very unimportant compared with the other processes.

2.14 Earth Radiation. Short-wave solar energy, absorbed at the earth's surface, is there transformed into heat. Through this absorption and conversion of insolation, the heated earth

becomes a radiating body. But although the atmosphere is capable of absorbing only relatively small amounts (14 per cent) of short-wave incoming solar energy, it is, on the other hand, able to retain up to 90 per cent of the outgoing long-wave earth radiation. As stated before, water vapor is the principal absorbing gas. This absorptive effect of water vapor upon outgoing earth radiation is illustrated by the rapid night cooling in deserts, the dry air and clear sky permitting a very rapid escape of energy. Obviously the effect of the atmosphere is analogous to that of a pane of glass in a greenhouse or a closed automobile, which lets through most of the incoming short-wave solar energy but greatly retards the outgoing long-wave earth radiation, thus maintaining surface air temperatures considerably higher than they otherwise would be and preventing great extremes between day and night. This is the so-called *greenhouse effect* of the earth's atmosphere (Fig. 2.8). The greenhouse depends for a large part of its heating upon the principle that the glass roof and sides permit free entrance of solar energy, but on the other hand, prevent the ready escape of long-wave heat energy. A more commonplace experience illustrating the greenhouse effect is the superheating of the inside of a parked automobile that occurs on a sunny day if the car's windows are closed.

Radiation of terrestrial energy from the earth's surface upward toward space is a con-

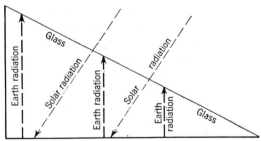

Fig. 2.8 Illustrating the "greenhouse effect" of the earth's atmosphere. The glass in the roof and sides of the greenhouse, like the atmosphere, is relatively transparent to the short-wave solar energy, but, by contrast, is relatively opaque to the long-wave earth radiation.

tinuous process. During the daylight hours up to about midafternoon, however, receipts of energy from the sun are in excess of the amount radiated from the earth, with the result that surface-air temperatures usually continue to rise until two to four o'clock in the afternoon. But during the night, when receipts of solar energy cease, a continued loss of energy through earth radiation results in a cooling of the earth's surface and a consequent drop in air temperature. Being a better radiator than air, the ground during the night becomes cooler than the air above it. When this condition prevails, the lower layers of atmosphere lose heat by radiation to the colder ground as well as upward toward space. This process is particularly effective during the long nights of winter when, if the skies are clear and the air is dry, excessively rapid and long-continued radiation takes place. If a snow cover mantles the ground, cooling is even more pronounced, for most of the incoming solar radiation during the short day is reflected by the snow and thus does not heat the earth's surface. At night, the snow, which is a very poor conductor of heat, allows little energy to come up from the ground below to replenish that lost by radiation at the top of the snow surface. As a result, the snow surface becomes excessively cold, and then in turn the air layer resting upon it.

Water, like land, is a good radiator, but the cooled surface waters keep constantly sinking to be replaced by the warmer water from below. Extremely low temperatures over water bodies are impossible, therefore, until they are frozen over, after which they act like a snow-covered land surface.

Humid air or a cloudy sky tends to prevent rapid earth radiation so that air temperatures remain higher, and frosts are less likely on humid nights and especially when a cloud cover prevails. There are authentic cases, in the dry air and under the cloudless skies of Sahara, of day temperatures of 90° followed by night temperatures slightly below freezing. When clouds cover the sky, all the earth radiation is completely absorbed at the base of the cloud sheet, which in turn reradiates a part of it back to the earth so that cooling of the earth is retarded. Under a sky with low clouds the net loss of heat from the ground is only about one-seventh the loss with clear skies. Water vapor likewise absorbs and reradiates outgoing terrestrial energy but not so effectively as liquid or solid cloud particles.

Unlike heat transfer by conduction, convection, and advection, for which some sort of material medium is required, radiation is the only process by which heat can be transferred through space. It is the single means, therefore, by which energy can be gained from a source outside the earth, such as the sun, or by which the earth can ultimately lose its energy to space. Since the earth appears to maintain a relatively constant temperature, it must be that its receipts of solar radiation from the sun are balanced by the losses of earth radiation outward toward space.

2.15 Warming the Atmosphere by Heat of Condensation. A relatively large amount of the solar energy which reaches the earth's surface is consumed in evaporating water. This converted solar energy is thus contained in the atmosphere's water vapor in latent or potential form. When condensation occurs and the water vapor is returned to the liquid or solid state this latent energy is again released into the atmosphere and heats it. Heat of condensation is a principal source of heat energy for the atmosphere (Fig. 2.5).

2.16 Transfer of Heat by Vertical and Horizontal Currents in the Atmosphere. Through these processes temperatures acquired through absorption of solar energy, through conduction and radiation processes, and by heat of condensation are transferred from one part of the atmosphere to another.

2.17 *Vertical transfer* results from convectional currents and eddy motions in the atmosphere. When surface air is heated by conduction and radiation it expands in volume and consequently becomes less dense. Hence it is forced upward by the surrounding colder, denser air which at the surface flows toward the warm source. Such a circulation (Fig. 2.9) is called a *convectional system*. Warm surface

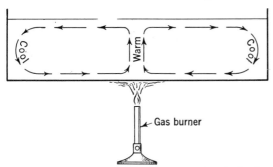

Fig. 2.9 Illustrating a simple convectional circulation. The expanded warm fluid rises over the heat source and settles over the colder areas. Aloft, the circulation is from warm to cool areas, while at the bottom the reverse is true and movement is from cool to warm areas.

air, expanded, and therefore less dense, is like a cork that is held under water; *i.e.*, it is unstable and inclined to rise. This convectional principle (which applies to liquids and gases only) is employed in the ordinary hot-air and hot-water heating systems. The rising masses of warmed air on a hot summer day make air transport relatively bumpy, since the airplane alternately crosses rising and sinking air masses.

Still another form of vertical heat transport is that resulting from mechanical turbulence and eddy currents which are so characteristic of the lower atmosphere. Turbulence is particularly well developed in strong gusty winds and is further increased by rough terrain. Vertical mixing by thermal convection, turbulence, and eddy currents is the most important method of carrying the warmth acquired by the surface air throughout the higher layers of the atmosphere (Fig. 2.5).

2.18 *Horizontal transfer* of temperature conditions, called *advection*, results from the movement of winds and air masses. Considering the earth as a whole this is the most important means of heat transfer. Moreover, it is this advection of air masses that causes most of the day-to-day weather changes and the storminess of winter climates in the middle latitudes. Even the layman has come to recognize that in Northern Hemisphere middle latitudes a south wind is usually associated with unseasonably high temperatures. In such a case the wind acts simply as the conveyer or importer of heat from lower latitudes where insolation is greater and higher temperatures are normal. Such an importation of southerly warmth in winter results in mild weather, with melting snow and sloppy streets. In summer, several days of south wind may result in a "hot wave," with maximum temperatures of over 90°.

If tropical air masses with associated south winds from regions that are usually warmer (Northern Hemisphere) import higher temperatures to the regions toward which they blow, then polar air masses with associated north winds from colder, higher latitudes, or from the cold interiors of continents, should in turn bring lower temperatures. These importations are particularly effective where there are no mountain barriers to block the wind movement. In eastern North America where lowlands prevail, great masses of cold polar air at irregular intervals pour down over the Mississippi Valley, oc-

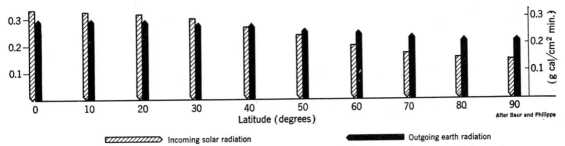

Incoming solar radiation Outgoing earth radiation

Fig. 2.10 In the lower latitudes, equatorward of about 37°, the annual amount of incoming solar radiation exceeds the losses from outgoing earth radiation. The reverse is true for the middle and higher latitudes, and losses from outgoing earth radiation exceed the gains from incoming solar radiation.

casionally carrying severe frosts even to the
Gulf States.

Not only the advection of air masses from
different latitudes but also that of those moving
from large water bodies onto lands bring contrasting temperatures in different seasons.

2.19 Heat Balance in the Atmosphere.
Since the mean temperature of the earth remains about the same, getting neither colder
nor warmer, it follows that the heat lost by the
earth through radiation to space is identical
with the amount of energy received from the
sun. But although this balance is true for the
earth as a whole, it is not true for individual
latitudes. In the low latitudes, equatorward
from about 37°, the incoming solar energy exceeds the outgoing earth energy, whereas poleward from latitude 37° exactly the reverse is
true (Fig. 2.10). Unless there is to be a constant increase in the temperatures of low latitudes and a constant decrease in the temperatures of the middle and higher latitudes, this
situation requires a continuous transfer of energy from low to high latitudes of the earth.
This transfer is accomplished by the winds and
the ocean currents. *In fact, in this unequal latitudinal distribution of solar and terrestrial radiation is to be found the ultimate cause for the
earth's atmospheric circulation and for much of
its weather.*

DAILY AND SEASONAL MARCH OF TEMPERATURE

2.20 All average temperatures for a month,
season, year, or even a long period of years are
built upon the *mean daily temperature* as the
basic unit. The daily mean is the average of the
highest and the lowest temperatures recorded
during the 24-hr. period.

The mean daily march of temperature chiefly
reflects the balance between incoming solar
radiation and outgoing earth radiation (Fig.
2.11). From about sunrise until 2:00 to 4:00
P.M., when energy is being supplied by incoming solar radiation faster than it is being lost by
earth radiation, the temperature curve usually
continues to rise (Figs. 2.11 and 2.12). Conversely, from about 3:00± P.M. to sunrise,

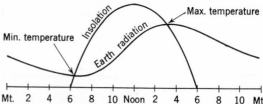

Fig. 2.11 Representation of the march of incoming
solar radiation and of outgoing earth radiation for
the daily 24-hr. period at about the time of an equinox, and their combined effects upon the time of
daily maximum and minimum temperatures.

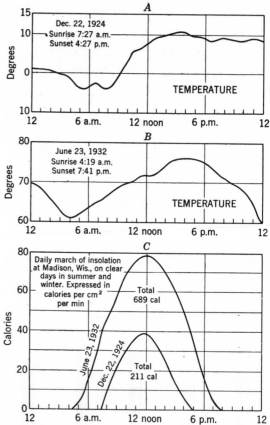

Fig. 2.12 Daily march of temperature (*A* and *B*)
and of insolation (*C*) on clear days in winter and
summer at Madison, Wis. The total solar energy
recorded was $3\frac{1}{4}$ times as great on June 23 as on
Dec. 22. Note that temperature lags behind insolation. South winds prevented normal night cooling on
Dec. 22.

when loss by terrestrial radiation exceeds receipts of solar energy, the daily temperature curve usually falls.

The annual march, or cycle, of temperature reflects the daily increase in insolation (hence heat accumulated in the air and ground) from midwinter to midsummer and the decrease in the same from midsummer to midwinter (Fig. 2.13). Usually there is a temperature lag of 30 to 40 days after the periods of maximum or minimum insolation. This reflects the balance between incoming and outgoing energy. The lag of the seasonal temperature maxima and minima over those of insolation may be even greater over oceans or along windward coasts in middle latitudes, where August may be the warmest month and February the coldest.

Distribution of Temperature: Vertical and Horizontal

VERTICAL DISTRIBUTION OF TEMPERATURE

2.21 Temperature Decreases with Altitude. Numerous temperature observations made during mountain, balloon, airplane, and kite ascents show that under normal conditions there is a general *decrease* in temperature with *increasing* elevation. Although the rate of decrease is not uniform, varying with time of day, season, and location, the average is approximately 3.3°F. for each 1,000-ft. rise (Fig. 2.14,*B*). The fact that air temperature is normally highest at low elevations next to the earth and decreases with altitude clearly indicates that most of the atmospheric heat is received directly from the earth's surface and only indirectly from the sun. But the lower air is warmer, not only because it is closest to the direct source of heat, but also because it is denser and contains more water vapor and dust, which cause it to be a more efficient absorber of earth radiation than is the thinner, drier, cleaner air aloft. This decrease in temperature upward from the earth's surface normally prevails throughout the lower 4 to 6 miles of atmosphere. The principal exception to the rule that temperature decreases with altitude is where temperature inversions prevail.

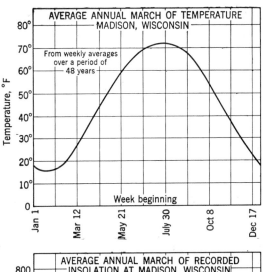

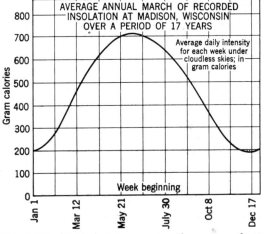

Fig. 2.13 Note that temperature lags a month or more behind insolation. The insolation curve has been smoothed slightly.

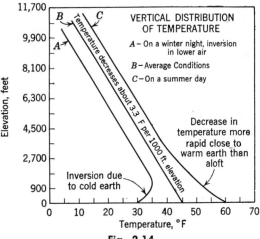

Fig. 2.14

2.22 Temperature inversions are said to exist when the normal lapse rate is reversed and there is an *increase* in temperature upward away from the earth. Such a condition may occur in the lowest layers of the atmosphere very close to the earth's surface or it may be found at altitudes of several thousand feet above the surface.

2.23 *Surface temperature inversions,* one of the commonest and most readily observed, originate as a result of cooling the air by radiation and conduction from the underlying cold earth's surface. Since the surface is a better radiator of heat energy than the atmosphere, at night the land surface cools more rapidly than the air. The air next to the cold earth is then chilled by radiation and conduction to the cold ground and thereby becomes colder than the air farther removed from the earth (Fig. 2.14,*A*).

Local, diurnal ground inversions of a few score or hundred feet in depth are well-known nighttime phenomena of the cooler seasons. Ideal conditions for these nocturnal radiation inversions are (*a*) long nights, as in winter, so that there will be a relatively long period when outgoing earth radiation exceeds incoming solar radiation; (*b*) a clear sky so that loss of heat by terrestrial radiation is rapid and unretarded; (*c*) cold, dry air that absorbs little earth radiation; (*d*) calm air so that little mixing will take place, and the surface stratum will, as a consequence, have time, by conduction and radiation, to become excessively cold; and (*e*) a snow-covered surface, which, owing to reflection of solar energy, heats little by day and, being a poor conductor, retards the upward flow of heat from the ground below the snow cover. At the Eiffel Tower in Paris there is throughout the year an increase in temperature upward from base to top between midnight and 4:00 A.M. Some of the deepest, most extensive, and most persistent inversions are those which prevail over the snow-covered northern parts of North America and Eurasia in winter. A very close relationship exists between temperature inversions and frost and fog, since conditions favorable for the one are also ideal for the others. Although temperature inversions are common on flattish land surfaces, they are, nevertheless, more perfectly developed in depressions.

During a temperature inversion when the cooler, denser air is at the surface the air is stable and nonbuoyant. There is no inclination for it to rise. Such a condition, therefore, is opposed to the formation of clouds and precipitation.

2.24 *Above-surface Inversions of Temperature.* These occur in the free atmosphere well above the earth's surface. Such inversions are usually produced by the settling or subsidence of air masses. They also operate to make the air stable and hence are opposed to vertical movement. Regions with well developed above-surface inversions of temperature are, therefore, likely to have small amounts of rainfall.

2.25 Surface Inversions and Air Drainage. In regions of uneven surface configuration, the cold stratum of air next to the earth's surface, because of its greater density, slips off the uplands and flows down to surrounding lowlands (Fig. 2.15). This phenomenon of the cold air drained from the adjacent slopes collecting in valleys and lowlands is designated as *air drainage.* It is a well-known fact that the first frosts of autumn and the last in spring occur in bottomlands, while the lowest minima on calm, clear winter nights are found in similar locations. On one occasion, during a cold spell, a

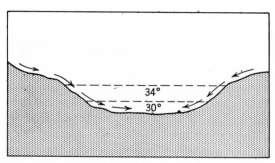

Fig. 2.15 Cold air, because it is denser, tends to settle in lower places. This drainage of the cold, dense air into depressions is the reason why frost and fog are more common in low places than on adjacent slopes.

temperature of —8.9° was registered on top of Mount Washington, N.H., while records of —23 to —31° were recorded in the surrounding lowlands. Citrus orchards in California, which are quite intolerant of frost, are located on the upper slopes of alluvial fans where air drainage causes a slipping off of the frosty air, while the colder lower slopes and bottoms are given over to hardier deciduous fruits and nuts or to field crops. Coffee in Brazil is prevailingly planted on the rolling uplands, while the frosty valleys are avoided. Resort hotels in the Swiss Alps shun the cold, foggy valleys and choose instead sites on the brighter and warmer slopes. So definite and sharp is the autumn frost line along certain of the valley slopes in the Blue Ridge Mountains that one can trace it by means of the color line between the darkened frozen vegetation below and the brighter living green of that above. At times the lower part of a bush may be frozen while the top is untouched.

2.26 Frost and Its Distribution. The term "frost" may be applied either (*a*) to the white deposit of condensed water vapor in solid form (hoarfrost) or (*b*) to a temperature of 32° or below, even though there is no deposit of white frost. There are frosts of various degrees of severity, but it is the "killing frost," which may be defined as a temperature condition "of sufficient severity to be generally destructive to the staple products of the locality," that is of principal interest to geographers. When it is difficult by direct observation of destructive effects to determine the dates of the first killing frost in autumn and the last in spring, and thereby the length of the frost-free, or growing, season, the first and last dates on which a minimum temperature of 32° was recorded are accepted. Throughout most of the middle latitudes frosts are of chief significance in autumn and spring, although in subtropical latitudes, such as California and Florida, midwinter frosts are critical because of the active growth of sensitive crops during that season (Fig. 2.16). On the poleward margins of the intermediate zones, on the other hand, in such regions as northern Canada and northern Eurasia, summer frosts not in-

frequently do serious damage to cereal crops. In tropical lowlands freezing temperatures are entirely absent.

2.27 *Conditions Favorable for Frost.* Ideal conditions for the occurrence of frost are those that are conducive to rapid and prolonged surface cooling, *viz.*, (*a*) a preliminary importation of a mass of dry, cool polar air, (*b*) followed by clear, dry, calm nights, during which the surface air, by radiation and conduction, may be reduced below freezing. The original importation provides the necessary mass of cool air, the temperature of which is already relatively low, although still somewhat above freezing, while further rapid loss of heat by earth radiation during the following clear night is all that is necessary to reduce the temperature of the surface air below freezing. But even though the generally favorable conditions for frost occurrence described above may prevail over extensive areas, the destructive effects very often are local and patchy. This is a matter chiefly of surface configuration and air drainage.

It is a common misconception that a weather-bureau warning of frost conditions is equivalent to a forecast of general freezing air temperatures. On the contrary, local frosts may occur in favorable locations when the average temperatures of the air over wide areas is still several degrees above freezing, or 32°F. It should be remembered that the weather bureau's forecasted temperature refers to conditions 5 or 6 ft. above the ground so that it is very possible to have below-freezing temperatures, and perhaps a deposit of white frost if the humidity is sufficient, on the ground and particularly in low places, while the general air temperature is above freezing.

2.28 Frost Prevention and Protection. The problem of artificial protection from frost is of genuine significance only in regions of highly sensitive and valuable crops which occupy restricted areas. It is obviously quite impossible to protect such extensively grown crops as corn or small grains, even when weather-bureau warnings are issued 12 to 24 hr. in advance of the anticipated freeze. The highly valuable citrus groves of California and Florida, how-

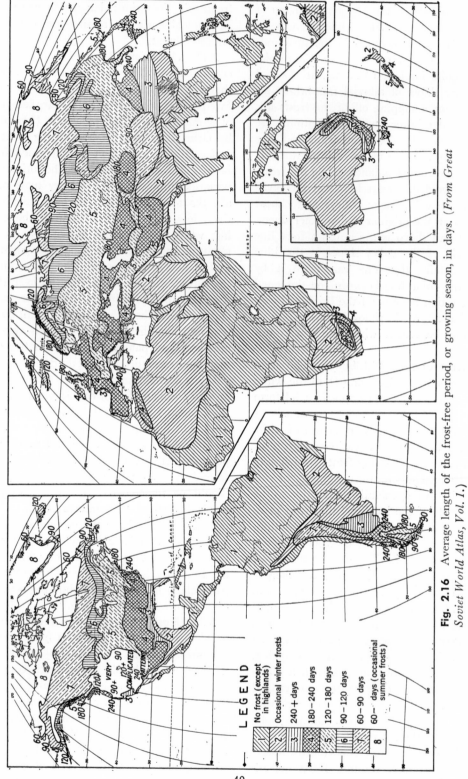

Fig. 2.16 Average length of the frost-free period, or growing season, in days. (*From Great Soviet World Atlas, Vol. 1.*)

LEGEND

1	No frost (except in highlands)
2	Occasional winter frosts
3	240+ days
4	180–240 days
5	120–180 days
6	90–120 days
7	60–90 days
8	60– days (occasional summer frosts)

ever, occupying only restricted areas, present a somewhat different problem. Whenever possible, sensitive crops should be planted on sites or locations where there is least danger of frosts. Because of air drainage, slopes are less frosty than are valley bottoms, so that fruit crops are characteristically located on hillsides. The windward shores of fairly large bodies of water, or peninsulas, are another example of favorable location.

For small-scale vegetable gardeners or fruit growers the simplest and most effective means of frost protection is to spread over the crop some nonmetallic covering such as paper, straw, or cloth, thereby intercepting the heat being radiated from the ground and plants. The purpose of the cover, quite obviously, is not to keep the cold out but to keep the heat in. This inexpensive type of frost protection is the one resorted to by the housewife in saving her garden plants from freezing. It is not so well suited to the protection of extensive orchard areas.

In California and Florida the huge losses in the citrus areas resulting from an occasional killing frost have inspired the most careful and sustained experimentation in frost-fighting methods. One single January frost in California resulted in a total citrus loss of 50 million dollars. A considerable number of protective devices, most of them of little or no practical value, have been constructed and tried out in the citrus groves. The orchard heater, consisting of a sheet-metal cylinder containing about a gallon of crude oil, is today, however, the only practical means known of obtaining complete protection from low temperatures in orchards. Smudging has proved ineffective. In the cranberry areas of Wisconsin and New England, the bogs are usually flooded if killing frost seems probable. The water surface created by flooding cools more slowly than a land surface and thereby lessens the frost hazard. Moreover, a protective cover of light fog is likely to develop over the flooded fields.

HORIZONTAL DISTRIBUTION OF TEMPERATURE

2.29 Isothermal Maps. Temperature distribution over the earth is shown on Figs. 2.17 and 2.18 by means of isotherms, *i.e.,* lines connecting places of the same temperature. Thus all points on the earth's surface through which any one isotherm passes have identical average temperatures. It would be entirely feasible to cover the world map with figures representing the temperatures of hundreds of stations, but such a map would be very cumbersome to use. Without scrutinizing each figure it would be difficult to determine, for instance, the regions of highest or lowest temperatures. But if lines are drawn on such a map connecting places of the same average temperature, then one can see at a glance many of the significant facts of thermal distribution. On Figs. 2.17 and 2.18 all temperatures have been reduced to sea level so that the effects of altitude are eliminated. If this were not done, the complications and details induced by mountains and other lesser relief forms would render the maps so confusing that the general world-wide effects of latitude and of land-and-water distribution would be difficult to perceive. These maps of sea-level isotherms are not so useful to agriculturists, engineers, and others who desire to put their data to practical use as are those showing *actual* surface temperatures.

Isotherms in general trend east-west, roughly following the parallels. This is not unexpected, since, except for differences in the transparency of the atmosphere, all places in the same latitude, or along the same parallel, receive identical amounts of solar energy. This east-west trend of isotherms indicates that latitude (or sun) is the greatest single cause of temperature contrasts. On no parallel of latitude at any season are temperature differences so great as between poles and equator. With increasing distance above the earth's surface the isotherms become more parallel to the latitude circles.

2.30 *General Features of Annual Temperature Distribution.* The highest average *annual* temperatures are in the low latitudes, where, for the year, the largest amounts of insolation are received, while the average lowest temperatures are in the vicinity of the poles, the regions of least annual insolation. Within a broad belt 40 to 50° wide in the tropics or low latitudes the temperature differences in a north-

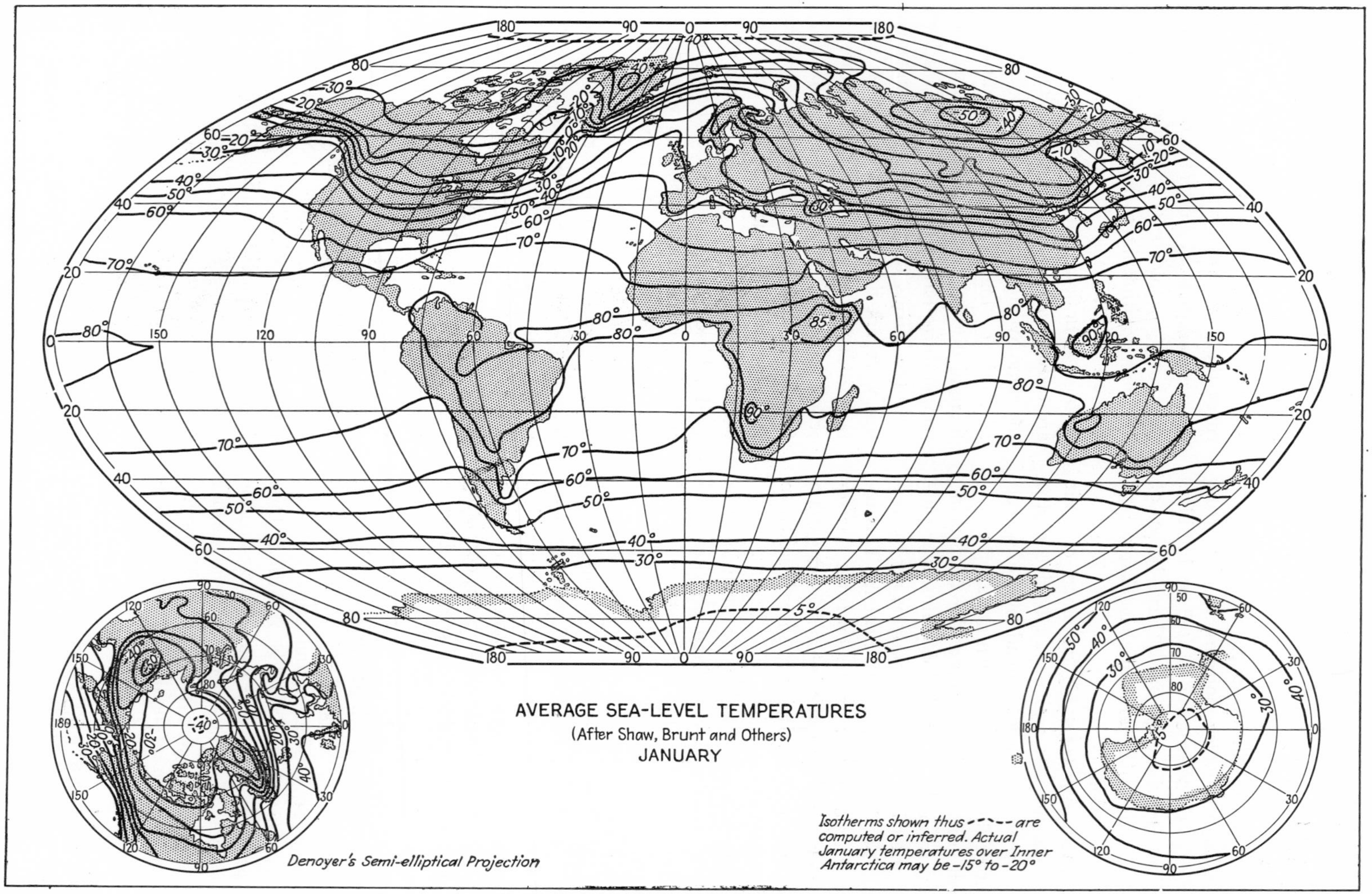

AVERAGE SEA-LEVEL TEMPERATURES
(After Shaw, Brunt and Others)
JANUARY

Denoyer's Semi-elliptical Projection

Isotherms shown thus ‒·‒·‒ are
computed or inferred. Actual
January temperatures over Inner
Antarctica may be –15° to –20°

Fig. 2.17

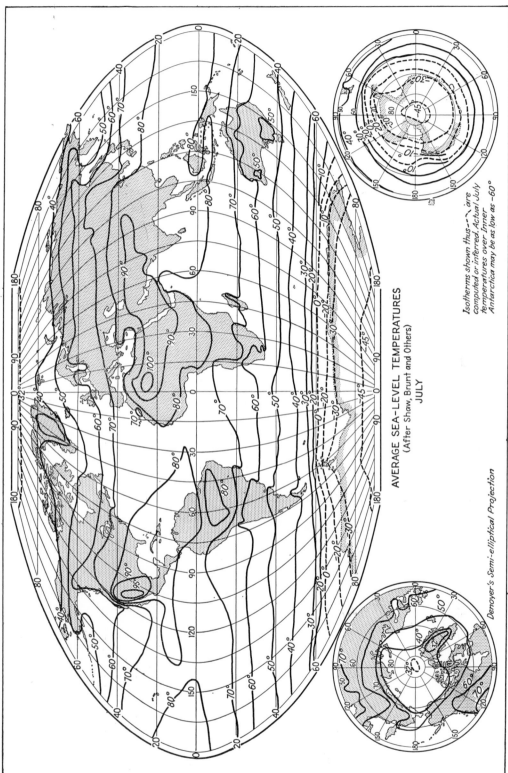

AVERAGE SEA-LEVEL TEMPERATURES
(After Shaw, Brunt and Others)
JULY

Denoyer's Semi-elliptical Projection

Isotherms shown thus---~ are
computed or inferred. Actual July
temperatures over Inner
Antarctica may be as low as −60°

Fig. 2.18

south direction are relatively slight and the thermal conditions are relatively uniform. It is chiefly in those latitudes poleward from 20 or 25°N. and S., and hence in the middle and higher latitudes, that the average annual temperatures decrease rapidly toward either pole.

Isotherms tend to be straighter and also more widely spaced in the Southern Hemisphere, the surface of which is more homogeneous, in this case largely water. The greatest deviations from east-west courses are where the isotherms pass from continents to oceans or vice versa. That is caused by the contrasting heating and cooling properties of land and water surfaces and the effects of ocean currents. After latitude or sun, land and water are the next most important control of temperature distribution. Cool ocean currents off the coasts of Peru and northern Chile, southern California, and southwestern Africa make themselves conspicuous through the *equatorward* bending of the isotherms. Similarly, warm currents in higher latitudes cause isotherms to bend *poleward*, this condition being most marked off the coast of northwestern Europe.

2.31 January and July Temperatures. For the earth in general, January and July represent the seasonal extremes of temperature. Following are some of the more significant features of temperature distribution as shown on the seasonal maps (Figs. 2.17 and 2.18). (*a*) From a comparison of the two maps it is obvious that there is a marked north-south shifting of the isotherms between July and January, following the north-south migration of sun's rays and insolation belts. (*b*) The migrations of isotherms are much greater over continents than over oceans because of the former's greater extremes of temperature. (*c*) The highest temperatures on both the January and July maps are over land areas, whereas the lowest temperatures in January emphatically are over Asia and North America, the largest land masses in the middle and higher latitudes. (*d*) In the Northern Hemisphere the January isotherms bend abruptly equatorward over the colder continents and poleward over the warmer oceans, whereas in July exactly the opposite conditions prevail. (*e*) No such seasonal contrasts between land and water as exist north of the equator are to be found in the Southern Hemisphere, for there large land masses are absent in the higher middle latitudes. (*f*) The lowest temperature on the January map is over northeastern Asia, the leeward side of the largest land mass in higher middle latitudes. The next lowest temperatures are over Greenland and North America. (*g*) Temperature gradients (rate of

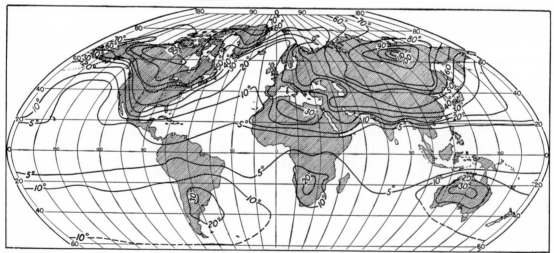

Fig. 2.19 Average annual ranges of temperature are smallest in low latitudes and over oceans. They are largest over continents in the middle and higher latitudes.

horizontal temperature change), like insolation gradients (Fig. 2.6), are steeper in winter than in summer. Steep gradients, represented by a relatively close spacing of the isotherms, are particularly conspicuous over the Northern Hemisphere continents in January.

2.32 *Annual Range of Temperature.* By annual range of temperature is meant the difference between the average temperatures of the warmest and coldest months. The largest annual ranges of temperature are over the Northern Hemisphere continents which become alternately hot in summer and cold in winter (Fig. 2.19). Ranges are never large (*a*) near the equator, where insolation varies little, or (*b*) over large water bodies. For the latter reason ranges are everywhere small in the middle latitudes of the Southern Hemisphere. In general, they increase toward the higher latitudes but much more markedly over the continents than over the oceans.

2.33 **Air Temperature and Sensible Temperature.** Correct *air temperature* can be obtained only by an accurate thermometer *properly exposed*. One of the principal items of correct exposure is to see that the instrument is *not* in the sun; otherwise it receives energy not only from the surrounding air but from the absorption of insolation as well. It also should be protected from direct radiation from the ground and adjacent buildings.

2.34 *Sensible temperature* refers to the sensation of temperature that the human body feels, as distinguished from actual air temperature which is recorded by a properly exposed thermometer. Unlike a thermometer that has no temperature of its own, the human body is a heat engine, generating energy at a relatively fixed rate when at rest. Anything, therefore, that affects the *rate of loss* of heat from the body affects physical comfort. Air temperature, of course, is one important factor, but so also are wind, humidity, and sunlight. Thus a *humid*, hot day is more uncomfortable than one of dry heat with the same temperature, since loss of heat by evaporation is retarded more when the air is humid. If the air is stirred by a fan on a hot day, the oppressiveness is decreased because of cooling by evaporation. A *windy, cold* day feels uncomfortable because the loss of heat is speeded up by greater evaporation. A sunny day in winter feels less cold than it actually may be owing to the body's absorption of direct insolation. Cold air containing moisture particles is particularly penetrating because the skin becomes moist, and evaporation results, while further loss of heat results from contact with the cold water. The rate of heat loss by radiation is greater in dry than in humid air. Because of its sensitiveness to factors other than air temperature, the human body is not a very accurate thermometer.

3

Atmospheric Pressure and Winds

3.1 Importance of Atmospheric Pressure and Winds as Climatic Elements and Climatic Controls. Compared with temperature and precipitation, atmospheric pressure (weight of the atmosphere) and winds are relatively insignificant as *elements* of weather and climate. To be sure, winds of high velocity may damage man's crops and structures, and there are, as well, certain adverse physiological reactions to strong air movement, but the sum total of these direct effects of wind is not of first importance. Still less is human life directly affected by the slight changes in air pressure which occur at the earth's surface. Although imperceptible to our bodies, these pressure differences are the reason for the existence of winds.

While not directly of first importance as climatic elements, both pressure and winds are indirectly of outstanding significance because of the effects which they have upon temperature and precipitation, the two genuinely important elements of weather and climate. The sequence of events might be as follows: A minor change in pressure (of little consequence directly) acts to change the velocity and direction of wind (also not of major importance directly), and this in turn brings about changes in temperature and precipitation, which together largely determine the character of weather and climate. Whether it is a south wind or a north wind is chiefly consequential because of the contrasting temperature conditions induced. An on-

shore wind as compared with an offshore one is climatically significant because of differences in moisture and temperature. It is chiefly as *controls* of temperature and precipitation, then, rather than as *elements* of weather and climate, that pressure and winds are worthy of attention. The two most important climatic functions of wind are (*a*) *the maintenance of a heat balance between the higher and lower latitudes in spite of their radiation unbalance and* (*b*) *the transportation of water vapor from the oceans to the lands, where that water vapor condenses and falls as rain.* Hence it is the winds from the oceans which provide the land masses with the necessary moisture supply for continental precipitation.

Because rainfall distribution over the earth is closely associated with the great pressure and wind systems, this chapter on pressure and winds precedes the one on moisture and precipitation. On the other hand, the discussion of atmospheric pressure logically follows the one on temperature, because some of the significant pressure differences and variations are induced by temperature.

3.2 Measurement of Air Pressure. A column of air 1 sq. in. in cross-sectional area extending from sea level to the top of the atmosphere weighs approximately 14.7 lb. This weight is balanced by a column of mercury nearly 29.9 in., or 760 mm., tall having the same cross-sectional area. Thus it has been customary to

Conversion scale

| Millibars | 948 | 956 | 964 | 972 | 980 | 988 | 996 | 1004 | 1012 | 1020 | 1028 | 1036 | 1044 |
| Inches | 28.0 | 8.2 | 8.4 | 8.6 | 8.8 | 29.0 | 9.2 | 9.4 | 9.6 | 9.8 | 30.0 | 0.2 | 0.4 | 0.6 | 0.8 | 31.0 |

measure air pressure in terms of its equivalent weight as expressed in inches or millimeters of a column of mercury—in other words, by a mercurial barometer. On all United States weather maps issued since January, 1940, pressure readings have been in millibars instead of inches. (The millibar is a force equal to 1,000 dynes per square centimeter.) One-tenth of an inch of mercury is approximately equal to 3.4 millibars, and sea-level atmospheric pressure may be expressed as 29.92 inches, 760 millimeters, or 1,013.2 millibars.

Relation of Pressure in Inches to Pressure in Millibars

Inches	Millibars	Inches	Millibars	Inches	Millibars
27.00	914.3	29.00	982.1	29.92	1,013.2
28.00	948.2	29.50	999.0	30.00	1,015.9
28.50	965.1	29.75	1,007.5	30.25	1,024.4

3.3 Pressure Differences and Their Origins. Differences in atmospheric pressure at sea level are to be observed on maps representing both different periods of time as well as areas of variable size. For example, on charts of average sea-level pressure for the entire earth (Figs. 3.4 and 3.5), a very conspicuous feature are the semipermanent cells of high and low pressure. Or if a daily weather map of the United States is analyzed it will be noted that there are numerous local *moving* pressure systems, both low and high, and that these moving pressure systems are accompanied by important weather changes.

There are two principal types of pressure systems: (*a*) high-pressure areas, called anticyclones or highs, and (*b*) low-pressure areas, called cyclones, depressions, or simply lows.

At present there is no adequate explanation for the general or average arrangement of pressure for the earth, or for the moving pressure systems which cause the day-to-day weather changes. Some of them appear to be essentially thermal in origin; others have dynamic causes, while still others are combinations. Since the density and weight of a given volume of air vary with temperature it is not unexpected that temperature contrasts will, on occasions, induce corresponding pressure differences. Thus air when heated expands and when chilled con-

tracts, so that a column of warm light air weighs less than a column of cold heavy air, both having the same height and cross-sectional area. Changes in air temperature produce changes in air density which set up vertical and horizontal movements resulting in differences in atmospheric pressure (Fig. 3.1). The above reasoning would lead to the conclusion that areas of high air temperature should be regions of low atmospheric pressure while low temperatures would favor the development of high pressure. While examples of thermally induced highs and lows are fairly common, there are too many instances where high temperatures and high pressures areally coincide and likewise low temperatures and low pressures, for the direct temperature-pressure relationship to be accepted as more than a partial explanation for world sea-level pressure distribution. Examples of thermally induced pressure systems are the great Asiatic High of winter and the lows over northwestern India, southwestern North America, and interior Asia in summer.

More widespread and numerous are those pressure systems which owe their origin largely or in part to nonthermal or dynamic causes, such as centrifugal force and friction. The precise operation of these mechanical processes

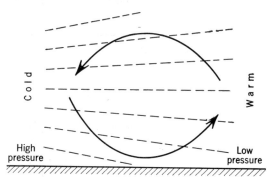

Fig. 3.1 Illustrating the *expected* relationship between air temperature, atmospheric pressure, and air flow. Dashed lines indicate surfaces of equal pressure. Since warm air is expanded and lighter, it might be expected that warm areas would be characterized by lower pressure at sea level than colder areas where the air is denser.

in producing low and high pressures is not completely understood.

Distribution of Atmospheric Pressure

3.4 Vertical Distribution. Since air is very compressible, it almost goes without saying that there is a rapid decrease in air weight or pressure with increasing altitude. The lower layers of the atmosphere are the densest because the weight of all the layers above rests upon them. For the first few thousand feet above sea level the rate of pressure decrease is in the neighborhood of 1 in., or 34 millibars (mb.), of pressure for each 900 to 1,000 ft. With higher altitudes the air rapidly becomes much thinner and lighter, so that at an elevation of 18,000 ft. one-half the atmosphere by weight is below the observer, although the whole air mass extends to a height of several hundred miles. The pressure is again halved in the next 18,000 ft., and so on. The human body is not physiologically adjusted to the low pressures and associated small oxygen content of the air at high altitudes, and nausea, faintness, and nosebleed often result from a too-rapid ascent. Oxygen tanks are a part of the normal equipment of aircraft operating at high altitudes.

3.5 Horizontal Distribution at Sea Level. *Average Conditions.* Just as temperature distribution is represented by *isotherms,* so atmospheric pressure distribution is represented by *isobars,* that is, lines connecting places having the same atmospheric pressure at a given elevation (Figs. 3.4 and 3.5). On the charts there shown all pressure readings have been reduced to sea level. Most pressure distribution charts represent sea-level pressures, although the need for understanding upper-air flow has in more recent years caused the development of pressure charts for high levels, commonly for about 10,000 ft. (750 mb.) and 18,000 ft. (500 mb.). Where isobars are closely spaced, there is a rapid horizontal change in pressure in a direction at right angles to the isobars. This rate and direction of pressure change is called the *pressure gradient.* Where isobars are widely spaced, the pressure gradient is weak.

A generalization of average sea-level pressure arrangement is reasonably well portrayed either by the idealized isobaric chart (Fig. 3.2) or by the meridional profile of pressure from pole to pole (Fig. 3.3). Both figures suggest that there is a zonal arrangement of pressure. But while pressure, averaged for all longitudes, certainly exhibits a belted arrangement, the so-called belts are more accurately described as centers, or cells, of pressure whose long axis is roughly east-west. Since the centers of the elongated cells of high pressure occupy nearly similar latitudes, the total effect is to produce an approximation of belts. The belted arrangement is more conspicuous in the relatively homogeneous Southern Hemisphere, suggesting that the great continents with their highlands

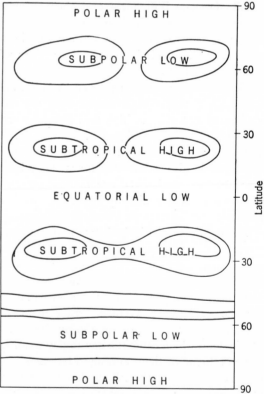

Fig. 3.2 Idealized arrangement of zonal sea-level pressure. Except in the higher latitudes of the Southern Hemisphere the zonal pressure "belts" are in the nature of cells of low or high pressure arranged in belts which are concentrated in particular latitudes.

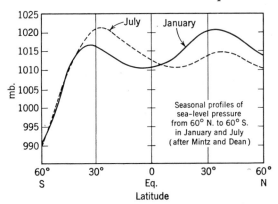

Fig. 3.3 Profiles of sea-level pressure from 60°N. to 60°S. averaged for all longitudes, at the time of the extreme seasons. Equatorial low, the subtropical highs, and the subpolar lows are conspicuous features of both profiles. Note the seasonal north-south movements of the pressure belts following the sun.

which obstruct the free flow of the atmosphere have much to do with the origin of pressure cells.

The most noteworthy features of generalized sea-level pressure, as derived from Figs. 3.2 and 3.3, are as follows: (a) The dominant and key element is the series of high-pressure cells which form irregular belts of high pressure at about 30°N. and S. These are the *subtropical highs.* Their origin is not fully understood, but certainly it is mechanical or dynamic, and not thermal. (b) Equatorward from the subtropical highs, in the vicinity of the geographic equator, is the *equatorial trough of low pressure.* It appears to be at least partly the result of the constantly high temperatures of the equatorial latitudes. (c) Poleward from the subtropical highs pressure decreases toward either pole with minima being reached in the vicinity of 65°N. and S. These are the *subpolar centers* or *troughs of low pressure.* What their origin may be is not so clear but it is due more to mechanical than to thermal causes. (d) Poleward from about latitude 65° aerological data are scanty so that the pattern of pressure distribution is not well known. It is generally assumed that fairly shallow surface highs, of thermal origin, occupy the inner polar areas.

If one were to inspect a weather map of the earth for a single day, the above-suggested arrangement of zonal surface pressure would not be so evident. This might indicate that the generalized cells and zones of surface pressure are, partly at least, in the nature of statistical averages of complicated day-to-day systems of moving highs and lows.

3.6 *Sea-level Pressure Distribution in January and July, Representing the Extreme Seasons.* (See Figs. 3.4 and 3.5.) Some of the features of seasonal pressure distribution which are of the greatest significance climatically are the following: (a) Pressure belts and cells, like those of temperature, migrate northward with the sun's rays in July and southward in January. This fact of latitudinal migration is most readily observed in Fig. 3.3 showing the profiles of pressure. In general, pressure is higher in the winter, or cold, hemisphere. (b) The subtropical highs are best developed over the eastern sides of the oceans and they tend to be weaker toward the western sides. In summer (January south of equator), the subtropical highs are weakened by the heated continents. In the Northern Hemisphere in July the subtropical highs along the eastern sides of the oceans extend well poleward into the middle latitudes, generally affecting the climate of the western sides of the continents. (c) The subpolar low is very deep and forms a continuous circumpolar trough in the Southern Hemisphere in both January and July, but in the Northern Hemisphere the subpolar low is represented by individual cells and these pressure cells are much more seasonal in character. In January two deep cells of low pressure occupy the North Pacific (Aleutian Low) and North Atlantic (Icelandic Low), but in July these oceanic lows are only faintly discernible. (d) In January a strong cell of high pressure has developed over the cold continent of Eurasia and a weaker one over smaller North America. In July these same continents, now warm, develop weaker thermal lows.

With increasing elevation above the earth's surface the cellular pattern of pressure, so conspicuous at sea level, gradually becomes less evident, and has become barely discernible at

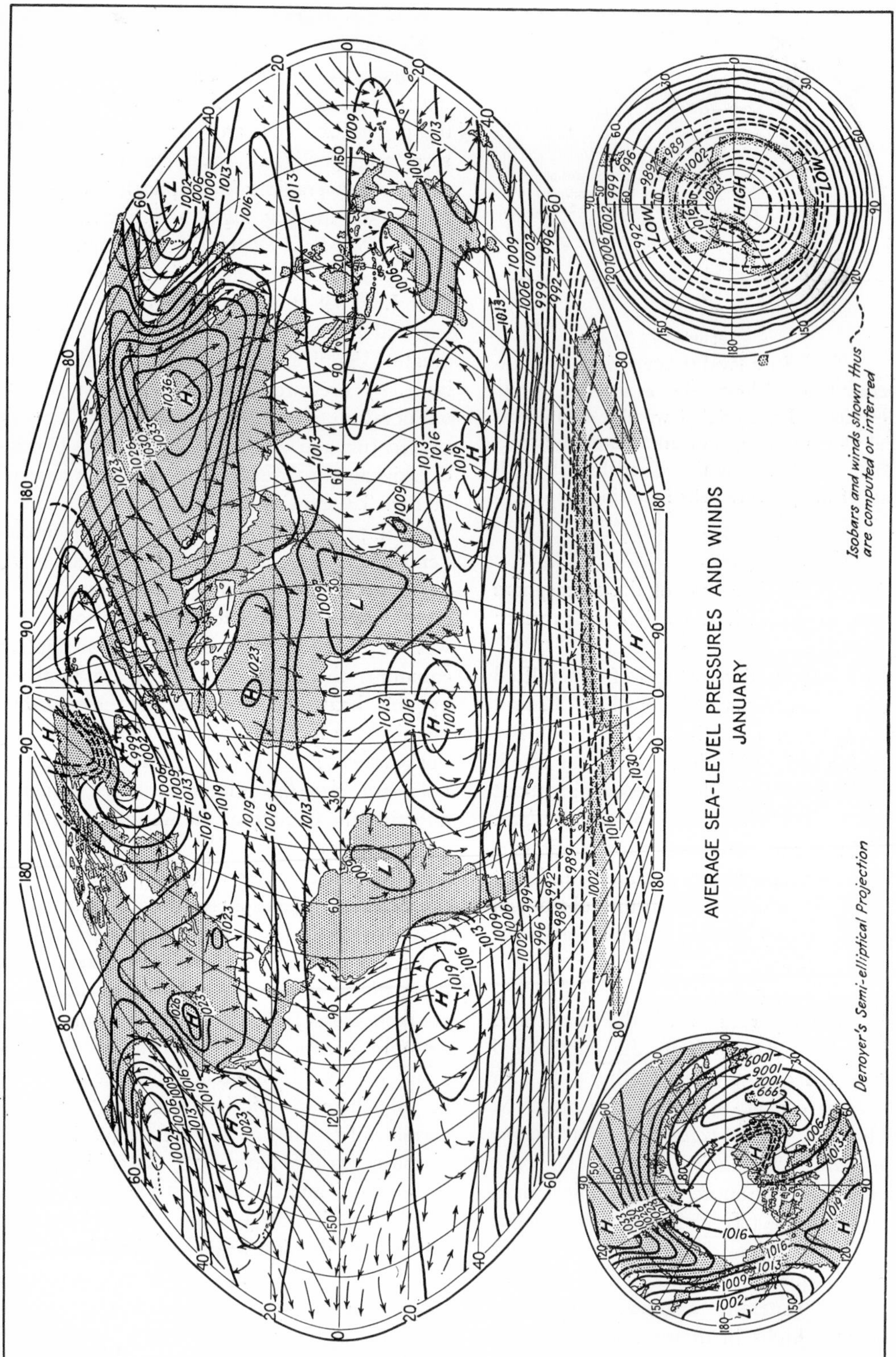

AVERAGE SEA-LEVEL PRESSURES AND WINDS
JANUARY

Denoyer's Semi-elliptical Projection

Isobars and winds shown thus
are computed or inferred

Fig. 3.4

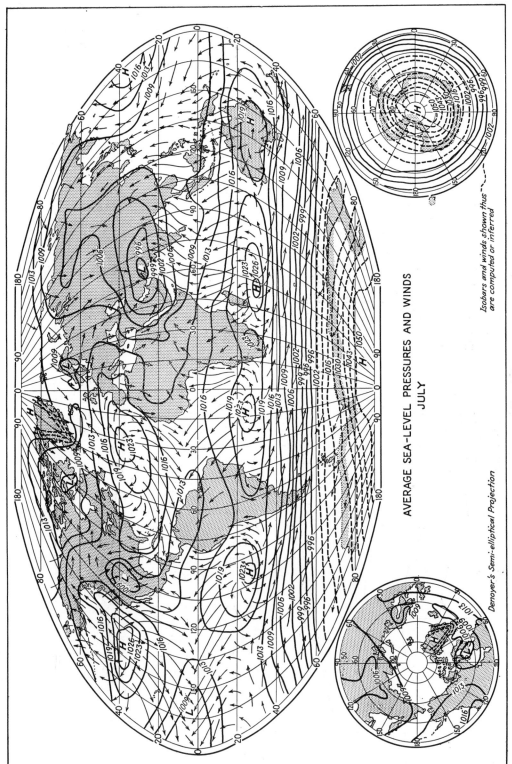

AVERAGE SEA-LEVEL PRESSURES AND WINDS
JULY

Denoyer's Semi-elliptical Projection

Isobars and winds shown thus ---
are computed or inferred

Fig. 3.5

10,000 ft. At this elevation pressure is highest in the low latitudes and decreases toward the poles.

Relation of Winds to Pressure

Resulting from latitudinal inequalities in the amount of incoming solar, and outgoing earth, radiation, large-scale vertical and horizontal movements of air are required to correct this unbalanced meridional distribution of energy. It is for this reason that the atmosphere is a restless medium in which movements of all scales of magnitude are characteristic.

3.7 Wind and the Pressure Gradient. Air that moves essentially parallel to the earth's surface is referred to as wind. Vertical air movements are more properly designated as currents, although the name is often applied to horizontal movements as well. Wind is usually caused by differences in air density, resulting in horizontal differences in air pressure. It represents nature's attempt to correct pressure inequalities. The rate and direction of change of pressure, as indicated by isobaric lines, are referred to as *pressure gradient,* or *barometric slope,* and it is this which indicates the velocity and general direction of air movements. Two very fundamental rules concerned with the relationships existing between pressure and winds are as follows: (*a*) The *direction* of air flow is from

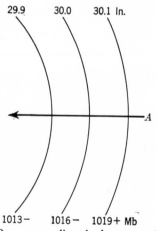

29.9   30.0   30.1 In.

A

1013−   1016−   1019+ Mb

Fig. 3.6 Pressure gradient is the rate and direction of pressure change. Gradient is represented by a line drawn at right angles to the isobars.

regions of greater to those of less density, *i.e.,* from high to low pressure or down the barometric slope, which may be represented by a line drawn at right angles to the isobars (Fig. 3.6). This follows the law of gravitation and is just as natural as the well-known fact that water runs downhill. Because of the deflective force of earth rotation, however, the flow of air from high to low pressure is very indirect and at more than 2,000 ft. above ground the winds nearly parallel the isobars.

(*b*) The rate of air flow, or velocity of the wind, is indicated by the steepness of the pressure gradient or the rate of pressure change. When the gradient is steep, air flow is rapid, and when it is weak, the wind is likewise weak. Just as the velocity of a river is determined largely by the slope of the land, or rate of change in elevation, so the velocity of wind is determined largely by the pressure gradient, or the rate of change in air pressure. One, therefore, can determine the steepness of the pressure gradient, and consequently the relative velocity of air movement, by noting the spacing or closeness of the isobars. Closely spaced isobars, like those in the vicinity of the subpolar trough in the Southern Hemisphere (Figs. 3.4 and 3.5), indicate relatively steep gradients, or marked pressure differences, and under these conditions winds of high velocity prevail. When isobars are far apart, gradients are weak, and winds are likewise. Calms prevail when pressure differences over extensive areas are almost, or quite, nil. At such times there is almost an absence of isobaric lines on the pressure map.

3.8 Deflection of Winds Due to Earth Rotation. On a nonrotating earth, air set in motion by pressure differences would flow along the pressure gradient at right angles to the isobars. But on a rotating earth where meridians and parallels are constantly changing direction, winds have an apparent deflection from the gradient direction so that they cross the isobars at an oblique angle. Over land surfaces where friction is relatively great the surface winds make an angle with the isobars of 20 to 40°. Over the oceans where friction is much less the angle may be as low as 10° and in the free

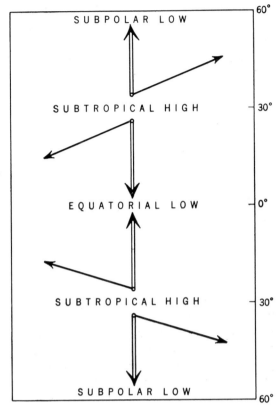

Fig. 3.7 Illustrating the apparent deflection of the planetary winds on a rotating earth. Double-line arrows indicate wind direction as it would be developed from pressure gradient alone. Solid-line arrows indicate the direction of deflected winds resulting from earth rotation.

toward the north, is called a south wind. The wind vane points *toward* the source of the wind. *Windward* refers to the direction from which a wind comes; *leeward,* that toward which it blows. Thus a windward coast is one along which the air is moving onshore, while a leeward coast has winds offshore. When a wind blows more frequently from one direction than from any other, it is called a *prevailing wind.*

Wind direction is referred to directions on a 32-point compass and is expressed in terms of letter abbreviations of the directions, by the number of the compass point, or by the number of degrees east of north (Fig. 3.8).

Wind velocity varies greatly with distance above the ground, and the variation is particularly rapid close to the ground. Wind is not a steady current but is made up of a succession of gusts and lulls of variable direction. Close to the earth the gustiness is caused by the irregularities of the surface which create eddies. Larger irregularities in the wind are caused by convectional currents. All forms of turbulence of the wind are important in the process of transporting heat, moisture, and dust into the upper air.

3.10 Cyclonic and Anticyclonic Circulations. As indicated earlier, sea-level pressure patterns

atmosphere several thousand feet above the earth's surface, winds nearly parallel the isobars, the angle being as low as 1 to 3°.

In the Northern Hemisphere earth rotation causes all winds to have an apparent deflection to the *right* of the gradient direction, and in the Southern Hemisphere to the *left* (Fig. 3.7). The above rule will not be apparent unless it is kept in mind that one must always face with the wind in order to observe the proper deflection. Only at the equator is deflective force of earth rotation absent and it increases with increasing latitude, *i.e.,* toward either pole.

3.9 Wind Direction and Velocity. Winds are always named by the direction from which they come. Thus a wind from the south, blowing

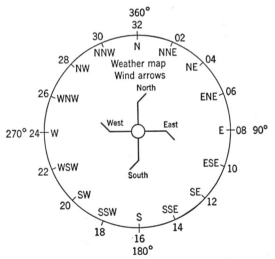

Fig. 3.8 Wind directions are named according to a 32-point compass.

The Beaufort Scale of Wind Force with Velocity Equivalents

Beaufort Number	General Description	Specifications for Use on Land	Miles per Hour
0	Calm	Smoke rises vertically	Less than 1
1	Light air	Wind direction shown by smoke drift but not by vanes	1 to 3
2	Slight breeze	Wind felt on face; leaves rustle; ordinary vane moved by wind	4 to 7
3	Gentle breeze	Leaves and twigs in constant motion; wind extends light flag	8 to 12
4	Moderate breeze	Raises dust and loose paper; small branches are moved	13 to 18
5	Fresh breeze	Small trees in leaf begin to sway; crested wavelets form on inland water	19 to 24
6	Strong breeze	Large branches in motion; whistling heard in telegraph wires	25 to 31
7	Moderate gale	Whole trees in motion	32 to 38
8	Fresh gale	Twigs broken off trees; progress generally impeded	39 to 46
9	Strong gale	Slight structural damage occurs; chimney pots removed	47 to 54
10	Whole gale	Trees uprooted; considerable structural damage	55 to 63
11	Storm	Very rarely experienced; widespread damage	64 to 75
12	Hurricane	. . . .	Above 75

are commonly cellular in character and on an isobaric chart these appear as systems of closed isobars. Such a system of closed isobars with the lowest pressure at the center is called a *cyclone*. When the highest pressure is at the center, it is an *anticyclone*. In a cyclone, or low-pressure system, the air flow is from the margins toward the center (Fig. 3.9). It is a *converging* wind system. Because of the deflective force of earth rotation the converging air moves obliquely across the isobars, anticlockwise north of the equator and clockwise to the south. In anticyclones air flows from the center toward the margins, so that it is a *diverging* wind system,

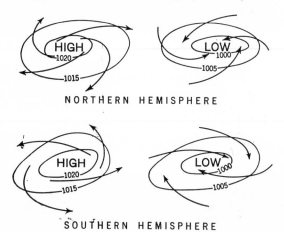

Fig. 3.9 Cyclonic circulations are *converging* systems of air movement, counterclockwise in the Northern Hemisphere and clockwise to the south of the equator. Anticyclonic circulations are *diverging* systems of air flow, clockwise in the Northern Hemisphere and anticlockwise in the Southern Hemisphere.

clockwise in the Northern Hemisphere and counterclockwise in the Southern (Fig. 3.9).

The Earth's Surface Winds[1]

3.11 The Zonal Pattern of Surface Winds. From the meridional profile of pressure (Fig. 3.3) or from the sketch showing a somewhat idealized arrangement of pressure belts (Fig. 3.2) one can readily visualize what the principal elements of the earth's zonal surface wind system will be. From the subtropical highs at about 30°N. and S. surface winds flow both from north and south toward the low-pressure trough near the equator. Earth rotation deflects these two air streams into oblique easterly winds so that they are appropriately designated as the *tropical easterlies*. They are also known as the *trade winds:* northeast trades north of the equator and southeast trades to the south of it (Fig. 3.10).

Poleward from the two subtropical high-pressure ridges, one in either hemisphere, winds flow downgradient toward the subpolar lows. By earth rotation these are turned so that they have a general west-to-east movement. These are the middle-latitude *westerlies:* southwest in the Northern Hemisphere and northwest south of the equator.

Poleward from latitudes 60 or 65° there are so few aerological observations that uncertainty exists relative to the average surface-wind systems of the two polar areas. Statistical aver-

[1] The term "surface wind" refers to the lower 1,000 to 2,000 ft. of the atmosphere.

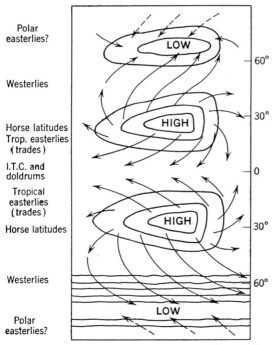

Polar easterlies?

Westerlies

Horse latitudes
Trop. easterlies (trades)

I.T.C. and doldrums

Tropical easterlies (trades)

Horse latitudes

Westerlies

Polar easterlies?

LOW — 60°

HIGH — 30°

— 0

HIGH — 30°

— 60°

LOW

Fig. 3.10 A much idealized representation of the earth's surface winds. Air flow is from an easterly direction in the low latitudes and from a westerly direction in the middle latitudes.

ages seem to indicate that easterly winds are most prevalent in the high latitudes, although they may not be a permanent feature of the circulation. These *polar easterlies* would appear to originate in shallow, thermally induced polar highs and flow toward the subpolar troughs of low pressure.

To summarize zonal surface winds, there is a predominance of easterly winds in the low latitudes or tropics and a prevalence of westerly winds in the middle latitudes. In the high latitudes easterlies probably prevail.

Between the converging trades, in the vicinity of the equatorial trough of low pressure, is a zone of variable and weak winds. This transition belt between the two trades has various names: *intertropical convergence* (I.T.C.), *doldrums,* and *equatorial belt of variable winds.* In the intermediate area between the diverging trades and westerlies, which is fairly coincident with the crests of the subtropical highs, is another

belt of weak and variable winds. These are the *horse latitudes* located at about 30° in each hemisphere.

3.12 Seasonal Surface Winds. While the concept of a simple zonal wind system as previously described is satisfactory as an introduction to the surface circulation patterns, it is not adequate for portraying a number of features of the atmospheric circulation which have important climatic significance.

In Figs. 3.4 and 3.5 the surface winds for July and January, representing the extreme seasons, are shown in a way that conforms somewhat more to actual conditions. From these seasonal maps one is less impressed with the zonal pattern of surface winds than with their cellular arrangement. The circulation appears not to occur so much in belts or zones as in the form of anticyclonic and cyclonic circulations around high-pressure and low-pressure centers or cells. Some of these appear to persist both in summer and in winter, while others are emphatically seasonal in character. Seasonal changes in the circulation pattern, and cellular pattern in general, are more conspicuous in the Northern Hemisphere with its larger land masses than in the more homogeneous Southern Hemisphere. The continents with their great seasonal temperature contrasts, and their mountain systems which interrupt the free flow of the atmosphere, not only emphasize the cellular as compared with the zonal pattern but they also make for greater seasonal variations in the circulation.

The most prominent features of the surface-wind flow are the large systems of divergent anticyclonic circulation concentrated in the subtropical latitudes. The equatorward branches of these anticyclonic circulations are the well-known tropical easterlies or trades, while the poleward branches are the middle-latitude westerlies. The subtropical anticyclonic wind systems dominate on both the January and July charts and no comparable systems of convergent cyclonic flow exist. The nearest approach are the relatively weak centers of converging cyclonic circulation over the Northern Hemisphere oceans in January.

On the January map (Fig. 3.5) the subtropical anticyclonic systems are relatively weak over the oceans of the Northern Hemisphere and they are largely confined to the eastern parts of the subtropical oceans. By contrast the subtropical anticyclonic systems are better developed and more continuous over the Southern Hemisphere oceans. In addition to these subtropical anticyclonic systems over the oceans there is the great continental anticyclonic system over eastern Asia. This seasonal diverging wind system of the Asiatic monsoon has its origin in the thermally induced high which develops in winter over the cold continent.

But January, which witnesses a weakening of the subtropical anticyclones over the Northern Hemisphere oceans, likewise shows an expanding and deepening of the oceanic lows and their converging cyclonic wind systems over the North Atlantic and North Pacific in middle latitudes. In the Southern Hemisphere in summer (January) a well-developed center of low pressure with its cyclonic circulation is conspicuous over the heated continent of Australia.

In *July* the anticyclonic circulations over the subtropical oceans of the Northern Hemisphere are more extensive and have shifted farther north (Fig. 3.4). Those of the Southern Hemisphere are little changed except that they are more continuous as a result of the cooler continents. Cyclonic circulations over the North Atlantic and North Pacific Oceans are weak, but on the other hand well-developed continental lows with their cyclonic circulations are prominent features over the heated lands of northwestern India, eastern Asia, and interior North America. In India and eastern Asia these cyclonic circulations are the well-known summer monsoons.

3.13 Zones and Areas of Horizontal Divergence and Convergence. From the preceding analyses of the zonal and cellular structure of the surface winds it becomes clear that there are on the earth certain zones or areas where the surface winds converge or tend to meet along a line or at a center. There are others where the winds diverge or move away from a common zone or center of origin. Facts con-

cerning the nature and distribution of atmospheric divergences and convergences are of the highest importance from the standpoint of understanding world climates. Where surface winds converge, there must of necessity be an escape of the air through upward movement or ascent, a condition which favors condensation, the development of storms, and associated clouds and precipitation. By contrast, where winds diverge, it is required that there shall be a downward movement of air from aloft (*subsidence*) in order to compensate for the divergent surface flow. Such a subsidence of the air heats and drys it so that divergence and subsidence are opposed to the development of storms and to the formation of clouds and precipitation (Fig. 3.11).

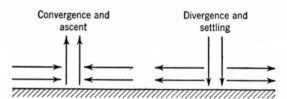

Convergence and ascent Divergence and settling

Fig. 3.11 Where surface winds flow toward each other, or *converge,* there is a resulting ascent of air. Where surface winds *diverge* there must be a settling or subsidence of the air.

3.14 *Zones of Divergence and Subsidence.* Most prominent and best developed of the divergence-subsidence zones are those associated with the subtropical anticyclones. These lines of divergence pass through the centers of the anticyclonic systems and extend poleward and eastward, and equatorward and westward from those centers (Fig. 3.10). These subtropical lines of divergence are scarcely continuous around the earth, for the high-pressure cells are strongest toward the eastern sides of the oceans and there subsidence is especially well developed. Toward the western sides of the oceans the anticyclones are weaker and subsidence is likewise. Other than in the subtropical anticyclones, divergence is also prominent in the winter high over central and eastern Asia and presumably also in the polar areas.

3.15 *Zones of Convergence and Ascent.* Most prominent of all the extended lines of wind convergence is that which is located between the Northern Hemisphere trades and the Southern Hemisphere trades in the general vicinity of the geographic equator. Throughout most of the year this intertropical convergence (I.T.C.) appears to be fairly continuous around the earth (Fig. 3.10).

Still other zones of convergence are those associated with the subpolar troughs of low pressure where the westerlies flowing from subtropical latitudes meet air of polar origin. These convergence zones appear to be less continuous both areally and temporally than is the I.T.C. near the equator. Much of the convergence here appears to occur in the individual moving cyclonic storms which are numerous in these latitudes, more especially over the oceans. Seasonal areas of convergence, associated with thermally induced lows, are to be found over eastern and southeastern Asia and over western interior United States in July.

THE INDIVIDUAL SURFACE WINDS AND THEIR CHARACTERISTICS

Winds of the Tropics

3.16 New Concepts. As a result of much new aerological data from tropical areas becoming available, a large part of it collected during the Second World War, some of the conventional notions concerning weather and winds in the low latitudes must undergo revision. Unfortunately there are still insufficient well-distributed data from these low latitudes to permit the creation of a satisfactory new concept of the earth's winds. The result is that considerable confusion exists at present regarding atmospheric circulation, and especially concerning tropical winds and weather.

Certain it is, however, that there must be a modification or revision of some of the conventional ideas. For example, the well-established notion of zonal uniformity of winds and weather in the low latitudes is no longer tenable. It has been discovered recently that tropical latitudes are affected by many more types of weather disturbances, or storms, than was formerly suspected, so that constancy of weather is by no means so characteristic as was previously thought to be the case.

A second circumstance which has obliged the revision of previous concepts is the discovery that the really steady and uniform trades occupy only a fraction of the total oceanic area within the tropics. In addition considerable uncertainty exists concerning the origin and distribution of weather disturbances, or storms, in the low latitudes, and also the direction of the winds and the nature of their convergence in the equatorial trough of low pressure.

3.17 The Tropical Easterlies or Trade Winds. Moving obliquely downgradient from the centers of the subtropical anticyclones toward the equatorial trough of low pressure, roughly between latitudes 30 or 35° and 5 or 10° in each hemisphere over the oceans, are easterly winds whose steadiness of flow over extensive areas has earned for them the name of trade winds (Fig. 3.10). Without doubt they are the most constant in direction and velocity of any of the earth's zonal winds (Fig. 3.12). Compared with the middle-latitude westerlies they have fewer interruptions in the form of weather disturbances so that moderate to fresh breezes averaging 10 to 15 miles an hour are fairly characteristic. In the days of sailing ships the trade-wind latitudes with their fine weather and steady winds with few severe storms were deservedly famed.

As pointed out in an earlier section, however, the uniformity of the trades has been overemphasized. The typical steady trades as described in textbook models of the general circulation are confined to more restricted areas within the tropics than had been supposed. The uniform trades are limited to belts of latitude which are usually less than 10° in width and they are much more conspicuous in the eastern than in the western parts of oceans. Constancy both in direction and in velocity declines sharply on their poleward and equatorward margins. Equally important is the fact that the proverbially steady trades are chiefly characteristic of the eastern parts of tropical oceans. In

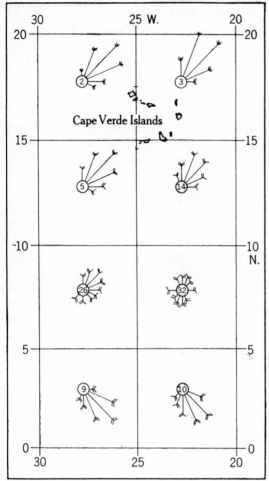

Fig. 3.12 Northeast and southeast trades and doldrums over the Atlantic Ocean, June, 1922. The wind rose is given for each 5° square. Arrows fly with the wind. The length of the arrow is proportional to the frequency of winds from that direction. The number of feathers on the arrow indicates the average force of the wind on the Beaufort scale. The figure in the center gives the percentage of calms, light airs, and variable winds. (*U.S. Hydrographic Office Pilot Chart.*)

their western parts they are more variable in character, for there they are interrupted more frequently by weather disturbances of various kinds. Not only are the trades more variable in their western parts but there also they have a smaller north-south component and may in parts blow nearly parallel with the equator, or even away from it.

Neither are the trades one homogeneous air mass and weather and climatic conditions vary

greatly in different parts. In general, the poleward parts of the trades which are closest to the centers of the subtropical anticyclones, where vertical subsidence and horizontal divergence are characteristic, are characterized by dry weather and much sunshine (Fig. 3.13). Here the air is said to be stable, for it lacks buoyancy and is opposed to deep convectional overturning. Very gradually as the trades move equatorward certain modifications occur which make them cloudier and rainier air masses. One of these modifications is the result of passing over great expanses of tropical ocean which results in large additions of moisture through evaporation. A second modification of great climatic significance is the fact that the trade-wind air is gradually leaving an area of strong subsidence in the subtropical anticyclones and is approaching the equatorial trough of low pressure where horizontal convergence and lifting are characteristic. Both modifications, the addition of moisture and increasing convergence and lifting, make the trades in their equatorward parts more buoyant and unstable. In such an environment atmospheric disturbances or storms are more readily developed, convectional overturning of the air is easier, and clouds and precipitation are more characteristic.

Not only do the trades change character in a north-south direction, but they likewise differ in their eastern and western parts. Normally

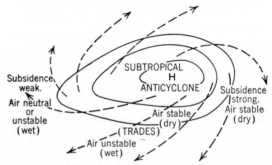

Fig. 3.13 The circulation pattern around a subtropical anticyclone with general areas of stability and instability shown. The eastern end of the cell is much more stable than the western. The poleward parts of the trades are more stable than the equatorward parts.

the subtropical high-pressure cells on whose equatorward slopes the trades originate are strongest and best developed toward the eastern sides of the oceans. It is in these same eastern parts, where subsidence is unusually strong, that the trades are driest and rain-producing storms are fewest. Farther west the anticyclone is weaker and subsidence is likewise, with the result that storms are more numerous and better developed and clouds and precipitation more frequent. Thus the trades are likely to be dry fair-weather winds in their poleward and eastern parts, while their equatorward and western margins are characterized by more weather disturbances and greater amounts of precipitation.

3.18 Winds of the Equatorial Convergence Zone. In the equatorial trough of pressure between the trades advancing from the Northern and Southern Hemispheres, the conventional description portrayed a relatively continuous belt around the earth in which calms and light and fickle winds prevailed. These were known as the *doldrums*. As the trades converged toward the equator, it was assumed that they were heated sufficiently to rise from the earth's surface in convectional currents leaving in the belt between them at low elevations this intermediate condition of relatively stagnant, humid air in which thunderstorms, cloud, and rainfall were abundant (Fig. 3.12).

It is now known that this doldrum condition

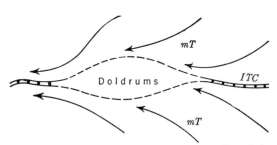

Fig. 3.14 Illustrating the winds in the region of the low-pressure trough near the equator and between the trades. In some longitudes the trades clash to form the Intertropical Convergence (I.T.C.). In other longitudes the trades do not meet at the surface and a condition of calms and variable winds prevails between them. These are the doldrums.

of light and fickle winds is neither uninterrupted around the earth near the equator nor is it continuous throughout the year. In reality winds near the equator are very complex and their systems are not completely understood. Doldrum conditions of variable latitudinal width do prevail in some longitudes, but in others they are pinched out by converging trades, which meet along a narrow zone of conflict, or by monsoon winds (Fig. 3.14).

Three fairly persistent areas of doldrums are now recognized, the most extensive one in the western Pacific and the Indian oceans, and two smaller ones, one in the eastern Atlantic and the other in the eastern Pacific.

Prevailingly the equatorial latitudes are an area of horizontal convergence in which the winds have a small constancy of both direction and velocity. Some longitudes appear to show a greater prevalence of easterly drift and others of westerly. Because of the prevailing convergence, however, there is a great deal of upward movement of air, resulting in abundant cloud and precipitation. But this condition of convergence and ascent, as shown on daily weather maps, is not continuous around the earth at all times but rather is to be thought of as occurring in the numerous atmospheric disturbances which prevail in these equatorial regions. The air masses which meet along the intertropical convergence (I.T.C.) are usually so similar in temperature and humidity that real density fronts such as characterize the middle latitudes probably are not so common.

3.19 Winds of the Subtropics. Latitudes 25 to 35° are characterized by the development of great anticyclonic circulations around zonally arranged oceanic high-pressure cells. Poleward from these cells flow the middle-latitude westerlies, while their equatorward branches are the tropical easterlies or trades. They are, therefore, transitional areas between diverging surface trades and westerlies. Since these horse latitudes with their anticyclonic circulations are associated with a divergence of surface winds, they must also be zones of subsidence or settling of the atmosphere in order to feed the diverging surface flow. As noted in an earlier section, horizontal divergence and vertical subsidence are opposed to the formation of clouds and precipitation so that the centers of the anti-cyclones are likely to be areas of meager cloud and precipitation (Fig. 3.15).

These same centers, with their character-istically weak pressure gradients, are areas of low wind velocity and of small constancy of wind direction. There is no *prevailing* wind, for the day-to-day air flow is from many points of the compass. What becomes clear is that the horse latitudes are like the equatorial regions in having much light and variable wind. They are quite unlike them, however, in their general weather conditions, for one is a region of con-verging surface winds, with accompanying as-cent, and the other of divergence and vertical subsidence.

In reality the horse latitudes (25 to 35°) are not longitudinally as similar in winds and weather as the previous discussion might indi-cate (Fig. 3.13). At the eastern and western ends of each of the anticyclonic cells, wind velocity and constancy of direction are both higher than toward the centers of the high. In addition, the western margins of each cell have less atmospheric subsidence than the centers and eastern parts, so that while the latter are characteristically dry, the western parts actually have a moderate amount of cloud and precipi-tation. Hence it develops that the eastern parts of the subtropical oceans and adjacent (west-ern) parts of continents have dry and subhumid climates, while the western parts of oceans and their bordering land areas, in the subtropics, have humid climates.

Winds of the Middle and Higher Latitudes

3.20 The Variable Westerlies of Middle Latitudes. Moving downgradient from the cen-ters of subtropical high pressure to the subpolar lows (roughly 35 or 40 to 60 or 65°) are the stormy westerlies. Particularly is the poleward boundary of this wind belt a fluctuating one, shifting with the seasons and over shorter peri-ods of time as well. The westerlies are distinc-tive among the wind belts in that they are not uniformly either strong or weak but instead are composed of extremes. Spells of weather are one of their distinguishing characteristics. At times, and more especially in the winter, they blow with gale force, and upon other occasions mild breezes prevail. Although designated as *westerlies,* westerly being, to be sure, the direc-tion of most frequent and strongest winds, air does blow from all points of the compass (Fig. 3.16).

The variability of winds, in both direction and strength, so characteristic of the westerlies, is largely the result of the procession of storms (cyclones and anticyclones) which travels from west to east in these latitudes. These storms, with their local systems of converging and diverging winds, tend to disrupt and modify the general westerly air currents. Moreover, on the eastern sides of Asia, and to a lesser degree North America, continental wind systems called *monsoons* tend to disturb the westerlies, espe-cially in summer. It is in the Southern Hemi-sphere, where in latitudes 40 to 65° land masses are largely absent, that the stormy westerlies can be observed in their least interrupted lati-

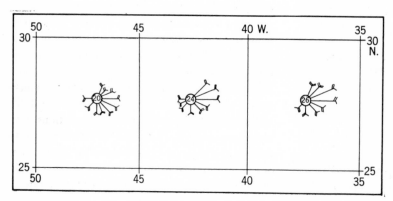

Fig. **3.15** The subtropical belt of variable winds and calms, or horse latitudes, over the North Atlantic Ocean in June. Winds are weak, calms are numerous, and the winds are from a variety of direc-tions. For an explanation of the symbols, see Fig. 3.12. (*U.S. Hydrographic Office Pilot Chart.*)

tudinal development. Over these great expanses of ocean, winds of gale strength are common in summer as well as winter. These are the roaring forties of nautical jargon. In the vicinity of Cape Horn they are often so violent as to make east-west traffic around the Cape not only difficult but even dangerous. It is a wild region where gale follows gale with only brief intervening lulls, where raw chilly weather, cloudy skies, and mountainous seas prevail.

The westerlies of the Northern Hemisphere, where the great land masses with their seasonal pressure reversals cause the wind systems to be much more complex, are considerably less violent in summer than in winter. In the former season gentle to fresh breezes prevail, and winds come from a great variety of directions with almost equal frequency. But in winter they are like their counterparts in the Southern Hemisphere, being strong and boisterous with a greater prevalence of winds from westerly directions. The poleward margins of the westerlies near the subpolar troughs of low pressure are particularly subject to great surges of cold polar air in the winter season. The sinuous line of discontinuity, known as the *polar front,* which separates the cold, dry polar air from that warmer and more humid mass coming from the subtropics in the form of the westerlies is the zone of origin for a great many middle-latitude cyclones and anticyclones. It follows, therefore, that the poleward margins of the westerlies are much more subject to stormy, variable weather than are the subtropical margins. Since this polar front and the accompanying belt of storms migrate with the sun's rays, retreating poleward in summer and advancing equatorward in winter, it also follows that storm control of weather in the middle latitudes should be much more pronounced in the winter season.

3.21 Winds of the Polar Regions. In the higher latitudes beyond about latitude 60 or 65° aerological observations are so few and so poorly distributed as to make an adequate description of the polar wind systems impossible at this time.

The subpolar low-pressure troughs, relatively continuous in the Southern Hemisphere, but

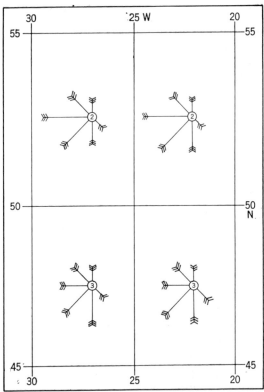

Fig. 3.16 The westerlies over the North Atlantic Ocean in January. Velocities are high, calms are few, and winds blow from a variety of directions. For an explanation of the symbols, see Fig. 3.12. (*U.S. Hydrographic Office Pilot Chart.*)

existing as isolated oceanic centers (Iceland Low and Aleutian Low) north of the equator, are extremely wild and stormy areas, for they are the routes followed by a large number of the cyclonic storms of high latitudes. Great surges of cold polar air originating in the inner polar areas cause the outlines of the subpolar troughs to be extremely sinuous, almost completely interrupting their continuity both frequently and at numerous points. Some of the surges of air from the polar areas reach deep into tropical latitudes.

In the north polar region available data appear to show that the average condition is a weak and shallow easterly flow, although in some years westerlies extend all the way from middle latitudes to the pole. Even in those years when easterlies predominate there may be periods of several days to several weeks in which westerly flow prevails. In the south polar region it seems probable that the average circulation is easterly in summer, while in winter easterlies characterize all but the interior of the Antarctic continent where the surface winds are inferred to be westerly.[2]

Features of the General Circulation of the Atmosphere

3.22   General Features. Up to this point the discussion has emphasized atmospheric circulation in the lower atmosphere, *i.e.*, the surface winds. Such low-level winds are of great importance climatically, for it is they which largely determine surface-temperature changes, and in some degree they likewise influence cloud and rainfall conditions. However, it is chiefly the air flow at higher levels which controls the general distribution of precipitation, and indirectly through the generation of atmospheric disturbances, or storms, affects surface weather conditions, including temperature. The topic of the general circulation, including both high-level and low-level winds is introduced at this point, therefore, in order that some of the larger distribution features of world weather and climate may be better understood. It must be admitted, however, that important elements of the general circulation are still unknown and some that are known are not understood.

The necessity for a general circulation of the atmosphere derives from the unequal latitudinal distribution of solar energy over the earth. Winds and ocean currents are the means by which the excess of energy received in the low latitudes is carried to the deficit regions farther poleward. But while the *ultimate* cause of the atmospheric circulation may be the unequal distribution of solar energy, it does not follow that the direct and immediate cause of the circulation in all its parts is latitudinal thermal differences. It seems likely that the exchange of air between high and low latitudes occurs in the form of irregular horizontal thrusts of polar

[2] Yale Mintz. The Observed Zonal Circulation of the Atmosphere. *Amer. Meteorol. Soc. Bull.*, Vol. 35, pp. 208–214, May, 1954.

air into the tropics and of tropical air into the middle and higher latitudes.

A west-to-east circulation prevails throughout the greatest volume of the earth's atmosphere. This westerly flow is often obscured at the earth's surface by the frictional effects of terrain irregularities and by numerous atmospheric disturbances in the form of storms. There are two exceptions to this general west-to-east movement of the earth's atmosphere. The first and principal one is the east-to-west flow in the low latitudes or tropics. These tropical easterlies or trades are deep near the equator where they may reach up to heights of 6 miles. Poleward from the equator they decline rapidly in depth until they cease to exist at about latitude 30 to 35°N. and S. (Fig. 3.17). The second exception to westerly flow are the somewhat doubtful and shallow surface easterlies of the polar areas.

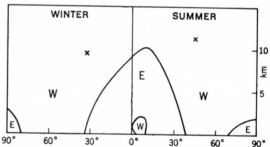

Fig. 3.17   A pole-to-pole cross section of the planetary winds up to about 8 or 9 miles above the earth's surface. E = tropical easterlies or trades; W = westerlies; x = average location of the jet stream; w = the somewhat doubtful belt of equatorial westerlies; e = polar easterlies. (*After Flohn.*)

3.23   *The Jet Stream, Upper-air Waves and Their Relationship to Surface Weather.* It was as late as about 1944 that the existence of a narrow stream of high-velocity air with speeds of 200 to 300 miles per hour at elevations of 20,000 to 40,000 ft. was discovered. This is the *jet stream.* Although the origin of the jet stream is still obscure, many of its rudimentary characteristics are now known. It appears to be in the nature of a narrow stream or streams of violently rushing air, one in either hemisphere, which completely encircles the earth in a meandering course (Fig. 3.18). Although it shifts latitudinally with the seasons, the average location of the jet stream is about 30 to 35° so that it overlies the subtropical anticyclones at the surface. Wind velocities in the jet stream are always high, although they do vary in different longitudinal sections and also with the seasons, being higher in winter than in summer. Across the jet stream horizontally temperature changes very rapidly, with cold air of polar origin on its poleward side and tropical air equatorward.

Although the jet stream, as well as the high-altitude westerly winds of which it is a part, are essentially zonal (west-east) in character, they do have north-south oscillations or waves of enormous length. These upper-air waves on the jet stream may be caused by the frictional and blocking effects of the continents and their mountain systems.

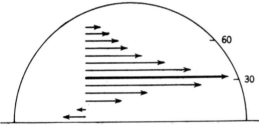

Fig. 3.18 To illustrate the location of the jet stream. At high altitudes westerly winds prevail over most of the Northern and Southern Hemispheres. Their velocities increase from the pole toward the equator until they reach a maximum at about 30°N. and S. This zone of maximum velocity to the north and to the south of the equator is the jet stream. (*After Namias.*)

It is now believed that the jet stream and its waves are intimately associated with surface weather conditions, although precisely what the connection is, and how it operates, is not yet clear. The waves on the jet stream are directly associated with the horizontal expulsion of great masses of polar and tropical air, which in turn are essential elements of the general circulation of the atmosphere. When the jet stream is very wavy, the latitudinal exchange of unlike air masses is very active and at such times storms are numerous in middle latitudes and weather

is very changeable. Less stormy conditions prevail when the oscillations on the jet are slight. Well-developed middle-latitude cyclones extend upward into the jet-stream waves and may have their origin in these waves. Rainfall appears to be concentrated in those areas lying below the jet. It may be safe to say that the jet stream has the effect of steering the storms, both cyclones and anticyclones, across the earth's surface.

3.24 *Important Terrestrial Modifications of the Earth's Surface Winds.* Some effects of the earth's surface upon air flow at lower atmospheric levels have been mentioned rather incidentally in the previous discussion of winds. At this point it seems wise to amplify and give organization to this topic. The principal terrestrial modifications result from (*a*) the inclination ($23\frac{1}{2}°$) and parallelism of the earth's axis, causing a uniform latitudinal shifting of the belts of solar energy during the course of a year; (*b*) a nonhomogeneous surface composed of both land and water areas, having contrasting temperature characteristics; and (*c*) land areas, the surfaces of which are variable in configuration and altitude.

3.25 Latitudinal Shifting of the Wind Belts. Consequent upon the parallelism and inclination of the earth's axis, during the annual period of revolution the sun's vertical noon ray shifts from $23\frac{1}{2}°$N. (summer solstice) to $23\frac{1}{2}°$S. (winter solstice), a total of 47°. The belt of maximum insolation actually undergoes a latitudinal shift of 70 to 80°. With the north-south migration of insolation there follows a similar shift in temperature belts which are largely sun controlled. Pressure and wind belts, in part thermally induced, likewise may be expected to migrate latitudinally with the sun's rays (Fig. 4.15). This north-south shifting of the wind belts is by no means so simple a thing as it may appear to be from the above description, for it varies in amount and rapidity of shift from one part of the earth to another. In general, there is a lag of a month or possibly two behind the sun. Over the oceans and along coasts where the migration is more readily observable the total migration is not great, usually not much over 10 to 15°. Over continents, on the other hand, where seasonal temperature changes are greater, the total latitudinal shift of pressure and winds is also greater, and the lag is considerably less than over oceans.

3.26 *Latitudes Affected by More than One Wind Belt.* This latitudinal shifting of the wind belts becomes climatically significant especially in those regions lying in an intermediate position between two wind systems having unlike weather conditions, as, for instance, between a converging and a diverging system. Such a position ensures the region of being encroached upon at the opposite seasons of the year by contrasting air masses and consequently of experiencing contrasting weather conditions. Two such transition belts will be noted (Fig. 4.15).

1. Latitudes 5 to 15° are roughly intermediate in position between the wet equatorial convergence zone (I.T.C. and doldrums) on the one hand and the dry subsidence and divergence zone of the subtropical anticyclones on the other. With the north-south seasonal shift of pressure and wind belts following the sun, these latitudes feel mainly the effects of the convergence zone and its rain-bringing disturbances at the time of high sun (summer) and of the subsidence in the subtropical anticyclones and their dry trade winds at the time of low sun (winter). One wet season and one dry season are the result. This condition is not so characteristic of the eastern sides of land masses.

2. Latitudes 30 to 40° are intermediate in location between the dry subtropical anticyclones and the middle-latitude westerlies with their numerous convergent wind systems associated with rain-bringing fronts and cyclonic storms. Drought associated with subsidence and divergence is therefore characteristic of the high-sun season (summer), while winter, or the low-sun period, receives adequate precipitation from moving fronts and cyclonic storms in the westerlies.

Actually this control producing dry summers and wet winters is operative only in certain restricted longitudes of the subtropics, chiefly the eastern sides of oceans and the adjacent western margins of the continents in latitudes 30 to 40°

where the summer subtropical anticyclone is well developed. In the western parts of subtropical oceans and adjacent eastern sides of continents, where the anticyclone is weaker and onshore monsoon winds are characteristic of the warm season, summer may actually be the wettest season.

3.27 Monsoon Winds. The conventional description of a monsoon wind states that it is a direct thermally controlled circulation in which there is a reversal of wind direction between summer and winter, and that the cause of this change in direction is the unequal heating of land and water surfaces. The chain of causation is from temperature, through pressure, to winds. In winter, for example, a large land mass in the higher middle latitudes is colder than the surrounding sea surface, so that the air is denser over the cold land surface, with the result that atmospheric pressure is relatively high over the land and lower over the ocean. Surface air flow consequently is from land to sea. This is the winter monsoon. Because it originates over a cold land mass it is likely to be dry and cold and generally opposed to cloud and precipitation (Fig. 3.19).

In summer, by contrast, the land surface is heated to a higher temperature than the surrounding ocean so that the pressure arrangement is reversed from what it was in winter, with the warm land showing a low-pressure center and the adjacent seas relatively higher pressure. As a consequence the surface air flow

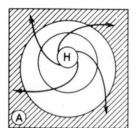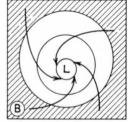

Fig. 3.19 To illustrate monsoons. Shaded areas represent oceans; white areas are continents. In winter (*A*) the land is cold, the pressure high, and the winds flow from land to sea. In summer (*B*) the land is warm, the pressure low, and the winds flow from sea to land.

is from sea to land (Fig. 3.19). This is the summer monsoon, and since it originates over water, it is humid and hence furnishes an environment favorable for the development of cloud and precipitation. The following diagram may help to fix the causation sequence described above for a monsoon system:

Winter — land cold — high pressure — surface winds from land to sea

Summer — land warm — low pressure — surface winds from sea to land

Actually monsoon winds are climatically significant chiefly because of their effects upon temperature and precipitation conditions of those parts of continents where they prevail. Ideally, monsoons should produce a climate characterized by seasonal extremes of both temperature and precipitation, with winters that are cold and dry and summers that are hot and wet.

While continents and oceans do tend to develop contrasting seasonal wind systems, the previous analysis has considerably oversimplified this situation. Always the monsoon system is superimposed upon the general planetary system of pressure and winds and does not wholly supplant it. It is in the nature only of a modification of the planetary system, so that elements of the latter are also present. Some look upon monsoons as essentially a latitudinal shifting of the planetary pressure and wind belts with their associated convergences and fronts. Thus, for example, in eastern Asia, winter finds the polar front far to the south over extreme southeastern China and the adjacent seas, so that northerly winds prevail on its western and northern sides. This would be the winter monsoon. In summer the polar front has shifted northward until it lies over northern China, and southerly winds, the summer monsoon, prevail on its southerly side.

It may be questioned, also, whether the seasonal highs and lows which generate monsoons are *exclusively* the results of the unequal heating of land and water. Moreover, the air streams of both the summer and winter monsoons are far from being regionally homogeneous and this fact is reflected in regional climatic differences within monsoon areas.

Neither the seaward flow of air in winter nor the landward flow in summer is steady and uninterrupted, for numerous moving cyclones and anticyclones with their converging and diverging wind systems greatly complicate the monsoonal flow patterns. Spells of weather consequently characterize both the winter and summer seasons in areas of monsoons. It is these same atmospheric disturbances which produce the rainfall which accompanies the summer monsoon, for while the humid air of oceanic origin may provide a favorable environment for precipitation, the summer rains are sporadic, not continuous, and they usually are associated with atmospheric disturbances. It may be seen, therefore, that the earth's monsoon winds, and their climatic effects, are far more complicated than conventional description would make them.

3.28 Monsoon Areas. Asia, the largest continent, exhibits the best-developed monsoons and likewise the most extensive area under the influence of these winds (Figs. 3.4 and 3.5). All of eastern and southeastern Asia from Manchuria, Korea, and Japan in the northeast to India and Pakistan on the southwest are affected by monsoon wind systems. Actually Asia has two monsoon systems with quite different and separate pressure centers of origin.

3.29 *The East Asia monsoon* which affects chiefly China, Japan, and Korea is characterized by much stronger winds in winter than in summer. In both seasons the monsoons are interrupted by moving atmospheric disturbances so that there are frequent weather changes. The strong land winds of winter result in abnormally low temperatures along the sea margins of eastern Asia, in fact the lowest for the earth at low elevations in these latitudes. Where the winter-monsoon air flow is strong and has few cyclonic interruptions, winters are very dry, as they are in North China and Manchuria. But where convergent systems in the form of cyclones and fronts are numerous, as in Japan and South China, the weather element is more marked and precipitation is moderate in amount, although considerably less than in summer. Rainfall in the summer monsoon likewise is associated with fronts and cyclones.

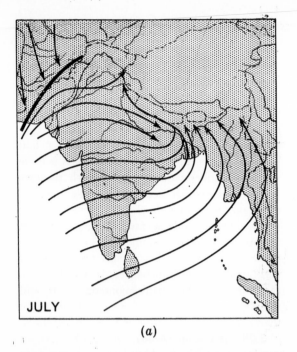

JULY

(a)

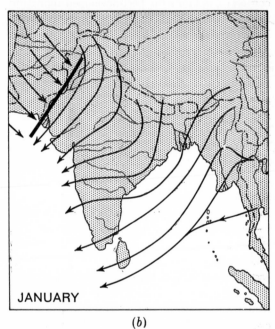

JANUARY

(b)

Fig. 3.20 Atmospheric streamlines over southern Asia in winter and summer. In winter the air flow is from land to sea, and in summer it moves from sea to land.

3.30 *The South Asia monsoon,* being of tropical origin, is characterized by a deep summer low over northern India and by a much stronger air flow in summer than in winter (Fig. 3.20). In reality the so-called winter monsoon of this region is nothing more than the normal trade winds of the planetary system. The heavy summer rainfall over lowlands is associated with moving atmospheric disturbances which find in the very humid tropical maritime air of the summer monsoon an ideal environment in which to generate abundant precipitation. In winter the land trades are dry and the cyclones few, so that little rain falls except where the winds are onshore along coasts bordered by highlands.

Other than in Asia, monsoon wind systems are imperfectly developed, although greatly modified monsoons are to be observed in a number of regions. Among these are southern and southeastern United States and northern Australia.

3.31 Minor Terrestrial Winds. There are certain small-scale winds generated by terrestrial peculiarities which have local climatic effects of some importance. Two of these will be mentioned only briefly. Chiefly along tropical coasts, and to a much less degree along those of middle latitudes, the daily *land and sea breezes* are a significant climatic phenomenon. They are identical in origin to monsoons except that the wind reversal is a daily rather than an annual occurrence. The sea breeze blows toward the heated land by day and from the cooler land by night. The depth of penetration of the sea breeze may be as much as 15 to 20 miles in the tropics, but in the middle latitudes, where it is largely confined to the summer season, its effects are felt only in a narrow belt a few miles in width. The sea breeze is especially strong along dry tropical and subtropical coasts which are paralleled by cool ocean currents and where as a result the afternoon temperature contrasts between land and water are unusually strong. The land breeze of night is a much weaker phenomenon.

Along tropical littorals the sea breeze is a remarkably important climatic phenomenon, causing them to be more livable and healthy places than they otherwise would be. The beginning of the sea breeze may cause a drop in temperature of 15 to 20° within $\frac{1}{4}$ to $\frac{1}{2}$ hr. At Joal, Senegambia (West Africa), the temperature at 12:30 P.M. on an April day was 100°F., with a land wind from the northeast and a relative humidity of 3 per cent. At 12:45 the wind direction was northwest, from the sea, temperature had dropped to 82°F., and the relative humidity had risen to 45 per cent (Hann). Coasts with well-developed sea breezes are inclined to have modified marine climates, with the daily temperature maxima much reduced.

3.32 *Mountain and valley winds,* like land and sea breezes, are local winds with a distinct diurnal periodicity. During the day the air of an enclosed mountain valley, or that adjacent to a slope receiving near vertical rays of the sun, becomes warmer than air at the same altitude over the adjacent plain, so that active convectional ascent of the warm and expanded air takes place up the valleys and along the mountain slopes. This daytime updraft of warm air, which is the *valley and upslope wind,* is indicated by the masses of cumulus clouds which collect about the peaks of mountains during summer days. They are the "visible tops of invisible ascending air currents." Daily summer afternoon showers are therefore common in mountains, and visibility, because of the cloud masses, is restricted during the warm

hours of the day. Actually a considerable amount of the precipitation in highland regions originates as a result of these daytime convectional updrafts of air. After sundown, as the rapidly cooling slopes commence to chill the air layers next to them, the cooler, heavier air begins to slip down the mountainsides into the valleys. This is a reversal of the day current and is known as the *mountain breeze.* It is often very perceptible at the mouth of a gulch; and where there are marked constrictions in a valley that drains a large area, strong winds may result.

NOTE: Surface ocean currents and drifts owe their origin chiefly to the frictional effects of winds. It is small wonder therefore that the general world patterns of ocean currents should show strong resemblance to those of the surface winds. It would not be illogical, therefore, to include a discussion of ocean currents at the close of this chapter on winds. Since, however, there is a later chapter which is devoted exclusively to the oceans (Chap. 18), it has seemed more appropriate to include the topic of ocean currents at that point. Nevertheless, since ocean currents are one of the controls of climate, there is good reason why the student should acquaint himself with their world pattern before proceeding to a study of climatic types and their distributions in Sec. A2.

4

Atmospheric Moisture and Precipitation

Humidity

4.1 Importance of Water Vapor. Water in gas form, or water vapor, in the atmosphere is referred to as *humidity*. Although it comprises only about 2 per cent of the total atmosphere, in terms of weather and climate water vapor is by all odds the single most important element of the air. Unlike most of the other gases, the proportion of humidity in the lower atmosphere varies considerably in both time and space (from nearly zero up to a maximum of 4 or 5 per cent) and this variability is of great importance for several reasons: (*a*) The amount of water vapor in a given mass of air is an index of the atmosphere's potential for yielding precipitation, one of the two major climatic elements. (*b*) Through its absorptive effects on earth radiation it regulates the rate of heat loss from the earth and thereby affects surface temperatures. (*c*) The greater the amount of humidity, the greater the amount of latent or potential energy stored up in the atmosphere for the development and growth of atmospheric disturbances or storms. The amount and vertical distribution of water vapor frequently determine whether an air mass will be stable and resist upward movement, or unstable and buoyant. (*d*) The humidity is likewise an important factor affecting the human body's rate of cooling, *i.e.,* the *sensible temperature*.

4.2 Evaporation and the Sources of Humidity. Like all other atmospheric gases, water vapor is invisible. It is derived from water in the liquid and solid form through the process of *evaporation*. The amount and rapidity of evaporation from a water surface depend upon the temperature of the air, its aridity, and its movement. On very hot, dry, and windy days evaporation is rapid. Certain generalizations regarding the distribution of actual evaporation are climatically significant: (*a*) Evaporation over oceans is greater than over continents where the water supply is more meager. (*b*) Evaporation is at a maximum in the low latitudes and it decreases poleward. Actually evaporation is greater at latitudes 10 to 20°, where the air is drier and the winds stronger and steadier, than at the equator.

The primary source of atmospheric humidity is the great oceans which cover approximately three-quarters of the earth's surface. By winds and diffusion methods, the water vapor evaporated from these bodies of water through the expenditure of solar energy is carried in over the continents. Less important, but nevertheless significant, sources of atmospheric moisture are the moist land surfaces, the vegetation cover, and the minor bodies of water. Plants give off more moisture to the air than does bare ground but not so much as does a freely exposed water surface. A constant turnover is forever in progress as regards the atmosphere's water vapor, additions being made through evaporation of water in its solid and liquid states, while some is being lost to the atmosphere by *condensation* and *precipitation*. By the process of condensation, water vapor, a gas, is changed back into the liquid or solid state, while through evaporation the liquid or solid water is converted into invisible gaseous water vapor. Half the water vapor in the air lies below an altitude of 6,500 ft.

4.3 The Hydrologic Cycle. For some time it has been known that the precipitation which falls upon the continents is far in excess of the runoff from the lands in the form of rivers and glaciers. Probably not more than 30 per cent of continental precipitation finds its way back to the oceans as water and ice. Much of the remaining 70 per cent of the continental precipitation is evaporated from the lands and carried back to the oceans by the seaward- and equatorward-moving dry polar continental air masses (Fig. 4.1). In the cycle of atmospheric exchange between land and sea, moist tropical maritime air masses carry oceanic moisture poleward into the middle-latitude continents, where it is cooled and precipitated. Conversely dry polar continental air masses carry much of the evaporated land moisture back again to the tropical oceans. The great surges of polar air moving southward over the United States are vast invisible "rivers," evaporating from the lands and transporting this moisture in vapor form back to the Gulf of Mexico and the tropical Atlantic.

4.4 Latent Energy in Water Vapor. It is common knowledge that energy is required in the form of heat to change ice (solid) into water (liquid) and water into vapor or steam (gas). The unit of heat energy, the calorie, is the amount of heat required to raise the temperature of a gram of water one degree centigrade. But it takes 79 calories to convert a gram of ice into a gram of water at freezing temperature, and 607 calories to evaporate the gram of water at 32° and convert it into water vapor at the same temperature. Since energy is required to change the solid into a liquid, and likewise the liquid into a gas, it follows that water vapor contains more potential energy than liquid water and water, in turn, more than ice. This stored-up energy in water vapor is known as *latent heat,* or *latent energy.* For the

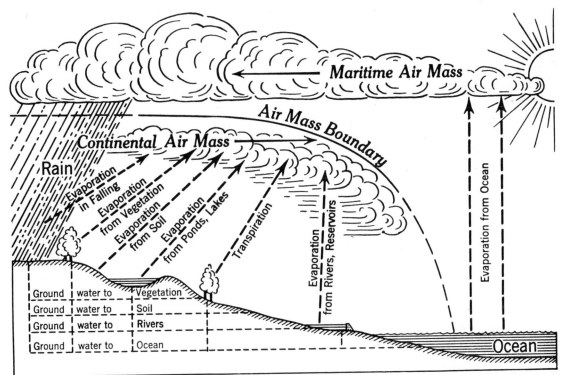

Fig. 4.1 To illustrate the hydrologic cycle. As dry continental air masses evaporate land moisture and carry it to the sea, so maritime air masses transfer moisture evaporated from the oceans to the continents where it falls as rain. (*After Holtzman.*)

most part it is transformed sun energy, which has been employed in evaporating water, ice, or snow and converting them into water vapor. One reason why bodies of water heat slowly is that so much energy is consumed in evaporating at their surfaces. That evaporation requires heat is evident from the cool sensation experienced when the skin is moistened with water or, even better, with alcohol. In this case heat is subtracted from the skin to convert the liquid into a gas. If energy is consumed in the process of evaporation, then, conversely, energy should again be released during condensation. This released heat, known as the *latent heat of condensation,* is an important source of energy in the growth of storms and in the production of precipitation. On a night when condensation takes place, cooling is retarded by the liberation of so much latent heat.

Evaporation—heat consumed

| Solid (Ice) | Liquid (water) | Gas (water vapor) |

Condensation—heat released

4.5 Atmospheric Humidity. The capacity of the air for containing water vapor depends almost exclusively on its temperature. Air that is warm or hot is able to contain much more water vapor than air that is cold. Moreover, the capacity of air for water vapor *increases at an increasing rate* as the temperature rises. This is indicated by the following table and by

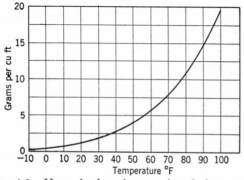

Fig. 4.2 Not only does the capacity of air to contain water vapor increase as the temperature of the air rises, but it increases at an increasing rate.

Maximum Water-vapor Capacity of 1 Cu. Ft. of Air at Varying Temperatures

Temperature, Degrees Fahrenheit	Water Vapor, Grains	Difference between Successive 10° Intervals
30	1.9	
40	2.9	1.0
50	4.1	1.2
60	5.7	1.6
70	8.0	2.3
80	10.9	2.9
90	14.7	3.8
100	19.7	5.0

Fig. 4.2. Thus by increasing the temperature of a cubic foot of air 10°, from 30 to 40°, the moisture capacity is advanced only 1 grain, while a similar 10° increase, from 90 to 100°, results in an increase of 5 grains. It is evident that the air on a hot summer day is able to contain much more moisture than is cold winter air and is likely, therefore, to have greater potentialities for abundant precipitation. Air over Madison, Wis., in July has a water-vapor capacity seven to eight times what it is in January. When a given mass of air contains all the water vapor that it is capable of retaining, it is said to be *saturated.*

4.6 *Distribution of Humidity.* The moisture content of the atmosphere is described in several ways. The actual amount of water vapor in the air is expressed either as specific humidity or as absolute humidity and for the purpose of this book they may be considered as similar. They both express actual water-vapor content of the air and hence are of some significance in gauging the atmosphere's capacity for precipitation. *Specific humidity* is the weight of water vapor in a unit weight of air and is usually expressed as the number of grams of water vapor contained in one kilogram of air. *Absolute humidity* refers to weight of water vapor per unit volume of air.

Since the earth's surface is the source of atmospheric humidity, it is to be expected that the *vertical distribution* of specific and absolute humidity shows the highest concentration near the earth's surface and a rapid decrease with altitude. The average *zonal* (north-south) *distribution* of specific humidity is largely a function of temperature and hence it is highest in the low latitudes near the equator and decreases poleward (Fig. 4.3). It is not unexpected also that the *seasonal distribution* of specific and absolute humidity shows much higher values in summer than in winter. Over north central United States in July air contains three to six times as much humidity as does the January air.

4.7 *Relative Humidity.* Relative humidity is always expressed in the form of a ratio, fraction, or percentage. It represents the amount of water vapor actually present in the air (absolute humidity) compared with the greatest amount that could be present at the same temperature. When the relative humidity reaches 100 per cent, the air is said to be saturated. As an illustration: air at 70° can contain approximately 8 grains of water vapor per cubic foot. If it actually contains only 6 grains (its absolute humidity), then it is only three-fourths saturated, and its relative humidity is 75 per cent. Relative humidity can be altered either by changing the amount of water vapor or by varying the capacity of the air, *i.e.*, changing its temperature. The following table shows how air which was saturated at 40° acquires

Temperature, Degrees Fahrenheit	Absolute Humidity, Grains	Relative Humidity, Per Cent Saturated
40	2.9	100
50	2.9	71
60	2.9	51
70	2.9	36
80	2.9	27
90	2.9	19

successively lower relative humidities simply by increasing its temperature, the water-vapor content remaining unchanged. Relative humidity is an important determinant of the amount and rate of evaporation; hence it is a critical climatic factor in the rate of moisture and temperature loss by plants and animals, including human beings.

Various humidity relationships are illustrated by Figs. 4.4*a* and 4.4*b*. Figure 4.4*a* shows a cubic foot of air subject to three different temperatures. At 0°F. only ½ grain of invisible water vapor can exist in a cubic foot. If the temperature rises to 40°F., nearly 3 grains of water

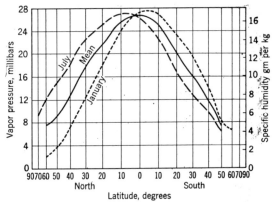

Fig. 4.3 Zonal distribution of the water-vapor content of the air. Specific humidity is highest in the vicinity of the equator and decreases toward the poles. There is a northward displacement in July and a southward displacement in January because of a similar distribution of temperature. Specific humidity at each latitude is higher in summer than in winter. (*After Haurwitz and Austin.*)

SATURATED CONDITIONS
(relative humidities 100%)

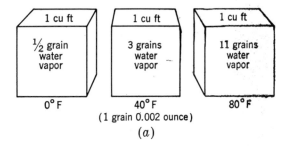

(1 grain 0.002 ounce)

(*a*)

UNSATURATED CONDITIONS

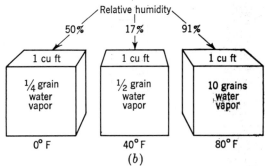

(*b*)

Fig. 4.4 To illustrate absolute and relative humidity.

vapor can exist in that same cubic foot of air, and at 80°F. there can be nearly 11 grains of water vapor in the same space. In all these cases, saturation conditions, or 100 per cent relative humidities, are assumed. If any of the cubes in Fig. 4.4a are cooled appreciably, the invisible water vapor will be condensed out as visible water or ice particles.

In Fig. 4.4b the same cubic-foot samples are shown except that they now represent unsaturated conditions; *i.e.*, they do not contain all the water vapor possible at those temperatures. The cube on the extreme left has only $\frac{1}{4}$ grain of water vapor. Since this is only one-half of what can be present under saturated conditions (see cube at left in Fig. 4.4a), the relative humidity is therefore $\frac{1}{4}$ grain divided by $\frac{1}{2}$ grain, or 50 per cent. The middle cube in Fig. 4.4b contains only $\frac{1}{2}$ grain of water vapor as compared with nearly 3 grains at saturation, making a relative humidity in this case of about 17 per cent. The same reasoning gives a relative humidity of about 91 per cent for the cube on the extreme right. A comparison of the cube on the extreme left in Fig. 4.4a with the center cube in Fig. 4.4b, *both of which contain identical amounts of water vapor*, reveals the former with 100 per cent cent relative humidity and the latter with only 17 per cent. This explains why relative humidity ordinarily goes down as temperature rises on a hot summer day and rises as temperature falls on a cool night.

4.8 *The zonal distribution of relative humidity* shows a strong maximum in the vicinity of the equator from which point there is a decline poleward with minima located at about 25 to 35°N. and S. (Fig. 4.5). These are the regions of the subtropical anticyclones. Poleward from the subtropics as temperature declines the relative humidity increases and maxima are located in the higher middle latitudes (60°±N. and S.). For the *daily period* relative humidity is usually highest in the early morning and lowest in midafternoon.

4.9 *Dew Point and Condensation.* If air that is not saturated is sufficiently cooled, its capacity for moisture thereby being reduced, a temperature is eventually reached at which the mass of air is saturated, even though the amount of water vapor has not been altered. This critical temperature at which saturation is reached is called the *dew point*. If air is cooled below the dew point, then the excess of water vapor, over and above what the air can contain at that temperature, is given off in the form of minute particles of water (if above 32°) or sometimes ice (if below 32°) and *condensation* has taken place. For example, when the temperature of the air is 80° and the absolute humidity 8 grains of water vapor per cubic foot, then the relative humidity is 73 per cent (table, page 70). If this mass of air is gradually reduced in temperature so that its capacity for water vapor is lowered, it eventually reaches

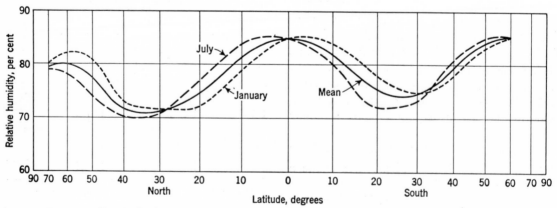

Fig. 4.5 Zonal distribution of relative humidity. Note that the north-south distribution of relative humidity is quite different from that of specific humidity (Fig. 4.3).

the dew point 70° and is therefore saturated at that temperature. Further cooling below the saturation point leads to condensation, the amount of water vapor condensed being the difference between the capacity of air at the different temperatures. Thus a cubic foot of saturated air at 70°, if reduced to 60°, will result in 2.3 grains of water vapor being condensed, this being the difference between the capacities of a cubic foot of air at those two temperatures. An equivalent amount of cooling of saturated air at different temperatures does not, however, yield the same amount of condensed water vapor. If a cubic foot of saturated air at 90° has its temperature reduced 20° (to 70°), 6.7 grains of water vapor are condensed (table, page 70), but a further cooling of 20° (to 50°) releases only 3.9 grains, and the next 20° drop only 2.2 grains. It is obvious that warm summer air has greater potentialities for abundant precipitation than does cold winter air.

Condensation

4.10 Condensation occurs in the atmosphere when a state of saturation is reached, or in other words, when the relative humidity approaches 100 per cent. The condition of saturation may be brought about either by reducing the temperature of the air below the dew point or by increasing the humidity in the air to the saturation point. The first of these two processes is much the more important in causing large-scale condensation, including the formation of all precipitation. By cooling the atmosphere its capacity for water vapor is lowered, and if sufficiently reduced, condensation must result. The dew point of any mass of air is closely related to its relative humidity. When the relative humidity is high, and the air is close to saturation point, only a slight amount of cooling may be required before the dew point is reached and condensation begins. On the other hand, when relative humidity is low, as it usually is over the hot deserts, a large amount of cooling is required before the dew point is reached.

Condensation, therefore, depends upon two variables: (*a*) the amount of cooling and (*b*) the relative humidity of the air. If the dew point is not reached until the temperature falls below 32°, some of the condensed water vapor *may* be in the form of tiny ice crystals (white frost, snow, and some clouds); if condensation occurs above the freezing point, it must be in the liquid state (dew, fog, and most clouds). Actually, much condensation which occurs at temperatures below freezing is in the liquid rather than the solid form and it appears to persist in this liquid form down to temperatures of −40°F.

All condensation in the free atmosphere occurs around hygroscopic nuclei. The most universal condensation nuclei are those of the sea-salt variety. These small salt particles are widely distributed throughout the lower atmosphere by wind. A more active type of hygroscopic nucleus, but more limited in its distribution, is that which is put into the air through the burning of sulphurous fuels such as coal and oil. The very dense fogs in the smoky atmosphere over low-lying industrial areas are associated with this second type of nuclei.

Forms of Condensation and Associated Methods of Cooling the Atmosphere

4.11 Condensation Forms at or near Earth's Surface. By direct cooling processes such as conduction and radiation from the overlying air to the cold earth, and by the mixing of two air masses of unlike temperatures and humidities, relatively shallow layers of air may be cooled below the dew point. However, the condensation forms (*dew, white frost,* and *fog*) resulting from the above-mentioned processes are of relatively small scale and are usually confined to the earth's surface or to shallow layers of surface air. Appreciable rainfall probably never results from such cooling processes. The cooling of deep and extensive masses of air well below the dew point, with associated large-scale condensation in the form of thick cloud masses capable of producing abundant precipitation, is always the result of expansion in rising air masses.

Fog. Of those forms of condensation which occur at the earth's surface, fog is decidedly of the greatest importance climatically speaking.

A very common type of land fog, known as *radiation* or *ground-inversion* fog, results from the cooling by radiation and conduction processes of shallow layers of quiet air overlying a chilled land surface (Fig. 4.6). Clear nights with little wind favor their development. They are deeper and more prevalent in valleys and depressions where, as a result of air drainage, the colder, heavier air collects. Radiation fogs usually are short-lived, being characteristic of the cooler night hours, for they tend to dissipate with sun heating during the day. In the vicinity of large industrial cities where sulphurous condensation nuclei are numerous they are likely to be denser and more persistent.

Another very common type of fog is known as the *advection-radiation* type which develops in mild, humid air as it moves over a colder surface and is chilled by radiation and conduction (Fig. 4.6). Here the emphasis is on *moving,* rather than quiet, air. Fogs of this origin are very common over oceans, especially in summer, along seacoasts and the shores of large inland lakes, and over middle-latitude land surfaces in winter. They are particularly prevalent

TYPES OF FOG

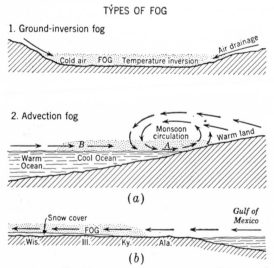

Fig. 4.6 To illustrate common types of fog and methods of their formation.

in the vicinity of cool ocean currents. Advection fogs in the interiors of continents are commonly associated with a poleward flow of mild, humid air from lower latitudes over a cold and snow-covered surface (Fig. 4.6). In general, advection fogs are less local in development than is the simple radiation type, and they tend to persist for longer periods of time so that days as well as nights may remain shrouded.

Still another fog type is that which is associated with belts of frontal rainfall. It originates as a consequence of falling rain saturating the cool surface air.

Distribution of Fog. Generalizations concerning fog distribution are not easy to make. Without much doubt it is more common over oceans than over continents and it is likewise more frequent over oceans in middle and higher latitudes than over those in the tropics. On the continents it is the coastal areas that have the greatest number of days with fog (Fig. 4.7).

Within the United States fog days are most frequent along the Pacific Coast, the North Atlantic Seaboard, and over the Appalachian Highlands. The least foggy area is the dry interior western country.

4.12 Condensation Forms in the Free Atmosphere. Clouds and Associated Precipitation. Although condensation forms in the surface air (dew, white frost, fog) are of some importance, they are, nevertheless, insignificant climatically compared with precipitation which is a product of condensation in the form of clouds. Clouds of great vertical thickness, capable of yielding moderate or abundant precipitation, are the product of one process of atmospheric cooling almost exclusively, *viz.,* cooling as a result of expansion in upward-moving thick air masses.

When air rises, no matter what the reason, is expands because there is less weight of air upon it at the higher altitudes. Thus if a mass of dry air at sea level rises to an altitude of about 18,000 ft., the pressure upon it is reduced one-half, and consequently its volume is doubled. A cubic foot of air at sea level would then, if carried to that altitude, occupy 2 cu. ft. In making room for itself as ascent and gradual expansion take place, other air has to be dis-

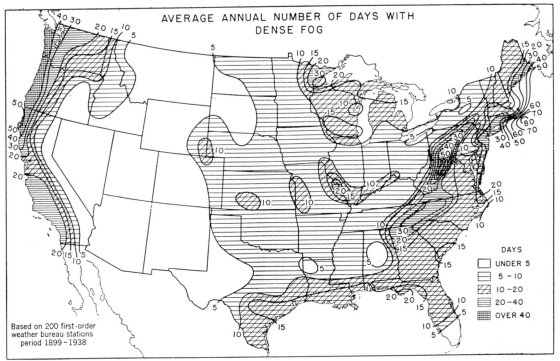

AVERAGE ANNUAL NUMBER OF DAYS WITH
DENSE FOG

DAYS
UNDER 5
5 - 10
10 - 20
20 - 40
OVER 40

Based on 200 first-order
weather bureau stations
period 1899–1938

Fig. 4.7 (*Courtesy of U.S. Weather Bureau.*)

placed. The work done in pushing aside the surrounding air requires energy, and this necessary energy is subtracted from the rising air mass in the form of heat, resulting in a lowering of its temperature. Conversely, when air descends from higher altitudes, it is compressed by the denser air at lower levels. Work is done upon it, and its temperature consequently is raised. It is a truism, therefore, that rising air cools, while descending air is warmed. The temperature changes occurring in the rising or subsiding air mass are not the result of additions of heat to, or withdrawals of heat from, outside sources, but rather are the consequence of internal processes of expansion and contraction. This is spoken of as *adiabatic temperature change.*

The rate of cooling or heating resulting from vertical movement of dry or nonsaturated air is constant and is approximately $5\frac{1}{2}°$ per 1,000 ft. change in altitude. This is the dry adiabatic rate. The rate of cooling of ascending air, therefore, is considerably more rapid than is the normal decrease of temperature (about 3.3° per 1,000 ft.) with increasing elevation, or the

lapse rate. These two rates, the adiabatic rate and the lapse rate, should be clearly distinguished as being very different things, for one represents the cooling of a rising and therefore moving mass of air, while the other represents the change in air temperature that would be recorded by a thermometer carried up through the atmosphere by a balloon or kite.

Heated air continues to rise until it reaches air layers of its own temperature and density. It bears repeating that *this process of cooling, by expansion of rising air currents, is the only one capable of reducing the temperature of thick and extensive masses of air below the dew point.* It is the only one, therefore, which is capable of producing condensation on such a large scale that abundant precipitation results. There is no doubt that nearly all the earth's precipitation is the result of expansion and cooling in rising air currents. The direct result of cooling due to ascent is *clouds,* a form of condensation characteristic of air at altitudes usually well above the earth's surface, just as dew, white frost, and fog are forms characteristic of the surface air. Not all clouds, to be

75

sure, give rise to precipitation, but all precipitation has its origin in clouds and is the result of processes that are supplementary to those causing condensation.

THE FORMATION OF CLOUDS AND PRECIPITATION IN ASCENDING AIR CURRENTS

Stability and Instability

4.13 Stability. Since upward vertical movement of the atmosphere is the cause of practically all precipitation, the conditions which promote or hinder such movements are of prime importance. When air resists vertical movement and tends to remain in the original position, it is said to be *stable*. Atmospheric stability may be likened to a cone resting upon its broad base. Such a cone is stable because it is difficult to tip over, and if it is forcibly tipped, it tends to return to its former position. Normally an air mass is most stable when colder and drier air underlies warmer air. Under such a vertical arrangement the denser air is below the lighter air, with the result that upward movement is difficult. Therefore an air mass in which a temperature inversion exists has a high degree of stability. In highly stable air abundant precipitation is unlikely.

Stability is promoted in at least two ways. If any air mass is chilled at its base through radia-

tion and conduction to a cold underlying surface, the density of the lower air is relatively increased and the stability is also increased. A surface temperature inversion, therefore, is an instance of stability. Still another way of developing stability in a mass of air is for it to subside and spread laterally (horizontal divergence). Such a process of stabilization occurs in high-pressure anticyclonic systems.

The relative stability of an air mass may be determined by noting its vertical temperature distribution or lapse rate and comparing it with the adiabatic rate. A small or weak lapse rate (less than the adiabatic rate of $5\frac{1}{2}°$ per 1,000 ft.), and especially one in which the temperature increases with altitude, indicates stable air (Figs. 4.8 and 4.9).

4.14 Instability. When air does not resist upward vertical displacement but, on the contrary, has a tendency to move upward away from its original position, a condition of *instability* prevails. Under such a condition where the air is buoyant, upward vertical movement is prevalent and cloud and precipitation are likely. Instability may be likened to a cone delicately balanced upon its small apex, for here the slightest impulse will cause it to tip over. Instability is characteristic of warm, humid air in which there is a rapid vertical decrease in temperature and humidity, *i.e.*, a steep lapse

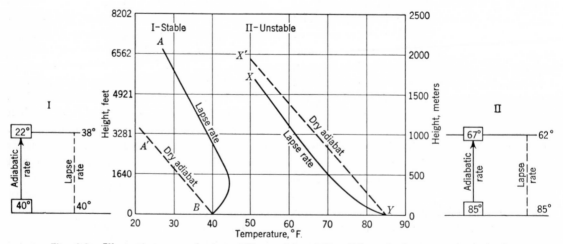

Fig. 4.8 Illustrating atmospheric stability and instability. When the lapse rate exceeds the adiabatic rate, instability prevails. When the reverse is true, the air is stable.

rate. When the lapse rate is greater than the adiabatic rate of $5\frac{1}{2}°$F. per 1,000 ft., a condition of instability prevails (Figs. 4.8 and 4.9).

Instability may be developed in an air mass if it is warmed and humidified in its lower layers. In summer when air from the Gulf of Mexico flows in over the warm land of the Cotton Belt states it is heated from below, made unstable, and much thunderstorm rainfall results. Instability is likewise promoted in a thick air mass by forcing it to rise. Hence the air in any converging system such as a low-pressure cyclonic system is likely to become unstable. Moreover, when humid air that is mildly stable is *forced* to rise over mountain barriers or over colder wedges of air, the resulting condensation may add so much heat to the ascending air that it becomes actually unstable and so continues to rise with accompanying heavy precipitation. Such humid air, which was originally stable but was made unstable as a result of condensation associated with forced ascent, is said to be *conditionally unstable*.

CLOUD TYPES

4.15 Clouds reflect the physical processes occurring in the atmosphere and consequently they are useful indicators of weather conditions. A detailed analysis of cloud types and the relationship of clouds to weather forecasting lies outside the scope of this book where the emphasis is geographical. On the other hand, a modest acquaintance with cloud types is highly useful to the geographer in his understanding of the daily weather out of which the composite climatic picture is composed. Only brief mention is made here of the 10 principal cloud types recognized in the international classification of clouds (Fig. 4.10).

Family A: High Clouds
(Mean lower level, 20,000 ft.)

1. *Cirrus.* Because of their high altitudes, all clouds of the cirrus family are composed of ice crystals instead of water droplets. Cirrus are thin featherlike clouds of delicate and fibrous appearance, white in color, and generally without shading (Fig. 4.10). They may be brilliantly

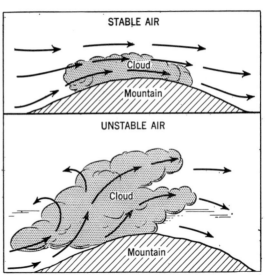

Fig. 4.9 Illustrating cloud formation in the forced ascent of air which is stable in one case and unstable in the other. With stable air, which is nonbuoyant, the clouds are not so thick and the resulting precipitation is likely to be lighter.

colored at sunset. When in the form of detached tufts and of irregular arrangement, they are indicators of fair weather. On the other hand, when they are systematically arranged in the form of bands and streamers, or when connected with cirrostratus or altostratus, they commonly are harbingers of approaching bad weather. The old proverb of the sailors, "Mackerel scales and mare's-tails make lofty ships carry low sails," has real merit.

2. *Cirrocumulus* exists in the form of patches of white flakes, or of globular masses, usually very small and without shadows. The cloudlets are arranged in groups or lines or more often in ripples. They form the so-called "mackerel sky."

3. *Cirrostratus* is a thin whitish veil of cloud which gives the sky a milky appearance. They do not cast a shadow and are never thick enough to obscure the sun. Halos around the sun or moon usually result from cirrostratus. Commonly they are signs of an approaching storm.

Family B: Middle Clouds
(6,500 to 20,000 ft.)

4. *Altocumulus* are flattened globular masses of clouds arranged in a layer. A patternful dis-

Fig. 4.10 A very generalized representation of the forms and elevations of the principal cloud types. (*From "Atmosphere and Weather Charts," published by A. J. Nystrom Co.*)

tribution, in the form of lines or waves, is common. They differ from cirrocumulus in consisting of larger patches, with definite dark shadings underneath.

5. *Altostratus* is a sheet cloud of gray or bluish color, frequently showing a striated or fibrous structure. It is like thick cirrostratus and often merges gradually with it. Although occa-

sionally and in spots it is thick enough to obscure the sun and moon completely, usually they are able to shine through it, although only wanly and with a faint gleam. Altostratus commonly is followed by widespread precipitation of a relatively continuous type.

Family C: Low Clouds
(From close to earth's surface up to 6,500 ft.)

6. *Stratocumulus* is composed of large globular masses or rolls of cloud with brighter spaces between. The cloud masses usually are regularly arranged, as in altocumulus, but they are much larger. They are dull gray in appearance, with darker parts.

7. *Stratus* is a low, uniformly gray layer of cloud, resembling fog, but not resting on the ground. It is capable of producing only light drizzle.

8. *Nimbostratus* is a dense, shapeless, and often ragged layer of low clouds, from which precipitation is likely to fall. However, it is not necessary for precipitation to be actually falling in order for the cloud to be classified as nimbostratus. It is darker than stratus, has no well-defined lower surface, and its elements are not regularly arranged as they are in stratocumulus.

Family D: Clouds with Vertical Development
(1,600 ft. to cirrus level)

9. *Cumulus* is a vertically thick cloud with a dome-shaped cauliflower top and a horizontal base. When seen from the sun side they exhibit great contrasts in light and shadow. When seen against the sun they appear dark and ominous, although they may have bright edges. Cumulus clouds are evidence of strong vertical convection currents, and this upsurge of air is visible in the "boiling" of the tops. Much cumulus cloud is of the fair-weather type, although sometimes they grow so high that they become cumulonimbus and produce precipitation of the thunderstorm type.

10. *Cumulonimbus* are overgrown cumulus which have reached such a height that they lose their clear-cut cauliflower shape. They often spread out on top and become anvil-shaped. Such clouds are associated with sharp showers, squall winds, lightning and thunder, and sometimes hail.

Precipitation

4.16 Origin. Although all precipitation originates in clouds, by no means do all clouds yield precipitation. It appears that some process other than just condensation in cloud form is required in order for precipitation to result. The reason why many, or even most, clouds do not yield precipitation is that condensation occurs around almost innumerable hygroscopic nuclei and the resulting cloud particles are so tiny that their buoyancy prevents them from falling to earth as rain. The precipitation process, therefore, requires the combining of the myriads of these almost microscopic cloud droplets into a smaller number of larger units capable of falling to earth. A good-sized raindrop may contain as much water as 8 million cloud particles and it falls 200 times as fast.

It is believed that this combining of cloud droplets to form raindrops is the result of two processes. One of these is the ascent of the cloudy air above freezing level where some of the liquid droplets are changed to ice. These ice particles then become very active nuclei around which the cloud water particles combine to form larger raindrops. The second precipitation mechanism is the collision and resulting coalescing of the cloud droplets as they fall at different velocities in the cloud.

4.17 Forms of Precipitation. *Rain,* which is much the commonest and most widespread form of precipitation, may be the result of cloud condensation in ascending air at temperatures above freezing. However, some of the earth's rain certainly was originally ice and snow particles, having been formed at temperatures below 32°, which subsequently melted as they fell through the warmer atmosphere closer to the earth's surface.

The most common form of solid precipitation is *snow.* Its fundamental form is the intricately branched, flat, six-sided crystal in an almost infinite variety of patterns. Numerous crystals matted together comprise a snowflake. Snow must develop from condensation which occurs at temperatures below freezing. On the other hand, it may originate in a cloud of supercooled water droplets or it may result from the direct sublimation of ice crystals from water vapor. On the average it requires about 1 ft. of snow to equal 1 in. of rain. Data on the amount and distribution of snowfall are very scant for much of the earth. Snow falls near sea level occasionally in subtropical latitudes but it does not remain on the ground; farther equatorward it is recorded only at relatively high elevations. At low elevations, a durable snow cover in winter lasting for a month or more is characteristic only of the interior and eastern parts of Eurasia and North America poleward from about 40°. In low and middle latitudes a *permanent* snow cover is characteristic only of elevated areas and the height of the snow line declines poleward. Thus while in the deep tropics permanent snow is found at elevations usually over 15,000 ft., at 60°N. in Norway snow remains on the ground throughout the year at an elevation of about 3,500 ft.

Other forms of solid precipitation are sleet and hail. They occur only very occasionally and are restricted in their distribution so that their total climatic significance is minor. Sleet is frozen raindrops. Hail, which falls almost exclusively in violent thunderstorms, is ice lumps which are larger than sleet.

TYPES OF PRECIPITATION CLASSIFIED ACCORDING TO THE CAUSE OF AIR ASCENT

Almost all of the earth's precipitation originates in ascending air which is adiabatically cooled. It is essential, therefore, to an understanding of the world distribution of precipitation to be familiar with the causes for the ascent of thick and extensive masses of air. Three main types of atmospheric lifting, and their associated precipitation, will be noted. It must be stressed, however, that none of these three usually exists in pure form. They are not mutually exclusive, but on the contrary are characteristically intermingled so that any particular unit of precipitation is commonly the result of the joint action of more than one type of atmospheric lifting.

4.18 Convectional Precipitation. As a result of the heating of surface air it expands and is forced to rise by the cooler, heavier air above and around it. Ordinarily such rising air, since it cools at nearly double the rate of the normal vertical temperature decrease, will rise only a few thousand feet before its temperature has been reduced to the point where it is the same as that of the surrounding air. At that point where the rising air reaches air strata of its own temperature and density, further ascent ceases. But if abundant condensation begins before this stage is reached, then heat of condensation is released, so that, with this added source of energy, the rising air will be forced to ascend much higher before reaching atmospheric strata of its own temperature. Thus on a hot, humid summer afternoon, when surface heating is intense and condensation abundant, the towering cumulonimbus clouds resulting from convectional ascent may be several miles in vertical depth, and precipitation from them may be copious.[1] Convectional ascent due to simple diurnal surface heating is largely restricted to land areas and is associated with the warmer seasons and with the warm hours of the day. Clearing toward evening is characteristic.

Thermal convection does not consist of the lifting of a widespread air mass, but rather it is in the form of local ascending and descending currents of relatively small horizontal dimensions. Consequently the cumulonimbus clouds associated with the ascending currents are not of great horizontal extent, so that each appears to be single and isolated and there is frequently clear sky between the individual cumuli. Because the cumulonimbus cloud is not extensive in character, the rainfall associated with it is usually of short duration. We speak of it as a thunder *shower* rather than as a thunder *rain*. Since convectional ascent is essentially a vertical movement of warm humid air, cooling is rapid and the associated rainfall is likely to be vigorous.

[1] Thunderstorms and their rainfall are dealt with in greater detail in the next chapter on storms.

Because convectional rain commonly comes in the form of heavy showers, it is less effective for crop growth, since much of it, instead of entering the soil, runs off in the form of surface drainage. This is a genuine menace to plowed fields, since soil removal through slope wash and gullying is likely to be serious. On the other hand, for the middle and higher latitudes, convectional rain, since it occurs in the warm season of the year when vegetation is active and crops are growing, comes at the most opportune time. Moreover, it provides the maximum rainfall with the minimum amount of cloudiness. Convectional showers resulting from surface heating are associated with warm regions and warm seasons. This type of rain reaches its maximum development in the wet tropics where heat and humidity conditions are relatively ideal for promoting local convection.

Of a somewhat different origin is rainfall resulting from the overrunning of warm and less dense air by colder, denser currents aloft. When this occurs, atmospheric overturning is likely, the cool, heavy air sinking to the earth and forcing the warm air upward, often violently. Heavy downpours may result.

Still another type of convectional precipitation is associated with humid air masses for which the initial upward thrust is provided by some obstacle such as a mountain range, or a cold wedge of air in a cyclonic storm, or where a simple horizontal convergence of air results in forced ascent. When condensation begins, so much heat of condensation may be added to the nonbuoyant ascending air that it eventually becomes unstable and buoyant, and convective ascent then carries it on to greater heights with convectional showers resulting. Such rain is a combination of orographic and convectional or of cyclonic and convectional. It is significant that cumulus clouds and convectional showers are most numerous in regions of horizontal convergence and in mountainous areas.

4.19 Orographic Precipitation. Large masses of air may be forced to rise when landform barriers, such as mountain ranges, plateau escarpments, or even high hills, lie athwart the paths of winds. Since water vapor is largely confined to the lower layers of atmosphere and rapidly decreases in amount upward, heavy orographic rainfall is the result of such forced ascent of air, associated with the blocking effect of landform obstacles. Witness, for example, the very abundant precipitation along the western or windward flanks of the Cascade Mountains in Washington and Oregon, along parts of the precipitous east coast of Brazil, which lies in the trades, or bordering the abrupt west coast of India, which the summer monsoon meets practically at right angles. The *leeward* sides of such mountain barriers, where the air is descending and warming, are characteristically drier (Fig. 4.11). This is called the *rain shadow*. The blocking effect of a mountain is normally felt at some distance out in front of the abrupt change in slope, the approaching wind riding up over a mass of stagnant air along its front. The most ideal condition for producing heavy orographic rainfall is when a high and relatively continuous mountain barrier lies close to a coast and the winds from off a warm ocean meet the barrier at right angles. Orographic rains have less seasonal and daily periodicity than do those of convectional origin. In monsoon regions, very naturally, the maximum is at the time when air is moving from sea to land, usually high sun, or summer. In other regions the strength of the winds, the angle at which they meet the mountain barrier, or the contrast between land and water temperatures may determine the season of maximum orographic rainfall.

It seems likely that a considerable part of the precipitation associated with highlands is not the result of direct forced ascent of the prevailing winds, in other words, not purely orographic

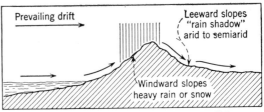

Fig. 4.11 To illustrate precipitation conditions on the windward and leeward slopes of highlands.

in type. Certainly of great importance are such indirect effects as (*a*) the production of convectional currents up mountain slopes exposed to strong insolational heating; (*b*) the "pinching" or "blocking" effect upon cyclonic storms; (*c*) orographically produced convergence in horizontal currents; and (*d*) the providing of a "trigger" effect that gives the initial upthrust to conditionally unstable air masses. Sometimes only a slight amount of lifting is necessary to bring these air masses to condensation level, after which they become unstable and so continue to rise, yielding abundant rainfall. Thus highlands of less than 3,000-ft. elevation, although perhaps inducing no great amount of direct orographic precipitation, may by these indirect means become much rainier areas than the surrounding lowlands.

4.20 Precipitation Resulting from Horizontal Convergence (Cyclonic and Frontal).

In any zone or area of horizontal wind convergence, an upward movement of air must result. Commonly this ascent is not the rapid vertical type, but rather is a more gradual, oblique ascent as along the slope of a mildly inclined plane (Fig. 4.12). In the heart of the tropics the converging air masses may be relatively similar in temperature and hence in density. But outside the tropics convergence usually produces a conflict between air masses of contrasting temperature and density, with the colder, denser air providing the obstacle over which the warmer lighter air is forced to ascend. The boundary between the unlike air masses is called a *front*.

Some of the commonest convergence areas of the earth are those associated with moving atmospheric disturbances in the form of pressure waves, troughs, and low-pressure centers called cyclonic storms. In parts of the earth these disturbances are so numerous that on mean pressure and wind charts their paths appear as average lines of convergence. The zone of convergence between the trades (I.T.C.) and those in the North Atlantic and North Pacific lows in winter may be partly of this origin. Thus the designation *cyclonic* or *frontal* precipitation is somewhat, although not completely, synonymous with precipitation associated with horizontal convergence.

Since in cyclones and along their fronts the air commonly is rising obliquely over mildly inclined surfaces of colder air, the cooling of the rising air is less rapid than is the case in vertical convectional currents.

As a result of the slower ascent and cooling, precipitation in cyclones is characteristically less violent than in thunderstorms and is inclined to be steadier and longer continued. The dull, gray, overcast skies and drizzly precipitation of the cooler months in middle latitudes, producing some of the most unpleasant weather of those seasons, are usually associated with cyclones. These storms and their associated fronts are most numerous and best developed during the cool seasons. Where they dominate weather conditions, therefore, they tend to produce fall or winter maxima in precipitation curves. Most of the winter precipitation of lowlands in the middle latitudes is cyclonic or frontal in origin. By no means all the precipitation in a convergent system is of the mild and prolonged type, however, for not infrequently the initial up-

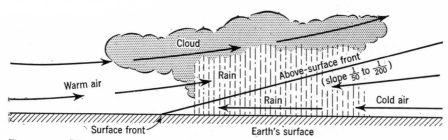

Fig. 4.12 Illustrating the origin of precipitation along a front. Here the warmer and less dense air cools due to expansion as it ascends over a wedge of cooler, denser air.

thrust of air along a front is sufficient to make it unstable so that intermittent showery rain may result.

4.21 Important Features of Precipitation. A satisfactory description of precipitation characteristics for the earth as a whole or for any of its regions involves not only the average total *annual amount,* but also the *seasonal distribution, reliability, intensity,* and *probability* of the rainfall. It is estimated that if the total annual rainfall were spread evenly over the earth's surface it would form a layer about 39 in. deep. Actually precipitation is spread very unevenly, for there are extensive areas that receive less than 5 in. and there are a few spots with over 400 in.

4.22 *Seasonal distribution* of precipitation is coequal in importance with amount. Geographically speaking, the fact that Omaha, Neb., receives 30 in.. of rainfall annually is no more significant than the fact that 17.4 in. (58 per cent) falls during the months from May to August and only 3.3 in. (11 per cent) falls during the period November to February. Seasonal distribution of precipitation becomes of greatest importance in the middle latitudes where there is a dormant season for plant growth imposed by low temperatures, *i.e.,* the winter season. In the tropics where frost is practically unknown except at higher elevations, rainfall is effective for plant growth no matter at what time of year it falls. In the middle latitudes, however, only that proportion of the annual precipitation which falls during the frost-free season may be called effective. In the more severe climates a strong concentration of rainfall in the warmer months when plants can use it is desirable.

4.23 *The dependability or reliability* of the annual or seasonal precipitation is an expression of its variability (Fig. 7.1). Data on rainfall reliability are scarcely less important than those concerned with amount and seasonal distribution. Variability may be defined as the deviation from the mean computed from 35 years or more of observations. In humid climates the annual variability is usually not greater than 50 per cent on either side of the mean, *i.e.* the

driest year may have about 50 per cent of the normal value while the wettest year may have 150 per cent. In dry climates these values vary between about 30 and 250 per cent. It is a general rule that variability increases as the amount of rainfall decreases. It is an inverse ratio. Variability of precipitation must be taken into consideration when agricultural plans are made, for it must be expected that there will be years when the precipitation is less than the average. In semiarid and subhumid climates where crop raising normally depends on a small margin of safety, rainfall variability is of utmost concern. Moreover, the agriculturist in such regions must bear in mind that negative deviations from the mean are more frequent than positive ones, which indicates that a greater number of dry years are compensated for by a few excessively wet ones. Variability of seasonal and monthly rainfall amounts is even greater than for annual values.

4.24 *Intensity and Probability.* There are many other types of useful precipitation data, although most of them are probably of less value than the three mentioned previously. For example the number of rainy days (defined as one having at least 0.01 in.. of rainfall) compared with the total amount of annual rainfall is an indication of the way the rain falls, or its *intensity.* At London, England, the annual rainfall of about 25 in. is spread over 164 rainy days which indicates a lower intensity than the conditions at Cherrapunji, India, where 440 in. falls in 159 days.. The *probability* of rainy days offers a kind of information that has considerable value to such people as farmers and resort owners. This may be readily computed by dividing the number of rainy days in a month or a year by the total number of days.

DISTRIBUTION OF PRECIPITATION

4.25 Distribution of Average Annual Precipitation Amounts. From a glance at Plate 1 it becomes obvious that the distribution of annual precipitation is very complicated. No simple explanation will suffice. Fundamentally it involves two things: (*a*) the factors which influence the lifting and subsidence of the air

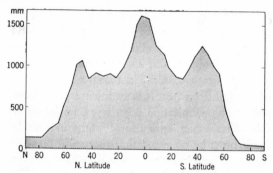

Fig. 4.13 Zonal distribution of precipitation. The amount for any latitude represents the average for all longitudes. (*After Brooks and Hunt.*)

and (*b*) the nature of the air itself, especially whether it is dry or moist. The first of these, which emphasizes vertical movement, is closely related to the distribution of (1) the principal zones of horizontal convergence and divergence, (2) atmospheric disturbances, (3) thermally induced convectional overturning, and (4) highland barriers. The nature of the air as regards its moisture content is chiefly determined by its place of origin: maritime or continental, tropical or high latitude. Some of these controls, for example, the zones of horizontal convergence and divergence, are strongly zonal in

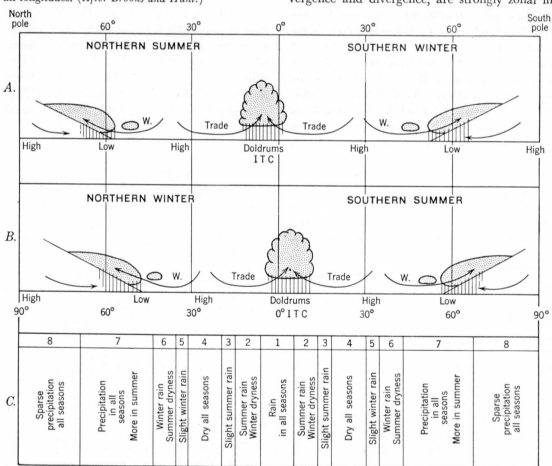

Fig. 4.14 Schematic cross section through the atmosphere showing the main zones of horizontal convergence and ascent, and of divergence and subsidence, together with associated precipitation characteristics; *A,* during the Northern Hemisphere summer; *B,* during the Northern Hemisphere winter; *C,* zones of precipitation. It needs emphasis that many nonzonal features of precipitation distribution cannot be adequately represented on this type of diagram. (*From Petterssen, "Introduction to Meteorology." McGraw-Hill Book Company, Inc., New York.*)

their influence. Others, like the distribution of land and water and of highlands, operate so as to produce modifications of the zonal controls.

4.26 *Zonal Features of Annual Rainfall Distribution.* Some of the most fundamental facts of world rainfall distribution may be presented in the form of a meridional profile showing the precipitation means for the different parallels. Such a profile is shown in Fig. 4.13. This suggests the existence of a strong primary maximum of rainfall amounts in the vicinity of the equatorial convergence (I.T.C.). Belts of lower rainfall are characteristic of subtropical latitudes where diverging wind systems and vertical subsidence are relatively strong. Poleward from the subtropics rainfall increases again so that secondary maxima are indicated for latitudes 40 to 50°N. and S. These are the middle-latitude convergences with their numerous cyclonic storms. Poleward from latitude 50 or 55° precipitation declines sharply with minima of 10 in. and less characterizing the very high latitudes where low temperatures and subsidence are characteristic (see also Fig. 4.14).

4.27 *Nonzonal Features of Annual Rainfall Distribution.* An analysis of Plate 1, and of Fig. 4.15 which attempts to generalize the features of precipitation on a hypothetical continent, reveals that precipitation amounts vary not only in a latitudinal direction, or zonally, but also longitudinally. Thus the typical areas with below-average precipitation (arid, semiarid, and subhumid) are asymmetrically developed in the tropics and subtropics, for they are concentrated in the western and central parts of a large land mass. This is the region of strong horizontal wind divergence and vertical subsidence associated with the stable eastern end of the subtropical anticyclone. Cool ocean currents along the tropical and subtropical west coasts serve to intensify the aridity. In the middle latitudes the dry and subhumid rainfall areas are located toward the center of the continent which is farthest removed from the oceanic sources of moisture supply. In the Southern Hemisphere only South America extends far into the middle latitudes and there

the land mass is so narrow that the feature of light precipitation extends to the east coast.

Abundant rainfall conditions extend across the entire breadth of the continent in the low latitudes close to the equator, with somewhat heavier precipitation characterizing the eastern and western oceanic margins. The equatorial zone of abundant rainfall is more restricted in width to the west where the subtropical anticyclone is strong, but broadens toward the east where the anticyclone is weaker, the coastal waters warmer, and the tropical easterly winds onshore. In the middle latitudes humid conditions are to be found both to the east and the west of the drier continental interiors, except, as noted earlier, in the case of South America. In the larger land masses of the Northern Hemisphere, well-developed cyclonic storms and a tendency toward onshore monsoon winds in summer along the eastern sides lead to the development of generally humid conditions along the eastern margins of the continents.

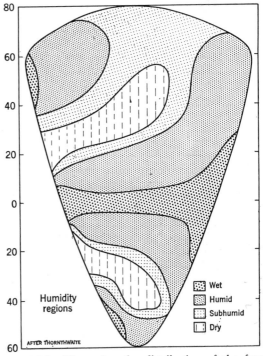

Fig. 4.15 Illustrating the distribution of the four great humidity provinces, based upon annual amounts of precipitation, on a hypothetical continent.

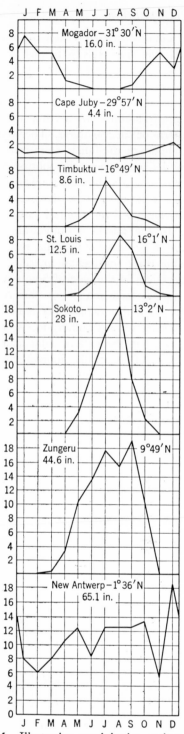

4.28 Seasonal Distribution of Precipitation.

Oceanic areas not only have greater total precipitation than do the lands but are also less seasonal in their concentration. Land masses, with their tendency to strong summer heating, associated thermal convection, and onshore summer winds, are likely to have more of the annual precipitation concentrated in summer. An additional factor making for dry winters over large land masses in middle and higher latitudes is the cold-season anticyclone with its diverging winds.

In the vicinity of the equator where the I.T.C. prevails at all seasons, rainfall is not only abundant but it falls throughout the year, there being no dry season (Figs. 4.14, 4.16, and 4.17). Farther away from the equator, from about 5 or 10° out to 15 or 20°, as rainfall decreases in amount it also becomes more seasonal, with a marked dry period in low sun or winter. The high-sun period, or summer, is wet (Figs. 4.16 and 4.17). This feature of high-sun rainfall

Fig. 4.16 Illustrating precipitation regimes in the low latitudes north of the equator in Africa. The stations are arranged according to latitude with Nouvelle Anvers (New Antwerp) closest to the equator.

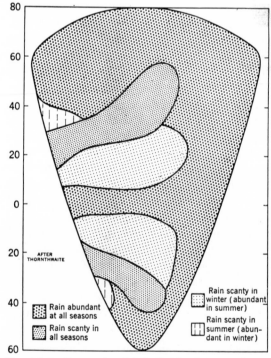

AFTER THORNTHWAITE

Rain abundant at all seasons

Rain scanty in all seasons

Rain scanty in winter (abundant in summer)

Rain scanty in summer (abundant in winter)

Fig. 4.17 Seasonal rainfall distribution on a hypothetical continent.

and low-sun drought is associated with the latitudinal shifting of the zones of convergence and divergence following the sun (Fig. 4.14*B* and *C*). These latitudes are affected by the I.T.C. at the time of high sun, while they feel the effects of the subtropical anticyclone and divergence at the time of low sun. It will be noted that this area of winter drought does not extend to the east side of the continent where the subtropical anticyclone is weaker.

In subtropical latitudes at about 30 to 40°, and restricted to the western side of the continent, are areas, usually of limited extent, where summer is the season of precipitation deficiency and winter is wet (Fig. 4.17). In such locations latitudinal migration of pressure and wind systems following the sun causes the stable eastern limb of the subtropical anticyclone to control the weather in summer and cyclones associated with the middle latitude convergence zone to prevail in winter (Fig. 4.17).

Throughout the middle latitudes (poleward of about 40°) there is usually no dry season, some precipitation falling at all times of year (Fig. 4.17). This is not to say that all seasons have equal amounts, however. The *western* or windward side of the continent characteristically has rain throughout the year. Along the immediate coast there is frequently a winter maximum. In the *interior* of middle-latitude continents summer commonly is the wettest season. The drier winters are related to the low temperatures and the anticyclonic wind systems of that season. *Eastern* margins of middle-latitude continents also have rain throughout the year, but usually summer is wetter than winter, although the seasonal concentration is not as emphatic as it is in the interior.

5

Air Masses, Fronts, and Atmospheric Disturbances

5.1 Climate, as indicated in an earlier section, is a generalization of the day-to-day weather prevailing in a locality or region. And the weather of an area is closely identified with the meteorological nature of the air which prevails there and with the atmospheric disturbances which develop. To the layman these disturbances are known as storms. Those areas which experience almost exclusively one type of air mass are likely to have relatively uniform weather. Such an area is the central Sahara in summer and the upper Amazon Basin at all times of the year. But much of the earth's surface experiences two or more air masses; in some parts the change from one to the other is largely seasonal in character, while in others, especially the middle latitudes, rapidly shifting air masses with striking temperature and humidity characteristics may produce highly changeable weather within a short period.

The zones of contact between unlike air masses, where air streams of contrasting temperature and humidity are converging, are called *fronts*. These frontal zones of converging air are the breeding areas for atmospheric disturbances of various kinds. Consequently, it is along air-mass boundaries or fronts that weather changes are concentrated and where much of the earth's precipitation is developed. From what has been said it should be clear that some understanding of air masses, fronts, and atmospheric disturbances is essential to an appreciation of the world pattern of climates the discussion of which follows in Sec. A2.

Air Masses and Fronts

5.2 Definitions and Characteristics. An air mass is an extensive portion of the atmosphere whose temperature and humidity characteristics are relatively homogeneous horizontally. Such an air mass develops whenever the atmosphere remains in contact with an extensive and relatively uniform surface for a sufficiently long period so that the properties of the air become similar to those of the surface on which it rests. These extensive and relatively uniform areas of the earth's surface where air masses develop are called *source regions*. Since the primary feature of an air mass is its relative uniformity, it follows that the earth's principal source regions are (*a*) where the surface is relatively uniform and (*b*) where at the same time the wind system is a divergent one. In regions of convergence unlike temperatures are brought close together so that thermal contrasts are great. Anticyclonic circulations, therefore, provide the most ideal source-region conditions. The snow-covered arctic plains of Canada and Siberia in winter, large areas of tropical ocean, and the hot, arid Sahara in summer are good examples of source regions.

As a rule air masses do not remain long in their source regions but sooner or later move outward from them into other areas whose weather as a result is affected by the invading air mass. Moreover, the moving air is itself modified by its new environment so that it begins slowly to change in character. Air masses are able to travel great distances from their regions of origin and still maintain many of the properties attained at their sources. Because of their great size and the slowness with which they are modified it is easy to trace the movement of an air mass from day to day and at the same time note the changes in the air mass imposed by the new environment which it is invading.

When air masses having different temperature and humidity characteristics come together, they do not mix freely with each other but tend rather to remain separated with more or less distinct sloping boundary surfaces between them, the warmer and therefore less dense air mass being forced aloft over the wedge of colder air (Fig. 5.1). The sloping boundary surfaces separating contrasting air masses are called *surfaces of discontinuity,* or *fronts.* Where a sloping surface of discontinuity in the free atmosphere intersects the earth's surface, a *surface front* is formed (Fig. 5.1). Fronts are not lines, but rather they are zones of appreciable width, varying from 3 to 50 miles in breadth. Usually marked changes in temperature and humidity can be observed as one crosses a front. The location of fronts, both at the earth's surface and aloft, and the nature of the contrasting air masses on either side of them are of great importance in weather forecasting, for along such fronts a great many storms and associated weather changes originate. Whenever there is a convergent movement of air masses, such as characterizes low-pressure systems, frontal discontinuities are likely to be present.

It is unusual for the fronts separating unlike air masses to remain very long in a stationary position. Usually one of the air masses is more active than the other and advances into the latter's domain. As a consequence the position of the front is shifted. When the warmer air mass is more aggressive and advances against the cold air, there is an active upward ascent of the lighter warmer air over the wedge of colder denser air (Fig. 5.2). This is a *warm front.* Where the colder air is the aggressor, it actively underruns the warmer air and forces

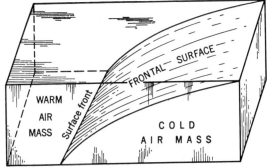

Fig. 5.1 A three-dimensional representation of an atmospheric front.

it upward. This is the *cold front.* Warm fronts and cold fronts differ in their weather features, but an analysis of these differences is postponed to a later section dealing with middle-latitude cyclones.

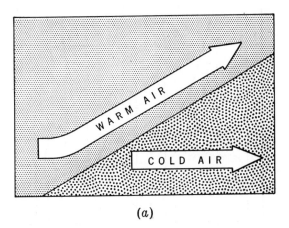

(a)

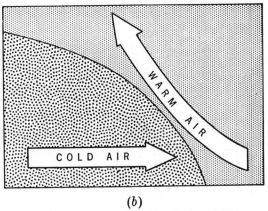

(b)

Fig. 5.2 Illustrating (a) warm front and (b) cold front. (*Courtesy of U.S. Weather Bureau.*)

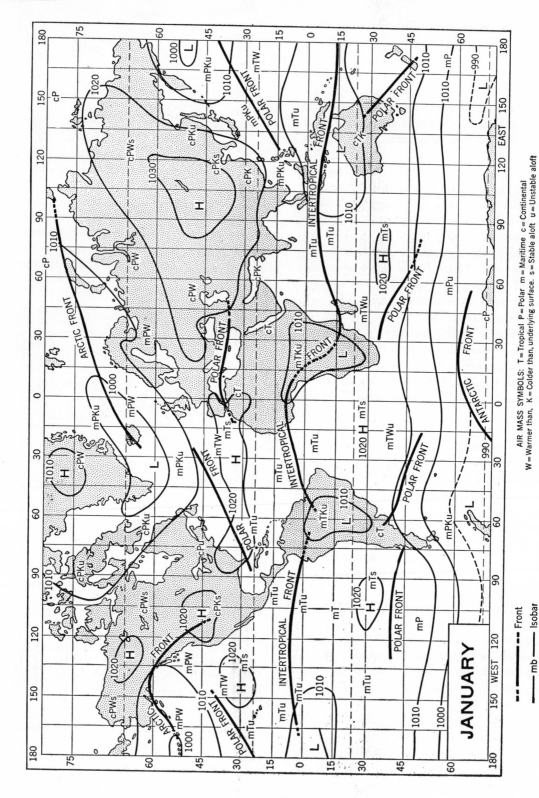

Fig. 5.3 Air masses and fronts in January. (*After Haurwitz and Austin.*)

AIR MASS SYMBOLS: T = Tropical P = Polar m = Maritime c = Continental
W = Warmer than, K = Colder than, underlying surface. s = Stable aloft u = Unstable aloft

Front - - - —
Isobar mb —

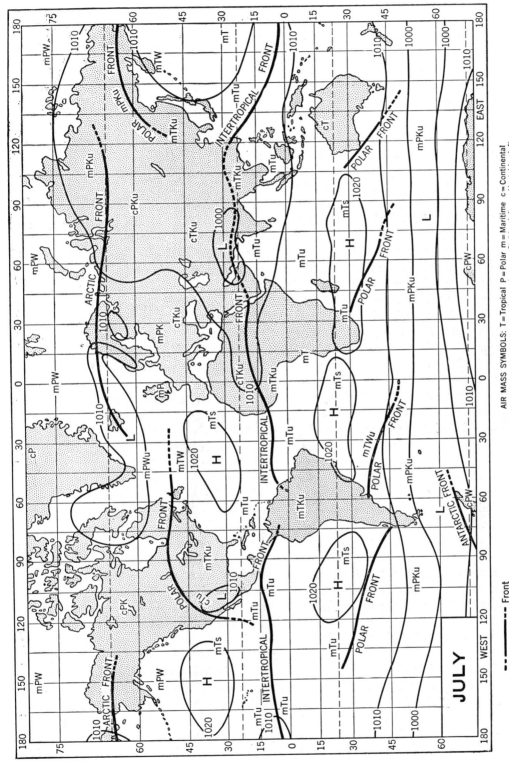

AIR MASS SYMBOLS: T=Tropical P=Polar m=Maritime c=Continental

W=Warmer than, K=Colder than, underlying surface. s=Stable aloft u=Unstable aloft

Fig. 5.4 Air masses and fronts in July. (*After Haurwitz and Austin.*)

91

The air-mass concept probably should be thought of as in the nature of a refinement or amplification of the earth's wind system. The discussion of air masses to follow is therefore largely supplementary to the treatment of winds in Chap. 3.

5.3 Classification of Air Masses. Any classification of air masses must be based primarily upon the characteristics of their source regions. For this reason air masses are designated by the name or abbreviation of the source region. The latter fall naturally into two groups, those of high latitudes or *polar* (*P*) and those of low latitudes or *tropical* (*T*). It is largely in the high and the low latitudes that there are large areas of relatively homogeneous surface conditions and relatively light air movement. The middle latitudes are the scene of intense interaction between the polar and tropical air masses and generally lack the uniformity of conditions essential to a source region (Figs. 5.3 and 5.4).

The air-mass classification may be further refined by dividing the polar (*P*) and tropical (*T*) source types, on the general basis of moisture and temperature differences, into *continental* (*c*) and *maritime* (*m*) subgroups. Thus, the symbol *cP* indicates a polar continental air mass, while *mT* indicates one of tropical maritime origin.

A principal way of modifying an air mass is through the transfer of heat between the bottom of the air mass and the surface over which it is moving. When an air mass is heated from below it becomes increasingly unstable, while chilling at the base causes stability. To indicate these important modifications two further letter symbols are added in the classification:

K: air mass colder than the underlying surface.

W: air mass warmer than the underlying surface.

But modifications of an air mass do not occur always at the surface. Horizontal convergences and divergences resulting in ascent and subsidence cause stability modifications. Thus convergence and ascent such as occurs in low-pressure cyclonic systems promote unstable conditions, while conversely divergence and settling which occur in high-pressure anticyclonic wind systems produce stability. A fourth letter is sometimes added to the air-mass symbol in order to indicate above-surface stability conditions (Figs. 5.3 and 5.4):

s: stable air aloft.

u: unstable air aloft.

It is further necessary to take into consideration the particular season of the year, for many source regions differ markedly from winter to summer, and consequently their air masses do as well.

5.4 North American Air Masses. The North American continent is a region of strong air-mass contrasts. The wide northern part permits the development of severely cold continental air masses in winter, while the lack of east-west relief barriers permits a free flow of polar air southward and of tropical air northward. On the other hand, because of the wide extent of mountains and plateaus in western North America, the entrance of maritime air from the Pacific is made difficult. *mP* air reaches central and eastern North America only in greatly modified form. In nearly all the above features North America stands in contrast to Europe.

5.5 *Polar Continental* (*cP*) *Air Masses.* The source region for the *winter cP* air in North America is the ice-covered northern interior of Canada, Alaska, and the Arctic Ocean (Fig. 5.5). At its source this air is always very cold, dry, and stable (*cPWs*). These distinctive properties result from (*a*) strong radiation cooling from the snow surface on which it rests and (*b*) subsidence aloft in the prevailing anticyclonic circulation. Excessive surface cooling produces a deep temperature inversion which may extend up to a mile or more above ground.

Severe winter cold waves are associated with rapid southward movement of *cP* air. Marked stability and a strong temperature inversion persist as long as the *cP* air mass moves southward over a snow-covered surface. Rarely does it become genuinely unstable in the Mississippi Valley before reaching the Gulf of Mexico. Cloudless skies are a distinctive characteristic.

Over northeastern United States and the Atlantic Seaboard *cP* air shows more cloudiness and has somewhat higher surface temperatures (Figs. 5.3 and 5.5). This results from passage over the open water of the Great Lakes in winter and the turbulence produced by the highlands in the eastern part of the country. Because of the general westerly air movement in middle latitudes, as well as the highland barriers, *cP* air only occasionally reaches the Pacific Coast. When it does, snow and severe subfreezing temperatures result.

Source properties of American *cP* air in *summer* are markedly different from those in

Classification of American Air Masses

Classification by local source regions				General classification after Bergeron (international)	Local air-mass names
Source by		Local source regions	Season of frequent occurrence		
Latitude	Nature				
Polar	Continental	Alaska, Canada and the Arctic	Entire year	cP or cPW, winter cPK, summer	Pc Polar Continental
		Modified in southern and central United States	Entire year	cPK	
	Maritime	North Pacific Ocean	Entire year	mPK, winter mP or mPK, summer	Pp Polar Pacific
		Modified in western and central United States	Entire year	cPW, winter cPK, summer	
		Colder portions of the North Atlantic Ocean	Entire year	mPK, winter mPW, spring and summer	Pa Polar Atlantic
		Modified over warmer portions of the North Atlantic Ocean	Spring and summer	mPK	
Tropical	Continental	Southwestern United States and northern Mexico	Warmer half of year	cTK	Tc Tropical Continental
	Maritime	Gulf of Mexico and Caribbean Sea	Entire year	mTW, winter mTW or mTK, summer	Tg Tropical Gulf
		Modified in the United States or over the North Atlantic Ocean	Entire year	mTW	
		Sargasso Sea (Middle Atlantic)	Entire year	mTW, winter mTW or mTK, summer	Ta Tropical Atlantic
		Modified in the United States or over the North Atlantic Ocean	Entire year	mTW	
		Middle North Pacific Ocean	Entire year	mTW, winter mTW or mTK, summer	Tp Tropical Pacific
		Modified in the United States or over North Pacific Ocean	Entire year	mTW	

Winter Characteristics of Some American Air Masses

Air mass	Station	Weather element	Elevation above sea level				
			Surface	1 km.	2 km.	3 km.	4 km.
cP	Ellendale, N.D.	Temp., °F.	−15	−13	−4	−7	−13
		Sp. humid., g./kg.	0.32	0.35	0.60	0.50	0.45
		Rel. humid., %	82	80	75	63	71
mP (Pacific)	Seattle, Wash.	Temp., °F.	46	32	18	7	−2
		Sp. humid., g./kg.	4.4	2.7	1.5	0.8	0.4
		Rel. humid., %	66	64	64	52	35
mT (Gulf)	Miami, Fla.	Temp., °F.	77	68	55	46	37
		Sp. humid., g./kg.	16.3	13.3	9.8	6.2	5.2
		Rel. humid., %	82	82	83	66	67
mT (Pacific)	San Diego, Calif.	Temp., °F.	68	59	50	43	34
		Sp. humid., g./kg.	11.9	9.8	6.8	4.0	2.1
		Rel. humid., %	86	81	70	51	33

Summer Characteristics of Some American Air Masses

Air mass	Station	Weather element	Elevation above sea level				
			Surface	1 km.	2 km.	3 km.	4 km.
cP	Ellendale, N.D.	Temp., °F.	66	61	50	39	27
		Sp. humid., g./kg.	6.3	5.6	3.9	3.1	2.9
		Rel. humid., %	42	45	43	44	57
mP (Pacific)	Seattle, Wash.	Temp., °F.	63	48	41	34	28
		Sp. humid., g./kg.	7.1	6.3	3.9	2.3	1.7
		Rel. humid., %	62	91	60	42	33
mT (Gulf)	Miami, Fla.	Temp., °F.	75	68	59	48	41
		Sp. humid., g./kg.	17.3	14.9	9.3	6.3	4.3
		Rel. humid., %	93	88	74	58	48
cT	El Paso, Tex.	Temp., °F.	75	81	75	64	
		Sp. humid., g./kg.	11.0	9.7	9.9	7.6	
		Rel. humid., %	52	37	43	43	

winter. Long days cause the snow-free land surface to become much warmed so that the air is heated from the ground (*cPK*) instead of being chilled from beneath as in winter. A fairly low moisture content, moderately low temperatures, and absence of clouds are characteristic of *cP* air in summer at or near its source. Precipitation is absent. As it moves southward from its source region, heat and moisture are constantly being added and instability increases. Occasionally modification is so great that thunder showers may develop (Figs. 5.4 and 5.5).

5.6 *Polar maritime* (*mP*) *air masses* (*Pacific*) which affect the western parts of North America have as their source region the northern part of the North Pacific Ocean. In winter this region is dominated by the circulation around the Aleutian Low. It is surrounded on all sides, except to the south, by *cP* source regions so that Pacific *winter mP* air was originally very cold and dry *cP* before it was drawn into the *mP* source region. Heating and humidifying the *cP* air at its base changes it from a cold, dry, stable air mass into one which is relatively unstable and whose surface strata, at least, are comparatively mild and humid (*mPKu,* Figs. 5.3 and 5.5). The instability aloft (*u*) is produced by the strong cyclonic circulation of the deep Aleutian Low.

As the unstable winter *mP* air advances against the coastal highlands of North America, or the colder air masses near the continent, much cloud and rain result. Important modifications occur as the Pacific *mP* air crosses the western mountains and reaches the interior of the country. By that time it has lost much of its moisture, its temperature has been lowered, and its stability has been greatly increased. Some of the finest winter weather east of the Rockies prevails when these Pacific *mP* air masses are in control—moderate winds, clear skies, and relatively moderate temperatures.

In summer the Pacific *mP* source region is geographically identical with what it is in winter. But in the warm season the waters of the North Pacific are colder than the surrounding lands, so that air entering the source region is chilled at the base and made more stable. Most of the eastern Pacific is dominated by the Pacific High in summer, and the strong subsidence in the eastern end of the cell makes for increased stability aloft. The high over the ocean and the low over the continent result in a flow of cool, stable *mPs* air southward along the west coast of North America so that clear skies and fair weather are the rule. The stabilizing and aridifying effect is increased as the summer *mP* passes over the cold water which upwells along the coast of California. In general, summer *mP* air at Seattle is more stable than *cP* air in the Upper Mississippi Valley.

5.7 *Polar maritime* (*mP*) *air masses* (*Atlantic*) which originate over the cool Atlantic waters between Cape Cod and Newfoundland

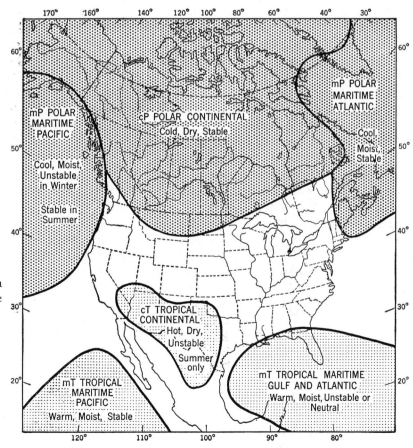

Fig. 5.5 North American air masses and their source regions.

were orginally *cP* air which moved off the continent and were modified over the cold waters. Owing to the prevailing west-east air movement, the North Atlantic is not an important source region for air masses affecting North America. This is especially true in winter. Seldom does Atlantic *mP* air extend its effect beyond the Appalachians. In *winter* Atlantic *mP* air is characteristically dry and stable aloft, while the surface layer is moderately unstable, moist, and chilly rather than cold. As compared with Pacific *mP* air, its lower levels are colder, drier, and more stable. As Atlantic *mP* air comes onshore in winter it results in weather with surface temperatures near freezing, high relative humidity, low visibility, and frequently light flurries of fine mist (Fig. 5.5).

Atlantic *mP* air masses have their greatest influence upon American weather in late *spring* and early *summer*. At that time of year the North Atlantic waters are abnormally cold compared with the adjacent continent so that they become a source region of genuinely cold air for the whole coastal area east of the Appalachians and north of Cape Hatteras. Atlantic *mP* summer air is distinctly cool, relatively stable, and shows only thin and broken clouds from which precipitation never falls.

5.8 *Tropical maritime (mT) air masses (Gulf and Atlantic)* which so greatly affect the weather and climate of North America east of the Rockies have their origin over the warm waters of the Gulf of Mexico and the Caribbean Sea or over the Sargasso Sea of the Atlantic proper. Gulf and Atlantic *mT* air at its source is characterized by marked warmth and high moisture content at lower levels. In *winter* as the *mT* air moves inland and poleward from the Gulf of Mexico, the ground strata are cooled and stabilized by contact with a colder earth, and where air movement is slight, dense fog frequently is the result. In rather strong air currents dense mist or fine drizzle is likely (Fig. 5.5). Convective precipitation rarely occurs within this *mT* air mass in the cool season, but along a front, where it is forced to ascend, precipitation may be extremely heavy. Combined with warmth and high humidity

there is likely to be considerable cloudiness of the low stratus type, especially during the night and early morning.

Because of prevailing sea-to-land pressure gradients over eastern United States in *summer,* Gulf *mT* air is able to extend much farther into the interior of the continent at that season than in winter. It is responsible for the oppressive humid heat which characterizes the summer weather of much of central and eastern United States. As it leaves its source region, summer Gulf *mT* air is somewhat warmer and more humid than it is in winter. Moving in over the continent and continuing northward over the warm land, there is a tendency for its surface layers to increase in temperature and therefore in instability (*mTKu*). Midday instability with numerous widely scattered local thunderstorms is characteristic of the air mass. Gulf *mT* air is the principal source of precipitation for the North American region east of the Rockies.

Although the source region of Gulf *mT* air is within the domain of the North Atlantic subtropical anticyclone, it is the weaker western margins of the cell which here prevail. Hence the strong upper-air subsidence and drought conditions which usually accompany anticyclones are not characteristic of this air mass in southeastern North America.

5.9 *Tropical maritime (mT) air masses (Pacific)*, which affect principally southwestern United States and northwestern Mexico, have their origin in the subtropical eastern Pacific ocean in almost identical latitudes to those in which Gulf *mT* air develops (Fig. 5.5). But while they both originate over subtropical oceans, the two *mT* air masses have fundamental contrasts. Pacific *mT* air is cooler, drier, and more stable than its counterpart in subtropical eastern North America. The lower temperatures result from the cool coastal waters, while the greater stability is a consequence of the strong subsidence in the *eastern* parts of the Pacific anticyclone (*mTs*) and of the chilling of the surface strata by the cool ocean waters (Figs. 5.3 and 5.4). Stable Pacific *mT* air is not a good rainbringer and thermal convection with associated thunderstorms is not characteristic of it. Only when it is forced to ascend, as for example over the western mountains or along a front in a cyclonic system, does it yield moderate precipitation. In summer when atmospheric disturbances are few, drought prevails.

5.10 *Tropical continental* (*cT*) *air masses* play an unimportant role in North American weather. Chiefly this is due to the fact that North America lacks an extensive land area in tropical latitudes. Only a relatively small area in southwestern United States and northwestern Mexico develops *cT* air, and moreover this occurs only in the warm season. During summer, as a result of strong insolation heating, the air in this source region becomes excessively hot and dry. As it moves eastward from the region of origin its influence is felt on the Great Plains, but as it moves farther eastward it mixes with other air masses and its identity is gradually lost. *cT* does not appear on the daily weather map east of the Mississippi River.

5.11   Eurasian Air Masses. Europe, excluding Soviet Russia, is lacking in a genuine source region. It is, rather, a transition zone where invading air masses are modified and transformed. The air masses which control the weather of western Europe are, in many respects, similar to those of western North America. Polar maritime air (*mP*), which plays such an important role in Europe's weather, resembles closely Pacific *mP* air in western maritime Canada and the United States. In *winter* it enters Europe as a fairly mild humid air mass of varying degrees of instability, depending on its route across the Atlantic. When caused to rise along fronts or over relief barriers, it yields plentiful precipitation. As it moves inland from the coast and is chilled at the base, its stability is increased. In *summer* the *mP* air is more stable, but as it moves slowly toward the interior it is warmed at the base and becomes increasingly unstable, so that cumulus clouds and convectional showers are fairly common (Figs. 5.3 and 5.4).

Tropical maritime (*mT*) air in western Europe resembles Pacific *mT* air in western North America, but it is cooler, drier, and more stable than Gulf *mT* air in southeastern United States. *Winter mT* air in western Europe has originated on the northern and eastern flanks of the Atlantic subtropical high and has traveled a northerly route over increasingly cooler waters. It is, therefore, relatively stable. It is warmer and moister than polar air, to be sure, but because of its stability it yields abundant rain only if lifted by relief barriers or along frontal surfaces. *Summer mT* is not common in Europe north of latitude 40°N. South of 40°N., it is a very stable (*mTs*) air mass.

Polar continental (*cP*) air masses are relatively infrequent in western Europe but become increasingly more prevalent in central and eastern Europe. The general west-east atmospheric circulation in middle latitudes makes westward thrusts of *cP* air difficult. The source region for this cold air is snow-covered Soviet Russia and Finland. European *winter cP* at its source resembles *cP* in Canada—low temperatures, with a surface inversion, low humidities, and a high degree of stability. By the time *cP* has reached central and western Europe it has been considerably modified, especially by relief barriers. Severe cold waves such as those common to the open Mississippi Valley are unlikely. *cP* air in the region of the Rhineland has a surface temperature of about 20°F. *Summer cP* is confined to northern Europe where it is a relatively cool, dry air mass.

5.12 *The Mediterranean Borderlands* in *winter* are a region of air-mass convergence, there being a relatively strong front developed over the warm waters of the Mediterranean Sea in the cool season. *mP* and *cP* air from Europe and *cT* from northern Africa enter the basin and are there modified in temperature and humidity. General instability and associated cyclonic storms with cloud and rain are the results. In *summer* the Mediterranean is a region of anticyclonic circulation and prevailingly warm, dry, stable *cT* air masses. Rainfall is consequently meager (Figs. 5.3 and 5.4).

5.13 *Eastern Asia* in its air-mass characteristics resembles eastern North America. In *winter* polar continental (*cP*) air from the extensive source region of the great Siberian anticyclone dominates the weather of central and eastern Asia. At its source this air is colder and drier then North American *cP*. As it surges southeastward from its source, it encounters rough terrain with the result that it is considerably modified before it descends to the plains of China and regions farther south, even into the tropics. India is largely protected from invasions of Siberian *cP* by the high mountain and plateau barriers bordering it to the north. North of about the Yangtze River *cP* so dominates the weather that winter precipitation is very meager. Southward, however, contact with *mT* air is more frequent, and as a result winters are much cloudier and rainier. *cP* that reaches Japan has been warmed, humidified, and made somewhat unstable by its passage over the Sea of Japan. When this air is forced aloft over the mountains of western Japan, it precipitates heavily in the form of snow. *cP* air in *summer* is of modest importance; for the most part it is confined to northern China and Siberia where it meets *mT* air along the polar front (Figs. 5.3 and 5.4).

Tropical maritime (*mT*) air masses dominate the weather of eastern and southern Asia in *summer*. This air closely resembles Gulf *mT* in that it is warm, moist, and unstable. As it moves inland over the warm lands its instability is further increased and heavy convective, frontal, and orographic rain results. Because of the anticyclonic circulation and the prevalence of polar air in *winter*, *mT* air has much greater difficulty entering eastern and southern Asia in the cool season. When it does invade, it makes fronts with *cP* resulting in cloud and rain. *cT* air is widespread in southern interior Asia in summer.

Atmospheric Disturbances

5.14 Atmospheric Disturbances as Generators of Precipitation. Simply because winds are onshore from over an extensive ocean, and probably contain an abundance of water vapor, is no assurance that the land precipitation will be abundant. A further requirement, in addition to the adequate supply of moisture, is some agency which will cause the humid maritime air to ascend and cool. Except where highland barriers are the cause for ascent, atmospheric disturbances or storms are the principal centers of rising air, with the consequence that they are likewise the earth's principal generators of precipitation.

These rain-bringing disturbances are of a great variety of kinds, origins, and intensities and are characterized by differences in direction and rate of movement. Some of them have long been known and studied; others have only recently been recognized. By no means are all classes of atmospheric disturbances well understood in either their characteristics or their origins. Many, but not all of them, can be observed on the surface daily weather map through isobar and wind patterns. On such a weather map of the United States, or still better one of the whole Northern Hemisphere, the traveling atmospheric disturbances may be so conspicuous and numerous that they tend to obscure the main lineaments of the general circulation (Fig. 5.6). It is somewhat analogous to a river being so full of whirls and eddies that it is difficult to distinguish the main current.

MIDDLE-LATITUDE DISTURBANCES: CYCLONES AND ANTICYCLONES

General Characteristics

5.15 Of principal importance in producing the frequent, erratic, day-to-day weather changes so characteristic of middle latitudes are the moving cyclones and anticyclones which fill the westerly wind belts. In such regions the fickleness of the weather is proverbial, and it is in these parts of the world that weather-forecasting services are most necessary and best developed. No two storms are exactly alike, so that the generalizations concerning cyclones and anticyclones which follow must not be expected to fit any particular storm in all respects. Moreover, they differ somewhat from region to region.

5.16 Nature and Location. Cyclones are low-pressure storms and commonly go by the

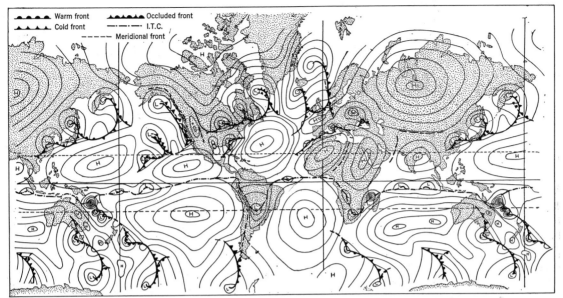

Fig. 5.6 A representative daily weather map of the world in the Northern Hemisphere winter. The most conspicuous features on the map are the numerous wave and vortex atmospheric disturbances. These disturbances are especially numerous in the middle latitudes. (*From M. A. Garbell, "Tropical and Equatorial Meteorology."*)

name of *lows,* or *depressions,* while anticyclones are high-pressure systems and are called *highs.* The cyclone must, therefore, be a mass of light air since surface pressures are low, while, conversely, the anticyclone, or high, is a mass of heavier air. Since cyclones develop as a result of air-mass conflict in the middle-latitude zones of convergence, they are characteristic features of the westerly wind belts and are best known, therefore, between latitudes 35 and 65° in each hemisphere. Because cyclones and anticyclones are traveling storms within the westerlies, it is expected that they will be carried by those winds in general from west to east, much in the same way that a whirlpool in a river is carried downstream by the main current.

5.17 Appearance. As one sees these storms on the published United States weather map they are represented by a series of closed, concentric isobars, roughly circular or oval in shape (Figs. 5.7 and 5.8). In the cyclone the lowest pressure is at the center, and it *increases* toward the margins; in the anticyclone, pressure is highest at the center and *decreases* outward. If the isobars in a low are imagined to be contours, then the cyclone resembles a circular or

oval depression, while the high has the appearance of a dome-shaped hill. There is no definite amount of pressure that distinguishes lows from highs; it is entirely a relative thing. Normally there are 10 to 20 mb., or several tenths of

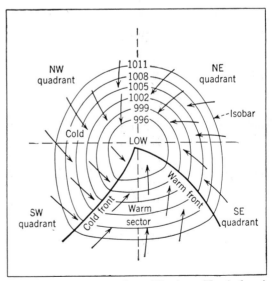

Fig. 5.7 A model cyclone (Northern Hemisphere) showing arrangement of isobars, wind system, warm and cold air masses, and surface fronts.

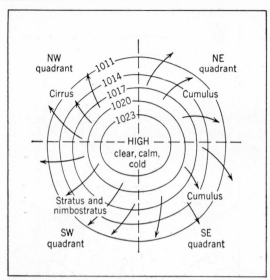

Fig. 5.8 A model cold anticyclone (Northern Hemisphere).

an inch, pressure difference between the center and circumference of a low. Occasionally a large and particularly well-developed winter cyclone may show a pressure difference of as much as 35 mb., or 1 in.

In highs the pressure difference between center and margins is usually in the neighborhood of 17 mb., or ½ in., although it may be double that in some instances. It is a general rule that both cyclones and anticyclones are less well developed, have smaller differences in pressure, have weaker pressure gradients, and travel at lower speeds in summer than in winter.

5.18   Size. There are great variations in the size of these storms, but on the whole they spread over extensive areas, sometimes covering as much as one-third of the United States, or 1 million square miles, although most of them are smaller. They are *extensive* rather than *intensive*. Thus a normal cyclone with a vertical thickness of 6 to 7 miles probably will have a short diameter one hundred times as great. Cyclones are inclined to be elliptical or egg-shaped, with the narrow end toward the equator. The long axis, extending in a northeast-southwest direction, is commonly nearly twice the length of the short one (northwest-southeast), so that a typical well-developed **winter** cyclone might show long and short

diameters of 1,200 and 650 miles, respectively. Anticyclones are inclined to be somewhat larger, their diameters averaging roughly 25 per cent greater than those of lows.

5.19   Direction and Rate of Movement. As noted in an earlier paragraph, lows and highs travel in a general west-to-east direction, carried along by the upper-air system of westerly winds in which they exist. That is not to say, however, that storms always move due eastward. To be sure, they follow different routes, and there are some regions of concentration and others of less frequency, but in spite of their vagaries in direction, as well as in rate of movement, their progress is, in general, eastward. The direction and rate of movement of cyclones are approximately those of the upper winds. It is easy to understand, therefore, why a weather forecaster in the middle latitudes bases his prediction upon weather conditions to the west, rather than to the east, of his station. Those storms to the east already have gone by; those to the west are approaching. There is a tendency for cyclones to follow certain general tracks, and a more detailed account of world-wide storm movements, and the routes followed, will appear later in the chapter.

Variability in rate of movement is characteristic, both as to season and as to individual cyclones. In the United States cyclones move eastward across the country at velocities averaging 20 miles an hour in summer and 30 miles an hour in winter, with the highs somewhat slower than the lows. In summer, when the whole atmospheric circulation is slowed down, storm speeds are reduced, and the contrasts between cyclones and anticyclones are less pronounced. As a consequence, warm-season weather is less changeable, and atmospheric disturbances are less vigorous. In the winter season a well-developed low characteristically requires 3 to 5 days for the transcontinental journey across the United States.

Just as temperature, pressure, and wind belts shift north and south, following the movements of the sun's rays, poleward in summer and equatorward in winter, so also do the storm tracks. This fact helps to explain the fewer and weaker storms over the lower middle latitudes in summer as compared with winter.

Because the cyclone is a low-pressure atmospheric disturbance, it is characterized by a converging system of surface winds of moderate velocity. By contrast, the anticyclone, or high, shows winds moving outward from center toward circumference; in other words, a horizontally diverging wind system.

Origin and Structure of Cyclones and Anticyclones

5.20 Origin of Cyclones and Anticyclones. It is entirely possible that atmosphere disturbances which are here grouped together under the heading of middle-latitude cyclones may be of somewhat different types and origins. Many of these storms, however, appear to have their beginnings as wavelike disturbances along surface fronts where air streams of contrasting temperature and density are converging. Regions with strong horizontal temperature contrasts and of air-mass convergence should, therefore, favor cyclonic development. Such areas of strong cyclogenesis are to be found along the coasts of eastern Asia and of eastern North America in winter, and along the margins of the Antarctic Continent. But although there are areas of concentrated cyclogenesis, it must be emphasized that all parts of the middle latitudes feel the effects of these storms.

Since most, if not all, fully developed middle-latitude cyclones appear to extend upward and make connection with an upper-air trough in the westerlies and their jet stream, it seems likely that these disturbances on the jet are also associated with cyclone origin, although the precise nature of the connection is not clear. What is altogether possible is that surface front and upper-air trough are themselves linked in a cause-and-effect relationship and that the cyclone, therefore, has a genetic connection with both.

There appear to be at least two quite different types of anticyclones. The rapidly moving *cold anticyclone* is essentially a mass of cold air which originates over a cold surface and is the product of heat transfer by conduction and radiation processes. Obviously such anticyclones are chiefly a phenomenon of the middle and higher latitudes and are most common and intense in the winter season. The slowly moving *warm anticyclone* is especially characteristic of the subtropics and of the lower middle latitudes in summer. Its origin is not well understood.

Middle-latitude cyclones and anticyclones may be thought of as ruptures in the zonal westerlies whereby great masses of polar and tropical air are displaced from their regions of origin. Through this latitudinal exchange of polar and tropical air associated with cyclones and anticyclones, it is believed that the unbalanced condition of radiation and heat between high and low latitudes is corrected.

5.21 Structure of Cyclones. On the daily weather map a cyclonic storm is often first noted as a slight indentation along a front. It takes the form of a very shallow thrust of warm air into the mass of colder air. As the wave or indentation deepens, the storm grows in size and intensity. Figure 5.9 illustrates a part of the life history of a cyclonic storm. It appears from this diagram that the storm is composed of two essentially different air masses (Fig. 5.10). To the south and southeast is a poleward projection of warmer humid air being fed by southerly currents from tropical latitudes. Enveloping this projection of tropical air on its western, northern, and northeastern sides is colder, drier air, often of polar origin. In the wind system acquired by the developing storm the air movement is such as to cause the tropical air to advance over the cold air in one part and for the cold air to underrun retreating warm air in still another part. The lifting of the warmer air over the cold commonly leads to condensation and precipitation.

That part of the front separating the two air masses which lies *ahead* of the advancing tongue of warm air is called the *warm front* (Fig. 5.10). Here the aggressive warm air currents leave the earth's surface and rise up over the retreating wedge of cold air along a surface of

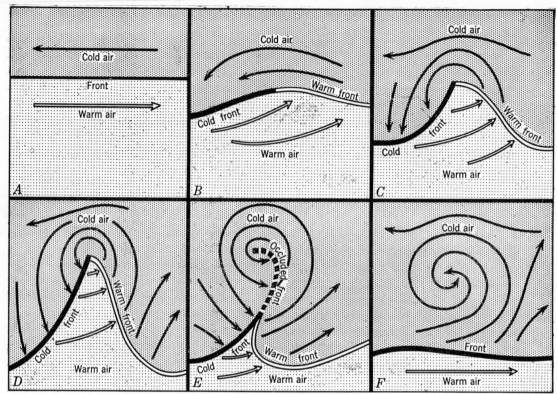

Fig. 5.9 Six stages in the life cycle of a frontal cyclone. Drawing *B* shows the beginning of a small horizontal wave along the front. In drawing *C* the wave development has progressed to the point where there is a definite cyclonic circulation with well-developed warm and cold fronts. Because of the more rapid movement of the cold front, drawing *D* shows a narrowed warm sector as the cold front approaches the retreating warm front. In drawing *E* the occlusion process is occurring, the cyclone has reached its maximum development, and the warm sector is being rapidly pinched off. In drawing *F* the warm sector had been eliminated; the cyclone is in its dying stages and is represented by only a whirl of cold air. (*Courtesy of U.S. Weather Bureau.*)

discontinuity. That part of the front lying *behind* the wedge of warm air is called the *cold front* (Fig. 5.10). Along this front the cold air is the aggressor, and it pushes in under the retreating warm air, forcing it to rise, often with vigor. The advance of the cold front is retarded by friction with the ground so that there is a tendency toward a piling of the cold air in the foremost portion of the advancing current. This often leads to an overrunning by cold air aloft of warm air at the surface. Warm air is thereby entrapped below the overrunning cold air, under which conditions violent convectional overturning may occur.

In normal cases the cold front advances more rapidly than the warm front so that it gradually

catches up with, and eventually overtakes, the warm front. When contact between the cold air masses, one on the front and the other on the rear of the storm, has been made, and the intervening warm air has been lifted above the earth's surface, an *occlusion* is said to have taken place (Fig. 5.9*E*). Occlusion is a normal development in the life history of middle-latitude cyclones, and as the process of occlusion advances the storm wanes in intensity and finally disintegrates. Precipitation along occluded fronts results from continued lifting of the warm air, now everywhere above the earth's surface, as well as from the vertical displacement of the less dense of the two cold air masses. Most of the cyclones that enter western

Europe and western North America are in the occluded stage of development.

Wind Systems of Cyclones and Anticyclones

Unlike tornadoes and hurricanes whose winds are violent and destructive, middle-latitude cyclones and anticyclones characteristically have winds of only moderate velocity. To be sure, an occasional winter cyclone or anticyclone of greater-than-average intensity may be accompanied by boisterous winds but these are the exception.

5.22 Wind System of Cyclones. Seen in the ordinary two-dimensional aspect as they appear on a United States weather map, where a cyclone is represented as a series of roughly concentric isobars with the lowest pressure at the center, air flow is from the circumference toward the center of the storm. In other words, it is a *converging* system of winds (Figs. 5.7 and 5.11).

This horizontal convergence of surface winds must of necessity be accompanied by an upward movement of air. Normally, this is not a rapid vertical updraft of air such as occurs in a thunderstorm, but rather a gliding of warmer air up over a mildly inclined wedge of colder, denser air. The rapidity of ascent, therefore, is not great. Cloud types in cyclones usually are of the flattish sheet type, typical of a situation where mild air is forced to ascend rather slowly along a thin wedge of cooler air.

Because of the effects of earth rotation the converging air flow in a cyclone tends to be-

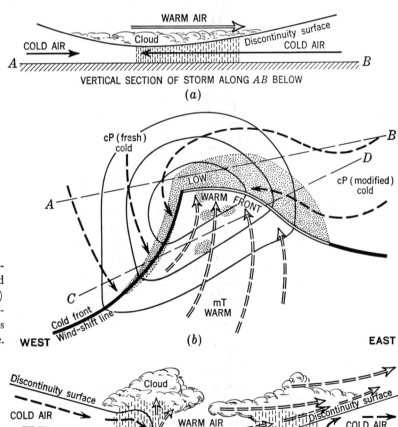

Fig. 5.10 The model cyclone. Ground plan (*b*) and vertical sections (*a* and *c*) of a fully developed wave cyclone in the middle latitudes of the Northern Hemisphere.

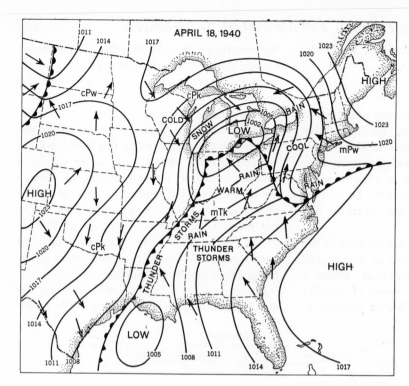

Fig. 5.11 A well-developed wave cyclone over eastern United States. This weather-map representation should be compared with the ground plan of the model cyclone in Fig. 5.10.

come an inward-spiraling or vortex system in which the wind arrows cross the isobars at an oblique angle. The moving cyclone's wind system may be diagrammatically represented as in Fig. 5.10*b*. Here convergence of air flow is conspicuous although the simple in-spiraling system is considerably modified. Most significant is the fact that the cyclone is seen as a conflict area between two unlike air masses, a colder, drier, and denser one which occupies the northeastern, northern, and western portions of the storm and a warmer less dense one of tropical or subtropical origin to the southeast and south of the center. Since the winds are usually easterly on the front of the storm and westerly on the rear, it is obvious that the easterly winds on the front are opposite in direction to the general movement of the cyclone itself.

5.23 Wind Shift with the Passing of a Cyclone. When a cyclonic center approaches and passes by an observer, the latter will experience general easterly winds as long as the low center is to the west of him, in other words, as long as he is on the front of the storm. As the center passes by, leaving him in the western, or rear, half of the low, the winds shift to the west.

Easterly winds, therefore, often indicate the approach of a cyclone with its accompanying rain and cloud, while westerly winds more often foretell the retreat of the storm center and the coming of clearing weather.

In many cyclones this shift from easterly to westerly winds is rather gradual and lacking in abruptness. In storms with a marked equatorward elongation, so that the isobars are roughly in the form of the letter V, the wind shift is likely to be abrupt (Fig. 5.26). Along the wind-shift line, which is approximately a line joining the apexes of the V-shaped isobars south of the center, winds of contrasting temperature, humidity, and density meet at a sharp angle, and violent storms and turbulent weather conditions often are the result. The wind-shift line is the cold front described in Art. 5.47.

5.24 *Veering and Backing Winds.* If the center of a cyclone passes to the north of the observer, so that he is in the southern quadrants of the storm, the succession of winds experienced will be southeast, south, southwest, and finally west and northwest (Fig. 5.12). This is called a *veering wind shift*. On the other hand, if the storm center passes south of the

104

observer, so that he is on the north side of the cyclone, he will experience in succession northeast, north, and finally northwest winds. This is known as a *backing wind shift.*

Backing and veering winds have important climatic significance. In a veering wind shift one experiences the effects of the tropical air in the warm quadrant of the cyclone and likewise the effects of the surface warm front and cold front. By contrast, the backing wind shift, in which the observer is to the north of the center, permits of experiencing chiefly cold air from higher latitudes, while surface fronts are less likely (Fig. 5.7). Therefore regions which prevailingly lie on the equatorward side of passing cyclones, and thus are subjected to veering winds, are likely to experience higher average temperatures, greater variability of temperature, stronger convection, more cumulus clouds, and less snowfall than those which are located on the poleward side of cyclonic tracks. Backing winds are associated with generally lower temperatures, less variability of temperature, a more continuous cloud cover, and greater likelihood of snow in winter.

5.25 Wind System of an Anticyclone. The term anticyclone was invented to designate the outflowing, or diverging, system of winds about a center of high pressure (Figs. 5.8 and 5.13). Deflection due to earth rotation causes the outflow of air about a high to develop something of a clockwise whirl (Northern Hemisphere).

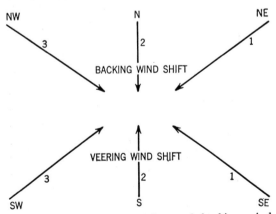

Fig. 5.12 Illustrating veering and backing wind shifts with the passing of a cyclonic storm.

Since surface air in the high is constantly spreading outward from the center, it follows that there must be a compensatory feeding in of air at higher elevations, and subsequent settling of it, in order to maintain the high. This characteristic subsidence in anticyclones causes the air in such circulations to be stable. The wind systems about highs and lows, therefore, are opposite (*a*) in direction of gradient-induced flow, (*b*) in direction of spiral deflection, and (*c*) in the direction of vertical movement.

Anticyclonic wind systems are usually less well developed than those of cyclones so that no characteristic wind shift is forecast as they pass by. In general, however, winds on the front (east) of an advancing high are westerly, while those on the rear are easterly. Since lows and highs often alternate with one another as they move across the country, it is evident that the westerly winds on the front of a high and the rear of a low have a similar origin and are much alike in character. Pressure gradients are usually less steep and wind velocities lower in anticyclones than in cyclones. Weak pressure gradients are particularly conspicuous toward the centers of highs where there is much light wind and calm. The strongest winds are likely to be found on the front margin of a rapidly advancing cold high where there is a merging with the preceding low. In this location between the cyclonic and anticyclonic systems the isobars tend to become nearly parallel straight lines trending in a general north-south direction. A strong horizontal pressure gradient from west to east is thereby developed, which is a consequence of combined westerly-wind gradients and storm gradients, vigorous west and northwest winds being the result. Cold waves and blizzards over central and eastern North America are associated with these strong outpourings of cold air in the transition areas between the rears of lows and the fronts of highs.

Precipitation in Cyclones and Anticyclones

5.26 Cyclones and Anticyclones Opposite in Precipitation Characteristics. As a general rule cloud and precipitation are characteristic of

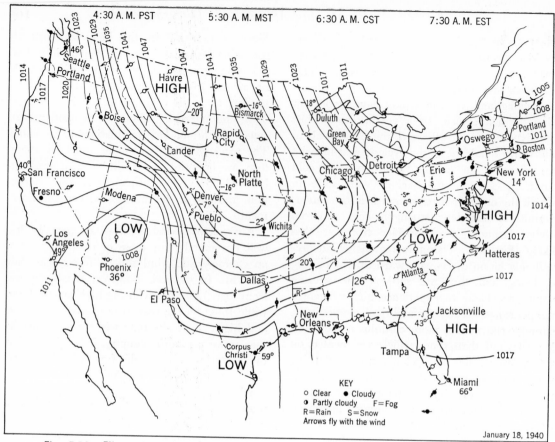

Fig. 5.13 Illustrating a well-developed cold anticyclone in winter. This cold anticyclone has moved into the United States from the arctic plains of Canada as a mass of cold, stable, polar continental (*cP*) air. St. Joseph, Mo., experienced a minimum temperature of 21° below zero and Galveston, Tex., on the Gulf of Mexico, 15° above zero. Such southward thrusts of polar air are essential elements of the hydrologic cycle and of the heat-balancing mechanism of the earth. (*Courtesy of U.S. Weather Bureau.*)

the cyclone, while much fair weather and little or no precipitation are normal for the anticyclone. This contrast is not unexpected, for the horizontal convergence and ascent of air in the low are conducive to the cooling of thick and extensive masses of air. Moreover, in most parts of the earth outside the heart of the tropics, convergence leads to a clash between air masses of different temperature and density, with the result that fronts are formed, which in turn promote active ascent of air. To be sure, not all cyclones yield precipitation, for the ascending air may be too dry for abundant condensation to develop.

In anticyclones, where horizontal divergence of surface air and associated subsidence are characteristic, atmospheric stability is fostered and condensation processes are opposed. But although fair weather is the rule in anticyclones, it is incorrect to assume that shower activity is never associated with these high-pressure systems. To cite one instance: maritime air derived from the western margin of a subtropical anticyclone, where subsidence is relatively weak, may become showery when subjected to intensive heating over a land surface.

5.27 Precipitation in Cyclones. Most of the cool-season precipitation which falls on lowlands in middle latitudes is cyclonic in origin. The fewer and weaker lows of summer may yield a smaller proportion of that period's rainfall since in summer thermal convection and

106

associated shower activity are more prevalent. Yet even a considerable amount of summer's convectional showers and thunderstorms are associated with the fronts of cyclonic storms.

Although cyclonic rain is the result of rising air, normally it does not rise because of local heating but rather because of forced ascent resulting from (*a*) a convergence of great masses of air toward a center, (*b*) the underrunning and lifting of warmer and lighter air masses by cooler heavier ones, and (*c*) the ascent of warm currents over colder ones (Fig. 5.10*b*). Unlike conditions in a thunderstorm, where rapid vertical ascent is characteristic, the lifting of air in cyclones, as noted earlier, is more often a gliding of warm, moist air up a mild slope formed by the upper surface of a colder, denser mass of air. Cooling is slower in the latter case, and rainfall less heavy. Cyclonic precipitation, therefore, inclines toward being light or moderate in rate of fall, but because of the greater areal extent of the storm it is of relatively longer duration than that of thunderstorms. Dull, gray, uniformly overcast skies, with steady precipitation, are typical of cyclonic weather. It should be stressed that precipitation in any storm would be minor in amount and of short duration if it were not that new supplies of water vapor are constantly being imported by winds to any area where rain is falling.

Neither the expectancy of precipitation nor its nature and origin are the same in all parts of a low. In general, the front or eastern half is more cloudy and rainy than is the rear or western half, although the latter is not completely lacking in precipitation. Clouds and rain extend out much farther to the front or east of the center than to the rear or west. This asymmetrical arrangement of cloud and precipitation in the low is partly the result of the structure of the storm's fronts to be described in the following article. It is likewise a consequence of the fact that the whole eastern half of a cyclone is an area of general horizontal convergence, while to the rear of the center, divergence and subsidence are more characteristic. In well-developed winter lows snow

is more common in the cooler northeastern part, whereas rain occurs more frequently in the warmer southeastern quadrant. Heavy snows over the eastern part of the United States usually arrive when storms travel the more southerly routes, so that the central and northern states are on the poleward sides of the cyclones.

5.28 Regions of Precipitation within a Cyclone. Three general regions of precipitation within a low may be distinguished. As a general rule the rain areas are associated with vertical displacement of mild and humid maritime air masses, often of tropical origin. The cold air masses act chiefly as barriers over which the warmer air is lifted, and only a small amount of precipitation is usually derived from the cold air itself (Fig. 5.10).

a. Warm-front Rain. To the north, northeast, and east of the storm center the warm, humid, southerly air masses meet the colder, drier air of polar origin. Because the latter is more dense, the warm air flows up over the gently inclined wedge of colder air just as it would flow over a mountain range and is lifted above the earth's surface (Fig. 5.10). As a result of rising over the wedge of cold air, the southerly currents are cooled by expansion, and widespread cloud and precipitation are the result. The most extensive area of precipitation within the cyclone is usually associated with the warm front.

Chilly, gray, overcast days with long-continued steady rain are typical of weather in this part of the storm. In the colder months this is also the region of heavy snowfall. Since the warm air is rising over the cold wedge along a gently inclined plane whose angle of slope is between 0.5 and 2°, its increase in elevation is slow, so that the resulting precipitation is likely to be only light or moderate in rate of fall, although, because of its long duration, the total amount may be considerable. It is not uncommon for warm-front rains to continue steadily for 24 hr. and more without letup. Such moderate rain is ideal in some respects, for it comes slowly enough for the ground to absorb most of it, and surface runoff and destructive slope wash and gullying are reduced to a minimum. In the warm seasons, if the air ascending over the cold wedge is conditionally unstable, warm-front rainfall may be relatively heavy.

It needs to be kept in mind that it is not from the cold surface air that the rain is chiefly coming but rather from the southerly currents aloft which are rising over the cold northerly air. Precipitation falling through the cold surface air, however, has its temperature reduced so that it reaches the earth as a chilly rain, and the day is inclined to be dark and dismal. It should be noted that the above-surface warm front usually extends for several hundred miles eastward and poleward from the storm center. It is this fact which helps to explain the greater amount of cloud and precipitation in the front, or eastern, half of the storm.

b. Cold-front Rain. To the south and southwest of the storm center is still another region of forced ascent. Here the cold west and northwest currents of polar origin meet and underrun the warm southerly currents, forcing them upward, sometimes with much vigor (Fig. 5.10). This cold-front rain belt is best developed in storms with a marked southward looping of the isobars, *i.e.*, a V-shaped cyclone, for under these conditions the contrasting air masses meet at a sharp angle with resulting vigorous overturning. In storms with more circular shape this is less likely to be the case. The cold front may be a region of great atmospheric turbulence, with associated severe thunderstorms and squall winds. Because of the rapid lifting and overturning of the warm air along the cold front, the accompanying rain is likely to be in the form of heavy showers but not of long duration. This cloud and rain belt, therefore, usually is much narrower than that along the warm front to the north and east of the storm center.

c. Nonfrontal or Air-mass Precipitation. A part of the precipitation occurring in a cyclone appears to be of an origin not associated with fronts. The general convergence of air characteristic of the eastern half of the low may be responsible for a portion of the storm's nonfrontal precipitation. Within the warm sector

of the cyclone where southerly winds predominate nonfrontal rain is especially likely (Fig. 5.10*b*). Here the mild, humid, southerly currents are forced upward by their own convergence as they move toward the center of the low. A part of it may be showery convection resulting from surface heating. This section of the cyclone commonly is not an area of continuous and heavy cloud cover, for although scattered showers are common and widespread, there also may be considerable broken sky and sunshine.

It should be stressed here that not all these three rainfall types or areas are present in each storm, nor are they always distinct from each other. There are numerous mergings, modifications, and intermediate conditions. Nevertheless, all three types are sufficiently common and distinct in cyclones to warrant their recognition.

Temperatures in Cyclones and Anticyclones

5.29   It is difficult to make significant generalizations regarding temperature contrasts between lows and highs. It is not true, as is sometimes stated to be the case, that, disregarding the season of the year, cyclones are always areas of high temperature and anticyclones of low. In themselves they are neither hot nor cold, but, depending upon the season as well as their own individual character (region of origin, path, velocity of movement), they may be either or both. An analysis of temperatures in cyclones and anticyclones chiefly resolves itself into a study of the air masses that comprise the storms, and of the nature of the cloud cover.

5.30   Temperatures in Anticyclones.   Certainly in the winter season a vigorous, well-developed high, advancing rapidly toward central and eastern United States from northern Canada, or from arctic Russia toward central and western Europe, progresses as a mass of cold, dry, polar continental air with clear skies. Such an anticyclone accounts for the *cold waves* and bitterest winter weather (Fig. 5.13). This type of high is cold for two reasons: (*a*) because it advances southward from the arctic regions as a mass of cold polar air associated with strong northerly winds and (*b*) because its dry, clear air provides ideal conditions for rapid terrestrial radiation during long winter nights. An anticyclone composed of *mP* instead of *cP* air, either in North America or Europe, brings less severe cold. Even in summer, a well-developed high approaching rapidly from higher latitudes gives low temperatures for the season, providing several days of clear, cool, delightful weather. It is not unusual in middle latitudes, then, for highs to have come to be associated with low temperatures for any particular season.

However, when in summer a large, relatively stagnant warm high, composed of tropical or subtropical air, spreads slowly over the south-central part of the country, excessively high temperatures, called *hot waves,* are likely to result over central and eastern United States (Fig. 5.14). The same clear skies and dry air that make for rapid terrestrial radiation during the long winter nights are conducive to maximum receipts of strong solar radiation during long summer days. Moreover, as tropical air from this anticyclone moves northward over the country, the south winds carry with them the heat absorbed in the lower latitudes. Clear, mild days in the cooler seasons likewise are usually associated with these same stagnant warm highs over the south-central part of the country. Large diurnal temperature variations are characteristic, because of the dry air and the general absence of clouds.

5.31 Temperatures in Cyclones. Well-developed cyclones, accompanied by extensive cloud cover and precipitation, are likely to bring higher-than-average temperatures in winter and somewhat lower-than-average temperatures in summer—just the opposite from those induced by the anticyclone. During the long winter nights the cloud cover and humid air of the cyclone tend to prevent rapid loss of earth heat, while these same conditions in summer, when days are long and sun stronger, tend to weaken incoming solar radiation.

5.32 *Temperature Contrasts within Different Parts of a Cyclone.* The foregoing general rule concerning lows and seasonal temperatures cannot be accepted too literally, however, for a cyclone, composed of unlike air masses,

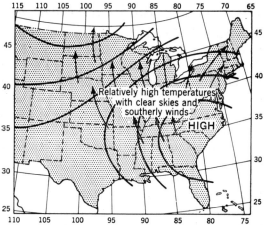

Fig. 5.14 Illustrating a warm anticyclone, relatively stagnant over southeastern United States. Such an atmospheric disturbance produces unseasonably hot weather over the central and eastern parts of the country.

usually has marked temperature contrasts within its several parts or quadrants. Thus the south and southeast part (front) of a low, where relatively warm air masses and southerly winds prevail, is considerably warmer than the north and west portion (rear), where air movement is from cooler higher latitudes. The effect of these air-mass temperature importations is to cause the isotherms in cyclones to trend north-northeast by south-southwest instead of the usual east-west direction, the south winds on the front of the storm pushing them poleward, and the northwest winds on the rear pushing them equatorward (Fig. 5.15).

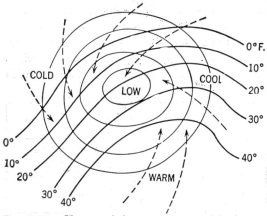

Fig. 5.15 Characteristic arrangement of isotherms in a winter cyclone over central and eastern United States in winter.

In general, the average rise of temperature above seasonal normal in front of a winter storm in eastern United States is not far from 10° although it may reach 20 or 30°. Between the front and rear of a well-developed winter cyclone in eastern United States the temperatures may differ by as much as 30 to 40° or even more. If the temperature of the center of a low is taken as a standard, the average departures of the four quadrants of well-developed winter cyclones in eastern United States are as follows: northwest, —8.7°; northeast, —5.6°; southeast, +6.3°; southwest, +2.6° (Ward). Stations on the southern side of a passing low, therefore, experience a greater *change* in temperature than do those to the north of the center, even though the temperatures are not so low.

5.33 Summary of Weather Changes with the Passing of a Well-developed Cyclone and a Following Anticyclone over Eastern United States.

The essence of cyclonic control in weather is its irregularity and undependability. Averages of the weather elements by days, months, or years give only a lifeless picture of the actual weather experienced, for such averages tend to mask the nonperiodic storm control. Rapid and marked weather changes are characteristic of regions and seasons where cyclones and anticyclones are numerous and well developed, as they are, for instance, over eastern United States in winter, and to a somewhat less degree in Europe. Temperature changes with passing storms are especially marked in winter, when latitudinal temperature gradients are steepest and importations by winds consequently most severe. In summer, with

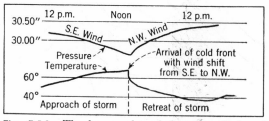

Fig. 5.16 The barograph and thermograph traces of the approach and retreat of a middle-latitude cyclone.

the poleward migration of the storm belt, cyclones are fewer and weaker; temperature gradients are milder; and sun control, with its daily periodicity, is more influential. In that season, then, weather changes are more regular and diurnal and less marked.

It is incorrect to conceive of cyclonic control as identical in different parts of the earth. Even within the United States storms act differently over the Pacific Coast or the western plateaus from the way they do in eastern United States. Northwest winds on the rear of a cyclone obviously cannot import very low temperatures if they come from over the ocean, as they do in northwestern Europe or the Pacific Coast of the United States. Storms differ in character with the regions and the seasons. Following is a description of a series of weather changes during the passage of a well-developed cyclone and a following anticyclone over central and eastern United States (Figs. 5.16 to 5.18).

As the cyclone approaches from the west and the barometer falls, there is a gradual clouding up in front of the storm. Far out in front of the center the sky becomes covered with fine veils, or films, of cirrus and cirrostratus clouds, which produce circles around the moon or sun. These distant heralds of the storm are associated with the warm-front discontinuity surface as much as 1,000 to 1,500 miles ahead of the surface warm front where the inclined wedge of cold air may be 3 to 4 miles thick. Contemporaneous with the appearance of the cirrus and cirrostratus clouds the wind sets in from an easterly direction and continues easterly until the center of the storm or the surface cold front has passed. As the storm center approaches closer and the cold wedge becomes thinner, the clouds gradually thicken, darken, and become lower in elevation. Precipitation usually begins several hundred miles out ahead of the surface warm front and continues until that front has passed. Temperature increases somewhat as the surface warm front draws nearer, but since the air on the front of the storm may be modified polar in character there is no abrupt temperature rise until the warm front at the surface passes. The passage of the warm front at the

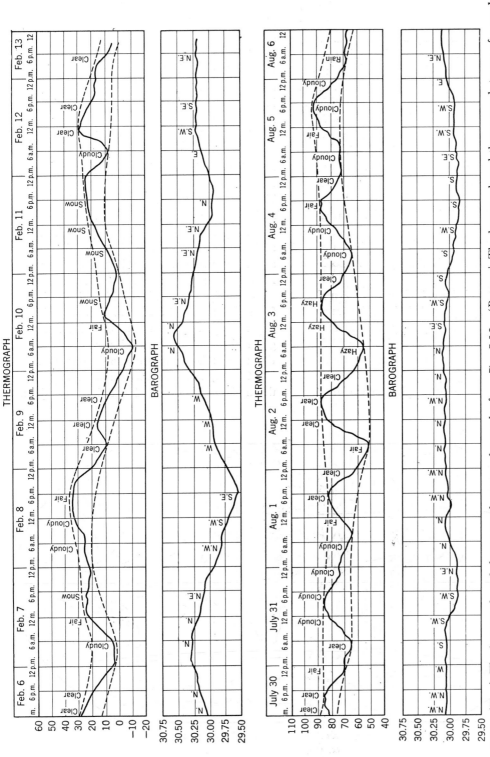

Fig. 5.17 (Top) The barograph and thermograph traces of a week of winter weather at a middle-latitude station. Note the marked pressure changes indicating the passage of well-developed cyclones and anticyclones with their contrasting air masses. The temperature belt rises as pressure falls and sinks when the pressure rises. (*After Ward.*)

Fig. 5.18 (Bottom) The barograph and thermograph traces of a week of summer weather at a middle-latitude station. Note the relatively flat barograph curve indicating weak cyclonic control. Regular daily temperature changes induced by sun control are more conspicuous than those nonperiodic ones associated with the contrasting air masses of cyclones and anticyclones. (*After Ward.*)

111

surface, with an associated shift from polar to tropical air, is marked by a number of weather phenomena, including (*a*) a slight wind shift, usually about 45°, the wind becoming more southerly as the warm air mass is entered; (*b*) a distinct rise in temperature; (*c*) a clearing in the weather conditions; and (*d*) a rapid increase in the amount of moisture in the air.

Within the warm air mass weather conditions may vary considerably, depending on the nature of the air and the season of the year. In summer if the air is from the Gulf of Mexico, hot sultry weather with local showers and thunderstorms is common. If the air is from a drier source, the heat will be less oppressive but more desiccating. In winter this tropical air mass gives rise to mild weather and rapid thaws, often associated with fog.

The passage of the cold front at the surface with an accompanying shift from the warm to the cold air mass is frequently associated with strong turbulence, particularly if the cold front is well developed. In summer severe thunderstorms with strong squall winds are common. Other associated weather phenomena are (*a*)

a marked rise in barometric pressure, (*b*) an abrupt drop in temperature heralding the arrival of the cold air, (*c*) a well-marked shift in wind direction amounting to from 45 to 180° (southerly to westerly), (*d*) heavy rains at the front but fairly rapid clearing and improvement in the weather conditions following its passage, and (*e*) a marked decrease in both specific and relative humidity. The advancing anticyclone moving southeastward as a mass of cold polar air with northwest winds continues to reduce the temperature until its center has passed. Toward the center of the high, winds are light and calms are prevalent, and in winter extremely low temperatures are likely to prevail. As the anticyclone retreats, the cycle is complete, winds again become easterly, and another approaching cyclone begins a new sequence.

Obviously there are considerable variations from the above description. These variations depend upon the nature of the air masses generating the storms as well as upon the routes the storms take with respect to the observer.

5.34 Cyclone Concentrations. All parts of the middle latitudes, and likewise the adjacent

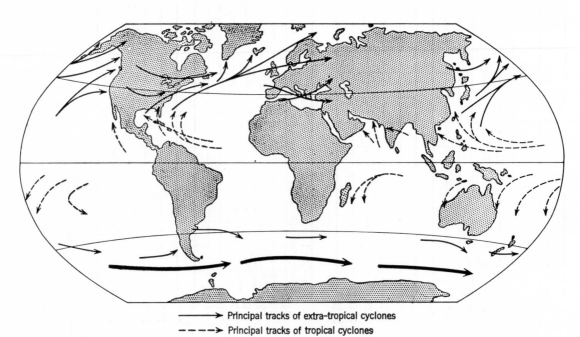

———▶ Principal tracks of extra-tropical cyclones
– – – ▶ Principal tracks of tropical cyclones

Fig. 5.19 The cyclone tracks here shown are greatly simplified. (*After Petterssen.*)

margins of the low and high latitudes, are affected by moving cyclones and anticyclones. All parts, however, are not affected to the same degree, for, although there is no rigid system of clearly defined *storm tracks,* there are, nevertheless, certain broad belts over which storms travel more frequently than elsewhere. These are the regions of most numerous and most active fronts. Of course the effects of a storm are felt far beyond the path of its center. Figure 5.19 shows in a generalized way the principal cyclonic tracks of the world.

In the *Southern Hemisphere,* as a result of a very stable and intense cold source over the Antarctic Continent providing abundant supplies of cold polar air throughout the year, there is great year-round vigor of cyclonic storms, in summer as well as in winter. The cyclones which develop along the Southern Hemisphere polar fronts greatly affect the weather of South America south of 30°S. and the southern extremities of Africa and Australia. The Cape Horn region of South America, extending as it does to nearly latitude 55°S., is a stormy area at all times of the year. Winter cyclones are likewise relatively numerous over the Pampa of Argentina.

5.35 *Northern Hemisphere Tracks.* The less vigorous (except in winter), and likewise less persistent, continental anticyclones forming over the arctic and subarctic regions provide the principal southward gushes of cold polar air for the formation of Northern Hemisphere storms. The arctic and subarctic anticyclones are relatively weak in summer, which accounts for the poleward migration of the storm tracks as well as for the general weakening of cyclonic control over the whole Northern Hemisphere in that season. In winter, on the other hand, when the arctic and subarctic high-pressure centers are much better developed, and therefore are able to provide the necessary southward surges of cold air, storms are both numerous and vigorous.

Two of the principal regions of cyclogenesis, especially in the cooler seasons, are in the areas of strong temperature contrasts along the Atlantic margins of North America and the Pacific

margins of Asia. Significantly these are also areas of persistent and well-developed upper-air troughs. Cyclones originating in these two regions move northeastward across the Atlantic and Pacific oceans, arriving in western Europe and western North America in an advanced stage of occlusion. In North America these cyclones may cross the western highlands and reach the central part of the continent where they often regenerate and become more active storms. A third region of active cyclogenesis is along the front which coincides with the Mediterranean Basin. This front is active in the cooler seasons only. Cyclones developing in the

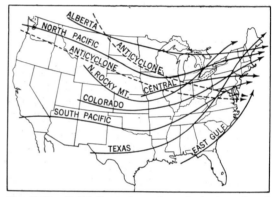

Fig. 5.20 Solid lines show the principal tracks of cyclones; broken lines represent tracks of cold anti-cyclones. Note how the cyclone tracks converge toward the northeastern part of the United States. Cold anticyclones have a dual origin. Those which move south from northern Canada (*cP* air) bring severe cold in winter; those from the Pacific northwest (modified *mP* air) bring only moderate cold.

Mediterranean Basin move eastward across western Asia, some of them eventually reaching northwestern India and Pakistan.

The United States and adjacent parts of Canada have the distinction of being the world's most cyclonic *continental* area. This is a consequence of the fact that North America east of the Rockies is a region of numerous secondary fronts resulting from the active clash of contrasting air masses which freely move across the extensive interior lowlands reaching from the Arctic to the tropics. Although the storm tracks are spread widely over the central part of the United States, it is highly significant climatically that the northern tracks are the most frequented ones. A marked bunching of cyclonic tracks occurs over the northeastern part of the country indicating that the Great Lakes–New England–Maritime Province region is one of highly variable weather with much cloud and precipitation (Fig. 5.20).

Cold anticyclones, one group from the North Pacific (*mP*) and the other from the arctic plains of Canada (*cP*), enter the United States at two far separated points, and travel in a general easterly and southeasterly course across the country (Fig. 5.20).

TROPICAL DISTURBANCES

5.36   Weather Element in the Tropics. Only recently has it come to be realized how important atmospheric disturbances are in the weather and climate of the tropics. Earlier it was believed that the sun largely controlled weather conditions in the low latitudes, producing a diurnal regularity that was relatively monotonous compared with the irregularity and variety of weather so characteristic of the middle latitudes. Without doubt the middle latitudes are still correctly thought of as surpassing the tropics in number and variety of atmos-

pheric disturbances, but this does not dim the importance of the discovery that tropical weather is characterized by a greater variety of weather than was even suspected a short time ago. Unfortunately, however, there does not exist as yet a satisfactory classification, description, and distribution analysis of the disturbances which affect tropical weather.

Most types of tropical disturbances, or perturbations, appear to be relatively mild affairs which in terms of pressure and wind features are not overly conspicuous on the daily surface weather chart. Their principal climatic significance is that they generate clouds and precipitation and hence they are noteworthy chiefly in terms of affecting one climatic element, *viz.*, precipitation. In the low latitudes, temperature changes induced by passing disturbances are relatively inconsequential. From the climatologist's point of view it is unfortunate that the single tropical disturbance which has been studied in most detail is the violent hurricane or typhoon. Spectacular though it is, the hurricane is much less numerous and is notably more restricted in its distribution than are the milder types of disturbances which are responsible for a large percentage of tropical rainfall.

5.37   Weak Tropical Lows. These shallow disturbances appear to be common throughout almost all the humid tropics although they are most numerous no doubt in the vicinity of the important convergence zones, especially the I.T.C. On the daily weather map they commonly can be detected by one or two closed isobars (Fig. 5.21). Their pressure gradients are weak and their wind systems poorly developed. The movement of such storms is usually slow and their paths poorly defined. It is in the rainfall element that they become particularly noteworthy. Compared with thunderstorm rainfall, that associated with weak tropical lows is much more extensive, usually is less vigorous but of longer duration, and falls from skies that are more uniformly overcast.

The origin of these shallow disturbances which so greatly affect the weather of the low latitudes is a controversial question. They appear to be most numerous in the regions of horizontal convergence but, on the other hand,

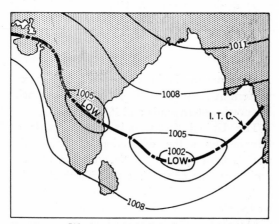

Fig. 5.21   Weak tropical disturbances of the summer-monsoon period over India and the Bay of Bengal. The storms are associated with the I.T.C.

there are many which seem to have no connection with convergence zones. Perhaps there are different types with somewhat different origins. Most of these weak disturbances never develop beyond the stage first described. A few appear to increase in intensity and become severe tropical storms or even develop into hurricanes.

5.38 Easterly Waves. In addition to the vortex disturbances with closed isobars there are others which are in the nature of pressure waves of small amplitude. On the weather map they are relatively inconspicuous, and appear only as slight bulges in the isobars (Fig. 5.22). These easterly waves are characteristic of the deep easterlies or trades and do not seem to be associated with zones of convergence. Their movement is from east to west. Ahead of the wave or trough, weather is fine, but behind it showery conditions prevail. Easterly waves were first detected in the Caribbean area, but more recently they have been identified in other parts of the tropics. A few of these weak wave disturbances grow in intensity, eventually reaching hurricane strength.

5.39 Tropical Disturbances of the Hurricane or Typhoon Variety. Very likely disturbances of all degrees of intensity are to be found in the tropics, but the most violent of all is the hurricane type. As indicated previously, these severe vortex storms have less climatic significance than the weaker disturbances, for they are of less frequent occurrence and are characteristic of more restricted areas. Moreover, since the hurricane develops and matures over water bodies only, the land areas which feel their effects are largely limited to coastal areas and islands.

These violent and destructive storms of the low latitudes in some respects resemble the middle-latitude cyclones, as, for instance, in the central area of low pressure, the converging cyclonic system of winds, and a relatively widespread area of cloud and rain. In other ways, however, the hurricane differs from its less intense counterpart of the middle and higher latitudes. Some of the more important features that distinguish it from the middle-latitude cyclone are as follows: (*a*) The isobars of the tropical storm are more symmetrical and more

nearly circular. Pressure gradients also are much steeper, so that winds are stronger. To be a genuine hurricane wind velocities in the storm must reach at least 75 miles an hour. (*b*) Rains are inclined to be more torrential and somewhat more evenly distributed about the center, although this latter characteristic is more common in nearly, or quite, stationary storms than in moving ones. (*c*) Temperature distribution around the center is relatively similar in every

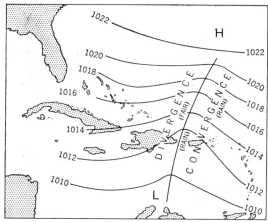

Fig. 5.22 A tropical disturbance in the form of an easterly wave. (*After Riehl.*)

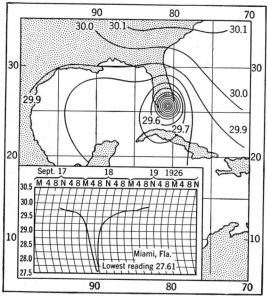

Fig. 5.23 A West Indies hurricane together with the barograph trace of this storm as recorded at Miami, Fla.

direction. There are no surface cold fronts or surface warm fronts as in the middle-latitude low. (*d*) There are no sharp wind shifts within the violent parts of the storm, the winds developing a perfect spiral whirl, with strong vertically ascending currents around the vortex, or core. (*e*) Tropical cyclones are most numerous in the warm season, rather than in winter. (*f*) Hurricanes have relatively calm, rainless centers, 5 to 30 miles in diameter. This area of descending air is called the "eye" of the storm. (*g*) The tropical cyclone has no anticyclonic companion. This is due to the fact that such a storm is maintained by heat of condensation and not primarily by temperature contrasts (Fig. 5.23).

The hurricane type of storm varies greatly in size, but in general it is smaller and more intense than the low of middle latitudes. The total diameter of the whirl may be 100 to 400 miles. Wind velocities are not always violent, but on the other hand they may reach such destructive speeds as 90 to 130 miles per hour. Tremendous damage to shipping and coastal settlements, with accompanying loss of life, is by no means rare. A considerable part of the property destruction, and loss of life from drowning, is due to the great avalanches of sea water piled up and driven onshore by the gale winds and to the excessive rainfall and associated floods that accompany the storm.

There is no generally accepted theory for hurricane origin. On the other hand it is clear that they develop only over water, and over warm water at that, probably 82°F. or higher. They are most numerous in summer and fall when the I.T.C. is displaced farthest from the equator. Many of these violent storms apparently have their beginnings in weak vortex and wave disturbances which subsequently mushroom into the intense and dreaded hurricane.

Tropical cyclones appear to occur over the warmer parts of all oceans, except possibly the South Atlantic where the I.T.C. does not migrate south of the equator. There are at least six regions of general concentration, however (Fig. 5.19). These regions are (*a*) the China Seas, the so-called *typhoons* of that region af-

fecting particularly the Philippines, southeastern China, and southern Japan; (*b*) the Arabian Sea and the Bay of Bengal, on either side of peninsular India; (*c*) the Caribbean Sea, with the West Indies, Yucatan, and southeastern United States all feeling the effects of hurricanes; (*d*) the eastern North Pacific in the region west of Mexico; (*e*) the South Indian Ocean east of Madagascar; and (*f*) the tropical waters to both the northeast and the northwest of Australia. The average number of severe tropical cyclones per year in the regions noted above is 22, 10, 5, 5, 13, and 13, respectively.

THUNDERSTORMS

5.40 General Characteristics. A thunderstorm is an intense convectional shower with which are associated lightning and thunder. In its mature stage it is characterized by several chimneys of vigorously ascending warm air, surrounded by compensating cooler downdrafts. Its structure, therefore, is one of multicellular convection. This characteristic turbulence is very evident in the seethings and convulsions that one can observe in the awesome cumulonimbus cloud or thunderhead (Fig. 5.24).

Rapid vertical upthrusts of air are commonly associated with high surface temperatures, so that it is not unexpected to find thunderstorms most numerous in the warmer latitudes of the earth, in the warmer seasons in the middle latitudes, and in the warmer hours of the day. It is obvious that heat and thunderstorms are closely related.

But heat is not the only requirement for thunderstorm development. The warm air must also be relatively rich in water vapor, for it is the abundant heat of condensation released in the rising air which is the principal source of energy for the storm's development. The intensity of the storm depends very largely upon this supply of latent energy in the form of heat of condensation. Without exception, the phenomena which one commonly associates with thunderstorms—torrential local rain, hail, violent squally winds, lightning, and thunder—are all directly related to the vigorous convectional overturning in warm humid air.

Fig. 5.24 A vertical section through a local heat thunderstorm and its cumulonimbus cloud.

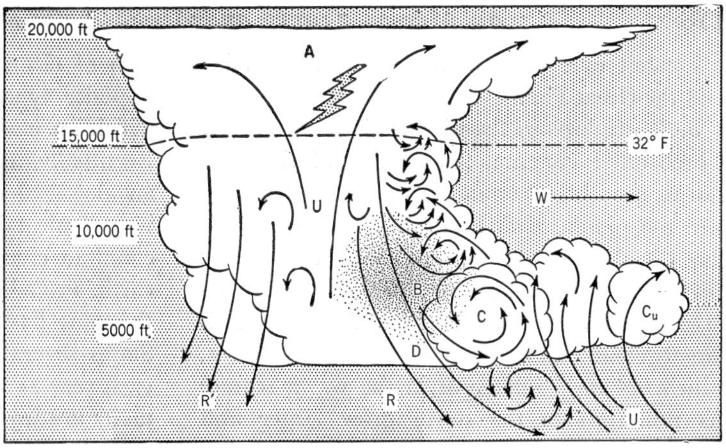

Key to diagram of cumulonimbus cloud

A – Anvil top
B – Dark area
C – Roll cloud
C_u – Advance cumulus clouds
D – Down drafts

U – Up drafts
R – Primary rain area
R′ – Secondary area
W – Wind direction

5.41   Precipitation in Thunderstorms. As indicated in an earlier section, rainfall in thunderstorms is likely to be more vigorous while it lasts, but of shorter duration, than that associated with cyclones. A cumulonimbus cloud is of relatively small areal extent so that it quickly drifts by and the rain ceases. One speaks of *thundershowers* rather than *thunder rains*. This downpour type of precipitation is related to (*a*) the more rapid vertical ascent of air in thunderstorms (at least 2,400 ft. a minute must often occur) than in most cyclones and (*b*) the higher temperature and, therefore, higher specific humidity of the air in the summer season when thunderstorms are prevalent. The vigorous nature of convectional rainfall, together with the fact that in middle latitudes it is concentrated in the growing season, has important economic consequences, some beneficial, others not.

5.42   *Hail.* Occasionally hail, the most destructive form of precipitation, is developed in very intense thunderstorms. Fortunately it occurs in only a few and usually falls in only restricted areas or belts within any particular storm. On first thought, it may appear peculiar that these relatively large globules of layered ice and snow should be a form of precipitation ordinarily concentrated in the warm season of the year. It is because they are associated with vigorous convectional systems such as are typical principally of the warm seasons. When convection is most violent and air currents are ascending at a rate of 25 to 50 miles an hour or more, raindrops caught in these upward-surging currents are carried up into regions of extreme cold, so that on mixing with snow they freeze as globules of cloudy ice. This ice pellet may grow into a hailstone as a consequence of a long fall from the high freezing level through a great thickness of subfreezing cloud layers, during which it captures supercooled water droplets and snow crystals with which it collides. Very large hailstones with a layered structure of concentric spheres of clear and cloudy ice result from the nonhomogeneous character of the cumulus cloud. When the strong upward-moving currents are temporarily halted, the hailstones fall to earth, often doing serious damage to crops, to structures such as greenhouses, and occasionally even killing livestock in the fields.

Strange as it may seem, hail frequency and thunderstorm frequency do not show the same distribution. For example, hail is practically unknown in the tropics where thunderstorms are most numerous. Within the United States hail rarely occurs in those warmer subtropical parts, such as Florida and the Gulf Coast, where thunderstorms are at a maximum. The distribution of hail frequency and hail damage are startlingly local in character, but frequency

117

is greatest over parts of the Rocky Mountains and the Great Plains.

5.43   Lightning, Thunder, and Squall Winds. Three other common phenomena of thunderstorms need brief comment: *lightning, thunder,* and the *squall wind.* Lightning is the result of the disruption of raindrops, with consequent development of static electricity, in rapidly ascending air currents. Like hail, therefore, it is largely confined to vigorous convectional storms, which are most numerous in the warm season. As raindrops in the storm grow larger and larger, they eventually reach such a size that their limit of cohesion is passed, and in the vigorous updrafts of air they begin to break up, the larger portions of the drops remaining at lower levels of the cloud or falling to earth, while the smaller particles, carried off as fine spray from the surface of the drop, are swept up into the upper and outer portions of the cloud (Fig. 5.25). The larger drops carry one type of electrical charge, the smaller ones the opposite type. Thus is created a situation in which an electrical discharge is likely to occur. Eventually, as these charges grow to great size, an electrical discharge in the form of a lightning flash takes place, more commonly from cloud to cloud but occasionally from cloud to earth. Probably not more than 1 per cent of the lightning flashes reach the earth. In the United States several hundred persons lose their lives each year as a result of lightning, and double as many are injured, while fire losses due to lightning amount to millions of dollars annually. The greatest losses result from the kindling of forest fires.

Thunder is produced by the violent expansion of the air caused by the tremendous heat of the lightning. It is due wholly to an explosive type of expansion consequent upon an extremely sudden and very great rise in temperature.

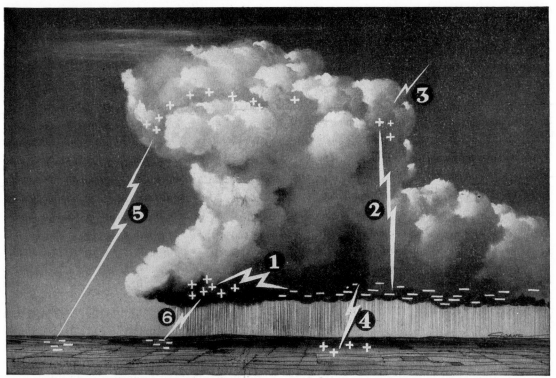

Fig. 5.25   Illustrating the development of electrical charges and lightning in a cumulonimbus cloud. (*Courtesy of Weatherwise.*)

5.44 *The Thundersquall.* The thundersquall is the strong outrushing mass of cool air just in front of the thunderstorm (Fig. 5.24). It is associated with the so-called squall cloud, an onrushing dark, gray, boiling arch or roll of cloud which is the forward projection of the lower portion of the storm cloud. The velocity of the squall wind at times attains hurricane violence, so that it may do serious damage. It should be carefully avoided by airplane pilots. The force of the squall is due in part to the cool air which has been brought down from aloft with the mass of falling rain. Being denser than the warm surface air, it spreads out in front of the storm, underrunning the warm air. In part its velocity is due also to the onrushing motion of the storm mass itself, so that forward and outward motions are combined.

5.45   Classes of Thunderstorms. Two main groups of thunderstorms are here recognized: (*a*) the simple convectional, or heat, type and (*b*) the frontal, type.

5.46 *Local Heat Thunderstorms.* These are the most common type. Since they owe their origin to the intense surface heating of humid air it is natural that they should be most frequent in latitudes, seasons, and daily periods of greatest heat. The heat, humidity, and convergent air movement characteristic of equatorial latitudes provide an ideal environment for their development and it is there that they are most frequent. Both in the tropics and in the middle latitudes they have a strong diurnal periodicity and reach a maximum frequency in the afternoon and early evening. They are local in character, occurring as isolated storms or groups of storms, and seldom cover a very extensive area. It is impossible therefore to forecast the exact time or place of their occurrence. Strong cumulus development gives warning of their imminence. Such local thunderstorms are of great economic importance for they furnish a considerable part of the warm-season rainfall in middle-latitude continents and a still larger proportion of that which falls in the tropics and subtropics.

Willis I. Milham gives the following excellent description of a local thunderstorm:

It has been a hot, sultry, oppressive day in summer. The air has been very quiet, perhaps alarmingly quiet, interrupted now and then by a gentle breeze from the south. The pressure has been gradually growing less. The sky is hazy; cirrus clouds are visible; here and there they thicken to cirro-stratus or cirro-cumulus. The temperature has risen very high, and the absolute humidity is very large, but owing to the high temperature the relative humidity has decreased somewhat. The combination of high moisture and temperature and but little wind has made the day intensely sultry and oppressive. In the early hours of the afternoon, amid the horizon haze and cirro-stratus clouds in the west, the big cumulus clouds, the thunderheads, appear. Soon distant thunder is heard, the lightning flashes are visible, and the dark rain cloud beneath comes into view. As the thundershower approaches, the wind dies down or becomes a gentle breeze blowing directly toward the storm. The temperature perhaps drops a little as the sun is obscured by the clouds, but the sultriness and oppressiveness remain as before. The thundershower comes nearer, and the big cumulus clouds with sharp outlines rise like domes and turrets one above the other. Perhaps the loftiest summits are capped with a fleecy, cirrus-like veil which extends out beyond them. If seen from the side, the familiar anvil form of the cloud mass is noticed. Just beneath the thunderheads is the narrow, turbulent, blue-drab squall cloud. The patches of cloud are now falling, now rising, now moving hither and thither as if in the greatest commotion. Beyond the squall cloud is the dark rain cloud, half hidden from view by the curtain of rain. The thunderheads and squall clouds are now just passing overhead. The lightning flashes, the thunder rolls, big, pattering raindrops begin to fall or perhaps, instead of these, damage-causing hailstones. The gentle breeze has changed to the violent outrushing squall wind, blowing directly from the storm, and the temperature is dropping as if by magic. Soon the rain descends in torrents, shutting out everything from view. After a time, the wind dies down but continues from the west or northwest, the rain decreasing in intensity; the lightning flashes follow each other at longer intervals. An hour or two has passed; it is growing lighter in the west; the wind has died down; the rain has almost stopped. Soon the rain ceases entirely; the clouds break through and become fracto-stratus or cirriform; the temperature rises somewhat, but it is still cool and pleasant; the wind has become very light and has shifted

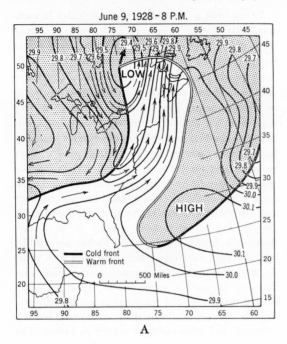

June 9, 1928 – 8 P.M.

A

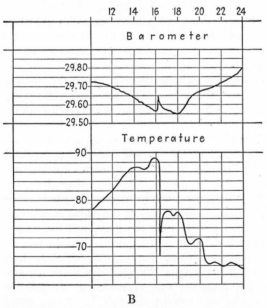

B

Fig. 5.26 (*A*) A V-shaped summer cyclone with a well-developed cold front and associated severe thunderstorms. Areas covered by continental polar air are shaded; those covered by air of maritime tropical origin are left unshaded. (*B*) Barograph and thermograph traces showing the approach and passage of the cold front shown in (*A*).

back to the southwest or south. Now the domes and turrets of the retreating shower are visible in the east; perhaps a rainbow spans the sky; the roll of the thunder becomes more distant; the storm has passed, and all nature is refreshed.[1]

5.47 *Frontal Thunderstorms.* Some thunderstorms are genetically associated with the fronts of moving cyclones and are the result of the upthrust of air that occurs in these areas of local convergence. Although thunderstorms may form along warm fronts and occluded fronts, they are most numerous and most severe along cold fronts, especially those of well-developed V-shaped summer cyclones (Fig. 5.26).

The cold front marks the abrupt meeting place of warm, humid, southerly currents on the front of the cyclone, with the cooler, heavier air of the northwest winds on the rear. Thunderstorms may form a nearly continuous series of active centers hundreds of miles long, the individual storms strung out along the cold front like beads on a string. Usually, however, they are some distance apart. When the cool westerly winds strike the side of the warm southerly currents along the cold front, they either underrun it like a blunt wedge or, owing to surface friction, overrun a portion of the warm air and entrap it (Fig. 5.10*c*). In either case vigorous overturning and upthrust take place with resulting turbulence and associated development of thunderstorms. Occasionally tornadoes, those most violent of all windstorms, likewise develop at or near the cold front of V-shaped cyclones. Since the cold-front variety of thunderstorm is associated with a frontal zone, it must of necessity travel with the latter, and its approach and passage, therefore, can be forecast with a considerable degree of accuracy.

In general, a cold-front storm can be distinguished from the local heat variety by the following criteria: (*a*) The former is commonly more severe although by no means always so. (*b*) It is not confined to any particular time of day, for its origin does not depend upon local surface heating. It may arrive, therefore, at any time of day or night. Local convectional storms,

[1] W. I. Milham. "Meteorology." Pp. 321–322. The Macmillan Company, New York, 1934.

on the other hand, more commonly are concentrated in the warmer hours of the day. (*c*) The cold-front thunderstorm is usually followed by a shift of wind from southwest, south, or southeast to northwest (from a tropical to a polar air mass) and by a consequent drop in temperature (Fig. 5.26). The local heat thunderstorm gives only a very temporary relief from the heat during the period of cloud cover and rain and is likely to be followed by the same kind of hot, humid weather that preceded it.

5.48 Distribution of Thunderstorms. The zonal distribution of thunderstorms, which shows the average number for any latitude, reveals a strong maximum in equatorial latitudes and a sharp decrease poleward in either hemisphere (Fig. 5.27). Beyond latitudes 60 or 70° thunderstorms are very few. In a general way, the pattern of zonal distribution is a function of temperature, but not wholly so, for while thunderstorm activity declines sharply between latitudes 0 and 20°, temperatures decline only slightly. The strong equatorial maximum, therefore, is not alone a consequence of high tem-

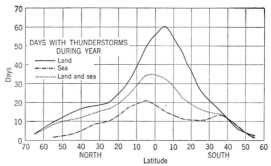

Fig. 5.27 Zonal distribution of average number of days with thunderstorms. (*After Brooks.*)

peratures, but also of the convergent nature of the air flow in these latitudes, while the sharp decline poleward from the equator reflects increasing subsidence and horizontal divergence in the marginal tropics and in the subtropics.

Greater frequency of thunderstorms over land areas than over oceans in similar latitudes is expected because of the higher summer temperatures of the former. Some equatorial land areas record over 100 days with thunderstorms

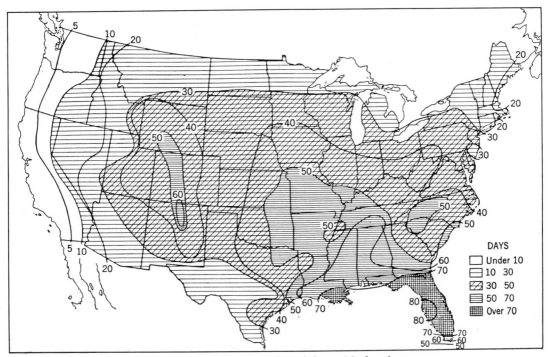

Fig. 5.28 Average annual number of days with thunderstorms.

during the year, while a few places have 200 such days.

In the United States the fewest thunderstorms are experienced in the Pacific Coast states which are dominated by stable anticyclonic air masses in summer. There are two regions of maximum occurrence: (*a*) the subtropical southeast and (*b*) the Rocky Mountain area in New Mexico, Colorado, and Wyoming. The eastern Gulf Coast region in the United States is the most thundery area outside the tropics, there being 70 to 80 days per year with thunderstorms. In this region heat and humidity combine to produce an environment ideal for the development of local convection (Fig. 5.28).

Section A2 CLIMATIC TYPES AND THEIR DISTRIBUTION

In the four preceding chapters the individual elements out of which climates are composed have been analyzed and their distributions over the earth's surface described. Variations in the amount, intensity, and seasonal distribution of these elements, as determined by the climatic controls, resulting in changeful combinations of the elements, are the reason for the existence of the variety of climates, the description of which is to follow.

Climates can be classified in a variety of ways and each of these has merit. It follows that there are a number of good classifications of climate. There is no one which is best, for some are better for one purpose and some for another. Nevertheless, they all have one goal which is the same, *viz.*, the reduction of almost innumerable local climates to a relatively few large groups or classes having important characteristics in common. This is the contribution of classification which is a process common to all sciences.

Classification by Temperature Zones. Perhaps the broadest and most general classification of climates is the one devised by the ancient Greeks who divided each hemisphere into three broad belts, or zones. Thus in the low latitudes is the *winterless* tropical region where temperatures are high throughout the year. Similarly in the high latitudes, in the vicinity of the poles, are the *summerless* polar regions, where there is a general prevalence of low temperatures. Between these two extremes, which are the tropical and the polar parts of the earth, are broad intervening belts where seasonal contrasts in temperature are marked, one season usually being warm or hot and the other cool or cold. These are the *intermediate*, or *middle, latitudes*,

sometimes designated as the "temperate zones," although obviously that name is not well chosen. The boundaries of these insolation or temperature zones as suggested by the ancients are the 23.5° and the 66.5° parallels in each hemisphere. For these unsatisfactory astronomical boundaries modern geographers have substituted certain critical isotherms, such as the 64° *coolest* month isotherm for the poleward limits of the tropics and the 50° *warmest* month isotherm for the poleward limits of the intermediate zones.

Climatic Regions and Climatic Types. This threefold classification of the earth's climates into tropical, middle-latitude, and polar types plainly does not take into consideration that other great climatic element, precipitation, since within both the low and the middle latitudes there are very wet as well as very dry climates, and still others which are intermediate in their amounts of rainfall. It is obvious that the geographer requires not only a more detailed and refined classification, but also one in which the climatic subdivisions are based upon precipitation as well as upon temperature characteristics. Such a subdivision of the land areas of the earth into climatic types and climatic regions is presented on Plate 2 (see the front endpaper).

Any portion of the earth's surface over which the climatic elements, and therefore the broad climatic characteristics, are similar (not necessarily identical) is called a climatic region. But it will be noted that not all the subdivisions on Plate 2 differ from one another climatically, for areas with similar climates are found in widely separated parts of the earth, although often in corresponding latitudinal and conti-

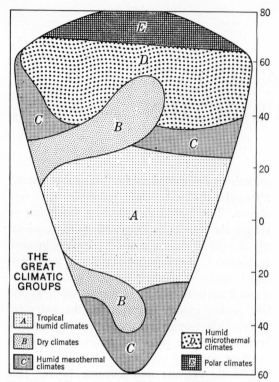

Fig. A.1 Arrangement of the principal groups of climate on a hypothetical continent of low and uniform elevation.

nental locations. This frequent approximating of climates in roughly corresponding positions on the continents suggests that there is order and system in the origin and distribution of the climatic elements. It likewise makes possible the classification of the numerous *climatic regions* into a relatively few principal *climatic groups* (Fig. A.1) and *climatic types* (Fig. A.2). The climatic region is a subdivision of the climatic type, and hence the type comprises a number of separate regions.

Observation of Plate 2 will show that there is a recognizable world pattern of climatic distribution, for the several climatic regions comprising a type are seen to fairly repeat each other in terms of latitudinal and continental locations. This is not unexpected since the greatest controls of climate are to be found in the distribution of solar energy and the general

circulation of the atmosphere, both of which have clearly distinguishable world patterns. The broader features of the world climatic distribution are presented in diagrammatic form in Figs. A.1 and A.2. Here an attempt has been made to show climatic arrangement as it might appear on a hypothetical continent of relatively low and uniform elevation. It is designed to show typical positions and arrangements of the climatic types divorced from peculiarities associated with individual continents by reason of their size, shape, or surface configuration. The important resemblances between Fig. A.2 and Plate 2 are obvious.

In studying the text materials on groups and types of climate to follow, constant reference should be made to Figs. A.1 and A.2 as well as to Plate 2.

Types of Climate*

Groups	Types
	I. Low Latitudes (The Tropics)
A. Tropical humid climates	1. Tropical wet (Af, constantly wet) (Am, monsoon variety)
	2. Tropical wet-and-dry (Aw)
	3. Low-latitude dry climates a. Low-latitude desert (BWh, arid) b. Low-latitude steppe (BSh, semiarid)
B. Dry climates	**II. Middle Latitudes (Intermediate Zones)** 4. Middle-latitude dry climates a. Middle-latitude desert (BWk, arid) b. Middle-latitude steppe (BSk, semiarid)
C. Humid mesothermal climates	5. Dry-summer subtropical (Cs) 6. Humid subtropical (Ca) 7. Marine (Cb, Cc)
D. Humid microthermal climates	8. Humid continental climates a. Humid continental, warm summer (Da) b. Humid continental, cool summer (Db) 9. Subarctic (Dc, Dd)
	III. High Latitudes (Polar Caps) or High Altitudes
E. Polar climates	10. Tundra (ET) 11. Ice cap (EF)
H. Undifferentiated highlands	

*Temperature and precipitation data for representative stations are included in the text for each type of climate. Supplementary climatic data can be found in Appendix A.

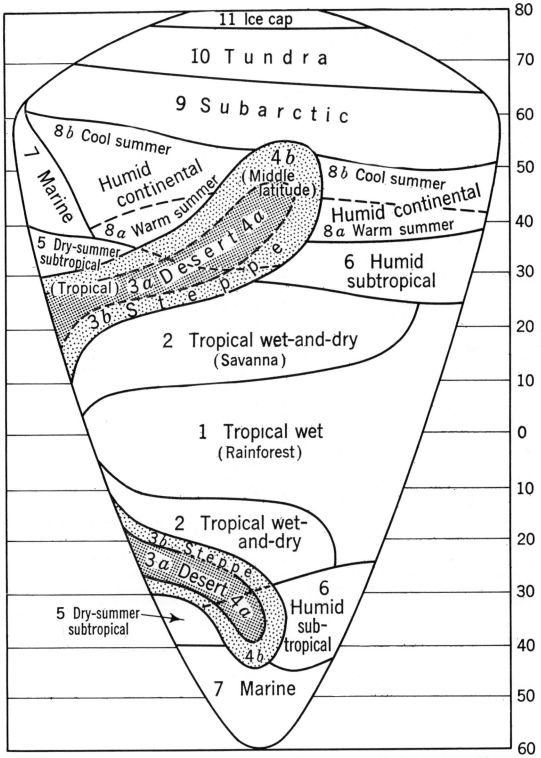

Fig. A.2 Arrangement of the principal types of climate on a hypothetical continent of low and uniform elevation.

Present Scheme of Climatic Classification. The plan of climatic classification employed in this book is a simplified and otherwise modified version of the well-known Köppen[1] system. Five great climatic groups (Fig. A.1) are recognized and each of these in turn is subdivided into a relatively few climatic types (Fig. A.2).

The five groups of climate are as follows (Fig. A.1). In the low latitudes near the equator is a winterless region with adequate rainfall. It is the humid tropics. This *A* group is called *tropical humid climates*. Poleward from the *A* group and extending far into the middle latitudes are the *dry climates, B.* The humid middle latitudes with their seasonal contrasts in temperature are divided into two climatic groups, one in which the winters are short and mild, the *humid mesothermal climates, C,* and the other in which they are severe and long, the *humid microthermal climates, D.* Finally, in the higher latitudes are the summerless *polar climates, E.* In more detail the outline of climatic classification is given on page 124.

In order to facilitate shifting back and forth between the Köppen system of classification and the modified and simplified form of that scheme here employed, the corresponding Köppen symbols appear in parentheses after each type of climate. Since the two classifications are *similar,* but not *identical,* the latter symbols indicate only somewhat comparable climates and should not be understood to imply complete agreement.[2]

---

[1] See W. Köppen, "Grundriss der Klimakunde." Walter De Gruyter & Company, Berlin, 1931. The particular value of Köppen's classification lies in the fact that it is a quantitative system, which uses numerical values for defining the boundaries of the climatic groups and types. Where exact definitions are given to the lines limiting the climatic types, the boundaries are subject to checking and revision as new data are available. The Köppen system has been so widely adopted that it is something of a world standard. Another valuable world classification of climates, likewise employing numerical values of temperature and rainfall for defining the boundaries of climatic types, is by C. Warren Thornthwaite (see references, p. 127). Both the Köppen and the Thornthwaite classifications, representing quantitative systems of comparative climatology, are particularly useful to professional geographers or to college students who are training to enter that field. It is the authors' belief, however, that in an introductory book in geography for college freshmen and sophomores, scarcely any of whom will become geographers, major emphasis should be placed upon the descriptive elements of a climate rather than upon the values employed to establish boundaries, especially since these values are still somewhat tentative. For this reason no attempt has been made to impress the student with the necessity of memorizing the specific Köppen formulas, the more important ones of which are given below for those who desire to use them. Definitions of other Köppen symbols are given in footnotes at the points where they may be useful.

A = temperature of coolest month over 64.4° (18°C.)
B = evaporation exceeds precipitation
C = coldest month between 64.4° (18°C.) and 26.6° (−3°C.)
D = temperature of coldest month under 26.6° (−3°C.); warmest month over 50° (10°C.)
E = temperature of warmest month under 50° (10°C.)

[2] One of Köppen's principal climatic types, *Cw,* is here omitted. It is felt that this climate is not sufficiently distinctive to warrant setting it apart, for the purpose of this classification, as a separate type.

References for Section A2

Ackerman, Edward A. The Köppen Classification of Climates in North America. *Geog. Rev.,* Vol. 31, pp. 105–111, 1941.

"Atlas of American Agriculture." Part 2, Climate. 3 sections: Frost and the Growing Season; Temperature, Sunshine and Wind; Precipitation and Humidity. U.S. Government Printing Office, Washington, D.C. Contains excellent and detailed maps of the climatic elements.

Blair, Thomas A. "Climatology, General and Regional." Prentice-Hall, Inc., New York, 1942.

Brooks, C. E. P. "Climate." Ernest Benn, Ltd., London, 1929.

Brooks, C. F., A. J. Connor, *et al.* "Climatic Maps of North America." Harvard University Press, Cambridge, Mass., 1936.

"Climate and Man." Yearbook of Agriculture, 1941. U.S. Department of Agriculture, Washington, D.C. Contains an abundance of climatic data on foreign countries as well as on the United States.

Hann, Julius. "Handbook of Climatology." Part 1, English translation by Robert De C. Ward. The Macmillan Company, New York, 1903. 4th rev. German ed. by Karl Knoch. J. Engelhorn's Nachfolger, Stuttgart, 1932.

Haurwitz, Bernhard, and James M. Austin. "Climatology." McGraw-Hill Book Company, Inc., New York, 1944.

Kendrew, W. G. "Climatology." 3d ed. of "Climate." Oxford University Press, New York, 1949. A particularly good treatment of the climatic elements.

————. "Climates of the Continents." 4th ed., Oxford University Press, New York, 1953.

Köppen, W. "Grundriss der Klimakunde." Walter De Gruyter & Company, Berlin, 1931. Contains a relatively complete analysis of the Köppen scheme of climatic classification.

———— and R. Geiger. "Handbuch der Klimatologie." Verlagsbuchhandlung Gebrüder Borntraeger, Berlin, 1930 and later. 5 vols.; not completed. Vol. I covers the field of general climatology; the other four are on regions. Those parts dealing with the United States, Mexico, West Indies, Central America, Australia, New Zealand, and parts of eastern Africa are in English; the other parts are in German. Vol. I, Part C, 1936, contains an analysis of Köppen's system of climates. The most complete and up-to-date compendium of information on general and regional climatology. Contains abundant climatic data.

Miller, A. Austin. "Climatology." 3d ed. E. P. Dutton & Co., Inc., New York, 1953.

Thornthwaite, C. Warren. The Climates of North America According to a New Classification. *Geog. Rev.,* Vol. 21, pp. 633–655, 1931.

————. The Climates of the Earth. *Geog. Rev.,* Vol. 23, pp. 433–440, 1933.

————. An Approach toward a Rational Classification of Climate. *Geog. Rev.,* Vol. 38, pp. 55–94, 1948.

Ward, Robert De C. "Climates of the United States." Ginn & Company, Boston, 1925.

6

The Tropical Humid Climates (A)

6.1 Location and Boundaries. The tropical humid climates form a somewhat interrupted belt 20 to 40° wide around the earth astride the equator (Fig. A.1, Plate 2). This region is distinguished from all other humid regions of the earth by reason of the fact that it is constantly warm; in other words, it lacks a winter. In the low latitudes heat is so constant that summer temperatures are of little importance in setting the poleward limits of tropical climates or of distinguishing their subdivisions. It is, rather, a season of coolness, during which there is some relief from tropical heat, and which provides a dormant season for vegetation that becomes critical. As a consequence, the poleward boundary of the tropical humid climates, except where they come in contact with the dry climates, is, according to Köppen, approximately the isotherm of 64° for the *coolest* month. Stated in a different way, within this climatic group there is no month with an average temperature of less than 64°. This temperature was selected because it was found to coincide reasonably well with the poleward limit of certain plants which grow only in the warmest regions and cannot tolerate a cool season. The chief interruptions in the belt of tropical humid climates over the continents are caused by mountains and plateaus, these elevated lands, even though near the equator, having temperatures too low to permit them to be classed as typically tropical.

Normally the tropical humid climates extend farthest poleward along the eastern or windward sides of the continents (Fig. A.1). Here tropical maritime air masses (trades), humid and relatively unstable, come onshore from off warm waters and provide atmospheric conditions conducive to thunderstorm and cyclonic precipitation. East-coast rainfall is especially heavy where the tropical air masses are forced to ascend highland barriers. On these windward sides of the land masses, therefore, the tropical humid climates extend poleward until they meet the humid subtropical climates of the middle latitudes.

In the interior, and toward the western sides of the continents, however, the humid tropics are bounded by the dry *B* climates (see Fig. A.1). Here the tropical air masses are more stable so that on the west sides and interiors dry climates are brought somewhat closer to the equator. Where cool equatorward-moving ocean currents parallel the west coasts in low latitudes, they may carry the dry climates to within a few degrees of the equator, notably constricting the breadth of the humid tropical belt. Likewise these western sides of tropical continents are fairly coincident with the eastern ends of subtropical high-pressure cells, where the subsiding air is stable and opposed to precipitation.

6.2 Precipitation. Rainfall is relatively abundant, rarely lower than 30 in., and usually it is well over that amount (Plate 1). Much of the precipitation is convectional in origin, the heavy showers often being accompanied by severe thunder and lightning. Rains associated with weak tropical disturbances of various kinds are likewise important. Unlike the uniform temperature conditions, rainfall is more variable in amount and in seasonal and areal distribution.

The two principal climatic types within the

humid tropics are distinguished from each other on the basis of their seasonal distribution of precipitation, one type, *tropical wet,* having ample rainfall throughout the year, while in the other, *tropical wet-and-dry,* there is a distinctly wet and a distinctly dry season.

Tropical Wet Climate (Af)[1] (Tropical Rainforest)

6.3 Type Location. (*a*) Uniformly high temperatures and (*b*) heavy precipitation distributed throughout the year, so that there is no marked dry season, are the two most distinguishing characteristics of the *Af* type, or tropical wet, climate. When typically located it is found astride the equator and extending out 5 or 10° on either side. The latitudinal spread may be increased to 15 or even 25° along the windward margins of the continents. This climate is closely associated with the doldrums and the intertropical convergence zone (Fig. 6.1). Characteristically tropical wet climate is bounded by the tropical wet-and-dry type (*Aw*) on its poleward sides. Along the wetter eastern margins of the continents, however, it usually extends farther poleward, so that there it makes contact with the humid subtropical climate (*Ca*) of middle latitudes (Fig. A.2).

6.4 Geographical Location. The Amazon Basin in northern South America and the Congo Basin and Guinea Coast in West Africa are the two largest contiguous areas with tropical wet climate (Plate 2). A third extensive but not contiguous area is composed of the East Indies, the Philippine Islands, and the Malay Peninsula in tropical southeastern Asia. In addition there are more isolated areas of tropical wet climate in eastern Central America, the windward parts of some islands in the West Indies, western Colombia, the coastal lowlands and slopes of sections of eastern Brazil, and eastern Madagascar.

[1] In the Köppen symbols *f* = moist (*feucht*) throughout the year; no month with less than 2.4 in. of rain.

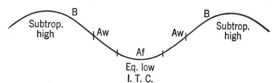

Fig. 6.1 Type locations of tropical wet climate (*Af*), tropical wet-and-dry climate (*Aw*), and dry climate (*B*) on the zonal profile of sea-level pressure.

TEMPERATURE

6.5 Annual and Seasonal Temperatures. Lying as *Af* commonly does athwart the equator and consequently in the belt of maximum insolation, it is to be expected that temperatures will be uniformly high, the yearly averages usually lying between 77 and 80°+ (see data, pages 131 and 134). Since the sun's noon rays are never far from a vertical position, and days and nights vary little in length from one part of the year to another, the annual insolation curve remains relatively constant, so that not only are the annual temperatures high, but there is likewise little seasonal variation (Fig. 6.2).

The annual temperature range, or difference between the warmest and coolest months, is usually less than 5°. Thus Belém and Iquitos in the Amazon Valley have annual ranges of 3° and 4°, respectively; Coquilhatville in central Africa, 2+°; and Singapore in southern Malaya, 3°. Over the oceans in these low latitudes ranges are even less, Jaluit in the Marshall Islands in mid-Pacific recording only 0.8° difference between the extreme months. It becomes evident from the very small temperature ranges that it is not the excessively high monthly averages but rather the *uniformity* and *monotony* of this constant succession of hot months, with no relief, that characterize the tropical wet, or *Af*, climate. Thus the average July temperatures of many American cities, such as Charleston, with 82°; Galveston, 83°; and Montgomery, 82°, may equal, or even exceed by a few degrees, those of the hottest months at stations near the equator. The hottest month at Belém (Amazon Basin) and at Akassa (Niger Delta) is only 80°.

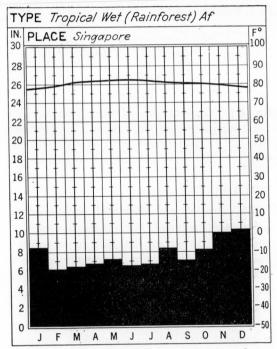

TYPE *Tropical Wet (Rainforest) Af*

PLACE *Singapore*

Fig. 6.2 Average monthly temperatures and precipitation for a representative station with a tropical wet climate (*Af*). Monthly temperatures are much more uniform than monthly amounts of precipitation.

6.6 Daily Temperatures. The daily or diurnal range of temperature (difference between the warmest and coolest hours of the day) is usually 10 to 25°, or several times greater than the annual range. For example, at Bolobo in the Belgian Congo, the average daily range is 16°, while the annual range is only 2°. During the afternoons the thermometer ordinarily rises to temperatures varying from 85 to 93° and at night sinks to 70 or 75° (Figs. 6.3, 6.4, and 6.5). It is commonly said, therefore, that night is the winter of the tropics. Even the extremes

of temperature are never very great, the average of the daily maxima at Belém being only 91.4°, and the average of the daily minima, 68°. The highest temperature ever recorded at Santarem (Amazon Basin) is 96.3°, while the lowest is only 65.3°. This absolute maximum of 96.3° may be compared with 103° for Chicago and 108° for St. Louis. Although the day temperatures may not be excessively high, the heat, together with slight air movement, intense light, and high relative and absolute humidity, produces an atmospheric condition with low cooling power. It is oppressive and sultry so that one's vitality and energy are sapped. *Sensible temperatures* are, therefore, excessively high, although the thermometer readings may not indicate abnormal heat.

Even the nights give little relief from the oppressive heat. Rapid nocturnal cooling is not to be expected in regions of such excessive humidity and abundant cloudiness. It is usually sufficient, however, to cause surface condensation in the near-saturated air, so that radiation fogs and heavy dew are common. The periods of less rainfall and clearest skies have the lowest night temperatures, the thermometer on rare occasions falling below 60°.

6.7 Daily March of Temperature. Figures 6.3, 6.4, and 6.5 show the daily march of temperature for the extreme months at representative stations within tropical wet climate. The graphs illustrate a temperature regime in which sun is almost completely in control. There is a marked diurnal regularity and periodicity about the changes, temperatures rising to about the same height each day and falling to about the same level each night, so that one 24-hr. period

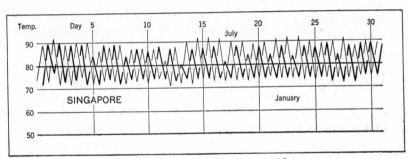

Fig. 6.3 Daily maximum and minimum temperatures for the extreme months at a representative station with tropical wet climate (*Af*). Diurnal solar control is almost complete, as shown by the regular daily rise and fall of temperature.

130

Climatic Data for Representative Stations with Tropical Wet Climate

Singapore, Straits Settlements (Malaya)

	J	F	M	A	M	J	J	A	S	O	N	D	Yr.	Range
Temp.	78.3	79.0	80.2	80.8	81.5	81.1	81.0	80.6	80.4	80.1	79.3	78.6	80.1	3.2
Precip.	8.5	6.1	6.5	6.9	7.2	6.7	6.8	8.5	7.1	8.2	10.0	10.4	92.9	

Belém, Amazon Valley

	J	F	M	A	M	J	J	A	S	O	N	D	Yr.	Range
Temp.	77.7	77.0	77.5	77.7	78.4	78.3	78.1	78.3	78.6	79.0	79.7	79.0	78.3	2.7
Precip.	10.3	12.6	13.3	13.2	9.3	5.7	4.9	4.3	3.2	2.5	2.3	5.1	86.7	

Nouvelle Anvers, Belgian Congo

	J	F	M	A	M	J	J	A	S	O	N	D	Yr.	Range
Temp.	79.2	80.1	79.2	78.1	79.2	78.4	76.5	76.3	77.0	77.4	77.9	78.1	78.1	3.8
Precip.	4.1	3.5	4.1	5.6	6.2	6.1	6.3	6.3	6.3	6.6	2.6	9.3	66.9	

almost duplicates every other. Irregular invasions of cold, a feature so common in the middle latitudes, are rare.

PRECIPITATION

6.8 Amount. Rainfall is both heavy and distributed throughout the year, there being no distinctly dry season (Fig. 6.2; see data below and page 134). Taken as a whole, tropical wet climate is coincident with the belt of the world's heaviest precipitation (Plate 1). Ward estimates the average rainfall of the doldrum belt to be in the neighborhood of 100 in., with less over the continents and more over the oceans. In this region close to the equator conditions are ideal for rain formation. Of primary importance is the fact that it is a region of rising air. This results in part from the lifting of trade-wind air masses along the intertropical convergence. In part it is due also to local convection in the warm, humid, unstable air of the doldrums. Both thunderstorms and weak cyclones are numerous, and only a small amount of lifting of the unstable air is required to produce abundant rainfall. Cloudiness, much of it

cumulus in character, is relatively high in the doldrums, averaging in the neighborhood of 58 per cent. At Manaos, in the Amazon Valley, cloudiness varies between $\frac{6}{10}$ and $\frac{7}{10}$ for each month. At Belém it is $\frac{4}{10}$ in the driest month and $\frac{8}{10}$ in the rainiest.[2]

6.9 Seasonal Distribution. Although it is true that there is no genuinely dry season in the tropical wet climate, it should not be inferred that the rainfall is, therefore, *evenly* distributed throughout the year. By comparison with the rainiest periods there are others that are less wet, but they are far from being dry (Fig. 6.2). There is no distinctive seasonal rainfall regime characteristic of the rainforest type of climate.

In the rainier periods precipitation falls on a large majority of the days, although there are usually a few days with none. Fewer rainy days and less rain on each day are characteristic features of the less wet seasons. At Belém in the Amazon Valley with 94 in. of rain, March (14 in.) has six and one-half times more rain than November, but even November has 10

[2] Cloudiness is here expressed in terms of the part of the total sky covered.

Fig. 6.4 Daily maximum and minimum temperatures for the extreme months at Manaos in the Amazon Valley. Periodic solar control dominates temperature. By contrast, the nonperiodic effects of atmospheric disturbances, or storms, are very weak.

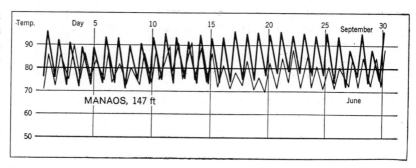

rainy days although March has 28. Precipitation varies much more from year to year than does temperature, although these variations are seldom enough to injure crops. Even the drier years are still relatively wet.

6.10   Nature of the Rainfall. Much of the rainfall is convectional in origin, falling in hard showers from towering cumulonimbus clouds. The maximum usually occurs during the warmer hours of the day, when local heating, and therefore convectional ascent, are at a maximum. Early mornings are often relatively clear, but as the sun climbs toward the zenith and temperature increases, cumulus clouds begin to appear, growing in number and size with the heat of the day, until by afternoon ominous thunderheads are common. Several thunderstorms, accompanied by thunder and lightning, in a single afternoon are not unusual, and the rain may continue on into the evening, although there is a tendency for the skies to become clearer as the heat wanes. The cloud cover and downpour of rain accompanying the storm temporarily cool the air, but with its passing and the reappearance of the sun, the usual oppressive conditions are reestablished. Within the doldrum belt thunderstorms reach their maximum development for any latitude of the earth, there being on the average 75 to 150 days with such storms during the course of a year. These paroxysms of nature, with their fierce lightning, crashing thunder, and deluges of rainfall, are awesome spectacles. One traveler[3] writes as follows concerning the heavy convectional showers in the tropical wet, or *Af,* climate:

The force of the downpour is another factor in the oecology of the forest. In the wet season thunderstorms of great violence are frequent, and the rain descends with a suddenness and volume unknown outside the tropics. The sun is shining, the forest glitters with a million lights, birds are on the move, and insects hum and dance from leaf to leaf. All at once a shadow is drawn over the sun, and all activity of bird and beast ceases as the sound of rushing rain rapidly approaches. An avalanche of

[3] Maude D. Haviland. "Forest, Steppe and Tundra." P. 39. Cambridge University Press, London, 1926.

water then crashes down, blotting out surrounding objects and, as it seems, sweeping the very breath from the nostrils, bewildering and benumbing the senses. Every twig and leaf is bent and battered, and in a few seconds streams pour down the paths and the world seems changed into a thundering cataract. Then, as suddenly as it came, the storm passes, and the sun blazes out again before the roar of the storm sweeping over the treetops has died away in the distance. Even before the leaves have ceased to drip, or the land crabs, tempted forth by the teeming water, have scuttled to cover again, the life of the forest is resumed. It is almost incredible how some fragile forms escape destruction under such terrific bombardments. . . .

In addition to the heavy local showers associated with afternoon thermal convection, there is also rainfall which accompanies the passage of extensive atmospheric disturbances of the cyclonic or the wave type. While such rainfall may be showery in nature, it is, on the other hand, more extensive than that associated with thermal convection, and the intermittent rains are characteristic of night as well as day. In such weak disturbances it is not uncommon also for the precipitation to fall continuously for many hours and from skies that are heavily overcast.

6.11   Winds. Pressure gradients are weak so that air movement is prevailingly slight. The whole region is poorly ventilated, and this, in conjunction with high temperatures and excessive humidity, makes for physical discomfort. Temporary relief may be brought by the strong squall winds associated with thunderstorms. Sea breezes are important climatic phenomena along coasts in the low latitudes. The importation of cooler air from the sea during the heat of the day is a great boon to residents along the littoral, causing tropical coasts to be much more livable than are the interiors.

6.12   The Weather Element. From the preceding description one would judge, and quite rightly, that sun control with its diurnal periodicity is dominant, causing one day's weather to closely resemble that of all the others. Monotony is characteristic. This is especially true of the temperature elements (Figs. 6.3 and 6.4). Diurnal regularity is not so complete in the

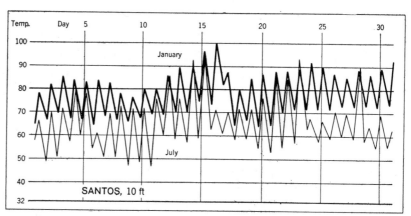

Fig. 6.5 Daily maximum and minimum temperatures for the extreme months at a station with tropical wet climate located on the east coast of Brazil at 24°S. Note the somewhat greater nonperiodic temperature changes as controlled by air-mass variations associated with atmospheric disturbances.

case of precipitation, for the passage of weak tropical disturbances gives rise to spells of unusually showery, rainy weather lasting several days. The following description by an eye-witness of daily weather conditions in the Amazon Valley may serve to synthesize and vivify the previous description:[4]

The heat increased rapidly toward two o'clock (92° and 93° Fahr.), by which time every voice of bird or mammal was hushed; only in the trees was heard at intervals the harsh whir of a cicada. The leaves, which were so moist and fresh in early morning, now became lax and drooping; the flowers shed their petals. Our neighbours, the Indian and Mulatto inhabitants of the open palm-thatched huts, as we returned home fatigued with our ramble, were either asleep in their hammocks or seated on mats in the shade, too languid even to talk. On most days in June and July a heavy shower would fall some time in the afternoon, producing a most welcome coolness. The approach of the rain-clouds was after a uniform fashion very interesting to ob-serve. First, the cool sea-breeze, which commenced to blow about 10 o'clock, and which had increased in force with the increasing power of the sun, would flag and finally die away. The heat and electric tension of the atmosphere would then become al-most insupportable. Languor and uneasiness would seize on every one; even the denizens of the forest betraying it by their motions. White clouds would appear in the east and gather into cumuli, with an increasing blackness along their lower portions. The whole eastern horizon would become almost sud-denly black, and this would spread upwards, the sun at length becoming obscured. Then the rush of a mighty wind is heard through the forest, swaying

[4] Henry Walter Bates. "The Naturalist on the River Amazon." Pp. 31–32. John Murray, London, 1910.

the tree-tops; a vivid flash of lightning bursts forth, then a crash of thunder, and down streams the deluging rain. Such storms soon cease, leaving bluish-black motionless clouds in the sky until night. Meantime all nature is refreshed; but heaps of flower-petals and fallen leaves are seen under the trees. Toward evening life revives again, and the ringing uproar is resumed from bush and tree. The following morning the sun again rises in a cloudless sky, and so the cycle is completed; spring, summer, and autumn, as it were, in one tropical day. The days are more or less like this throughout the year in this country. . . . It is never either spring, sum-mer, or autumn, but each day is a combination of all three. With the day and night always of equal length, the atmospheric disturbances of each day neutralising themselves before each succeeding morn; with the sun in its course proceeding midway across the sky, and the daily temperature the same within two or three degrees throughout the year— how grand in its perfect equilibrium and simplicity is the march of Nature under the equator!

MODIFIED TYPES OF TROPICAL WET CLIMATE

6.13 Windward Coasts. Where tropical wet climate is found along windward coasts at some distance (15°–20°) from the equator, it exists in slightly modified form. Close to the coast the sea breeze makes the humid heat easier to bear. In addition, the closer proximity to middle latitudes permits greatly modified polar air to reach these areas occasionally in winter. The result is a greater nonperiodic variation in tem-perature than is true of the typical rainforest climate. Slightly lower winter minimum tem-peratures and somewhat greater annual ranges of temperature are also characteristic. See data

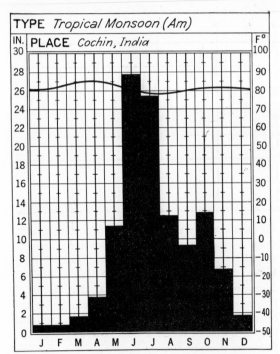

TYPE *Tropical Monsoon (Am)*

PLACE *Cochin, India*

Fig. 6.6 Average monthly temperatures and precipitation amounts for a representative tropical wet station where monsoon control is strong (*Am*).

for Belize below and also Fig. 6.5, illustrating conditions at Santos.

6.14 Monsoon Rainforest Climate (*Am*). In this subtype the total annual rainfall is commonly heavier than the average for tropical wet climate. It differs from the typical rainforest climate in that precipitation is not so well distributed throughout the year, there being at least a short dry season. In annual rainfall distribution, therefore, this subtype somewhat resembles the tropical wet-and-dry climate, although the total amount is much heavier and the dry period commonly is not so long (Fig.

6.6). The maximum precipitation usually occurs at the time of high sun, which is the period of the onshore monsoon. In spite of a distinct dry season, variable in length, the precipitation is so heavy that the ground remains sufficiently damp throughout the year to support a relatively dense, semideciduous forest. Temperatures usually reach a maximum during the period of clearer skies just before the season of heaviest rainfall and cloud, even though the latter is the period of highest sun (see data for Calicut below). This subtype is best developed in the monsoon lands of tropical southeastern Asia and on the western Guinea Coast of Africa.

6.15 Resource Potentialities of the Tropical Wet Realm. Although approximately 10 per cent of the earth's land surface is characterized by tropical wet climate, by no means do these areas contain 10 per cent of the earth's population. Moreover, within the earth's tropical wet areas there are the widest variations in population densities. The New World tropics are far emptier than those of the Old World. The huge Amazonian region lies at one extreme with fewer than 1,500,000 people within its 1,500,000 square miles, while at the opposite pole is tiny Java with over 800 per square mile and the Ganges Delta with over 600.

Tropical wet is the most lavish and prolific of all climates. Here there is no dormant season for plant growth imposed either by a season of cold or a season of drought. In no other climate do plants grow so continuously and so rapidly, and since plants provide the ultimate food resource for human beings this would seem to suggest a potential maximum food production within the rainforest regions. An offsetting

Climatic Data for Belize, British Honduras, on a Windward East Coast at about 17°20′N.Lat.

	J	F	M	A	M	J	J	A	S	O	N	D	Yr.	Range
Temp.	74.8	76.8	79.2	79.2	81.9	82.4	82.6	82.6	82.0	79.3	76.1	73.6	79.3	9
Precip.	5.1	2.6	1.6	1.5	4.1	9.1	9.6	8.5	9.4	11.0	10.2	6.3	79.0	

Climatic Data for Calicut, India, a Representative Monsoon Rainforest Station

	J	F	M	A	M	J	J	A	S	O	N	D	Yr.	Range
Temp.	77.8	79.8	81.6	83.6	83.1	78.5	76.7	77.4	78.3	79.1	79.5	78.3	79.5	6.9
Precip.	0.3	0.2	0.6	3.2	9.5	35.0	29.8	15.3	8.4	10.3	4.9	1.1	118.6	

factor, however, is the handicap which this same climate imposes upon the health and general well-being of the people who live in it. Numerous tropical diseases, among them malaria, sleeping sickness, yellow fever, and tropical dysentery, have been veritable scourges to the inhabitants of the low latitudes. By some the constant heat and humidity are considered to be insuperable obstacles to the maintenance of mental and physical vigor. Nevertheless, there is a growing optimism that modern hygiene and sanitation, together with electrical refrigeration and the creation of artificial indoor climates, may greatly reduce the hazards and discomforts associated with living in a tropical climate.

But if the tropical wet climate provides a bountiful climate for plant growth, its low-grade residual soils, on the other hand, offer a serious counterbalance and make the growth of crops, other than the bush and tree crops with deeper roots, difficult. The strong leaching effects of the abundant and warm rains continuing throughout the entire year leave the soil deficient in mineral plant foods and in organic material. A very few years of cropping is sufficient to exhaust the topsoil so that the native agriculturist is forced to migrate or at least to shift his fields. On the other hand, these soils which are deficient in mineral plant foods are, at the same time, coarsely granular in structure, so that they are friable and easy to till. This characteristic recommends them to the native agriculturist who operates with relatively ineffective tools.

Like the climate, the vegetation resource is abundant, at least as far as quantity is concerned. No other climate produces such a dense growth of large trees. To the agricultural settler who is obliged to clear the land, this forest is much more of a handicap than a resource. On the other hand, no other of the earth's forest regions provides such a storehouse of wood and lumber, although the exploitation of this resource is associated with many obstacles.

Unoccupied land is plentiful in some of the tropical wet regions, but the value of these areas for future settlement is a fiercely debated question. The matter is far from settled, although there is more optimism at present relative to their future than at any other time. Of all the earth's extensive areas of meager population, there is more hope for colonization in the wet tropics than in either the high-latitude or the dry lands.

Tropical Wet-and-Dry Climate (Aw)[5] *(Savanna)*

This climate differs in two principal respects from tropical wet climate: (*a*) It usually has less total precipitation; and (*b*) rainfall is unevenly distributed throughout the year, there being a distinctly wet and a distinctly dry season. These climatic contrasts result in the dense forest cover, typical of areas near the equator, being replaced by open forest and tree-studded grassland in the wet-and-dry climate.

6.16 Type Location and Boundaries. In Fig. A.2, showing the distribution and characteristic locations of types of climate on a hypothetical continent, tropical wet-and-dry areas lie on the poleward and interior sides of the tropical wet climate and between it and the dry climates. Toward the rainier eastern side of a continent the wet-and-dry climate commonly makes contact with humid subtropical climate of the middle latitudes. The typical latitudinal location of the wet-and-dry climate is about 5 or 10° to 15 or 20°, and it may extend still farther poleward on the eastern or windward side of the continent. This typical location places tropical wet-and-dry in an intermediate position between the intertropical convergence and its unstable air masses on the equatorial side and the subtropical anticyclones with their stable subsiding and diverging air masses on the poleward side (Fig. 6.1). During the course of the year with the north-south shifting of insolation belts, and as a consequence a similar migration of pressure and wind belts, latitudes 5 to 15° are alternately encroached upon by the wet I.T.C. and dol-

---

[5] In the Köppen symbols *w* = dry season in winter or low-sun period: at least one month with less than 2.4 in. of rain.

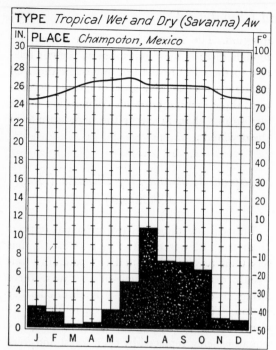

TYPE *Tropical Wet and Dry (Savanna) Aw*
PLACE *Champoton, Mexico*

Fig. 6.7 Average monthly temperatures and precipitation amounts for a station with tropical wet-
and-dry climate (*Aw*) in Mexico at 19°21′N. and
90°43′W.

drums at the time of high sun, and by the
drier parts of the trades and the subtropical
anticyclones at the time of low sun. The result
is rainy "summers" and dry "winters."

6.17 Geographical Location. It becomes
evident from a comparison of Plate 2 and Fig.
A.2 that most of the extensive areas with
tropical wet-and-dry climate actually are
located on the individual continents in approximately the positions suggested in the analyses
of type location which preceded. The Llanos of
the Orinoco Valley (Colombia and Venezuela)
and adjacent parts of the Guiana Highlands in

northern South America; the Campos of Brazil
south of the equator in that same continent; in
Africa the extensive Sudan area north of the
Congo Basin and the veld to the south of it, the
great wet-and-dry area in northern Australia,
and that in tropical southern and southeastern
Asia are all approximately situated as represented on the hypothetical continent (Fig. A.2).
Most parts of these representative areas lie between latitudes 5 or 10° and 15 or 20° and have
a tropical wet climate on their equatorward
sides and a dry climate or a humid subtropical
climate on their poleward frontiers.

6.18 The temperature elements in tropical
wet-and-dry climate and in tropical wet climate
are not greatly unlike. Constantly high temperatures are still the rule, for the noon sun is
never far from a vertical position, and days and
nights change little in length from one part of
the year to another. In general, however, yearly
ranges are somewhat greater (although still
small) than in typical rainforest regions, usually
over 5° but seldom exceeding 15° (Fig. 6.7).
These larger ranges may result from the fact
that the high-sun months are slightly hotter
and the low-sun months are slightly cooler than
in regions nearer the equator (Figs. 6.8 and
6.9).

It is significant that the hottest month or
months many times do not coincide with the
time of highest sun but usually precede it somewhat and thus occur before the height of the
rainy period, when the more persistent cloud
cover and heavier precipitation tend to lower
the temperature. Thus March, April, and possibly May are likely to be hotter than June or
July, which are the rainiest periods for Northern Hemisphere tropical wet-and-dry climate.

Climatic Data for Representative Stations with Tropical Wet-and-Dry Climate

Timbo, French West Africa (10°40′N.)

	J	F	M	A	M	J	J	A	S	O	N	D	Yr.	Range
Temp.	72	76	81	80	77	73	72	72	72	73	72	71	74	9.7
Precip.	0.0	0.0	1.0	2.4	6.4	9.0	12.4	14.7	10.2	6.7	1.3	0.0	64.1	

Calcutta, India

	J	F	M	A	M	J	J	A	S	O	N	D	Yr.	Range
Temp.	65	70	79	85	86	85	83	82	83	80	72	65	78	21
Precip.	0.4	1.1	1.4	2.0	5.0	11.2	12.1	11.5	9.0	4.3	0.5	0.2	58.8	

Cuiabá, Brazil (15°30′S.)

	J	F	M	A	M	J	J	A	S	O	N	D	Yr.	Range
Temp.	81	81	81	80	78	75	76	78	82	82	82	81	80	6.6
Precip.	9.8	8.3	8.3	4.0	2.1	0.3	0.2	1.1	2.0	4.5	5.9	8.1	54.6	

Precipitation

6.19 Amount of Rainfall. Since temperatures are not greatly different within the tropics, rainfall becomes the more critical element in setting apart the several climatic types of the low latitudes. Characteristically, the total amount of rainfall of the wet-and-dry type is less than that of the tropical wet climate, 40 to 60 in. being more typical of the former. But since the wet-and-dry type usually occupies transitional belts between the constantly wet and the constantly dry climates, it naturally follows that there will be considerable contrast between the amount of rainfall on its two margins. As a general rule there is a decrease poleward.

6.20 Rainfall Regime. It is the seasonal distribution rather than the total amount of precipitation, however, which chiefly distinguishes the two climates of the humid tropics, for one is constantly wet while the other has a distinct dry season (Fig. 6.7). This contrast between the two types is principally due to their latitudinal locations, for although the tropical wet type is almost constantly within the intertropical convergence where there is a large-scale ascent of warm, humid, unstable air masses, the wet-and-dry type is on the margins of the I.T.C. and, therefore, in an intermediate position between it and the dry settling air masses of the subtropical anticyclone and the poleward margins of the trades (Fig. 6.1).

The Sudan of northern Africa may be used as a concrete example to clarify further the mechanics of the tropical wet-and-dry rainfall regime. As the sun's vertical rays move northward from the equator after the spring equinox, their thermal effects cause pressure and wind belts to shift in the same direction, although lagging a month or two behind in time. As the I.T.C. with its unstable air masses and heavy

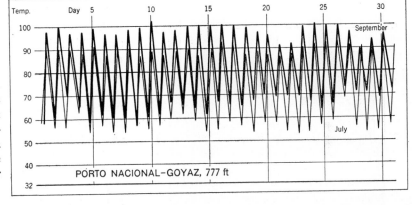

Fig. 6.8 Daily maximum and minimum temperatures for the extreme months at a station with tropical wet-and-dry climate (*Aw*) in Brazil. Note the dominance of the periodic or solar control.

PORTO NACIONAL–GOYAZ, 777 ft

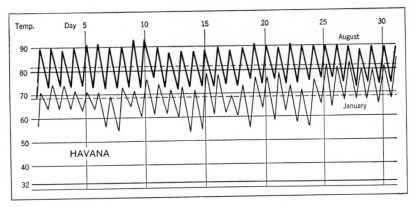

Fig. 6.9 Havana represents a tropical wet-and-dry climate with a strong marine influence. Note that the daily ranges are relatively moderate and there is some evidence of nonperiodic air-mass control of temperatures in January.

HAVANA

rains gradually shifts northward, thunderstorms begin to appear in March and April over the Sudan, and the rainfall continues to increase in amount until July or even August, when the I.T.C. reaches its maximum northward migration. With the southward retreat of the I.T.C., following the sun, the rains decline in amount, until by October or November the dry, settling, stable air masses (subtropical anticyclone and poleward margins of trades) are prevailing over the Sudan, and drought grips the land. The length of the wet and the dry seasons is variable, depending upon distance from the equator.

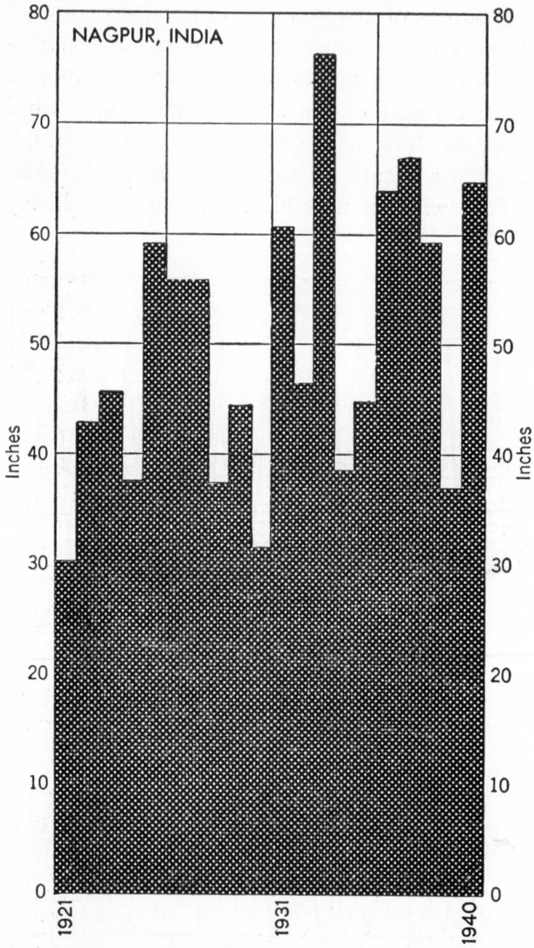

There is no abrupt boundary between the constantly wet and the wet-and-dry climates, but a very gradual transition from one to the other (Fig. 4.16). Thus on the equatorward margins of the wet-and-dry type the rainy season persists for almost the entire year. In such locations there even may be a slight depression at the crest of the precipitation curve, this falling off of the rains occurring in the short interval of time between the northward and southward migrations of the I.T.C. (Fig. 4.17, Zungeru). The farther poleward one travels in the Sudan, the shorter is the period of I.T.C. control and the longer that of the drier settling air masses, so that the dry season increases in length while the wet period shrinks. For the sake of emphasis it bears repeating that the rainy season closely coincides with the period of high sun and the dominance of converging unstable air masses, whereas the dry season is identified with the period of low sun when stable, diverging and subsiding air masses prevail. Most emphatically, rainfall follows the sun. This rule holds for either hemisphere, although it should be kept in mind that December to February is the period of high sun (summer) south of the equator and June to August the period of low sun (winter). It is obvious, therefore, that when a Northern Hemisphere tropical wet-and-dry climate is having its rainy season, a similar region south of the equator is experiencing drought, and vice versa.

6.21 Rainfall Reliability. Not only is rainfall in the tropical wet-and-dry type less in total amount, and more seasonal in its distribution throughout the year, as compared with tropical wet climate, but it is likewise less reliable, there being wider fluctuation in the amounts from year to year. One year may bring such an abundance of rain as to flood the fields, rot the crops, and increase the ravages of injurious insects and fungi, while the following year may witness even more severe losses from drought. In northern Australia the average rainfall variation from the normal is as much as 25 per cent (Fig. 6.10).

Fig. 6.10 Variations in amounts of annual rainfall over a 20-year period at Nagpur, India, a station with tropical wet-and-dry climate. Large annual variations in precipitation are characteristic of this type of climate.

6.22 Seasonal Weather. During its rainy season the weather of tropical wet-and-dry climate closely resembles that of tropical wet climate at its worst. This period usually is ushered in and out by violent thunderstorms and severe squall winds, which in Africa are called tornadoes. In these transition periods the weather is very trying, "violent short deluges of rain and intensely hot sunshine alternating." During the height of the rains violent thunderstorms appear to be less frequent than they are at the transition periods, while on the other hand heavy, long-continued, and more general rains reach their maximum at that time. These latter probably originate in tropical disturbances of the weak-cyclone and wave varieties.

In the low-sun, or dry, season the weather is like that of the deserts. The humidity becomes very low so that the skin is parched and cracked. In spite of the aridity, the dry season is welcomed after the humid, oppressive heat of the rainy period. An occasional shower may occur during the months of drought, the number depending upon which margin of the wet-and-dry type is being considered. On the dry margin the period of absolute drought may be of several months' duration, while on the rainy margin, where it makes contact with tropical wet climate, there may be no month absolutely without rain. During the dry season the landscape is parched and brown, the trees lose their leaves, the rivers become low, the soil cracks, and all nature appears dormant. Smoke from grass fires and dust fill the air, so that visibility is usually low.

The following quotation[6] is a description of the seasonal weather and related landscape changes in a wet-and-dry region. It should be emphasized, in order to avoid confusion, that the region described is Zambezia, Africa, which is *south* of the equator. As a result of Southern Hemisphere location, the months included within the several seasons are exactly opposite from what they are in regions north of the equator.

The winter months, or dry season, extend, with a slight variation, from April to November. They are,

[6] R. C. F. Maugham. "Zambezia." Pp. 383–388. John Murray, London, 1910.

as I have said, pleasant and healthy in the extreme. Now the traveller and hunter of big game make their appearance; the deciduous trees are leafless; the grasses dry, yellow, and ready for the chance spark or deliberate act which, with the aid of a steady breeze, will turn vast expanses of golden grasslands into so many hideous, bare deserts of heat-tremulous black. All nature seems to be at a standstill, hibernating. The rivers are low. Where, but a few short months since, wide, watery expanses rushed headlong toward the sea . . . there now remain but tranquil, placid channels, flowing smilingly at the bottom of steep, cliff-like banks. . . .

With October the heat becomes very great. Vast belts of electrically charged, yellowish clouds, with cumulus, rounded extremities, begin to gather and at the close of day are seen to be flickering in their murky centres with a menacing tremor of constant lightning. This may go on for a week or more, and then Nature arises like a strong man in anger and looses the long pent-up voice of the thunder and the irresistible torrents of the early rains. The first manifestation may come at evening and is a soul-moving display of natural force. . . .

After such a disturbance as the one I have just described, rain is fairly continuous for some time, and the effect of this copious irrigation makes itself felt in every branch of animal and vegetable life. Within a few days the change is startling; the paths and roadways choke themselves with a rich clothing of newly sprung grasses, whilst the trees, the extremities of whose twigs and branches have been visibly swelling, now leap into leaf and blossom. The mosses, which for months past have looked like dry, bedraggled, colourless rags, regain once more their vivid, tender green. Now the forest throws off its puritanical greyness and, with an activity and rapidity beyond belief, decks itself in flowers of a thousand gorgeous shades of colour, from chrome-yellow and purple to grateful mauve.

The birds now put on their finest feathers, the animals appear in their brightest hues. Colour and warmth run riot in the brilliantly clear air now washed clean from the mist and smoke which for so many months have obscured it. The clear verdant green of rapid-springing grasses and opening fronds clothes the landscape, and the distant peaks of the mountains lose their pale, bluey-grey haziness and stand boldly out in the light of the sun. The months succeed each other, bringing with them new and strange beauties, for summer is now at its height, and trees and flowers at their most perfect period. . . . April comes, and suddenly Nature holds her

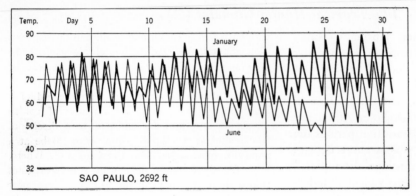

Fig. 6.11 Daily maximum and minimum temperatures for a station with tropical wet-and-dry climate on the Brazilian plateau. Note the lower temperatures imposed by altitude. While solar control is dominant, non-periodic air-mass control is also conspicuous.

hand. The swollen rivers and inundated plains shake themselves free from the redundant waters. The grasses have now reached a formidable height. The rains now cease, and the land begins to dry up. Rich greens turn to copper, and brown, and yellow, and little by little, with the advent of May, the winter returns with its sober greyness.

6.23   Upland Wet-and-dry Climate   (Cw).[7] In tropical latitudes on several continents, but especially Africa and South America, there are extensive upland areas, possessed of many of the normal characteristics of tropical wet-and-dry climates but differing chiefly in their somewhat lower temperatures, which are the result of higher altitude (Fig. 6.11). Some of these uplands, such as those of eastern Brazil and of eastern Africa, are among the best developed tropical areas, for the lower temperatures make them more attractive to agricultural settlers. These uplands are included within the general wet-and-dry type but on Plate 2 are set apart from the more standard lowland variety by a light stippling. (For climatic modifications imposed by altitude, see Chap. 10.)

6.24   Resource Potentialities of the Tropical Wet-and-Dry Realm. Tropical wet-and-dry climate characterizes close to 15 per cent of the

[7] According to the Köppen classification, *Cw* climates appear in two characteristic locations: (*a*) tropical wet-and-dry uplands, where because of altitude the temperature is lowered below that of the surrounding lowlands (*Aw*); and (*b*) mild subtropical monsoon lands such as exist in southern China. It is the first group that is here being classified as the subtype upland savanna. The other group is included within the humid subtropical climates of the middle latitudes.

earth's land area. On a map showing the distribution of the earth's inhabitants, many of the wet-and-dry areas are conspicuous because of their dearth of people. This is especially true of the wet-and-dry regions of the New World and of Australia. Peninsular India is the most striking exception, for there human life is abundant. Portions of the African Sudan and of the upland wet-and-dry areas of East Africa are somewhat intermediate in their population densities.

Although temperatures are constantly high in tropical wet-and-dry climate, the fact that there is a dormant season imposed by drought considerably reduces the productiveness of wet-and-dry, as compared with tropical wet, climate. The smaller total amount of precipitation, and its variability as well, emphasize this contrast still further. Reflecting the reduced climatic energy, the vegetation cover is one of tall coarse grasses with scattered trees and of open forest with grass instead of a dense evergreen forest such as characterizes the tropical wet climate. Much of the woodland is of little value commercially, while the grasses are too tall, coarse, and unnutritious to support an important grazing industry. To the native agriculturist the tough grass sod offers a more formidable obstacle than does the luxuriant rainforest. Little is known about the mature soils of the wet-and-dry climate, but as a general rule they appear to be leached and infertile. There is some evidence that they are inferior to those that develop under the tropical rainforest. As in most regions of infertile or difficult soils, the fresh, young, unleached alluvial surfaces are the most attractive sites for cultivation.

7

The Dry Climates (B)

7.1 Definition and Boundaries of Dry Climates.
The essential feature of a dry climate is that potential evaporation from soil and vegetation shall exceed the average annual precipitation. As a result of rainfall deficiency there is no surplus of water with which to maintain a constant ground-water supply, so that permanent streams cannot originate within such areas. It may be possible, however, for streams to cross them, as do the Nile and the Colorado, for instance, provided they have their sources in more humid regions.

If the above definition of a dry climate, *viz.,* one in which potential evaporation exceeds precipitation, is accepted, then, since evaporation varies greatly in different parts of the earth, it follows that no specific amount of rainfall can be used to bound dry climates over the world as a whole. Potential evaporation is greater in warm than in cold regions, so that while 25 in. of precipitation may be effective in producing a humid landscape with forests in cool northwestern Europe, the same amount falling in the hot tropics results in semiarid conditions. Moreover, if a large amount of the annual precipitation in subtropical climates comes in the warmer months when evaporation is higher, more is lost through evaporation and less is available for plant growth. Thus barley is grown in parts of southern California where the rainfall is not much more than 10 in. and the climate is arid or semiarid. This is possible, however, because the meager precipitation is concentrated in the cool season when evaporation is at a minimum. Its effectiveness for plant growth is therefore great.

7.2 Desert and Steppe.
Two subdivisions of dry climates are commonly recognized: (*a*) the arid, or desert, type and (*b*) the semiarid, or steppe, type. In general, the steppe is in the nature of a transitional belt surrounding the real desert and separating it from the humid climates beyond. The boundary between arid and semiarid climates is a relatively arbitrary one, but by Köppen it is defined as one-half the amount separating steppe from humid climates. For example, if in a particular region 19 in. of rainfall marks the outer, or humid, boundary of dry climates in general, then $9\frac{1}{2}$ in. may be taken as the boundary between steppe and desert for that same region (Fig. A.2). Of all the climatic groups dry climates are the most extensively developed over the continents, occupying as much as 26 per cent of the earth's land surface. By contrast only 4 to 5 per cent of the ocean surface is characterized by dry climate.

7.3 Type Location.
From Fig. A.2 and Plate 2 it can be noted that dry climates are to be found both in the tropics and in the middle latitudes and that commonly the dry climates of low and middle latitudes join to form a continuous area of drought. Apparently drought-making controls exist in a wide range of latitudes.

Dry climates in the tropics are concentrated between latitudes 15–20° and 30°. They are likewise patternfully developed longitudinally in that they are shifted away from the eastern or windward side and toward the interior and the western side of a continent. Here the effects of the strong subsidence and the diverging winds of the subtropical anticyclones are best developed.

In the middle latitudes drought conditions are best developed in the deep interiors of the great land masses, areas which feel the effects of the cold anticyclones of winter and which are farthest removed from the oceanic sources of moisture.

7.4 Temperature. Since dry climates exist in a wide range of latitudes, it is impossible to make valid generalizations regarding their average *annual* temperatures. Some are hot, others cold, and there are still others which are intermediate in character.

On the other hand, dry climates as a class are characterized by relatively severe *seasonal* temperatures compared with the average for any particular latitude. In other words, summers in dry climates are likely to be abnormally warm or hot and winters abnormally cool or cold as compared with the seasonal temperatures of those humid types of climate in the same latitude. Large annual ranges of temperature are representative, therefore. Such seasonal extremes and large annual ranges are related to the leeward and interior locations of most dry climates, and to the prevailingly clear skies and dry atmosphere.

Even more striking, however, are the large *daily* extremes and ranges of temperature, the clear, cloudless skies, and relatively low humidity permitting an abundance of solar energy to reach the earth by day but likewise allowing a rapid loss of earth energy at night. Large diurnal ranges in deserts also are associated with the meager vegetation cover, which permits the dry barren surface to become intensely heated by day. It is a physical law that the higher the temperature of a body, the more rapid is its loss of heat by radiation and consequently the more rapid its reduction in temperature. Deserts, therefore, not only acquire, but likewise lose, heat rapidly. In humid regions with a more complete vegetation cover, more of the solar radiation is consumed in evaporating moisture from plant surfaces and from the damp earth, so that extreme temperatures, like those of deserts, are less likely. Where vegetation is abundant, water vapor is likely to be also, and night cooling is consequently retarded.

7.5 Precipitation and Humidity. Rainfall in the dry climates is always meager. In addition it is extremely variable from year to year so that the average is not to be depended upon (Fig. 7.1). Significantly, also, there are more years when rainfall is below the average than above, for it is the occasional humid year which tends to lift the average. It is a general rule, worthy of memorization, that dependability of precipitation usually decreases with decreasing amount. Two handicaps, therefore, (*a*) meagerness and (*b*) unreliability of rainfall, seem to go together. No part of the earth, so far as is known, is absolutely rainless, although at Arica, in northern Chile, the average yearly rainfall over a period of 17 years was only 0.02 in. During the whole 17 years there were only three showers heavy enough to be measured.

Relative humidity is (with a few exceptions) low in the dry climates, 12 to 30 per cent being usual for midday hours. Conversely, evaporation is extremely high. Absolute humidity, on the other hand, is by no means always low, for hot desert air usually contains a considerable quantity of water vapor, even though it may be far from being saturated. The amount of sunshine is great and cloudiness small. Direct as well as reflected sunlight from the bare, light-colored earth is blinding in its intensity.

7.6 Winds. Dry regions are inclined to be windy places, there being little friction of the moving air with the lowly and sparse vegetation cover. In this respect they are like the oceans. Moreover, the rapid daytime heating of the lower air over deserts leads to convectional overturning, this interchange of lower and upper air tending to accelerate the horizontal surface currents during warm hours when convection is at a maximum. "In the desert the wind is almost the only element of life and movement in the domain of death and immobility. A journey in the desert is a continuous strife against the wind charged with sand and, in moments of crisis, a painful physical struggle." (Gautier.) Nights are inclined to be much quieter. Because of the strong and per-

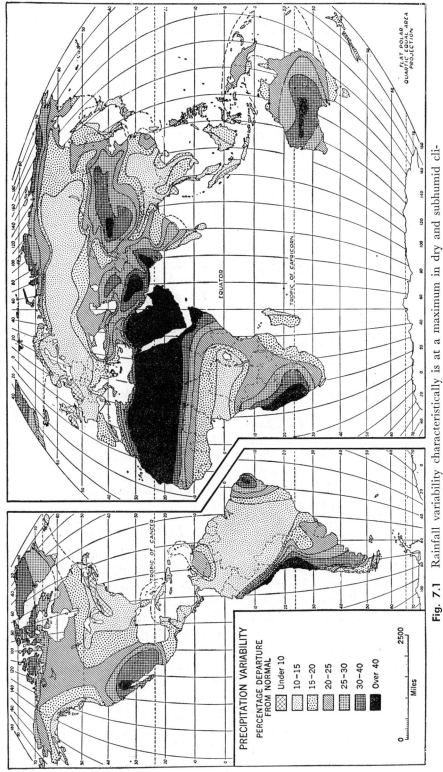

Fig. 7.1 Rainfall variability characteristically is at a maximum in dry and subhumid climates. (*After Biel, Van Royen, and others.*)

PRECIPITATION VARIABILITY

PERCENTAGE DEPARTURE
FROM NORMAL

Under 10
10–15
15–20
20–25
25–30
30–40
Over 40

0   2500
Miles

143

sistent winds, desert air is often murky with fine dust which fills the eyes, nose, and throat, causing serious discomfort. Much of this dust is carried beyond the desert margins to form the loess deposits of bordering regions. The heavier, wind-driven rock particles, traveling close to the surface, are the principal tool of the wind in sculpturing desert landforms.

In the classification of climates here employed, two great divisions of dry climates, based upon temperature contrasts, are recognized: (*a*) the dry climates of the tropical low latitudes, or the *hot* steppes and deserts; and (*b*) the dry climates of the middle latitudes, or the *cold* (in winter) steppes and deserts.[1]

Low-latitude (*Tropical and Subtropical*) Dry Climates (*BWh and BSh*)[2]

7.7   Type Location. The heart of the tropical dry climates (Fig. A.2) is in the vicinity of latitudes 20 or 25°N. and S., with the average positions of their extreme margins at approximately 15°± and 30°±. They are fairly coincident with the abnormally dry subsiding air masses and horizontally diverging wind systems of the subtropical anticyclones (Fig. 6.1). Subsidence and drought are by no means confined to the centers of the anticyclonic cells, for these same characteristics extend out onto the equatorward slopes of the highs into the trade winds. Ordinarily the dry climates do not extend to the eastern margins of the continents, humid climates characteristically taking their places on these windward margins. Here the offshore waters are warm, the subtropical highs are less well developed, and subsidence is not conspicuous. Hurricanes as well as other tropical disturbances add to the rainfall of some of these east coasts.

[1] Köppen uses the mean annual isotherm of 64.4° (18°C.) as the boundary between the two principal latitudinal subdivisions of dry climates. For North America at least, the January isotherm of 32° appears to be a better boundary between the hot and the cold dry climates.

[2] In the Köppen symbols, *W* = desert (*Wüste*); *S* = steppe; *h* = hot (*heiss*): annual temperature over 64.4° (18°C.).

Along west coasts in these latitudes, on the other hand, dry climates extend down to the sea margins and even far beyond over the oceans. Here to the drought-producing effects of strong anticyclonic control are added those of cool ocean currents which characteristically parallel tropical west coasts. These cool ocean currents tend to intensify the aridity and frequently cause steppe and desert conditions to be carried 5 to 10° farther equatorward than normal. It appears to be a general rule, then, that humid tropical climates extend unusually far poleward along the eastern (windward) sides of the continents (eastern Brazil, eastern Central America, eastern Madagascar), while dry climates are carried equatorward beyond their normal latitudes along the western littorals (western Peru, western Angola in southwestern Africa).

7.8   Geographical Location. The most extensive uninterrupted dry area in the tropics and subtropics is that which extends from the Atlantic coast of North Africa eastward for nearly 6,000 miles to northwestern India and Pakistan. This includes the entire breadth of North Africa, Arabia, and much of southwestern Asia. Central and western Australia rank next in extensiveness, with smaller areas of tropical dry climate in southwestern Africa, western South America in Peru and northern Chile, and in northern Mexico and adjacent parts of southwestern United States (Plate 2).

Low-latitude Desert (*BWh*)

7.9 The low-latitude deserts probably are the most nearly rainless regions on the earth. Next to the deserts of snow and ice on the polar ice caps, they are also the most hostile to life. Since they occupy regions of warm, dry, settling, and diverging air currents, conditions are unfavorable for the development of convectional showers. This same divergence is opposed to the development of fronts and cyclonic storms. Moreover the desert air is so dry that rain falling from a cloud is often evaporated before it reaches the earth. Too far equatorward to be reached by the equatorward advance of middle-latitude fronts and cyclones on the poleward side, too far poleward to be affected by the I.T.C. advancing from the low latitudes, and too far interior from eastern littorals to be affected by the onshore winds and tropical disturbances, these low-latitude deserts are outside the realms of the usual rain-bringing winds and storms. Some of the extensive low-latitude deserts, particularly the Sahara and the Australian desert, are large enough to be source regions for tropical continental air masses.

PRECIPITATION AND HUMIDITY

7.10 Annual Rainfall. Although no exact amount of rainfall can be accepted as defining the outer, or humid, margins of the hot deserts, the figure usually lies somewhere between 10 and 20 in. Over much of the Sahara precipitation is under 5 in., a condition true, as well, of large parts of the other low-latitude deserts, *viz.*, Kalahari in South Africa, Atacama-Peruvian desert in western South America, Australian desert, Thar in northwestern India, and Sonora in northwestern Mexico and southwestern United States. At Cairo, Egypt, the annual rainfall averages 1.2; at Lima, Peru, 2; William Creek, Australia, 5.4; Yuma, Ariz., 3.3; and Port Nolloth in southwestern Africa, 2.3 in. In parts of northern Chile rain may not fall for 5 or 10 years in succession..

However, averages are of little value in giving a correct impression of the annual amount and seasonal distribution of desert rainfall, for not only is it small in amount, but it is likewise erratic and uncertain in its time of fall. Over most of the low-latitude deserts the rainfall variability shows a 40+ per cent departure from the normal (Fig. 7.1). It is, therefore, almost impossible to speak of a *typical* rainfall curve, or an *average* annual rainfall, for desert stations. As an illustration: At Iquique in northern Chile, during a period of 4 years, no rain fell. Then on the fifth year one shower gave 0.6 in., which made the "average" annual rainfall for the 5-year period 0.12 in. On another occasion 2.5 in. of rain fell in a single shower.

7.11 Desert Downpours. General, widespread rains are almost unknown over large parts of the hot deserts, most of the precipitation coming in violent convectional showers which cover no very extensive area. Seven single storms brought nearly one-quarter of the total rain (30.7 in.) that fell at Helwan in the Egyptian Sahara in the 20-year period 1904–1924. These sudden and heavy downpours may be disastrous in their effects, causing more damage than they do good. Because of the violence of tropical desert rains and the sparseness of the vegetation cover, temporary local runoff is excessive, and consequently less of the total fall becomes effective for vegetation or for the crops of the oasis farmer. This "dash" character of hot-desert showers, plus their local nature and their erratic seasonal distribution, makes them of little direct use for agriculture, so that no immediate dependence is placed upon them as a source of water.

On the *poleward* margins of low-latitude deserts there are occasional widespread rains of a less violent nature. These are usually associated with the fronts of middle-latitude cyclones and are largely confined to the low-sun period.

7.12 Cloudiness and Sunshine. Skies are prevailing clear in the low-latitude deserts so that sunshine is abundant. In the Sonora desert of the United States and Mexico 75± per cent of the possible sunshine is experienced in winter and 90± per cent in the other seasons. Over much of the Sahara, December and January have a cloudiness of only 1/10, while from June to October it drops to about 1/30. The pitiless glare of sunlight in the tropical deserts is such an essential characteristic of their landscapes that the occasional dark or rainy day, being so unusual, is said to be depressing. Strong surface heating, due to the intense insolation and the nearly bare ground, must give rise to vigorous convectional currents, but the whole mass of air is too stable and has too low a relative humidity to allow these rising air currents, except infrequently, to reach condensation level and produce "thunderheads." Dark cumulonimbus clouds do form occasionally, sometimes accompanied by thunder and lightning, but the streamers of rain that can be seen descending from them usually are evaporated in the arid atmosphere before they reach the earth.

7.13 *Evaporation,* due to the high temperature and low relative humidity, is excessive, often being twenty or more times the precipitation. At Yuma the average evaporation during the hot months is 55 in., while the average rainfall during the same period is not quite 1 in. Relative humidities as low as 2 per cent, with temperatures of over 100°, have been recorded in the Egyptian Sahara. It was the excessively dry air which allowed the Egyptians to mummify their dead.

But even though the air may be *physiologically dry* and have unusual evaporating power, there is usually a moderate amount of moisture in the atmosphere. Thus the air at Yuma, Ariz., contains nearly as much moisture in July, and double as much in January, as does that at Madison, Wis., in the same months, although the relative humidity is only one-half to two-thirds as great in either season.

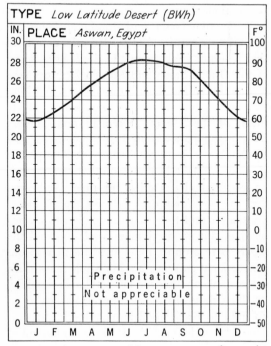

Fig. 7.2 Average monthly temperatures for an interior desert station in low latitudes. Note the relatively large annual range for the latitude.

TEMPERATURE

7.14 Seasonal Temperatures. During the high-sun period scorching, desiccating heat prevails (Fig. 7.2). Hot-month temperatures average between 85 and 95° (Yuma, 91°; Timbuktu, 94.5°; Nullagine, Australia, 90°), and midday readings of 105 to 110° are common at this season. At Yuma, in one summer the daily maxima exceeded 100° for 80 consecutive days, except for one day (Fig. 7.3). At this time of the year, although the lower night temperatures are a distinct relief by contrast with the days, they are by no means cool. At Phoenix, Ariz., the midsummer daily maxima usually exceed 100°, and the minima are close to 75 or 76°. At Azizia, 25 miles south of Tripoli, 136.4° has been recorded, this being the highest air temperature in the shade ever registered under standard conditions. The highest official air temperature ever recorded in the United States is 134°, in Death Valley in the California desert.

During the period of low sun the days still are warm, with the daily maxima usually averaging 65 to 75° and not infrequently reaching 80° (Fig. 7.3). Nights are distinctly chilly at this season, with the average minima in the neighborhood of 45 to 55°. Occasionally light frosts are experienced in these tropical deserts, and heavy night dews are frequent. The average temperature of the winter months commonly is between 50 and 60°.

7.15 Annual and Diurnal Ranges of Temperature. Annual ranges of temperature in the low-latitude deserts are larger than in any other type of climate within the tropics, 20 to 30° being usual (Fig. 7.2). Aswân, in the Sahara, has a mean temperature of 59° in January and 93° in July, resulting in an annual range of 34°. Such ranges, which even exceed those of some middle-latitude climates, reflect not only the clear skies, bare earth, and low humidity but also the higher latitudes of the deserts, and their somewhat greater extremes of insolation, as compared with most of the humid tropics. It should be emphasized that it is the excessive "summer" heat, as well as the "winter" cold,

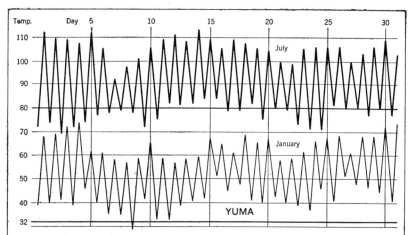

Fig. 7.3 Daily maximum and minimum temperatures at a station with low-latitude desert climate (*BWh*). While solar control is dominant, the nonperiodic airmass control is fairly conspicuous, especially in winter.

which leads to the marked differences between the seasons.

Daily ranges average 25 to 45° and in rare instances even reach 50 or 60°. The same conditions that make for relatively large temperature differences between the extreme months are likewise conducive to wide differences within 24 hr. On Dec. 25, 1878, at Bir Milrha, south of Tripoli in the Sahara, a minimum temperature of 31° and maximum of 99° were recorded on the same day.

7.16 Daily Weather. Sun very much controls the weather in tropical deserts so that one day is much like another. Diurnal regularity of weather is striking (Fig. 7.3). Along the poleward margins of the deserts, which lie close to the middle latitudes, there is somewhat less weather uniformity, especially in winter. This results from the effects of infrequent cyclonic storms whose centers lie farther poleward. Such storms bring occasional overcast days with rain and likewise invasions of cool air from higher latitudes. On the equatorward margins of the deserts occasional convectional showers are experienced during the hot season when the I.T.C. has migrated farthest poleward.

Low-latitude Steppe (*BSh*)

7.17 Location. It is again necessary to emphasize the fact that low-latitude steppe climates characteristically surround the low-latitude deserts, except possibly on their western sides (Fig. A.2), and are, therefore, transition belts between them and the humid climates both to the north and to the south. Because they are less at the heart and more on the margins of the dry, settling tropical air masses associated with subtropical highs and trades, and are, therefore, one step closer to the humid climates than are the deserts, the steppe lands are encroached upon for a short period of the year by rain-bearing winds and their associated storms. It is this brief period of seasonal rains which causes them, although still a dry climate, to be semiarid rather than arid.

PRECIPITATION AND HUMIDITY

7.18 Precipitation Meager and Erratic. Rainfall in the steppes, like that in the deserts, is not only meager but also variable and undependable (Fig. 7.1). This characteristic is perhaps even more dangerous in the semiarid

Climatic Data for Representative Stations in Low-latitude Deserts

	J	F	M	A	M	J	J	A	S	O	N	D	Yr.	Range
						Jacobabad, India								
Temp.	57	62	75	86	92	98	95	92	89	79	68	59	79	41
Precip.	0.3	0.3	0.3	0.2	0.1	0.2	1.0	1.1	0.3	0.0	0.1	0.1	4.0	
						William Creek, Australia								
Temp.	83	83	76	67	59	54	52	56	62	70	77	81	68	30.5
Precip.	0.5	0.4	0.8	0.4	0.4	0.7	0.3	0.3	0.4	0.3	0.4	0.3	5.4	

Climatic Data for a Representative Low-latitude Steppe Station with High-sun Rainfall

Kayes, French West Africa

	J	F	M	A	M	J	J	A	S	O	N	D	Yr.	Range
Temp.	77	81	89	94	96	91	84	82	82	85	83	77	85	19.2
Precip.	0.0	0.0	0.0	0.0	0.6	3.9	8.3	8.3	5.6	1.9	0.3	0.2	29.1	

Climatic Data for a Representative Low-latitude Steppe Station with Low-sun Rainfall

Benghazi, Libya

	J	F	M	A	M	J	J	A	S	O	N	D	Yr.	Range
Temp.	55	57	63	66	72	75	78	79	78	75	66	59	69	24
Precip.	3.7	1.8	0.7	0.1	0.1	0.0	0.0	0.0	0.1	0.3	2.1	3.1	11.9	

than in the arid lands, for in the latter precipitation is never enough to tempt settlers to make agricultural conquest other than at oases, while occasional humid years in the steppe may be sufficiently wet to lure inexperienced persons to attempt it. But a few humid years are invariably followed by more dry ones, and with these comes disaster to settlers who have ventured too far beyond the safety line. Only where irrigation water supplements the normal rainfall is agriculture safe, so that the grazing of animals becomes a more widespread form of land use.

7.19 *Steppes with Low-sun Rainfall.*[3] Those belts of steppe lying on the poleward sides of tropical deserts, and usually in fairly close proximity to Mediterranean climate, have nearly all their rain in the cool seasons. Like the Mediterranean climates on whose margins they lie, they receive their rain from fronts associated with middle-latitude cyclones which, because of sun migration, characteristically travel more equatorward routes in winter than in summer. During most of the year, however, these steppes are dominated by dry settling air masses associated with the subtropical anticyclones. Because rainfall is concentrated in the cool season, evaporation is less, and consequently the small amount that falls is relatively effective for plant growth. Moreover, variability is not so great as in those steppes having a high-sun rainfall maximum. In steppe lands with a low-sun rainfall *spells of weather* associated with the air masses and fronts of passing cyclonic storms are not unusual in the winter season.

[3] Köppen subtype *BShs,* in which *s* stands for summer drought.

Not only cloud and rainfall, but changes in temperature as well, are involved. In spite of winter being the rainiest season, it is nevertheless prevailingly sunny, the precipitation coming in showers of rather short duration. Occasional gray, overcast days with rain do occur, however.

7.20 *Steppes with High-sun Rainfall.*[4] Those tropical steppe lands lying on the equatorward margins of the deserts, and therefore between them and the wet-and-dry type, are likely to have a very brief period of relatively heavy rains at the time of high sun, when unstable *mTu* air and the I.T.C. are farthest poleward. Rainfall periodicity is like that of the tropical wet-and-dry climate except that the dry season is longer and the total precipitation less. Since the rainfall arrives in the hot season less of it is effective for vegetation, and consequently these steppes bordering the savannas usually are characterized by a greater total rainfall and rainfall variability than are their poleward counterparts. Temperatures are not greatly different from those of the adjacent desert.

Cool Marine Dry Climates (Bn)[5]

7.21 **Location.** The normal features of tropical dry climates—hot summers, large annual and diurnal temperature ranges, low humidity and small amount of cloudiness—are modified to a considerable degree along the littorals of a number of tropical deserts where cool ocean currents parallel the coast (Fig. 7.4). The presence of cool currents is especially marked along

[4] Köppen subtype *BShw,* in which *w* stands for winter drought.

[5] *n* = frequent fog (Nebel).

the desert coasts of Peru and northern Chile and the Kalahari in southwestern Africa, but their influence is also felt along the Atlantic coasts of the Moroccan Sahara, northwestern Mexico, and Somaliland in eastern Africa. Most of these regions, it will be noted, are to be found along tropical *west* coasts and centered in latitudes 20 to 30°, although in some instances they may extend equatorward to nearly 10°. These are the latitudes of the stable eastern limbs of the subtropical anticyclones. The Somaliland coast in eastern Africa is the principal exception to west-coast location.

7.22   Temperature. In most of these coastal dry climates three features of temperature are strikingly in contrast to those of tropical dry climates in general: (*a*) summer temperatures are markedly lower, (*b*) the annual range of temperature is greatly reduced, and (*c*) the daily range of temperature is likewise abnormally small (Figs. 7.5 and 7.6; compare Figs. 7.3 and 7.6; see climatic data of Lima). Coastal Peru has annual temperatures as much as 10° lower than those of the Atlantic coast of Brazil in similar latitudes. During the hottest month the temperature at Callao is only 71° (similar to July at Madison, Wis.), while during the coldest month it is 62.5°. This annual range of only 8.5° is extraordinarily small for a desert, but it needs to be emphasized that it is principally the result of the unusually cool summer. The daily range of temperature at Mollendo, Peru, is only about 10°, or from one-third to one-half that of a normal dry-climate station (Fig. 7.6).

7.23   Precipitation and Fog. Rainfall along these cool tropical coasts is extremely low (2.3 in. at Port Nolloth in southwestern Africa, 1.2 in. at Callao in Peru), even lower than in the great interior continental deserts, and the drought conditions may extend to within a few degrees of the equator. The intensified aridity

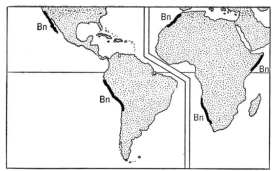

Fig. 7.4   Distribution of cool coastal dry climates (*Bn*) in the tropics. Here fog is prevalent. Characteristically this subtype of tropical dry climates is located along coasts paralleled by cool ocean currents.

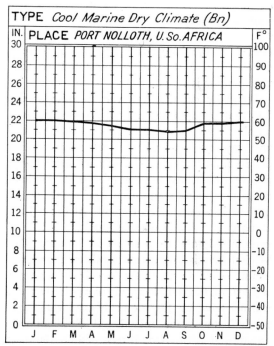

Fig. 7.5   Average monthly temperatures for a marine desert station located on a coast paralleled by a cool ocean current. Temperatures are abnormally low and the annual range is very small. Compare with Fig. 7.2.

Climatic Data for a Representative Desert Station on a Cool-water Coast

Lima, Peru

	J	F	M	A	M	J	J	A	S	O	N	D	Yr.	Range
Temp.	71	73	73	70	66	62	61	61	61	62	66	70	66	12.8
Precip.	0.0	0.0	0.0	0.0	0.0	0.2	0.3	0.5	0.5	0.1	0.0	0.0	1.8	

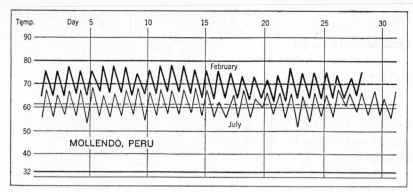

Fig. 7.6 Daily maximum and minimum temperatures for a low-latitude desert station located on a coast paralleled by a cool ocean current. Note the abnormally low average temperatures and the small daily ranges. Compare with Fig. 7.3.

is the result of two phenomena: (*a*) these tropical western littorals are under the influence of the eastern ends of the oceanic subtropical high-pressure cells with their subsiding and drying air, and (*b*) they are paralleled by cool ocean currents. As warm air from over the tropical ocean proper drifts landward over the cool waters closer to the coast, the *mT* air is chilled at the base, its lapse rate is thereby decreased, and its stability increased, so that precipitation is very unlikely.

Peculiarly enough, however, in spite of the fact that precipitation is very meager, there is an abundance of low stratus cloud so that skies are gray and the brilliant sunshine of normal deserts is uncommon. The relative humidity is also very high, and fog and even mist are characteristic phenomena over the cool ocean current and the adjacent coasts. At Cape Juby in northwest Africa relative humidity is 91 per cent in July and 82 per cent in January. The foggiest belt is several miles offshore, and the condition is brought to the land by winds from the sea. As the cool, foggy air moves in over the warmer land, the fog is quickly evaporated and rarely extends far inland. At Swakopmund (Southwest Africa) fog is recorded on 150 days in the year. Sea breezes along these coasts, intensified by the cool ocean water offshore, are extraordinarily strong.

In Peru the heavy fog, or "wet mist," is sufficient to make for a meager showing of vegetation on the coastal hills. Darwin, in his book "The Voyage of the Beagle," describes these Peruvian mists as follows:

A dull heavy bank of clouds constantly hung over the land, so that during the first sixteen days I had only one view of the Cordillera behind Lima. It is almost become a proverb that rain never falls in the lower part of Peru. Yet this can hardly be considered correct; for during almost every day of our visit there was a thick drizzling mist which was sufficient to make the streets muddy and one's clothes damp; this the people are pleased to call "Peruvian dew."

In occasional years these desert west coasts, more especially the sections closest to the equator, may have their cool desert climate terminated abruptly and the high temperatures and heavy rainfall of the tropical wet climate established in its place. These climatic reversals are the result of the weakening or poleward displacement of the high-pressure cell and a substitution of warm water for the prevailingly cool current. The temporary, abnormal conditions are quickly ended with the reestablishment of the high-pressure cell and the cool ocean current.

Middle-latitude Dry Climates (*BWk* and *BSk*)[6]

7.24 Location. The middle-latitude steppes and deserts are less the result of location within a particular pressure or wind system than are those of low latitudes. Dry climates in the middle latitudes usually are found in the deep interiors of the great continents, far from the oceans, which are the principal sources of the atmosphere's water vapor (Fig. A.2, Plate 2). Asia, the greatest land mass in the middle latitudes, has the largest area of dry climates, and North America is next in order. Further in-

[6] In the Köppen symbol k = cold (*kalt*): average annual temperature below 64.4° (18°C.).

tensifying the aridity of these deep interiors is the fact that they are largely surrounded by mountain or plateau barriers that block the entrance of humid maritime air masses. Where high mountains closely parallel a coast as in western North America, arid climates approach relatively close to the sea.

Although tropical dry climates characteristically extend down to the ocean margins on the leeward (western) sides of continents, the leeward (eastern) sides of land masses in the westerlies may be far from dry. Witness, for example, eastern North America and Asia. This shifting of middle-latitude dry climates interior from the leeward coasts is associated with the presence of monsoons and cyclonic storms along the eastern sides of land masses in the westerlies. Owing to an unusual combination of circumstances, dry climates do reach the east coast in Patagonia (Argentina), but this is the exception. There the land mass is so narrow that all of it lies in the rain shadow of the Andes, where descending currents make for drought conditions. This same small land mass precludes the development of onshore monsoon winds in summer. The cool Falkland Current lying offshore may likewise induce aridity, while the principal frontal zones are to the north and south of the area in question. Moreover, those storms that do cross the high Andes temporarily are so disrupted that they are unable to bring much rain to the Patagonian uplands. With the exception of South America, none of the other Southern Hemisphere continents extends into sufficiently high latitudes to permit the development of very extensive middle-latitude steppes and deserts.

7.25 Temperature. Although dry continental climates of middle latitudes duplicate the arid and semiarid climates of the tropics in their meager and undependable rainfall, they differ from them in having a season of severe cold, which is of course absent in the low latitudes (Fig. 7.7). On the other hand, they are like the *humid* continental climates of comparable latitudes in their temperature and weather characteristics but they are unlike them in that they receive less rainfall.

The interior locations of most middle-latitude dry climates assure them of having relatively severe seasonal temperatures and consequently large annual ranges. Because they have such a wide latitudinal spread (15 or 20° in both North America and Asia) it is difficult to speak of *typical* temperature conditions, for they are very different on their equatorward and poleward margins. Yet for any given latitude temperatures are severe. Summers are inclined to be warm or even hot, and winters are correspondingly cold. The temperature at Tashkent, U.S.S.R., at 41°N. ranges from 32° in January to 81° in July, while for Urga, Mongolia, at 48°N. the comparable figures are −16 and 63°. Diurnal ranges are inclined to be large and for the same reasons as noted in the discussion on tropical steppes and deserts (Figs. 7.7 and 7.8).

7.26 Precipitation. Locational reasons for the aridity of middle-latitude dry climates have been given in Art. 7.24. An additional reason for winter drought in these regions is the well-developed winter anticyclones that cover all but

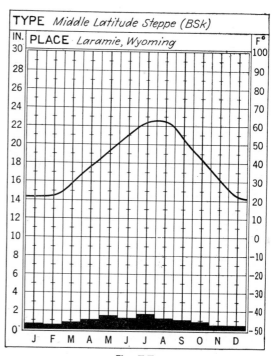

Fig. 7.7

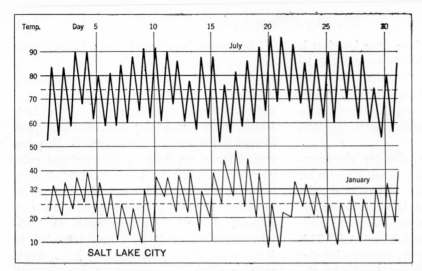

Fig. 7.8 Daily maximum and minimum temperatures for a middle-latitude steppe station (*BSk*). Note the strong nonperiodic air-mass control, especially in winter.

their subtropical margins. In winter, therefore, they become source regions for dry, cold, continental air masses. Unlike the dry climates of the tropics, those of middle latitudes receive a portion of their precipitation in the form of snow, although the amount is characteristically small, and the winter snow cover is not deep.

Seasonal Distribution. It is not easy to generalize concerning seasonal distribution of precipitation in the dry climates of middle latitudes. In the more interior and continental locations, however, summer is usually the period of maximum precipitation (see data for Urga and Williston). This is related to the higher temperatures, greater absolute humidity, and inblowing system of monsoonal winds in summer. Most of interior Asia and the Great Plains region of the United States are dry lands with a distinct summer maximum in their precipitation curves. Urga, Mongolia, for example, receives 84 per cent of its 7.6 in. of rainfall in the three summer months.

On the other hand, those dry climates which occupy subtropical latitudes and lie on the interior margins of Mediterranean climate, are likely to have dry summers and wetter winters (see data for Fallon, Nev., and Quetta, Pakistan). This is the typical Mediterranean regime of rainfall and is particularly characteristic of west margins of continents in the lower middle latitudes. The dry lands of southwestern Asia—Anatolia, Iran, Mesopotamia—most perfectly represent this subtropical type with winter pre-

cipitation. In the Great Basin of the United States it is present in less ideal form (see climatic data, page 153).

7.27 The Weather Element. The nonperiodic weather element in middle-latitude dry climates is much stronger than it is in those of the tropics (Fig. 7.8). This is to be expected, because the middle latitudes are open to invasion by air masses from both the tropics and the polar regions, and cyclones and fronts are therefore better developed. Over large parts of the middle-latitude dry climates, where the winter continental anticyclones are strong, the weather of that season is inclined to be clear, cold, and relatively calm. The occasional passage of well-developed fronts may be accompanied by strong winds and snow. On the North American Plains this weather type is the famous blizzard. Low temperatures, high wind velocity, and blinding wind-driven snow make such storms dangerous to human beings as well as to livestock. Summers are hot and windy, but the irregular weather changes associated with cyclones and their fronts are less striking.

Middle-latitude Deserts (BWk) [7]

7.28 Because of their generally lower temperature, and therefore reduced evaporation rate, the humid boundaries of the middle-latitude deserts have lower rainfalls than those of tropical deserts. This does not mean that

[7] See footnote on p. 150 for interpretation of symbol.

they are necessarily more arid. In fact the opposite is probably true, for some precipitation, no doubt, falls in middle-latitude deserts every year, so that they are not so generally rainless as are certain of their tropical counterparts. Characteristically, this subtype of the middle-latitude dry climates occupies the low-altitude basinlike areas in the continental interiors. Tarim, the Gobi, Dzungaria, Russian Turkistan, and central Iran are all of them surrounded, in part at least, by highland rims. Such is likewise the case with the principal desert area in the United States, where it practically coincides with the Great Basin. As a result, these are regions of rain shadow with descending currents, so that excessive aridity is developed. A further consequence of enclosure, when combined with low elevation, is the excessively high summer temperatures, with warm-month averages in some instances even approaching those of tropical deserts. At Turfan, in the Turfan depression of Central Asia, the July average is 90°, while the daily maxima for that month often rise to 110° and more, although this is an extreme case. At this same station, where 118° has been recorded, the January mean is only 13°.

Patagonia, in the Argentine, does not correspond in some respects to the description given above for middle-latitude deserts. Being a narrow land mass, with cool waters offshore, temperatures are more marine than continental, summer temperatures being unusually low. Winters are likewise mild, considering the latitude. Thus Santa Cruz at 50°S. has a January (hottest month) temperature of only 59°, while in July it is 35°.

Middle-latitude Steppes (BSk)

7.29 Middle-latitude steppes, like their counterparts the semiarid lands of the tropics, occupy transitional, or intermediate, positions between deserts and the humid climates (Figs. 7.7 and A.2). The general characteristics of these continental steppes have already been analyzed. Because of the greater precipitation than in deserts, the steppes are somewhat better fitted for human settlement, but this, together with the unreliable nature of the rainfall, also makes them regions of greater economic catastrophe (Figs. 7.1 and 7.9). A succession of humid years may tempt settlers to push the agricultural frontier toward the desert, but here also drought years are sure to follow, with consequent crop failure and ensuing disaster. Years with below-normal rainfall are more numerous than those in which it is above. Over a considerable part of the American semiarid country, in 30 to 40 per cent of the years, rainfall is less than 85 per cent of the average. During the period 1871–1920, at Ogden, Utah, whose average annual precipitation is 15.2 in.., there was one year with rainfall as high as 25 in. and another as low as 6.5.

A unique feature of the North American steppe lands east of the Rocky Mountains, from Alberta to Colorado, is the frequency and strength of chinook winds. Rapid changes in temperature over short periods of time and large variations in the mean winter temperatures of different years are the result.

7.30 Resource Potentialities of the Dry Realm. Dry climates are characteristic of over one-quarter of the earth's land surface, a pro-

Climatic Data for Representative Stations in Middle-latitude Deserts

Santa Cruz, Argentina

	J	F	M	A	M	J	J	A	S	O	N	D	Yr.	Range
Temp.	59	58	55	48	41	35	35	38	44	49	53	56	47.5	24
Precip.	0.6	0.4	0.3	0.6	0.6	0.5	0.7	0.4	0.2	0.4	0.5	0.9	6.1	

Turfan, Sinkiang, China (−56 Ft.)

	J	F	M	A	M	J	J	A	S	O	N	D	Yr.	Range
Temp.	13	27	46	66	75	85	90	85	74	56	33	18	56	77
Precip.	No data													

Fallon, Nev. (3,965 Ft.)

	J	F	M	A	M	J	J	A	S	O	N	D	Yr.	Range
Temp.	31	36	41	50	56	65	74	72	61	51	40	32	50.6	42.7
Precip.	0.6	0.5	0.5	0.4	0.6	0.3	0.1	0.2	0.3	0.4	0.3	0.6	4.7	

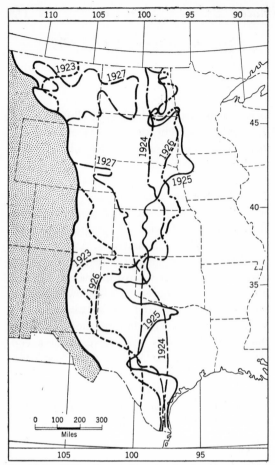

Fig. 7.9 Wide fluctuations in the location of the boundary separating dry from humid climates over a period of 5 years in the region east of the Rocky Mountains. (*After Kendall.*)

ducing precipitation from clouds composed of supercooled water droplets by seeding them with powdered dry ice seems to have revived the hope that man eventually will be able to cause abundant rains to fall in dry climates. This likelihood appears to be exceedingly remote, however, for to begin with, nature must first produce the clouds before man has a chance of stimulating precipitation, and thick clouds are uncommon features in arid lands. Up to the present time, also, it is only clouds whose top portions, at least, contain supercooled droplets which have been made to yield precipitation artificially, and such clouds are still more rare. What is more, a considerable part of the precipitation falling from clouds in dry climates would be evaporated before reaching the earth's surface.

Further reducing the effectiveness of the meager dry-land precipitation is its great variability from year to year and the pelting nature of the few rains that do fall. Pelting rains are relatively ineffective because such a small proportion enters the ground where it can be used by plants, while a large part disappears in the form of surface runoff thereby causing destructive gullying and slope wash. It would appear as though the expansion of settlement in lands with dry climates will be associated with (*a*) an increased use of irrigation methods and (*b*) the further development and greater use of drought-resistant plants and their cultivation by dry-farming methods. One can scarcely be optimistic, however, about the promise that either of these methods holds for opening up extensive areas of dry land for future agricultural settlement.

The niggardly climate is responsible for a sparse vegetation cover which has relatively low resource value. Some deserts are almost barren wastes, practically devoid of plants having economic value. Other deserts have a thin mantle of widely spaced woody shrubs with some short desert bunch grass. The grazing value of this vegetation is very low. Over the desert area of southwestern United States, more than 75 acres are required to supply natural forage for 1 steer. In the semiarid

portion larger than for any of the other climatic groups. It is unfortunate that such an unproductive climate should be so extensively distributed. For the most part dry climates are coincident with great gaps or blank spaces on the world-population map. In this respect they are like the thinly populated wet tropics and the cold polar and subarctic lands. These three —the dry, the cold, and the constantly hot climates—offer the greatest obstacles to a large-scale redistribution of population on the earth.

Owing to insufficient rainfall it appears that a large part of the earth's land surface is doomed to remain relatively unproductive, the most arid parts of it even barren wastes. Very recently the success attained in artificially pro-

Climatic Data for Representative Stations in Middle-latitude Steppes

Williston, N.D.

	J	F	M	A	M	J	J	A	S	O	N	D	Yr.	Range
Temp.	6	8	22	43	53	63	69	67	56	44	27	14	39.2	62.7
Precip.	0.5	0.4	0.9	1.1	2.1	3.2	1.7	1.7	1.0	0.7	0.6	0.5	14.4	

Quetta, Pakistan (5,500 Ft.)

	J	F	M	A	M	J	J	A	S	O	N	D	Yr.	Range
Temp.	40	41	51	60	67	74	78	75	67	56	47	42	58.1	38.2
Precip.	2.1	2.1	1.8	1.1	0.3	0.2	0.5	0.6	0.1	0.1	0.3	0.8	10.0	

Urga, Mongolia (3,800 Ft.)

	J	F	M	A	M	J	J	A	S	O	N	D	Yr.	Range
Temp.	−16	−4	13	34	48	58	63	59	48	30	8	−17	28	79
Precip.	0.0	0.1	0.0	0.0	0.3	1.7	2.6	2.1	0.5	0.1	0.1	0.1	7.6	

regions, or the steppes, short, shallow-rooted, widely spaced grasses prevail. This steppe vegetation has a considerably higher grazing value than has the desert shrub, so that it is capable of supporting more livestock per unit area. Although the humid margins of some middle-latitude steppes have been brought under the plow, it appears that the meager and unreliable rainfall will tend to keep the larger part of the world's steppe lands out of cultivation and in natural grasses. Grass, the greatest natural asset of the steppes, forms the basis for a grazing industry, but grazing is an economy which is able to support only a meager population.

Soils are of little consequence in deserts largely because the deficient rainfall makes it impossible to use them for agricultural purposes. In the middle-latitude steppes the very modest amount of leaching and the humus derived from the root mat of the grasses make for dark fertile soils of high resource value. Unfortunately this admirable soil resource of middle-latitude semiarid lands cannot be exploited to anything like its capacity because of the precipitation handicap. It is the old story of fruitful soils and prolific climates seldom being areally coincident. Soils of the tropical steppes appear to be inferior to those of the semiarid lands in middle latitudes.

8

The Humid Mesothermal¹ Climates (C)

8.1   General Character and Type Locations.
Lacking the constant heat of the tropics and the constant cold of the polar caps, middle-latitude climates, of which mesothermal is one group, are characterized by a very definite seasonal rhythm in temperature conditions. Thus temperature becomes coequal with rainfall in determining the various types of middle-latitude climates. In the tropics seasons are designated as wet and dry; in the middle latitudes they are called winter and summer, and the dormant season for plant growth usually is one of low temperature rather than of drought.

In the intermediate zones the changeableness of the weather is a striking characteristic. This results from the fact that the middle latitudes are the natural region of conflict for contrasting air masses expelled from the tropical and polar source regions. Other than the equatorial region, they are the only great zones of horizontal air convergence. As a consequence cyclonic storms and fronts, with their accompanying weather changes, are numerous. The science of weather forecasting is best developed and most useful in the intermediate zones where irregular and nonperiodic weather changes are the rule.

Since winters in mesothermal climates of necessity must be relatively mild, the climates of this group are found only in those type locations which preclude severe and long continued winter cold. They are, as a consequence, restricted either (*a*) to the equatorward margins of the middle-latitude continents where

latitude ensures winter mildness or (*b*) to marine locations, usually on the windward or western side of continents farther poleward (Figs. A.2 and 8.1). Two of the mesothermal climates, *dry-summer subtropical* and *humid subtropical*, occupy the first of the type locations mentioned above, while the third, *marine climate*, is typically found in the second.

Dry-summer Subtropical Climate (Cs)² *(Mediterranean)*

8.2   General Features. In its simplest form this climate is characterized by three striking features: (*a*) a concentration of the modest amount of precipitation in the winter season, summers being nearly or completely dry; (*b*) warm to hot summers and unusually mild winters; and (*c*) a high percentage of the possible sunshine for the year and especially in summer. Quite deservedly this climate with its bright, sunny weather, blue skies, few rainy days, and mild winters, and its usual association with abundant flowers and fruit, has acquired a glamorous reputation. It has the unique distinction of being the only one of the earth's humid climates having drought in summer with a strong rainfall maximum in winter. The dry-summer subtropical type is strongly marked in its climatic characteristics, these being duplicated with notable similarity in the five regions where it occurs, *viz.*, the borderlands of the Mediterranean Sea, central and coastal south-

---

¹ Meso-, from Greek *mesos,* middle. Mesothermal, therefore, refers to "middle," or moderate, temperatures.

² In the Köppen symbol, *s* = dry season in summer of the respective hemisphere.

ern California, central Chile, the southern tip of South Africa, and parts of southern Australia.

8.3 Type Location. Mediterranean climate characteristically is located on the tropical margins of the middle latitudes (30–40°) along the western sides of continents. Lying thus on the poleward slopes of the subtropical high, it is intermediate in location between the dry subsiding air masses of the subtropical anticyclone, on the one hand, and the rain-bringing fronts and cyclones of the westerlies, on the other. With the north-south shifting of wind belts during the course of the year, these Mediterranean latitudes at one season are joined to the dry tropics and at the other season to the humid middle latitudes. Tropical constancy, therefore, characterizes them in summer, and middle-latitude changeability in winter. Emphatically, this is a transition type between the low-latitude steppes and deserts and the cool, humid, marine climates farther poleward.

As previously stated, Mediterranean climates are usually confined to the *western* sides of continents, roughly between latitudes 30 and 40° (Fig. A.2, Plate 2). Here they feel the strong subsidence characteristic of the eastern limb of the anticyclone. In both central Chile and California, mountains terminate the type abruptly on the land side, steppe and desert prevailing interior from the mountains. In South Africa and southwestern Australia the farthest poleward extent of these continents carries them barely to Mediterranean latitudes, so that the dry-summer subtropical climate occupies southern and southwestern extremities rather than distinctly west-coast locations. Only in the region of the Mediterranean Basin, which is an important route of winter cyclones, does this type of climate extend far inland, perhaps for 2,000 miles or more, the extensive development there being responsible for the climate's regional name. It is the relative warmth of the Mediterranean Sea in winter, and the resulting low-pressure trough coincident with it, that makes the Mediterranean Basin a region of air-mass convergence with a resulting development of fronts and cyclones. Interiors and eastern margins of continents, where the summer

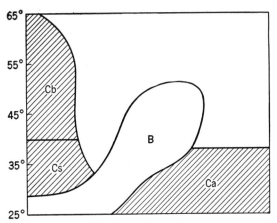

Fig. 8.1 Type locations of the three mesothermal types of climate (*C*) on a hypothetical continent.

anticyclone is relatively weak, and where there is a tendency toward a monsoon wind system, are not conducive to the development of Mediterranean climate, more especially its characteristic rainfall regime.

TEMPERATURE

8.4 Mild Winters. Both because of its latitudinal location and because of its characteristic

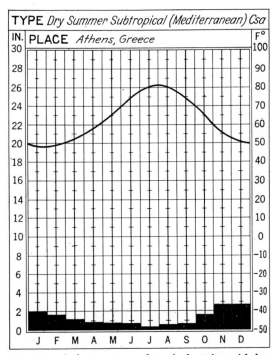

Fig. 8.2 A dry-summer subtropical station with hot summer (*Csa*).

157

position on the continents, Mediterranean climate is assured of a temperature regime in which cold weather is largely absent (Fig 8.2). Usually the winter months have average temperatures of between 40 and 50°, and the summer months between 70 and 80°, so that mean annual ranges of 20 to 30°+ are common. These are relatively small for the middle latitudes but are larger than those of most tropical climates, except possibly the low-latitude steppes and deserts.

8.5 Subdivisions of Dry-summer Subtropical Climate. Based principally upon the degree of summer heat, which in turn is a function of location, two subdivisions of this climate are recognized: (a) an interior subtype with hot summers (*Csa*) and (b) a coastal subtype with cooler summers (*Csb*).[3]

[3] In the Köppen symbols *Csb* and *Csa*, the letter *b* indicates cool summers with the temperature of the warmest month under 71.6° (22°C.) but with at least 4 months over 50° (10°C.). The letter *a* indicates hot summers with the temperature of the warmest month over 71.6° (22°C.).

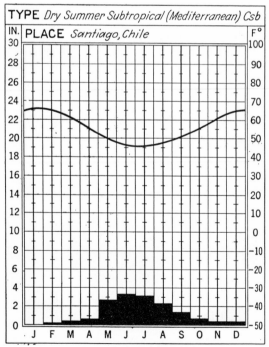

Fig. 8.3 A Southern Hemisphere dry-summer subtropical station with cool summer (*Csb*).

8.6 Marine Locations (*Csb*). Littoral locations are likely to have somewhat modified Mediterranean conditions. Summers are unusually cool, owing partly to the general marine location, but this condition many times is accentuated by the cool ocean currents offshore (Figs. 8.3 and 8.4; see data for Santa Monica, page 161). Thus Mogador, on the Atlantic coast of Morocco, has a hot-month temperature of only 68°, while San Francisco records only 59°, and Valparaiso, Chile, 66°. Fogs are frequent, as they are along the desert coasts somewhat farther equatorward. Winters are unusually mild, frost being practically unknown. Thus the average cool-month temperature at Valparaiso, Chile, is 55°; Perth, Australia, 55°; and San Francisco, 50°. In such marine locations the annual temperature range is uncommonly small, approximately 9° at San Francisco and 11° at Valparaiso. Daily ranges are likewise small (Fig. 8.4).

8.7 Interior Locations (*Csa*). Interior from the coast a short distance, however, Mediterranean climate has a more continental temperature regime (Figs. 8.2 and 8.5; see data for Red Bluff, page 161). Winters, of course, are still mild, for the latitude is distinctly subtropical, and in most regions mountains or bodies of water protect against strong importations of low temperatures from higher latitudes. Redlands, an interior station in California, has a January temperature of 51°, which is only slightly cooler than coastal stations in similar latitudes.. Summers, however, are distinctly hotter than in marine locations (July at Redlands, 77°; Santa Monica, on the coast, 66°) so that annual ranges may be 15°± greater.

8.8 Summer Temperatures. Except along cool-water coasts, summer temperatures in dry-summer subtropical climates have many resemblances to those of tropical steppes and deserts slightly farther equatorward. Thus, Red Bluff in the Sacramento Valley has a July temperature of 81.5°, which is distinctly tropical in nature and approximately 16° higher than the July average at Santa Monica, Calif., farther south but situated on a cool-water coast. Stations in Mediterranean Europe have average

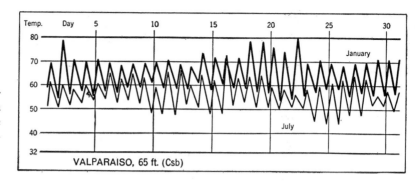

Fig. 8.4 A coastal dry-summer subtropical station in Chile (*Csb*). Note the small diurnal range of temperature and the cool summer.

VALPARAISO, 65 ft. (Csb)

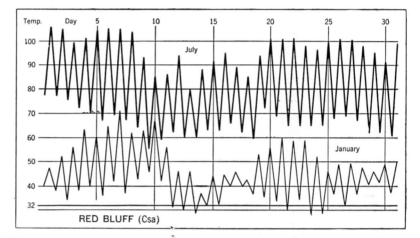

Fig. 8.5 An interior dry-summer subtropical station (*Csa*). Note the hot summer and the large diurnal range of temperature. Solar control is dominant in summer, but irregular, nonperiodic air-mass control is conspicuous in winter.

RED BLUFF (Csa)

hot-month temperatures approximating 75°; those of North Africa are in the neighborhood of 80°. Summer days, quite obviously, are likely to be excessively warm (Fig. 8.5). On the other hand, they are not sultry, for relative humidity is low. Dry heat like that of the steppes and deserts is the rule, and oppressive, muggy weather is almost unknown.

The averages of the daily maxima of cities in the Great Valley of California are usually between 85 and 95°+. Sacramento in a year selected at random had 27 days in July and 16 days in August with maxima over 90°; while the respective figures for Red Bluff were 30 and 30 days. Sacramento has recorded a temperature as high as 114°, and Red Bluff 115°. The clear skies, dry atmosphere, and nearly vertical sun are ideal for rapid and strong diurnal heating.

However, these conditions that give rise to high midday temperatures with a blazing sun are at the same time conducive to rapid nocturnal cooling, so that there is marked contrast between day and night. This feature is typical of most dry climates. At Sacramento, in the Great Valley, hot, clear summer days, with afternoon temperatures 85 to 100° and over, are followed by nights when the thermometer sinks to between 55 and 60°. The daily range in July for this same city is 30 to 40°, figures thoroughly characteristic of deserts. The relatively cool nights, following hot glaring days, are much appreciated by the inhabitants of Mediterranean climates (Fig. 8.5). A light overcoat may feel distinctly comfortable when motoring on a summer night. One 24-hr. period is usually much like another in summer, for sun is in control.

8.9   Winter Temperatures. It is for the characteristically mild bright winters, with delightful living temperatures, that Mediterranean climates are justly famed. Peoples of the higher latitudes seek them out as winter playgrounds and health resorts. Even interior locations have average cold-month temperatures 10 to 20° above freezing. Thus Sacramento has an **aver-**

159

age January temperature of 46°, Marseille 43°, and Rome 44°. In southern California, in January, midday temperatures rise to between 55 and 65° and at night drop to 40°± (Figs. 8.4 and 8.5).

8.10 Frost. The growing season is not quite the whole year, for frosts occasionally do occur during the three winter months. To say that the growing season is 9± months does not, however, adequately describe the situation, for while freezing temperatures are by no means unknown during mid-winter months, they occur on only relatively few nights, and rarely are they severe. During a period of 41 years at Los Angeles, there were 28 in which no killing frost occurred; in other words, the growing season was 12 months in length. During a recent January at Red Bluff, Calif., there were 10 nights, and at Sacramento 7, when the temperature dropped below 32°. The lowest temperature ever recorded at Los Angeles is 28°, at Naples 24°, and at Sacramento 17°. Even on the very occasional nights when temperatures do slip a few degrees below freezing, the following day sees them well above 32° again. Never does the thermometer stay below the freezing point for the entire day. Such frosts as do occur

Temperatures for Selected Mediterranean Cities*

	Av. Annual Minimum	Absolute Minimum	Av. Annual Maximum	Absolute Maximum
Valencia	31	19	99	109
Naples	30	24	94	99
Athens	29	20	100	105

* W. G. Kendrew. "The Climates of the Continents," 3d ed. P. 246. Oxford University Press, New York, 1942.

are usually the result of local surface cooling, following an importation of *cP* air, the low temperatures being confined to a shallow layer of surface atmosphere and particularly to depressions in which the cool dense air has collected. For this reason such sensitive crops as citrus are characteristically planted on slopes. Occasionally fires may be lighted among the citrus trees in order to prevent serious damage from freezing. Upon first thought it may seem odd that in Mediterranean climates, where frosts

are neither frequent nor severe, unusual losses should result from low temperatures. But it is this infrequency and the small degree of frost that make it so treacherous, since the mild winters tempt farmers to grow types of crops, such as out-of-season vegetables and citrus, that are particularly sensitive to cold.

PRECIPITATION

8.11 Amount and Distribution. Rainfall is generally less than moderate, 15 to 25 in. being a fair average. More characteristic than the amount of rain, however, is its distribution over the year, for there is a pronounced maximum during the cooler months, summer being nearly, if not absolutely, dry (Figs. 8.2 and 8.3). If the relatively modest amount of rain typical of dry-summer subtropical climate fell in the hot summers when evaporation is high, semiarid conditions would be the result. But coming as it does in the cooler seasons, much less is evaporated, and more, therefore, is available for vegetation. As a result, Mediterranean climate is more correctly described as subhumid than as semiarid. The name *dry-summer subtropical* is useful, therefore, in distinguishing this climate from its wetter counterpart, the *humid subtropical climate* located on the eastern sides of continents in similar latitudes.

Over three-quarters of the precipitation in Los Angeles falls during the period December to March, and 2 per cent during June to September. The rainfall regime, therefore, is alternately that of the deserts in summer and of the cyclonic westerlies in winter when rain is relatively abundant. This seasonal alternation of drought and rain results from the latitudinal shifting of air-mass control and rain belts following the sun, poleward in summer, bringing Mediterranean latitudes under the influence of the subtropical anticyclone, and equatorward in winter when they are brought within the zone of middle-latitude fronts and cyclones. Rainfall therefore is chiefly of frontal or cyclonic origin (Fig. 8.6).

Lying as they do between the dry climates on their equatorward sides and the rainy marine climate farther poleward, dry-summer sub-

Climatic Data for Representative Dry-summer Subtropical Stations

Red Bluff, Calif. (Interior)

	J	F	M	A	M	J	J	A	S	O	N	D	Yr.	Range
Temp.	45	50	54	59	67	75	82	80	73	64	54	46	62.3	36.3
Precip.	4.6	3.9	3.2	1.7	1.1	0.5	0.0	0.1	0.8	1.3	2.9	4.3	24.3	

Santa Monica, Calif. (Coast)

	J	F	M	A	M	J	J	A	S	O	N	D	Yr.	Range
Temp.	53	53	55	58	60	63	66	66	65	62	58	55	59.5	13.6
Precip.	3.5	3.0	2.9	0.5	0.5	0.0	0.0	0.0	0.1	0.6	1.4	2.3	14.78	

Perth, Australia (Coast)

	J	F	M	A	M	J	J	A	S	O	N	D	Yr.	Range
Temp.	74	74	71	67	61	57	55	56	58	61	66	71	64	19
Precip.	0.3	0.5	0.7	1.6	4.9	6.9	6.5	5.7	3.3	2.1	0.8	0.6	33.9	

tropical climates show a gradual increase in rainfall from equatorward to poleward margins. This is well illustrated by three California cities, arranged in order from south to north. San Diego, farthest south, has only 10 in. of rain, Los Angeles 15 in., and San Francisco 20 in. Precipitation also tends to increase from the interiors toward the coasts, except where elevations may modify the rule.

8.12 Snowfall. A snow cover is absent at low elevations, and even snowfall is rare. Over central and southern California (excluding the mountains) annual snowfall averages less than 1 in., and there is none at all along the coast from San Luis Obispo southward. In all Mediterranean regions snow is so rare that it is a matter for comment when it does fall. Where highlands are present in Mediterranean regions, as they commonly are, they may have a moderate to heavy snow cover. This snowfall in highlands provides an invaluable source of irrigation for the adjacent drier lowlands.

8.13 Winter Rainfall and Cloudiness. But although winter is the rainy season, it is by no means dismal and gloomy as are the west-coast regions farther poleward at that season. Since Mediterranean latitudes usually are on the equatorward sides of the storm centers, and far removed from most of them, they experience a less persistent cloud cover, and sunshine is abundant even in winter. To be sure, winters are considerably cloudier than summers, but still there is much bright sunny weather. In interior California, midsummer months have over 90 per cent of the possible sunshine, but in winter this is reduced to 50 per cent or less, although farther south in the vicinity of Los Angeles it reaches 60 to 70+ per cent. Dull gray days with persistent long-continued rain are by no means rare, but showery conditions with a broken sky are more common. After the rain the sun seems to shine more brilliantly than ever in the washed and dust-free atmosphere.

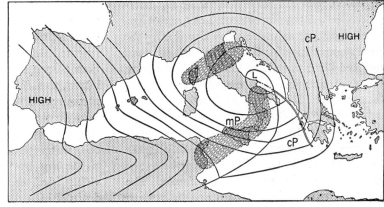

Fig. 8.6 A winter cyclone in the Mediterranean Basin producing widespread cloud and precipitation. The precipitation in dry-summer subtropical climates is predominantly of frontal cyclonic origin.

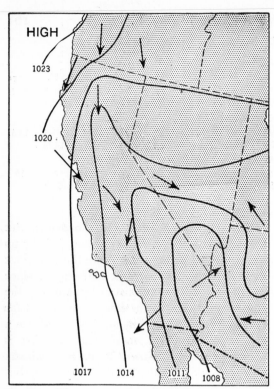

Fig. 8.7 The summer drought of dry-summer subtropical climate is associated with strong subsidence and divergent surface air flow in the stable eastern parts of a subtropical anticyclone.

8.14 Summer Drought and Sunshine. Summers in the dry-summer subtropics are periods of brilliant sunshine, extremely meager precipitation, nearly cloudless skies, and desertlike relative humidity (Fig. 8.7). Thus Sacramento has no rain at all in July and August, and in those months the percentage of the possible sunshine received is 95 and 96, respectively. Afternoon relative humidity is in the neighborhood of only 30 to 40 per cent. Los Angeles has, on the average, only one rainy day during the three summer months; San Bernardino has two; and Red Bluff, three. The low rainfall, dry heat, abundant sunshine, and excessive evaporation characteristic of summers in interior locations are ideal for out-of-doors drying of fruits on a large scale. In spite of the summer heat, thunderstorms are rare, except possibly in the mountains or hills, two to four a year being the usual number in southern California. The strongly subsiding air of these regions in summer and the onshore winds from over cool ocean currents are scarcely conducive to the formation of cumulo-nimbus clouds.

Coastal regions, especially if paralleled by cool ocean currents, are characterized by high relative humidity and much fog. Rarely does it remain foggy for the entire day, the mists usually being burned off by the ascending sun after 9:00 or 10:00 A.M. Nights, however, may be damp and unpleasant. The coast of California is one of the foggiest areas in the United States, parts of the littoral having 40+ days with dense fog per year. These coastal sections with their cool, humid, and less sunny summers are really a subtype of general Mediterranean climate.

8.15 Dependability of Precipitation. Like most subhumid climates, this one suffers from a rainfall that is none too reliable, although it fluctuates less than a summer-maximum regime having the same amount. At San Bernardino, Calif., where the annual rainfall averages 16.1 in., during a 48-year period it has been as low as 5.5 and as high as 37.1. In 5 of the 48 years it has been below 10 in. The somewhat precarious, as well as subhumid, character of the precipitation compels a relatively great dependence upon irrigation.

8.16 Weather. Daily weather is less fickle in the subtropical climates than it is farther poleward, where moving cyclones and anticyclones are more numerous and better developed. A typical *summer* day in the dry-summer subtropical type is almost a replica of one in a low-latitude desert. Moreover, one day is much like another. Drought, brilliant sunshine, low relative humidity, high daytime temperatures, and marked nocturnal cooling are repeated day after day with only minor variations. Along seacoasts, and for a short distance inland, the daily sea breeze is often a marked phenomenon, greatly meliorating the desert heat. Regions with Mediterranean climates are famous for their well-developed sea breezes, the cool water offshore and the excessive heating of the dry land under intense insolation providing ideal conditions for strong daytime indrafts of air.

In *autumn* winds become less regular and uniform. As the cyclonic belt creeps equatorward, following the sun's rays, an occasional cyclone with its associated cloud cover and rain makes itself felt. The dry and dusty land begins to assume new life under the influence of increasing precipitation. Temperatures are still relatively high. As sun control loses something of its summer dominance, daily weather becomes more uncertain, and "spells of weather" become more frequent.

Winter witnesses an increase in the frequency and strength of cyclones, and it is in that season that irregular, nonperiodic weather changes are most marked (Fig. 8.7). Rainy days, brought by lows the centers of which are often well poleward from Mediterranean latitudes, are sandwiched in between sunny ones, in which the days are comfortably mild, even though the nights may be chilly with occasional frosts.

Spring is a delightful season of the Mediterranean year: fresh and yet warm. On the whole it is cooler than autumn. This is the harvesting period for many grains. Passing cyclones gradually become fewer as summer approaches, but nonperiodic weather changes are still significant.

8.17 Resource Potentialities of the Mediterranean Realm. This, the most restricted of all the principal climatic types, embracing less than 2 per cent of the earth's land surface, is, nevertheless, one of the most unique and glamorous. Its abundance of sunshine, fruit, and flowers; its mild and relatively bright winter weather offering resort and outdoor sport attractions; its blue skies and even bluer waters create for it a reputation and renown far out of proportion to its small area. Perhaps, also, the fact that the ancient civilizations, from which stem some of the most important elements of our present culture—literature, religion, science, art—developed within the Mediterranean Basin and bear an indelible imprint of that environment may have had no small part in establishing the fame of this climate.

In the dry-summer subtropical climate is found a unique combination of elements, some of which make for high agricultural productive capacity, and others which have the opposite effect. It is more particularly in the temperature elements—long, warm-to-hot summers with abundant sunshine; mild, bright winters; and almost a year-round frost-free season—that this climate exhibits its highest potentialities. For any part of the middle latitudes the two subtropical realms represent the nearest approach to the bountiful temperature regime of the tropics. This close approach to tropical temperature conditions, while still lying within the middle latitudes and profiting by proximity to their markets, gives to these two realms a considerable part of their distinctive character. In them is permitted the development of certain heat-loving or frost-sensitive crops, some of them of a luxury type—citrus, figs, viniferous grapes, rice, sugar cane, cotton—which can be grown in few other parts of the middle latitudes. The subtropical climates likewise permit the development of out-of-season vegetables and flowers for the markets of regions farther poleward, where a season of severe cold imposes a long dormant period. The possibility, within the Mediterranean realm, of utilizing the middle-latitude winter as an active growing and producing season offers unusual possibilities. In addition, the mild and moderately bright winters make this realm attractive as a winter playground for peoples from the higher middle latitudes. Here snow and ice and frigid temperatures are left behind, and out-of-doors living can be enjoyed even in midwinter. The proximity of the sea is a further attraction. There is no doubt that climate, especially winter climate, is one of the Mediterranean realm's greatest natural assets.

On the other hand, it is (*a*) the relatively meager total precipitation as well as (*b*) the long summer drought which place definite climatic limitations upon production within the realm. It is this deficiency of water, especially in the warm season, which makes of summer, in spite of its abundant heat, a naturally dormant season. The large-scale development of irrigation within the Mediterranean realm is evidence of man's attempt to overcome the handicap of summer drought and thereby provide a year-round growth for crops. Except where irrigation is practiced the relatively meager total precipitation and the arid summers tend to place limitations upon the kinds of crops grown, emphasizing drought-resistant perennials such as the olive and vine or those annuals which mature quickly such as barley and wheat. Fortunately, the usual 15 to 25 in. of rain is concentrated in the cooler seasons of the year when evaporation is at a minimum. If the same amount fell during the hot summer when evaporation is excessive, much less of it would be effective for plant growth.

The modest precipitation coupled with the summer drought produce a vegetation cover characterized by woody shrubs and widely spaced stunted trees. In some Mediterranean regions scattered patches of desert bunch grass are also present. This plant cover is of modest value for grazing, particularly of sheep and goats. Only on the higher hill lands and the mountain slopes are the forests of genuine commercial value, the stunted trees and the bushes of the valleys and the lower slopes being useful chiefly as checks to erosion.

Because of the widespread occurrence of hill land in this realm, mature residual soils are not common. On the slopes soils are inclined to be thin and stony, and to a considerable extent they remain uncultivated. It is the young alluvial soils of the valleys which are the attractive sites for cultivation.

Humid Subtropical Climate (*Ca*)[4]

8.18   Three principal differences distinguish the humid subtropical from the dry-summer subtropical climates: (*a*) the former is characteristically located on the eastern rather than on the western sides of continents; (*b*) it has a more abundant precipitation; and (*c*) this precipitation is either well distributed throughout the year or else concentrated in the warm season. Even where the warm-season maximum is not emphatic, summer is still humid and usually has adequate rainfall for crops.

[4] In the Köppen symbols, *f* = humid throughout the year; *w* = dry season in winter of the respective hemisphere; and *a* = temperature of warmest month over 71.6° (22°C.).

8.19   Type Location. In latitudinal position the two subtropical climates are similar, both of them being on the equatorward margins of the intermediate zones but with the humid subtropical type extending slightly farther equatorward. Characteristically it extends from latitude 25°±, poleward to 35 or 40° (Figs. A.2 and 8.1, Plate 2).

In continental location, however, the two subtropical types are dissimilar, for humid subtropical is typically situated on the eastern side of land masses (Fig. 8.1). Of principal importance in favoring this east-side location is the weaker subsidence and less stable air in the western limb of the subtropical anticyclone which affects these subtropical eastern parts of continents in summer. Moreover, along the subtropical eastern sides of the continents where the summer anticyclone is relatively weak there is some tendency for a monsoon system of winds to prevail. This in turn favors summer precipitation.

Since warm ocean currents characteristically parallel subtropical east coasts this situation provides an additional reason why a warm-summer type like humid subtropical is found along eastern littorals rather than western where cool water prevails.

Lying as they do on the equatorward margins of the middle latitudes, and just beyond the poleward margins of the tropics, the humid subtropical and the dry-summer subtropical climates are transitional types. But here the similarity in location ends, for while Mediterranean climate is characteristically bordered by low-latitude steppe and desert on its equatorward side, humid subtropical climate is terminated by humid tropical types. This contrast has a marked effect upon the thermal importations from the low latitudes in the two types, parching dry heat accompanied by dust in the one case and humid sultry heat in the other. On their poleward sides they likewise make contact with contrasting types, for while dry-summer subtropical generally merges into the mild rainy marine climate, humid subtropical not infrequently makes contact with severe continental climate. This is particularly true of North

America and Asia, where there are extensive land masses in the higher middle latitudes. On their landward or western margins humid subtropical climates gradually grade into dry types characteristic of the continental interiors (Fig. A.2).

TEMPERATURE

8.20 Temperatures Subtropical. In temperature characteristics the humid subtropics are similar to dry-summer subtropical climate, but there is somewhat less contrast between coastal and interior locations (Fig. 8.8). This similarity is not unexpected since the two types roughly correspond in their latitudinal locations. However, because warm, instead of cool, ocean currents wash the subtropical eastern coasts of continents, there can be no distinctly cool littorals such as are characteristic of some dry subtropical coasts. Cool, foggy stations, like San Francisco or Mogador, are absent.

8.21 Summer. Average hot-month temperatures of 75 to 80° are characteristic. Along the immediate coasts, especially of the smaller Southern Hemisphere land masses, they are as often below as above 75°. But everywhere summers are distinctly warm to hot, and this is particularly true of North America and Asia. Thus hot-month temperatures average 81° at Charleston, S.C.; 80° at Shanghai, China; 77° at Brisbane, Australia; 77° at Durban, South Africa; and 74° at Buenos Aires, Argentina.

Not only the air temperature, but also the absolute and relative humidity are high. The high humidity in conjunction with the high temperatures produces a sultry, oppressive condition with low cooling power. Sensible temperatures, therefore, are commonly higher in the humid- than the dry-summer subtropics, even when the thermometer registers the same. Summer heat in the American Gulf States, where *mT* Gulf air prevails, closely resembles that of the tropical wet climate. At New Orleans during June, July, and August the average temperatures are 2 to 3° higher than they are at Belém in the Amazon Valley, while the amount of rainfall is nearly the same. The average of the daily maxima in July throughout

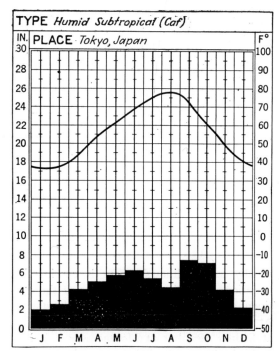

Fig. 8.8 Compare with Fig. 8.2. Seasonal rainfall is quite in contrast in the two subtropical climates.

most of the American Cotton Belt is between 90 and 100°, while the highest temperatures ever observed are usually between 100 and 110° (Figs. 8.9 and 8.10).

8.22 *Night Temperatures.* Not only are the days hot and sultry, but the nights are oppressive as well, the humid atmosphere with more cloud preventing the same rapid loss of heat that takes place in the drier air and clearer skies of dry-summer subtropical climates. The sultry nights are an additional item of resemblance to the wet tropics. The slower night cooling results in relatively small diurnal ranges, usually only one-half to two-thirds as great as those in the dry-summer subtropics (compare Fig. 8.5 with Fig. 8.9). Since the sun is very much in control of the daily weather, one day in summer is much like another in the humid subtropics.

8.23 Winter. Winters are, of course, relatively mild in these subtropical latitudes, cool-month temperatures usually averaging between 40 and 55°. Thus Montgomery, Ala., has an average cool-month temperature of 49°; Shanghai, China, 38°; Buenos Aires, Argentina, 50°; and Sydney, Australia, 52°. Annual ranges are

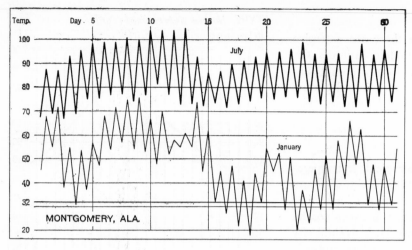

Fig. 8.9 Daily maximum and minimum temperatures for the extreme months at a humid subtropical station. Note the strong periodic, or solar, control in summer. By contrast, winter shows strong nonperiodic or air-mass control.

usually small, although there is considerable variation, depending upon the size of the continent and the latitudinal location of the station. At Buenos Aires the annual range is only 23°, at Sydney 19°, but at Montgomery it is 32°, and it is 43° at Shanghai. Apparently the larger the land mass and the better the development of monsoon winds, the colder are the winters and the larger the annual ranges. In eastern Asia the strong monsoonal outpouring of cold polar continental air in winter from the large land mass to the rear results in the lowest *average* winter temperatures in those latitudes for any part of the world.

The midday temperatures in winter are likely to be pleasantly warm, the thermometer usually rising to 50 or 60°. On winter nights temperatures of 35 to 45° are to be expected. These certainly are not low, but combined with the high humidity they are likely to produce a

sensible temperature which is distinctly chilly and uncomfortable. Summer is so much the dominant season that little thought is given to the heating systems in homes, and as a result they are likely to be inefficient and ineffective. Consequently, one is often more uncomfortable indoors than he is in colder regions farther poleward where adequate provision is made for winter heating.

8.24 *Minimum Temperatures and Frost.* It is to be expected that the growing season, or period between killing frosts, will be long. It is usually at least 7 months and from that up to nearly, if not quite, the entire year. Even though freezing temperatures may be *expected* during a period of several months, they actually occur on only a relatively few nights of the winter season. As in the dry-summer subtropical climates, so too in these, the long growing season and infrequent severe frosts make them ideal

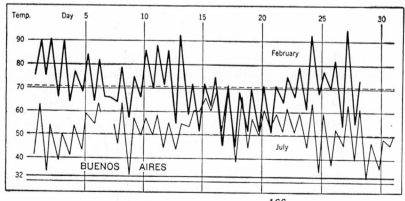

Fig. 8.10 A humid subtropical station in Argentina. Nonperiodic or air-mass control is conspicuous in both winter and summer.

Climatic Data for Representative Humid Subtropical Stations

Charleston, S.C.

	J	F	M	A	M	J	J	A	S	O	N	D	Yr.	Range
Temp.	50	52	58	65	73	79	82	81	77	68	58	51	66.1	31.4
Precip.	3.0	3.1	3.3	2.4	3.3	5.1	6.2	6.5	5.2	3.7	2.5	3.2	47.3	

Shanghai, China

	J	F	M	A	M	J	J	A	S	O	N	D	Yr.	Range
Temp.	38	39	46	56	66	73	80	80	73	63	52	42	49	42.8
Precip.	2.8	2.0	3.9	4.4	3.3	6.6	7.4	4.7	3.9	3.7	1.7	1.3	45.8	

Sydney, Australia

	J	F	M	A	M	J	J	A	S	O	N	D	Yr.	Range
Temp.	72	71	69	65	59	54	52	55	59	62	67	70	63	20
Precip.	3.6	4.4	4.9	5.4	5.1	4.8	5.0	3.0	2.9	2.9	2.8	2.8	47.7	

regions for sensitive crops and for those requiring a long maturing period. In sections of the Southern Hemisphere humid subtropics, frost does not occur every winter and usually is light when it does come. Thus the *average lowest winter temperature* at Brisbane, Australia, is 37°, and at Sydney 39°. The lowest temperature *ever recorded* at Buenos Aires is 23°; at Montevideo, Uruguay, 20°; and at Brisbane, Australia, 32°.

One of the distinguishing features of the South Atlantic and Gulf States of the United States, a region where the *average winter temperatures* are relatively high, is the unusually *low winter minima,* even lower than those of China. Thus while southeastern China has lower *average* winter temperatures, the American humid subtropics have severer *cold spells* and consequently lower minima. Several killing frosts are of annual occurrence, and temperatures as low as 10° have been recorded along the ocean margins of all the Gulf States (Fig. 8.11). No other part of the world near sea level in these subtropical latitudes experiences such low winter minima. This is due to the open nature of the North American continent east of the Rocky Mountains which permits the surges of cold polar continental air to move rapidly southward into subtropical latitudes. In Mediterranean California, mountain barriers prevent such severe invasions of cold air, so that there the absolute minima are much higher. Thus while commercial citrus production extends north to about 38° in California, it is confined to regions south of latitude 30 or 31° in southeastern United States. In China the more hilly and mountainous surface configura-

tion prevents such unrestricted latitudinal importations of cold air.

PRECIPITATION

8.25 Amount and Distribution. Rainfall is relatively abundant (30 to 65 in.) within the humid subtropics, but still there are considerable differences within the several regions. On the landward frontiers of this type, where it makes contact with steppe climates, rainfall reaches the lowest totals. In general, there is no

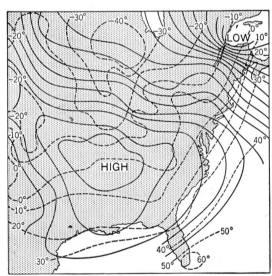

Fig. 8.11 Weather controls giving rise to a spell of severe subfreezing weather in the American humid subtropics. A cold anticyclone advancing southward from arctic Canada as a mass of cold *cP* air produced a minimum temperature of 20° at New Orleans and 8° at Memphis. The isotherm of 20° approximately coincides with the Gulf and South Atlantic coasts.

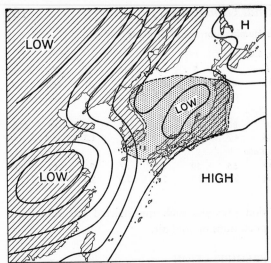

Fig. 8.12 A common weather type of the summer season in the humid subtropics of Asia. Cyclonic storms are responsible for a considerable part of the summer precipitation. The area of precipitation has a stippled shading. (*After Japanese weather map.*)

marked drought season as there is in the dry-summer subtropics, although summer usually has more precipitation than winter (Fig. 8.8). In the Southern Hemisphere where the monsoon tendency is weak, the seasonal accent is less marked. China and India, by contrast, with the best-developed monsoons and the fewest cyclonic interruptions in winter, have the greatest rainfall contrasts between summer and winter.[5] Probably because of the strong cyclonic control in late winter and early spring, portions of the American humid subtropics inland from the Gulf and Atlantic have more rain in the winter half year than in the summer half.

8.26 Warm-season Rainfall. A considerable part of the summer rainfall at low elevations originates in convectional storms, many of them accompanied by thunder and lightning. In fact the American humid subtropics are the most thundery part of the United States, a large portion of that area having over 60 electrical storms a year, while a small part of Florida has over 90. These storms are mostly of local origin, resulting from strong surface heating of the potentially unstable mT Gulf air masses. The

[5] Parts of the Asiatic humid subtropics have genuinely dry winters. These are Köppen's Cw areas.

high temperatures and high humidity of the mT air provide an ideal environment for vigorous development of local convection.

In addition to the thunderstorm rain, falling from cumulus clouds, a considerable part is also obtained from weak cyclonic storms and, in the late summer and early fall, from tropical hurricanes as well (Fig. 8.12). In the weak shallow lows rain often falls steadily from gray overcast skies and is general over larger areas than is true of thunderstorm precipitation. Hurricane rainfall is largely confined to the American and Asiatic humid subtropics, contributing in both those regions to the late-summer maximum in their precipitation curves.

In spite of the abundant summer rainfall characteristic of the humid subtropics, sunshine is relatively abundant, although much less so than is true of summers in Mediterranean climates. Montgomery, Ala., receives 73 per cent of the possible sunshine in June and 62 per cent in July.

8.27 Cool-season Rainfall. In winter the ground is cooler than the poleward-moving tropical air masses so that the latter are chilled at the base and made more stable. As a consequence local convection is unlikely. Only as the tropical maritime air masses are forced to rise over relief barriers or over masses of cold air does precipitation usually occur. Winter rainfall over lowlands is chiefly frontal and cyclonic in origin. It is, therefore, usually associated with a general and persistent cloud cover extending over wide areas, from which precipitation may fall steadily during a large part of a day or even more. On the whole the rainfall is less violent, but of longer duration, than is that of the summer thundershowers. Because of the more numerous cyclones, winters are cloudier than summers. At Shanghai, China, in an average January, only 2 in. of rain falls, but there are 12 rainy days, whereas the 6 in. of August precipitation falls on only 11 days. Each rainy day in August, therefore, accounts for three times as much precipitation as a rainy day in January. Montgomery, Ala., which has 73 per cent of the possible sunshine in June, receives only 49 per cent in January and 44 per cent in December. Gray overcast days with rain are unpleasantly chilly.

Snow falls occasionally when a vigorous winter cyclone swings well equatorward, but it rarely stays on the ground for more than a day or two. On the northern margins of the American Gulf States snow falls on 5 to 15 days a year, and the ground may be covered for an equally long period.

8.28 Seasonal Weather. Irregular nonperiodic weather changes are usually less marked in the humid subtropics than they are farther poleward, where the conflict between air masses is more marked and fronts more numerous. In *summer* when the frontal belt or storm belt is farthest poleward, and the sun is largely in control, irregular weather changes are at a minimum (Fig. 8.9). Weak cyclones may bring some gray days with general widespread rains. Humid, sultry days with frequent thundershowers, each day much like the others, are the rule. The thermometer rises to about the same height each day and sinks to similar minima each night. *Late summer and fall* are the dreaded hurricane season, and, although these storms are not numerous, their severity more than makes up for their infrequency. Sunny autumn days furnish delightful weather, although the equatorward advancing cyclonic belt gradually produces more gray cloudy days and unseasonable temperature importations as winter closes in.

In *winter* the belt of fronts is farthest equatorward, so that irregular weather changes are most frequent and extreme at that time. The arrival of tropical air masses may push the day temperatures to well above 60 or even 70°, whereas the subsequent northwest winds of polar origin may reduce the temperature as much as 30° within 24 hr., resulting occasionally in severe freezes. Bright, sunny winter days are distinctly pleasant and exhilarating out of doors. *Spring* again sees the retreat of the cyclonic belt and the gradual reestablishment of regular diurnal sun control.

8.29 Resource Potentialities of the Humid Subtropics. Without doubt this is the most productive climate of the middle latitudes. Temperature and rainfall here combine to produce the closest approach to humid tropical conditions outside the low latitudes. Those temperature assets stressed for the Mediterranean realm in an earlier section are closely duplicated in this second of the subtropical climates. But if the two subtropical climates are similar in their temperature potentialities, they are in greater contrast as regards rainfall. It is the more abundant precipitation of the humid subtropics, in conjunction with the lack of a genuinely dry season, which makes this realm potentially more productive climatically than its subhumid counterpart. To be sure, its sultry tropical summers are far from being ideal for human comfort, but they are, nevertheless, excellent for a luxuriant plant growth.

The abundant climatic energy, expressed in rainfall as well as temperature, induces an equally abundant vegetation, usually of forests, although in regions of more modest precipitation grasses may replace trees. Grasses are particularly prevalent in the westernmost parts of the American humid subtropics, in the Argentine Pampa and parts of Uruguay, and in the higher parts of the Transvaal and Orange Free State of South Africa. The character of the forests varies so greatly among the humid subtropical regions that generalizations are difficult to make. Broadleaf trees, both deciduous and evergreen, no doubt predominate although conifers, or needle trees, are common at higher elevations and in areas of stony and sandy soils. The most valuable remaining stands of commercial forest within the humid subtropics are those of the United States and of southeastern Brazil, both of these areas having large stands of conifers. In southeastern Asia long occupance by civilized man has resulted in serious forest denudation so that the only remaining stands of valuable timber are in the more inaccessible mountain areas. Trees grow more rapidly in the humid subtropics than they do in other climates of the middle latitudes so that natural or artificial reforestation is a quicker process than it is farther poleward.

The mature forest soils of the humid subtropics are characteristically of low fertility, a resource feature that tends to offset seriously the effects of the realm's highly productive climate. The soil inferiority is not unexpected, however, considering the high leaching power of the climate and the low humus-producing character of the forest vegetation. In a general way the red and yellow soils of the humid subtropics resemble those of the wet tropics, although the former are not so completely leached. Under cultivation they deteriorate rapidly. It seems like a geographic imperfection of first magnitude that the most productive climate of the middle latitudes should be associated with such infertile soils. Thus while the climate is suited to produce a great variety of crops, the inferior soils place serious limitations upon agriculture, especially the cereal types.

Where grasses replace forests, as they do in the subhumid portions of the subtropics, the soils are darker in color and much more productive. The lower rainfall results in less leaching, while the grasses provide a greater abundance of organic matter. It is the South American humid subtropics, especially the Argentine Pampa and Uruguay, that have the most extensive development of these fertile grassland soils. The productivity of the Pampa is almost proverbial. In the humid subtropics of southeastern Asia it is the regions possessing fertile, relatively unleached new alluvial soils that have become the centers of population and of agricultural production.

Marine Climate (Cb)[6]

8.30   Type Location. These mild marine climates characteristically occupy positions on the western or windward side of middle-latitude continents, poleward from about 40°, where the onshore westerly winds import to them conditions from the oceans (Fig. A.2, Plate 2). In their general atmospheric characteristics, therefore, they are like the seas from which the imported air is derived. Where land areas are relatively narrow, as, for instance, in the case of islands, such as Tasmania, New Zealand, and

[6] See footnotes on pp. 158 and 164 for interpretation of individual letters in the Köppen symbol.

Great Britain, or where the continent extends for only a short distance into the belt of westerlies, as do the Southern Hemisphere land masses of Australia and Africa, marine climate may not be limited completely to the western margins. An extensive development of the type on the eastern sides of large continents in middle latitudes is unlikely, however (in spite of the proximity of oceans), by reason of the severe temperatures resulting from leeward location and the monsoon wind systems.

On its equatorward margins this climate characteristically makes contact with the dry-summer subtropical type. On its poleward side marine climate extends far into the higher middle latitudes, where it is eventually terminated by either the subarctic or the tundra type. The far poleward extension of this mild climate is the result of a prevalence of mild maritime air masses. Warm ocean currents, which parallel the west coasts of continents in middle latitudes, tend to accentuate the normal tempering effects of the ocean proper.

The depth to which the marine climate extends into the interior of a continent is determined largely by surface configuration. Where mountains closely parallel the west coast, as in North and South America and Scandinavia, marine conditions are confined to relatively narrow strips of territory seaward from the highlands. But where extensive lowlands prevail, as in parts of western Europe, the effects of the sea are carried well inland. On their land sides marine climates are characteristically bordered by severe continental types, either dry or humid.

TEMPERATURE

8.31   Summer. Although there are good and sufficient grounds for objecting to the use of the word "temperate" as applied to many middle-latitude climates, it is relatively suitable for the particular one under discussion (Fig. 8.13). Summers are moderately cool and, while more or less ideal for human efficiency and comfort, their temperatures are somewhat too low for the best growth of many cereal crops. The characteristically cool summer should be emphasized as one of the principal contrasts between this third of the triumvirate of mild mesothermal climates, on the one hand, and the two subtropical types, on the other. Seattle, Wash., has a mean July temperature of only 63°; Dublin, Ireland, 60°; Bergen, Norway, 58°; and Paris, 66°. Night cooling is considerably less rapid in these humid, cloudy marine climates than is characteristic of Mediterranean summers. The average of the daily minima in July is only 55° at Seattle and 51° at Bellingham, Wash., while the daily maxima are 73 and 72°, respectively, so that the normal diurnal range is in the neighborhood of only 20° (Figs. 8.14 and 8.15). Occasional hot days may occur when the effects of a tropical continental air mass are felt. Under such conditions Seattle and Bellingham have experienced a temperature as high as 96°, and Paris 100°. Severe and prolonged hot waves, however, are few (see temperature data, page 173).

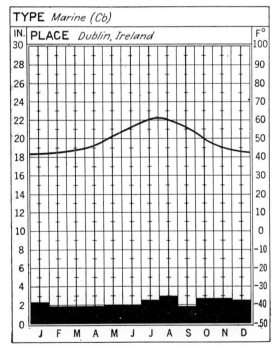

Fig. 8.13 Temperature and rainfall characteristics of a lowland marine station in western Europe. Note the small range of temperature and the modest amount of precipitation well distributed throughout the year.

8.32　Winter. Winters, on the whole, are more abnormally mild for the latitude than the summers are cool. This is particularly the case with western Europe, where a great mass of warm water, the North Atlantic Drift, lies offshore. Thus the most marine parts of western Europe are 20 to 30° too warm for their latitudes in January. In winter isotherms tend to parallel these coasts rather than follow the lines of latitude, indicating the dominance of land-water control. The decrease in temperature is much more rapid from the coast toward the interior than it is going poleward. Thus Paris is 7° colder in January than Brest, which is 310 miles nearer the ocean. January averages of 35 to 50° in western Europe are matched by others of 0 to —40° in the continental climates of interior Asia in similar latitudes.

8.33　*Winter Minima and Frosts.* The average cold-month temperature at London is 39°; at Seattle, 40°; at Valentia, Ireland, 45°; and at Valdivia, Chile, 46°. Annual ranges are small: 15° at Valentia, 23° at London, 13° at Valdivia, and 24° at Seattle. For Seattle the average of the January daily minima is 35°, so that on a majority of nights frost is absent. At Paris frost occurs on about one-half of the nights in the three winter months, whereas in London the thermometer remains above the freezing point on more January nights than it goes below. At Seattle the thermometer has fallen as low as 3°. The prevailingly cloudy skies and humid atmosphere in winter tend to retard nocturnal cooling, thereby reducing the diurnal range of temperature (Figs. 8.14 and 8.15).

Frosts are more frequent, as well as more severe, and the frost-free season is shorter than in Mediterranean climates. Nevertheless the growing season is unusually long for the latitude, 180 to 210 days being characteristic of the American North Pacific Coast region. Seattle has only 4 months when temperatures below freezing are to be expected. However, winter is usually severe enough to produce a dormant season for plant life, which is not true for the dry-summer subtropics farther equatorward. During unusually cold spells temperatures may

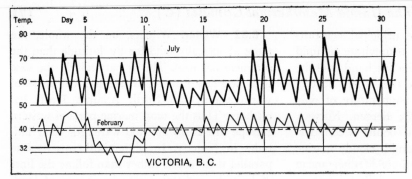

Fig. 8.14 A marine station on the Pacific coast of Canada. Note the small diurnal range, especially in winter when skies are prevailingly cloudy.

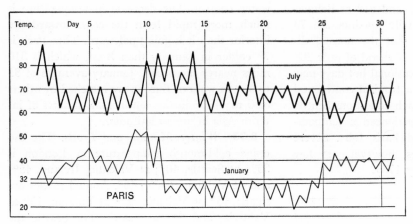

Fig. 8.15 A station in western Europe inland from the coast, with a marine climate. Nonperiodic air-mass control of temperature is conspicuous.

remain constantly below freezing for a period of several days. Midday temperatures of normal winter days are relatively high, however, the average of the daily maxima for January at Seattle being 44° and the daily range less than 10°. On the whole, the day-to-day temperature changes are slightly less regular in winter than in summer, the former season being more completely controlled by the succession of cyclones and anticyclones.

8.34 *Cold Spells.* Unusual cold spells in these marine climates characteristically are caused by importations of cold polar continental air from the anticyclonic interiors. But such invasions of polar continental air are infrequent for they are opposed to the general westerly air movement of the middle latitudes. The American North Pacific Coast is further protected against invasions of cold continental air by mountain barriers. Northeasterly, and not northwesterly, winds bring the coldest weather to the American North Pacific Coast and to western Europe (Fig. 8.16). During an unusual

February cold spell in Europe the influence of the continental high persisted for several weeks. During that spell temperatures in eastern Kent, England, remained continuously below freezing for 226 hr., the Thames was frozen over in many parts, and practically the whole of the British Isles was frost-bound for 5 weeks (Kendrew). On the continent at this same time German coastal cities recorded temperatures below zero, while the Rhine was frozen throughout almost its entire course.

PRECIPITATION

8.35 Amount. These are humid climates with adequate rainfall at all seasons (Fig. 8.13). The total amount, however, varies greatly from region to region, depending in a large measure upon the character of the relief. Where lowlands predominate, as they do in parts of western Europe, rainfall is only moderate, usually 20 to 35 in. But, on the other hand, where west coasts are elevated and bordered by mountain ranges, as is the case in

Norway, Chile, and western North America, precipitation may be excessive, even reaching such totals as 100 to 150 in.

In addition to this contrast in amount is a further contrast in regional distribution, for where lowlands exist, moderate rainfall prevails well into the interior of the continent; but where coastal mountains intercept the rain-bearing winds, precipitation is confined pretty much to the littoral. East of the mountains drought conditions may prevail. There is no doubt that an *extensive* distribution of *moderate* rains is economically more desirable than the concentration of large and unusable quantities on a mountainous coast. Unfortunately, Europe is the only one of the three continents extending well into the westerlies where the windward side of the land mass is freely open to the entrance of the rain-bearing winds. The precipitation of these marine climates has a high degree of reliability, and droughts are of rare occurrence.

8.36 Annual Distribution. With respect to annual distribution of precipitation, the thing to be emphasized is *adequate rainfall at all seasons*, rather than a particular season of marked deficiency. There is no dormant period for vegetation because of lack of rain. In some very marine locations winter may have slightly more precipitation than summer. Thus at Brest, France, and Valentia, Ireland, between 50 and 60 per cent of the total annual precipitation falls during the winter half year. A winter maximum is likewise characteristic of those parts of marine climate lying closest to the dry-

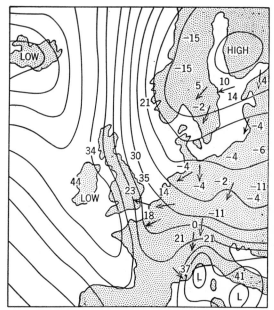

Fig. 8.16 Weather controls favoring unseasonably low winter temperatures in western Europe. A cold anticyclone to the north and east is delivering cold *cP* air to the regions west and south of its center. (*After Kendrew.*)

summer subtropical where the drought-producing effects of the anticyclone are felt in summer (see data for Seattle below).

8.37 Snowfall. In spite of the fact that winter is characteristically a wet season, snowfall is not abundant, temperatures being too high on the lowlands for much snow. "Snow is sufficiently rare in most of northwest Europe to be a topic of conversation when it lies more than a few days. . . . " (Kendrew.) Paris has, on the average, 14 snowy days during the year;

Climatic Data for Representative Marine Stations

Valentia, Ireland

	J	F	M	A	M	J	J	A	S	O	N	D	Yr.	Range
Temp.	44	44	45	48	52	57	59	59	57	52	48	45	50.8	15
Precip.	5.5	5.2	4.5	3.7	3.2	3.2	3.8	4.8	4.1	5.6	5.5	6.6	55.6	

Seattle, Wash.

	J	F	M	A	M	J	J	A	S	O	N	D	Yr.	Range
Temp.	40	42	45	50	55	60	64	64	59	52	46	42	51.4	24
Precip.	4.9	3.8	3.1	2.4	1.8	1.3	0.6	0.7	1.7	2.8	4.8	5.5	33.4	

Paris, France

	J	F	M	A	M	J	J	A	S	O	N	D	Yr.	Range
Temp.	37	39	43	51	56	62	66	64	59	51	43	37	50.5	29
Precip.	1.5	1.2	1.6	1.7	2.1	2.3	2.2	2.2	2.0	2.3	1.8	1.7	22.6	

Hokitika, New Zealand

	J	F	M	A	M	J	J	A	S	O	N	D	Yr.	Range
Temp.	60	61	59	55	50	47	45	46	50	53	55	58	53	16
Precip.	9.8	7.3	9.7	9.2	9.8	9.7	9.0	9.4	9.2	11.8	10.6	10.6	116.1	

in the Puget Sound Lowland there are some 10 to 15 such days, and the duration of snow cover is approximately the same length. The snow that falls is wet and heavy, reflecting the relatively high winter temperatures. Upon the ground, it quickly turns to slush, making for unpleasant conditions underfoot.

Where mountains border these west coasts, receiving abundant orographic and cyclonic winter precipitation, snowfall is extremely heavy. On the western slopes of the Cascade Range 300 to 400 in. of snow falls on the average each year. Snowfall is likewise heavy on the western slopes of the British Columbia Coast Ranges, the Scandinavian Highlands, the mountains of southern New Zealand, and the southern Andes. In each of these regions the mountain snowfields have in the past given rise to numerous valley glaciers, which in turn have been responsible for the characteristically irregular, fiorded coasts.

8.38   Origin of Precipitation. Over lowlands precipitation is chiefly frontal or cyclonic in origin, falling as steady long-continued rain, often only drizzle, from a gray, leaden sky (Fig. 8.17). It is in winter that these storms reach their maximum development, and it is at that time of year that cloudy, rainy days are most numerous. In spite of the fact that cyclones are weaker and less numerous in the warm seasons, because the absolute humidity is higher, and the entrance of lows into the continents is facilitated by lower pressures, summer rain may be nearly, if not quite, as great, although it falls in sharper showers on fewer days. Thus at London, July has 13 rainy days with 2.4 in. of rain, whereas in January the respective figures are 15 and 1.9. Summers, therefore, are usually brighter and sunnier than winters. The cool maritime air masses are not conducive to thunderstorm formation. The North American Pacific Coast records only two to four thunderstorms a year.

A distinguishing feature of the precipitation of these marine climates is the relatively small amount of rain that falls, considering the large number of cloudy, rainy days. Thus although Paris has only 22.6 in. of precipitation, it is

spread out over 188 rainy days (average 0.12 in. for each rainy day). Seattle, with 32 in. of precipitation, has 151 rainy days; London has 24.5 in. and 164 rainy days; while Sumburgh Head, on the Shetland Islands, has 36.7 in. spread out over 260 rainy days. London has had 72 rainy days in succession. Where coasts are precipitous, abundant rains of direct or indirect orographic origin supplement those from cyclones and the few convectional storms.

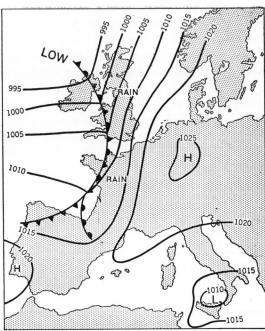

Fig. 8.17   A strongly occluded storm in western Europe, producing light but steady and widespread rainfall, a low ceiling, and low visibility. Most of the cyclones which affect western Europe are in an advanced stage of occlusion. Such storms are inclined to produce much cloud but only a modest amount of precipitation on lowlands.

8.39   Cloudiness and Sunshine. Marine climate is one of the cloudiest climates of the earth. The American North Pacific Coast region has the highest cloudiness and least sunshine of any part of the United States, the mean annual cloudiness of that region being 60 to 70 per cent. Over wide areas of western Europe cloudiness is greater than 70 per cent, the sun sometimes being hidden for several weeks in succession. Winter, the season of maximum cyclones, is much darker and gloomier than summer. Seattle, which has only 22 per cent of the possible sunshine in November and 21 per cent in December, has 65 per cent in July and 60 per cent in August, so that summers there are relatively bright and pleasant. Valentia, Ireland, has only 17 per cent of the possible sunshine in December but in May 43 per cent. But even though summers are sunnier than winters, they are still much cloudier than those of Mediterranean climates. Fog and mist are characteristic weather elements of the marine climate. The American North Pacific Coast has over 40 days with dense fog during the year; Bergen, Norway, has 37.7; and Fanö, Denmark, 53.6.

8.40 Seasonal Weather. Since cyclonic storms are both numerous and vigorous, it is to be expected that the nonperiodic weather element will dominate (Fig. 8.17). *Winter,* in spite of its mild temperatures, is a stormy period. In coastal locations gales are numerous as one storm follows another in rapid succession. The high seas generated by winter winds are strong enough to make navigation difficult, and unusually severe storms may do serious damage to shipping. The fog and mist make for poor visibility and add to the difficulties of navigation. Precipitation is relatively abundant and very frequent, most of it being in the form of rain rather than snow. Long periods of dark, gloomy, dripping weather are characteristic, so that winters are depressing and hard to endure. Between the frequent cyclones there are occasional sunny days with crisper weather, but these are the exception rather than the rule. Night frosts are not unusual, especially when skies are clear, but ordinarily they are not severe. A pushing westward of polar continental air masses now and then leads to a succession of clear days in which temperatures may remain continuously below freezing.

As the days lengthen with the advance of *spring,* cyclones become fewer and sunshine more abundant. The air is still cool, but the sun is warm, and in western Europe spring is acclaimed the most delightful season. *Summer*

temperatures are pleasant for physical well-being, and where sunny days are numerous, as they are in the American Pacific Northwest, a more pleasant summer climate would be hard to find. More especially in the higher middle latitudes, or in very exposed marine locations, chilly, gray, overcast days are numerous even in summer. Rain is still relatively abundant, but it falls on fewer days than in winter. *Autumn* witnesses the equatorward swing of the storm belt again and, as a consequence, a rapid pick-up in cloudiness and precipitation.

8.41 Resource Potentialities of the Marine Realm. Two of the most significant climatic elements affecting the potential productivity of the marine realm are (*a*) its unusually long frost-free season, considering the latitude, and (*b*) its relatively mild winters. To be sure, there is a marked dormant season imposed by killing frosts, so that those sensitive and out-of-season crops characteristic of both the dry-summer subtropics and the humid subtropics are excluded from this realm. Nevertheless a frost-free period of 6 to 8 months and the relatively mild winters permit many cereal crops to be fall sown, and animals can graze out of doors nearly, if not the entire, 12 months. Large-scale storage of animal feeds for winter use is therefore much less necessary than in the more severe continental climates.

Somewhat offsetting the advantages associated with relatively mild winters and a long frost-free season is the deficiency of summer heat, for just as the winters are marine so also are the summers. Thus, while warm-month temperatures of 60 to 65° are ideal for human comfort, and may represent the optimum conditions for physical activity as well, they are not ideal for many crops. Maize, for example, is seriously handicapped. On the other hand, grass finds here almost ideal conditions, so that pastures are usually excellent and hay and forage crops thrive. An adequate amount of rainfall and no season of marked drought are climatic assets of first magnitude. Constancy and dependability of the precipitation year in and year out are reflected in high uniformity of crop yields.

In these mild, humid west-coast regions the original vegetation cover was chiefly forest, and because of the hilly and mountainous nature of large parts of the realm, trees still cover extensive areas. In Europe the original forest was composed largely of broadleaf deciduous trees, with oaks predominating. Conifers, or needle trees, occupied chiefly the highland and sandy areas. Centuries of occupance by civilized peoples has resulted in a removal of the forest cover from the plains and even those of the highlands have been greatly modified. In the North American marine region is the earth's finest coniferous forest which is the world's principal source of high-grade softwood lumber. The Douglas firs of this region are large trees growing in dense stands so that the yield in lumber per unit area is very large. Forests of the Southern Hemisphere marine regions are relatively dense and luxuriant, but they are composed of species most of which produce inferior lumber.

8.42 *Soils and Surface Features.* The gray-brown podzolic soils which are fairly characteristic of lowlands with this type of climate are the best of the world's forest soils. They are by no means the equal of the dark-colored grassland soils, for they have been moderately leached and the supply of organic matter from the forest cover is not abundant. On the other hand, they are distinctly better than the red and yellow soils of the wet tropics and subtropics. Under constant cultivation they deteriorate, to be sure, but less rapidly than the other light-colored soils, and with less care and attention they can be kept in good condition and fitted for a variety of crops.

This is the first of the climatic realms studied where surface and drainage features resulting from continental and mountain glaciation are at all prominent. Except on the European lowlands the glacial features are almost exclusively those resulting from the work of mountain or valley glaciers. Where highlands closely approach the sea as they do in the higher latitudes of Pacific North America, Norway, Scotland, southern Chile, and the southern island of New Zealand, the heavy snowfall is conducive to the development of valley glaciers. A few of these reach the sea even at present, but in those past periods when glaciers were much more extensive, hundreds of valley glaciers reached the ocean along these west coasts in higher middle latitudes. The result is typically fiorded coast lines, ragged in outline, with numerous long, narrow, and steep-walled arms of the sea and innumerable islands. Repetition of this pattern of rugged, island-studded, fiorded coasts and glaciated mountain hinterlands within the four far-separated segments of the marine realm is extraordinarily striking.

In western Europe extensive continental glaciers covered most of the area down to about the Elbe River in Germany and all but the southernmost parts of England and Ireland. On the highlands, composed of resistant crystalline rock, ice scouring removed the weathered rock and soil, grooved and polished the bed rock, and gouged out numerous lake basins. On the lowlands, composed of less resistant rocks, features associated with ice deposition are conspicuous. Among these are numerous lakes and swamps.

9

The Humid Microthermal[1] Climates (D)

9.1 Type Location. Colder winters, a durable snow cover, a longer frost season, and larger annual ranges of temperature distinguish the severe microthermal climates from the mesothermal types. This greater severity results primarily from locational differences, with respect to both (*a*) latitude and (*b*) position on the continents, for microthermal climates lie poleward from the subtropical types and occupy more interior and leeward locations on the great land masses than does the marine climate (Fig. A.2, Plate 2). Emphatically, microthermal climates are land controlled and are, therefore, distinctly continental in their characteristics. It is because they are land controlled, being associated with large continents in higher middle latitudes, that they are confined exclusively to the Northern Hemisphere. Only Eurasia and North America are able to produce them. Of the Southern Hemisphere continents, South America alone extends poleward sufficiently far to permit of severe climates, but the narrowness of that land mass south of latitude 35° prevents genuinely severe conditions in spite of the latitude.

Microthermal climates are excluded from the western, or windward, coasts because of the dominance there of maritime air masses. They occupy, instead, the interiors of land masses and commonly extend down to tidewater on their leeward or eastern sides, where, in spite of proximity to the sea, modified continental conditions likewise prevail.

Unlike the mesothermal climates, those of the microthermal group differ substantially from

one another only in degree, and that chiefly in one element, temperature. For this reason the general aspects of microthermal climates as a group are discussed before the individual types of climate are analyzed.

9.2 Temperature. Because of a wide latitudinal spread, there are marked temperature contrasts within those regions classed as microthermal. However, for any particular latitude, these climates are sure to have relatively severe seasons, so that annual ranges are large. Of the two extreme seasons, it is the winter cold, rather than the summer heat, which is most characteristic and distinctive. Nevertheless, summers are warm for the latitude. Not only are the seasons extreme, but they are likewise variable in temperature from one year to another. In marine climates, for instance, one winter is likely to be much like another, but wide departures from the normal seasonal temperature are characteristic of severe continental climates—in extreme instances as much as 30°.

9.3 *Effects of a Snow Cover upon Temperature.* Only in the microthermal, polar, and highland climates is the snow cover of sufficiently long duration to have a marked effect upon cool-season temperatures. Once a region is overlain by such a white snow mantle, the ground itself ceases to have much influence upon air temperature. Sunlight falling upon snow is largely reflected so that little of the solar energy is effective in heating the ground or the atmosphere. Moreover, although loss of energy by earth radiation goes on very rapidly from the top of a snow surface, the low conductivity of snow tends greatly to retard the flow of heat from the ground below to replace that

---

[1] Micro-, from Greek *mikros,* small. Microthermal, therefore, refers to "small," or low, temperatures.

which is being lost. Observations made at Leningrad, after a fall of 20 in. of loose, dry snow, showed a temperature of —39° at the top of the snow surface, whereas the ground underneath recorded only 27°, a difference of 66°. Obviously, the effect of a snow cover is markedly to reduce winter temperatures. As spring advances it acts to retard the warming of the air, for the reason that much of the solar energy is expended in melting the snow and ice. On the other hand, the snow cover tends to keep the ground warmer and prevents deep freezing.

9.4 Precipitation. Although winters are not without precipitation, summer is normally the season of maximum. This seasonal distribution is related to the following conditions: (*a*) The specific humidity or reservoir of water vapor in the atmosphere is much less over the continents during the cold winter than it is in summer when temperatures are much higher. (*b*) During winter the settling air in the continental seasonal anticyclone is likewise conducive to low specific humidity. This same subsidence makes for increased stability of the atmosphere. (*c*) The continental anticyclones, which develop over the colder, more northerly parts of the land masses in winter, are areas of diverging air currents, a condition that is antagonistic to the development of fronts and cyclones. In summer, although cyclones may be fewer and weaker, they can, nevertheless, penetrate deeper into the continents. This applies particularly to the more severe microthermal climates, such as the subarctic, where the winter anticyclone is best developed. (*d*) Convection is at a maximum during the warm summer months, for at that season the warm land surface has a tendency to make unstable the air masses moving over it. In winter, on the other hand, the cold snow surface tends to increase the stability of air masses. (*e*) Consequent upon the seasonal extremes of temperatures, and hence of pressure, a tendency toward a monsoon system of winds is developed, which leads to an inflow of tropical maritime air with high rainfall potentialities in summer and to an outflow of dry, cold *cP* air in winter. No such re-

versal of winds is experienced along marine west coasts in similar latitudes where seasonal temperature extremes are not well developed.

In severe climates with short frost-free seasons it is of the highest importance that rainfall be concentrated in the warm growing season. This is especially true where the total amount of precipitation is relatively modest, as it is over extensive areas within this group of climates. In the tropics it matters not at all when the rain falls since it is constantly hot. Even in the subtropics winter rainfall is effective for plant growth. In the microthermal climates, however, where the severe winters create a completely dormant season for plants, it is highly essential that periods of sufficient heat and sufficient rainfall coincide.

Two principal types of climate are included within the microthermal group, *viz.*, (*a*) humid continental climate, including both warm-summer and cool-summer phases, and (*b*) subarctic climate. The first type, which is an important agricultural climate, characteristically lies on the equatorward margins of the subarctic type, the latter occupying such high latitudes that agriculture ceases to be of great importance.

Humid Continental Climates (Da, Db) [2]

9.5 Location. Depending upon the presence or absence of mountain barriers, marine climates of the west coasts change abruptly or gradually into the more severe continental climates of the interiors (Plate 2). In North America, where mountain chains parallel the west coasts, the change is sudden and abrupt; on the west European lowlands, on the other hand, it is very gradual. A further contrast distinguishes the two great Northern Hemisphere continents as regards arrangement of climates. In North America, arid and semiarid conditions separate marine west coasts from the continental climates farther east. This results from the abrupt halting of the moisture-bearing winds from the west by mountain barriers, so that to

[2] The individual letters included in these symbols have been defined in footnotes in earlier chapters,

the leeward of the highlands it is dry. A humid marine climate, therefore, passes over directly into a dry continental one. In Eurasia, on the other hand, where, except in Scandinavia, the absence of high mountains permits the deep entrance of marine air into the land mass, humid continental climate lies *both* to the east and to the west of the dry interior. Consequently this type is to be found both in central and eastern Europe and in eastern Asia (Plate 2).

In North America the humid continental climates lie poleward of latitude 35 or 40°. On their equatorward margins they pass over into the humid subtropical type and on their poleward sides make contact with subarctic climate. This same arrangement is repeated in eastern Asia. In Europe, on the other hand, Mediterranean replaces humid subtropical climate on the southern frontier (Plate 2).

It may be noted with some surprise that severe land-controlled climates should extend eastward to the ocean margins. In part this is due to the fact that the eastern is the leeward side of the continent, and here the ocean is relatively ineffective in greatly modifying temperature conditions. The general west-to-east atmospheric circulation in these latitudes makes deep entrance of maritime air into the continent on its leeward side relatively difficult. In addition, the tendency toward monsoons on the eastern sides of large middle-latitude continents tends to accentuate their temperature extremes, making for cold winters and relatively warm summers.

TEMPERATURE

9.6 Seasons Severe. Warm-to-hot summers and cold winters are characteristic of the humid continental climate. Depending principally on latitudinal location, mean July temperatures usually vary between about 65 and 75° while average January temperatures range from zero or below up to 25 or 30°. Annual ranges consequently are large and they tend to increase with increasing latitude. At Peoria, for example, in central Illinois at about 41°N., the January and July averages are 24 and 75° so that there is an annual range of about 50°. At Winnipeg

at about 50°N.. the comparable figures for cold and warm months are −4 and 66° and the range is 70°. In general, the rigorousness of the climate increases from south to north and likewise from the coast toward the interior. Westerly winds and winter monsoons tend to carry continental air masses down to the eastern littorals, but there is some maritime air of cyclonic or summer-monsoon origin which acts to meliorate conditions slightly, with the result that east coasts have *modified* continental climates. For example, at New York City and Omaha, Neb., in similar latitudes, but the former on the Atlantic Seaboard and the latter deep in the interior, the July temperatures are 74 and 77°, respectively, while their January temperatures are 32 and 22°. The annual range, consequently, is 42° at New York and 55° at Omaha. The higher atmospheric humidity of the air along the seaboard causes the summer heat to be more oppressive and sultry, and the winter cold more raw and penetrating, than are the drier extremes of the interior. The degree of marine modification is greatest where coasts are deeply indented, as, for example, in extreme eastern Canada, in the region of the Maritime Provinces.

9.7 Seasonal Gradients. Summer and winter in the continental climates present marked contrasts in latitudinal temperature gradients (Fig. 9.1). In the warm season the few isotherms that cross eastern United States are spaced far apart so that one does not experience marked temperature changes in going from north to south, the rate of change being in the neighborhood of 1° for every degree of latitude, or approximately 70 miles. These same weak summer gradients are characteristic of eastern Asia.

In winter, on the other hand, temperature changes very rapidly from north to south in eastern United States, the rate being 2.5° for each degree of latitude. Between Harbin, Manchuria, and Hankow, China, there is only 13° difference in July, but there is 42° in January. Between St. Louis and Winnipeg the January contrast amounts to 35°; the July contrast to only 13°. Obviously, there is much more reason

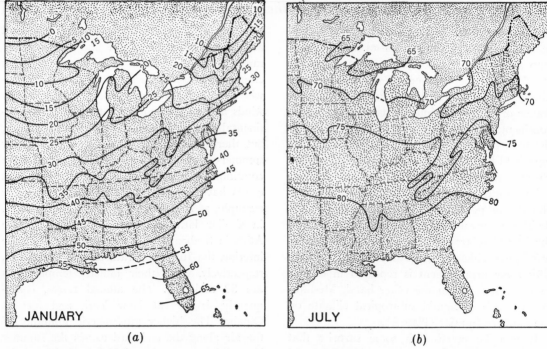

Fig. 9.1 Surface temperature gradients in the microthermal climates are much steeper in January (*a*) than in July (*b*).

for northerners to go south to escape winter cold than for southerners to go north to escape summer heat. Because of the steeper temperature gradients in winter, sudden and marked temperature changes associated with shifts in wind direction are much more common in that season than in summer. These same latitudinal temperature contrasts make the development of cyclonic storms much more likely in winter.

The growing season varies greatly in length from north to south in the continental climates, approaching 200 days on the low-latitude margins and decreasing to 100± days on the subarctic side.

PRECIPITATION

9.8 Amount and Distribution. Rainfall decreases (*a*) from the seaward margins toward the interiors and (*b*) usually toward the higher latitudes as well. Thus along their interior margins the humid continental climates make contact with dry climates, and these interior sections are definitely subhumid. The regions of the grasslands, to be found in both interior

Eurasia and North America, illustrate this drier subtype.

For reasons previously stated, these land-controlled climates are likely to receive their most abundant precipitation in the warm season, although winters are not necessarily dry. More especially it is (*a*) the deep continental interiors and (*b*) the regions with marked monsoonal tendencies, in which summers are emphatically rainier than winters. At Mukden in Manchuria, a station typical of regions having well-developed monsoons, December and January each have only 0.2 in. of precipitation, while July and August have 6.3 and 6.1 in., respectively. Omaha, Neb., typical of an interior regime in North America, has 0.7 in. in January and 4.7 in June. Over much of the United States *east* of the Mississippi, however, the discrepancy between winter and summer precipitation is not so marked. New York City, which receives 3.3 in. in each of the three winter months, has only slightly more, 4.1 and 4.3 in., in July and August, respectively. Its total for the year, however, is 42.5 in.

9.9 *Early-summer Maximum.* In the more subhumid interior locations the period of maximum rainfall, more often than not, is in early summer and late spring, rather than at the time of greatest heat (Fig. 9.2). This is the case in the Danube Basin and in the western prairie region of the United States. At Belgrade, Yugoslavia, June is the wettest month, and May has more precipitation than July. At Omaha, June likewise receives the maximum amount. Lacking a forest mantle, the shallow snow cover of these subhumid lands melts rapidly with the advance of spring, and the dry earth warms quickly under the strong insolation. By May or June, therefore, the lower air has become relatively warm although the upper layers, in which

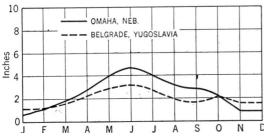

Fig. 9.2 Illustrating the early-summer maximum of precipitation characteristic of interior subhumid parts of humid microthermal climates.

there is a greater seasonal temperature lag, are still cool. Atmospheric instability, and consequently convectional overturning, is therefore greatest in early summer when there is a maximum temperature contrast between lower and upper air. Later in the summer, even though surface temperatures are higher, there is less vertical contrast. Since the largest water requirements of the small-grain cereals occur during the earlier stages of their growth, this early summer maximum of precipitation is of great economic importance.

9.10 Winter Precipitation. Cool-season precipitation is largely frontal or cyclonic in origin. In North America *mT* Gulf air masses move poleward up the Mississippi Valley with no relief obstacles to interfere. The cold ground surface chills the Gulf air and consequently stabilizes it. Occasionally the tropical air may flow poleward at the ground as far north as Iowa and the southern shores of the Great Lakes. More commonly, however, it comes into conflict with colder heavier air masses before reaching so far inland and is forced to ascend over them, with widespread precipitation resulting. The North American continental climates, therefore, have a moderate amount of winter precipitation, nearly all of it cyclonic in origin. In northeastern Asia where the winter monsoon is stronger, the *cP* surges more continuous, and the relief barriers formidable, *mT* air is unable to advance so far poleward so that winter precipitation in North China and Manchuria is very meager.

A portion of the winter precipitation is in the form of snow, and a permanent snow cover, varying from a few weeks to several months in duration, is typical (Fig. 9.9). Owing to the fact that (*a*) it takes 5 to 15 in. of snow to equal 1 in. of rain and (*b*) snow tends to remain on the ground whereas rain does not, the smaller total of winter precipitation may be more conspicuous and impressive than summer's greater amount. This contrast is further accentuated by the fact that the cyclonic winter precipitation is continuous over longer periods of time than are the sharper convectional showers of summer. In those parts of northeastern United States and Canada where winter cyclones are particularly numerous and well developed (Great Lakes region, St. Lawrence Valley, New England, and the Canadian Maritime Provinces), snow becomes excessively deep. Thus northern New England and New York have more than 7 ft. of snowfall during an average winter, and the snow cover remains on the ground for more than 4 months. In parts of the Adirondack Mountains 150 in. or more of snow falls annually. Over the American Great Plains, on the other hand, it amounts to only 20 to 30 in.

9.11 Summer Precipitation. Summer rains, somewhat more convectional in origin, often fall in sharp showers from cumulo-nimbus clouds and frequently are accompanied by thunder and lightning. The warm humid *mT*

Gulf air that enters deep into the North American continent in summer provides favorable conditions for convectional development over eastern and central United States. In Hungary 61 per cent of the rain in June falls on days with thunderstorms (Kendrew). A fair percentage of the thunderstorms of continental climates are of the local heat variety resulting from surface heating. As a rule the local heat thunderstorms decline in frequency, and frontal thunderstorms increase, with increasing latitude. Long-continued cyclonic rains falling from gray overcast skies are not absent, to be sure, but this type of weather is less frequent in summer than in the cooler seasons. On the whole, cyclonic weather in summer is most typical of the poleward margins of the continental climates.

SEASONAL WEATHER

9.12 Nonperiodic Weather Changes Characteristic. In no other types of climate are rapid and marked nonperiodic weather changes so characteristic as in the humid continental, for it is in these regions that the conflict between polar and tropical air masses reaches a maximum development. It is in the cold season, when the sun has retreated farthest south, and with it the storm belt, that the continental climates experience the strongest nonperiodic control of weather. At that season the diurnal sun control is usually subordinate, and weather conditions are dominated by moving cyclones and anticyclones associated with rapidly shifting polar and tropical air masses and the fronts that develop along their boundaries. The daily rise and fall of temperature with the sun many times is obscured by the larger nonperiodic oscillations caused by invasions of polar and tropical air masses (Figs. 9.8 and 9.11). Central and eastern United States, which are freely open to the movements of air masses both from north and south, are regions of unusual storminess. Storm control is less marked in eastern Asia. In the deep interiors and higher middle latitudes of the continents the effects of the winter continental anticyclone are more pronounced, and the weather as a consequence is drier, colder,

and somewhat less fickle. In summer, throughout the humid continental climates, air masses are more stagnant, fronts are fewer, and the weather is more regular and sun controlled.

9.13 *Special Seasonal Weather Types.* The normal cycle of weather changes with the passage of a well-developed cyclone, followed by an anticyclone, has been described in an earlier part of this book. In reality, however, there is almost an infinite variety of weather variations, depending upon the season, the size and intensity of the storm, the nature of the air masses involved in the storm, the track followed by the storm, and the contrasting patterns of high-level atmospheric circulation. As a consequence of the great variety of weather combinations no satisfactory classification of weather types has ever been developed. Nevertheless, even a layman is aware of the fact that there are some weather types which are sufficiently distinctive that they have been given names. Warm wave, cold wave, Indian summer, blizzard, and January thaw are illustrations of this group. Much more numerous are the unnamed ones. Certain it is that no real comprehension of humid continental climates is possible without an appreciation of the variety of weather types which in combination produce the seasonal climates. This requires a study of the daily weather map, or synoptic chart, in conjunction with a firsthand observation of weather conditions. A very few of the weather types characteristic of the humid continental climates are illustrated by sketches of synoptic weather charts of parts of North America (Figs. 9.3 to Fig. 9.6). These are worthy of careful study.

Winter, the season of maximum temperature gradients and of greatest air mass contrasts, is the period of greatest weather variety. A well-developed anticyclone arriving from arctic Canada as a mass of fresh *cP* air may produce bitterly cold weather with subzero temperatures (Fig. 5.13). This sharp drop in temperature as brought by the northwest wind is the well-known *cold wave.* If the cold anticyclone is characterized by unusually steep pressure gradients, blizzardlike conditions with violent winds

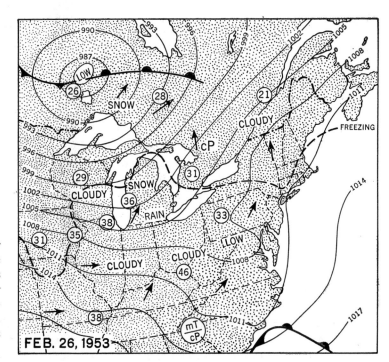

Fig. 9.3 A common winter weather type. Here a cyclone traveling on a northern track is producing cloudy, mild weather and light precipitation over extensive areas of northern central United States. Temperatures shown are for 1:30 A.M.

may usher in the anticyclone. But if the invading cold anticyclone is composed of modified *mP* air from west of the Rocky Mountains, skies will be clear and temperatures only moderately low. This control produces some of the finest winter weather. A deep cyclonic storm, especially if it originates in the Texas area and takes a route northeastward across the country, is more than likely to bring extensive and heavy snowfalls to the humid continental

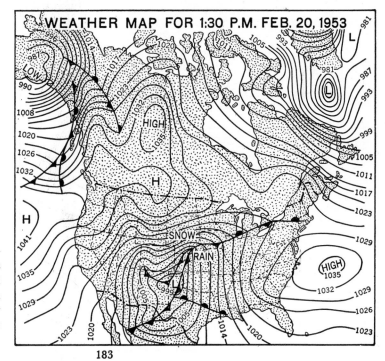

Fig. 9.4 A well-developed winter storm originating in the Texas area and moving northeastward across the United States. Such storms are likely to bring heavy precipitation, much of it in the form of snow.

climates of the Mississippi valley and the east (Fig. 9.4). If the vigorous cyclone travels a more northerly route, the weather is milder and the rain area is more extensive. A weak low following a route to the north of the Great Lakes may give generally gray overcast weather but with only very modest amounts of rain or snow (Fig. 9.3). But these are only a few of the far more numerous weather types which in combination produce the winters of humid continental climates.

In *summer,* temperature gradients are weaker, air-mass contrasts less striking, and altogether the weather element as controlled by passing atmospheric perturbations is less well developed. But while sun control and diurnal regularity are relatively stronger than at other seasons, this period of high sun is by no means lacking in nonperiodic weather irregularities. A somewhat stagnant anticyclone to the south and east may envelop the humid continental area of the United States in a prolonged heat wave with a succession of days when the daily maximum

temperature rises to between 90 and 100° (Fig. 9.5). If the heat is of a humid variety, local afternoon thunderstorms may be numerous. Such a heat wave may be suddenly brought to an end by the passage of a V-shaped cyclonic storm with a well-developed cold front with which are associated severe cold front thunderstorms (Fig. 5.26). Following the passage of the cold front with its strong convectional activity there may be several days of delightfully cool weather, as an anticyclone with air of polar origin dominates the weather.

Spring and fall, the transition seasons, witness a more even struggle between storm and sun control. At times the one and then the other is in the ascendancy, so that there is something of an oscillation between summer and winter conditions. Mild, warm days in April and early May, with regular diurnal rise and fall of the thermometer, resembling summer, may be followed by a reestablishment of winter conditions as a passing cyclone lays down a snow cover and the following *cP* invasion drops the tem-

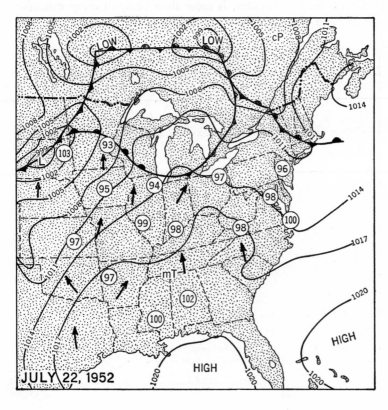

Fig. 9.5 A summer weather type in the form of a July heat wave over the central and eastern parts of the country. Temperatures shown are the maxima for the 12 hr. preceding. Tropical air from the warm anticyclone over the Gulf of Mexico controls the weather.

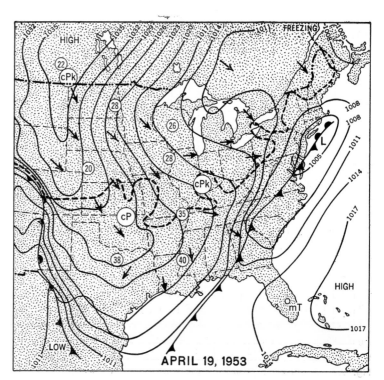

Fig. 9.6 A spring weather type. Here a cold anticyclone advancing southward as a mass of cold *cP* air with northwest winds carries low temperatures deep into the subtropics and results in a severe spring freeze in the North Central States.

APRIL 19, 1953

peratures to an unseasonable frost (Fig. 9.6). Continental climates are famous for their fickleness of spring weather.

Autumn brings some of the loveliest days of the entire year but likewise some of the rawest, gloomiest weather. Bright, clear weather with warm midday temperatures and crisp, frosty nights comes with anticyclonic control. A reestablishment of hot-wave gradients in October and November, after severe frost and perhaps even snow have been experienced, causes a temporary return of summer conditions. The result is those much cherished spells of warm weather with hazy, smoky atmosphere, known as *Indian summer*. But well-developed cyclonic storms of this season may also bring those raw, gray days with chilly rain, and occasionally a temporary snowy winter landscape may be produced as early as October.

SUBDIVISIONS OF THE HUMID
CONTINENTAL CLIMATE

9.14 The Subtypes and Their Locations. Humid continental climate may be conveniently subdivided into two subtypes, the *warm-summer* subdivision (*Da*) and the *cool-summer* subdivision (*Db*). The former is the milder phase of humid continental climate and the latter the more severe. Since these two subtypes are relatively similar climatically except that one has cooler summers and colder winters than the other, it is to be expected that when typically located, the milder subtype will be found on the equatorward margins of humid continental climate, while the more severe subtype will be found farther poleward. Thus the warm-summer subtype is bordered by one of the subtropical types on its equatorward side, while the cool-summer subtype extends poleward until it meets the subarctic type (Fig. A.2).

Three representative areas of the warm-summer subtype should be noted on Plate 2. One of these is in central and eastern United States and it extends from about central Kansas in the West through Iowa, Illinois, and Indiana to Pennsylvania and New Jersey in the East. Within this North American segment is to be found the greater part of the American Corn Belt. The second extensive area includes parts of the Danube and Balkan countries in Europe. The third is in eastern Asia and includes North China, central and southern Manchuria, and the northern part of the main island of Japan.

Three far separated areas likewise comprise

185

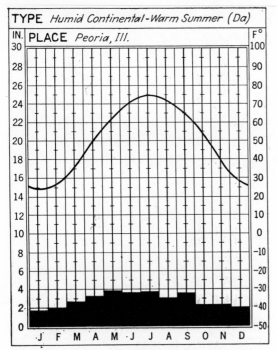

TYPE *Humid Continental-Warm Summer (Da)*

PLACE *Peoria, Ill.*

Fig. 9.7 A station representing the warm-summer subtype of humid continental climate. Large annual range of temperature and precipitation concentrated in the warm season is characteristic.

the cool-summer subtype of humid continental climates. In North America it is found east of about the 100° meridian and includes the northern tier of states in the United States and adjacent portions of southern Canada. In Europe it characterizes eastern Germany, Poland,

and a large part of the central plain of the U.S.S.R. between about latitudes 50 and 60°. The third area in eastern Asia includes northern Manchuria, southeastern Siberia, and the northern island of Japan.

9.15 Temperature. In the warm-summer subtype summer months are only 5 to 10° warmer than those of the cool-summer subdivision but this is sufficient to make for marked differences in their agricultural potentialities. Moreover, while the frost-free season is 5 to 6 months in length in the warm-summer subtype, it is shortened to 3 to 5 months in the other (Figs. 9.7 and 9.8). Summers in the warm-summer phase are likely to have many days when it is uncomfortably hot and humid so that human comfort is better served by the cooler summers farther north even though they may offer more handicaps to agriculture.

Winter temperatures, on the other hand, are usually 15 to 20° colder in the cool-summer subtype, and subzero temperatures and long spells of cold weather are more common. In both of the humid continental subtypes successive winters may vary greatly in average temperature conditions, some winters being well above normal and others below (Figs. 9.9 and 9.10).

9.16 Precipitation. The two subtypes are not conspicuously different in amount and sea-

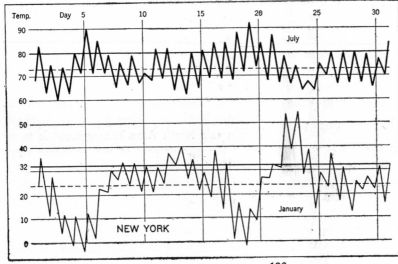

Fig. 9.8 Daily maximum and minimum temperatures for the extreme months for a station with humid continental warm-summer climate. Nonperiodic air-mass control is conspicuous, especially in winter.

Climatic Data for Representative Stations in the Humid Continental Warm-summer Subtype (Da)

Peoria, Ill.

	J	F	M	A	M	J	J	A	S	O	N	D	Yr.	Range
Temp.	24	28	40	51	62	71	75	73	65	53	39	28	51	52
Precip.	1.8	2.0	2.7	3.3	3.9	3.8	3.8	3.2	3.8	2.4	2.4	2.0	34.9	

New York City

	J	F	M	A	M	J	J	A	S	O	N	D	Yr.	Range
Temp.	31	31	39	49	60	69	74	72	67	56	44	34	52	43
Precip.	3.3	3.3	3.4	3.3	3.4	3.4	4.1	4.3	3.4	3.4	3.4	3.3	42.0	

Bucharest, Rumania

	J	F	M	A	M	J	J	A	S	O	N	D	Yr.	Range
Temp.	26	29	40	52	61	68	73	71	64	54	41	30	51	48
Precip.	1.2	1.1	1.7	2.0	2.5	3.3	2.8	1.9	1.5	1.5	1.9	1.7	23.0	

Peking, China

	J	F	M	A	M	J	J	A	S	O	N	D	Yr.	Range
Temp.	24	29	41	57	68	76	79	77	68	55	39	27	53	55
Precip.	0.1	0.2	0.2	0.6	1.4	3.0	9.4	6.3	2.6	0.6	0.3	0.1	24.9	

sonal distribution of precipitation. However, in those parts farther south somewhat more of the summer precipitation is from convectional showers of thermal origin, while farther north a larger part of the winter precipitation is in the form of snow. As a consequence the snow cover is more durable and long continued in the northern parts. In the American Corn Belt, for example, snow falls on about 20 to 30 days, the total snowfall is 10 to 40 in., and snow remains on the ground for 15 to 60 days. By contrast, northern Minnesota has 60 to 80 days with snowfall, the total amount is 40 to 60 in., and there is a continuous snow cover for about 4 months (Fig. 9.11). The total effect of the more continuous snow cover is to reduce winter temperatures.

9.17 Resource Potentialities of the Humid Continental Realm. This is one of the greatest producing realms of the earth. Natural assets of a high order, therefore, would appear to be present. Within the realm are portions of the world's three great population clusters. The North American segment contains the industrial and agricultural heart of that continent, while a portion of Europe's manufacturing belt likewise lies within this realm.

Climatically the realm is less bountiful than the humid subtropics, chiefly because of the shorter growing season. This deficiency of heat tends to exclude many of the more sensitive crops or those requiring a long period between frosts. Greater dependence upon quick-maturing annuals is the result. As compared with the

subtropics, there is likewise a shorter period during which animals can forage for their food and a much longer one during which they must be protected against the cold and fed from feeds stored in barns and granaries. A further

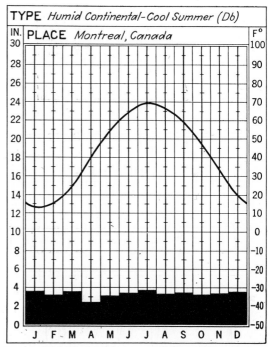

Fig. 9.9 Illustrating the cool-summer subtype. Note the large annual range of temperature. At this station there is an absence of any seasonal concentration of precipitation, a feature characteristic of northeastern United States and adjacent parts of Canada where winter cyclones are numerous.

Climatic Data for Representative Stations in the Humid Continental Cool-summer Subtype (Db)

Madison, Wis. (marginal in location)

	J	F	M	A	M	J	J	A	S	O	N	D	Yr.	Range
Temp.	17	20	31	46	58	67	72	70	62	50	35	23	46	55
Precip.	1.2	1.3	1.9	2.6	3.7	3.4	3.5	3.3	4.1	2.3	2.0	1.4	30.6	

Montreal, Canada

	J	F	M	A	M	J	J	A	S	O	N	D	Yr.	Range
Temp.	13	15	25	41	55	65	69	67	59	47	33	19	42	56
Precip.	3.7	3.2	3.7	2.4	3.1	3.5	3.8	3.4	3.5	3.3	3.4	3.7	41	

Moscow, U.S.S.R.

	J	F	M	A	M	J	J	A	S	O	N	D	Yr.	Range
Temp.	12	15	23	38	53	62	66	63	52	40	28	17	39	54
Precip.	1.1	1.0	1.2	1.5	1.9	2.0	2.8	2.9	2.2	1.4	1.6	1.5	21.1	

Harbin, Manchuria

	J	F	M	A	M	J	J	A	S	O	N	D	Yr.	Range
Temp.	−2	5	24	42	56	66	72	69	58	40	21	3	38	74
Precip.	0.1	0.2	0.4	0.9	1.7	3.8	4.5	4.1	1.8	1.3	0.3	0.2	19.3	

climatic handicap grows out of the fact that over extensive areas rainfall is only modest in amount and is inclined to be undependable. In northern China, including Manchuria, southern Soviet Russia, the Danube plains, and the western prairie regions in North America, the rainfall handicap is most striking. The relatively wide fluctuations in crop yields from year to year in these same regions reflect the above handicap. Somewhat compensating for the disadvantage of modest and variable precipitation is the feature of its seasonal concentration in the period of greatest heat.

Forests in the more humid portions and tall-grass prairie in the subhumid interiors—such is the characteristic pattern of native vegetation within the realm. In their virgin state the prairies provided some of the finest natural grazing land on earth. Almost all the prairie land has long since come under the plow, however, for this represents some of the world's best agricultural land. The forests of the more

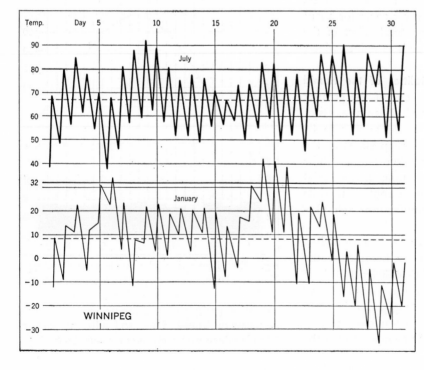

Fig. 9.10 Illustrating the cool-summer subtype of humid continental climate. Note the very large and irregular temperature changes, evidence of strong air-mass control associated with cyclones and anticyclones.

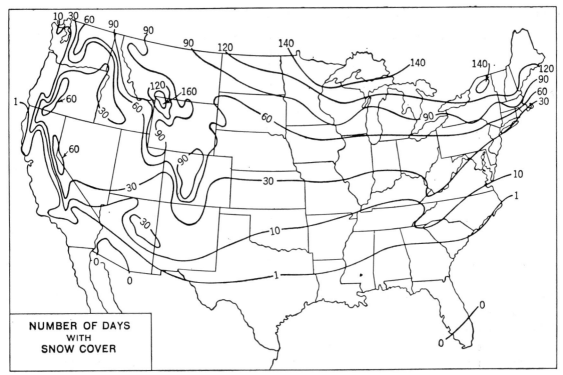

NUMBER OF DAYS
WITH
SNOW COVER

Fig. 9.11

humid sections of the realm were of a variety of types. A representative north-south cross section of the forests would show conifers predominating toward the northern margins of the realm, with mixed forests and purer stands of deciduous broadleaf trees prevailing farther south. Without doubt the virgin forests of the humid continental realm were among the finest and most extensive of the earth. For decades they were the world's principal source of lumber, and they are still important producers. However, because they were composed of such superior lumber trees and because of ready accessibility, they have suffered rapid cutting. Much of the forest was removed by settlers in search of farm land. In less desirable agricultural regions it was the great lumber companies that logged off the forest and left behind a desolate cut-over country.

Soils in the humid continental realm show great variations, depending upon the nature of the climate, the original vegetation, and the recency of glaciation. Gray-brown soils of moderate fertility are characteristic of those areas with mixed or deciduous forests. These, the best of the forest soils, have already been described in the earlier analysis of the resource base of the marine realm. On the cooler poleward margins of the humid continental realm where needle trees tend to replace the broadleaf varieties, the soils are inferior, being more strongly leached of mineral plant foods and having a much lower humus content. These gray, ash-colored soils (known as podzols) are one of the poorest of the earth's soils. In the subhumid sections of the realm, on the other hand, where prairie grasses predominated, are to be found some of the earth's superior soils. The lower rainfall results in less leaching, and the grasses provide an abundance of organic matter so that the soils are high in soluble minerals and dark in color. Such excellent soils help to compensate in part for the less abundant and also less reliable rainfall.

Considerable areas in both the north American and European section of the realm have been subjected to recent glaciation by continental ice sheets. Where the relief is relatively great or the bedrock resistant, as for example, in New England, northern New York State,

189

and parts of Norway, Sweden, and Finland, ice erosion has been dominant, so that soils are thin and stony and lakes are numerous. In other regions, where ice deposition prevailed, the drainage lines have been disrupted so that lakes and swamps are numerous and a rolling and somewhat patternless terrain arrangement of rounded hills and associated depressions is characteristic. The soils are usually deep, but they vary greatly in composition and quality.

Subarctic Climates (Dc, Dd) [3]
(Taiga)

9.18 Location. This is the extreme in microthermal climates, subarctic having the largest annual temperature ranges. It is found only in the higher middle latitudes (50 or 55 to 65°) of the great Northern Hemisphere continents (Fig. A.2, Plate 2). On its poleward side it makes contact with tundra, one of the polar climates. This northern boundary is approximately the isotherm of 50° for the warmest month (usually July), which is critical because it closely coincides with the poleward limit of forest growth. On its southern margin, the subarctic climate usually makes contact with the cool-summer phase of humid continental climate or, in places, with middle-latitude steppes and deserts.

The Eurasian subarctic area (the taiga of the Russians) extends from Sweden and Finland in Europe, across the whole of the continent to the coast of Siberia. It widens toward the Pacific, or leeward, side as continentality increases. In North America the subarctic belt stretches from Alaska on the Pacific, across Canada to Labrador and Newfoundland on the Atlantic.

TEMPERATURE

9.19 Summer. Long, bitterly cold winters, very short summers, and brief springs and autumns are characteristic (Fig. 9.12). Since the isotherm of 50° for the warmest month has been adopted as the poleward boundary of this

[3] In the Köppen symbols, *c* = cool summers with only 1 to 3 months above 50° (10°C.); *d* = cold winters with the temperature of the coldest month below —36.4° (—38°C.).

type of climate, at least one month must have an average temperature of 50° or above. At Yakutsk, Siberia, nearly 62°N., representing the extreme in subarctic climates, July, the warmest month, has an average temperature of 66°, which is higher than the same month at London or Berlin and 6° higher than July at San Francisco. Midsummer daily maxima of 80° are common at Yakutsk, and the thermometer occasionally reaches 90°. The absolute maximum is 102°. At this same station, however, June and August have mean temperatures of only 59°. It needs to be emphasized that at Yakutsk there are only 3 months in which the mean temperatures exceed 50°, for both May and September have averages in the low forties. At Fort Vermilion, at 58°27′N. in Canada, another representative subarctic station, July is cooler than it is at Yakutsk, having an average temperature of only 60°, while June and August have temperatures of 55 and 59°, respectively. The mean of the daily maxima in July

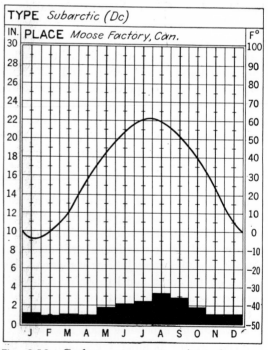

Fig. 9.12 Cool summer, severe winter, large annual range of temperature, and modest precipitation concentrated in summer are characteristic of subarctic climate.

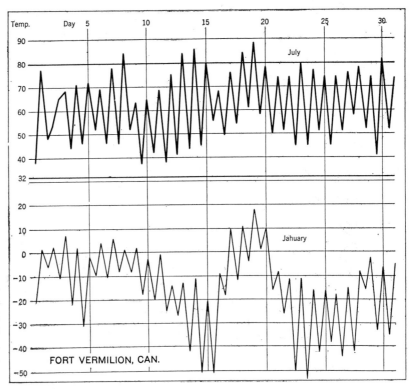

Fig. 9.13 A subarctic station in Canada. Note the unusually strong nonperiodic air-mass control of temperature changes in winter. Summer shows greater diurnal regularity.

is 74°, and of the minima, 46°. Temperatures over 90° have been recorded at Fort Vermilion in both June and July. Subarctic summer days, then, are pleasantly warm and occasionally even hot (Fig. 9.13).

9.20 *Long Summer Days.* Somewhat compensating for the short and none-too-warm summers are the unusually long days in these higher latitudes. Thus, although the intensity of sunlight is not so great, the large number of hours during which the sun shines is an offsetting factor. Moreover, the short nights do not permit a long period of cooling. For example, at latitude 55°N. June days average 17.3 hr. of possible sunshine; latitude 60°N., 18.8 hr.; and latitude 65°N., 22.1 hr. Moreover, since twilight continues when the sun is as much as 18° below the horizon, it is evident that in summer the hours of genuine darkness are very much limited. At the time of the summer solstice the daily surface receipts of insolation at latitude 60° are equal to those at the equator.

9.21 *Growing Season.* Unfortunately, the subarctic lands have very short periods that are entirely without frost. The growing season in

the Mackenzie Valley of Canada varies from about 50 to 75 days, and many stations must expect freezing temperatures in July and August in at least half of the years. A shift of wind to the north at any time brings with it the chill of the ice-laden Arctic. Thus while it is the occasional *midwinter* frosts which are dangerous in the subtropical climates, it is, on the other hand, the *midsummer* frosts which are of peculiar significance in this subarctic type. The characteristic coolness, shortness, and precariousness of the growing season are the most serious handicaps of the subarctic climates for agricultural development. In fact, these are the principal conditions that have retarded permanent settlement, so that at present much of the subarctic has only a meager sprinkling of frontier farmers and of people exploiting the mineral, forest, and wild-animal resources.

9.22 **Winter** follows on the heels of summer with only a very brief intervening autumn season. Frosts may arrive in late August, and ice begins to form on pools in September. By the middle of October navigation for small craft is made difficult on the subarctic lakes of Canada.

At Verkhoyansk, Siberia, the mean temperature drops 40° from October to November. Subarctic Siberia holds the records for minimum temperatures at low elevations, even lower than those of polar climates. Verkhoyansk, in the northeastern part, boasts an average January temperature of 59° below zero, while an absolute minimum of —90° was recorded in February, 1892. This, of course, is an extreme case. At Yakutsk, however, where July has an average temperature of 66°, the January mean drops to approximately —46°, producing an annual range of 112°. For 7 months at Yakutsk the average temperatures are below freezing, and during 5 months they are below zero. No other type of climate can show such contrasts between summer and winter temperatures.

Concerning the Siberian winter, Hann writes:

It is not possible to describe the terrible cold one has to endure; one has to experience it to appreciate it. The quicksilver freezes solid and can be cut and hammered like lead; iron becomes brittle, and the hatchet breaks like glass; wood, depending upon the degree of moisture in it, becomes harder than iron and withstands the ax so that only completely dry wood can be split. Every step in the dry snow can be heard for long distances; the bursting of the ice cover and the frozen ground sound like the cannonading of distant batteries.

Subarctic winters in North America are not quite so severe as are those of Siberia. This comes about in part as a result of Asia's being a broader land mass. Moreover, it contains no such extensive arm of the sea as is Hudson Bay in North America. In addition the mountains of eastern Siberia retard the eastward flow of the cold continental air, thereby aiding in an excessive accumulation of cold air over the continent. Representative stations such as Churchill, Dawson, and Fort Good Hope show average January temperatures of —20, —22, —32°, respectively. At Dawson, in the Yukon, at 64°3′N., the thermometer, on an average January night, falls to approximately —29° and rises to nearly —16° during the warmest hours of the day (Fig. 9.13).

The excessive and long-continued cold of the subarctic winters causes large parts of taiga

regions to be permanently frozen down to great depths. Over extensive areas of the subarctic lands only the upper few feet thaw out during the short summers. The depth to which frost penetrates and the depth of the summer thaw vary greatly from one part of the subarctic lands to another. Cleveland Abbe notes the case of a mine in the Klondike (Yukon) which passed out of the permanently frozen zone at a depth of 220 ft.

Just as long days are characteristic of subarctic summers, so long nights are characteristic of the winters. For example, on Dec. 21 all places on the 60°N. parallel can receive a maximum of only 5.7 hr. of sunshine, while on latitude 65°N. the maximum is only 3.3 hr. These long daily periods of darkness are not only depressing and hard to bear, but they are, in a considerable measure, responsible for the low winter temperatures.

Spring, like autumn, is a short and inconspicuous season. At Yakutsk there is a difference of 25° between the mean temperatures of April and May, and 18° between May and June. The average April temperature at Yakutsk is like that of Madison, Wis., in January, while May is only 4 to 5° lower than April at Madison.

PRECIPITATION AND HUMIDITY

9.23 Amount. Precipitation in subarctic climates is usually meager (Fig. 9.12). Over much of the Siberian taiga it is no more than 15 in., while most of subarctic Canada receives less than 20, and parts receive less than 15 in. The modest precipitation is related to (*a*) the low temperatures and associated low specific humidity, (*b*) the well-developed winter anticyclone with its settling air and diverging wind systems, and (*c*) the great breadth of the land masses in the subarctic latitudes. It is principally along the oceanic margins in both Eurasia and North America that rainfall exceeds 20 in. In most middle-latitude climates these small amounts, characteristic of the taiga, would be classed as semiarid, but where such low temperatures and, therefore, low evaporation rates prevail, and where the ground is frozen so

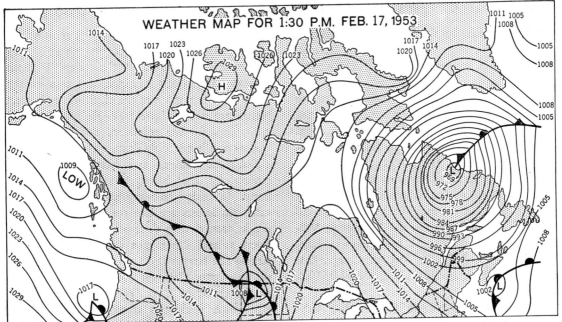

Fig. 9.14 A subarctic winter-weather type. A well-developed cyclone accompanied by strong winds and extensive precipitation prevails over the subarctic and tundra region of northeastern Canada. A cold anticyclone is conspicuous over northernmost Canada.

much of the year, the precipitation is sufficient for forest growth.

9.24 Annual Distribution. Precipitation is concentrated in the warmer months (Fig. 9.13). At Yakutsk, where the total annual rainfall is 13.7 in., August is the wettest month with 2.6 in., and February the driest with 0.2 in. At Dawson in the Yukon the total is 12.5 in., with 1.5 in July and 0.8 in January (0.7 in. in February and 0.5 in March). Winter, with its low temperature and specific humidity, strong anticyclone, and diverging surface winds, presents a total setup which is antagonistic to precipitation. It is over east-central Siberia, in particular, that winters are especially dry, the three

winter months there having only 10 per cent of the annual precipitation, while the three summer months have 58 per cent. This is the region of most intense cold and the strongest winter anticyclone.

Over lowlands the meager winter precipitation, practically all of it in the form of snow, is cyclonic in origin (Fig. 9.14). The few fronts that cross these areas yield sufficient precipitation, in the form of relatively dry, hard snow, so that a permanent snow cover, lasting 5 to 7 months, is common. Because of the shelter provided by the forest, little melting or evaporation occurs, so that the winter snows accumulate to a depth of 2 to 3 ft. in the taiga. This

Climatic Data for Representative Subarctic Stations

Fort Vermilion, Alberta, Canada (58°27′N.)

	J	F	M	A	M	J	J	A	S	O	N	D	Yr.	Range
Temp.	−14	−6	8	30	47	55	60	57	46	32	10	−4	27	74
Precip.	0.6	0.3	0.5	0.7	1.0	1.9	2.1	2.1	1.4	0.7	0.5	0.4	12.3	

Moose Factory, Canada (51°16′N.)

	J	F	M	A	M	J	J	A	S	O	N	D	Yr.	Range
Temp.	−4	−2	10	28	42	54	61	59	51	39	22	5	30	66
Precip.	1.3	0.9	1.1	1.0	1.8	2.2	2.4	3.3	2.9	1.8	1.1	1.1	21.0	

Yakutsk, Siberia, U.S.S.R.

	J	F	M	A	M	J	J	A	S	O	N	D	Yr.	Range
Temp.	−46	−35	−10	16	41	59	66	60	42	16	−21	−41	12	112
Precip.	0.9	0.2	0.4	0.6	1.1	2.1	1.7	2.6	1.2	1.4	0.6	0.9	13.7	

same protection by the forest leads to slow melting of the snow cover in spring. In east-central Siberia, winter precipitation is so meager that sleighing is sometimes difficult.

Summer, the season of maximum surface heating, steepest vertical temperature gradients, and highest humidity, provides conditions that are relatively most favorable for rainfall. Warm-season precipitation is also largely frontal in origin. Thunderstorms are not numerous, the total number in the Mackenzie Valley of Canada being in the neighborhood of 5 to 10 a year. Fort Vermilion, in the Mackenzie Valley, has on the average 5.3 rainy days in June, 9.1 in July, and 7.5 in August. Comparable data for Dawson, in the Yukon, are 11.7, 10.3, and 10.9.

9.25 Resource Potentialities of the Subarctic Realm. In spite of the fact that this is one of the most extensive of the earth's geographic realms, it is also one of the least productive. Like the dry lands, and parts of the wet tropics, the subarctic realm is coincident with relatively blank areas on the world-population map. The extractive industries, such as hunting, fishing, mining, and logging, which are of more than usual importance, are capable of supporting only a meager population. The landscape, therefore, is one composed predominantly of natural features; man has left but a faint imprint.

In productive capacity the realm is fundamentally handicapped by a niggardly climate which sets very definite and low limits upon agricultural development. The primary handicaps are associated with (*a*) the briefness of the summers and (*b*) the relatively low summer temperatures. It is obviously impossible to draw a line that accurately defines the northern limits of agriculture as set by temperature conditions. Some quick-maturing vegetables grow almost as far poleward as the Arctic Circle. In certain favorable years both wheat and barley have been matured in 70 to 80 days, but summer frosts in any year may prevent a harvest. At present, however, commercially successful agriculture is not likely in regions where the frost-free season is less than 80 or 90 days, and this

condition prevails in all except the most southerly portions of the subarctic realm. Along the southern margins of the taiga, in both Eurasia and North America, are two of the great frontier regions of the earth where human beings are struggling to push their agricultural settlements farther poleward. But the progress is slow and is probably destined to remain so.

Subarctic Eurasia and North America are covered by what is largely a virgin coniferous forest. In their immensity and monotony these subarctic forests are like the sea, and travelers are impressed with their emptiness and silence. Even animal life is not abundant. They are among the largest and least-known wildernesses of the earth. Conifers usually occupy in the neighborhood of 75 per cent of the forest area with such deciduous trees as birch, poplar, willow, and alder comprising most of the remainder. In both continents spruce and fir are the dominant trees, although larch and pine are plentiful. Neither in the size of the trees nor in the density of the stand is taiga forest impressive, so that it does not represent nearly so great a potential supply of forest products as its area might seem to indicate. In the ice-scoured Canadian subarctic extensive areas of lake, swamp, and bare rock are practically without forest. Subarctic timber is probably much more universally valuable for firewood and pulpwood than for good lumber. Moreover, the inaccessibility of these northern forests involving the severe handicap of distance to world markets greatly reduces their resource value.

The subarctic forest lands are the home of many of the earth's most important fur-bearing animals and are the source of a large proportion of the wild pelts taken annually. The lakes and swamps and the forest cover provide the satisfactory habitat conditions for various types of animals, while the long and severe winters induce thick, heavy pelts. In many parts the forest animals are more valuable than the vegetation cover under which they live. Ruthless hunting and trapping have, however, caused the numbers of fur-bearing animals to dwindle alarmingly.

An impoverished soil environment is characteristic of the subarctic realm. This infertile soil, combined with a climate of low potentialities, causes the subarctic lands to offer what appear to be almost insurmountable difficulties to the agricultural settler. The needles from the coniferous forest provide a very meager supply of organic material for the soil, while the ground water, high in organic acids derived from the raw humus, results in an excessive leaching of the soil minerals.

After climate and soils, the third ranking handicap to agricultural settlement within the subarctic realm is deficient drainage. This prevalence of poorly drained land is partly the result of a permanently frozen subsoil, a condition which prevails throughout the higher latitudes of the realm. Over most of subarctic North America and in Scandinavia, Finland, and western Soviet Russia the abundance of lakes and swamps is a consequence of continental glaciation. The name Finland, derived from "fen land," suggests the prevalence of lake and marsh in that country where they occupy about one-third of the entire area. Still another cause of the realm's deficient drainage is associated with the fact that many of its streams flow poleward into the Arctic Ocean. Such rivers thaw out in their upper and middle courses while the lower courses are still frozen and therefore unable to carry the drainage waters. As a result, where lowlands prevail, widespread spring inundation is the result.

10

Polar Climates and Highland Climates

Polar Climates (E)

10.1 As the tropics are characterized by lack of a cool season, so the polar regions are wanting in a period of warmth. It is the prevalence of monotonous heat that typifies the low latitudes. In the high latitudes monotonous and long-continued cold is the greatest handicap.

10.2 Phenomena of Light and Darkness. A distinctive feature of the polar climates is their peculiarities with respect to periods of light and darkness. At the poles the sun is out of sight entirely for approximately 6 months, while for an equal period it is constantly above the horizon, although never very high in the heavens, so that insolation is weak. At the Arctic and Antarctic Circles, which lie near the equatorward margins of polar climates, the daily period of sunlight varies from 24 hr. at the time of the summer solstice to a complete lack of sunlight at the winter solstice. At points between the poles and the 66½° parallels the lengths of the periods of sunlight, and absence of sunlight, are intermediate in character between the two extremes noted.

10.3 Locations and Boundaries. Polar climates are largely confined to the high latitudes of the earth. Somewhat similar conditions can be found at high altitudes in a great variety of latitudes. But these latter regions of continuous cold usually are very isolated and fragmentary and in this book are included within the group designated as highland climates.

The poleward limit of forest is usually accepted as marking the boundary separating the polar climates from those of the intermediate latitudes. In continental locations this vegetation boundary approximately coincides with the isotherm of 50° for the *warmest month*, so that this seasonal isotherm is commonly employed in defining the outer margins of the polar climates.[1] It is significant that, while for the boundary of the humid tropics a *cool-month* isotherm is employed, a *warm-month* isotherm serves in the same way for polar climates (Fig. A.2). It suggests that, while a period of coolness is of critical importance for plants and animals in the low latitudes, a period of warmth is much more significant in high latitudes. In the Southern Hemisphere the only conspicuous land area having polar climates is the ice-covered Antarctic Continent. In the Northern Hemisphere it is the Arctic Sea borderlands of Eurasia and North America, together with extensive island groups north of both continents, and ice-covered Greenland, which are included.

10.4 Arctic and Antarctic. Since the Arctic is almost a landlocked sea, while the Antarctic is a seagirt land, certain important climatic differences are to be expected between the two regions. As a consequence of its single land mass being centered at the Pole and surrounded on all sides by extensive oceans of uniform temperature, the Antarctic shows much greater uniformity and simplicity in its climate than does the Arctic. Wind and pressure systems are symmetrically developed about the South Pole, and there is little change in these elements throughout the year, whereas lack of symmetry

---

[1] In order to exclude certain cool marine climates which are not distinctly polar in nature, the definition might further stipulate a mean annual temperature of 32° or below.

and seasonal variations in these controls are characteristic of the north polar regions.

10.5 Temperature and Precipitation. Polar climates claim the distinction of having the lowest *mean annual,* as well as the lowest *summer,* temperatures for any part of the earth. In spite of the long duration of sunshine in summer, temperatures remain low, the sun's rays being too oblique to be genuinely effective. Moreover, much of the solar energy is reflected by the snow and ice or is consumed in melting the snow cover and evaporating the water, so that neither the land surface nor the air adjacent to it becomes warm. Winters are bitterly cold, but there is some doubt as to whether the thermometer ever sinks as low in the polar regions as it does in the subarctic climate of northeastern Siberia. In spite of the cool summers, winter cold is sufficiently severe to develop large annual ranges.

Precipitation is meager throughout the high latitudes. Over large parts of the land areas it is less than 10 in. But in spite of its meagerness, the low evaporation permits of some runoff, part of it in the form of glaciers. It is because of the low evaporation and the small amount of melting that great permanent snow and ice fields several thousand feet thick have been able to accumulate on Greenland and the Antarctic Continent, and this in spite of the low precipitation. A dearth of polar precipitation does not seem unusual when one considers the prevailingly low absolute humidity which must accompany the low temperatures. The reservoir of water vapor is small at all times. Moreover, in these latitudes there is a general settling of the cold upper air masses which creates a condition unfavorable to condensation. Precipitation is usually heavier in the warmer months when the moisture supply is most abundant.

10.6 Tundra and Ice Caps. Polar climates are usually subdivided into two types, with the *warmest month* isotherm of 32° serving as the boundary between them. Where the average temperatures of all months are below freezing, the growth of vegetation is impossible, and a permanent snow-and-ice cover prevails. These are the *ice-cap climates.* Where one or more of

the warm-season months has an average temperature above 32° (but not over 50°), so that the ground is free from snow for a short period, and a meager and lowly vegetation cover is possible, the climate is designated as *tundra.*

Tundra Climate (ET) [2]

10.7 Location. Tundra climate is transitional in character between the ice caps, or regions of perpetual snow and ice, on the one hand, and middle-latitude climates, usually subarctic, on the other (Fig. A.2, Plate 2). Its accepted equatorward and poleward boundaries are the warmest month isotherms of 50 and 32°, respectively, which, as indicated previously, are reasonably coincident with important vegetation boundaries.

Tundra climate over land areas is almost exclusively confined to the Northern Hemisphere. In the Antarctic, ocean prevails in those latitudes where the tundra would normally develop. Only the most northerly fringes of the Antarctic Continent, and certain small Antarctic islands, have sufficiently warm summers for them to be included. The most extensive tundra areas are the Arctic Sea margins of both North America and Eurasia. Most of the Arctic archipelago of the former continent, as well as the coastal fringe of Greenland, is likewise included.

TEMPERATURE

10.8 Summer. Long cold winters and very short cool summers are the rule (Fig. 10.1). By the definition of boundaries for tundra climate, previously stated, the average temperature of the warmest month can be no lower than 32° and no higher than 50°. The cool character of the summer is therefore relatively fixed. Raw and chilly, the warmest months of the tundra resemble March and April in southern Wisconsin and are like January in the American Cotton Belt. Usually only 2 to 4 months have average temperatures above freezing, and killing frost is likely to occur at any time. Along coasts, where water, ice, and land are in close

[2] *ET,* warmest month below 50° (10°C.) but above 32° (0°C.).

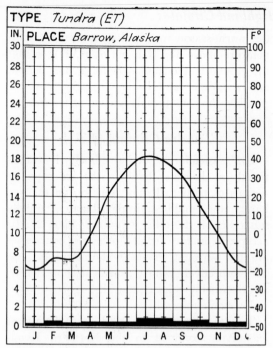

TYPE *Tundra (ET)*

PLACE *Barrow, Alaska*

Fig. 10.1 A tundra station of the severe continental type. Note the large annual range of temperature and the meager precipitation.

the permanently frozen subsoil, subsurface drainage is deficient, and bog and swamp are prevalent. Myriads of mosquitoes and black flies make life almost unbearable for man and beast alike during the summer period of wet earth.

At Ponds Inlet, Canada, a tundra station at 72°43′N., where the average July temperature is 42°, the thermometer in that month rises to about 49° during the warmest hours of the day and, on the average, sinks to 35 or 36° at night. Daily ranges in summer are relatively small, for the sun is above the horizon for all or a greater part of the 24-hr. period. On most July nights no frost occurs, but on the other hand it is not unusual for the thermometer to slip a few degrees below freezing (Fig. 10.2). Warm days occur now and then, Ponds Inlet having recorded, on at least one occasion, a temperature of 77°.

10.9 Winter. While summer temperatures are not greatly different from one tundra region to another, there are greater variations in the winters. Thus along the Arctic coasts of Siberia, average January and February temperatures are in the neighborhood of −35 or −40°, and it is appreciably colder farther inland. At this season winds in general are from the bitterly cold subarctic region to the south, and these importations serve only further to intensify the severity of temperatures in the tundra. Along

proximity, fog is very prevalent. These fogs may last for days at a time and are extraordinarily depressing. Under the influence of unusually long summer days, the snow cover begins to disappear in May, and the lakes are usually rid of their ice cover in June. Because of

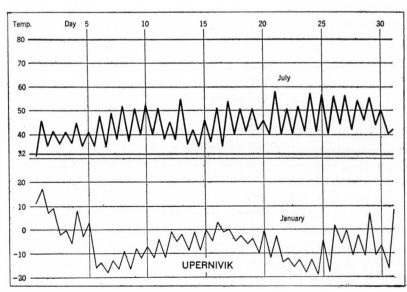

Fig. 10.2 A tundra station in Greenland.

Climatic Data for Representative Tundra Stations

Sagastyr, Siberia, U.S.S.R. (73°N., 124°E.)

	J	F	M	A	M	J	J	A	S	O	N	D	Yr.	Range
Temp.	−34	−36	−30	−7	15	32	41	38	33	6	−16	−28	1	77
Precip.	0.1	0.1	0.0	0.0	0.2	0.4	0.3	1.4	0.4	0.1	0.1	0.2	3.3	

Upernivik, Western Greenland (73°N., 56°W.)

	J	F	M	A	M	J	J	A	S	O	N	D	Yr.	Range
Temp.	−7	−10	−6	6	25	35	41	41	33	25	14	1	16	61
Precip.	0.4	0.4	0.6	0.6	0.6	0.6	1.0	1.1	1.0	1.1	1.1	0.5	9.2	

the arctic borderlands of North America winters are not quite so severe. A coastal station in Labrador shows a January mean of −8°; Ponds Inlet in Canada records an average of −28° for January, −30° for February, and even −24° for March (Fig. 10.1). At the latter station 5 months, November to March, have average temperatures below zero, while 9 are below freezing.

PRECIPITATION

10.10 Amount and Distribution. Over most of the tundra lands precipitation is not over 10 or 12 in. (Fig. 10.1). In portions of eastern arctic Canada, particularly the Labrador peninsula, it is somewhat greater. Low summer temperatures and winter anticyclonic conditions are, in general, not conducive to abundant condensation, while convectional effects are largely absent. Summer and autumn, the warmest seasons, are likewise the periods of maximum precipitation throughout the tundra as a whole. In the more marine locations, where cyclones are greater in number, fall and winter may show larger totals than summer. Precipitation is principally cyclonic in origin. Much of that which falls in the warm season is in the form of rain, with occasional wet snows.

The meager winter snowfall is usually dry and powdery in character so that it forms a very compact cover. It is only this very compact snow, 2 in. of which may equal an inch of rain, that the Eskimos use in constructing their igloos. The actual amount of dry sandlike snow that falls is not easy to measure, since it is often accompanied by strong blizzard winds which heap it up in depressions and on the lee sides of hills, while at the same time sweeping bare the exposed surfaces. There are no forests,

as in the taiga, to break the force of the wind and anchor the snow cover. Stefansson estimates that 75 to 90 per cent of the surfaces of the Arctic lands is nearly free of snow at all seasons. Both as a result of the small amount of snow and as a result of its strong tendency to drift, sledging commonly is difficult.

Ice-cap Climate (EF)[3]

This least well known among the world's climatic types is characteristically developed over the great permanent continental ice sheets of Antarctica and Greenland and over the perpetually frozen ocean in the vicinity of the North Pole. Only fragmentary data have been obtained from these deserts of snow and ice where the average temperature of no month rises above freezing.

10.11 Temperature. The mean annual temperature of interior Greenland has been calculated to be −26°; that of the South Pole −22 to −31°; that of the North Pole −9°. These, without doubt, are the lowest annual temperatures for any portion of the earth. Observed temperatures for the *warmest* months in the neighborhood of the South Pole, at the time of continuous insolation, were −9° (December) and −19° (January). A temperature of −58° has been recorded in the Antarctic Continent in this season. Unquestionably, therefore, Antarctica has the distinction of being the earth's coldest spot in summer. While the North Pole and interior Greenland are certainly below freezing in July and August, they are far from being as cold as the south polar plateau at the time of continuous day. To be sure, the figures given above are for interior portions of Antarc-

[3] *EF*, warmest month below 32° (0°C.).

Climatic Data for a Representative Ice-cap Station

Little America, Antarctic Continent (79°S., 164°W.)

	J	F	M	A	M	⌈J	J	A	S	O	N	D	⌈ Yr.	Range
Temp.	22	(9)	(−7)	−24	−27	−29	−34	−34	−29	−14	9	24	−11.3	58
Precip.	No data													

tica and hence represent extreme conditions. Along the margins of that continent warm-month temperatures are considerably milder (McMurdo Sound, 25°; Little America, 22°).

During the period when the sun is constantly below the horizon, excessively cold weather prevails, although exact and reliable data are not available. On the Antarctic plateau the average winter-month temperatures are probably in the neighborhood of 35 to 45° below zero. It is not impossible that in some of the wind-protected depressions of that region, cold-month and minimum temperatures are as low as those of subarctic northeastern Siberia.

10.12 Precipitation. If little is known about the temperatures of the ice-cap climates, still less is known concerning their precipitation. There is no doubt that it is meager, and probably all of it falls as snow, most of it in the form of dry, hard, sandlike particles which are readily driven before the wind. The origin of the precipitation over the ice caps is not well understood. In such regions, although streams are practically absent, there is some loss by evaporation as well as through glaciers moving out to the sea. Enough precipitation must be accounted for to more than offset these losses. No doubt a portion of the inland snow has its origin in the cyclonic storms that move along the margins of the ice plateaus. Still more originates in the moving cyclonic storms that pass in over the ice cap. At Eismitte in interior Greenland precipitation fell on 204 days in the year and the annual snowfall amounted to about 12 in. or 3 to 4 in. of water.

Highland Climates (H)

10.13 Altitude and Exposure as Climatic Controls. Next to the distribution of land and water, elevation above sea level is the most important control causing differences in climate in similar latitudes. The climatic effects of such elevated land masses as mountains and plateaus are expressed through the two factors (*a*) *altitude* and (*b*) *exposure*.

It needs to be emphasized, however, that there is no such thing as a *highland type of climate* in the same sense that there is a subarctic or a humid subtropical type. Almost endless varieties of local climates exist within a mountain mass, the atmospheric conditions varying markedly with altitude and exposure and of course with latitude as well. The enclosed valley or plateau is very different climatically from the exposed peak; windward slopes contrast markedly with those having leeward positions, while flanks inclined toward the sun are dissimilar to those oppositely inclined. And each of these in turn is different at various *altitudes* and *latitudes*. Above an elevation of 5,000 or 6,000 ft. marked differences in temperature are conspicuous between sunshine and shade, wind and calm. Representative temperature and rainfall curves for highland climates scarcely can be said to exist, and only the most flexible generalizations are broadly applicable. On Plate 2, which emphasizes a relatively small number of simple types of climate, no attempt has been made to show the varieties of climate within great mountain masses. Instead most of the *high* mountain and plateau areas in low and middle latitudes have been included within one general group, *highland climates*. In contrast, regions of *moderate* elevation and relief have been included within the general climatic type characteristic of the surrounding lower lands, even though they may represent a modified form of the lowland climate. Up to an altitude of about 4,000 or 5,000 ft. the peculiarities of altitude climate are not prominent, but above 6,000 ft. they are usually very noticeable (*cf.* Plates 2 and 4).

10.14 Atmospheric Pressure in Mountains. At low elevations the minor changes in air pressure from day to day, or from season to season, are not directly perceptible to the human body. However, the very rapid decrease in the atmosphere's weight with increasing elevation and the very low pressures that prevail in high mountains and plateaus cause this element to be a genuinely important one in highland climates. At an elevation above sea level of about 17,500 ft., pressure is reduced to approximately one-half its sea-level value. The highest human habitations are found below this level, although there are said to be settlements in Tibet and the Bolivian Andes the elevations of which approach it. Physiological effects (faintness, headache, nosebleed, nausea, weakness) of decreased pressure aloft are experienced by most people at altitudes above 12,000 to 15,000 ft. Sleeplessness is common, and exertion is difficult. Usually mountain sickness is a temporary inconvenience that passes away after a week or so of residence at high altitudes. Some persons, however, never become acclimated to the reduced pressure.

TEMPERATURE AND INSOLATION

10.15   Insolation. Intensity of sunlight increases aloft in the cleaner, drier, thinner air of mountains. This is to be expected, since dust, moisture, and other principal scattering and absorbing elements of solar radiation in the atmosphere are much more abundant at lower elevations. On a clear day probably three-fourths of the insolation penetrates to 6,000 ft., but only one-half to sea level. The great relative intensity of the sun's rays attracts the attention of nearly all persons going to high elevations. This intensity of insolation causes soil temperatures to be relatively high as compared with the cooler air temperatures.

Insolation not only is more intense in the higher altitudes, but it also is proportionally richer in the shorter wave lengths of energy, or the violet and ultraviolet rays. One therefore burns and tans quickly in mountain sunlight. The greater therapeutic quality of this short-wave radiation is one reason for establishing many sanatoriums in the higher altitudes.

10.16   Air Temperature. Probably of most fundamental importance among the climatic changes resulting from increased elevation is the decrease in air temperature (on the average, about 3.3° per 1,000 ft.), and this in spite of the increased intensity of insolation. Quito, Ecuador, on the equator, at an elevation of 9,350 ft., has an average annual temperature of 55°, which is 25° lower than that of the adjacent Amazon Lowland. But although the clear, rare air at that elevation, which is incapable of absorbing and retaining much energy, remains chilly, the sun is intensely strong. It is a climate of *cool shade and hot sun*. Viscount Bryce has the following to say concerning his experience on the Bolivian plateau: "The keen air which this elevation gives has a fine bracing quality, yet there are disadvantages. One is never warm except when actually in the sunlight. . . . The inhabitants get accustomed to these conditions and shiver in their ponchos, but the traveler is rather wretched after sunset and feels how natural was Sun worship in such a country."

Vertical temperature gradients along mountain slopes are many times steeper than the most severe winter horizontal gradients on lowlands. In the low latitudes, by a railroad trip of only a few hours, one can be transported from tropical to polar temperatures. This fact of steep vertical temperature gradients in mountains is particularly significant in the low latitudes, where, as a result of the prevailingly high temperatures of the lowlands, people look with favor upon elevated regions where they are able to escape the oppressive heat. Largely because of their lower temperatures, elevations in the tropics commonly become the centers of concentration for the population. In tropical

Climatic Data for a Highland Station in the Tropics

Quito, Ecuador (9,350 Ft.)

	J	F	M	A	M	J	J	A	S	O	N	D	Yr.	Range
Temp.	54.5	55.0	54.5	54.5	54.7	55.0	54.9	54.9	55.0	54.7	54.3	54.7	54.7	0.7
Precip.	3.2	3.9	4.8	7.0	4.6	1.5	1.1	2.2	2.6	3.9	4.0	3.6	42.3	

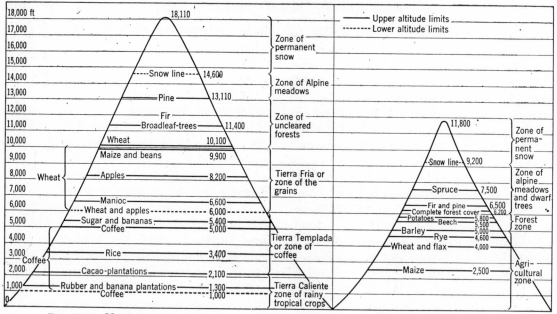

Fig. 10.3 Vertical temperature zones and altitude limits on a tropical mountain (left) and a middle-latitude mountain (right). (*After Sapper.*)

Latin America, for instance, the capital cities of Venezuela, Colombia, Bolivia, and five of the Central American republics are on highlands. In India, the so-called "hill stations" of the sub-Himalayas, such as Darjeeling, Simla, Murree, and Naini Tal, at elevations of 6,500 to 7,500 ft., become havens for residents from the lowlands during the long, hot season.

10.17 Vertical Temperature Zones on Tropical Highlands. As a consequence of steep vertical temperature gradients there is a striking zonation of climates on tropical mountains. In the mountains of tropical Latin America four such vertical zones of climate are recognized, *viz.*, the *tierra caliente* (hot lands), *tierra templada* (temperate lands), *tierra fria* (cool lands), and *tierra helada* (lands of frost) (Fig. 10.3). Quite naturally these altitudinal belts are not defined by identical elevations throughout the entire tropics. In general, the bounding elevations become lower with increasing distance from the equator. The lowest zone, or caliente, normally extends from sea level to 2,000 or 3,000 ft. (annual temperature roughly 83 to 75°). Where precipitation is abundant, **the caliente** is characterized by a luxuriant

vegetation cover of trees, or of trees and tall grass, and by such crops as rubber, bananas, and cacao. The tierra templada lies above the caliente and extends up to 6,000 or 6,500 ft. (temperature roughly 75 to 65°). Within this climatic belt is produced a great variety of crops, among them coffee, maize, tea, cotton, and rice. Tierra fria, lying above the templada, prevails up to 10,000 to 11,500 ft. (temperature 65 to 54°). There middle-latitude crops such as wheat, barley, apples, and potatoes are at home, and the pastoral industries frequently are well developed. At still higher elevations is the *tierra helada* which is above the tree line and beyond the zone of agricultural production. Here are located the alpine pastures on which large numbers of animals are grazed. The pastures are terminated along their upper margins by the permanent snow fields. Local trade of considerable importance, fostered by the vertical zonation of products, is carried on between the inhabitants at various altitudes.

10.18 *Middle-latitude Highlands.* While within the tropics mountains and plateaus may be climatically favored because of their lower temperatures, this same characteristic causes

Climatic Data for a Representative Altitude Station in Middle Latitudes

Longs Peak, Colo. (8,956 Ft.)

	J	F	M	A	M	J	J	A	S	O	N	D	Yr.	Range
Temp.	23	22	26	33	41	51	55	55	48	39	31	24	37	33
Precip.	0.7	1.2	2.0	2.7	2.4	1.6	3.6	2.2	1.7	1.7	0.9	0.9	21.6	

highlands in the middle latitudes to be climatically inferior to lowlands. The difference lies in the fact that tropical lowlands have an *excess* of heat, so that any reduction of temperature with altitude usually is counted as an advantage, for human comfort as well as for the greater variety of products than can be grown. In the middle latitudes, on the other hand, even the lowlands usually are none too warm, so that reduction of temperature with altitude, causing a cooler summer and shorter growing season, materially decreases the opportunities for agricultural production. In other words, there are fewer *utilizable* temperature zones in middle-latitude highlands.

10.19 Diurnal and Seasonal Temperatures. The thin, dry air characteristic of mountains and high plateaus permits the entry of strong solar radiation by day and of rapid loss of earth energy by terrestrial radiation at night. Rapid heating by day and cooling by night are the result, so that large diurnal ranges of temperature are characteristics of highland climates. In tropical highlands the great temperature difference between day and night, or the diurnal range, stands in contrast to the very small temperature difference between the averages for the months or the seasons. At high altitudes in

tropical highlands the large diurnal range in temperature results in numerous days in which there is night freezing and daytime thawing. This frequent and rapid oscillation between freeze and thaw has a marked effect upon vegetation and soil characteristics. It is obvious that one of the distinctive features of high plateaus and mountains in the tropics is the combination of large *daily* and small *seasonal* ranges of temperature.

The lower temperatures at elevated sites have led to the statement that mountains in the tropics enjoy perpetual spring. Quito's annual temperature of 54.7°, for instance, is not greatly unlike the May average at Madison, Wis. However, the great variety of elevations within a tropical mountain mass obviously results in all gradations of temperature.

But although the thermometer stands lower on a tropical mountain than it does on an adjacent lowland, both locations have a similar uniformity in monthly and daily mean temperatures. Small *annual* ranges and the same monotonous repetition of daily weather belong alike to tropical highlands and plains (Figs. 10.4 and 10.5). At Quito, for instance, the temperature difference between the warmest and coolest months is only 0.7°, which is very

Fig. 10.4 Daily maximum and minimum temperatures of the extreme months at a tropical mountain station located at moderate altitudes. Note the diurnal regularity of temperature change indicating sun control. Diurnal range is greater in July, the drier season, when there is the least cloud.

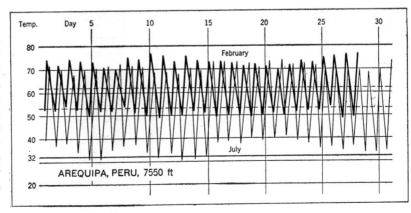

similar to that of the Amazon Lowlands in the same latitude (Fig. 10.5). Mexico City at 7,474 ft. has an average annual temperature 17° below that for Veracruz on the coast; yet their annual ranges are almost identical—11.5 and 11°, respectively. One climatologist has stated the situation tersely by saying: "The pitch changes; the tune remains the same." Highland climates in the tropics present the unique feature of a cold climate with a small annual range of temperature.

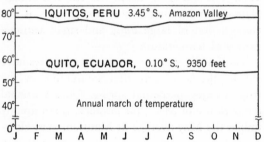

Fig. 10.5 A comparison of the annual march of temperature at Iquitos, a tropical lowland station, and at Quito, a tropical highland station. Note the generally lower temperature at Quito. On the other hand, a small annual range of temperature is characteristic of both stations.

Farther away from the equator the annual range of temperature characteristic of highlands increases in magnitude. This is similar to the situation for lowlands. In fact, the annual range for highland stations and lowland stations in similar latitudes is approximately the same.

PRECIPITATION

10.20 Increased Precipitation in Mountains. Precipitation is characteristically heavier in highlands than it is on surrounding lowlands. Thus on a rainfall map mountains are conspicuous as "islands" of heavier precipitation. This fact is admirably illustrated by the Pacific Coast mountains in the United States, by the Abyssinian Highlands in northeastern Africa, and by the Himalayas in southern Asia. The reasons for the increased precipitation in highlands has been discussed in an earlier section

of this book. Whether or not rainfall continues to increase with increasing elevation, up to the tops of high mountains, or whether there is a zone of maximum precipitation above which the total amount declines, is not known for sure.

It is especially in dry climates, no matter in what latitude, that the heavier rainfall of highlands is of such critical importance. In regions of drought, mountains, besides being "islands" of heavier precipitation, are islands of heavier vegetation cover and more abundant agricultural production as well. In both arid and semiarid lands, highlands are likely to bear a cover of forest in contrast to the meager grass and shrub vegetation of the surrounding drier lowlands. The Black Hills of western South Dakota are "black" because their dark-green forests present such a color contrast with the tawny-hued steppes surrounding them.

Not only are settlements attracted to the humid slopes and to the well-watered mountain valleys, but streams, descending from the rainier highlands, carry the influence of highland climate far out on the dry lowlands. The waters of the Colorado River, with its principal sources in the Rocky Mountains, make possible the agricultural utilization of the dry Imperial Valley of southern California, over 700 miles distant. From the Andes come the 50 or more small streams that, crossing the Peruvian Desert, nourish the parallel irrigated strips of that otherwise waste land.

The heavier precipitation associated with highlands has important consequences in terms of power. This accumulation of water and snow at high elevations represents a reservoir of potential energy, for as it moves in the form of streams to lower elevations, its energy may be harnessed to produce hydroelectric power.

10.21 Snowfall and the Snow Line. Because of the lower temperature at higher elevations snowfall is more abundant and the snow cover is more durable in mountains than on adjacent lowlands. The snow line, which marks the lower boundary of permanent snow, as a general rule increases in elevation toward the equator. This reflects the influence of higher temperatures.

Actually the highest snow line is not at the equator where precipitation is heavy, but 15 to 25° north and south of the equator where precipitation is less. As a rule the snow line is lower on snowier windward slopes and higher on drier leeward slopes. It is also lower on the shadier slopes which are inclined away from the sun.

WINDS

10.22 On exposed mountain slopes and summits, where ground friction is small, winds are usually strong. Mountain valleys, on the other hand, are particularly well protected against violent winds. Owing to the great variety of relief and exposure in highlands, there are also a number of local winds characteristic of such areas. The diurnal reversal of wind direction, upslope by day and downslope by night, has been discussed previously under the head of *mountain and valley winds.*

10.23 Foehn, or Chinook. Still another local vertical wind, characteristic of mountains, is the cyclonic-induced *foehn,* which in the United States and Canada is known as the *chinook.* It is a relatively warm, dry wind which descends a mountain front when a cyclonic storm causes air to cross the range from the opposite side of the divide (Fig. 10.6). For ex-

ample, as a well-developed low travels southeastward down the Great Plains, paralleling the Rocky Mountain front, air is induced to ascend over the Rockies from the western side and descend their eastern slopes. The relatively high temperature and aridity of the chinook originate as follows: As the air ascends on the western side of the Rockies, condensation occurs, so that the rising air reaches the top of the divide with much of its moisture gone *but still retaining a relatively high temperature* as a result of liberation of heat of condensation during ascent. As this air descends on the side of the mountain toward the cyclone, it is further heated by compression and made relatively drier, so that it arrives at the eastern base of the Rockies as a mild, arid wind. The warmth of the chinook, therefore, is of dual origin: (*a*) heat of condensation and (*b*) heat resulting from compression. Usually its temperature is not over 40° in winter, but this appears very warm, by contrast at least, after a period of anticyclonic weather with intense cold. If snow lies on the ground, it vanishes as if by magic before the warm blast of the chinook. A rise in temperature of 40° within 24 hr. is not unusual. At Kipp, Mont., there is the extraordinary record of a 34° rise within an interval of 7 min.

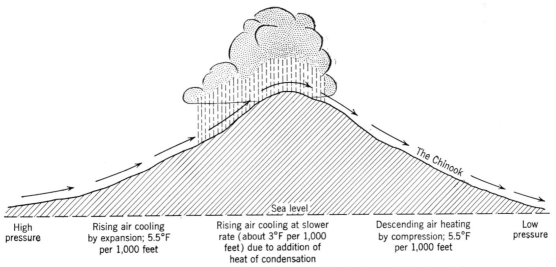

| High pressure | Rising air cooling by expansion; 5.5°F per 1,000 feet | Rising air cooling at slower rate (about 3°F per 1,000 feet) due to addition of heat of condensation | Descending air heating by compression; 5.5°F per 1,000 feet | Low pressure |

Fig. 10.6 Illustrating the origin and nature of the foehn, or chinook, wind.

The genuine chinook country is the High Plains at the eastern foot of the Rockies from southern Colorado northward to the limits of settlement in Canada. The milder winters of this western portion of the plains, as compared with regions farther east, are associated with the prevalence of these local mountain winds. Here the snow cover is less persistent, so that grazing can go on throughout the winer. Foehn winds are by no means confined to the eastern Rocky Mountain foothill country but, on the contrary, are found in almost all mountain areas where cyclonic storms are prevalent. No doubt the region where they are best known is the Swiss valleys on the northern side of the Alps.

DAILY WEATHER

10.24 In highlands the weather changes within the 24-hr. period are likely to be greater than they are on adjacent lowlands. Violent changes from hot sun to cool shade, from chill wind to calm, at one period gusts of rain or possibly snow, and then again intense sunlight—such is the erratic nature of the daily weather. Even within the tropics, the complex sequence of daily weather stands out in marked contrast to the uniformity of temperature conditions between the months.

The night and early mornings are cold and raw, but the powerful sunshine raises the temperature rapidly, and by noon it feels hot in the sun, though in the shade it is still cool. About midday clouds gather and there is often a violent thunderstorm in the afternoon with heavy rain, hail, and frequently snow. These clouds and storms are essentially convectional, and they die away after the heat of the day which caused them. . . . The early mornings are fine, and the air at these great altitudes (Quito, Ecuador) is remarkably clear; but in the afternoons the clouds hang low over the gloomy landscape, and hail, snow, and rain chill the air, so that the mountains are almost invariably hidden.[4]

[4] W. G. Kendrew, "The Climates of the Continents," 3d ed. P. 320. Oxford University Press, New York, 1942.

Section B LANDFORMS AND THE SEAS

The earth upon which man lives is characterized by great and often pleasing variety in its surface features. High lands and low, level expanses and steep slopes, plains, tablelands, hill lands, and mountains are arranged in endless combinations. Because there are so many kinds of landforms, it may sometimes seem that they are distributed over the earth without order and that an understanding of their nature and arrangement is beyond the ability of the beginning student. Such is not the case. It is quite as possible to understand the meaning of earth features and to perceive them in their interrelationships as it is to reach an understanding of the major climatic types of the world.

The study of climates in the preceding chapters was approached through a consideration of the individual *elements* or ingredients out of which climatic types are compounded, and of the processes or *controls* which cause these elements to vary from place to place and from time to time. With the basic material in hand, the distinctive climatic types were then examined, in terms of their identifying characteristics, their areas of occurrence, and the reasons why they exist where they do. The study of landforms will be approached in the same general manner, beginning with a brief consideration of the elements or ingredients that combine to give any section of the land surface its essential character. A study of the agents or processes that produce different sorts of terrain will follow, and finally attention will be directed to the distinctive classes of terrain, what they are like and where they occur and why. It will become evident that terrain exists in recognizable and recurrent types over the face of the earth and that these types and their pattern of occurrence may be characterized and accounted for in a reasonably systematic way.

11

The Elements and Types of Terrain

Elements of Terrain

11.1 The Major Groups of Elements. When one looks about at the seemingly endless variety of forms and features that the surface of the land displays, it may seem almost hopeless to introduce any degree of order into landform description. But if many small sections of terrain are carefully compared, with the intention of determining precisely in what ways each piece differs from the others, there is soon accumulated a long list of specific elements or *differentiating characteristics* with respect to which terrain samples differ. And if this list is examined, it becomes apparent that the many elements may be grouped under the four major headings of (*a*) slope, (*b*) surface material, (*c*) arrangement, and (*d*) dimensions. That is, the differences between any two sections of the land surface may be expressed in terms of these four major aspects.

11.2 *Slope* refers simply to the inclination of the land surface at a particular spot. Normally any section of the surface measuring a few miles across is made up of many small bits of sloping land, each one differing from its neighbors in steepness. Steep slopes, gentle slopes, and slopes of intermediate steepness may all be present in a single area. However, there is a great difference between one area and another in the relative frequency or degree of predominance of each of these major slope classes. For example, a section of the Texas coastal plain near Houston may have 95 per cent of its area occupied by very gentle slopes, while a section of hilly southwestern Wisconsin may be only 30 per cent gently sloping, with

intermediate and steep slopes occupying the majority of the area (Fig. 11.1). It is doubtful that any other single item of information could tell as much about the fundamental contrast between those two landform regions. For any piece of terrain, the relative predominance of slopes of various degrees of steepness represents a valuable body of specific information that is an aid not only to the visualization and evaluation of that area, but to its objective comparison with other areas.

11.3 *Surface Material.* Another surface characteristic that varies from place to place is the nature of the *surface material*. Over most of the earth's land surface relatively finely divided mineral matter occurs, commonly with some admixture of partially decomposed organic debris. Wherever such *soil* (using the term in a very broad sense) does *not* make up the surface layer, it is a fact worth knowing. Surfaces of bare bedrock, of loose sand, of cobbles and boulders, of permanent ice, or of standing water are fundamentally different from soil surfaces, not only in appearance and feel, but in origin and function as well. It may reasonably be maintained that the character of the bedrock many feet below the surface and also the chemical and detailed physical properties of even the surface layers do not as a rule belong in a list of terrain elements. But clearly the *gross physical nature of the surficial materials* cannot be omitted from a terrain description without running the risk of serious misrepresentation. It would, for example, be futile to attempt a characterization of Finland or of much of northern and eastern Canada without mentioning almost at the outset that standing

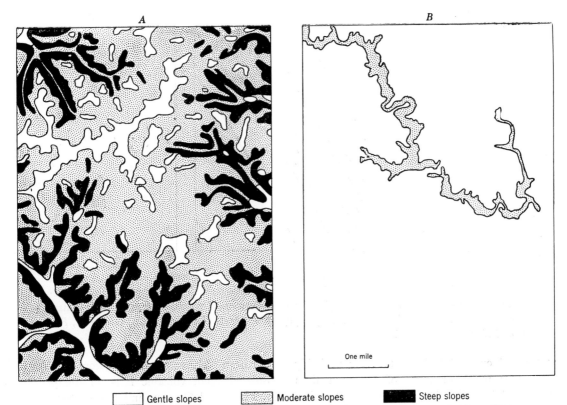

Gentle slopes ☐ Moderate slopes ▦ Steep slopes ■

Fig. 11.1 An example of contrast between areas in terms of slope. *A* is from Driftless Hills of southwestern Wisconsin; *B* from coastal plain near Corpus Christi, Tex. (*From U.S. Geological Survey topographic sheets: Boaz, Wis., and Petronilla, Tex.*)

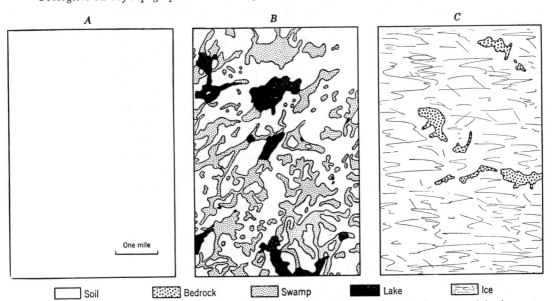

Soil ☐ Bedrock ▦ Swamp ▦ Lake ■ Ice ▦

Fig. 11.2 An example of contrast among areas in terms of nature of surface material. *A* is from rolling prairies of northwestern Missouri; *B* from morainic plains of northern Minnesota; *C* from southern Alaska. (*From U.S. Geological Survey topographic sheets: Bethany, Mo., Ely, Minn., and Seward A-8, Alaska.*)

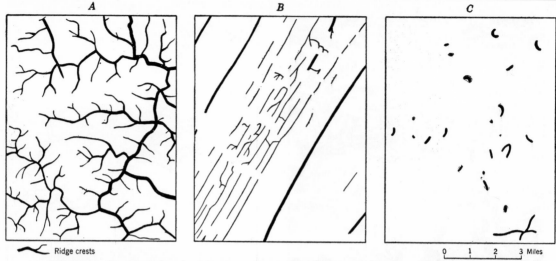

Fig. 11.3 An example of contrast among areas in terms of pattern of ridge crests and summits. *A* is in the Driftless Hills of southwestern Wisconsin; *B* in the Appalachian Ridge-and-Valley section of central Pennsylvania; *C* in an area of volcanic cones in south-central Oregon. (*From U.S. Geological Survey topographic sheets: La Farge, Wis., Orbisonia, Pa., and Newberry Crater, Ore.*)

water and exposed bedrock together probably occupy as much or more of the area than is covered by soil. The ice cap of Antarctica, the sand-dune "seas" of the Libyan Sahara, and the great coastal marshes of South Carolina and Georgia all owe much of their distinctive character to their unusual surface materials (Fig. 11.2).

11.4 *Arrangement.* When information about the occurrence of various classes of slopes and different kinds of surface material is complete for a given area, characterization is well underway, but for most kinds of terrain much more must be known before the land surface can really be visualized. In particular, something must be known of the *arrangement* of these slopes and materials.

The arrangement of features in the horizontal plane, that is, the shapes and relative positions they display on maps or on aerial photographs taken from directly above, may be termed *pattern.* In some regions pattern is one of the most striking of all characteristics, especially where it departs from the usual treelike arrangement of valleys or streams and the divides between them. The remarkably parallel arrangement of ridges in the middle belt of the Appalachians between central Pennsylvania and

northern Alabama, the random dotting of isolated small volcanic hills on the plains of south-central Oregon, and the aimless and unsystematic maze of lakes, swamps, and streams in northeastern Minnesota represent obvious and indispensable ingredients of any meaningful description of these regions (Fig. 11.3). The patterns of several different kinds of features such as crests or summits, valleys, streams and other water features, steep slopes, flats, or patches of various sorts of material may all serve to give distinctive character to the terrain. In addition they may be highly significant, either as clues to the geological history of the region or in their relationships to other geographical patterns, such as that of soils, of native vegetation, or of agricultural utilization of the land.

There are also significant aspects of arrangement in the vertical plane, especially *profiles,* a profile, in this sense, being the change of slope or gradient along a given line. Under this heading would come such items as the cross-section forms of valleys; the evenness, jaggedness, or presence of deep clefts in major mountain crests; and the various changes in gradient of streams from their headwaters down to their mouths. Regional contrasts in these respects are sometimes striking and important. The continuously high crest lines of the Sierra Nevada of California and the Colorado Rockies differ most significantly from the deeply cleft divides of the Cascade Range in Washington or of the northern Rockies in Montana and Idaho (Fig. 11.4). The gentle, unbroken gradients of the Mississippi and Amazon Rivers contrast sharply with the profiles of the Congo or Nile, both of which are broken by impassable falls or rapids. The very essence of the contrast between a plateau or tableland, such as that about the Grand Canyon in northern Arizona, and a

basin-and-range landscape like that covering most of Nevada is the fundamental difference in general cross-section profile. Both have much gently sloping land; both have some areas of steep slopes, and both exhibit large local differences in elevation. But the tableland has its gentle slopes at high level, with its steep slopes and elevation differences provided by deep, steep-walled canyons carved into the upland, while the basin-and-range section is just the opposite, with gently sloping plains surmounted by steep-sloped mountain ranges (Fig. 11.5).

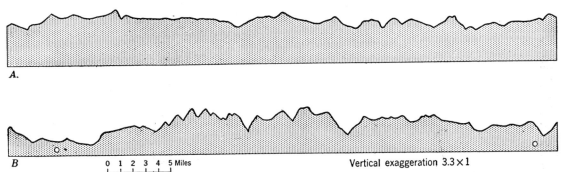

0 1 2 3 4 5 Miles   Vertical exaggeration 3.3 × 1

Fig. 11.4   The continuously high crest line of the Sierra Nevada of California (*A*) contrasts sharply with the deeply serrated crest of the Cascade Range in Washington (*B*). The openings near the ends of the lower profile are railroad tunnels. (*From Army Map Service series V502, Fresno and Wenatchee sheets.*)

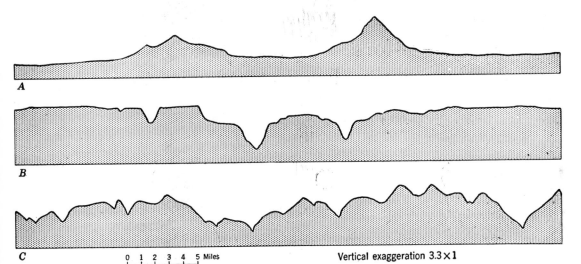

0 1 2 3 4 5 Miles   Vertical exaggeration 3.3 × 1

Fig. 11.5   Example of contrasting transverse profiles in areas of high relief. *A* is from Basin and Range section in Nevada; *B* from Colorado Plateau in northern Arizona; and *C* from Rocky Mountains of Idaho. (*From U.S. Geological Survey topographic sheets: Sonoma Range, Nev., Diamond Creek, Ariz., and Lolo, Idaho.*)

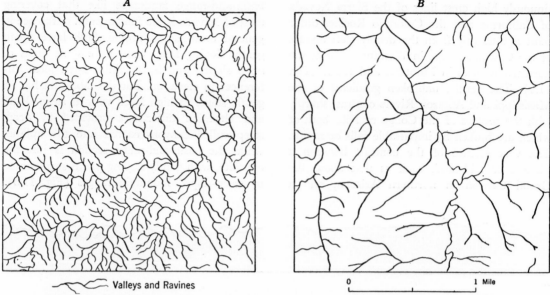

Valleys and Ravines

Fig. 11.6 Example of contrast in texture, or spacing of valleys and ravines. The patterns are similar, but the textures are strikingly different. *A* is from the Badlands of southwestern South Dakota; *B* from central Missouri. (*From U.S. Geological Survey topographic sheets: Cuny Table E, S. Dak., and Nelson, Mo.*)

Cross-section profiles of valleys and divides and the longways profiles of streams are especially valuable sources of information to the student of earth history; for they may sometimes be used to determine such things as previous uplifts of the earth's crust in that area, earlier variations in the volume of the streams, or the effects of the nature of the rocks upon the processes of erosion. The examples mentioned above will suggest that profiles of the terrain may relate also to other aspects of geography, including utilization of the land by man.

11.5 *Dimensions,* the fourth major group of terrain characteristics, are also readily con-

sidered in terms of their horizontal and vertical components.

Horizontally one may consider such items as spacings of valleys, ridges, streams, or other features, and widths of patches of gentle or steep slope, bodies of water, or patches of some particular surface material. Sometimes the term *texture* of terrain is used to refer to the prevalent horizontal dimensions of features in various areas. Thus the "badlands" of South Dakota are noted for their extremely fine texture, that is, the extremely close spacing of the ravines and gullies that dissect the area into such an inhospitable maze. The High Plains of

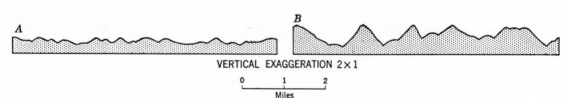

VERTICAL EXAGGERATION 2×1

Fig. 11.7 Contrasting local relief in two areas of rough lands. *A* is from Missouri Ozarks; *B* from Appalachians in central West Virginia. (*From U.S. Geological Survey topographic sheets: Round Spring, Mo., and Bald Knob, W. Va.*)

western Kansas, on the other hand, are notably coarse textured, their broad, smooth uplands being cut by significant stream valleys only at intervals of many miles (Fig. 11.6).

In the vertical direction, the dimensions of the terrain of a limited area are given by various expressions of *local relief,* or difference in elevation. For a general expression of local relief, the difference in elevation between the highest and lowest points in the small area is sometimes used. Or a figure may be used that indicates the average or prevalent height of crests above the adjacent valley bottoms in the area (Fig. 11.7). The relief along crest lines, on local uplands, along valley floors or streams may also be of interest. Local relief is a characteristic of considerable descriptive value, suggesting at once something of the scale of features and the degree of irregularity within the area being considered. If the local relief in an area is only 50 ft., it is immediately evident that the surface must be either nearly flat or marked by only small roughnesses. But a local relief of 5,000 ft. immediately suggests a landscape of considerable grandeur, though without specifying what form its great features may take. When combined with data on slopes and profiles, local relief becomes one of the most revealing of all generalized expressions of terrain character. The more specific sorts of relief measurement, such as, for example, the amount of necessary climb along a given mountain-pass route, may be of very direct importance in evaluating an area from a particular point of view.

The Principal Types of Terrain

11.6 Recognition of Terrain Types. Careful analysis in terms of the specific characteristics just discussed can be made to yield as accurate and as detailed a picture of a given piece of terrain as may be desired. Since the information is specific and systematic, it makes possible a characteristic-by-characteristic comparison of this bit of the earth's surface with any other small areas similarly described. And if in this manner large numbers of terrain samples from

all over the world are compared, it becomes apparent that certain combinations of major characteristics recur again and again in widely separated places. And thus comes the realization that there may be defined, at least in general terms, a number of distinct types of terrain that may be recognized wherever they occur, and that together make up the entire surface of the continents. These types of terrain, defined in terms of a few major characteristics, are comparable to the similarly defined climatic types discussed in the earlier chapters. While these types will be discussed later in some detail, it will be well to obtain a general idea of their characteristics and variety before proceeding to the discussion of the processes by which they originate.

11.7 Major Classes of Terrain. The scheme of terrain types to be used here is based upon similarities and differences with respect to three major characteristics: relative amount of gently sloping land, local relief, and generalized profile. On the basis of the first two characteristics alone we may distinguish among: *plains,* having a predominance of gently sloping land, coupled with low relief; *plains with some features of considerable relief,* again dominated by gently sloping land, but having moderate to high local relief; *hills,* characterized by a predominance of steeper slopes, but with low or moderate relief; and *mountains,* which have little gently sloping land and high local relief.

The second group, *plains with some features of considerable relief,* may be further subdivided on the basis of whether the existing large amount of gently sloping land lies in the lower part of the profile or in the upper part. If most of the gently sloping land lies at relatively low levels, with steep slopes rising above it, the surfaces may be designated *plains with hills or mountains.* If, on the other hand, most of the nearly level land lies relatively high, with the steep slopes of canyons or escarpments dropping down from it, the surfaces may be called *tablelands.* If the relief is slight, or if the amount of gently sloping land is not large, this profile distinction is less fundamentally significant, and therefore it is not used here as a basis for sub-

A

B

C

Fig. 11.8 Examples of tne three smoother classes of terrain. *A*, rolling plains in southwestern Iowa. (*Photo by Soil Conservation Service, U.S.D.A.*). *B*, a remarkably clear-cut example of a tableland. Canyon de Chelly National Monument, in northeastern Arizona. (*Spence Air Photos.*) *C*, Hopi Buttes, near Winslow, Ariz., a plain with hills and mountains. (*Spence Air Photos.*)

A

B **Fig. 11.9** Examples of the two rougher classes of terrain. *A,* a portion of the Allegheny-Cumberland hill land near Parsons, W.Va. Local relief is 700 to 800 ft. (*Photograph by John L. Rich, courtesy of the Geographical Review, published by American Geographical Society of New York.*) *B,* high mountains in the Rockies of central Colorado. Local relief 2,000 to 4,000 ft. View northward over Berthoud Pass (11,300 ft.) along the crest of the Continental Divide. (*Photograph by T. S. Lovering, U.S. Geological Survey.*)

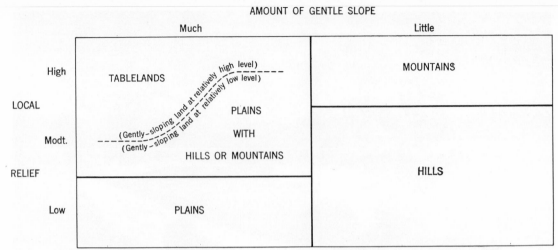

Fig. 11.10 Diagram illustrating how the principal classes of terrain are defined and how they are related to one another.

dividing plains, hills, and mountains. Figures 11.8 and 11.9 give examples of the principal terrain classes. Figure 11.10 shows schematically how the classes are defined.

It must be fully realized that within each of these five major classes of land surfaces, which have been defined in terms of only two or three characteristics that seem particularly important to visualization or to utility, there exists a vast range of variety, based upon differences with respect to other characteristics. Some plains, for instance, are conspicuously flat and swampy, others are rolling and well drained, and still others are simply broad expanses of smooth ice. Similarly, some mountains are low, smooth-sloped, and arranged in parallel ridges, while others are exceedingly high, with rugged, rocky slopes and great glaciers and snow fields. The subdivision that has been outlined is intended to bring out only the most striking contrasts among land surfaces and to provide a general basis upon which to develop a systematic discussion of landforms and their origin, or a consideration of the general surface character of the various continents.

11.8 Distribution of Terrain Types. Plate 3 shows the distribution of the major terrain classes over the earth. Note that several additional subclasses have been shown, the conspicuously flat plains, for example, being distinguished from the more irregular ones, and the particularly high-relief mountains from the low. The few broad ice caps of the world have been shown by an entirely separate symbol.

Plate 3 is fundamental to the study of terrain geography. As the succeeding material is studied, frequent reference should be made to the map, so that by the time the end of the section on landforms is reached, the terrain patterns of the different continents, and the occurrence over the world of the different terrain types, will be quite familiar.

12

The Earth's Crust and the Tectonic Processes

12.1 The Forces Involved in Surface Molding. Landforms, whether large or small, result from the interaction of certain forces with the materials of the earth's surface through longer or shorter periods of time. Some of the forces may be described as geologic, some as climatic, and still others as biologic. They accomplish their various kinds of work by means of *processes* of whose operation at least the rudiments must be understood. The forces work by means of these processes upon an earth crust made up of rocks of different kinds and degrees of resistance, arranged in different positions and attitudes with respect to each other and to the surface of the earth.

The various forces involved in the production and alteration of landforms may be grouped for convenient study in more than one way to suit different objectives. For the present purpose it will be helpful to think of them as belonging to two major groups: (*a*) those forces which originate *within* the earth and (*b*) those which originate from *without,* or beyond, the earth.

The members of the first group derive their energy mainly from changes occurring in the earth's interior, changes such as heating through radioactivity or chemical recombination, expansion or contraction, or the removal of molten material from one place to another. This group may be called the *tectonic forces.* They are made manifest through processes called *diastrophism* and *vulcanism.* Diastrophism includes those processes which are involved in the breaking, bending, and warping of the earth's crust and the elevation, depression, or displacement of one part with respect to another.

Vulcanism includes those processes which involve the transfer of molten material from one place to another within the earth's crust or its expulsion at the earth's surface. *The ultimate tendency of the tectonic forces and their processes is to cause differences in surface elevation on the earth* and, by heaving up the crust here and depressing it there or by pouring out upon it great masses of molten lava, to construct surface features of great height and areal extent.

The members of the second group derive their energy mainly from the sun. They may be called the *forces of gradation.* They operate largely through the work of agents such as wind, running water, moving snow and ice, and living organisms, working in conjunction with the force of gravity. *The ultimate tendency of the forces of gradation and their processes is to bring the surface of the land to a uniform low slope or grade.* This is done by tearing down all elevations, such as may be produced by the tectonic forces, and by filling up depressions. The process of gradation may be thought of as consisting of four steps: (*a*) the preparation of rock material for removal, (*b*) the picking up of the rock fragments, (*c*) their transportation, and (*d*) the deposition of the transported fragments. Step (*a*), which involves the various processes of rock breakdown collectively termed *weathering,* does not directly include any movement of the weathered products, and hence does not by itself produce a modification of the shape of the land surface. Steps (*b*) and (*c*) together result in a tearing down of the relatively high-standing parts of the surface, and are accordingly referred to as *degradation*. Step (*d*), by which tectonic basins and other depressions are filled with sediment and thus raised in surface level, is sometimes called *aggradation*.

The two groups of forces, *tectonic* on the one hand and *gradational* on the other, are at work continuously and simultaneously, and therefore are in endless conflict. The one causes features having differences in elevation; the other, though it may temporarily and locally roughen the surface, tends in the long run to reduce it to a low and uniform plain. The hills, valleys, and other relief features that now exist simply show the present, but temporary, state of this perpetual battle.

12.2 The Time Element in Physical Geography. The student of landforms and of the processes by means of which they have evolved must adopt a different conception of time from that employed in considering the events of human history. Although some of the processes of nature are sudden and violent, accomplishing notable results in a short space of time, such are the exception rather than the rule. Most of the common landforms have been produced by the slow and long-continued operation of forces and processes still at work. Understanding of the fact that they are able to produce so little effect within a lifetime or within the span of human history requires merely the use of a different time scale for their measurement.

It is estimated by geologists that the age of the earth probably exceeds three billions of years. Of this vast span of time the record of the first five-sixths is vague and largely lost in antiquity. It is like that long period in human development before man learned how to make any written record of his doings. More is known of the latest one-sixth of earth history (around 500 million years). But even that time is so long that it dwarfs human history to a moment by comparison. However, most of the present landforms of the earth trace their origins to events in that time and especially in the later or more recent periods of that time. It is not desirable to enter here upon a study of the periods of time into which geologic history is

divided, although it may be convenient in some connections to make references to them. As a basis of reference, and to provide a better conception of the time element in the evolution of landforms, as well as for its general interest, a simplified form of the geological column is reproduced in Appendix E. This tabular arrangement of the periods of earth history in major outline shows also some of the principal events in the biologic sequence which geological science has interpreted from the records of the rocks.

12.3 The Earth's Interior. Since the tectonic processes involve the moving, bending, and breaking of the earth's crust, together with the moving through the crust of masses of molten material, it is important to have at least an elementary conception of what that crust is like, and what relation it bears to the deeper interior of the earth. It is neither appropriate nor feasible in a book of this type to enter deeply into this complex and highly theoretical subject, but an understanding of a few basic ideas should make more clear how the seemingly rigid outer crust of the earth can indeed be made to suffer large-scale deformation.

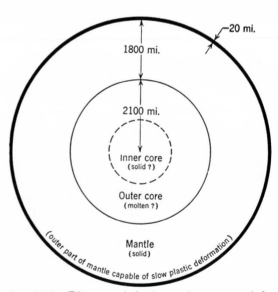

Fig. 12.1 Diagram of the internal structure of the earth. The heavy outer line represents the crust, too thin to be shown otherwise.

Largely from study of the behavior of earthquake waves, students of the earth's interior have inferred that the earth is composed of a great central *core* and a series of surrounding layers known collectively as the *mantle* (Fig. 12.1). The core, having a radius of about 2,100 miles, is made up of exceedingly dense material, probably in large part nickel and iron. The outer portion of the core is probably molten; the inner portion may be solid. The mantle, about 1,800 miles thick, appears to be composed principally of certain of the denser rock-forming substances that are found at the earth's surface. In spite of the extremely high temperatures that are known to exist within the earth, this mantle is known to be solid, probably because the tremendous pressure exerted by the overlying material raises the melting point of the material to levels higher than the temperatures that actually occur.

Most of the mantle is very dense, roughly twice as dense as the rocks that occur at the surface of the earth. But near the surface the nature of the mantle abruptly changes, and the outermost shell is composed of familiar types of surface rocks. This outer shell, of low density, is called, rather illogically, the *crust*.

12.4 The Earth's Crust. The thickness of the crust varies from almost nothing to nearly 40 miles, with the average being not far from 20 miles. The crust is much thicker under the continents than under the ocean basins, and is almost absent from parts of the central Pacific basin.

Although the rigidity of the earth's crust seems great by human standards (it is actually about as rigid as cold steel), it is surprisingly small in terms of the forces to which it is subjected. Under the influence of great stresses, of uncertain origin but of immense power, the crust is readily warped, buckled, and shattered. Furthermore, there is evidence that the portion of the dense mantle that lies immediately beneath the crust is in a state of temperature and compression that permits it to behave almost as if it were an extremely viscous fluid, on which the less dense crust may be considered to "float." Thus, with a relatively weak crust rest-

ing upon a layer that is capable of plastic deformation, the stage is well set for deformation of the crust itself, provided only that there are sufficient forces available to produce it. Since there is abundant evidence that the crust has in fact been deformed, we know that such forces do exist, though their nature and origin are not at all well understood. One body of theory holds that the major deforming forces stem from slow flowing movements in the plastic layer beneath the crust, these movements perhaps resulting from temperature differences produced by radioactivity in the outer part of the mantle. Other processes that have been called into account are the expansion or shrinkage of the earth as a whole, and the redistribution of surface load caused by the removal of material from one part of the surface and its deposition elsewhere.

DIASTROPHISM

12.5 The Nature of Diastrophism. Deforming of the crust has occurred widely and has assumed many different forms. Most of our knowledge of diastrophism comes from observations of the structure and arrangement of the layers of rock that are exposed at the surface or that have been reached in deep borings or excavations. Such observations indicate clearly that the crust has been subjected to almost every conceivable sort of bending, breaking, uplift, or depression. From the relations between these geological structures and the ages of the rocks involved, it has also been determined that deformation has occurred throughout the course of determinable geologic history, and that there have been several periods during which the activity was especially strong.

12.6 Crustal Fracture. Stresses sufficient to cause crustal fracture have developed so many times that the solid rock is nearly everywhere traversed by cracks called *joints*. These are so numerous near the surface that the hard exterior of the earth must resemble the crackled glaze on a piece of antique china (Fig. 12.2). However, the joints become smaller and fewer with depth and below a dozen miles or so are believed not to exist. The joints permit the water

Fig. 12.2 Jointing in granite. Joint planes commonly occur in sets, all the members of which trend in the same direction. The sets may be vertical, inclined, or horizontal. (*U.S. Geological Survey photograph.*)

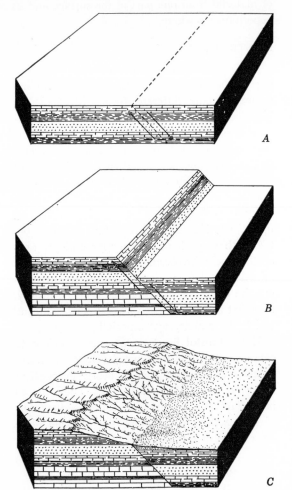

A

B

C

of the ground to circulate more freely within the rocks and enable the agents of gradation to work more readily. In some places also they play a part in the details of shape in landforms.

Under severe stresses rocks not only break but sometimes move along the plane of fracture and are displaced. Such displacements are called *faults*. The motion that produces the dislocation often is sudden but usually is limited in amount to fractions of an inch or a few feet. The displacement is sometimes in a vertical direction, the rocks on one side of the fault being elevated as compared with those on the other. Then a cliff is produced which is called a *fault scarp*. Some faults are produced by tensional or stretching forces as in Fig. 12.3*A* and *B*, others by compressional or crowding forces, as in Fig. 12.4. In some faults the displacement is horizontal rather than vertical, resulting in the breaking and offsetting of roads and boundary lines.

When many successive vertical faults occur along the same plane at intervals during thou-

Fig. 12.3 Diagram to show the development of a tensional fault in sedimentary rock. *A*, the strata before faulting; *B*, fault, showing direction of displacement and the fault scarp; *C*, the modification of the fault scarp by erosion.

220

sands of years, the resulting escarpment along the line of the fault plane may attain the size of hills or even mountains. Most of the Basin Ranges in Nevada are the result of tensional faults which have uptilted great masses of rock, and so is even the towering east face of the Sierra Nevada Range of California (Fig. 12.5). The Lewis Range of Montana, in Glacier National Park, is likewise the result of faulting but of the compressional type, which caused the broken edge of the rock layers to slip up over the rocks of the adjacent plains and ride out upon them for a distance of several miles. These giant displacements required a long time for their accomplishment during which the growing escarpments were attacked by destructive agents, lowered, and carved up into mountain peaks (Figs. 12.3C and 12.4).

In a few places in the world parallel faults of great length have permitted the segments of earth between them to drop down. These become broad valleys, flanked on either side by fault scarps, and are known as *grabens*, or rift valleys (Fig. 12.6). Of this origin are such famous valleys as the Lowlands of Scotland, the

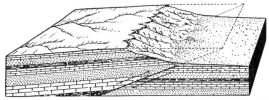

Fig. 12.4 A diagram to illustrate the manner of displacement in a compressional fault. The dotted lines show the volume of rock removed by erosion during the growth of the fault scarp.

middle Rhine Valley, the depression in which the Dead Sea lies, and those vast trenches in East Africa occupied in part by lakes Tanganyika and Nyasa. In other places the land between parallel faults has been elevated rather than depressed. The result is a blocklike uplift called a *horst*. Some of the Basin Ranges are of that origin. To some extent faulting has a part in the making of almost all mountains.

12.7 Crustal Bending. In certain earth deformations the stresses have been applied to rocks so slowly or under such conditions of confinement that instead of fracturing they

Fig. 12.5 The rugged eastern face of the Sierra Nevada in California is a dissected fault scarp. Mt. Whitney, at right, rises nearly 8,000 ft. above the gentle slopes in the foreground. (*Spence Air Photos.*)

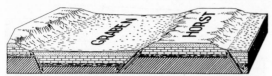

Fig. 12.6 A diagram to illustrate block faulting and the formation of a graben and a horst. The arrows indicate direction of relative displacement.

bend or even fold. The bends and folds may be either small or of mountainous proportions and either simple or complicated. In some mountain regions sedimentary rock strata have been shortened by horizontal compression and have been pushed up into a series of wavelike folds (Fig. 12.7*A*). The arch, or crest, of one of these simple folds is called an *anticline,* and the trough of the wave a *syncline* (Fig. 12.8). In the Alps and some other mountains the folding has been so intense as to cause the wavelike structures to jam together and tip over (Fig. 12.7*B*). In most folded mountains the arrangement of the rocks is further complicated by severe faulting and, in many places, by intrusions of volcanic materials also. The present ridges and valleys of highly folded mountain regions seldom represent the original anticlines and synclines, because time and the degradational processes have intervened, greatly altering the appearance of these structures. How-

ever, the position and arrangement of the remnants of the folded rocks, resistant and non-resistant, are generally reflected in features of mountain relief.

12.8　Crustal Warping. Similar to folding in nature, less intense but even more important, are broad deformations of the earth's crust which may be called warping. Gentle crustal bending of this sort affects vast areas and probably is continuously in progress, but it requires thousands of years to produce notable results. Through warping, broad areas of low plains land, such as formerly existed on the present site of the North Sea basin, have been lowered slowly a few feet or a few scores of feet and added to the shallow sea bottoms. By the same process great expanses of shallow sea bottom have been elevated slowly and added to the areas of the continents. Most of the state of Florida is a relatively recent addition to the area of North America. Through an understanding of this process one comes to an appreciation of the meaning of the stratified sedimentary rocks, containing the fossil remains of sea animals, that now are found far in the interiors of each of the continents. The fossil evidences in these rocks indicate that some of them were uplifted from the sea far back in geologic history, others in comparatively recent time. Similar evidence shows that some areas have been alternately elevated and depressed

A. Simple folding

B. Complex folding and faulting

Fig. 12.7 Diagrams to illustrate simple and complex deformation of the crust. *A* shows simple open folding in the Appalachian Ridge-and-Valley section in West Virginia–Pennsylvania. (*After U.S. Geological Survey Geological Folio 179.*) *B* shows combined folding and compressional faulting in the Rocky Mountains of southeastern Idaho. (*After U.S. Geological Survey Professional Paper 238.*)

Fig. 12.8 A portion of a buried anticlinal structure that has been exposed in a stream valley. (*U.S. Geological Survey photograph.*)

relative to sea level not only once but several times. There are few broad areas of sedimentary rocks that do not show evidence of some warping.

12.9 Diastrophism and Rock Structures. From the foregoing it may be seen that the attitudes and arrangements of the rocks are subject to the greatest variation. Sediments put down horizontally do not always remain so. Likewise, igneous rocks are subject, long after their formation, to distortion and fracture. The position and arrangement of rock formations with respect to each other are called the *rock structure,* and rock structure is one of the very important elements in that complex of conditions out of which landforms of the earth are evolved.

12.10 Present Diastrophism. While most of our knowledge of diastrophism has been gathered from the study of rock structure, additional valuable information can be derived from the observation of certain happenings that disclose the working of crustal deformation at the present time. Since the diastrophic processes normally proceed very slowly, their manifestations within any brief period of human history are quite small, though they may sometimes be accompanied by frightening and even disastrous side effects. Evidence of present-day diastrophism is of two principal types: (*a*) slow changes in the elevation of a section of the surface and

(*b*) earthquakes and observed displacements along faults.

Slow vertical movements of the crust have been observed at many places on the earth, usually along the sea coasts where the sea surface provides a ready reference level. Here, during the course of the last few centuries, low-lying plains have become marshy, or have disappeared beneath the waters. Ancient buildings have been discovered wholly or partially submerged. Wharves and other harbor works have been gradually raised above the sea until they could no longer serve their intended purpose. Parts of the shores of the Baltic Sea in northern Europe are known to be rising at a rate of about 3 ft. per century, while the outer part of the Mississippi River delta in Louisiana is apparently sinking at a similar rate. Records of such local movements, though not made very systematically, give unmistakable evidence of crustal movements which, if continued for thousands of years, could effect great changes in the elevation of the surface and in the form of the continents.

12.11 *Earthquakes.* Earthquakes are relatively small vibratory movements of the earth's crust. Probably they are all initiated by the sudden displacement of the rocks along fault lines. Often these displacements may be seen on the surface, in the form of small scarps or horizontal offsets of roads or fences. Usually the visible displacements accompanying a single earthquake are very small, but movements amounting to several feet have been recorded. In the violent San Francisco earthquake of 1906, the maximum observed displacement was 21 ft., indicated by the horizontal offset of a road. Most earthquakes, however, appear to originate at great depth, and are not accompanied by visible dislocations at the surface.

The shock of the sudden displacement generates a system of compressional and transverse waves that radiate from the point of origin and travel rapidly and to a great distance through the earth's crust and through the deeper interior of the earth. It is these small vibrations that are registered by the delicate recording instruments called *seismographs* and that may be felt by man if they are sufficiently strong. Most earthquakes are too slight to be noticeable, and most of those that can be felt are too weak to do more than rattle windows or dishes on the shelf. But when shocks of unusual strength do occur, they may be sufficiently violent to shatter masonry buildings, throw down more flexible wooden structures, and break pavements and water mains. Some of the greatest natural disasters of history have resulted from violent earthquakes that have

occurred in the neighborhood of large cities. Fortunately some of the greatest recorded earthquakes, such as the great 1950 earthquake in Assam, in the northeast of India, have occurred in sparsely settled areas. Earthquakes that originate beneath the sea sometimes set in motion gigantic waves that travel great distances across the oceans.[1] These waves sometimes reach proportions that carry them far up onto low-lying shores, inundating coastal towns and farm lands and causing great damage and loss of life.

Since earthquakes result from the fracturing and displacement of rocks, their pattern of occurrence should provide a fair indication of where the greatest diastrophic activity is centered at the present time. Figure 12.9 shows how the principal earthquake regions lie in a belt that circles the basin of the Pacific Ocean and extends westward across southern Eurasia. Comparison with Plate 3 will reveal a close coincidence with the high mountain regions of the world, a not surprising coincidence, since high mountains are themselves indicative of strong tectonic activity in late geologic time.

[1] In common speech these are often referred to as tidal waves, but since they have nothing to do with the tides, the term should be avoided.

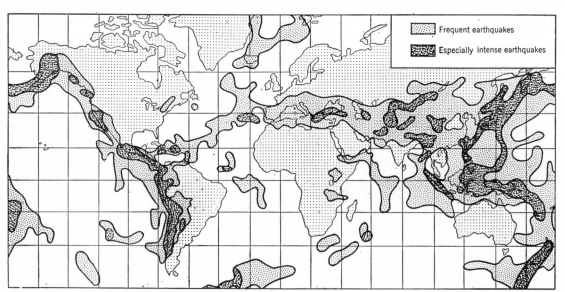

Fig. 12.9   The principal earthquake regions of the world. (*After Leet.*)

VULCANISM

12.12 Vulcanism and Volcanic Activity. Repeatedly during earth history there have developed in the lower part of the earth's crust, or immediately beneath the crust, large pockets of molten rock material. The reasons for the development of these pockets are not fully understood, but a lowering of the melting point accompanying a release of pressure through faulting is probably involved in some instances. Whatever their cause, the masses of molten or *igneous* material, once formed, may make their way toward the surface, eventually cooling and hardening again into rock. During the process, gases are given off, water in the ground is boiled into steam, and molten rock, or *lava,* is forced upward through fractures in the outer crust. These products sometimes reach the surface, causing the often spectacular phenomena known as volcanic activity, or *extrusive* vulcanism. Much of the molten material, however, cools and hardens to rock before reaching the surface, its subterranean movement and the associated effects being referred to as *intrusive* vulcanism. These intrusive rocks become exposed at the surface only when erosion strips off the overlying material, an event that may occur millions of years after the rocks were first formed. Both types of vulcanism are directly or indirectly responsible for the development of certain types of surface features.

12.13 Igneous Extrusions. The principal product of volcanic extrusion is lava, or molten rock. Some lavas quickly become viscous and solidify as they approach the surface or before they have flowed far. Extrusions of these sometimes are accompanied by gases and steam which find difficult escape through the viscous mass and cause *explosive* eruptions.

In a typical explosive eruption great volumes of superheated steam and other suffocating or poisonous gases are blown into the air. Mingled with the gases are large quantities of fragmented rock, shattered or blown to dust while still in the molten state by the expansive force of included gases. A giant black cloud of steam and dust billows skyward and hangs above the

Fig. 12.10 Volcano Parícutín, Mexico, in violent eruption. Typical steep-sided cinder cone. (*Photograph courtesy of the American Museum of Natural History.*)

mountain, but eventually it drifts with the wind and is dispersed over large areas. A hail of rock fragments, cinders, bits of lava, and ash falls about the crater or even upon the outskirts of the cone. Condensing steam and condensation in ascending air currents provide torrents of rain which are accompanied by lightning and thunder. Saturated with dust and ash, the runoff may turn into flows of volcanic mud which reach and bury portions of the bordering lowland.

The explosive phenomenon over, and the pent-up pressure released, the eruption is likely to continue more quietly. Although not all eruptions involve the extrusion of lava, it is commonly the case that a flow of lava and the quiet emission of steam bring the period of eruption to a close, and there ensues a period of quiescence which lasts for months, years, or, in some volcanoes, hundreds of years.

Extremely violent eruptions have been the

Fig. 12.11 The great shield volcanoes on the island of Hawaii. The summit of Mauna Loa (13,018 ft.), with several craters, is in the foreground; the broad cone of Mauna Kea (13,784 ft.) in the background. The largest crater shown is three miles long and nearly two miles wide. (*Official U.S. Navy Photograph.*)

cause of several appalling catastrophes. Examples often cited are the eruptions of Vesuvius in A.D. 79; of Krakatao, near Java, in 1883; and of Mount Pelée, in the West Indies, in 1902. Many other eruptions of great violence have passed with brief historical record, either because the regions in which they occurred were unpeopled or because no witness wrote an account.

Explosive phenomena normally produce steep-sided cones which ultimately may attain mountainous proportions. This process is well illustrated by the origin and growth of the volcano Parícutin in Mexico. It began with the opening of a new crater in a tilled field on Feb. 20, 1943, and in less than 4 years developed a steep-sided cinder and lava cone more than $\frac{1}{3}$ mile high (Fig. 12.10). It is situated near the Pacific margin of Mexico on a line of structural weakness along which are several other volcanoes which have been active within historic times.

Other volcanoes extrude lavas that remain liquid as they approach their solidification points rather than becoming more and more viscous as they cool down. Therefore, included gases bubble through these lavas with less tendency to explosive violence, and the eruptions are said to be *quiet*.

Volcanic eruptions, even of the quiet type, are awe-inspiring phenomena. Molten rock seethes within the crater; steam and other gases are emitted; and upwelling lava spills over the crater rim. Erupted lavas of the slow-hardening type may flow some distance from a volcanic crater before they congeal in nearly horizontal sheets. Thus is produced a cone of relatively larger area and more gentle slopes than are those formed by quickly solidifying lavas. Mauna Loa and other volcanoes in the Hawaiian Islands, and indeed the Islands themselves, furnish examples of this type of cone. They are called shield volcanoes (Fig. 12.11).

Lava flows are perhaps the most extensive of the extrusive features. They issue from limited volcanic vents or pour from long crevices in the earth. In many places there are flows of solidified lava the extent of which is to be measured in square miles or scores of square miles. In a few places, and at various times in earth history, there have issued from crevices or numerous vents lavas so liquid and so copious that layer after layer, at intervals, have flooded and buried the original surface over many thousands of square miles. They give rise to great expanses of dark-colored rock of a type known as basalt which, in some regions, breaks down into soils of notable fertility. Among the great basaltic lava flows of the world are those of the Deccan (peninsular India), Ethiopia, southern Brazil, and the Columbia Plateau in northwestern United States. In the last-named region successive flows, over a long period, covered a total area of more than 100,000 square miles to an average depth of $\frac{1}{2}$ mile. In the process, valleys were filled, hills were buried, and mountains were left standing like islands in a nearly level sea of lava plains.

12.14   Igneous intrusions occur in a vast range of forms and sizes. The largest, known

as *batholiths*, are immense masses of granite or similar rocks measuring several tens, or even hundreds, of miles across and thousands of feet in thickness. In the cores of many of the great mountain belts of the world long-continued erosion has laid bare such deep-lying intrusive bodies. Much of the unbroken expanse of mountains in the Rockies of central Idaho, for example, is hewn out of a huge igneous mass measuring about 250 by 100 miles. The major portion of the Sierra Nevada of California represents the exposed and deeply eroded surface of a batholith 400 miles long. Many deep intrusions assume similar form, but are much smaller. When molten material is forced into the rocks near the surface of the crust, it often makes its way into vertical joints and other fractures, where it solidifies into sheets of rock known as *dikes*, or works laterally in between the strata of layered rocks to form horizontal sheets called *sills*. Where lava has been forced onto the surface, the volcanic pipe or vent eventually becomes clogged with solidified material in the form of a volcanic *neck*. Some-

Fig. 12.12   An igneous dike which stands in relief because it is more resistant to erosion than the rocks on either side of it. Near Spanish Peaks in southern Colorado. (*U.S. Geological Survey photograph.*)

Fig. 12.13 Agathla Peak, a great volcanic neck in northeastern Arizona. (*Courtesy of the American Museum of Natural History.*)

times a larger mass is forced in between rock strata near the surface, raising the overlying beds in the form of a great blister on the face of the earth. The hardened filling of such a blister is known as a *laccolith*.

The principal significance of these various igneous intrusions lies in the fact that the rock of which they are composed is sometimes more resistant to weathering than the surrounding rock into which it has been intruded. When

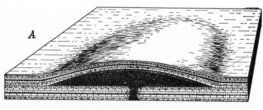

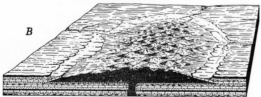

Fig. 12.14 A diagram to illustrate the effects of the intrusion of a giant laccolithic mass into horizontal sedimentary rocks (*A*) and the features resulting from its subsequent erosion by running water (*B*).

subsequent erosion strips off the overlying material and exposes the intrusions, their superior resistance may then, as gradation proceeds, cause them to remain higher than their surroundings. Resistant dikes may come to stand out as wall-like outcrops (Fig. 12.12), volcanic necks as stumplike projections, sometimes of considerable size, and laccoliths may be carved into groups of hills or mountains when the weaker rocks around them are stripped away (Figs. 12.13 and 12.14). Thus from the point of view of landform development the real importance of intrusive vulcanism is commonly not made evident until long after the molten material was actually forced up into the crust.

12.15 Regions of Volcanic Activity. The distant past of geologic time includes an era of almost world-wide vulcanism, but later periods of earth history show it generally much restricted. In different periods one region or another has been affected only to have its volcanoes grow dormant and disappear. Usually, notable volcanic activity appears to have been closely associated with regions of principal diastrophism. It is not unreasonable that the two should be associated. Zones of crustal breaking or bending may well be the zones of weakness through which deep-seated masses of

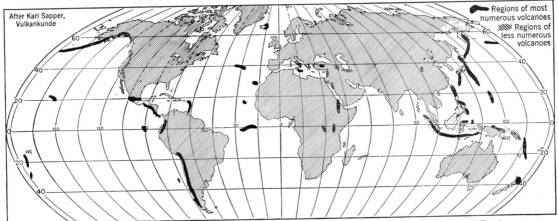

Fig. 12.15 The principal volcanic regions of the world. (*Denoyer's Semielliptical Projection.*)

molten rock find their way to the surface most readily.

In view of this probable relationship it is not surprising to find that the world regions of greatest current volcanic activity are closely comparable to those of present diastrophism (Fig. 12.15). Within the zones previously described, including the borderlands of the Pacific Ocean, southern Asia, southern Europe, and the West Indian region, are included not all the 300 or more active volcanoes of the world but a large proportion of them.

13

The Agents and Processes of Gradation

13.1 Gradational Agents and Processes. It has been noted previously that the tectonic forces are opposed by forces of gradation which tend ultimately to reduce to a low and uniform level all those features produced by diastrophic uplift or volcanic outpourings. Most important among the *agents* that accomplish this work are water, ice, and wind, acting in conjunction with the force of gravity. The energy of the sun evaporates the waters of the oceans, which are then precipitated upon the land and returned to the sea as running water or moving ice. Solar energy and the force of gravity likewise are responsible for the winds, which remove some quantities of earth from the land surface and which largely condition the precipitation of moisture over the lands and the work of waves along the margins of the seas. Organic agents such as plants, animals, and man play parts in the slow gradation of the land. Their activities also are conditioned by solar energy, particularly as it is expressed in climates. At times the force of gravity acts independently as a gradational agent, moving loosened materials down to the base of the slope from which they have been dislodged.

It is convenient to divide the work of gradation into two parts or stages, although it must be remembered that the parts are so intimately related that often it is difficult to determine at just what point one ends and the other begins. The first part involves no significant movement of material. It represents rather the preparation of the material for removal by breaking down bedrock into smaller pieces, or into softer or more soluble substances. The processes by which this is accomplished are collectively termed *weathering*. The second part of the gradational sequence involves the actual picking up, moving, and redepositing of the prepared material. It is by these processes of *degradation* and *aggradation,* and not by weathering, that landforms are carved or constructed. Indeed, it may for this reason be argued that weathering itself should not be included as a part of gradation, but it is so vitally necessary a preparatory measure and so intimately bound to the "picking-up" processes that it seems almost impossible to disassociate it from the mobile processes that follow so closely on its heels.

13.2 The importance of gradation to the development of landforms can hardly be emphasized enough. Its agents are constantly at work on every part of the continental surfaces, carving, grading, and filling, so that there is no place that does not show the marks of their handiwork. Even in those areas where the tectonic processes are working most rapidly and with the greatest effect, the forms that may be seen are almost never purely tectonic, but show more or less gradational modification. For as soon as tectonic forces begin to produce a surface irregularity, the gradational agents begin their unceasing labor of evening it off again.

Rock Materials and Weathering

13.3 The Breaking Down of Rock. Even the most powerful of agents can accomplish little against massive, unweathered bedrock. Therefore, the weathering processes, by which solid rock is disintegrated, decomposed, or otherwise made more easily removable, are of great importance. Weathering may be either mechanical or chemical in nature. Mechanical weathering includes all those processes by which solid rock is disintegrated or reduced to fragments, but left chemically unchanged. Chemical weathering includes all those processes of rock decomposition or decay in which some of the rock substances undergo chemical change. Usually both are to some degree involved in the preparation of rock material for removal. These processes vary considerably in their nature and rate of working, depending upon the physical structure and chemical composition of the rocks they are attacking. In order, therefore, to understand the activities and the results of weathering, it is necessary to gain some understanding of the nature of the rocks themselves.

ROCK MATERIALS

13.4 Minerals. The rocks that compose the earth's crust are aggregations of particles of various substances called *minerals*. The term is here applied not in the sense of an earth product having marked economic value, such as coal or petroleum, but rather in the sense of any natural earth substance having a nearly constant chemical composition and fairly definite physical characteristics. The latter usually include a fairly definite crystalline form, a certain hardness, a limited range of color, and a characteristic structure and mode of fracturing.

Minerals are sometimes composed of a single chemical element, such as pure copper or gold. More commonly they are combinations of two or more elements in chemical union. All of the 92 known chemical elements exist in the crust, but many of them are extremely rare. Some others are more common, but still do not make up a great part of the crust. Only eight are really abundant, together comprising 98 per cent of the known crust of the earth. In order of abundance these are: oxygen (47 per cent), silicon (28 per cent), aluminum (8 per cent), iron (5 per cent), calcium (4 per cent), and sodium, potassium, and magnesium (2 to 3 per cent each). These eight are the commonest

components of minerals. It is interesting to note that of the familiar and valuable metallic elements only iron and aluminum are really abundant in the crust.

In minerals the elements are united to form substances which are very different from any of the constituent elements. Thus, iron, a metallic element, may unite with oxygen, a gas, and water, a liquid, to form a soft brown earthy mineral, limonite, which is familiar as iron rust. The list of known minerals contains many hundreds of names, but, as with the elements, a few are so much more common than the rest that they make up the bulk of the crust.

Among the minerals deserving special mention is *silica*, a compound of silicon and oxygen, most familiar in the hard, glassy form called *quartz*. Silica is noted for its hardness and resistance to chemical decomposition and is the commonest material in sand. Also important are the *feldspars*, a group of light-colored minerals that are physically hard, but quite liable to chemical breakdown. They are compounds of aluminum, silicon, and oxygen (aluminum silicates), with various other elements such as potassium, sodium, or calcium. Other important aluminum silicates are the *ferromagnesian* minerals, dark, heavy substances containing iron, magnesium, and various other elements. Like the feldspars, they are fairly hard, but not very resistant to decomposition. The *clay minerals* are also aluminum silicates, chemically stable, and usually occurring in very fine particles. The *carbonates* are a group of minerals most abundantly represented by calcium carbonate, or *calcite*, a clear, soft, crystalline substance that decomposes readily, as do many of the minerals of the group. Among the *metallic oxides* the most familiar and abundant are the various oxides of iron, mostly reddish or brownish in color, often earthy, and relatively difficult to break down chemically.

It will be seen that there is great contrast among these common minerals in hardness and resistance to decomposition. It is to be expected then that these properties of the minerals will be transmitted to the rocks which they compose and that because of their varied mineral composition the rocks will themselves vary in physical and chemical resistance.

13.5 Rocks. In rocks the component minerals exist separately in distinct grains or particles and not in chemical combination. Moreover, the component minerals in various specimens of the same class of rock are not necessarily identical in kind or amount. The particles are locked together in an almost infinite array of patterns, which depend upon the nature and proportions of the component minerals, their peculiarities of crystalline structure, and the history of the rock since its origin. It is clear that, since there are hundreds of minerals that may be combined in a great variety of ways and proportions and then subsequently changed by events in the history of the rock, the total number of different kinds of rock is very large. The many kinds are most commonly grouped, according to their origin, into three general classes: (*a*) igneous, (*b*) sedimentary, and (*c*) metamorphic rocks.

13.6 *Igneous rocks* are those which have been solidified from a molten state. They are, therefore, the rocks most directly associated with vulcanism, and are represented by the lavas that have been forced out onto the earth's surface as well as by the intrusive rocks that have cooled and solidified underground, often at great depth. Aside from their common mode of origin and the fact that all are aggregates of particles or grains of individual minerals that have crystallized separately out of the molten mass, there is little that can be said about the igneous rocks as a class. The majority, in particular the intrusive rocks, are not layered or stratified, but many of the extrusive rocks have accumulated in very definite strata. There are great variations among them in respect to grain size, color, mineral composition, and physical and chemical resistance.

The igneous rocks are commonly distinguished and classified on the basis of grain size and mineral composition. Some igneous rocks have grains of microscopic size, giving a smooth, dense, or even glassy appearance. In others the grains may readily be seen and identified with the naked eye, imparting a distinctly granular texture. Generally speaking, the very fine-grained rocks have developed from extrusive materials and from dikes near the surface, for here the cooling and solidification have been too rapid to permit the growth of large crystals. The granular rocks usually represent batholiths and other deep intrusive masses that have cooled very slowly, allowing the development of a coarse, interlocking crystalline structure.

In terms of mineral composition, the igneous rocks range from *acidic* (dominated by quartz and feldspar, with only minor amounts of the ferromagnesian minerals) to *basic* (dominated by the ferromagnesian minerals and certain feldspars, but with no quartz). Among the common acidic rocks are *granite,* a gray, white, or pink rock made up of clearly distinguishable grains, chiefly of quartz and feldspar, and *rhyolite,* a dense rock with indistinguishable particles, but having the same mineral composition as granite. On the basic side are *gabbro,* a dark-colored granular rock composed largely of ferromagnesian minerals with some feldspar, and its fine-particled equivalent, *basalt,* a common dark-colored lava rock.

13.7 *Sedimentary rocks* are those that have been developed from deposits of clay, silt, sand, gravel, or chemical precipitates such as lime that have been transported and laid down by the various gradational agents. Some are the deposits of wind, ice, or streams on the land, but more largely they are put down on the nearly level floors of the shallow seas or of lakes. The sediments themselves are simply the products of the decomposition and disintegration of other rocks, of any class whatever. The soft sediments become consolidated into rock by compression resulting from the great weight of the overlying accumulations and by the cementing action of infiltering chemical materials.

The accumulation of sediment is rarely continuous, nor does the character of material being deposited remain unchanged over long periods of time. These interruptions and variations make themselves felt in the occurrence of distinct beds or *strata* in the deposit. Successive strata will commonly differ slightly from one another in size or kind of material, and will be separated by planes of weakness called *bedding planes* (Fig. 13.1). The normal attitude of most water-laid sedimentary strata is practically horizontal, and when such rocks are found in positions greatly inclined from horizontal it is an indication that there has been a disturbance of the materials after their deposition.

Sedimentary rocks are of two principal sorts. One sort, called the *clastic* rocks, is derived from the accumulation of solid rock fragments and mineral particles that have been transported, laid down, and cemented together. The other type is formed from materials that have been carried in solution in the water and either chemically precipitated upon the bottom or removed from solution by certain organisms, such as corals and the various shellfish, that use them in the formation of their own skeletal and protective structures. Rocks derived from these precipitates or from accumulations of the shells or skeletal structures may be called the *chemical and organic* rocks.

The clastic rocks are distinguished from one another chiefly on the basis of the size of the particles of which they are composed. Thus the microscopically fine-particled clays give rise to the dense, compact, nonporous rock called *shale*. Sand, in turn, yields the granular and often porous *sandstone*. Gravel may be cemented together to form coarse *conglomerate*. The mineral composition of the clastic rocks may vary greatly, but quartz, because of its great hardness and extreme resistance to decomposition, is by far the commonest ingredient of sands and gravels, and is therefore the dominant mineral in sandstones and conglomerates. Very important in determining the properties of the finished clastic rock is the nature of the cementing material. This may be calcium carbonate, which is weak and soluble, or it may be silica, which is hard and chemically resistant. Clay and iron oxides also sometimes appear as weak cementing agents.

The chemical and organic sediments are represented most importantly by *limestone*, composed of calcium carbonate precipitated in sea water or derived from the accumulations of

Fig. 13.1 Stratified rock. An exposure of thin-bedded sedimentary rock grading upward into regolith and soil. (*Wisconsin Geological Survey photograph.*)

shells. Limestone takes many forms, but is commonly soft and light colored, and may be either dense or coarsely crystalline. A similar and closely related rock is *dolomite*, which is made up of the somewhat less soluble calcium magnesium carbonate. Both of these types of rock often contain thin beds or masses of a dense silica rock known as *chert*, which is also removed from the water by chemical precipitation or by organisms.

13.8 *Metamorphic Rocks.* The term "metamorphic" signifies "changed" or "altered," and is applied to rocks of this group because they are formed by the changing or altering of other rocks. The commonest causes of change are pressure, heat, and the cementing action of percolating waters underground. In some metamorphic rocks the change appears to have been produced in a relatively short time (geologically speaking) by means of the great pressures accompanying diastrophism or by the great heat resulting from the intrusion of molten lavas into older rocks or by both at once. Other rocks appear to have been changed by the extremely slow alteration or replacement of minerals by underground waters.

Metamorphism in some rocks has involved a change so great as to produce minerals not present in the parent rock. Some of the valuable mineral ores are formed in that way. In others the changes are mainly those of form, produced by recementation, by recrystallization, or by rearrangement of the crystals.

Nearly every common igneous or sedimentary rock has a well-known metamorphic equivalent. Granite, for example, may have its grains compressed, crushed, and stretched to form a distinctive coarsely banded or streaked rock called *gneiss*. Basalt yields the more finely banded *schist*. A sandstone may be metamorphosed into an almost solid mass of silica, forming *quartzite,* a rock of extreme hardness and resistance to weathering and erosion.

A shale subjected to great pressure has its particles further flattened and arranged in more perfect parallelism, so that the rock readily splits or cleaves. It is called *slate,* a rock of considerable economic value. A pure limestone, under similar processes, becomes recrystallized, sometimes takes on a translucent or waxy appearance, and is called *marble*. Bituminous coal becomes anthracite when metamorphosed or, if the process is carried far enough, *graphite,* the substance used in pencil leads.

13.9   The Significance of Rock Types. The rocks that underlie a region are associated in many significant ways with other of its natural and cultural features. For example, there is in some places a close relationship between the underlying rocks and the soil, since the weathered rock is the parent material from which the soil is derived, and is itself a principal constituent of some soils. The character of the underlying rock may strongly affect the availability and manner of occurrence of water in the ground (19.4). Or the rock may itself serve as a resource in the form of building stone, limestone for fertilizer, or otherwise (24.22, 24.23).

But from the point of view of the student of landforms, the chief importance of the bedrock lies in its varied response to the weathering processes. The rate and progress of degradation depend upon the rate of rock weathering. Therefore local and regional differences in the physical and chemical resistance of the rock will be reflected in local and regional differences in the nature and speed of landform

evolution, and hence in the present nature of the landforms themselves. Some of the specific relationships between rocks and weathering will be mentioned later (13.12).

13.10   Lithic Regions. Since rock types are significant in so many ways, it is worthwhile to obtain a general picture of the world pattern of occurrence of the major classes of rocks. In many regions the rocks are of such different kinds, and change from one kind to another within such short distances, that they may be described only as regions of complex rocks. However, there are certain large regions in each of which a single class of rocks, such as recent sediments or ancient intrusive and metamorphic rocks, is so widespread that it imparts at least some degree of fundamental unity to the region in which it is dominant. The larger of the world regions of rock similarity are shown in Plate 4, which is entitled "Lithic Regions."

From that map it will be seen that, although sedimentary rocks are included in some of the world's regions of mountainous relief, still larger expanses of them are found in the great interior plains and coastal plains of the several continents (Classes 2 and 3, Plate 4). In total, they underlie the larger part of the land surface of the earth.

In several parts of the earth are vast areas of rocks of great age and complexity. Some, doubtless, originally were igneous, others sedimentary. Whatever their original nature, they have been subjected, during the long progress of geological time, to deformative processes and igneous intrusions. In some regions these processes have been repeated on a vast scale more than once. As a result the older rocks of these regions generally are metamorphosed to a high degree and have been largely recrystallized. Associated with them are masses of intrusive rocks of somewhat more recent age. Regions of that kind are sometimes broadly characterized as "areas of ancient crystalline rocks" or more commonly simply as *shields*. There are several large areas of ancient crystalline rocks (Class 1, Plate 4), especially in northeastern North America, Scandinavia and Finland, Central

Asia, eastern and northern Brazil, eastern Africa, and western Australia. There are other areas of similar rocks too small to be shown on that map.

It will be seen that there are only a few large areas in which extrusive igneous rocks are dominant (Class 4), although many small ones are included in the mixed rocks, which are characteristic of most of the mountainous regions of the world (Class 5).

WEATHERING

13.11 Mechanical Weathering. Of the two main groups of processes that serve to break down solid rock, the simpler in principle is the group that accomplishes mechanical breaking or disintegration without necessarily involving any chemical change. But in spite of the simplicity of the process, the means by which it is accomplished are by no means fully understood. Probably among the more important of the methods of rock breaking are the following: (*a*) the formation of joint planes by diastro-

phism or as the result of stresses set up during the cooling or compaction of rocks, (*b*) the expansive force of freezing water in rock crevices, and (*c*) the wedging effect of the growth of plant roots in rock crevices. The intense heating of rocks, as by forest fires, and their sudden cooling cause internal stresses which also end in rock disruption. It may be that intense insolation and rapid cooling, as between day and night in desert climates, are sufficient, when repeated for many years, to accomplish a similar end. However, it seems unlikely that the latter process is the principal cause of rock weathering even in deserts, as was formerly believed. In addition, all scraping, grinding, scouring, or striking of the surface, by whatever agent, may break off fragments from an outcrop of bedrock.

Mechanical weathering occurs everywhere, though it will be particularly rapid in areas where one or another of the above-mentioned agents is especially favored, as, for example, in areas where repeated and frequent freezing and

Fig. 13.2 Angular rock debris covering surface of ground at 11,000 ft. elevation in the Beartooth Mountains, Montana. At these high altitudes, low temperatures favor mechanical weathering by freezing water, but inhibit chemical weathering.

thawing occur. In warm and humid regions its products are to a considerable degree obscured by the more abundant products of chemical weathering. It is in regions of cold or arid climates, where the chemical processes act slowly, that the rock fragments produced by mechanical means are most strikingly in evidence. In these regions coarse and angular materials often comprise a large part of the weathered debris forming the surface cover (Fig. 13.2).

13.12 Chemical weathering results principally from the chemical union of oxygen, carbon dioxide, or water with elements in the rock minerals or from the dissolving of some of them. These chemical processes are called, respectively, (*a*) oxidation, (*b*) carbonation, (*c*) hydration, and (*d*) solution. They are of great importance, because the chemical changes result in the formation of new minerals which have properties different from those from which they were derived. They greatly increase the

rate at which solid rock is prepared for removal (*a*) by producing new minerals which are softer, more finely divided, or more soluble than the old or (*b*) by the disrupting effect caused by the crowding of expanding substances.

The rusting of iron is a familiar example of both oxidation and hydration, for yellow iron rust is a hydrous oxide of iron. Some igneous rock minerals contain iron, and many sedimentary rocks include iron oxide as a cementing material. These minerals are subject to oxidation and hydration and are changed thereby. Other of the igneous rock minerals contain combinations of elements such as potassium or calcium which, under favorable conditions, recombine with the carbonic acid in ground water. The resulting carbonate crystals are larger in size and different in shape from those of the original minerals. This change exerts a strong wedging force, tending to crowd apart the associated rock crystals and, therefore, to weaken or break up the crystalline

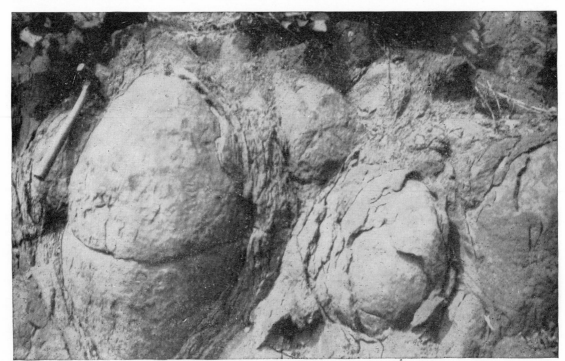

Fig. 13.3 Weathering granite. The disintegration of granite in place, here in a spherical manner, is accomplished chiefly by the chemical decomposition of its feldspar grains. (*Wisconsin Geological Survey photograph.*)

structure of the rock (Fig. 13.3). The carbonates are also commonly more soluble than the minerals from which they were derived. Hydration tends to produce the same crowding effect, being attended, according to Merrill, by an increase in the bulk of some minerals of as much as 88 per cent.

Solution works in a different way. Certain minerals, such as calcium carbonate, become soluble in the water of the ground. Their removal in solution is called *leaching*. It leaves the rocks that contained them somewhat porous, or at least less solid and resistant than before, and the process may end in the nearly complete disappearance of such rocks as are composed largely of soluble minerals.

The chemical decomposition of rock is not local but widespread in its effects, operating upon all types of rocks. Rain water in falling through the air absorbs carbon dioxide gas and becomes a dilute carbonic acid. In the ground it obtains other acids from decaying vegetation. In general, therefore, the water of the ground is really a weak acid and is capable of dissolving lime and other substances and of making chemical changes not possible in pure water.

The processes of chemical weathering are promoted by high temperatures and abundant moisture. Chemical weathering is, therefore, most rapid and complete in the humid tropics and least rapid and complete in regions of aridity or cold. But even in these less favorable areas some small amount of decomposition occurs.

13.13 The Regolith. The accumulated materials resulting from weathering and awaiting transportation often cover to some depth the parent rocks from which they have been derived. These accumulations of disintegrated and decomposed rock fragments are referred to as the *regolith* or *mantle rock* (not to be confused with the earth's mantle, discussed in Chap. 12). The thickness of the regolith depends upon the relative rates of its formation by weathering and its removal by the gradational agents. On steep slopes where gravity or rain wash removes rock fragments about as fast as they are loosened, or in dry or cold areas where weathering

is very slow, the mantle rock may be thin or patchy, permitting the bare and solid rock to be seen. These exposures are referred to as *outcrops*.

On the flat surfaces, even in rainy regions, the products of weathering tend to accumulate to greater depths because of the slowness of the processes of transportation there. In such situations the accumulated regolith may grade downward from fine surface materials, which are completely changed by chemical and mechanical weathering, through partly changed and coarser fragments into the unweathered parent rock beneath (Fig. 13.1). In the humid tropics, where chemical weathering is most active, the regolith is porous, and the surface is protected from erosion by a thick covering of vegetation. There the regolith may accumulate on some gentle slopes to a depth of 100 ft. or more. In most regions it averages considerably less than that depth.

13.14 Differential Weathering. Under a given set of conditions, different kinds of rock will ordinarily weather at different rates because of differences in mineral composition and the degree of ease with which water may penetrate into the rock. Even on an outcrop of a single type of rock the rate of weathering may vary from place to place, either because of minor variations in the composition or texture or because of local differences in the numbers and sizes of joints and crevices that allow penetration of water. If the weathered material is continually being removed by the gradational agents, the places of most rapid weathering gradually are etched out to form low spots in the surface, while the places where weathering is particularly slow come to stand above the rest. Thus *differential weathering* leads to *differential erosion*, which is a major factor in landform development. It is responsible not only for the minor irregularities of rock outcrops, but also, on a large scale, for many surface features of great size (Fig. 12.2) and even for striking regional contrasts.

Since silica is notable for its hardness and resistance to decomposition, rocks that contain large amounts of that mineral are usually relatively resistant to weathering and erosion. Quartzite and the similar silica-cemented sandstones, which are almost entirely silica, are the most obdurate of all common rocks. Many groups of high-standing hills and mountains, like the Baraboo Hills in southern Wisconsin or the higher mountains of the Brazilian Upland north of Rio de Janeiro, owe their height to the relative resistance of their quartzite rocks to degradation. A rock such as granite that contains grains of both quartz and feldspar is somewhat less resistant, for while the quartz grains remain almost unweathered, decomposition of the feldspar grains results in a reduction of the rock to clay and quartz sand.

In humid climates the rocks made up largely of feldspars and ferromagnesian minerals, such as gabbro, basalt, and many schists, are not very resistant to weathering. Generally least resistant under humid conditions are the shales, the limestones, and those clastic rocks in which calcium carbonate is the cementing substance. Some limestones and dolomites have their resistance increased by the presence of large quantities of chert.

In dry regions, where chemical weathering is feeble, the physical structure of the rock appears to be the most significant factor. Here the most resistant rocks are generally those that are massive, fine-grained, and free from close jointing. Even limestones, if they are fine-particled and thick-bedded, are very resistant in dry climates, as are the dense basalts, rhyolites, and quartzites. The coarse-grained granites and weaker sandstones, all thin-bedded sedimentary rocks, and the more flaky or platy types of metamorphic rocks yield somewhat more readily. It must be kept in mind, however, that weathering as a whole proceeds much more slowly in arid regions than where water is abundant.

THE MOBILE PROCESSES

13.15 Erosion and Transportation. The weathering processes commonly are followed, but not always immediately, by *degradational* processes which remove the weathered rock fragments from the places of their origin. Spe-cifically, these include *erosion,* or the picking up of loose material, and its *transportation.* The term erosion is often applied to the two processes combined, but since they are governed by different laws and occur in different places, there is a distinct advantage to treating them separately. Together with weathering they produce the general result of degradation, which is the wasting away of the land and its reduction to the lowest possible level and the gentlest possible slope, or grade.

The principal agents of gradation were listed above, but they may be repeated here, since they will be used as a basis for organization in the remainder of this discussion of the agents and processes of gradation. Weathered rock is transported by the force of *gravity* which may act either directly or, on a broader scale, through the agencies of *running water, water in the ground, moving snow and ice, wind,* and *waves.* To a small degree transportation is accomplished also by organic agencies, including man, and in other minor ways. Clearly, transportation is the essential element of degradation. It is accomplished whenever the material (*a*) is carried in dissolved form, and is therefore invisible, or (*b*) is lifted bodily and carried in suspension by wind, stream, wave, or ice, or (*c*) merely rolls, slides, or is pushed downslope by any of these agents.

13.16 Deposition. Since each of the agents of erosion, under proper conditions, is capable of transporting material, it will be evident that, under other conditions, they will put it down again. This process may be called *deposition.* By it *aggradation* is accomplished, and elevations below the local grade are brought up to it by filling. Just as materials are carried in different physical conditions and by the different agents, so they may be deposited either from solution or from suspension, or they may merely come to rest after having fallen or slid some distance. They may be deposited by the wind, by running water, by moving ice, or by the waves. The various agents and conditions combine to produce classes of deposits which often are associated with the development of distinctive landforms.

From these general considerations the discussion may turn to the specific gradational agents and the various processes by which each carries on its work and aids in the development of landforms. The emphasis in this brief survey will be upon the nature of the *processes* involved. Description of the features produced, the principal concern of the student of geography, will be reserved for more detailed consideration in later chapters.

Gravity as a Direct Agent of Gradation

13.17 Gravity and Mass Movement. The importance of the force of gravity as a source of driving power for such obvious gradational agents as running water and moving ice is familiar and needs no elaboration here. But the work of gravity as a gradational agent in its own right is less well known and is often under-

estimated. Among students of landform development, however, the realization is growing that *mass movement*, or the downslope translocation of material under the largely unaided urging of gravity, is one of the most widespread and effective of all the means of gradation, perhaps scarcely less important than running water itself.

The force of gravity is present everywhere and at all times. On any slope, whenever regolith or fractured rock finds itself insufficiently supported from below it will immediately slide, roll, or flow downward until it reaches the bottom of the slope or a place of secure lodgment on the slope. Such movements may involve single particles or huge masses of material; they may be rapid or slow; and they may be a small fraction of an inch or many thousands of feet in distance traveled. But they occur almost everywhere, and always their direc-

Fig. 13.4 The Gros Ventre landslide of 1925, near Jackson Hole, Wyo., produced an immense scar on the mountainside and temporarily dammed the creek flowing in the valley below. (*U.S. Forest Service.*)

Fig. 13.5 Slumping and earthflow resulting from rain saturation of the ground on a shaly hill slope in eastern Ohio. The lower slope shows turf bulges resulting from flowage beneath the sod, and the upper shows tension cracks. (*U.S. Soil Conservation Service photograph.*)

tion is downward, so that in the long run their cumulative effect is very great. Together with the unchanneled surface wash of rain water, they represent one of the most important means by which weathered material is moved down the slopes to the drainage channels or collecting basins at the foot.

13.18 Rapid Mass Movements. On steep slopes it is not uncommon for masses of regolith, and sometimes fractured bedrock as well, to detach themselves from their underpinnings and fall, slide, or tumble at high speed into the valley below. *Landslides* of this kind are usually quite small, sometimes involving the fall of but a single dislodged block. Occasionally, however, they achieve great size, sending thousands of tons of soil and rock thundering down the mountainsides, sometimes causing much damage and destruction if the lower slopes or valley floors are inhabited. One of the larger recorded slides of this type occurred in 1925 in the Gros Ventre Mountains in western Wyoming. A mass of 50 million cu. yd. of material slid some 2 thousand feet downslope and a short distance up the opposite side of the valley (Fig. 13.4). The debris dammed up the stream in the valley bottom, forming a large lake which eventually overtopped the dam, washed out part of it, and flooded the valley below the slide, causing damage and loss of life.

Landslide movements, large or small, ordinarily occur only on steep slopes, and are especially favored by the existence of unusually thick regolith or weak, fractured, or stratified bedrock, especially if the fractures or bedding planes are steeply inclined. The slide may be initiated by undercutting of the slope through stream or ice erosion or man-made excavation, by lubricating of potential slippage surfaces through the soaking-in of water, by earthquakes, or any of various other agencies. In areas where large-scale shaft-and-tunnel mining is practiced or where subsurface solution by ground water has formed large caverns, sudden collapse of the roofs of these cavities sometimes occurs, forming pits or depressions at the surface.

A somewhat different type of rapid mass movement is that which involves the actual flowing downslope of a limited mass of regolith that has become saturated with water. Such *earthflows* commonly result from the saturation of slippery silty clay subsoils during long-continued rains (Fig. 13.5). The movement is much slower than in landslides, though still perceptible, and may occur even on relatively gentle slopes.

The rapid forms of mass movement are relatively spectacular, both in occurrence and effect. Usually a hollow scar is left on the slope where the movement originated, while the mass that has moved forms an irregular bulge or heap at the foot of the scar, or sometimes a broad, hummocky accumulation across the floor of the valley below. But in spite of the occasional large size of those slides and earthflows, and the obviousness of the resulting surface features, the relatively restricted areas in which

they occur reduces their over-all significance. For the earth as a whole they are probably less important than the slower, less obtrusive, but more widespread types of mass movements that will be considered next.

13.19 Creep and Solifluction. The rapid movements discussed above are usually well defined, individual phenomena, each involving the displacement of a limited, sharply bounded section of the regolith. But there is evidence that on practically all slopes the entire mantle of regolith is engaged in an imperceptibly slow downhill movement, to most forms of which the term *creep* is applied. In creep the regolith behaves essentially as though it were flowing at an exceedingly slow rate. In detail, however, it appears that this is the cumulative effect of innumerable semi-independent movements, usually tiny, of individual soil or rock particles. Although creep proceeds too slowly for its motion to be perceived, there is abundant evidence that it occurs. Some of these manifestations are illustrated in Fig. 13.6.

Any action or happening that permits or forces a single soil particle to move downhill a minute fraction of an inch thereby becomes

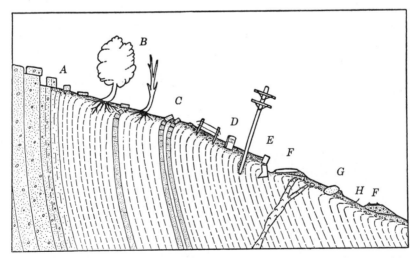

Fig. 13.6 Common evidences of creep: (A) moved joint blocks; (B) trees with curved trunks; (C) downslope bending and drag of fractured and weathered rock; (D) displaced posts, poles, etc.; (E) broken or displaced retaining walls; (F) roads and railroads moved out of alignment; (G) turf rolls downslope from creeping boulders; (H) stone-line near base of creeping soil. (*From C. F. S. Sharpe, Landslides and Related Phenomena, Columbia University Press. Reproduced by permission of author and publishers.*)

a contributing agent to creep. And since gravity is ever-present, nearly all soil-disturbing forces, of which there are many, are likely to produce at least a slight net downslope transfer of particles. The growth of frost crystals lifts particles and then upon melting permits them to settle downhill. Expansion of the soil accompanying the freezing of water, swelling of the soil when it is wetted, and expansion of rock fragments when heated are followed by subsequent contraction upon melting, drying, or cooling. All such expansion and contraction are greatest in the downhill direction, because of the help of gravity. The filling of cracks, burrows, or root cavities in the soil proceeds chiefly from the uphill side. The prying by wind-blown trees or shrubs and the compaction produced by walking animals force soil downslope. Thus slowly but steadily the regolith moves downward, to be carried away by streams or other transporting agents, or if these are lacking, to accumulate as a gently sloping deposit at the foot of the original incline.

In areas where the entire regolith may sometimes become saturated with water there occurs a type of slow downhill flowage of the whole mass (not a localized rapid movement as in earthflow). This process, termed *solifluction,* is especially significant in the subpolar regions and at high altitudes, where the surface layers may thaw out while the lower part of the regolith is still frozen. Much water is released by the melting, but the impervious frozen layer beneath traps the water in the surface layers, which then become almost jellylike and ooze slowly downhill.

Except for the accumulations of regolith that sometimes form at the bottom of a slope, creep and solifluction do not produce obvious and striking landforms. Instead their effect is more general, gradually wearing back slopes and lowering the surface by widespread, unobtrusive erosion.

Gradation by Running Water

13.20 Surface Runoff and the Origin of Streams. Running water has a larger part than any of the other agents of gradation in the modeling of landforms. Some of the work is done by the direct impact of raindrops or by thin sheets of water moving over the ground during downpours of rain. The larger part is done by streams, because in them the water is deeper and faster flowing and therefore has greater erosive and transporting power. The turbulent force of running water over the land surface dislodges and removes weathered rock, and in the process it develops channels or valleys. It is the patterns and peculiarities of stream-cut channels and valleys that give character to most of the lands of the earth.

Streams are fed (*a*) by the immediate runoff of water during rains; (*b*) by the release of water temporarily held in storage in lakes, swamps, snow, and glaciers; and (*c*) by the underground water issuing through seepage and springs. The amount and velocity of surface runoff, which is that part of the precipitation that does not at once soak into the ground or evaporate into the air, are determined by a number of factors which themselves thus become important conditioners of the rate of erosion. Conditions especially favorable to copious and rapid runoff are: (*a*) intense downpours of rain; (*b*) steep slopes; (*c*) clayey, impervious soil; and (*d*) absence of a protective cover of vegetation.

EROSION

13.21 The Erosional Work of Running Water. The most widespread degradational activity of running water is accomplished by the hydraulic action or surface wash of the runoff. The actual loosening or picking up of material is accomplished principally by turbulence or eddy currents in the flowing water and by the striking or scouring action of grains of silt, sand, or rock already being carried by the moving mass. On a bare soil surface much dislodgment of particles is caused by the splashing impact of raindrops.

The degree of turbulence and the force of particle impact are both dependent chiefly upon the velocity of flow, and hence chiefly upon the *gradient,* or degree of inclination of the slope or bed upon which the water is flowing. A dense cover of vegetation on a slope creates in-

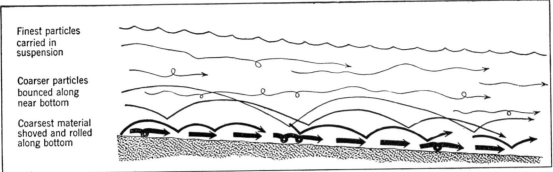

Finest particles carried in suspension

Coarser particles bounced along near bottom

Coarsest material shoved and rolled along bottom

Fig. 13.7 Diagram illustrating ways in which solid materials are transported by running water.

numerable tiny dams that impede the flow of runoff and also serve to protect the soil surface against the direct impact of raindrops. Therefore only very slow water erosion can occur on slopes that have a solid cover of forest or grass, and it is probable that on many such slopes creep is the more important gradational agent. The ease and rate of erosion are also affected by the particle size of the materials that must be moved. Up to a certain point, a decrease in size of particles is accompanied by greater and greater ease of erosion. With very fine silts and even finer clays, however, the relationship is reversed, so that very fine clays are about as difficult to erode as rather coarse gravels. One apparent reason for this surprising reversal is that with clays it is very difficult for eddy currents to penetrate into the tiny spaces between the flat-lying particles and then flip them up into the moving water. Most easily eroded are very fine sands and coarse silts.

The particles that have been dislodged from the bed are transported in several ways (Fig. 13.7). The heavier materials cannot be raised from the bottom and may simply be rolled or shoved along by the force of the current and the striking of other particles. Somewhat smaller grains are thrown or bounced up into the current and carried downstream until their weight causes them to settle, strike the bottom again, bounce once more, and so to proceed by a series of leaps. The finest particles are so light that they can be kept up in the body of the stream simply by the force of the churning eddy currents. This portion of the transported load is called the *suspended load,* in contrast to the

bed load that is rolled or bounced along the bottom. The ability of a stream to transport material depends upon (*a*) the velocity of flow, (*b*) the volume of water, and (*c*) the particle size of the material to be moved.

The carrying capacity of a stream increases rapidly with increase in the velocity. If its velocity is doubled, the maximum volume of the pieces of rock it will be able to move may, under ideal conditions, be increased in proportion to the sixth power of its velocity, or sixty-four times. According to Geikie, a stream having a velocity of about $\frac{1}{8}$ mile per hour will barely carry fine clay. At the velocity of $\frac{1}{4}$ mile per hour it will move fine sand; at $\frac{1}{2}$ mile, coarse sand; at $\frac{2}{3}$ mile, fine gravel; and at $1\frac{1}{2}$ miles per hour it will transport pebbles about 1 in. in diameter. The relationship between particle size and transportability is a direct one, so that clay, while it is difficult to erode, is the easiest of all materials for a stream to carry. Usually it is carried in suspension, even in very sluggish streams.

13.22 Valley Deepening and Stream Gradients. The runoff may start its work as a sheet of water, but ordinarily it does not progress far before it is concentrated into rivulets which eventually are enlarged and are maintained by springs and the seepage of underground water. Streams flow in valleys, and most valleys start as gullies. It is the work of running water to make them *deeper, wider,* and *longer.*

Valleys are deepened when their streams, following the principles of erosion and transportation outlined above, remove rock materials from their beds and carry them off downstream.

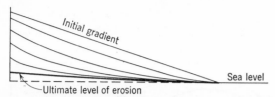

Fig. 13.8 Diagram showing idealized development of a stream profile. Lower reaches of stream achieve gentle gradients first, resulting in concave profile.

Since the level of the mouth of a large stream system is usually fixed by the level of the sea or other body of water into which it flows, continued lowering of the rest of the stream bed will result in a gradually decreased gradient. The lower reaches, having the smallest vertical distance through which to erode, will achieve gentle gradients first, and gentling of the bed will then proceed progressively upstream. Therefore in a river system the newer tributaries and headwater streams usually have steeper gradients than the waters of the middle and lower courses (Fig. 13.8). For that reason the tributary streams may be eroding rapidly while the main stream, in its lower course, may have a gradient so low that it is no longer able to cut downward, and more material may collect in its channel than it is able to transport. In this circumstance some aggradation will occur in the lower section of the system while the headwaters are still actively deepening their valleys, a situation that may be observed in many places.

The term *graded* has often been used to designate a section of a stream which has achieved a gradient that no longer permits significant downcutting, but which just permits the transporting of the load fed to it from above. While this precise equilibrium condition is rarely achieved in nature, the concept has some value as the theoretical goal toward which the gradational activity in any section of a stream is at all times directed.

Different streams and different sections of the same stream often contrast sharply in the rate at which downcutting proceeds. The principal controlling factors are the gradient with which the stream began, which is often the result of tectonic happenings, and the nature of the rock material. Sections of the stream that pass over easily eroded material cut down more rapidly and achieve gentle gradients sooner than sections developed on resistant rocks. Thus a stream that crosses several belts of rock of sharply differing resistance will develop a lengthwise profile of alternating steep and gentle segments (Fig. 13.9). Outcrops of especially resistant rocks may be marked by rapids or even waterfalls in the streams that cross them. As the long process of erosion continues, such irregularities are eventually evened out, and the stream achieves a smooth profile.

13.23 Baselevel. The lowest level that can be achieved by any part of a stream system is the level of the body of water into which it empties, and only the mouth of the stream can reach this level. Every other point in the system

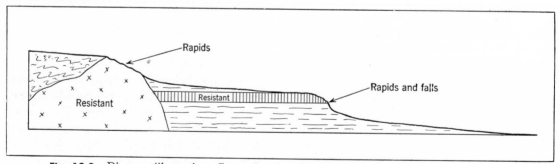

Fig. 13.9 Diagram illustrating effects of rock resistance upon stream profile. Weaker rocks erode more rapidly and allow stream to achieve gentle gradients, while resistant outcrops, because they yield more slowly and are undercut from below, develop steep gradients, rapids, and falls.

will remain enough higher to permit the water to flow. The limiting elevation for the stream mouth is called the *baselevel*.

Not all inactive streams, however, have reached the lowest levels to which they are ultimately capable of eroding. Many are prevented from continuing their downward cutting by the existence of *temporary baselevels*. Thus, for example, some of the streams of northern Ohio have reached gentle gradients because they empty into Lake Erie, the elevation of which establishes a baselevel for them. This, however, is, geologically speaking, temporary, since the level of Lake Erie is maintained by a resistant rock ledge at Niagara Falls, and below this are the rapids of the St. Lawrence River. In time these obstructions may be removed by erosion, and then the tributary streams in Ohio will (barring tectonic interruption) be able to reduce their channels to the ultimate and lowest possible grade, which is established by the level of the sea. The same is true of certain arid-land streams which do not ultimately discharge into the sea but into basins of interior drainage (14.25). The floor of such a basin, whatever its elevation above or below sea level, establishes a temporary baselevel for the streams tributary to it.

13.24 Valley Widening and Cross-section Profiles. At the same time that the stream is deepening its valley by erosion of its bed, the valley is also being widened by erosional attack upon the valley walls. A small part of this attack may be laid to undercutting at the base of the slope by the stream itself. Much of it, however, is accomplished by rainwash, gullying, and mass movement, such as will occur on any exposed slope. The rate at which the driving back of the valley walls proceeds is dependent upon the already familiar controls of erosion in general: amount and intensity of precipitation, density of the vegetation cover, resistance of the rocks, and initial steepness of the slope, which is largely determined by the rate of downcutting by the stream. Generally speaking, loose materials or materials that wash or slide easily give rise to gentler slopes than more compact and resistant types of rock.

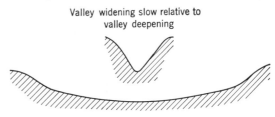

Valley widening slow relative to valley deepening

Valley deepening slow relative to valley widening

Fig. 13.10 A stream that cuts down rapidly relative to the rate of valley widening develops a narrow, steep-sided valley. Slow downcutting permits valley widening to open up a broad, flaring profile.

Since downcutting and valley widening go on simultaneously, the cross-section profile of a valley is in considerable part determined by the relative rates at which these two processes are advancing. If stream cutting is rapid relative to valley widening, the resulting valley will be narrow and steep-walled (provided that the rocks are sufficiently compact). Slow deepening and rapid widening will result in a valley that is broad and open (Fig. 13.10). It has been seen that stream gradients, and hence rates of downcutting, tend to decrease gradually as erosion continues. There is, however, no reason to expect a corresponding change in the rate of valley widening. Therefore, in valleys that are in the earlier stages of development and are still actively downcutting, it is common to find relatively narrow, V-shaped cross sections. But where streams have achieved gentle gradients

Fig. 13.11 A gully head which is almost visibly gnawing its way up a slope which directs the flow of rain water into it. (*Photograph by F. W. Lehmann, C. B. & Q. Railroad Company.*)

Fig. 13.12 As a gully grows in length by headward erosion, tributary gullies branch from its sides and grow in like manner. (*Photograph by F. W. Lehmann, C. B. & Q. Railroad Company.*)

and are sluggish and inactive, continued active widening will usually have changed the cross section into one that is wide and flaring.

13.25   The Development of Stream Systems. A normal gully begins at the base of a slope and grows in length by erosion at the point where surface water pours in at its upper end. In a sense it gnaws its way *headward* into uneroded land (Fig. 13.11). New gullies branch from the sides of the first one and lengthen in the same manner (Fig. 13.12). In rock or regolith of uniform resistance the gullies normally have a branching, treelike, or *dendritic*, relation to each other. Gullies of this kind may grow on unprotected slopes in such numbers as to create a great problem in the control of soil erosion (22.18). Not all gullies thus formed grow to great length, but in time some of them may. During that time each long gully will have acquired tributaries, each tributary will have subtributaries, and these in turn will end in a multitude of gullies which reach and drain all parts of the region.

A major stream of water and its tributary streams is called a *river system*. The higher land separating two adjacent stream valleys is called an *interfluve*. The entire area of land drained by a river system is called a *drainage basin*. The line along an upland separating two adjacent drainage basins is called a *divide*. On the divide surface drainage destined for the respective streams is parted, as on the ridge of a house roof, although some divides are low, and the line of water parting is therefore indistinct.

As stream systems develop, so do the relief features of the regions through which they flow. In areas where tributaries are undeveloped and few, and the interfluves are broad and little dissected (Fig. 13.13*A*), it is evident that the streams have only just begun the task of reducing the whole block of land to its ultimate low baselevel. A region with a surface of that kind is said to be in a stage of *youth*.

As erosion proceeds, many new tributary streams and a large number of gullies are formed. These dissect the former broad interfluves. Valleys grow deeper and wider, and the divides between adjacent streams grow narrower, until finally little remains of the former broad upland. The whole area is then char-

246

acterized by sloping rather than flat land (Fig. 13.13*B*). This stage of development may be called *maturity*. In it the flat upland of youth has ceased to exist, and the new and extensive flat lowlands of old age have not yet come into existence.

Progress of erosion beyond maturity enables the streams, first the larger ones and then the tributaries, to reach gentle gradients and cease active downcutting. Beyond this point there is continued degradation of the land surface as the divide areas are slowly reduced by weathering and slope wash. The region ultimately acquires broadly open and level-floored valleys separated by low, inconspicuous divides which are but the remnants of the former youthful interfluves (Fig. 13.13*C*). This stage of development may be called *old age*.

It is not intended that the terms "young," "mature," or "old," as applied to relief features, should be interpreted in terms of years, but rather in terms of the stage of advancement or completion of the work of reducing the local land mass to the uniform low slope of old age. The actual time required for a region to pass through all the erosional stages from the features of youth to those of old age will depend upon a number of factors, such as the height of the original youthful plain above its baselevel, the kinds of rock to be eroded, the quantity of runoff, and the vegetation cover. Measured in terms of years, the time required must be, at the very least, extremely long. It is estimated, for example, that the material carried into the Gulf by the Mississippi River is sufficient to reduce the average elevation of the entire drainage basin 1 in. in about 800 years, but that the rate of degradation in the Colorado Basin is nearly twice as fast. Undoubtedly the growth of a complete system of tributaries, which transforms a youthful surface into a mature one, is accomplished much more quickly than the slow widening of valleys and wasting away of divides that carries the same surface from maturity to old age.

In few places in the world are there plains that illustrate the extreme of erosional old age. In most instances, the slow process of their final reduction has been terminated by diastrophic changes which have lifted them somewhat farther above the sea. Thus the streams are given new baselevels, acquire steeper gradients, and start upon dissection of the plains in new cycles of erosion. If the slow process is not interrupted, a plain of low relief is formed with undulating surface and occasional hill remnants of the once broad uplands. Such a plain is called a *peneplain*, and any remnant hills are called *monadnocks*.

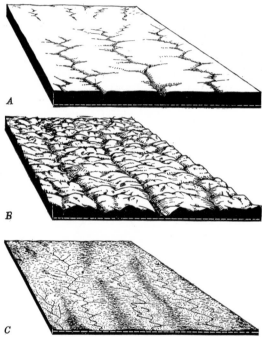

Fig. 13.13 The ideal stages in the development of a land surface by stream erosion, from youth (*A*) through maturity (*B*) to old age (*C*). The dashed white line indicates the baselevel toward which the streams are working.

13.26 Stream Patterns. The patterns which stream systems assume are governed principally by (*a*) the initial slopes of the area in which they develop and (*b*) local differences in resistance of the rocks. Initial slopes, which may be produced by tectonics or inherited from an earlier cycle of erosion, rather naturally determine the direction of flow of the first streams

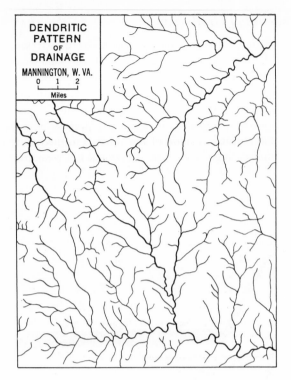

DENDRITIC
PATTERN
OF
DRAINAGE
MANNINGTON, W. VA.
0   1   2
Miles

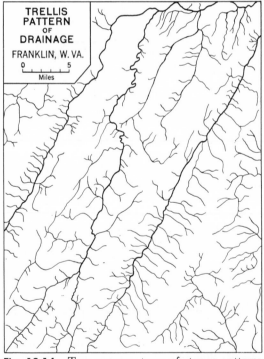

TRELLIS
PATTERN
OF
DRAINAGE
FRANKLIN, W. VA.
0   5
Miles

Fig. 13.14 Two common types of stream patterns. The dendritic pattern develops where there are no strong, systematically arranged contrasts in rock resistance. The trellis pattern sometimes occurs where weak and resistant rocks alternate in long parallel bands.

that develop. On a broad, smooth plain that is gently and uniformly inclined, the first major stream courses may, for example, develop as roughly parallel channels, all directed down the regional slope. On a new structural dome, uplifted fault block, or volcanic cone, the first streams will commonly radiate from the crest of the uplift.

Local differences in rock resistance make themselves felt later during the course of development of the stream system. Areas of weaker rocks are relatively rapidly eroded and hence tend to form valleys and lowlands, while more resistant materials maintain higher elevations. Even prominent joint planes, fault lines, and belts of shattering in the rocks frequently serve as lines along which erosional attack is especially effective. During the development of tributary systems, therefore, the areas of weakness are particularly favorable sites for valley growth, and their pattern of occurrence is reflected in the pattern of the stream system that evolves. If there is no strong local variation in rock resistance, the tributaries usually develop in a random branching (*dendritic*) pattern (Fig. 13.14). Strongly marked joint systems may induce a striking rectangularity of pattern, while a belted arrangement of alternately weak and resistant rocks may give rise to a stream system in which the major tributaries follow the belts of weak rock, while smaller tributaries flow down the sides of the intervening ridges. Such an arrangement is sometimes called a *trellis* pattern.

DEPOSITION

13.27 Deposition by Running Water. If the supply of weathered rock available for stream transportation exceeds the carrying capacity of the stream, it becomes overloaded, and some of the load will be deposited.

Streams become overloaded in several ways, such as by having much new sediment brought to them without corresponding increase in carrying power, or by loss of water through decrease in rainfall, through seepage, or through evaporation. However, it is likely that the most common cause for stream deposition is loss of velocity. Decrease in stream velocity may come about gradually, as a result of the decreasing gradient from the headwaters toward the mouth, or it may come about suddenly. A sudden decrease in velocity may occur at an abrupt change in land slope, as, for example, where a mountain stream flows out upon a flat plain, or it may occur as a result of the checking of the stream current where it enters a body of standing water, such as a lake or the sea.

The term *alluvium* is applied to stream deposits of all grades and forms of accumulation. The action of running water tends to sort the transported material roughly according to the size and weight of its particles before putting it down. This sorting action causes stream deposits to accumulate as beds of gravel, sand, silt, and clay. In the process of deposition streams put down the coarsest and heaviest parts of their loads first, because they carry such material less easily. Thus the principal deposits of a swift Rocky Mountain tributary of the Mississippi system may be large stones and boulders, while those of the lower Mississippi itself are only fine sands, silts, and clay. However, the carrying power of a stream changes often between flood and low water, and it is common to find beds of alluvium of different grades one above another.

The different conditions that cause streams to deposit cause the deposited materials to accumulate in several characteristic places with reference to the stream course and in several commonly recognized forms.

13.28 *Deposition on Valley Floors.* If aggradation begins in a section of a stream that occupies a well-defined valley, the alluvial deposit will take the form of an elongated strip in and along the sides of the channel on the valley floor. In time, as accumulation proceeds, the bottom of the valley becomes filled with alluvium, the nearly flat surface of which is termed a *floodplain.* When a sediment-laden stream rises in time of flood, overflows its channel, and spreads out upon the floodplain, much material is deposited immediately along the stream banks where the water first goes out of its proper channel and loses its velocity. There the alluvial accumulation is thickest, and

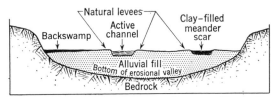

Fig. 13.15 A cross-section diagram illustrating typical floodplain features. The highest ground is along the natural levees.

it generally forms very low, broad ridges bordering the stream. They are called *natural levees* (Fig. 13.15).

The width of floodplains ranges from a few yards to many miles, depending chiefly upon the original width of the erosional valley which is being filled and upon the thickness of the deposit. Some small widening of the plain may also be accomplished by undercutting and caving of the valley walls at points where the stream channel swings against them.

The development of a floodplain suggests that something has occurred, either abruptly or gradually, to change the activity of that part of the stream from downcutting to aggradation. Such a change is usually brought about by an alteration of the gradient of the stream, or of the amount of load being supplied to that section of the stream.

A decrease in gradient may come about gradually through the normal process of erosion. It is not uncommon to find, in a large stream system, that active growth of the tributary system is still going on after the lower reaches of the stream have achieved very gentle gradients and have therefore become sluggish. Thus as the load being supplied by headwater streams continues to increase, the lower stream trunk finds itself increasingly unable to handle the supply, and deposition begins.

A decrease in gradient might also be achieved through a diastrophic backward-tilting of a portion of the stream course. Construction of an extensive delta has the effect of lengthening the stream without changing the level of its mouth. This necessarily decreases the average gradient of the stream near the mouth, and may induce deposition on and above the delta head.

An increase in load may come about simply through growth of the system of tributaries, or it may occur as a result of some specific change that permits more debris to be brought into the existing stream system. Any thinning of the vegetation cover, exposure of more easily eroded materials, or climatic change in the direction of more intense downpours of rain might, by enhancing erosion, augment the load fed into the headwaters. During glacial times great quantities of debris were carried by streams that drained melt water away from the ice edge, and extensive floodplains were built by those streams, the Mississippi and many of its northern tributaries among them.

13.29 *Deposition at the Stream Mouth.* Nearly all streams are able to carry some sediment down their entire courses and out at their mouths. Usually most of that sediment has been a long time on its way, having been incorporated into bars and floodplains, re-eroded, and put down and picked up thousands of times on its journey. Finally it is deposited where the stream velocity is checked upon entering a lake or the sea. Extensive accumulations of sediment in that kind of location are called *deltas*. Not every stream has a delta. Some carry out little sediment; others deposit their loads on sinking coasts or upon such as have deep waters or are so exposed to violent wave and current action that the sediment is spread over the adjacent sea floor and thus is prevented from making large accumulations.

The process of delta building is accomplished by deposition on either side of the stream channels during overflow and by the building of an alluvial embankment and the formation of bars beyond the mouth of the stream. The deposition of a bar opposite the open end of the lengthening channel often forces the channel to bifurcate, flowing at either side of the obstruction. As the channels lengthen and repeat the process, the stream acquires increasing numbers of outlets, which are called *distributaries* (Fig. 13.16).

13.30 *Deposition at Sharp Decreases in Valley Gradient.* The velocities of mountain streams are checked suddenly where their courses extend out upon adjacent plains. It is at this point that some streams choke their own courses with alluvium, turn aside and choke again, and repeating the process, ultimately build broad fan-shaped or conical piles of alluvium which are called *alluvial fans* (Fig. 13.17). In humid regions many mountain streams have sufficiently large and constant volumes to be able to move their loads of debris still farther down their courses and do not form alluvial fans. Even in humid regions, however, fans of large size accumulate at the bases of very steep mountain slopes, and those of small size often are to be seen at the mouths of small gullies where there are no permanent streams but where much water runs during a rain. Along a fresh road cut, on a sidewalk, or at the mouths of little gullies fans may be seen, perfect in shape but no more than a few inches across.

It is in dry regions, however, that alluvial fans reach their greatest development. There the slowness of chemical weathering and the meagerness of the protective cover of vegetation favor active erosion of coarse debris from the higher slopes during occasional downpours. Abrupt checking of velocity at the mountain foot results in immediate deposition of much of the coarser part of this abundant load. Quick cessation of rain, absorption by the porous alluvium, and loss through evaporation rapidly diminish the stream volume, and the remainder of the debris is strewn along the channel, usually within no more than a few miles of the mountain front. Along the bases of some mountain ranges every stream has its alluvial fan, large or small, and they are so crowded that adjacent fans spread and join, making a continuous *piedmont alluvial plain.*

13.31 **Stream Behavior on Alluvial Surfaces.** Streams that are flowing on alluvial surfaces are noteworthy for their tendency to alter and shift their channels continually. This tendency is due in part to the ease with which stream banks in unconsolidated alluvium may be undercut and made to collapse and in part to the repeated choking and diversion that occur in a channel in which alluvium is being

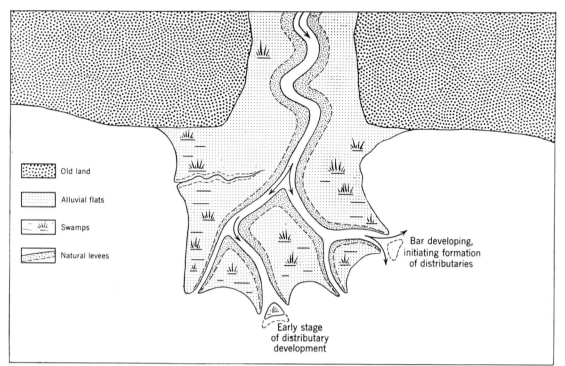

Fig. 13.16 Diagram illustrating characteristic features of a delta plain. Distributaries form when the stream, as it extends itself to seaward, divides around a bar which has been deposited directly opposite the mouth.

Fig. 13.17 A small and steep alluvial fan in Nevada. The apex of the fan lies at the mouth of the gully from which the fan material was eroded. (*Photograph by John C. Weaver.*)

rapidly laid down. A stream that is flowing in silty or fine sandy alluvium, but not actively depositing, characteristically assumes a highly sinuous or *meandering* pattern, such as that exhibited by the lower Mississippi River. These bends or meanders do not remain fixed in place, but rather tend to widen and become more looping. Often a meander is completely severed from the main channel by diversion of the stream across the narrow neck of the loop during flood stage. Thus on a floodplain one may often see not only the present meandering channel, but also many abandoned loops that have been cut off by continued shifting of the stream (Fig. 13.18). Streams flowing in less easily eroded materials, while they may display some irregularity of pattern, rarely show true

meanders, because of the great difficulty involved in shifting their stream channels laterally. Most of the smooth meanders that do exist in solid bedrock were probably formed originally on floodplains. A renewal of downcutting then permitted the streams to lower their sinuous courses down through the alluvium and to entrench them in the bedrock beneath (Fig. 13.19).

A stream that is very actively depositing coarse alluvium characteristically exhibits, at low water, a broad, sandy bottom on which there is developed a complex system of many small interconnected channels separated by bars. At high water, the stream spreads broadly over the entire bottom, depositing quantities of sand and rearranging the pattern of channels and

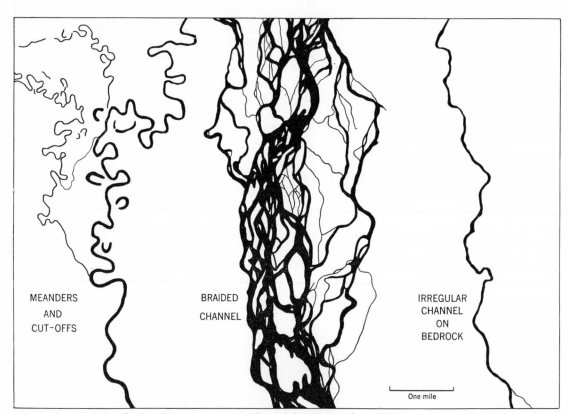

MEANDERS
AND
CUT-OFFS

BRAIDED
CHANNEL

IRREGULAR
CHANNEL
ON
BEDROCK

One mile

Fig. 13.18 A sluggish stream on a floodplain commonly exhibits a pattern of shifting meanders. A stream moving and depositing quantities of sand and gravel often develops a complex system of intertwined, shallow, sand-choked channels. Streams cutting on bedrock characteristically show relatively narrow channels of irregular pattern. (*From U.S. Geological Survey topographic maps:* Fairbanks D-1, Alaska, Fairbanks C-1, Alaska, and Fairbanks A-4, Alaska.)

Fig. 13.19 Renewed downcutting by a meandering stream has produced a remarkable series of entrenched meanders along the San Juan River, in southeastern Utah. (*Spence Air Photos.*)

bars (Fig. 13.18). Such *braided* channels are common where quantities of coarse alluvium are being fed into a section of the stream which cannot handle them because of gentle gradient or diminishing volume. Most streams on alluvial fans, many on floodplains, and even a few on deltas display braided patterns.

Ground Water and Its Gradational Processes

13.32 Ground water exists in the pore spaces of the regolith, in porous rocks, and in the joint cracks and other crevices of all rocks, in regions of humid climate, as far down as crevices and pore space extend. The greater part of the pore space, and therefore of the water, is within a few hundreds of feet of the surface, and many impervious or tightly covered rocks at great depths are essentially dry. The ground-water supply is maintained from the land surface by that part of the precipitation that seeps into the ground rather than immediately running off in streams or evaporating into the air. The surface addition of water seeps downward, as it would in a glass full of sand, until it joins with that already in the ground and fills the lower spaces. Ordinarily there is not sufficient water to fill all the pore space, and the upper part of the earth is merely moist while the lower part is saturated.

The top of the saturated zone is called the *ground-water table*, or ground-water level. In areas of uniform rock character it is not a horizontal surface but tends to seek a common level by slow outward movement from its higher portions (Fig. 13.20). It is not found at a uniform depth below the surface but is usually at greater depths beneath hills and at less depths below valleys, at greater depths after protracted droughts, and at less depths after rains. In humid regions it may be near the surface, and in arid regions far below it. In areas underlain by complex rock structures, the average depth of the ground-water table beneath the land surface may be irregular, some of the rocks being more permeable than others. In some compact rocks, owing to the capillary movement of the water upward in the small pore spaces, there may be no definite ground-water table but merely a gradual decrease in degree of saturation upward from the fully saturated horizons underneath.

Even where the ground-water table is definite, it seldom remains long at any given depth beneath the land surface. In wet seasons or cycles of wet years it rises because of abundant additions from above. In dry seasons or cycles of dry years it sinks to lower levels because the rate of seepage and other losses exceeds the rate of addition. As a consequence three horizons may be recognized: (*a*) an upper one which seldom if ever is saturated, (*b*) a deeper one which always is saturated, and (*c*) an intermediate one which sometimes is and sometimes is not saturated. This condition has much to do with the permanency of springs and wells (19.7, 19.10).

13.33 The gradational work of ground water is accomplished through both chemical and mechanical processes. However, the chemical processes are undoubtedly more widespread, penetrate the earth more deeply, and bring about greater total changes. In most rocks the ground water moves too slowly to accomplish much mechanical erosion, but it is effective in promoting landslides or soil flowage and the slow downslope creep of the regolith. This it does by increasing the weight of the weathered material and by acting as a soil lubricant. The chemical effects of ground water on landforms are accomplished largely through (*a*) solution and (*b*) the redepositing of dissolved minerals.

Solution is a widespread phenomenon. It has been discussed as a phase of chemical weathering, and that perhaps is its most significant aspect. It is, however, a process capable of giving rise to certain landforms. In regions of pure limestones especially, underground solution may remove rock to the extent that large caverns are formed or the rock is honeycombed with small cavities. The surface becomes dotted with depressions caused by solution cavities or by the collapse of cavern roofs (14.27). Such regions are said to have *karst* features, and in them a large part of the drainage flows in underground channels rather than in surface streams.

Under favorable conditions ground water may become overcharged with dissolved minerals and be forced to deposit some. These conditions include (*a*) evaporation of some of the water, (*b*) decrease in its temperature, (*c*) loss of some of its dissolved carbon dioxide, and (*d*) changes in other conditions that tend to hold minerals in solution. The deposited minerals are chemical precipitates, comparable to those which accumulate in a teakettle. In a somewhat different way, minerals are deposited from underground water also by chemical exchange with other minerals in the rocks through which the water passes and by the work of microorganisms. The process is accomplished slowly, molecule by molecule.

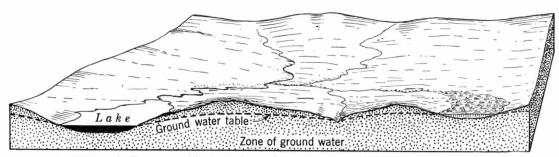

Fig. 13.20 A diagram to illustrate the undulating surface of the ground-water table and its relation to relief and drainage features.

A well-known illustration of deposition by ground water is the formation of stalactites and stalagmites which grow in underground caverns through precipitation from percolating water. Of much greater importance are certain less spectacular phases. For example, ground water charged with lime may build a lime filling in the pore spaces of a bed of sand, cementing the grains of sand together into a limy sandstone. Or water charged with silica may remove the molecules of a previously deposited lime cement, replacing them with the silica, thus producing a quartzite. In the same manner silica or lime, either alone or in combination with valuable metals, such as gold, may be deposited in a rock crevice, making a *vein*. Wood, bone, or shells are *petrified* by the removal of their substance, molecule by molecule, and its replacement by lime or silica, even the microscopic details of internal structure often being kept.

It will be seen subsequently that the removal and replacement of minerals by ground water are important factors in the formation of certain earth resources, such as soil and mineral ores, as well as in the making of landforms.

Moving Ice and Its Gradational Processes

13.34   The Development of Glaciers. Wherever annual snowfall exceeds annual melting, there will remain on the ground at the end of the melting season a portion of the snow from the previous winter. The snow of the following winter is piled on top of this residue, and at the end of the next melting season not only the older residue, but also some of the newer snow remains on the ground unmelted. In this way, by yearly addition, there develops a thick accumulation of snow that may in time reach a thickness of many tens or hundreds of feet. But the snow that makes up the accumulation does not remain unchanged in form. Through the effects of compression by the overlying layers and internal melting and refreezing, the powdery or flaky snow is gradually transformed into hard, granular form and finally into solid ice. If the solid ice becomes thick enough, per-

haps 150 to 250 ft., it begins, simply by its own weight, to flow outward or downslope from the area of accumulation. While the precise physical process of glacial movement is not fully understood, it is at least outwardly like the flow of an exceedingly viscous fluid. Rates of movement rarely exceed a fraction of an inch per day, though exceptional rates of several feet per day have been recorded.

Since the primary requirement for glacier development is an annual excess of snowfall over melting, it follows that glaciers may originate either where snowfall is very great or melting very slight or both. Accordingly, glaciers develop not only in the polar regions, where melting is at a minimum, but also in those areas in middle and low latitudes that experience unusually heavy snows and have a short and cool melting period. Most of the glaciers outside the polar regions are found at high altitudes, for only there are summer temperatures low enough to permit snow, however thick, to persist through the summer. But dryness, as well as warmth, is an enemy of glacier development, and many high mountain ranges and even many sections within the polar circles are free of glaciers because of the insufficiency of snowfall.

13.35   The Form and Behavior of Glaciers. Most of the world's glaciers may be grouped under one or another of two headings: (*a*) *mountain* or *valley glaciers* and (*b*) *ice caps* and *continental glaciers*.

For the first group the place of accumulation of the snow is the upper slopes and high valley heads in mountainous terrain. Winds and avalanches carry the snow from the slopes into the heads of the valleys below, where it reaches great thickness and is eventually transformed into ice, which then begins to flow down the valley bottoms.

The protruding ice tongue that creeps forward conforms to the shape of the valley in which the ice lies. Its rate of movement is governed principally by (*a*) the thickness of the ice, (*b*) the steepness of the valley gradient, and (*c*) the temperature of the ice. The advancing end of the ice tongue, extending down the valley, ultimately reaches lower elevations, where higher average temperatures prevail and the ice wastes by melting and evaporation.

So long as the supply of snow is renewed from above, the glacier will continue to move. So long as the average forward movement of the ice is greater than the amount lost by wasting, the front of the ice tongue will continue to advance. When the rates of advance and wasting are equal, the ice front will remain in the same position. If a series of warm years increases the rate of wasting, or if the amount of snowfall decreases, so that wasting exceeds the rate of ice supply, the ice front will recede up the valley. The glacier is said then to be in retreat. It is, however, only the location of the ice front that retreats, for the ice continues to move downslope or at most remains stagnant.

Some valley glaciers in high latitudes, for example in Alaska, are able to push so far down their valleys that they reach the sea. There, instead of melting away, their ends are continually broken off by wave undercutting and the buoyancy of the sea water, and the pieces float away in the form of icebergs (Fig. 13.21).

A continental glacier is in some respects like a valley glacier but in others different. It starts with the accumulation of snow fields, but not necessarily in regions of high altitude. Having attained considerable depth and area the snows are slowly transformed into ice, and the mass spreads outward under its own weight in all directions. It is fed by snowfall over its entire surface, especially at its margin. The only requirement for continental glaciation is that the snowfall be just enough greater or the temperature enough lower than at present so that the snow of one year is not quite all melted when

Fig. 13.21 A tidal glacier. In the foreground is floe ice. It has toppled off the front of this Alaskan glacier, which descends to sea level. Unusually large masses sometimes break off, forming icebergs. This separation, commonly along crevasses, leaves the ice front sheer. (*U.S. Geological Survey photograph.*)

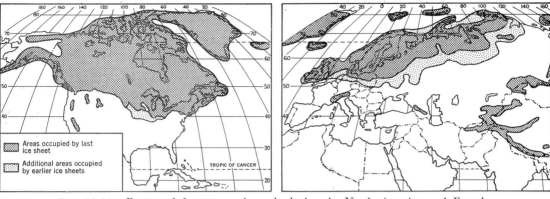

Fig. 13.22 Extent of former continental glaciers in North America and Eurasia. (*After Flint.*)

that of the next year begins to fall. If that condition prevailed the accumulation would spread inch by inch and century by century until its irregular margin reached a position where loss by melting and evaporation equaled the rate of advance.

The disappearance of a great glacier, conversely, would result from a decrease in snowfall or an increase in temperature of an amount such that the average wastage exceeded the additions from snowfall. This would result in the eventual thinning of the ice, probably in its marginal stagnation and ultimate melting away.

13.36 Former Continental Glaciers. At various times during the last million years of geologic history, great continental ice sheets, such as now occupy most of Greenland and Antarctica, covered northern North America, most of northern Europe, and probably much of Siberia (Fig. 13.22).

The European ice sheets radiated from centers located in the Scandinavian region and Scotland and extended southward into England, the Netherlands, Germany, Poland, and Russia. In Siberia, glaciers originating in the Ural Mountains, the northern uplands, and the far eastern mountains appear to have spread thinly over the surrounding plains. It is possible that several of these merged into glaciers of great extent. However, in the relatively dry environment of northern Siberia the ice sheets apparently did not attain such great thickness or extent as did those originating in the centers of Scandinavia and northern Canada, and perhaps they did not exist at all during the time of the latest ice advance in Europe and America.

The centers of North American glaciation were situated adjacent to Hudson Bay. From the American centers ice spread outward, but most extensively southward. At one time or another it reached to a line that trends from New York City westward across southern New York State to northeastern Ohio and from there nearly along the present courses of the Ohio and Missouri Rivers toward the Rocky Mountains. Adjacent to the glacier margins the ice may have been only of moderate depth, but it increased northward to thicknesses that may well have been a mile or more, sufficient at least to bury the mountains of New England. A large area in southwestern Wisconsin and adjacent parts of Illinois, and possibly of Iowa and Minnesota, was never buried by the ice. Apparently this region, known as the *Driftless Area*, was at no time completely surrounded by ice. Instead, each succeeding ice sheet passed it by on one side or the other, probably because of the blocking effect of the broad area of high ground to the south of Lake Superior.

The growth of glaciers during this "Great Ice Age" or *Pleistocene* period (see Appendix E) was not confined to the continental ice sheets. Mountain glacier systems developed or expanded beyond their normal limits on most of the high ranges of the world, though less in the tropical regions than in the higher latitudes.

While many of the details of glacial history are not yet known, it is generally agreed that both in Europe and North America ice sheets formed, expanded, and wasted away at four different times during the Pleistocene period. In addition, there were numerous minor advances and retreats during each of the four major cycles. By the standards of the geologic time scale, the last of the great glaciations occurred surprisingly recently, reaching a maximum perhaps 15,000 to 25,000 years ago. The final disappearance of ice from south of the Canadian border probably occurred no more than 8,000 years ago. The reasons for the changes in temperature and snowfall that brought the glaciers into existence and later destroyed them are not definitely known. However, it is improbable that the changes were extreme, or that the climatic conditions that stimulated the beginnings of glacial growth were greatly different from those of the present time.

The vast quantity of water locked up in these great ice sheets was extracted from the oceans by evaporation, and it returned to them upon the disappearance of the glaciers. It is believed that the quantity was sufficient to cause a general lowering of the level of the sea by at least several scores of feet during the periods of glacier growth, and a corresponding rise in sea level during the periods of glacial shrinkage, including the present time. This would obviously have had considerable effect on the areas of the continents and the shapes of their coastal outlines. Large areas of the continental

shelves, now covered by shallow seas, may well have been land during periods of great glacial advance.

13.37   How Glaciers Erode. A glacier is a highly competent agent for transporting large quantities of rock and regolith over considerable distances. Much of the material which glaciers transport, particularly valley glaciers, is carried onto the surface of the ice by wash or mass movement from the slopes above. But an even larger portion of the load is dislodged and picked up by the ice itself. Because of the virtual impossibility of actually seeing glacial erosion at work, there is some uncertainty about the exact methods by which the erosion is accomplished and the relative importance of each. However, it is now generally believed that most erosion is done by *quarrying*. In this process the plastic ice molds itself about particles of regolith or blocks of bedrock and then, as the ice continues to move forward, drags them out of place and gradually incorporates them into the lower layers of the moving mass (Fig. 13.23). This plucking of particles out of place is probably aided by local melting of the ice under extreme pressure, followed by penetration of the water into crevices where it refreezes, seizing loosened fragments in a grip of ice. Quarrying would be particularly effective in stripping off the mantle rock and eroding in thinly bedded or closely jointed rock.

Using as tools the rocks thus obtained, the

Abrasion by debris dragged over surface

Joint blocks removed by plucking

Fig. 13.23   Diagram to illustrate the way in which a glacier erodes by plucking and abrasion.

ice is able to accomplish another, though less important, part of its erosion by the process of *abrasion*. Angular boulders, pebbles, and sand which are frozen into the bottom of the ice are held down by its weight and pushed forward by its great force. In their slow motion they gouge, groove, scratch, and polish the rock surface over which they pass. In the process the tools are themselves scoured, scraped, and reduced in size. They lose their sharp angularity and become partially rounded, or "subangular" (Fig. 13.24).

Fig. 13.24 A subangular boulder, showing glacial scratches. (*U.S. Geological Survey photograph.*)

Long-continued glaciation has in many places accomplished notable erosion, but, in general, the resulting features are not so prominent or distinctive as those of stream erosion. Rather, they appear to be, in the main, the reshaped features of previous stream erosion.

Glacial erosion can occur almost anywhere within the area covered by the glacier. Near the outer edge of the glaciated area, however, melting greatly reduces the thickness, and hence the effectiveness, of the ice. It also releases much of the material being carried, so that this becomes primarily a zone of deposition, with little erosion in evidence. Speaking generally, the most active degradation will occur (*a*) where the ice is especially thick, (*b*) where the rate of movement is greatest, and (*c*) where the underlying material is weakest or most reduced by weathering. Deep, constricted valleys oriented in the direction of ice movement are very good sites for powerful glacial erosion.

13.38   How Glaciers Deposit. The load of a glacier is comprised of rocks and earth inter-

mingled without regard to size or weight. It is carried in part upon the ice surface or frozen into its mass, but especially in its bottom, because that is where most of it is obtained. The lower layers of ice in some glaciers are so crowded with clay, sand, and boulders that the earthy material is more abundant than the ice. When its bottom is so greatly overloaded, the glacier readily loses its frozen grasp upon some of the material, which then is left resting upon the ice-scoured bedrock below. Near the margin of the glacier melting occurs at both the top and bottom of the sheet, releasing still more of the load (Fig. 13.25). Upon the top of this deposited layer the still-burdened ice creeps slowly forward. If a glacier finally wastes away, its entire remaining load is let down upon that already accumulated. Thus were formed, in the areas covered by the great continental glaciers, vast expanses of unassorted or poorly sorted earthy material, called *till* or *boulder clay*. Specific glacial deposits are called *moraines*, and

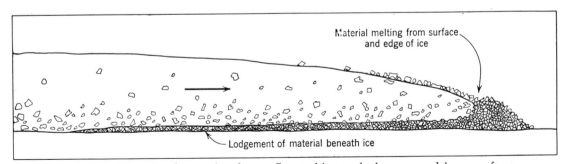

Material melting from surface and edge of ice

Lodgement of material beneath ice

Fig. 13.25 Near its edge, an ice sheet suffers melting on both upper and lower surfaces. Thus some of the debris it contains is lodged beneath the ice, and the rest is dropped at the outer edge.

259

the till sheet, because much of it was held in the bottom of the ice, is called the *ground moraine*.

In regions of nonresistant bedrock and near the margins of the regions of former glaciation the till has accumulated to thicknesses of many feet or even several scores of feet. In regions of resistant bedrock and near the centers of glacial origin it is generally less abundant and is entirely lacking in some localities. In the latter regions the ice was less able to secure debris and, being less heavily burdened, was able to move most of the available material outward toward its margins.

13.39   Where Glaciers Deposit. The ground moraine that is formed under the ice is only one of several forms of glacial deposit, or *glacial drift*. At places where ice advance is for a long time nearly balanced by the rate of melting, the edge of the ice remains almost stationary for years or scores of years. About these stagnant margins accumulate great ridges of drift, which, as a class, may be called *marginal moraines*. Those formed about the margin of the ice at its most advanced position are called *end moraines*. Similar ridges formed at times of pause or slight readvance during its stagnation and final wastage are called *recessional moraines*. Marginal moraines are comprised of drift that is in part shoved or plowed in front of the moving ice but in larger part fallen or washed out of its melting margin.

There is much of the glacial load, however, which is carried beyond the ice margin by the streams of water that result from the melting of the ice. Like all stream-transported earth, this material is sorted somewhat according to weight, the fine muds being carried farthest, and the coarse heavier materials being put down close in front of the ice. The deposit of a glacial stream is classed generally as *glacio-fluvial* rather than as glacial material. When these stream-sorted glaciofluvial deposits are arranged in floodplain form, they are known as *valley trains*. When they are spread in broader fanlike deposits about the ice margin, they are called *outwash plains* (Fig. 14.41).

13.40   Glacial Disturbance of Drainage. The processes of both glacial erosion and deposition disturb the normal processes of stream development. Glacial erosion, unlike stream erosion, acts spottily, producing surfaces with numerous rock basins and ice-scoured hills. The irregular pattern of arrangement of these features reflects peculiarities in the direction of ice flow, its variable erosive capacity, and all inequalities in the rock resistance. In regions of glacial deposition there is also little of local plan or order in the thickness and arrangement of the drift. Consequently, the drainage of both ice-eroded and drift-covered regions appears without pattern. Streams wander aimlessly, falling here over a ledge of rock or collecting there as lake or swamp in a depression. Such stream patterns do not grow entirely as the result of headwater erosion but come immediately into existence on whatever irregular surface is uncovered when the glacier melts away.

13.41   Newer and Older Drift. Among the glacial deposits of North America and Europe are striking contrasts in apparent age. In the younger drift freshly scratched boulders, newly piled hills, and unfilled depressions indicate an origin in very recent geologic time. Other deposits, clearly glacial in nature, contain many weathered boulders, hills much subdued by rainwash, and depressions generally filled, or else drained by a system of well-integrated valleys, so that lakes and swamps are few. From these and other evidences it is known that the continents were invaded by ice sheets at least four times at intervals of many thousands of years. As a rule, only those deposits that were laid down during the last of the great glacial advances (called in this country the *Wisconsin* glaciation) still retain well-defined morainic features and poorly integrated drainage.

The Gradational Processes of the Wind

13.42   How the Wind Degrades. The wind is an important transporting agent. The air is never without dust in suspension, and winds of high velocity are capable of moving sand and

Fig. 13.26 The pebbles and rock fragments of a desert pavement in western Nevada. (*Photograph by John C. Weaver.*)

even pebbles for some distance. Some of the materials carried by the wind are thrown into the air by volcanic explosions, but the greater part is obtained by the wind directly from the earth. This process of surface degradation, during which sand or dust is whipped up by the wind and is transported from one place to another, is called *deflation*.

There are definite limits to the conditions under which deflation can work. It can pick up only dry, finely divided material, and its action is almost completely inhibited by any considerable cover of vegetation. Hence it is effective only (*a*) in regions of aridity and scanty vegetation such as the deserts, (*b*) in exposed areas of beach sand, (*c*) on the dried-out beds of rivers during low-water periods, (*d*) in areas of newly deposited glacial drift, or (*e*) on bare plowed fields. In these areas large sections of the surface may, over a period of years or centuries, be lowered several feet by gradual removal of the finer particles of the regolith. Often this selective winnowing out of the finer materials leaves behind a surface covering of coarser pebbles and gravel that is

termed *desert pavement* (Fig. 13.26). The process of deflation is to some extent aided by wind abrasion. The wind-transported particles scratch, polish, and reduce each other and to some extent the solid rock, producing fine particles which in their turn are removed from the region. Except for some broad, shallow depressions and various sand-blasted bedrock forms, deflation is not responsible for the production of conspicuous surface features.

13.43 How the Wind Aggrades. Wind, like running water, deposits its load of coarse material promptly if its velocity is significantly reduced, but is able to carry fine particles farther and distribute them more widely.

Loose sands are supplied in abundance by the weathering of desert rocks or by wave deposition on shorelines. Where the sands are not anchored by vegetation or moisture, they are whipped up by wind and drifted into heaps, often in the sheltered lee of some obstruction, where the decrease in wind velocity permits some to be deposited. Thus is begun the growth of a sand dune which, by its own height and roughness, interferes with the blowing sand and

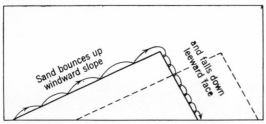

Fig. 13.27 A sand dune moves because the individual grains of which it is composed are continually driven forward by the wind.

promotes its own growth. The growth of a dune often is accompanied or followed by a change of its location. A film of sand is stripped from the windward slope of the dune and deposited in the lee of the crest. By continuous subtraction from the windward and addition to the leeward side, the dune moves slowly, but seldom far, from the source of sand supply (Fig. 13.27).

In contrast, dust supplied by rock weathering and abrasion in dry regions is drifted by prevailing winds over wide expanses to the leeward. There probably is a considerable quantity of wind-borne dust in most soils, but in regions immediately to the leeward of arid lands, where deflation is active, it is particularly abundant and may attain great thickness. In several areas of the earth are found widespread and thick accumulations of an unstratified, buff-colored, calcareous, silty material called *loess*, at least most of which appears to have been deposited as wind-borne dust. In northern China there are particularly thick and extensive deposits which may have been carried in from the wind-swept desert plains to the northwest.

The Gradational Processes of Waves and Currents

13.44 Where Land and Sea Meet. The oceans, seas, and lakes of the earth cover more than 71 per cent of its surface and are important agents in the making and changing of landforms. Their work is accomplished by means of movements of the water, especially waves and currents. These are induced mainly by the wind and, to a lesser extent, by the tides and other causes. Although waves and currents are found in the open seas as well as in coastal waters, they do not reach the bottoms of deep seas and so produce no change there. Their gradational work is restricted to the shallow sea margins with waters of less than about 600 ft. depth. Even in these ocean shallows by far the greater part of the wave work is performed along the coastal margins in waters no more than a few feet or a few tens of feet deep. The total areas subject to change by this force are, however, considerable, since the shorelines of all the lands have a combined length of many thousands of miles.

The work of waves and currents, like that of rivers and glaciers, has two phases: degradational and aggradational, or erosional and depositional.

13.45 How Waves and Currents Degrade Land. The greater part of marine erosion is accomplished by waves. Waves, most of which are caused by the wind, are undulatory motions of the water. In small waves the motion is confined to surface waters, but in great ones there is sufficient agitation to cause some churning of the bottom at considerable depths.

There is little forward motion of the water in the waves of the open sea. A wave is the motion of a shape, not of a mass. The wave form moves forward just as waves may be seen to run across a field of standing grain or may be sent along a shaken rope. However, as a wave enters shallow water a change comes over both its shape and its motion. The wave form shortens horizontally and increases in height. It drags on the bottom, inclines forward, eventually to topple, or *break*, with a motion that throws forward a considerable amount of water (Fig. 13.28). The water thrown forward by breaking waves rushes upon the shore only to lose its velocity and run back, under the pull of gravity, beneath other oncoming waves. The returning water is called the *undertow,* and it has sufficient force to be an important factor in erosion.

The erosive work of waves is accomplished both by the forward motion, or slap, of the water as the waves break and by the sand and rocks that they carry and use as tools. In either case the principal work is done where the waves break.

On coasts where deep water lies immediately offshore, even great waves do not break until they reach the shoreline. There the force exerted by the sheer weight of the water in great waves is truly impressive. Blows of a ton or more per square foot are not uncommon. This is sufficient to dislodge and move about rock fragments of great weight. The effect of the undertow is to move the broken fragments away from the shore into deeper water where they are caught by oncoming waves and moved

shoreward again. By this means waves are furnished with tools that greatly increase their erosional effectiveness. Sand, pebbles, and sometimes great boulders are hurled upon the shore, especially at the bases of exposed headlands. There they are thrown forward and rolled back in endless repetition, scratching and grinding against each other and the solid rock of the shore, accomplishing notable erosion. The general effect of such erosion is to cut back coastal projections, decreasing the area of the land, straightening the coast, and developing, in the process, several characteristic coastal features such as wave-cut cliffs and marine benches (17.7).

On exposed coasts of easily eroded rock the rate of cutting is sufficiently rapid so that whole

Fig. 13.28 A wave breaking. (*Ewing Galloway.*)

shorelines are known to be retreating landward at measurable rates. The shoreline of one part of England, for example, is known to have been cut back as much as 2 miles since the time of the Roman conquest. Shorelines of resistant rock retreat much more slowly.

Where shallow water extends far offshore, the waves break long before reaching the coast itself. In this circumstance, the force of their breaking is directed downward against the shallow bottom, where it may be sufficient to dislodge quantities of sand or mud along the line of breaking. Some of this loosened material is carried out to deeper water by the undertow. The remainder is thrown up ahead of the breakers in the form of a low ridge, which sometimes grows until it reaches the level of the water surface as a long bar parallel to the shore. Wave erosion of this type tends to deepen the water along the breaking line, and if continued, carries the deepening steadily closer to the shore, always driving the bar ahead of it (17.9).

13.46   How Waves and Currents Aggrade. The products of wave erosion, together with sediments emptied into the sea by rivers, are shifted about by waves and currents but ultimately are deposited by them. Much of the material is carried out by the undertow, to be deposited in deeper water. Because wave activity does not extend to great depths, the sedi-

ment does not spread far from shore. The coarsest is deposited first, and the finest is carried farthest out. This process results in a general assortment of deposits according to their sizes. Large boulders seldom are moved far from the places of their origin. Sands are more easily moved, cover vast expanses of shoreline, and extend out into waters of some depth. Beyond these are collected the silts and muds that remain longer in suspension and are deposited in the quiet offshore waters of greater depth. In areas so situated that little mud is deposited there, lime is precipitated from solution and accumulates, together with the limy and siliceous shells of small marine organisms. Thus are originated the sands, muds, and limes which in many regions have been uplifted from shallow sea margins and have become the stratified sedimentary rocks of the continents.

In addition to the material carried out to sea, much is deposited on or near the shore by wave action. Large wind-driven waves are usually destructive, but lesser waves and gentle swells often have a net constructive effect, washing sand or gravel up onto the shore to form beaches.

When the direction of the wind is such that waves strike a shore obliquely, the combined effects of the diagonal shoreward motion of the breaker and the offshore motion of the undertow is to cause both water and the wave-transported material to progress slowly, by angular, in-and-out paths, along the shore. Where the winds are prevailingly from one direction, there is set up by this means a continuous transport of material along the shore in that direction (Fig. 13.29) The transported debris is eventually dropped in sheltered spots behind islands, in bays and inlets, or on the lee side of projecting points or angles in the coast. These accumulations may be subsequently thrown up into various sorts of bars and beaches by waves that drive in at right angles to the coast. These depositional features, by filling in the coastal indentations, tend ultimately to smooth out the shoreline. Thus both wave erosion and wave deposition have the general effect of reducing the irregularity of the coast.

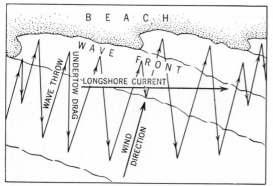

Fig. 13.29   A map diagram to illustrate the in-and-out path of a pebble under the combined forces of oblique waves, undertow, and longshore current.

14

Plains

The two preceding chapters have discussed the processes which have been most significant in shaping the surfaces of the continents. It is now feasible to return to a consideration of the major classes of terrain, discussed briefly in Chap. 11, with the purposes of (*a*) studying their basic characteristics and distinctive types of features in somewhat more detail; (*b*) discovering the combinations of processes, materials, and events that have brought them into existence and produced their various features; and (*c*) considering specific examples that illustrate particular assemblages of characteristics or particular lines of development. In reading the following chapters, constant reference should be made to the brief discussions of materials and processes in the two preceding chapters and to the map plates in the back of the book, especially Plate 3 (Types of Terrain) and Plate 4 (Lithic Regions).

14.1 General Characteristics of Plains. In Chap. 11, plains were defined as surfaces having a predominance of gently sloping land, coupled with low local relief.[1] Within the broad limits allowed by this definition, however, plains exhibit a surprising degree of variety. Some approach as near to perfect flatness as it is pos-

sible for a land surface to become, while others are so rolling or dissected as barely to avoid being classed as hills. Some are marshy or seasonally waterlogged, while others are arid sand, gravel, or soil. Some are rock-floored; others are surfaced with permanent snow or ice. Some lie near sea level; others are thousands of feet higher. The only statements that apply to all are that most of their slopes are gentle and that the differences in elevation within limited areas are small.

But these two attributes are in themselves sufficiently important to justify setting apart the lands that possess them. Not only are such lands visually conspicuous by virtue of their relative smoothness, but also, taken as a group, they stand out in terms of their utility to man. While there are many conspicuous exceptions to the rule, it may safely be said that plains offer a greater amount of favorable land for human use than any other terrain class. It is not surprising therefore that they contain the chief centers of world population (Plate 7). Except for certain swampy, rocky, or icy areas, they are easily traversed by routes of transportation, and the surfaces of those that are, by conditions of climate and drainage, suited to crops are largely capable of tillage.

14.2 The Origin of Plains. The very existence of broad areas of low relief, dominated by gentle slopes, implies certain things about their developmental history. For a surface to possess low relief, at least one of the following must be true: (*a*) the area has undergone prolonged degradation or aggradation that has cleared away or covered all formerly existing features of high relief; (*b*) the area has not, at least in

---

[1] It is not the authors' primary intention to emphasize a set of precise boundary values for the different classes of terrain, and for this reason somewhat generalized verbal definitions are used in the body of the text. "Low" relief would not exceed a very few hundred feet. "Gently" sloping land would have an inclination of no more than three or four degrees. In plains a majority of the area is occupied by such gentle slopes. In "flat" plains (Plate 3), nearly all slopes are gentle, and the local relief is no more than a few tens of feet.

late geologic time, suffered uplift sufficient to carry it many hundreds of feet above the local baselevel and thus to permit streams to cut deep valleys into it; or (*c*) if major uplift has occurred, it has been so recent and so rapid that streams have not yet had time to dissect the uplifted surface deeply.

The most extensive of the world's plains, such as those of interior North America and South America and northwestern Eurasia, generally satisfy conditions (*a*) or (*b*). In either instance, the conclusion would be that these vast plains represent sections of the earth's crust that have not lately been subjected to great tectonic disturbance. Indeed, geologic evidence indicates that for parts of those areas, for example much of the American Middle West, there has been no tectonic activity beyond slow, intermittent uplift and gentle warping for several hundred millions of years.

A number of fairly extensive plains, however, have had a much more eventful history, which in some instances involves very recent disturbances of considerable magnitude. Especially noteworthy are the plains produced by the deep accumulation of alluvium in structural depressions formed in very late geologic time. Examples are the Central Valley of California and the Tigris and Euphrates Plain in the Middle East. A few plains, notably the southern parts of the Columbia Plateau in southeastern Oregon and southern Idaho, owe their existence to the outpouring of immense quantities of basalt lavas, which covered most of the pre-existing landscape and formed a new plain at a higher level. Some of the smoother parts of the Colorado Plateau southeast of the Grand Canyon in Arizona, together with the flatter sections of the high uplands of Tibet and the so-called Altiplano of the central Andes, represent subdued surfaces which have been brought to high level so recently that stream dissection has not yet been able to destroy them completely All, however, are being encroached upon by headward erosion, and in the geological time scale their destruction will be swift.

To be sure, not all areas of low relief are smooth enough to be classed as plains, but those

that are not are exceptions to the general rule. Nearly all depositional surfaces, with the exception of some moraines and sand-dune areas, are conspicuously lacking in steep slopes. Even stream-eroded terrain is usually predominantly gently sloping if the depth of valleys is small. Only in the mature stage of erosional development are gentle slopes likely to be deficient in extent, and then only under conditions especially favorable to the formation of steep slopes. One such condition would be unusually copious surface runoff combined with either easily gullied or very massive subsurface materials.

14.3   General Distribution of the World's Plains. A study of the location and distribution of the world's great plains (Plate 3) will reveal the significant fact that many are tributary to the Atlantic and Arctic Oceans. Only the smaller plains of southern and eastern Asia, east Africa, Australasia, and western America face upon the Pacific or Indian Oceans. This is to be expected, since the borders of the Pacific comprise the most extended world region of young and growing mountains. Reference to Fig. 12.9 will show that the most extensive plains lie outside the areas within which tectonic activity is now greatest.

14.4   The detailed features of plains, that is, the specific uplands and lowlands, ridges and valleys, swells and hollows that together make up the surface of each plain and give it its particular character, cannot be explained simply by reference to the general tectonic history. These features are, with few exceptions, the result of *gradational* happenings during the last few million years. Therefore, the surface detail of any particular plain reflects the nature and workings of the gradational agents that have been most active there during that geologically brief span of time. The operations of the gradational agents are conditioned by the inherited rock structure upon which the agents must work. Also important are the tectonic happenings that occur either just before or during the course of gradational activity, as well as such external factors as climate and vegetation cover.

The surface of any given plain usually shows the effects of one of the principal agents or

Fig. 14.1 A rock-controlled drift surface in southern Wisconsin. The principal hills are rock thinly covered with till, but the intervening lowlands have a deep drift cover. (*Wisconsin Geological Survey photograph.*)

processes much more strongly than any other, and to a degree each of the agents or processes tends to produce an array of features that is peculiarly its own. For this reason it will be convenient to consider in turn the assemblages of features that characterize plains sculptured primarily by one or another of the major agents.

It is not expected that the classes of plain surfaces to be discussed are mutually exclusive or that they will include every part of each of the world's great plains. There are certain omissions and some overlaps. For example, the plain of southeastern Wisconsin is fundamentally a stream-eroded plain, but it is covered by a veneer of glacial drift which in some places quite obscures and in others only partly obscures its stream-eroded features. The same region may be considered, therefore, as an illustration of both stream-eroded and glaciated plains (Fig. 14.1).

Plains Sculptured by Stream Erosion

14.5 Differences among Stream-eroded Plains. Since surface runoff is an almost universal phenomenon, there are few plains that have not been at least somewhat affected by its gradational work. It is appropriate, then, to consider first those plains which owe their surface detail largely to the work of running water. And because the effects of stream erosion are so completely different from those of stream deposition, it will be convenient to consider the two separately, even though on any given plain erosional and depositional features may both occur. It is also true that in stream-sculptured plains mass movement is constantly at work modifying the forms of all slopes. But since it operates in the same fashion on the slopes of all types of plains, it may be omitted from the heading of any individual class.

Plains that have been sculptured chiefly by stream erosion differ among themselves in two principal respects: (*a*) the *width and cross-section form* of valleys and interfluves and (*b*) the *pattern* of valleys and interfluves. Differences of the first sort represent differences in the stage of erosional development, while differences of the second sort usually reflect variations in initial slopes and underlying rock structure. In the immediately succeeding sections, the nature and causes of these differences will be explored

267

in somewhat more detail. First will be considered the simple features of a plain in the youthful stage of erosional development on a homogeneous rock structure, and subsequently the features associated with the later stages of degradation and with more complex rock structures will be analyzed.

14.6 Youthfully dissected plains are, by definition, those which are characterized by broad, smooth interfluves, widely spaced major valleys, and only a limited development of tributaries. Tributaries are usually most numerous close to the main valley, where they produce a fringe of dissected terrain (sometimes called "river breaks") between the upland and the main valley floor (Fig. 13.13*A*).

Most of the land of particularly gentle slope is found on the interfluve crests and represents the undissected portions of the original surface on which valley cutting began. This surface may have originated in any of the ways in which smooth plains can develop. It may be an old-age erosional surface from a previous cycle of erosion. Or it may be an old alluvial plain, a former sea floor or lake bottom, the surface of a broad lava flow, or a plain of glacial drift. Its detailed features will depend upon which of these modes of origin brought it into being. The only requirement is that it be conspicuously smooth and that its relief be low relative to the depth of the valleys now being cut into it. The specific characteristics of smooth surfaces of each type will be mentioned in the appropriate sections below.

While the upland accounts for most of the gentler slopes, it is not uncommon also to find broad valley floors along the larger streams. Because streams in plains have not far to cut before they reach the limits of valley deepening, the major streams quickly achieve gentle gradients and become sluggish. But valley widening continues, and the growth of active cutting of tributaries continues to feed alluvium into the principal streams, which may find themselves unable to carry it. Thus one frequently encounters plains in which the major streams are winding along broad valley floors, even though tributaries are still short and most of the upland is still undissected. The tributary valleys are usually narrow and their gradients are sometimes steep and irregular.

The steepest slopes on a youthfully dissected plain are the valley walls. But even these are not necessarily precipitous. Where valley deepening has been very slow, where chemical weathering is rapid, and where the slopes are protected by a dense cover of vegetation, the valley walls may be very gentle indeed. But if, as is common during the early stages of erosional development, stream cutting is much more active than slope wash and mass movement, then the valley walls will be steep, breaking sharply downward from the edge of the upland above. This is common among desert streams, where the weathering attack on the valley walls may be slow and tributaries few.

The stream systems of young stream-eroded plains generally are dendritic, or treelike, in pattern (Fig. 13.14). In regions of horizontal strata or uniform rock they are likely to remain so throughout their development. In regions of inclined strata or diversified rocks other patterns sometimes develop as a result of adjustments of streams to structure during later erosional stages.

In regions of young plains the broad interfluves generally are the principal sites of agricultural settlement, transportation routes, and urban centers (Fig. 14.2). Minor valleys are narrow and subject to flood. Their walls are steep and are the least usable lands on the plains. The broad bottoms of some major valleys contain usable land. Some are important commercial thoroughfares, as for example, the Platte River valley in Nebraska. In dry regions they are more easily adapted to the requirements of irrigated agriculture than are the uplands.

Prominent among the youthfully dissected plains of the United States are the High Plains that lie east of the Rocky Mountains in Colorado, New Mexico, Kansas, Oklahoma, and Texas; much of the dissected till plains of Illinois, Iowa, and northern Missouri; and the outer portion of the Atlantic and Gulf Coastal Plain between Virginia and Texas.

Fig. 14.2 The undulating surface of the inner coastal plain in central Georgia. The broad, low interfluve is cultivated, but the slopes and bottoms of the creek valleys are wooded.

14.7 *Newly emerged coastal plains,* because of their widespread occurrence and distinctive surface character, deserve special mention among plains upon which dissection has as yet made little headway. It has been indicated previously that the shallow sea bottoms are the sorting and settling places for the sands, muds, and limes which come directly or indirectly from the adjacent land (13.46). Because they are continually worked over by waves and currents, the sediments are so evenly distributed within their respective zones that the surfaces of the continental shelves are smooth and essentially flat.

The slow emergence of a portion of the sea floor would add to a continental margin a low and almost featureless plain. It would be comprised of loosely compacted and alternating layers of sands, muds, and lime which normally would be nearly horizontal or would have a slight inclination seaward. Such a plain would be mainly of depositional and tectonic origin, since weathering and erosion would have had, as yet, little opportunity to change its features.

Plains of this origin have been formed in various parts of the earth during its long history,

but although they may be flat following their emergence, they do not long remain featureless. As the land emerges, inch by inch, it is attacked by the agents of degradation. Streams, originating far inland, continue their courses across the new land of the coastal margin. Rainwash develops tributary gullies in it and produces erosional landforms. However, the valleys of low coastal plains cannot be deep because base-level is close below the surface. Even where streams are numerous, their gradients are likely to be so low that their tributaries are unable to erode quickly into all parts of the interstream areas. The latter tend therefore to remain flat and to be poorly drained. They contain swamps, small and large, which lie in minor depressions of the ancient sea bottom or coastal margin and do not have streams with gradients sufficiently steep to drain them (Fig. 14.3).

There are several plains in the world whose characteristic landforms indicate that they belong to the newly emerged class. Among them is that portion of the United States included in the coastal margins of Virginia, the Carolinas, Georgia, and the Gulf states from Florida to Texas (Fig. 14.4). Most of this plain is flat, local

Fig. 14.3 The flat, marshy surface of the Florida Everglades, part of a relatively new plain not yet dissected by streams.

Fig. 14.4 Flat but well-drained coastal plain in Texas.

relief being less than 50 ft., and although the difference in their elevations is slight, there are large areas of both river-bottom and upland swamps. The upland swamps (Fig. 14.3) generally are small, but a few are of notable extent. The largest are the Everglades of Florida; the Okefenokee Swamp, located astride the Florida-Georgia boundary; and the Dismal Swamp of North Carolina and Virginia. The swamps of the Atlantic and Gulf Coastal Plains, both upland and river bottom, are so numerous and so large that, altogether, they comprise nearly two-thirds of all the ill-drained lands of the United States.

Other coastal lowlands also are characterized by the presence of large swamps. Such is the nature of the broad coastal flats of eastern Nicaragua, the eastern coast of South Africa, and the arctic fringes of Alaska and of the U.S.S.R.

14.8 Maturely dissected plains are defined as those in which tributary development has progressed so far as to have largely destroyed the original smooth upland. Normally this is the stage of development in which gently sloping land is at a minimum. If a low-relief surface is at any time going to depart from the "plains" designation, it will be at this stage, when most of its area is occupied by valley sides. Only if the sides are gently sloping can it qualify as a plain (Fig. 14.5).

A plain rarely achieves "ideal" maturity, in which there are no upland or lowland flats, but only valley slopes. The main streams achieve low gradients quickly, and by the time tributaries have reached their way headward to the point of destroying the upland, the valleys of the principal streams usually have become wide and flat-floored.

In plains of early maturity, the interfluves, although narrowed by increasing dissection, often have more flat land than do the valleys and are the areas of principal settlement. However, continued development involves an increase in the proportion of land in slopes and corresponding decrease in the area of flat land. In later maturity the interfluves are reduced to mere ridges; and the farms, roads, and villages are more largely concentrated in the broadened valleys.

Rolling plains typical of erosional maturity are found in parts of the dissected till plains of northern Missouri, southern Iowa, and eastern Nebraska, in much of the inner Coastal

Fig. 14.5 The rolling surface of a mature plain in northwestern Missouri.

Plain, the Appalachian Piedmont east of the mountains in Georgia and Carolina, and in scattered areas of the continental interior between the Rocky Mountains and the Missouri River.

14.9 Old-age plains, or peneplains, are typically dominated by broadly open valleys. The remnants of former interfluves exist only as low rolling divides between the streams, too low to have any notable relation to the human occupance and use of the plains (Fig. 13.3). Some peneplains have developed from the long-continued gradation of plains which originally had youthful relief features but have passed through the stages of maturity and old age. However, it is certain that others were originally not plains at all but mountain regions of highly complicated structures. The time required for the complete leveling of high and geologically complex mountain regions is so long, and the later stages of the process are so slow, that few if any of the peneplains of this latter type ever were perfectly finished. Unreduced portions in the form of erosion remnants, or *monadnocks,* are to be found standing in bold relief above the general level of their surfaces as reminders of the greater heights at which the regions once stood.

Significantly, there are in the world at present very few true peneplains that have developed near baselevel and that still remain there. Evidently tectonic unrest and fluctuations of sea level in late geologic times have been too great to permit the long, slow process to be carried to completion or to permit already existing peneplains to lie undisturbed where they were formed. Perhaps the closest approach to an existing and still evolving peneplain is the eastern part of the Guiana section of northeastern South America. There only a few remnant hill groups and small ranges rise above an almost featureless plain developed on crystalline rocks (Fig. 14.6).

There do exist, however, many examples of old-age erosion surfaces that have suffered uplift sufficient to permit the streams to begin downcutting once again and to carve the plains into the forms typical of youth or maturity. The *Appalachian Piedmont* may be cited as an example of a former crystalline peneplain that has been moderately uplifted and dissected to a rolling plain in early maturity. The remnants of the ancient surface are locally still fairly broad, and rising above the upland are many monadnocks, such as Stone Mountain, near Atlanta, Ga., King's Mountain, famed as a battleground in the American Revolution, Spencer Mountain, North Carolina (Fig. 14.7), and others. Some peneplains have been so greatly elevated that portions of their former flattish surfaces are now found among the heights of hill regions or mountains.

Fig. 14.6 Remnant hills left standing upon an erosional plain developed on crystalline rocks, British Guiana. (*Photograph by D. Holdridge. Courtesy of the Geographical Review, published by the American Geographical Society of New York.*)

Fig. 14.7 Spencer Mountain, a monadnock on the partially redissected peneplain of the Appalachian Piedmont, near Gastonia, N.C.

14.10 *Pediments.* A type of old-age erosion surface that appears to originate principally under arid or semiarid climatic conditions is the *pediment.* A pediment is a gently sloping, smooth-surfaced erosional plain, sometimes thinly veneered with alluvium, that is left behind as a mountain range or tableland is gradually eroded away. The plain slopes away from the foot of whatever portion of the highland still remains. Usually there is a remarkably sharp break between the steep slopes of the mountain and the gentle slopes of the pediment. In surficial appearance pediments are often indistinguishable from the sloping piedmont alluvial slopes that commonly develop in similar places (13.18). The true identity can be ascertained only by excavation that will determine whether the alluvium is but a thin covering over a rock floor or an accumulation scores of feet thick.

The unusual smoothness and lack of valleys and the relatively greater inclination that together distinguish pediments from other old-age stream-eroded surfaces have occasioned much discussion. Most earlier studies placed much emphasis upon the effects of sidewise cutting by streams that had already achieved low gradients, the ultimate effect being the clearing away of intervening spurs and the planing off of the surface. More recently, however, the tendency has been to attach much less importance to such lateral planation and more to the work of relatively unchanneled runoff. The mountain front or escarpment is driven back by the combined effects of weathering, rainwash, gullying, and mass movement, and as it retreats, there evolves at its base a plain across which the debris is carried by a dense network of small channels. The inclination of this plain will necessarily remain great enough to permit the transportation of the relatively coarse debris that is the typical product of desert weathering.

Pediments are abundantly developed about the mountain ranges of the North American desert (Fig. 14.8), and are evidently equally widespread in northern Chile, southwestern Africa, parts of the Sahara, and perhaps in most of the formerly mountainous deserts.

Fig. 14.8 The long-eroded slope of this pediment, which borders one of the basin ranges of Nevada, has a veneer of desert alluvium. (*Photograph by John C. Weaver.*)

Because of the prevalent rockiness and thinness of their soils these plains are usually unfavorable for plant growth or irrigated agriculture, in contrast to the piedmont alluvial plains, which assume similar forms but are underlain by deep regolith.

14.11 Erosional Features Related to Rock Structure. Rock structures make themselves felt by presenting to the gradational agents certain arrangements of materials of differing degrees of resistance. Degradation proceeds more rapidly on the weaker rocks, and hence the weak-rock areas pass more quickly through the stages of erosional development than do the adjacent zones of resistant materials. Because they offer greater opportunity for weathering and removal, even minor lines of weakness such as fracture zones or joint planes often become favored sites for tributary growth and valley cutting. Thus they influence the pattern which the valley systems eventually achieve.

Resistant outcrops tend in time to stand out as areas of higher summit elevation and relatively more youthful forms than the areas about them. In some instances the monadnocks on peneplains owe their preservation to the superior resistance of their rocks. The Wichita and Arbuckle Mountains, in southwestern and southeastern Oklahoma, respectively, represent ancient hills that were buried by sedimentary deposits before erosion had time to destroy them. More recently erosion has stripped away part of the weaker sedimentary material, uncovering the buried hills, which now, by virtue of the resistance of their rocks, remain standing as prominent features above the general degradational level.

Unequal resistance in the rocks of a valley wall sometimes results in the formation of rock benches or terraces along the valley sides. The upper surface of a resistant rock stratum forms a terrace while its eroded edge forms the steeper slope below.

In extreme cases a horizontal stratum of great resistance may so inhibit downcutting as to serve for a considerable time as a temporary baselevel. Continued wasting of the weaker materials above eventually produces a surface which practically coincides with the upper surface of the resistant stratum. Such plains are called *stripped plains*. They account for many of the smooth upland surfaces in the high Colorado Plateaus in northeastern Arizona and southeastern Utah.

14.12 *Cuestaform Plains.* Many plains have been developed by stream erosion of gently inclined sedimentary strata of varying resistance. Streams have carved more readily into the less resistant of these formations, leaving the exposed edges of the more resistant standing in

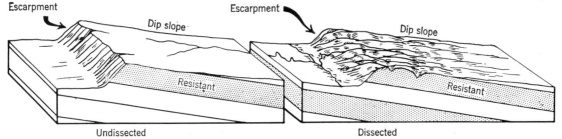

Fig. 14.9 Diagram to illustrate form and structure of cuestas. Example at left is sharp and regular. Dissected form at right is more typical, especially in humid regions.

relief. Owing to the inclination of the rocks, long low ridges are thus produced, alternating with broad lowlands. The ridges trend parallel to the pattern of outcrop and are asymmetrical, usually presenting gentle slopes in the direction toward which the strata are dipping and steeper faces in the opposite direction. The relation of the alternating ridges and lowlands to each other and the manner of their erosion by streams will become readily apparent from a study of Fig. 14.9. Ridges of this kind are called *cuestas.* Their steeper faces are called *escarp-*

ments; their gentler slopes are *dip slopes;* and the valleys between the ridges are called *lowlands.* Extensive plains that include a series of cuesta ridges and intervening lowlands may be spoken of as *cuestaform plains.*

Some of the cuestas present features of bold relief, the height and irregularity of their crests depending much upon the thickness and resistance of the rock formations to which they are due (Fig. 14.10). In general, however, the ridges of cuestaform plains, especially in humid lands, are not sharply defined features but are

Fig. 14.10 White Rock escarpment, the west-facing front of a low cuesta on the Texas Coastal Plain near Dallas.

dissected into belts of hills whose heights are not great when compared with the widths of the intervening lowlands.

Minor features upon these plains include groups of hills which are remnants of the cuesta escarpments, detached and left isolated by differential weathering and erosion. Such hills, which lie out beyond the margin of the main body of the rock of which they are composed, are called *outliers*.

Cuestaform plains may develop wherever long erosion has exposed the edges of gently inclined strata that differ in resistance. Such a condition sometimes occurs on a coastal plain, where the rock strata, usually weakly consolidated, are inclined toward the coast at low angles, but not so low as the inclination of the plain surface. In coastal plains the dip slopes face seaward and the escarpments face inland.

Where strata dip outward in all directions from the crest of a structural dome, erosion may produce a series of concentric cuestas with escarpments facing inward toward the center. Conversely, cuestas developed from a structural basin will have their escarpments facing outward from the center (Fig. 14.11).

Much of the Middle Western United States is occupied by cuestaform plains (Fig. 14.12). Throughout this area the strata are gently warped into a series of domes and basins that have suffered long erosion. Massive, often cherty limestones and dolomites and some thick sandstones are the chief ridge makers, and many of the escarpments may be traced for scores or even hundreds of miles. One of the most persistent is the Niagara cuesta, an outcrop of dolomite that traverses northern Illinois, eastern Wisconsin, upper Michigan, and peninsular Ontario and finally dies out in western New York. Its projecting crest is the cause of the Door Peninsula of Wisconsin, Manitoulin Island, the Bruce Peninsula of Ontario, and the

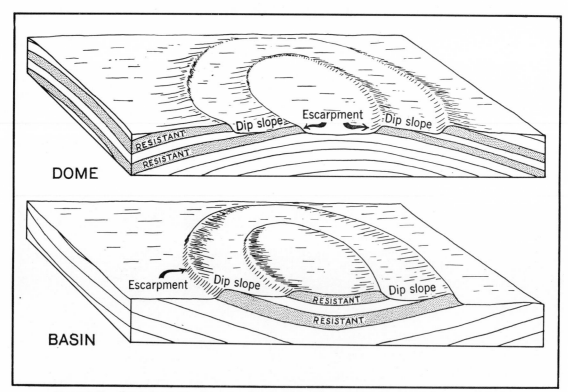

Fig. 14.11 Diagram to illustrate the development of cuestas in structural domes and basins. Dip slopes face outward from center of dome; inward toward center of basin.

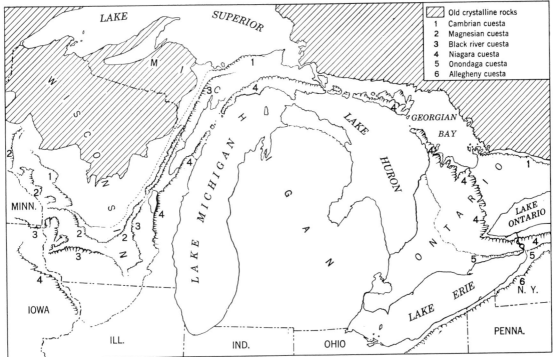

Fig. 14.12 The Niagara cuesta and other less-marked ridges produced by stream erosion in the gently warped sedimentary rocks of the Great Lakes region. Parts of some of the ridges are deeply covered by glacial drift, and their approximate positions are shown by broken lines.

escarpment that gives rise to Niagara Falls. The Mounds of southern Wisconsin are notable outliers of this cuesta.

The Gulf Coastal Plain, especially in Alabama and Texas, displays a fine series of cuestas, in which sandstones are the chief ridge makers (Fig. 14.13). The broad inner lowlands on both the Alabama and Texas Coastal Plains are eroded in chalky limestones which have given rise to soils of great productivity. These lowlands, which are called the *Alabama Black Belt* and the *Texas Black Prairies,* have become major centers of population and agricultural wealth.

In southeastern England the Lincoln Wolds, the Cotswold Hills, the several Downs, and other ridges are cuestas formed by the differential erosion of inclined rock strata (Fig. 14.15). Mainly the ridge-making rocks are porous chalky limestones which have resisted erosion by their absorptiveness.

The Paris Basin of France is another notable example of a plain of this class (Fig. 14.14). Its

five or six low cuestaform ridges have been partially dissected by streams and stand as concentric but broken ridges upon a fertile plain. The shapes, heights, and arrangements of these

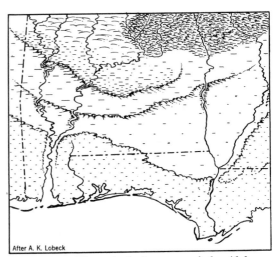

After A. K. Lobeck

Fig. 14.13 The principal cuestas of the Alabama Coastal Plain. The escarpments face generally northward, as the rock strata dip toward the sea.

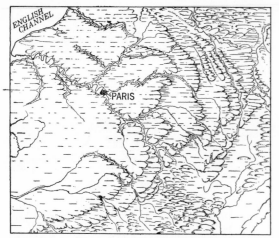

cuestas have played important parts in the appearance of the plain, its agricultural uses, the pattern of its avenues of transportation, and the military defense of Paris, which is its natural focus.

Plains Shaped by Stream Deposition

14.13 Alluvial Plains. It has been mentioned previously that reduced velocity, decreased volume, and the feeding in of an unduly great load of debris are the factors that may induce a stream to deposit alluvium (13.27). It has also been noted that there are three characteristic localities in which alluvial deposition commonly occurs: on valley floors, at the stream mouth, and at sharp decreases in valley gradient.

Alluvial deposits almost invariably assume the form of plains, usually plains that are conspicuous by their flatness. Indeed, stream deposition is directly responsible for many of the most extensive flat surfaces in the world, and is indirectly responsible for most of the remainder, in which material supplied by streams has been further smoothed by wave action in lakes or shallow seas.

The detailed features of alluvial plains vary somewhat according to the place and mode of deposition. In particular, distinction may be made between (*a*) floodplains, (*b*) delta plains, and (*c*) piedmont alluvial plains.

14.14 Floodplains are formed wherever a stream deposits significantly along its valley floor. The alluvial accumulation may be no more than a thin covering over the erosional

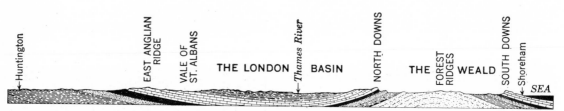

Fig. 14.15 A north-south cross section through the outskirts of London, showing the surface features and rock structures of the London Basin and the Weald. The section is 100 miles long, and its vertical scale is several times greater than the horizontal.

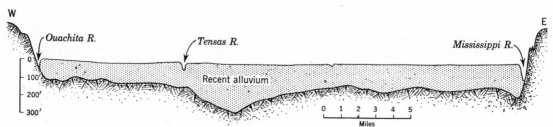

Fig. 14.16 Cross section of the alluvial valley of the lower Mississippi at Natchez, Miss. Note the great depth of alluvium and the irregular, stream-eroded form of the bedrock valley floor. (*After Fisk.*)

surface beneath, or it may be a deep fill scores of feet thick. The depth of alluvium beneath the lower Mississippi River floodplain is known to exceed 100 ft. generally, and to reach 400 ft. near the mouth. Drillings reveal that the buried bedrock floor has the profile of a broad, though typically formed erosional valley (Fig. 14.16). Probably few floodplain deposits significantly exceed this thickness, but as more and more subsurface exploration is done, it is becoming clear that deep alluvium is much more characteristic of floodplains than has generally been realized. But whatever the depth of the alluvium beneath them, and whatever the profile of the bedrock valley they conceal, nearly all floodplains display a characteristic association of surface features.

14.15 *The Floodplain Surface.* While the surface of a floodplain is characteristically flat, it is not without internal variety which, though of small degree, is highly important. The floodplain represents an assemblage of four types of features: (*a*) active stream channels; (*b*) abandoned stream channels; (*c*) natural levees associated with active and abandoned channels; and (*d*) flat areas lying between channels or behind the natural levees.

Stream channels on floodplains are usually either strongly sinuous or braided. The degree of sinuosity depends upon the width of the floodplain compared to that of the river, and upon the nature of the alluvial material. If the alluvial plain is wide enough, a stream will tend to develop smooth, looping meanders. But the breadth of a fully developed belt of meanders is usually fifteen to twenty times the width of the stream channel, and unless the floodplain is at least that wide, free meandering cannot occur. If the width is not adequate, the stream will swing from side to side of the alluvial surface, the curves being flattened and distorted where they encounter the bedrock valley side. Small tributary streams crossing a broad floodplain to join the major stream often develop their own meanders, but on the small scale appropriate to the small width of their channels. Streams flowing in tough clay or partially cemented alluvium that cannot be readily

Fig. 14.17 The braided channel of the Rio Grande in northern New Mexico. During flood the entire belt of channels and sandy islands will be covered with water. (*Spence Air Photos.*)

eroded rarely develop smooth meanders at all (Fig. 13.18).

The braided channels characteristic of streams that are actively moving great quantities of coarse alluvium usually appear clearly only at low-water stage. During high-water periods the entire channel belt is covered by a relatively thin sheet of water, which scours and shifts channels and deposits bars in the sand and gravel beneath. At low water, most of the channel belt is laid bare, with only a few narrow and shallow threads of water following the deeper channels. The bars and shallower channels form dry expanses of sandy surface, usually free of vegetation. In desert streams, which are very commonly braided, the channel may contain water only a few days out of the year, immediately following rains. The rest of the year it is only a dry, barren strip of channeled sand, sometimes called a *wash*. In some valleys the braided channel belt occupies the full breadth of the floodplain, but in valleys of unusual width, channels cover only a portion of it, being sunk a few feet below the remainder of the surface (Fig. 14.17).

Since stream channels on alluvial surfaces are continually shifting their position, it follows that abandoned channels will be common features on floodplains. A meander curve becomes elongated by deposition occurring on the inside of the bend, while deepening of the channel and slumping of the banks occur on the outside. Eventually meanders that have grown overlong are cut off and abandoned by the stream when it shortens its course by cutting through the narrowed neck of alluvium. The ends of the abandoned meander channel presently are filled with silt, and the unfilled portion exists as a horseshoe-shaped pond,[2] bordered by its levees.

Lakes of this kind no sooner are formed than they begin to be filled and obliterated (*a*) by sediment deposited during general river floods, (*b*) by sediment washed by rain from the ad-

[2] Lakes of this kind have often been called *oxbows*, but the ox yoke and its parts have become such unfamiliar objects that the term conveys no visual impression and should probably be abandoned.

jacent surface, and (*c*) by the growth and decay of aquatic vegetation. The surfaces of broad floodplains are likely, therefore, to contain many such features in all stages of modification. Some, which are of recent formation, appear as curving open lakes; others remain as boggy, sedge-filled marshes; while still others may be described only as *meander scars*. The latter are marked by bits of woodland swamp or low ground, the horseshoe-shaped outlines of which hardly would be noticed save from an airplane (Fig. 14.18). Not only the major stream, but tributary streams as well will leave on the floodplain these scars marking channels they once followed.

Both the active and abandoned channels on most floodplains are bordered by natural levees, which usually furnish the highest and best-drained land to be found on the floodplain surface. However, they rarely rise more than a few feet above the lands behind them, and were it not for their superior drainage, which is sometimes reflected in the vegetation cover or land use, they would scarcely be discernible on the ground. The natural levees of the lower Mississippi near New Orleans are locally nearly a mile in breadth, but they rise only 5 to 10 ft. above the neighboring swamps. On smaller streams the levees are correspondingly small. However, these levee lands are highly significant to man, because they may be tilled with less necessity of artificial drainage and with a lower frequency of inundation than the slightly lower lands behind them (Fig. 13.15).

The lands behind the natural levees, because they are slightly lower, are likely to suffer the difficulties attendant upon a high water table. Sometimes they are permanently swampy (known as *backswamps*); always they are liable to seasonal waterlogging or flooding. If they are to be used successfully, they must usually be diked and kept reasonably dry by pumping. On the Mississippi floodplain, large areas of swampland remain unreclaimed. On some Old World floodplains, however, such as those of the Nile and Yangtze, where fertile land is scarce and life and labor cheap, even the swamps are drained and cultivated.

Fig. 14.18 A horseshoe-shaped swamp and other great meander scars on the lower Mississippi floodplain, viewed from the air. The shades of gray in the photographs indicate differences in the vegetation, either natural or cultivated, which in turn indicate differences in soil or drainage. (*Official photographs, U.S. Army Air Corps. Courtesy of U.S. Geological Survey.*)

14.16 *Alluvial Terrace Lands.* Many floodplains are fringed at intervals with smaller alluvial plains which stand at elevations somewhat above that of the present plain. These are called *alluvial terraces,* or benches. Although they lie above the floodplain, they are unlike the valley walls which flank them in that they are stream deposits. Usually they are bordered by abrupt descents of a few feet to the level of the newer plain. They are the remnants of older and higher floodplains into which the stream has subsequently eroded a new valley, owing to some cause that has decreased its load of sediment or has increased its carrying capacity. Some valleys exhibit a series of alluvial terraces at different levels which mark stages in

the erosion of the old valley filling (Fig. 14.19). Because alluvial terrace land is sufficiently above present river level to be free from floods, it generally is well drained and admirably adapted to cultivation. However, because the terrace is above the present flood level its soils are no longer enriched by additions of alluvial mud and, being older, they are, in regions of abundant rainfall, likely to be somewhat leached. Sites of this kind are suitable also for river towns.

14.17 *Floodplains and River Floods.* The flatness of floodplains, the nature and direction of their levee slopes, and indeed the very manner of their formation indicate that they are subject to river overflow. In some rivers

Fig. 14.19 A diagram to illustrate the development of alluvial terraces by renewed downcutting in an older deposit of alluvium. Natural levees border the present stream course.

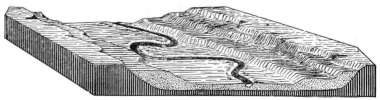

Fig. 14.20 High water on the lower Mississippi floodplain. The artificial levee is the only land remaining unsubmerged. The main channel of the river is seen in the far distance. (*Official photograph, U.S. Army Air Corps.*)

floods are of periodic occurrence, and in others they come at irregular intervals, while some streams are so controlled by nature as to be little subject to flood.

Periodic floods, such as those of the Nile, the Orinoco, and other tropical streams, result from the marked seasonal character of the precipitation over the river basin. Nile floods have been for many centuries the means of renewing the fertility of the alluvial soil of that populous valley by the addition of an annual layer of silt. The recent construction of dams reduces the inconvenience of floods and enables a more economical use of both the land and the water, but it largely prevents the distribution of the fertile mud over the floodplain by causing it to settle in the quiet waters above the dams. The alternation of protracted drought with widespread flood on the floodplain of the

Orinoco has so far had the effect of retarding attempts to make effective use of that broad and flat plain.

Disastrous floods on the Mississippi and its tributaries usually occur in the early spring. They result from heavy rainfall on a frozen or saturated earth, frequently supplemented by the rapid melting of a winter's accumulation of snow. Sometimes both of these conditions come at the same time in different parts of the basin. The general deforestation of the eastern half of the Mississippi Basin during its settlement and agricultural utilization probably has increased the flood menace by removing the forest litter which formerly absorbed moisture and served to retard the runoff. As settlement on the Mississippi floodplain increased, protection from flood became as necessary as it did on the delta. Artificial levees of earth were extended from the delta to the floodplain and now total hundreds of miles in length. It was found that the height of the early levees was not sufficient to prevent overflow, and their level has been raised several times. In consequence of the building of higher levees the river has been forced to transport material that otherwise would have been spread over the floodplain. This in turn has caused silting of the channel and a raising of the river grade. As the levees have increased in height, therefore, so have the succeeding floods, and there is no more security from them now than formerly (Fig. 14.20). The problem of flood control is one given much study, but the method of its solution is complicated, expensive, and, as yet, by no means certain.

14.18 Delta plains are the surfaces of newly built accumulations of river sediments which are deposited at the mouths of streams upon their entry into bodies of quiet water. The method of delta growth through additions at the extremities of channels and, during flood periods, at the sides of channels, has been outlined previously (13.29). As a delta grows seaward, the decreased stream gradient induces deposition not only at the delta head, but then progressively upstream in the lower stream valley (13.28). Hence floodplain and delta are sometimes intimately related, and it is difficult to say where the one begins and other ends. However, not all delta-building streams have floodplains, and not all streams having floodplains are able to form deltas.

14.19 *The Delta Surface.* Although it is true that delta plains are very flat, they, like floodplains, are not devoid of distinctive surface features. Indeed, the features which characterize deltas are closely analogous to those of floodplains, the principal differences being the presence of distributaries, a generally higher water table, and the existence of a changing coastal margin. But the delta surface, like the floodplain surface, is made up of the familiar trio: channels, natural levees, and backswamps.

The channels of delta-building streams may be straight, irregular, meandering, or even braided, in the same manner and for the same reasons as floodplain streams. The one distinctive feature of them is their tendency to branch in a downstream direction, forming a more or less fan-shaped network of distributaries. On the older parts of the delta there is some tendency for lesser distributaries to be abandoned and sealed off from the major channels though they may continue to serve as local drainage ways carrying runoff from the delta itself (Fig. 14.21).

The major channels and all distributaries as well are bordered by natural levees. These are both higher and broader on the older upstream portion of a delta than near its newer seaward margin. Thus they taper down to small size toward the stream mouths, finally disappearing in the coastal marshes at the delta edge (Fig. 14.22). Although the levees rise gently but a few feet above the surrounding swamps and marshes, drainage detects the difference. While the higher parts near the stream banks are generally well drained, their lower portions, which slope away from the stream, end in the swamps. For this reason the levees

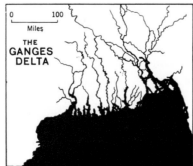

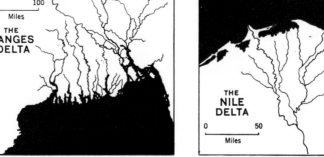

Fig. 14.21 Delta outlines and distributaries.

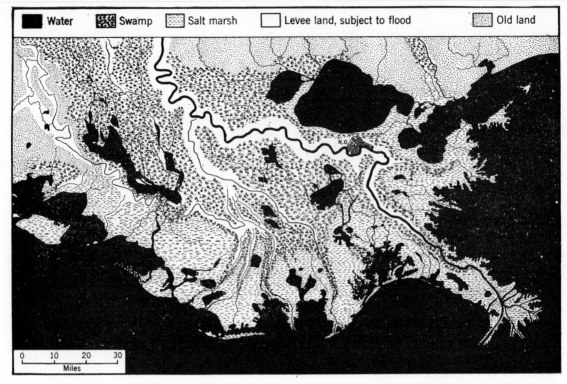

0   10   20   30
Miles

Fig. 14.22 The Mississippi River Delta has fringing areas of salt-marsh grass and reeds, belts of wooded swamp, and strips of tilled levee lands. Note that the levee lands grow narrow downstream and disappear.

are the principal sites for human settlements, tilled fields, and transportation lines. But even these lands are water-covered when the river rises in general flood.

On a delta, the highest parts of which may be only a few feet above sea level, the low lands behind the levee receive the runoff from the sloping back sides of the levees, and are usually marshy. Only on the older and higher sections of the inner delta are dry lands likely to be found anywhere except on the levees themselves. Between the levees the seaward margin is built up so slowly and is so flat that, on large deltas, vast areas of the coastal fringe are scarcely above salt water, much being tidal marsh. The delta margin is often marked by the outer limit of marsh grass rather than by a true shoreline dividing land from sea (Fig. 14.23). These low-lying swamps and marshes can be utilized only if extensive drainage and diking operations are undertaken. Since the backswamps make up a majority of delta lands, their wetness constitutes the major problem to delta utilization.

On some deltas, notably that of the Mississippi, the whole broad surface appears to be sinking very slowly, perhaps in part as a result of the great weight of sediment being continually added. The effect of this submergence is to drown the delta swamps, especially in those parts of the delta where sedimentation is least active at present. This forms shallow lakes and bays in the low sections, leaving the natural levees and the regions of most active deposition protruding seaward like spread fingers (Fig. 14.22).

14.20 *Some Famous Deltas.* Some of the most extensive delta plains may readily be discovered on the maps of a student atlas. They are the delta of the Nile, from which all such deposits take their name (its triangular central portion resembles in shape the letter Δ of the Greek alphabet), and the deltas of the Rhône, Po, Rhine, Volga, Indus, Ganges, Irrawaddy,

Hwang, Orinoco, Colorado, and Mississippi. There are many more delta plains of almost equal size, but less well known, such as those which fringe the east coast of peninsular India. Of small deltas there are thousands.

The Mississippi Delta is not only one of the most familiar and most thoroughly studied, but also one of the world's largest delta plains. It has a frontage of more than 150 miles along the Gulf of Mexico, and extends a similar distance inland from the present mouth of the river. At its head it merges imperceptibly with the great floodplain of the lower Mississippi, which reaches for several hundred miles northward to the southern tip of Illinois with a width of from 25 to 125 miles. The floodplain and much of the present delta have been deposited in a broad, shallow, gradually sinking structural trough reaching northward from the Gulf. While the history of the valley is too complex for treatment here, most of the present flood-plain and delta appear to have been deposited during and since the late stages of the last glaciation. Much of the alluvium is probably glacial outwash brought down from the Great Lakes area and laid down as a braided stream deposit in an existing erosional valley that had been cut in earlier alluvial fill. Only in the last 5,000 years, since the sea reached its present level, has the floodplain section of the stream become meandering and relatively inactive.

At the active stream mouth the delta grows rapidly seaward, deposition proceeding at present at an estimated rate of two million tons of sediment per day. However, as distributary systems have been formed and abandoned, the center of depositional activity has shifted from one side of the delta to the other. And because the whole area is sinking, only the place of most active deposition grows outward at any given time. The rest of the coast line creeps gradually shoreward, so that there is now probably little net growth to the delta as a whole.

Human occupance of the Mississippi Delta is almost entirely confined to the natural levees. Here are located the towns, roads, railroads, and farms. The lowland swamps and marshes are frequented by muskrat trappers and the

Fig. 14.23 Broad marshes and shallow channels on the seaward margin of the Mississippi Delta. The distant row of trees occupies the remnant of a levee which borders an abandoned distributary channel.

outer fringes by shrimp fishermen, but almost no other activity is possible without reclamation, which has not yet been extensively attempted. The city of New Orleans, built on the natural levee and on diked and drained swampland adjacent to the levee, has had a most interesting history of development, much of it involving continual contention with the high water table typical of the delta environment. Not only surface drainage, but the excavation of foundations, the construction of footings for large buildings, the disposal of sewage, and even the digging of graves have all posed unusual problems that have been met with remarkable perseverance and ingenuity.

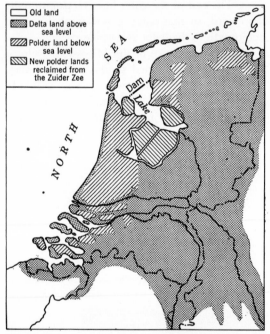

Fig. 14.24 The extent of reclaimed land in the Netherlands in relation to the area of the Rhine Delta.

The Netherlands coast includes the merged deltas of the Rhine, Meuse, and Scheldt Rivers. Originally the region had the features common to delta surfaces, and the streams, by flood, built their levees and extended the coastal marshes seaward. Through several centuries a growing need for land has encouraged the

inhabitants of this region to reclaim the marsh lands and actually to crowd the sea off the delta margin. Small areas of lower levee and interlevee swampland have been, one after another, made secure from flood by constructing artificial levees, or dikes, entirely around them. Each enclosed area, called a *polder,* is kept sufficiently drained for agriculture by a network of drainage ditches leading to a pump at the lowest corner of the polder. This lifts the water from the polder into a bordering stream or canal which lies between dikes or in channels on top of the dikes. The newest and greatest project has been designed to cut off and drain the Zuider Zee, a great and shallow coastal embayment, which was much like Lake Pontchartrain near New Orleans (Fig. 14.24).

14.21 *Some peculiarities of delta development* are exhibited by the Hwang River of North China, and by the Colorado River and the Sacramento–San Joaquin system in the western United States.

The Hwang is so burdened with silt that it is extremely liable to choking and shifting of its channel. Some of the changes are minor, but the stream has several times shifted its course from one side of the hilly Shantung Peninsula to the other, a distance of 250 miles (Fig. 14.25). Such a change on a densely populated plain is a major disaster, accompanied by an appalling loss of human life.

The Colorado River, by building its delta across the head of the Gulf of California, completely isolated the head of the Gulf. Under the desert climate the waters evaporated, leaving the Salton Basin, a part of whose floor lies nearly 275 ft. below sea level. The southern part of the basin, known as the Imperial Valley, is an important agricultural region irrigated by water from the Colorado (Fig. 14.26).

The Sacramento and San Joaquin Rivers of California have built their combined delta in a nearly enclosed arm of the sea. The delta has features characteristic of most plains of its kind, but it is almost entirely surrounded by higher land. Connection with the sea is made by way of the Golden Gate, San Francisco Bay,

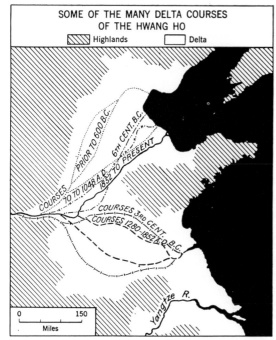

Fig. 14.25 The great Hwang Ho Delta of North China, its relation to the Shantung Peninsula, and some of the many channels the river has occupied within historic times. (*After maps by G. B. Cressey and D. W. Mead.*)

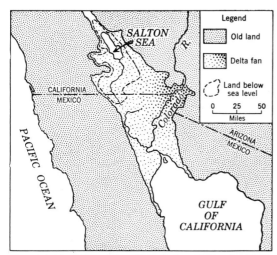

Fig. 14.26 The delta fan of the Colorado River has blocked off the head of the long embayment into which it is built. The location and extent of the Salton Sink, once part of the Gulf of California, are indicated by the broken line. Salton Sea lies in its lowest portion, its bottom 274 ft. below sea level.

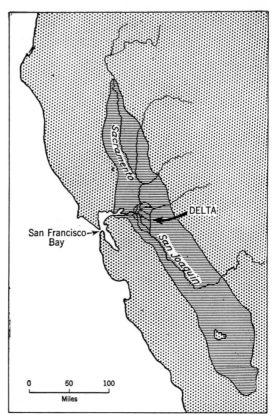

Fig. 14.27 An arm of the sea once reached through San Francisco Bay into the heart of the Central Valley of California. The combined delta of the Sacramento, San Joaquin, and other rivers that drain the valley has been built in the head of this embayment, far from the open sea.

and a long relatively narrow channel through a gap in the Coast Ranges (Fig. 14.27).

14.22 Piedmont Alluvial Plains. The bases of mountain slopes in dry and subhumid climates commonly are fringed by alluvial fans so closely spaced that their margins are merged in one continuous plain. The surface features of these *piedmont alluvial plains* may be understood better if the configuration of the simple alluvial fan is first considered.

Streams with steep gradients furnish abundant sediment, much of it coarse in texture. The material clogs the stream channel at the point where the mountain gradient changes to that of the bordering plain. The choked stream breaks over its banks, tending to form distributary channels. The rapid accumulation of material

Fig. 14.28 These large alluvial fans at the eastern foot of the Sierra Nevada of California are beginning to merge, forming a piedmont alluvial plain. (*Spence Air Photos.*)

encourages frequent shifts of channel which have the effect of causing the building to proceed evenly upon all parts of the fan margin. This produces a nicely rounded or semicircular outline and gives the feature its fanlike shape (Fig. 14.28).

Piedmont alluvial plains are comprised of coalesced fans, some of which are large and some small, their size depending upon the volumes and deposits of the several streams draining the mountain front. The heads of the several fans may be distinguished at the mouths of the valleys (Fig. 14.29).

The deposition of material, especially the heavy or coarse material, is most abundant at the apex or head of the fan, where the stream

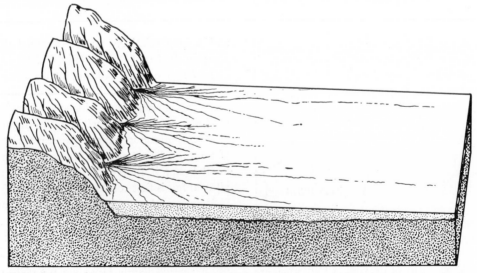

Fig. 14.29 A piedmont alluvial plain is formed by the growing together of many extensive alluvial fans at the foot of a mountain range.

velocity is first checked. At no great distance from the mountain front, however, the slopes of the bordering fans flatten out, their soils become finer, their margins spread, and they merge into a continuous alluvial plain (Fig. 14.30). Such a plain may appear practically level; yet it is not so in fact. Not only does it slope away from the mountain base, but each of its component fans has its faintly convex surface, and where they are blended together the resulting plain has a scalloped margin.

Many piedmont alluvial plains are covered only with desert shrubs or sparse grasses, but the fine dry-land soils are high in mineral plant foods, and such as have available supplies of irrigation water are capable of great productivity. Although their surfaces are dry, natural conditions provide many alluvial fans with supplies of water for irrigation.

The water of the mountain stream that builds a fan may be impounded in its mountain valley, whence it may be led out upon the fan surface. Because of the radial slope of the fan, irrigation water applied at its upper end may be distributed by gravity to all parts of the fan surface. Their porous soils and bouldery surfaces cause the higher parts of the fans to be somewhat avoided for intensive agricultural use, although they may furnish gravel and sand for constructional purposes.

The natural stream flow disappears, except in time of flood, into the coarse debris of the fan head. However, it collects underground in the great storage reservoir of porous fan material and slowly seeps outward toward the fan margin. This water also is commonly recovered for use in irrigation, in some regions through wells, and in others, as in parts of Asia, through tunnels driven underneath the fan surface. Provided the supply of water is sufficient, it is sometimes led by canals out beyond the irrigated areas of the fans and applied to the

Fig. 14.30 A section of the piedmont alluvial plain bordering the San Gabriel Mountains of southern California near Los Angeles. The head of this fan lies at the mouth of the mountain valley. (*Photograph by Fairchild Aerial Surveys, Inc., Los Angeles. Courtesy of California Fruit Growers' Exchange.*)

alluvial valley bottoms as far as the supply permits.

Piedmont alluvial plains often occur in intimate association with pediments, which they resemble so closely that distinction between them can rarely be made on the basis of surface form. A common arrangement finds the pediment at the immediate foot of the mountain front, with a deep alluvial covering farther out, on the lower slopes of the plain. However, if the rate of alluvial deposition is sufficiently rapid, alluvium will accumulate in fans right at the mountain foot, and no bedrock pediment surface will appear.

14.23 *Noted Piedmont Alluvial Plains.* Because piedmont alluvial plains have deep fertile soils and are admirable sites for the practice of irrigation, some of them, which have abundant and dependable water supplies, are noted for their agricultural wealth. Among them are the Sacramento and San Joaquin Valleys of California, the Los Angeles–San Bernardino lowland of southern California, the Vale of Chile, the Samarkand district of Russian Turkestan, and many others. Conditions in the San

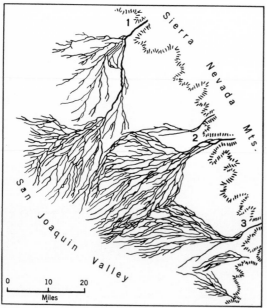

Fig. 14.31 A map showing the intricately branching patterns of the temporary distributary channels on the alluvial fans of the (1) Kings, (2) Kaweah, and (3) Tule Rivers in the Central Valley of California.

Joaquin Valley illustrate the landforms developed by valley filling.

The San Joaquin Valley is a portion of the Central Valley of California, a structural trough between the Sierra Nevada and the Coast Ranges. From the latter more than 50 small wet-weather streams flow eastward into the basin, bringing alluvium which is spread in a seemingly flat and quite featureless plain along the western margin of the valley. Drainage from the abundant snows and rains on the windward, west-facing slopes of the higher Sierra Nevada Range is carried down to the eastern margin of the valley by eight large streams and more than a dozen smaller ones. These have contributed the larger amount of alluvium to the general filling of the valley and have, in addition, built large alluvial fans. The largest of the fans is that of Kings River. It spreads outward into the valley 50 miles from the mountain base, crosses the axis of the structural trough, and blocks the drainage of its dry southern end (Fig. 14.31). Thus Tulare and Buena Vista Lakes are created, and areas about the margins of the fans are made marshy.

Large supplies of irrigation water from the snowy Sierras supplied to the gently sloping and highly tillable piedmont plain have turned each great fan into an oasis upon which there is an intensive agriculture devoted principally to fruits. This contrasts sharply with the extensive livestock-ranch type of agriculture that prevails on the western margin of the plain which lies in the rain shadow of the Coast Ranges and has only limited supplies of irrigation water.

14.24   Delta Fans. Some streams that have fairly steep gradients and are abundantly supplied with sediment enter the sea and build deltas. As these grow, their flat surfaces serve further to check stream velocity, fans form upon the delta tops, and the two grow in association. Such features may be called delta fans, and some of them are of great size. The delta of the Colorado River is, in fact, a large delta fan. Small delta fans occupy fringing embayments of many mountainous coasts, as, for example, in Japan, where various of the small marginal plains are delta fans. In a land so generally mountainous as Japan, these fragmentary but

Fig. 14.32 A playa basin in Nevada. Its deep alluvial filling has a glistening white crust of salt, and wind-blown salt clings to the rock island included within it. (*Photograph by John C. Weaver.*)

fertile plains are densely peopled and intensively used. Of similar construction are the productive lowlands of Valencia, Spain, the gently sloping surfaces upon which much of Los Angeles and its surrounding agricultural lands are located, and the Canterbury Plain, a gently sloping plain 40 miles wide and 175 miles long on the east coast of South Island, New Zealand. Each of them, however, is made up of the combined delta fans of several streams which drain the bordering mountains, and they might properly be called "piedmont alluvial delta-fan plains," if one wished to employ a term so awkward.

14.25   Alluvial Basins of Interior Drainage. In many arid plains are structural basins into which are discharged the drainage waters of the plain and with them great quantities of alluvium which aggrade and flatten the basin floors. Upon the flanks of some, especially the smaller and deeper ones, the filling is collected in the form of encircling alluvial fans. Basins of that type have been called *bolsons*. In many of the shallower basins the alluvium is spread uniformly over the gently sloping plain.

In humid lands streams that flow into structural basins fill them with water, creating lakes which overflow the lowest point upon the rim, and the drainage ultimately reaches the oceans.

Few streams in arid plains have sufficient volume or permanence to flow to the ocean. They flow intermittently, though sometimes with great volume, only to be swallowed up in the desert floor or to spread in shallow lakes over the lowest parts of their basins, where exposure to sun and dry winds soon evaporates them. Flood water, therefore, moves toward the center of the basin, but none flows out. For that reason the desert plain may be said to be typically a region of *interior drainage*. Only a few streams, those of greatest volume and permanence, and especially those streams that derive most of their waters from highlands beyond the desert (called *exotic* streams), are able to flow across it and reach the sea. Only for the exotic streams is baselevel determined by sea level. For the others it is determined by the levels of the alluvium-filled basins or temporary lakes into which they flow.

The lowest portion of the typical basin of interior drainage shows evidence of concentration of drainage there in the form of marshes or lakes. If the general rate of inward drainage is approximately equal to the average rate of loss through evaporation, a lake is likely to exist. It will be a salt-water or alkaline lake, because water is continually removed from it by evaporation while the salts contained in the inflowing water, especially the common salt, remain behind in solution and eventually reach concentrations that make some salt lakes more salty than the oceans. If the rate of evaporation generally exceeds the rate of inflow, temporary, or *playa*, lakes will result. These will contain water for a short time following heavy rains, but become dry during protracted droughts. The marshy beds of the ephemeral lakes commonly are mud-covered and are strongly charged with salt or soluble soil alkalies. When thoroughly dried they commonly are incrusted with salts and sometimes are glistening white in color (Fig. 14.32). In these deposits are not only common salt and other compounds of sodium and calcium, which are called *alkali*, but also some salts of economic value. Among the latter are the borax deposits of southwestern United States and the famous sodium nitrate deposits of northern Chile (24.22).

The great salt lakes of the world lie, as may be expected, in basins of interior drainage, some of which are plains of great size. Noted salt lakes are the Great Salt Lake, in Utah; the Aral and Caspian Seas, which are surrounded by the plains of Russian Turkestan; and Lake Eyre in southern Australia. The latter usually is a dry salt plain and its level is, like that of the Caspian, lower than sea level.

14.26 Plains of Older Alluvium. Many plains which are now being more or less actively eroded by streams were originally formed by alluvial deposition. Because of general uplift relative to baselevel or some significant change in the volume of streams or the availability of load, stream activity has been changed from aggradation to valley cutting. Hence the smooth alluvial surface has come to be the smooth "upland" which is undergoing dissection. Many of the youthfully dissected plains which are noteworthy for the flatness of their interfluves have had this origin. The largest plains of this type are distributed around the margins of great mountain systems and were no doubt, at the time of their formation, vast piedmont alluvial plains.

In the United States almost the entire eastern front of the Rocky Mountains is bordered by plains of older alluvium known collectively as the Great Plains. These were deposited as a piedmont alluvial plain by the shifting courses of former streams which flowed from the mountains. The original surface of this vast plain, which extends from the Llano Estacado (Staked Plains) of Texas northward to Montana, probably was very flat at the time of its formation. Changed conditions have led to erosion of the plain by the same drainage that formed it.

Fig. 14.33 The remarkably smooth surface of the Great Plains upland in southwestern Kansas, a plain of older alluvium. (*Photo by Soil Conservation Service, U.S.D.A.*)

Fig. 14.34 The Argentine Pampa, near Rosario, a low, flat plain comprised largely of older alluvium. (*Photograph by H. G. Olds.*)

All the streams that traverse the Great Plains have cut new valleys which have dissected the older alluvium into striplike, flat-topped interfluves with an east-west trend. In the process of eroding their present courses some of the streams have cut steep-walled valleys several scores of feet in depth and have built new floodplains from one to several miles in width. The prevailing dryness of the area, together with the porosity of much of the material, has inhibited the growth of tributaries, especially in the southern sections from Kansas to the Panhandle of Texas (Fig. 14.33).

Similar plains occur to the south of the Himalayas in the middle and upper valleys of the Ganges and Indus Rivers, and also in the northern part of the Po Valley of Northern Italy, along the south flank of the Alps. Much of the extensive interior plain of South America stretching eastward from the foot of the Andes is an old alluvial surface now undergoing shallow dissection. The best-known portion of it is the Pampa of Argentina, a flat and fertile region of great agricultural significance. Because of low rainfall, low elevation, and

almost imperceptible slope, the Pampa has not suffered much dissection, but neither is it still being aggraded (Fig. 14.34).

Karst Plains

14.27 Solution Features. In various parts of the world are small plains, and there are some of considerable size, the distinctive surface features of which result from the solvent work of underground water rather than from stream erosion. They may be called *karst* plains (13.33). Regions of this kind are underlain by rock strata which include layers of pure limestone. In some karst plains the soluble limestones make up the surface rock formations and are covered only by residual earth; in others they lie beneath some thicknesses of other rocks. In either case, however, the surface features show evidence of the removal of material beneath the surface and mainly in solution.

In contrast with stream-eroded plains, karst plains are distinguished by a general absence of valleys. They are not always entirely lacking, since some large streams originating in border

293

areas may cut entirely across a karst plain. Small valleys, however, generally are not numerous, some districts of hundreds of square miles' extent having few if any.

Instead of stream-eroded drainage patterns, karst plains have undulating, rolling, or sometimes rough surfaces in which numerous depressions without visible outlets are separated by low irregular ridges or hillocks without definite pattern of arrangement. Some of the depressions are large and irregular in outline; others are small and nearly circular. The depressions and their intervening ridges result from the unequal solution of the underlying limestones. Some of the basins are produced by surface solution, the water finding its outlet through the bottom into solution caverns, along joints, or into other underground channels. More, on the other hand, appear to be the result of the subsidence of the roofs of former caverns. They vary in size from a few feet in diameter to sprawling depressions several miles in extent. Commonly they are designated by the general term *sinks* (Fig. 14.35).

Some sinks are many feet deep, are steep-sided, and have obvious openings through which the surface drainage runs underground. Others are so shallow as almost to escape notice. In some the bottom outlets are partially or wholly stopped by clay or other materials, and the drainage escapes so slowly that swamps, temporary lakes, or even permanent lakes accumulate in them. Seldom, however, do the lakes rise to the point where they overflow their basins and spill into neighboring depressions through surface channels.

Associated with the underground drainage of karst plains is the formation of numerous caverns, mainly small, which in some regions thoroughly honeycomb the soluble limestones beneath. Fed by surface drainage, the waters of many solution cavities pass along joint planes or dissolved channels and sometimes join ultimately in underground streams of considerable size or issue as springs of remarkable volume (19.8). In a few karst areas thick limestone formations have permitted the solution of caverns of great size and extent, such as Mammoth Cave, Kentucky. The partial collapse of cavern roofs in these regions results also in the formation of natural bridges. Features of that kind are not uncommon, but mainly they are of small size.

14.28   Notable Karst Regions. Areas of solution features take their name from the Karst, a rough denuded limestone hill region which lies back of the Adriatic shore of Yugoslavia. Of the same rock type is the neighboring lowland of Apulia, the rolling plain of the "heel" of Italy. Broad sinks, there called *dolines,* are interspersed among barren limestone uplands. Because the sinks are low and soil-floored they are the principal tilled areas, but in the rainy season the underdrainage cannot remove the inflowing water fast enough to prevent them from being very wet or even flooded.

Other karst plains are found in North America, especially on limestone platforms bordering the Gulf of Mexico. The rolling limestone plain of central Florida is covered in large part by sands of some depth, but occasionally there are found admixtures of thin strata of clay. Sink-

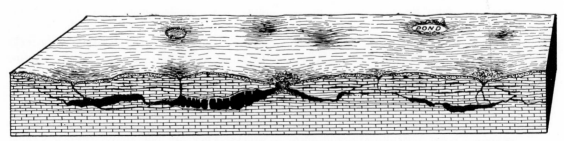

Fig. 14.35 A diagram illustrating karst plain features. Sinks of various types are shown in relation to features of limestone solution underground.

holes of all sizes are separated by low sandy ridges, or hills; small caverns are numerous; and underground drainage issues in springs, one of which has the largest flow of water of any spring in the United States. The region as a whole is not without surface streams, but one of its most persistent characteristics is its lakes, ponds, and pools, which lie in solution depressions that have their underdrainage impeded by accumulations of clay over their bottoms (Fig. 14.36).

Another karst region in the United States is the irregular section in south central Kentucky which is underlain by a cavernous limestone. Considerable parts of this region are so dominated by solution features that sinks and their associated knolls and ridges are the principal relief features. Under primitive forest conditions many if not most of the sinks had free underdrainage. Since clearing, soil erosion has stripped clay from the adjacent hills and deposited it in sinks until many of them now are ill drained and contain at least temporary ponds. In the underlying limestone are many springs and caverns, often with hillside openings. Mammoth Cave, in this region, is widely known for its giant cavities and great underground extent.

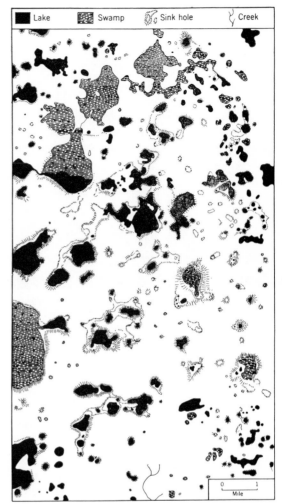

Fig. 14.36 Numerous sinks, lakes, and swamps dot this Florida karst plain, but there are almost no surface streams.

Plains Modified by Glaciation

14.29 Origins of Glaciated Plains. In northern North America and northwestern Eurasia are extensive plains that were covered, at one or more times during the last million years or so, by great continental ice sheets. Although the larger relief features of these plains were produced by tectonic forces or by stream erosion, their surfaces were extensively remodeled by the ice. Hence, most of the details of landform that characterize their present appearance are the result of glacial action.

The last of the major ice sheets was in existence so very recently that the features it produced are still strikingly fresh and but little modified by subsequent stream erosion. A number of areas, however, though covered by one or more of the earlier ice sheets, were not overrun by the last. The glacially produced features of these regions have been exposed to erosion long enough to permit streams to destroy much of their distinctive character. The plains that are distinctively "glacial" in surface form are, therefore, largely those covered by the most recent, or Wisconsin, ice sheet (Fig. 13.22).

All phases of glacial activity were involved, and their imprints are left upon the plains. In many localities there may be found in close association, and in great variety of detail, the forms produced by glacial erosion, glacial deposition, and deposition by the waters that flowed from the melting ice. Some areas, however, have

Fig. 14.37 The rounded uplands and rock basins of an ice-scoured surface in northern Canada, where vegetation is scant. Note the different elevations of the lakes. (*Royal Canadian Air Force photograph.*)

predominantly the kinds of surface features that result from glacial erosion, while in others the features are mainly those that result from glacial or glaciofluvial deposition. Plains thus distinguished may be called *ice-scoured plains* and *drift plains,* respectively.

Plains of the ice-scoured type are most prevalent in regions of crystalline rocks and on the inner rather than on the marginal portions of the glaciated areas (Fig. 13.22). There the thin regolith, the general resistance of the rocks, and the lesser frequency of melting provided relatively small amounts of local glacial drift. That which was formed was comprised in large part of rocks resistant to crushing, and these remain as coarse boulders intermingled with some quantities of finer material.

The plains of deep glacial drift are found more commonly in association with sedimentary rocks, which generally were more deeply weathered and more easily crushed than those of the crystalline areas. In both North America and Europe, the direction of ice motion happened to be generally away from the regions of crystalline rock toward those of sedimentary formation. That is the reason for the numerous *erratic boulders* of igneous or metamorphic

rock found in drift plains which are underlain by sedimentary rock only.

The features of the two classes of glaciated plains may be discussed separately.

14.30 The Features of Ice-scoured Plains. The major stream-eroded features that previously existed on the plains over which the great continental ice sheets crept probably were almost universally reshaped, but rarely completely erased, by glacial erosion and deposition.

The surface configuration of the crystalline plains where ice scour was predominant is characterized by rounded rock hills, often conspicuously bare of soil, and broad open valleys and basins. The first ice invasion of a region doubtless was sufficient to remove the mantle of soil and weathered rock which had accumulated there under previous conditions. The quarrying out of areas of much-jointed rocks left an uneven surface of knobs and hollows on the massive rocks beneath (Fig. 14.37). Upon this the ice continued to flow, smoothing and rounding but unable to effect further great change. Many of the rock knobs, scoured and polished by abrasion, bear the grooves and striations scratched upon them by ice-pushed boulders. Some of the larger hills have striking inequalities of slope. A long and gradual incline marks the side up which the ice pushed its slow and grinding way, and the lee slope is left shorter and steeper as a result of the plucking action of the ice as it pulled away jointed blocks of rocks in its forward motion (Fig. 13.23).

Over the present valley floors a thin veneer of glacial debris may serve inadequately as the parent material of a soil. Strewn with sub-angular boulders torn from the adjacent slopes by the ice, the drift of ice-scoured plains commonly is neither deep enough nor continuous enough to be tillable except in patches or localities. It may, however, serve as anchorage for thin stands of forest, especially the shallow-rooted conifers.

The changes in relief produced by ice scour are not of a large order of magnitude as compared with some produced by other agents, but they are sufficient to disarrange completely the preexisting drainage. It may be supposed that, during the long period of preglacial erosion, streams had become somewhat adjusted to the kinds and structures of the rocks of the plains and that they had developed definite patterns as the result of that adjustment. The present drainage of the ice-scoured plains is noted particularly for its indefinite pattern and its lack

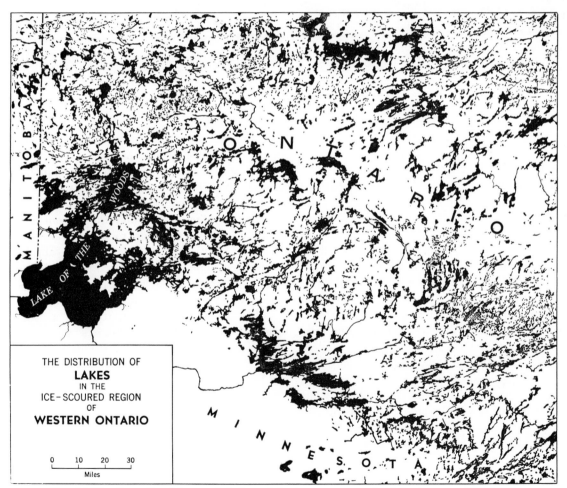

Fig. 14.38 Sprawling lakes, mainly in rock basins, occupy much of the ice-scoured plain of western Ontario. They are proving a valuable resource in the development of the summer-resort industry. (*After Map 24A, Province of Ontario, Department of Surveys.*)

Fig. 14.39 An air view of the lake-dotted, forest-clad plain of ice-scoured crystalline rocks north of Lake Superior. (*Royal Canadian Air Force photograph.*)

of adjustment to rock structures. The universal effect of the accident of glaciation is to return the drainage of a region to a stage of youth in which it is characterized by numerous lakes, waterfalls, and rapids.

Lakes are particularly numerous in plains of severe ice scour (Fig. 14.38). There are said to be more than 35,000 lakes in Finland, and they occupy more than 11 per cent of the country. Certain sections of the district lying north and west of Lake Superior in Minnesota and Ontario are more than 25 per cent lake area, but that is not true of the ice-scoured region as a whole. Many of them lie in rock basins eroded by the ice with its characteristic disregard for uniform gradient. Such basins often are broad, only moderately deep, and are dotted with islands which are ice-scoured rock hills of the irregular plain (Fig. 14.39). Because of the prevalent resistance of the rocks and the clearness of the water, glacial lakes of the rock-basin type are likely to be enduring as well as numerous.

Some small rock-basin lakes show almost no tendency to destruction even after the vast lapse of time since the disappearance of the

last ice sheet. On the other hand, there are some that were shallow by origin and have been filled subsequently by the remains of marsh vegetation such as sphagnum moss. In Canada bogs of that type are called *muskeg*.

The same disregard for uniform gradient that enabled glaciers to erode rock basins caused them to leave rock ledges or other abrupt changes of slope to be discovered by the drainage of ice-scoured plains. Streams in such regions developed their wandering courses by overflow from basin to basin after the ice was gone. On such ungraded courses falls and rapids are numerous, and in regions of hard rock they are, like the lakes, enduring (Fig. 14.37). The potential utility of these streams for water-power development is high compared with that of streams in plains of other kinds. The streams are relatively free of silt; the falls, though seldom great, are numerous and widely distributed, and the discharge of water over them is much regulated by the presence of many natural lakes and swamps and by the floors of widespread forests in the drainage areas.

14.31 *Extensive Ice-scoured Plains.* The most extensive ice-scoured plains of the world are found close to the centers from which the great Pleistocene glaciers of Europe and North America radiated. These regions are (*a*) the Laurentian upland plain of Canada and (*b*) the plains of Sweden and Finland. The fact that the preglacial surface in each of these regions was a plain of ancient crystalline rocks instead of less resistant sedimentary rocks probably had much to do with the cleanness of ice scour and the preservation of the ice-eroded forms. The time that has elapsed since the last glaciation, although it is several thousands of years, has not been sufficient for slow weathering under high-latitude climate to produce any great change in the ice-carved forms of the hard rocks.

14.32 The General Relationships of Drift Plains. Those parts of the areas of continental glaciation which are characterized by the deposition of a thick mantle of drift are more extensive and of much greater human significance than those in which ice scour was dominant. They occupy most of the broad outer margins of the glaciated plains of both North America and Europe and are underlain mainly by sedimentary rocks (Fig. 13.22). Over them are spread the debris carried from the ice-scoured plains, intermingled with a much larger quantity obtained locally or transported only a short distance. Their features are the products of the deposition of drift together with a limited amount of ice scour.

In general, the effects of continental glaciation upon relief were to smooth and make more level the regions in which deposition was the dominant activity. This was brought about chiefly by a greater deposition of drift in the valley bottoms than on the hilltops and, secondarily, by somewhat more severe erosion of hilltops than of valley bottoms (Fig. 14.40*B*). In some localities drift completely buries the rock surface under an unbroken mantle which may be several tens of feet or even 400 or 500 ft. in thickness. In such areas the surface features of the drift are relatively independent of those of the underlying rock (Fig. 14.40*A*). Where thick rough moraine was deposited upon a smooth rock surface, the end product might be a sur-

A. Burial of rolling surface by thick, smooth drift

B. Partial burial of rough land — A rock controlled drift surface

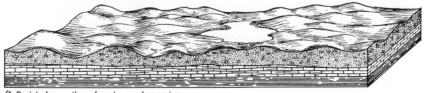

C. Burial of smooth surface by rough moraine

Fig. 14.40 Different effects of glacial deposits upon previous rock surfaces.

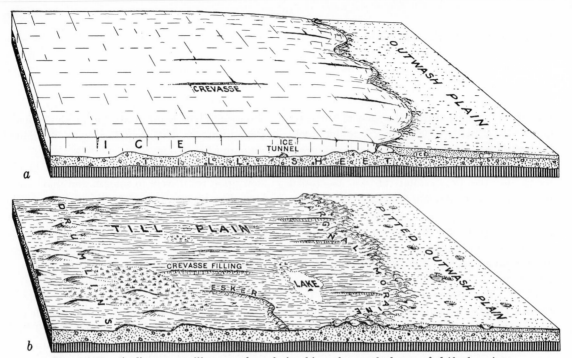

Fig. 14.41 A diagram to illustrate the relationships of several classes of drift deposits to the parts of the glacier by which they were formed: (*a*) a plain partly covered by the margin of a glacier; (*b*) the same plain after the ice has disappeared. Since till extends on beneath the outwash to the right, the marginal moraine shown is recessional rather than end.

Fig. 14.42 An exposure of glacial till showing the unassorted clay, pebbles, and boulders of which it is composed. (*Wisconsin Geological Survey photograph.*)

face actually rougher than the original (Fig. 14.40*C*).

It has been noted previously that glacial drift is comprised of several classes of deposits, some of which are put down underneath the body of the ice itself, whereas others are associated with its margins or with the streams of melt water flowing from the ice (13.38). Because of this fact the drift plain, in areas of most recent glaciation, has various classes of features arranged in diverse but recognizable patterns. The most extensive and fundamental element in this complex is the till sheet or ground moraine, an undulating surface which covers most of the area once occupied by the glacier. About the margins of the till sheet, and also upon its surface, may be found ridgelike marginal moraines (end or recessional), often arranged in broad festoons, one behind another (Figs. 14.41 and 14.47). Bordering them, either beyond the till sheet or upon its surface, are areas of stream-sorted and deposited sand and gravels or beds of fine sand and clay which accumulated in transient stream channels or temporary lakes.

14.33 Features of the Till Plain. The till sheet, or ground moraine, is a widespread mantle of unsorted and unstratified drift, containing materials of all sizes from huge boulders to fine clay (Fig. 14.42) It was deposited in part beneath the glacier and in part by being let down onto the ground surface when the ice edge melted back or the glacier wasted away. Usually much of the till is composed of materials which are of local origin. However, there are often pebbles or boulders which may be recognized as being foreign to the area in which they are found, sometimes being traceable to source regions scores or even hundreds of miles away. Such rocks, called *erratics,* occasionally provide valuable evidence of the direction in which the glaciers moved.

Till derived from jointed but resistant rocks is likely to be excessively stony (as, for example, in New England), while that obtained from weaker rocks, especially shales, usually contains few boulders and much clay. Unlike normal weathered regolith, which grades downward into the underlying bedrock from which it is derived, the till sheet rests directly upon the little-weathered surface of the ice-scoured bedrock beneath. The principal and widespread characteristic of the till plain is a gently undulating surface which includes broad low hills,

Fig. 14.43 The undulating surface of a till plain. (*Wisconsin Geological Survey photograph.*)

or swells, and wide shallow depressions, or swales, the latter often without outlets (Fig. 14.43). These result from the unequal deposition of the ground moraine. The various elevations and depressions are arranged according to no recognizable pattern, and commonly the local relief is less than 100 ft. Exceptions to this condition are found in areas that had a considerable preglacial relief or where the till sheet is thin. There the principal hills are but thinly veneered protrusions of a rock surface having a relief too great to be completely buried by the till sheet (Figs. 14.40B and 14.1).

Rising above the undulating surface in a few localities are sizable groups of low, smooth, half-egg-shaped hills composed of till. Each hill is usually a considerable fraction of a mile in length, and is elongated in the direction of glacier flow, with its steeper end facing the direction from which the ice came. These peculiar features, known as *drumlins*, were deposited beneath the marginal sections of the ice sheets and were streamlined by ice movement, but the exact manner of their formation is not known (Figs. 14.44 and 14.45).

Because of the filling of preglacial stream valleys and the generally uneven and patternless dumping of the till sheet, drainage conditions on the young till plain surface are scarcely better than those on the ice-scoured surface. Lakes and swamps accumulate in the swales and depressions of the ground moraine, and streams wander aimlessly from one depression to another (Fig. 14.46). Rapids and falls are not uncommon, especially where the streams cross uncovered ledges of rock.

Some of the largest lakes, as, for example, the chain of four at Madison, Wis., occupy depressions in thick drift that only partially filled the broad and deep valleys of large preglacial rivers. Even the larger lakes are usually quite shallow, and this factor, combined with the relative ease of stream cutting in the drift rim and the usual existence of a considerable silt load in the inflowing streams, favors rapid filling or draining.

Fig. 14.44 A drumlin on the till plain of central New York. Its shape indicates that the glacier movement was from right to left. (*U.S. Geological Survey photograph.*)

In the till plains of America, even before the agricultural occupancy of the land during the past century, thousands of the lake-filled basins left at the retreat of the last glacier had been filled or drained by natural processes, including the growth of vegetation, and converted into marshes. Generally the basins are partly filled with peat, the acid half-decayed remains of rank vegetation. Some are now covered with grasses and appear as marsh meadows. During the last century other thousands of small lakes and ponds in America have dwindled in size or have become marshes, owing to the increased rate of fill resulting from clearing and plowing on adjacent hillsides or to the lowering of the ground-water table which follows general deforestation. Also, thousands of acres of small marshlands have been artificially drained and their surfaces put to agricultural or pastoral uses.

14.34 Marginal moraines represent relatively thick heapings of drift that accumulated around the edge of an ice sheet during periods when the ice margin remained nearly stationary for a considerable time.

It appears that variations in atmospheric temperature, the supply of snow, or other elements of environment caused the rate of glacial disappearance to be most irregular. Advances, or slight readvances, during which marginal moraines great or small were formed, alternated with periods of waste so rapid that only small amounts of marginal deposit were put down upon the surface of the till. This is indicated by successive morainal ridges separated by areas of till plain. Moraines put down about the margin of the ice at its most advanced position are called *end moraines*. *Recessional moraines* were built upon the top of the till plain at places of hesitation or temporary readvance during glacial wastage.

The location of marginal moraines indicates the position of the ice edge at various times during glacial wastage. The scalloped or festooned pattern of their occurrence shows that the ice front neither advanced nor wasted away as a unit, but rather assumed the form of a series of lobes or tongues (Fig. 14.47).

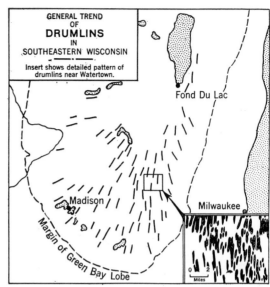

Fig. 14.45 Drumlins are thickly clustered in the area once covered by the extremity of the Green Bay lobe of the Wisconsin ice sheet. Their trend follows closely the direction of ice movement.

The variety of surface detail on marginal moraines reflects the variety of depositional processes that are represented at the edge of the ice sheet. Much material is simply dropped in heaps and ridges where the ice has melted from around it. Some is washed from the glacier surface or from under the ice by streams of melt water, the coarser debris being deposited

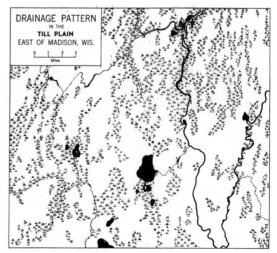

Fig. 14.46 The drainage pattern on a portion of a Wisconsin till plain.

303

as steep deltas or alluvial cones against the ice edge. Locally some may be pushed up into a ridge, bulldozer fashion, by a small but rapid advance of the ice. Most of the finer material is carried away from the ice front by melt water, leaving a concentration of gravelly and bouldery material in the morainic accumulation.

The result of these diverse happenings is an irregular, jumbled deposit of till and partially sorted water-laid material, forming a belt of

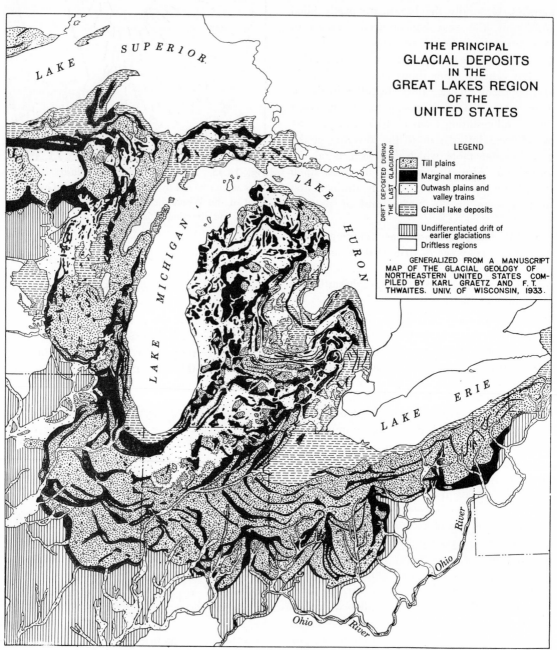

**THE PRINCIPAL
GLACIAL DEPOSITS
IN THE
GREAT LAKES REGION
OF THE
UNITED STATES**

LEGEND

DRIFT DEPOSITED DURING THE LAST GLACIATION

- Till plains
- Marginal moraines
- Outwash plains and valley trains
- Glacial lake deposits

- Undifferentiated drift of earlier glaciations
- Driftless regions

GENERALIZED FROM A MANUSCRIPT MAP OF THE GLACIAL GEOLOGY OF NORTHEASTERN UNITED STATES COMPILED BY KARL GRAETZ AND F. T. THWAITES. UNIV. OF WISCONSIN, 1933.

Fig. 14.47 The pattern of arrangement of the drift deposits in the Great Lakes region. (*Reproduced by permission of F. T. Thwaites.*)

Fig. 14.48 Small kettle ponds surrounded by boulder-strewn knobs in a marginal moraine near Whitewater, Wis.

distinctive terrain around the margin or across the surface of the till plain. The surface of a well-developed marginal moraine is most often somewhat higher, stonier, and noticeably more irregular than that of the neighboring till plain. The gravel cones and piles of till form many small rounded knobs or ridges, and between these are small hollows or depressions, some of which contain small ponds or swamps. The descriptive term *knob-and-kettle* may be applied to such surfaces (Fig. 14.48).

Some marginal moraines are so low, smooth, or meager as to be detectable only to a practiced eye. Others form the most conspicuous features for many miles around. Generally speaking, moraines in stony and gravelly drift are more upstanding and have rougher, more broken surfaces than moraines in clay drift. The clay moraines of northeastern Illinois, for example, though large in volume, form low, gentle swells that would hardly be recognized by a person familiar only with the hilly, stony moraines of eastern Wisconsin. The highest and broadest marginal moraines represent situations in which (*a*) the ice edge has oscillated over a

limited zone for an unusually long time or (*b*) a vast mass of drift has accumulated in the narrow zone between two slightly separated lobes of the ice sheet. An example of the latter is the remarkably high and rough Kettle Moraine of eastern Wisconsin (Fig. 14.49).

Because of their prevalent roughness and stoniness, marginal moraines often stand out as belts of relatively unused land. In the Great Lakes area of North America, some moraines may be traced across the countryside as belts of wood lots left when the more favorable land was cleared and cultivated. Broad moraine belts, because of their pleasant irregularity, their lakes, and their woodlands, often serve as valuable recreational areas.

14.35 Features of Stream-deposited Drift. Some marginal moraines, both end and recessional, are fringed for miles with *outwash plains* of water-sorted and therefore stratified drift which was washed out from the ice front and spread fanwise by many shifting and temporary channels (Fig. 14.41). These are characterized by flat surfaces and an internal structure of rudely stratified sand, gravel, and small boul-

Fig. 14.49 The unusually rough, knobby surface of the Kettle Moraine, in eastern Wisconsin. (*Photograph by John R. Randall.*)

Fig. 14.50 A cut through an outwash plain, showing sand and gravel washed free of clay and rudely stratified according to size. (*Wisconsin Geological Survey photograph.*)

Fig. 14.51 The nearly flat surface of an outwash plain. (*Wisconsin Geological Survey photograph.*)

Fig. 14.52 The undulating surface and numerous hollows of a pitted outwash plain. Note the surface similarity to a till plain. (*Wisconsin Geological Survey photograph.*)

ders (Fig. 14.50). In general, the clay component of the drift is not present in the deposits because it was carried farther on by the streams that built them. The largest boulders, on the other hand, usually were left behind on the moraines.

The generally flat surfaces of some outwash plains that are underlain by till are dotted with *kettle holes* which appear to have resulted from the melting of stranded, and perhaps buried, ice blocks left during glacial wastage (Figs. 14.51 and 14.52). Plains of that kind are called *pitted outwash*. They are common among the extensive outwash plains of southern Michigan. During spring thaws, when the soil still is frozen, the kettles are likely to contain small ponds, but they are not commonly occupied by permanent lakes because of the free drainage of surface waters through the underlying gravels.

Because of the materials of which outwash plains are composed, they commonly are of rather low agricultural productivity as compared with till plains. Even though their surfaces are very flat, they are in some places stony and in others sandy. Usually they are subject to drought because of the free underdrainage.

They are, however, provided with naturally crushed and rudely sorted sands and gravels for constructional use, and the supply is abundant, since some of the outwash deposits are many feet thick (Fig. 14.53). The large commercial gravel pits of the Great Lakes region mainly are located in outwash plains.

Some glacial streams flowed in definite valleys and for this reason deposited outwash only along their valley floors, rather than broadly over the upland surface. These aggraded glacial stream beds are called *valley trains,* and they bear the same relationship to outwash plains that floodplains bear to piedmont alluvial plains. Valley-train gravels and sands now are found in the floodplains or alluvial terraces of the Mississippi, lower Wisconsin, and other streams that led away from the front of the great North American glacier.

Many broad valleys were eroded in the drift or in bedrock where ice-front or marginal-lake drainage cut across low divides into established river valleys leading to the sea (Fig. 14.54). Such *glacial spillways* are now either abandoned or else occupied by streams that often seem ridiculously small in valleys that

Fig. 14.53 A view showing outwash gravels and marginal moraine in association. The smooth surface of the outwash plain is shown above the gravel pit, and the position of the bordering moraine is indicated by the low hills in the right background. (*The Sheboygan Press.*)

Fig. 14.54 The flat-bottomed channel of a former glacial spillway, not now occupied by any stream. (*Wisconsin Geological Survey photograph.*)

appear to have been eroded by streams of the size of the Mississippi. Some of these valleys, because of their gentle gradients, have served as routes for canals connecting important inland waterways. Examples are the spillway connecting Lake Michigan with the Illinois River, the Mohawk Valley (Erie Canal) route across New York, and the network of spillways utilized by the extensive canal system connecting the rivers of the North European Plain (Figs. 14.55 and 14.58).

Many of the temporary streams that discharged from the glacier margin flowed under the ice, sometimes at the bottoms of deep crevasses and sometimes in ice tunnels (Fig. 14.41). Being heavily loaded, they aggraded their beds and built narrow deposits of glaciofluvial drift within the confines of crevasse or tunnel. If the stagnant ice melted away without sufficient forward motion to erase so fragile a feature, it clearly would remain to mark the course of the ancient stream. Such deposits are not uncommon and are called *eskers*. They appear as sinuous ridges of gravel somewhat like an abandoned railroad grade. Some of them continue, with interruptions, for many miles (Fig. 14.56).

14.36 Glacial Lakes and Lake Plains. It has been observed that the lakes of the drift

plains are due to some kind of glacial obstruction of present drainage. This is in some degree true even of the Great Lakes. However, in an earlier stage in their history the drainage of the Great Lakes, and of several other large lakes which have now disappeared, was obstructed by the ice of the glacier itself. Where the glacier rested upon a surface that sloped inward toward the ice front, melt water could not escape and therefore was impounded in a lake that had the ice front as one margin. The lake rose until it found an outlet at the lowest point on its rim. Temporary glacial lakes of that kind are known as *marginal lakes*. The gradual wast-

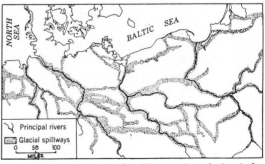

Fig. 14.55 The glacial spillways that drained the long European ice front toward the west at its various stages of disappearance. (*After Paul Wold-stadt. Das Eiszeitalter.*)

Fig. 14.56 A narrow, sinuous ridge of the esker type. It contains stratified drift and may have been deposited in an ice tunnel or in a crevasse. (*Photograph by John R. Randall.*)

age of the ice barrier back of a marginal lake permitted drainage to find new and lower outlets, and thus the lake dwindled in size or disappeared entirely. During the periods of their existence marginal lakes modified the land surfaces that they covered and in their disappearance left behind unmistakable features which are called *lake plains* or *lacustrine plains*. Their

Fig. 14.57 The extremely level surface of a glacial-lake plain near Saginaw, Mich.

distinguishing features are strikingly level surfaces which are comprised largely of the wave-worked ingredients of the drift, silts and clays where they were abundant, but sometimes sand also (Fig. 14.57). They include also shore features such as abandoned beach ridges, offshore bars, and deltas spread at intervals that mark successive stages in the lowering of the outlet and the decrease of the lake area.

14.37 *Notable lacustrine plains of North America* include the lake-plain margins of the present Great Lakes, the Lake Agassiz plain, the southern part of the Ontario Clay Belt, and the sand plain of central Wisconsin.

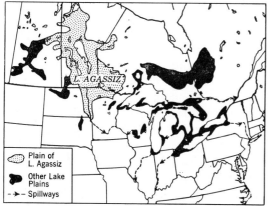

Fig. 14.58 A map showing the plain of glacial Lake Agassiz, together with the plains of other ice-margin lakes that existed at various times during the wastage of the Wisconsin ice sheets. Also shown are some of the spillways through which these lakes drained during the time that their normal drainage was blocked by the ice.

During certain stages in the wastage of the last ice sheet the southern portions of the Great Lakes were exposed, while the great ice dam still lay across the present outlet through the St. Lawrence Valley. During that time the lake levels stood higher than now, and the waters overflowed southward through various higher outlets (Fig. 14.58). The margins of the floors of those more extensive lakes, containing unleached glacial silt and clay, are now exposed as flat and fertile plains in northern Ohio, eastern Michigan, western New York, and else-

where. Even the city of Chicago stands in large part upon one of them. They are bordered by a series of beach ridges and other shore features which mark the lake levels associated with successive outlets.

In the same manner glacial drainage was impounded in a large marginal lake between the wasting ice front in central Canada and the higher land of central Minnesota. A broad and shallow lake created upon this slope found for a long time its lowest outlet through the course of the present Minnesota River into the Mississippi. The wave-worked sediments that were spread over the floor of that formerly extensive body of water, which is known as Lake Agassiz, now comprise the flat and fertile Red River plains. Lakes Winnipeg and Winnipegosis now occupy the lowest portions of the depression, the remainder of the lake having disappeared when the ice dam was removed.

Upon the ice-scoured surface of the Canadian Shield where morainic deposits generally are scant, coarse, and infertile is a region known as the Ontario Clay Belt. It is a district of growing agricultural value, comprised in part of fine sediments laid down in a marginal lake. In the plain of central Wisconsin, on the other hand, both the drift from which the sediments were derived and the lake bed upon which they were deposited were composed largely of sandstones. That plain is therefore flat but sandy and infertile.

14.38 Association of Drift Features. In the preceding discussion different types of drift features have been discussed separately for the sake of convenience. However, it must be remembered that the drift plains of North America and Europe are actually complex surfaces which combine till plains, marginal moraines, patches and ribbons of outwash, lake plains, groups of drumlins, and even patches of exposed, scoured bedrock, in close and often intricate association. A glance at Fig. 14.47 will yield a general idea of this complexity, though only the larger features are shown.

Because of the great differences in surface material, drainage condition, and surface irregularity that exist among these groups of features, and even among individuals of a single group, it is impossible to generalize about the utility of drift plains to man. The excessively stony, sandy, swampy, or rough-surfaced areas are ordinarily of little agricultural value, though they may be useful as sources of sand or gravel, as wildlife refuges, or as recreational areas. On the other hand, some of the smoother, reasonably well-drained, stone-free, loamy till plains and lake plains rank among the most valuable agricultural lands of the New or the Old World.

It should also be recalled that large areas of drift plains that were not occupied by the last great ice sheet have been so modified by stream erosion that they no longer retain their distinctively "glacial" features. These "older drift plains" (Fig. 13.22) now more properly belong, as do the "plains of older alluvium," to the class of "plains sculptured by stream erosion."

14.39   The Great Ice Caps. While the great ice sheets that still cover most of Greenland and the Antarctic continent are fundamentally different features from the plains sculptured by older ice masses, it is convenient to consider them at this point in connection with glaciation in general.

For the most part, the surfaces of the ice caps actually are relatively smooth plains, on which are various systems of low ridges and swells a few feet in height, which result principally from the work of the wind and drifting snow. But, owing to the cold, there are no streams, and consequently there are no significant erosional features. Only upon their margins do the great ice caps exhibit any important variety. In this respect the Antarctic and Greenland caps differ considerably.

The vast expanse of the Antarctic ice sheet includes an area about one and two-thirds times the size of the United States, almost entirely ice-covered. The surface slopes rapidly up from the coast to a flattish interior which has an average elevation of about 6,000 ft. and a maximum of about 10,000 ft. in the region inland from the Pacific Coast. The relief features of the underlying Antarctic Continent are little known, but its average elevation is believed to be considerable. It may be that the ice sheet over the interior does not in many places exceed 2,000 ft. in thickness and that in some places it is very thin.

The ice surface of Antarctica descends from the high interior, and the marginal ice thins and is traversed by deep cracks. Except in a few localities, where it is held back by fringing mountains, the ice everywhere overruns the land margin so that the exact position of the shoreline of the continent is difficult to determine. The ice edge, whether it is at the land

Fig. 14.59 Margin of the Antarctic Ice Cap. Floating pack ice in foreground. (*Official U.S. Navy Photograph.*)

Fig. 14.60 Tongues from the Greenland Ice Cap protrude coastward through the fringing mountains. (*Photograph by Rasmussen. Courtesy of the Geographical Review, published by the American Geographical Society of New York.*)

margin or well out into the adjacent sea, is marked by sheer cliffs. From these walls great icebergs are split off along crevasses as a result of undercutting by waves and the buoyant effect of the sea water. Some of them are tens of square miles in area, tabular in form, and almost mesalike in their relation to the parent mass. The icebergs, large and small, disintegrate by melting and disperse as masses of floe or drift ice which fringe the continent for many miles and combine with the ice wall to make it relatively unapproachable (Fig. 14.59).

The Greenland cap is to a degree intermontane, since its ice is largely held within fringing mountain walls. This mountainous rim and the higher summer temperatures prevailing there produce somewhat different features upon its margin. Not everywhere does it descend to the sea. Since it is held back by the highlands, much of its southern and western front wastes by melting some distance inland.

Where it does discharge into the sea it does so by means of tongues of ice, some narrow, some wide, which protrude through gaps in the bordering highland. Between parts of the ice tongues and surrounded by them are islands of rock, called *nunataks*, which are the peaks of ice-enveloped hills or mountains. These become more numerous near the margin where the hills are higher and the ice thinner (Fig. 14.60). There are nunataks in Antarctica also, but they are less numerous and more widely scattered. From the tongues of Greenland ice which discharge directly into the sea are derived irregular icebergs which, although they are not so large as some seen in Antarctica, are of ample size to

create a hazard to navigation when they drift southward into the foggy North Atlantic steamship lanes in the spring.

Plains Modified by the Wind

14.40 Wind-eroded Surfaces. It has been suggested previously that wind erosion or deflation is not a major shaper of the earth's surface. Even in the deserts, running water is, or has recently been, the most significant sculpturing agent. There are, however, many areas of considerable extent, especially in the sparsely vegetated deserts, that bear some marks of deflation in their surface detail.

Most important is the whipping up of quantities of fine material from the floors of alluviated basins, resulting in a general lowering of the surface over a broad area. Because this process is seldom concentrated in a limited space, only occasionally does a clearly excavated depression appear. Some broad hollows a few feet deep that have been found in the semiarid grass-covered plains of the world have been ascribed to this cause. A local destruction of the vegetation, by animals, excessive alkalinity, or any other cause, would open up a bare spot upon which deflation would go to work, producing a shallow *blowout* depression. In a few places tablelike remnants of the former surface remain, showing the amount of lowering that deflation has accomplished. Generally, however, the wind accomplishes its erosion so broadly and so gradually that its degree of importance can scarcely even be approximated.

As a by-product of its selectivity, deflation is

responsible for the widespread occurrence of gravel-clad surfaces in the desert plains. Only the finer silts and clays are picked up; pebbles and coarse sand are left behind. In this way, such coarser materials become concentrated at the surface, producing the familiar *desert pavement,* beneath which fine material may still remain (Fig. 13.26). Where no coarse material exists in the regolith, no desert pavement is formed, and the finer dust may be stripped off to considerable depth.

14.41 Aeolian Sand Plains. From the foregoing it is clear that the popular conception of the arid plain as a sea of wind-blown sand is not well founded. Not many large desert areas are so much as one-fourth sand-covered. However, there are many regions of sandy desert, the largest lying in the central and eastern Sahara and in southern Arabia. Their abundant sands are derived chiefly from the disintegration of sandstone and other bedrock in the locality or from local accumulations of sandy alluvium (Fig. 14.61).

Unlike fine silt and clay, sand is rarely moved by the wind far from its place of origin. It does not enter into suspension, but is rolled or bounced along the ground like the bed load in a stream, rarely getting more than a few feet above the surface. It accumulates in heaps, ridges, or sheets that assume an astonishing variety of forms (Fig. 14.62). While the mechanisms of dune formation are imperfectly understood, the factors believed to be especially significant in affecting depositional forms are (*a*) the amount of sand, (*b*) the strength of the sand-moving winds, (*c*) the consistency of direction of the sand-moving winds, and (*d*) the nature of the vegetation cover.

Especially common forms in wind-deposited sand are crescent-shaped dunes, transverse

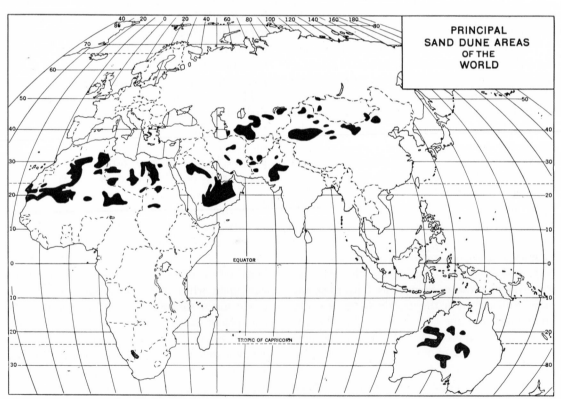

Fig. 14.61 Extensive areas of sand dunes are largely confined to the deserts of the Eastern Hemisphere continents.

Fig. 14.62 The billowing, wind-rippled forms of one of the small patches of sand dunes in the American desert. Note the mud floor and some vegetation in the depressions or pockets where water has stood. The most distant features are low mountains, not sand dunes. (*Photograph by Ewing Galloway.*)

dunes, and elongated, peaked ridges. Crescent-shaped dunes, or *barchans,* appear to form where there is a limited amount of sand and a consistent direction of wind. Transverse dunes, resembling the wind-driven waves of the sea, are probably no more than crowded, merged barchans, forming in places where the sand supply is more copious. The long ridges, or *seifs,* though common, are more mysterious features, there being little agreement among authorities regarding their origin (Fig. 14.63).

Most dunes that are barren of vegetation, and especially those occurring in areas of fairly constant wind direction, are actively moving. High winds drift sand up their gentle windward slopes and over their crests, where the grains roll down or drop in the shelter of their steep leeward slopes. By this process the dune form is maintained while the whole feature slowly migrates (Fig. 13.27). Observed rates of movement vary from imperceptibly slow to as much as 50 to 100 ft. per year.

Where a dune is moving over a vegetation-covered surface, its movement is more or less strongly impeded. If vegetation is able to gain a foothold on the dune itself, movement may be stopped entirely. There are many regions of the world in which sand dunes have become fixed by the growth of a grass cover on them, in some instances undoubtedly reflecting a change of the climate in the direction of greater

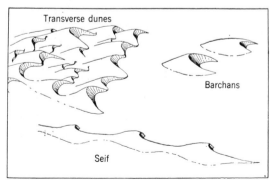

Fig. 14.63 Common types of sand dunes. In all the examples shown, the prevalent direction of strong winds is from left to right.

315

Fig. 14.64 An elongated depression between ridges in the grass-covered sand hills of Nebraska.

Fig. 14.65 A recent road cut through a loess hill in the prairie region of eastern Nebraska.

rainfall. This is true of a broad belt across western Africa along the southern margin of the Sahara. In north central Nebraska there is a large "sand-hill" region in which the sands are now anchored by a thick cover of grass. The sands were derived from the weathering of weak sandy-clay sediments which still make up the cores of some of the larger ridges. This vast area, once a sea of sand dunes, perhaps during the late glacial period, is now a favored region for the grazing of great herds of cattle (Fig. 14.64).

14.42 Loess Plains. The finer materials, largely silts, that are picked up by the wind from the dry lands, river beds, bare drift deposits, or other exposed surfaces are carried in suspension for great distances, and are spread broadcast over the countryside downwind from the source. Most of the extensive deposits of the silty material known as *loess* are thought to have been laid down in this way, with perhaps some small alteration by weathering having occurred following deposition.

Not all loess deposits are plains, for aeolian dust comes to rest upon hill and valley alike and is found in regions of great relief as well as upon smooth lands. The loess merely covers and perhaps increases the levelness of plains sculptured by whatever agents.

Loess has certain physical peculiarities that lead to the development of distinctive features under stream erosion and mass movement. The material is unstratified, highly porous, and characterized by fine vertical tubes which probably are related to the existence of former plant roots. Owing to its structure it has the property of standing in vertical faces when cut through by streams or roadways, even though it is so soft as to crumble to dust when pressed between the fingers (Fig. 14.65). Erosional slopes are characteristically steep, which gives to some loessial landscapes an unusually broken appearance. If the vegetation cover is thin, gullying is very likely to occur, leading to rapid and intricate dissection. Slumping mass movement on valley sides in deep loess often produces a steplike profile that is distinctive (Fig. 14.66).

There are in the world many extensive loess-covered plains, several of which are fertile and productive agricultural regions. Much of the

Fig. 14.66 An eroded and slumped hillside in deep loess in central Nebraska.

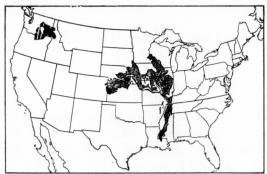

Fig. 14.67 The principal loess deposits of the United States. (*After C. F. Marbut, U.S. Department of Agriculture.*)

flat Pampa of Argentina, for example, is mantled with loess which was probably derived from the dry plains near the foot of the Andes to the west. A vast area of interior North China is thickly loess-covered, though this area can scarcely be called a plain. Here the loess is believed to have come from the arid plains to the westward, and was laid down over hilly topography. Deep erosion has further roughened the surface and has provided much of the sediment load of the appropriately named Hwang, or Yellow, River. This sediment has been redeposited to form much of the great delta plain of North China (14.21). In western Eurasia are other loess deposits extending over the plains in a long belt reaching from central Germany through south central Russia into the basins of central Asia.

Loess is an important surface deposit over a large area in interior United States (Fig. 14.67). There, as in Europe, the principal deposits are believed to have been derived from exposed fresh drift and from the braided floors of glacial drainageways during the wastage of Pleistocene ice sheets. These bare surfaces appear to have been subject to deflation for thousands of years under semiarid climatic conditions.

The deepest accumulations are found in southern and eastern Nebraska and the western margin of Iowa. There the loess in many places reaches a thickness of 60 to 100 ft. Much of the loess in south central Nebraska is believed to represent silty material winnowed out of the same weak sediments that gave rise to the sand hills (14.41). Other deep and extensive accumulations of loess cover much of eastern Iowa, adjacent parts of Wisconsin, central Illinois, and extend down the eastern bluffs of the Mississippi River. These generally are less deep than those of the Missouri River region, but locally they attain great thickness. Still another notable deposit occupies a part of the rolling plateau of eastern Washington and Oregon, where it buries the lava surface.

While most of these North American loessial areas would classify as plains, several, notably those in central Nebraska and in southeastern Washington, have been sufficiently dissected to form low hills (Fig. 14.66).

15

Tablelands, and Plains with Hills or Mountains

15.1 Plains with Some Features of High Relief. There are many extensive areas of land that, like plains, are occupied largely by slopes of gentle inclination, but that cannot rightly be called plains because of the existence of some relatively steep-sided features of high relief. Were it not for these exceptional or aberrant features the surfaces would be characteristic plains (11.7).

The "steep-sided features of high relief" that exclude these surfaces from the plains class may be of several sorts. They may be valleys or canyons that are incised deeply into the plain surface. They may be hills or mountains that rise sharply above the plain at broad intervals. Or they may take the form of escarpments that separate one plain at a high level from another at a lower level. The plains themselves may also vary, exhibiting any of the characteristic associations of features discussed in the preceding chapter.

All these varieties of terrain have in common two distinguishing characteristics: (*a*) most of their area is in gentle slope and (*b*) their local relief is moderate to high, that is, from several hundred feet to several thousand feet. However, the differences between plains cut by deep canyons and plains studded with hills or mountains are so fundamental that it is advantageous to consider the two types separately. Accordingly, the distinction is made between *tablelands,* in which the major portion of the gently sloping land is at relatively high level, with deep valleys or escarpments falling below, and *plains with hills or mountains,* in which the major portion of the gently sloping land lies at relatively low level, with steep-sided eminences rising above.

Tablelands

15.2 The Origin of Tablelands. In considering the origin of a two-part surface such as a tableland, attention must be given to the formation of each of the parts, in this instance: (*a*) the upland plain and (*b*) the valleys or escarpments. It is true that sometimes the two are developed at the same time. More frequently, however, the plain is formed first and is afterward subjected to the beginnings of dissection.

Most tablelands, then, represent nothing more than plains on which stream dissection has worked deeply, but in which tributary growth has not yet advanced beyond the early stages of the developmental sequence. The distinguishing profile of the tableland, with its broad upland and widely spaced valleys, is simply a high-relief version of the familiar profile of erosional youth. Tablelands develop under conditions that permit streams to cut more deeply than on youthfully dissected plains, while still largely preserving the upland against the inroads of tributary growth.

Deep downcutting can occur only if the plain surface has been brought many hundreds or even several thousands of feet above baselevel. Usually this implies a relatively late broad uplift of the area. A few examples exist in which the plain surface has been built up to high level by thick and extensive deposition of lava.

Fig. 15.1 The ragged edge of an escarpment that is being driven back by erosion. Painted Desert, northeastern Arizona. (*Spence Air Photos.*)

Preservation of the upland surface against tributary cutting, with such high reliefs, usually requires something more than mere shortness of time. Most commonly it may be related to one or both of two factors: (*a*) the existence of only a few streams of significant size, principally because of aridity, or (*b*) the existence of some sort of protective layer on the upland. In many dry regions local runoff is insufficient to give rise to a system of tributaries that are large and powerful enough to cut deep valleys. This restricts canyon cutting to those few exotic streams that enter the region from more humid sections round about. Between these widely spaced canyons the upland remains no more than shallowly etched by intermittent streams. Protection may be afforded to the upland plain by the existence of an underlying stratum of unusually resistant rock or, with almost equal effectiveness, by a thick cover of porous sand or gravel that absorbs rainfall and reduces surface runoff. In view of the importance of these factors, it is not surprising that tablelands are especially common in the drier parts of the world and in sections underlain by strong, nearly horizontal stratified rocks

or by porous deposits of older alluvium. The few exceptional cases that fit none of these qualifications must be accounted for chiefly by extreme recency and rapidity of uplift.

The escarpments that form the margins of some tablelands generally originate as fault scarps or as erosional features such as steep valley sides or as bluffs produced by differential erosion. These steep scarps will, under the attacks of weathering and erosion, be driven back from their original positions, often retaining much of their initial steepness. As they retreat, they continually encroach upon the upland surface, reducing its area and, if enough time is available, eventually obliterating it (Fig. 15.1).

15.3 The detailed features of tablelands, like those of plains, are largely the result of the recent operations of the various gradational agents. Strictly speaking, there are no types of landforms that occur only on tablelands. Rather, these surfaces are assemblages of the same sorts of features that have already been discussed in connection with plains or that will be encountered again in the chapter on hills and mountains. However, canyons and escarpments are of such especial significance to tablelands that they merit more detailed consideration here. So also do the various smaller features that are associated with the erosion of well-consolidated horizontal strata under arid or semiarid climatic conditions.

The existence of deep, narrow, steep-walled valleys or canyons is favored by the very factors that are responsible for tablelands in general. Relatively late uplift to a level well above grade means that at present many streams will still be deepening their valleys at a rapid rate. The factors, such as aridity or the existence of a protective cap, that favor preservation of the upland plain tend also to reduce the rate of valley widening and thus to maintain the steepness of the valley walls. Even so, canyons are rarely as narrow as they seem. The Grand Canyon of the Colorado is nearly ten times as wide (from rim to rim) as it is deep, and even the slitlike gorge of its tributary, the Little Colorado, is twice as wide as it is deep (Fig. 15.2).

The typical dry-plateau canyon is not a natural thoroughfare. Its narrow bottom offers little place for a roadway, and its stream, if any, seldom is navigable. Its course is likely to be steep, boulder strewn, and interrupted by rapids and falls. Moreover, it is subject to sudden and large changes in stream level. Its bottom is reached from the upland plain only by a steep climb down a precipitous valley wall or by the difficult route of a tributary canyon. It is too deep and too steep to be crossed easily and yet too wide to bridge economically. The deep dry-plateau canyon is more effective as a barrier to transportation than as a route of transportation.

Generally the faces of tableland escarpments are scarred by many ravines, their upland rims are etched into sharp promontories, and often these in turn are notched by gullies. Weathering attacks through joint planes, thus working behind and detaching portions of the rock mass. This gives to many escarpments fringed or crenate outlines of great intricacy of detail. In some kinds of rock the weathered features stand as colonnades or pyramids of complicated form (Fig. 15.3). Piles of *talus* (earth and rocks dislodged from above by the processes of weathering, which the forces of erosion are unable to remove as fast as they accumulate) lie in abundance against the bases of dry-land escarpments except in places so situated that they are swept at rather frequent intervals by the erosion of intermittent streams.

Canyon formation tends to separate and ultimately to isolate portions of the upland margin, and these become outliers. As the valleys are widened, the marginal blocks are

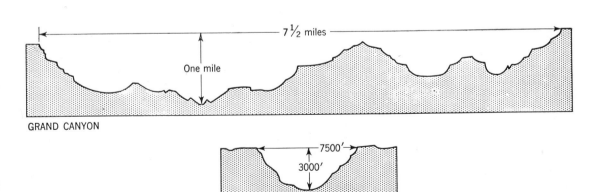

Fig. 15.2   Cross-section profiles of the Grand Canyon of the Colorado at Powell Memorial, and of the canyon of the Little Colorado about two miles above its mouth. Vertical and horizontal scales are the same. (*From U.S. Geological Survey topographic sheet: Grand Canyon National Park, East Half.*)

Fig. 15.3 Fantastic details resulting from the differential weathering and erosion of a dry-land escarpment in Bryce Canyon, Utah. The steep sides and flat top of the mesa in the middle distance are well shown. (*National Park Service, U.S. Department of the Interior.*)

reduced in area through erosional attack on all sides, but they retain their flat tops. In American dry lands, an upland of small to moderate size and tabular form (flat top and steep sides) is called a *mesa*. Features of the same origin but of smaller size often are called *buttes* (Fig. 15.4).

The upland plains may display any conceivable sort of configuration, depending upon the agencies that sculptured them, either before or after canyon cutting began. Some are typical stream-eroded or alluvial surfaces. Others, like the Colorado Plateaus, are separated by escarpments into several upland levels at different elevations. Some bear upon their surfaces irregularities caused by volcanic activity or faulting. Still others display the typical features associated with glacial deposition. Since many

Fig. 15.4 A small mesa (right) and several buttes in Monument Valley, Ariz. (*Courtesy of the American Museum of Natural History.*)

322

tablelands have developed on nearly horizontal rock strata under relatively dry climates, the features characteristic of erosional plains formed under such conditions are worthy of special mention. Generally it may be said that the features of such uplands are simply small-scale editions of the larger elements that make up the tablelands themselves. Narrow, steep-sided ravines, low escarpments and ledges maintained by single resistant strata, and small mesas all combine to give such uplands the appearance of being made up of miniatures of the more extensive tablelands of which they are a part.

In some tablelands erosion has almost completely destroyed the flat upland. Only small mesas, buttes, and pinnacled divides remain, separated by fantastically carved canyons and ravines. Surfaces of that kind merge without distinction into mountains or into hill country of the badland type.

15.4 Examples of Tablelands. There are in North America several extensive areas that fit the tableland designation and that illustrate various interesting modes of development.

The Great Plains region, lying immediately to the east of the Rocky Mountains, has been discussed previously as a former piedmont alluvial plain, built during earlier periods of strong tectonic activity and active erosion in the Rockies. Since then the plain has suffered general uplift, erosion in the mountains is less active, and the streams crossing the plain from the west have changed their regime from one of deposition to one of erosion. The southern part of the area, between the Rio Grande and the Platte Rivers, has been affected by valley cutting only at wide intervals and remains one of the flattest plains of the continental interior. But for reasons not well understood the section to the north of the Platte River, thus lying in the western Dakotas, in eastern Montana and Wyoming, and in Alberta and southern Saskatchewan, has been rather deeply incised by many streams and formed into a tableland of moderate relief. This section is sometimes called the *Missouri Plateau*. The cutting and widening of the valleys have been accomplished in several stages, so that erosional terraces and benches

are numerous and everywhere present. Perhaps 50 to 70 per cent of the area is occupied by gentle slopes. In a few sections, notably along the White, Cheyenne, and Little Missouri Rivers in the western Dakotas, intricate gullying of the weak sandy clays has produced fantastically rugged badland terrain which extends along the sides of the major valleys as belts of "river breaks" several miles wide. The Canadian section of the tableland and a narrow fringe south of the international boundary shows, by the existence of lakes and morainic features, the effects of thick glacial deposition.

In eastern Washington and Oregon and southern Idaho is a vast area, as large as New York, New Jersey, and Pennsylvania combined, that is underlain by black basaltic lavas. These occur in flows of variable thickness superimposed one upon the other (Fig. 15.5). The total depth ranges from a few hundred feet to nearly a mile, generally sufficient to have buried all but a few peaks of the mountain-and-basin surface that existed beforehand. In this way an upland plain was produced, not by uplift, but by construction.

The basalt area as a whole is usually called the *Columbia Plateau*, but only a few sections of it have the form of tablelands. Since the plain was formed, parts of it have been warped, folded, and carved into low mountains. The rest remains as a plain upon which canyon cutting has made only limited headway. The aridity of the climate and the porosity of the lava afford little local runoff. Nearly all dissection is accomplished by exotic streams. In southeastern Oregon no large streams exist, and the surface is still an almost undissected plain. In southern Idaho a single exotic river, the Snake, has cut a deep canyon across the wide basalt fill. Only in eastern Washington and the northern margin of eastern Oregon has enough dissection occurred to produce a typical tableland. The Columbia River, the Snake River, and several of their tributaries are responsible for the largest canyons. But in east central Washington are many smaller channels, now abandoned, that were cut by melt-water streams during the late Pleistocene period, when the

Fig. 15.5 An exposure of the Columbia Plateau basalts in a canyon wall, showing beds that result from successive lava flows. The base of the wall is flanked by talus slopes. (*U.S. Geological Survey photograph.*)

edge of the continental ice sheet lay along the immediate northern edge of the basalt plain. The largest abandoned channel, called the Grand Coulee, was cut by the Columbia River itself at a time when its present course around the west edge of the plateau was blocked by the encroaching ice. It is through this old drainage-way that water pumped from the Columbia is now being conducted to reach irrigable lands in the central part of the state.

The *Colorado Plateaus,* on either side of the Colorado River in Utah, Arizona, Colorado, and New Mexico, offer an example of a table-land formed by canyon cutting in an uplifted erosional plain. In this vast region, which is equal in area to the combined areas of Ohio, Indiana, and Illinois, sedimentary strata which total several thousands of feet in thickness lie in nearly horizontal position upon a foundation of crystalline rocks. In some places the sediments are faulted, slightly arched, or covered

with recent volcanic products, but the principal surface features result from the erosion of nearly horizontal strata.

The bulk of the canyon cutting in this arid region has been performed by the exotic Colorado River and its larger tributaries, most of which, like the Colorado, rise in the more humid mountains to the north and east. The Grand Canyon of the Colorado River in Arizona is the most magnificent of its kind. It is the work of a silt-laden, mountain-fed stream of high gradient. The stream crosses high arid plateaus from which it receives but few permanent tributaries. In one part of its valley it has cut through more than 4,000 ft. of nearly horizontal sedimentary strata and more than 1,000 ft. into crystalline rocks beneath. The erosion of the latter has produced a narrow inner gorge, above which the walls rise in a series of giant steps which are etched by under-cutting in the unequally resistant sediments. The exposed edges of the more resistant sedimentary strata form the sheer rises and some of the benches. Those of the less resistant strata form the intervening slopes (Fig. 15.6). The intricate forms of the walls, which hold most of the scenic grandeur, result from arid-land weathering and erosion on a large scale along both joint and bedding planes.

In North America as elsewhere in the world, there are few tablelands in the humid sections. The best-developed examples in this country are certain limited sections of the western Appalachians, especially the Cumberland Plateau, in eastern Kentucky and Tennessee, and several smaller areas in northern Pennsylvania. In both of these localities preservation of the upland surface is favored by a thick and resistant cap-rock layer.

Considering the world as a whole, extensive tablelands are not especially numerous, compared with other types of terrain. Several are broad enough to warrant special mention. In South America, much of the upland of interior Brazil is occupied by tablelands developed on the sandstone and lava sheets that provide a covering for the interior parts of the crystalline shield. Youthful dissection is provided by the major tributaries of the Amazon and Paraná Rivers. In southern Argentina the old piedmont plains to the east of the Andes have been uplifted and dissected in much the same manner as the Missouri Plateau, producing a surface known as the Patagonian Plateau. Many of the valleys were cut by melt-water streams pouring out of Andean glaciers during the ice ages, and are not now occupied by streams.

It is customary to refer to Africa as a plateau of continental size, because its margins are abrupt and much of the interior is a relatively subdued upland. However, only a few parts of the continent are actually characterized by terrain that would fit the definition of a tableland. Most of the upland of Africa is occupied by broad plains, hilly country, or plains studded with groups of hills and mountains. The most extensive tablelands are found in the central

Fig. 15.6 The Grand Canyon of the Colorado River in Arizona. The narrow inner gorge is cut in crystalline rock; the steps and benches above in nearly horizontal sedimentary strata. Resistant layers form the cliffs, weak strata the gentler slopes.

and northern Sahara, where erosion of gently warped sedimentary strata has produced a landscape somewhat like that of the Colorado Plateaus, but with lower elevation and much less deep canyon cutting (Plate 3).

Plains with Hills or Mountains

15.5 The Origin of Plains with Hills or Mountains. The second class of terrain belonging under the heading of "plains with some features of high relief" is, like the first, a two-part surface. As with tablelands the major part of such an area is a plain, while the remainder is occupied by relatively steep-sided features of considerable height. But unlike tablelands, the plain in this terrain type forms a floor, above which rise, at wide intervals, the hill or mountain features that provide most of the relief.

As before, the existence of moderate to high relief requires that at least some portions of the surface must have been carried tectonically well above the surroundings or well above base-level. The existence of broad plains, on the other hand, requires the strong action of gradational agents. There are at least two fundamentally different sequences of events that combine those two aspects of development in such a way as to produce plains surmounted by hills or mountains. The *first* involves the erosional reduction of a mountainous area to early old age, leaving only a few remnants standing upon an erosional plain. The *second* starts with a plain and then roughens it at intervals by diastrophism or vulcanism. There are in the world examples of both.

15.6 Erosional Plains with Remnant Hills. Long-continued gradation in a mountainous or hilly region produces a gradual widening of all valleys and a narrowing and lowering of the divides between them. Eventually, in what may be termed early old age, valleys have so broadened and merged as to form a low-level plain of irregular outline. There still remain, however, significant numbers of steep-sided though narrow divides, small ranges, and isolated hills

or hill groups to give to the area irregularity and a considerable relief.

Extensive areas of mountain-studded plains of this origin do not occur in North America, but there are several small examples of the type. On the inner section of the Appalachian Piedmont in Virginia and the Carolinas, and again on both the northern and southern fringes of New England, are areas of rolling plains surmounted by sizable monadnocks and hill groups. Both regions have had complex gradational histories, but the major features of the terrain owe their existence to long-continued erosion of mountainous surfaces (Fig. 15.7).

Terrain of generally similar character and origin is better and more extensively developed in other parts of the world. Much of the Guiana region of northeastern South America, for example, is a broad erosional plain developed on crystalline rocks and surmounted by numerous ranges and groups of low mountains. In the western part of the area bits of a once extensive cover of quartzitic sandstone remain atop some of the larger remnants, giving them the form of huge and spectacular mesas. On the crystalline upland of eastern Brazil are large areas of terrain somewhat like eastern Guiana, but at higher elevation (Plate 3).

The crystalline uplands of central and western Africa, which are similar both in structure and developmental history to those of eastern South America, also exhibit large areas of hill-studded erosional plains. In many sections erosion has proceeded so far as to leave only a few small hills that jut from the almost featureless plains like islands from the sea.

In eastern Sweden and northern Finland the crystalline shield was apparently similarly reduced to early old age, but has more recently been given a highly distinctive character by strong and repeated glacial scour.

15.7 Plains Roughened by Tectonic Disturbance. A plain of any sort may be converted into a plain with hills or mountains through the formation of widely spaced peaks or ranges by any of various kinds of tectonic disturbances. Scattered volcanic cones may be built up from the plain; or anticlinal folds, horsts, or tilted fault blocks may be thrust up at wide intervals to break the general smoothness. Like all tectonically produced irregularities, these features are assailed by erosion as soon as they begin to appear, so that by the time they reach their full height they are often so modified by gradation that their structure is no longer clearly revealed by their outward form.

One of the world's more extensive plain-and-mountain areas is the Basin and Range region, which occupies much of the southwestern United States and nearly all of northern Mexico. From southern Oregon to Mexico City this landscape of dry plains and rather small but rugged mountain ranges extends without a break and with only a moderate degree of in-ternal variation. Most of the ranges are believed to have originated as raised and tilted fault blocks. Some of these, especially near the northwestern corner of the region, are fairly fresh and undissected. Most, however, are strongly eroded and reduced in size, much of the debris of their destruction having been deposited on the plains between them (Fig. 15.8). Some show evidence of more than one major period of tectonic disturbance. A few volcanic mountains exist, but only at the southern end of the region, in central Mexico, do they become numerous. In that section, however, there are hundreds of cones, ranging from cinder hillocks to the majestic and snow-capped Popocatepetl.

Many of the plains between the ranges in the Basin and Range area are basins of interior

Fig. 15.7 Near the western edge of the Appalachian Piedmont, numerous small monadnocks remain standing upon an erosional plain developed on crystalline rocks. Big Cobbler Mountain, in northern Virginia. (*Photograph by John L. Rich, courtesy of the Geographical Review, published by the American Geographical Society of New York.*)

Fig. 15.8 Deeply eroded ranges alternate with smooth basin floors in the Mojave Desert of southeastern California. Note the great alluvial fan in the foreground. (*Spence Air Photos.*)

drainage, partly filled with alluvium and occupied in large part by the gentle slopes of pediments and alluvial fans. Even those that have exterior drainage are much the same, lacking only the playa lakes or alkali flats that are characteristic of the enclosed basins. Some of the basins, like the famous Death Valley in southeastern California, are actually down-faulted blocks or grabens. Others may have suffered relatively little disturbance. Nearly all have been smoothed and widened by erosion about their margins and by deposition on their floors. It cannot now be determined how smooth a plain there was before the fault blocks were formed.

Elsewhere in the world are many other extensive areas similar in surface form and in general mode of origin to the North American Basin and Range region. The chief differences among them lie in the scale of the features, the precise structure or origin of the ranges, and the degree of erosional destruction of the ranges. In northwestern Argentina, for example, the ranges are unusually large and widely spaced. In the high Altiplano, on the crest of the central Andes in Peru and Bolivia, and in the highland of Tibet, the basin floors themselves lie at elevations of from 10,000 to 16,000 ft. above sea level, with the summits of the ranges often exceeding 20,000 ft.

Much of the great cordilleran belt of south-ern Eurasia is mountain and plain rather than unbroken mountains (Plate 3). Large parts of Spain, Turkey, Iran, Afghanistan, western Pakistan, Tibet, Mongolia, and innermost China bear a fundamental similarity to our own Southwest. The features, however, are often on a grander scale, and there is much variation and complexity in the structure of the mountains. Northwestern Africa, extreme southern Africa, and west central Australia also furnish broad expanses of plains roughened by tectonic disturbance.

15.8 Lakes in Dry Basins. Many of the basin plains in the areas mentioned above contain notable salt lakes. Such are Sevier Lake and Great Salt Lake, Utah; Mono Lake, California; Tengri Nor, Koko Nor, and others, in the basins of Central Asia; the lakes of Iran; and Lake Poopó, Bolivia. Not all lakes of dryland basins are salt. Some of those at higher elevations overflow into lower basins and are kept fresh thereby. That is true of Lake Titicaca, Bolivia, which overflows into Lake Poopó, and of Utah Lake, which overflows into Great Salt Lake.

There is abundant evidence to show that some of the present salt lakes are only the dwindled remnants of once greater lakes, some of them fresh-water lakes. Great Salt Lake, for example, was so much larger and higher during glacial times that it overflowed the rim of its basin and discharged northward into the Snake River and so to the Pacific Ocean via the Columbia. It was then a great fresh-water lake. When the water supply from shrinking mountain glaciers decreased, the level of the lake began to lower, owing to the excess of evaporation over inflow. Presently it had no outlet, and its salt content began to increase. Abandoned shore terraces and broad salt flats now mark various levels at which the dwindling lake stood at certain stages during the long process of reduction to its present small size and salt saturation.

Many basins have not enough water to maintain permanent lakes, but contain salt marshes. Examples are seen in the "pans" of South Africa, the Tsaidam Swamp of Central Asia, the Salar de Uyuní of Bolivia, and the Humboldt Salt Marsh of Nevada.

16

Hills and Mountains

16.1 Hills and Mountains Distinguished. In common use, the words "hill" and "mountain" are applied loosely and with little discrimination to landforms of many sorts and sizes. Generally both terms imply predominantly steep slopes and considerable vertical development, and a "mountain" is usually a higher and bigger feature than a "hill" in the same area. But the Black Hills, in South Dakota, and the Khasi Hills, in northeastern India, are many times larger and higher than Rib Mountain, in central Wisconsin, or Stone Mountain, near Atlanta, Ga. Much depends on what is available near at hand for comparison.

For purposes of the present study it will be worthwhile to be more restrictive and consistent in the use of the words. Both terms will be applied to lands that are distinguished by having little of their area in gentle slope. Those that possess low or moderate relief (generally expressible in hundreds of feet) will be designated as hills; those having high relief (generally expressible in thousands of feet) will be called mountains. Hill lands thus differ from plains by having a greater prevalence of at least fairly steep slopes and in some instances, higher relief. In the same manner hills and mountains may both be distinguished from plains with hills or mountains and from tablelands by the absence or insignificance of upland or lowland plains.

Although steep slopes are among the distinguishing features of hills and mountains, few of them are in fact so steep as popular belief would make them. The average slope of most great mountains probably does not exceed an angle of 20 or 25° from horizontal. A few exceed 35°, especially near their summits, where erosion proceeds rapidly along joint planes. The fact that mountain slopes commonly are made up, stairlike, of gentle inclines separated by abrupt rises or sheer cliffs has led to a popular exaggeration of the extent of the latter. Seldom is the sheer or overhanging mountain precipice more than a few score feet in height. The great and seemingly vertical walls hundreds of feet high found in some mountains are not vertical. In fact, they seldom exceed angles of 70° and are capable of ascent, at least by the animals whose habitat they are.

The local relief of mountains in places reaches extremes of 10,000 to 15,000 ft., but such high figures are relatively rare. In the United States, even the higher mountains of the West seldom exhibit relief in excess of 5,000 ft., figures of 2,000 to 4,000 ft. being more nearly the rule.

Several terms commonly applied to hill and mountain country should be introduced at this point, since they will be needed in the subsequent discussion. A *range* of hills or mountains is an elongated arrangement of many peaks, ridges, and their included valleys (Fig. 16.1). Ordinarily a range displays a general unity of form, structure, and geologic age. The term *group* is sometimes used to describe an array of peaks and ridges of rangelike size but nearly circular, nodal, or massive in outline (Fig. 16.2).

Several associated ranges or groups are referred to as a *mountain system* if they have some linkage of position, form, or structure but are separated by trenches or basins. The

Fig. 16.1 The crest line of a linear mountain range in Colorado, showing some of its peaks, saddles, and lateral ridges or spurs. The crest is part of the Continental Divide.

Rocky Mountain system is an example. The term *cordillera,* although it originally meant an extended range or chain, has come to be applied to a very extensive belt of mountain systems.

16.2 Significance of Rough Terrain. Several of the distinguishing features of hills and mountains conspire to make them the least habitable of the major groups of landforms. Narrow valleys and the large proportion of land in slope limit the area of tillable land to a small part of the total. Steep slopes often are stripped of their regolith, and where soil is present it is in constant danger of destructive erosion if disturbed by the plow. Forests and grass serve to utilize the soil on slopes and to aid in its

Fig. 16.2 Abajo Mountains, a mountain group in eastern Utah. This dissected laccolith is about 6 mi. in diameter and rises nearly 4,000 ft. above the upland of the Colorado Plateaus. (*W. Cross, U.S. Geological Survey.*)

retention. They are, therefore, among the most important resources of the rough lands.

The conditions of mountain origin that give rise to complexity of rock structure commonly give rise also to mineral ores, and these may be added to the list of rough-land resources having potential value for human use. So also may the potential water powers created by abundant precipitation and high stream gradients. Moreover, hills and mountains adjacent to great centers of population on plains have large actual or potential use as playgrounds. A considerable part of the population of the Alps and some other mountains subsists upon income derived from those who come to view mountain scenery or to enjoy mountain climate or mountain sports.

Steep gradients, narrow and tortuous valleys, and high divides are among the numerous factors that tend to make hill and mountain belts barriers to travel and transport. However, there is much variation in this regard. Some mountains may be easily traversed by way of valleys that cut completely through them. The Columbia River gorge through the Cascade Range and the Hudson Valley through the New England–Appalachian highland are examples of such passageways that have become important routes of trade. Other mountainous areas have relatively low gaps in the divide that may be approached by gentle-gradient routes from either side, thus affording less extreme difficulty than the general ruggedness or summit elevations might suggest. The Alps and the northern Rocky Mountains offer several such pass routes. There are some ranges, however, that have such continuously high crests and such steep and difficult approaches as to provide maximum difficulty for crossing. The southern Sierra Nevada in California, the central Andes, and the tremendous wall of the Himalayas are examples of this type.

16.3 The Origin of Hills and Mountains. The two distinguishing characteristics of mountains, high relief and steep slopes, are both attributable, either directly or indirectly, to strong uplift in relatively recent geologic time. Only through uplift that carries at least parts

of the area far above baselevel, or above the surrounding areas, can high relief be realized. And steep slopes, in turn, most commonly stem from the work of streams that are cutting very rapidly downward toward grade, which usually means that they have started well above that goal.

The same factors are important to the development of the hill lands of moderate relief, the difference being chiefly one of degree. As suggested in Chap. 14, hills of *low* relief usually represent plains in a mature stage of dissection, under conditions especially favorable to the development of steep slopes. Easily gullied materials insufficiently protected by vegetation would provide one such favorable circumstance, while a combination of copious runoff and resistant rocks would also serve.

In practically all rough-land areas that have been studied, there is abundant evidence that uplift has occurred not merely once, but repeatedly during the course of late geologic history. Each time, erosion has carved the uplifted mass into hills or mountains and has then continued until these features were greatly reduced or completely erased. The last uplift has in each case occurred so recently that time has not permitted the destruction of the rough-land features that developed as a result of it. Since it appears likely that even a great mountain range can be virtually destroyed in a few tens of millions of years, the events that have brought the present generations of mountains or hills into being must in all instances have occurred within the last few million years. Some rough lands are known to have suffered uplift during or just preceding the ice ages, and some are still being raised.

As an illustration of these principles, the ranges of the Rocky Mountains of Wyoming and Colorado represent probably the third generation of mountains that has existed on those sites. The first generation came into being somewhat more than 70 million years ago. These mountains were largely destroyed by erosion, but renewed uplift brought a second generation into being, and these too were attacked by the gradational agents. Remnants of the erosion surface produced during the reduction of the second generation of mountains can still be seen as relatively smooth upland areas on the interfluve crests. Many of the highest peaks of today represent remnants of that second generation that were still standing when the last uplift occurred. Features of these same general sorts can be found in most of the world's mountainous or hilly areas.

16.4 The Great Cordilleran Belts. Most of the mountains of the earth, and many areas of hill country as well, are found in a few broad and long cordilleran belts. Each continent contains at least a part of one of these complex arrays of mountain systems, though the apportionment among the continents is very unequal. A glance at Fig. 16.3 will reveal that all of the cordilleran belts are in fact connected, forming a nearly complete ring around the Pacific Ocean, and extending westward across southern Eurasia.

Plate 3 shows that the cordilleran belts vary greatly from section to section in breadth, height, and complexity. In the western United States, northern Mexico, and Alaska the North American cordillera is conspicuously wide and "frayed out," with many plains and tablelands interspersed among the loosely linked ranges. In Canada and in Central America, however, the belt narrows down markedly, and is less broken, though generally no higher. The Andean Cordillera of South America, by contrast, is noteworthy for its narrowness, its continuity, and its height. From northern Peru to central Chile the elevation of the crest line does not fall below 10,000 ft., and even outside this section, the belt is rugged and high, with few low passes.

The Eurasian cordillera in its western half is somewhat similar to that of western North America. Loosely arrayed systems and ranges are separated by wide valleys and basins, certain of those in Europe being at very low elevation (*e.g.,* the Po Valley of northern Italy and the Hungarian Plain). There are several gaps affording easy passage across the belt, notably the Rhône Valley of southern France and the straits of the Dardanelles and Bosporus that

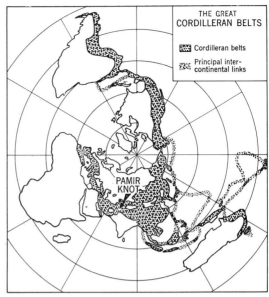

Fig. 16.3 The great cordilleran belts of the world are all interconnected. They may be considered as three great arms radiating from the "Pamir Knot," two of them embracing the Pacific basin, the third reaching westward across southern Europe.

lead from the Mediterranean into the Black Sea. In the Pamir region, to the northwest of India, however, the ranges come together in a tight and high "knot," from which they then fan out eastward to cover practically the entire eastern part of the continent and even the great island systems offshore. This is the broadest and most complex cordilleran section anywhere on the earth. From this tangle of ranges streamers extend northeastward across the Bering Strait and the Aleutian Islands into Alaska to connect with the North American belt. To the southeastward other lines follow through the East Indies into the mountain systems of Australia and New Zealand.

Africa, strictly speaking, does not have a cordillera of its own. A few strands of the Eurasian belt cross the Mediterranean to form the Atlas system in the extreme northwest. With that exception, however, Africa's mountains are scattered and discontinuous. The area most resembling a cordillera is the great faulted rift-valley zone that extends from north to south along the eastern side of the continent, but neither in structure nor in surface form is this belt comparable to the other cordilleras of the world.

Comparison of the pattern of the cordilleran belts with the zones of greatest tectonic activity (Plate 3 and Fig. 12.9) reveals a high degree of correspondence. This is hardly surprising, in view of the fact that mountains must have undergone late uplift in order to exist at all at the present time. Studies of the geological structure within the cordilleran areas indicate that these are zones in which there has been repeated active folding and faulting during the Cenozoic era (approximately the last 70 million years; see Appendix E). They may be considered as bands of the crust which have been laterally compressed, or jammed together, producing a complex pattern of wrinkling, buckling, and shortening of the crust. The forms, patterns, and structures of individual ranges and systems within the cordilleran belt display an extreme range of variety.

Outside of the major cordilleran belts are other areas of mountains and hills, few of which achieve the height or ruggedness of the larger cordilleran ranges. Many of these systems, such as the Appalachians of the eastern United States, the highlands of Scandinavia and the British Isles, and the Urals of the north central U.S.S.R., were originally folded at a much earlier time than most of the cordilleran mountains. Repeated uplifts have continually renewed them, but as a rule the uplifts have grown successively weaker, so that the present generation of rough lands is commonly not especially impressive.

16.5 Stream-eroded Features of Rough Lands. Few hill or mountain regions derive many of their features directly from faulting, folding, or volcanic activity. Instead, they acquire them as a result of weathering and erosion of highlands of various origins and structures. The minor relief features are nearly all of erosional origin, and they are of different forms because of differences in rock structure, climatic condition, and stage of erosional development, the same conditions referred to so often in other connections. Some of the more important of the erosional characteristics, including the depths and shapes of the valleys, the patterns of the minor ridges and spurs, the prevalent slope angles, and the heights and forms of the summits, may be considered at greater length.

16.6 *Valleys and Slopes*. Rough-land streams usually have the steep gradients of youth. A few have not. The latter are the occasional major streams that have reached grade, or those minor streams the erosional progress of which is held up by a temporary baselevel. Such streams flow in open, flaring valleys or meander on flat alluvial floors. In most, however, rapid downward cutting discovers rocks of unequal hardness and develops falls and rapids as well as the V-shaped transverse profile of youth (Fig. 16.4). With recent cutting in resistant rock the V is narrow and the valley a gorge or canyon, but more commonly it is broadly open. The Royal Gorge and several other canyons cut into the Front Range of the Rocky Mountains are examples of stream-eroded valleys of the narrow and steep-sided type. Such a narrows, or gorge, is sometimes utilized as a site for the economical construction of a dam to impound water in a reservoir which will lie in the more open upper part of the valley.

Rough lands of ideally mature dissection are simply a succession of narrow ridges and V-shaped valleys in which level land may occupy less than 5 per cent of the total area (Fig. 16.5). Others, however, have not yet reached full maturity and still retain parts of an old

Fig. 16.4 Overlapping spurs in the narrow Rimac Valley in the Andes of Peru. The steepened lower slopes indicate a renewed vigor of stream erosion. (*Courtesy of Economic Geography and Preston E. James.*)

upland surface in the form of broadly rounded or flat-topped interfluves which are separated by narrow and steep-sided valleys. Still other regions have been so long subjected to erosion that they are past the extreme irregularity of maturity. Such a region may retain only remnants of its former high interfluves in the form of subdued hills of small summit area, among which open rolling valleys and basins are interspersed.

Unless strong control is present in the form of a systematic arrangement of weak and resistant rock outcrops or some unusual pattern of initial slopes, valleys and ridges develop with no clearly systematic arrangement. On broad areas of essentially homogeneous rocks or on horizontally stratified rocks, the valleys usually assume the familiar dendritic pattern. However, because complexities of rock structure and initial slopes are so common in hill and mountain belts, departures from the random branching arrangement are more frequently encountered here than they are in plains. Some of these peculiarities will be discussed later (16.10).

Because of the prevalent steepness of valley sides in hill and mountain lands, both rapid surface erosion and the swifter forms of mass movement are especially likely to occur. Thinning or clearing of the natural vegetation cover enhances the amount, velocity, and erosional effectiveness of surface runoff, often leading to severe washing and gullying on the slopes and to flooding and deposition of debris on the valley floors. Landslides and, in the winter, avalanches of ice and snow constitute a particular hazard to habitation or travel in these rough lands. Hillside soils are characteristically thin and stony.

Mechanical weathering is especially rapid on the exposed upper slopes of deep mountain valleys. Blocks of rock, dislodged by frost, fall below. There they accumulate as talus slopes, the upper parts of which commonly include coarse newly fallen blocks piled more steeply than the older and more weathered rock beneath (Fig. 15.5). At the mouths of steep ravines on the valley walls the talus piles are particularly large and tend there to be cone shaped.

Fig. 16.5 An aerial view in the Allegheny hill region of West Virginia shows it to be a stream-dissected upland with a dendritic valley pattern. (*Photograph by John L. Rich. Courtesy of the Geographical Review, published by the American Geographical Society of New York.*)

Such piles are called alluvial cones or *gravity cones,* and they are like the upper ends of steep alluvial fans, into which they merge without sharp distinction.

It has been noted previously that mature dissection of uplands in poorly consolidated sediments may produce very rough surfaces. Some of that nature have a high degree of local relief and, under subhumid climate, have been eroded into astonishingly complicated hill forms and patterns. It was the bewildering maze of sharp hills and dry ravines that led the French fur traders to call those of the Great Plains, near the Black Hills, *mauvaises terres pour traverser* (literally "bad lands to cross"), from which has been derived the term *badlands,* now applied generally to terrain of this sort. They are eroded in thick beds of sandy clay, and in large part are but deeply and minutely dissected plains (Fig. 16.6). Still other badlands

Fig. 16.6 The features of badlands in western North Dakota. (*U.S. Geological Survey photograph.*)

are found in certain easily eroded rock formations in the dry southwestern plateaus and mountain borders. However, extremely rapid dissection in almost any uniform material will produce similar features. Badland forms eroded in crystalline metamorphic rock of uniform texture are known in the treeless highlands of dry northern China.

16.7 *Crests, Peaks, and Spurs.* Between rough-land valleys are the interfluves, persisting remnants of the original highlands. Their varied forms hold much of the attractiveness of mountain scenery. The forms and patterns of some crest lines are the result of faulting or folding, and many peaks are volcanic cones superimposed upon pre-existing uplands. By far the greater number of the countless peaks and ridges of the earth, however, are the result of differential erosion in the uplands of which they are a part. Owing to superior resistance, to condition of structure, to accident of position, or to other causes, they have been preserved from erosion while adjacent rocks have been reduced to lower levels. Of a whole tectonic uplift the serrate crest line of a rugged mountain range, therefore, may mark only a narrow remnant, into which deep notches already have been cut. Indeed, it is the notches that dis-

tinguish the peaks. Each notch marks the erosional progress of a valley or gulch which, through headward erosion, is gnawing at the backbone of the range. Some notches result from the headward approach of two valleys, one on either side of the range, toward the same part of its crest (Fig. 16.7).

Spurs are the lateral projections of an upland mass into the flanks of which tributary valleys are etched. In a youthful stage of erosion the spurs are likely to be steep, and as they approach the irregular course of the main stream from opposing uplands, they may even overlap, obscuring the view up or down the valley and complicating the problems of transportation (Fig. 16.4). Spurs with their alternating valley heads create complicated patterns of relief, and some rough lands are so difficult of access that they are areas of extreme isolation.

Rainfall on the crests separates according to the surface slopes and descends by countless rivulets into adjacent valleys, modeling the upland as it goes. The crests are, therefore, properly called "water partings," or *divides*. The minor spurs, or extensions, of the upland serve merely as divides between small tributaries of the same stream. Crests in more strategic locations may part the waters of great river systems, and some separate the drainage destined for opposite sides of a continent. The latter are called *continental divides*.

On some mountain uplands the divide is a conspicuous feature. Rock structure and the process of erosion combine to produce a bold and narrow ridge upon which the water parting is a sinuous line almost as sharply defined as the ridge of a house roof. On others the divide is not so well defined, since the uplands were originally extensive plateaus. Mature dissection by streams and their numerous perennial tributaries has destroyed the upland surface and reduced the whole to a maze of hills and valleys not characterized by a definite crest.

16.8 The Effects of Structure. As in other classes of terrain, the pattern and nature of the original tectonic activity and the attitudes and patterns of outcrops of resistant and weak rocks often have profound effects upon the form of the surface. Because of the magnitude and complexity of the tectonic disturbances involved, the structures of hill and mountain lands are often especially large and diverse and their reflection in the surface forms striking and far-reaching. Structural effects are especially noticeable in the detailed forms of slopes and in the patterns of ridges and valleys.

The rock structure produced during the formation of one generation of mountains remains, at least in part, even after that generation is destroyed by erosion. Re-uplift of the area will be followed by renewed erosion that will carve new hills or mountains out of the stumps of these old structures. Thus in the Appalachian area folded structures produced during the original mountain making, perhaps 250 million years ago, are still exercising a profound control upon the erosional development of ridges and valleys, even though the later tectonic events

Fig. 16.7 Brown Pass, a saddle-shaped notch in Glacier National Park, Montana. The white arrow point touches the crest of the pass, which crosses the Continental Divide. Note talus slopes at foot of cliffs at right. (*National Park Service, U.S. Department of the Interior*).

have been no more than small general uplifts, without a renewal of folding.

16.9 *Details of Slope and Crest.* The relatively rapid erosion of steep slopes tends to expose rocks of unequal resistance and to produce angular and sharply defined contours. The tendency is less evident in hills than in high mountains and in warm, humid climates than in those that are prevailingly cold or dry. However, in most mountain valleys the slope, as viewed from a distance, is interrupted by steep bluffs where resistant formations outcrop and by more gently inclined benches or terraces where the rocks weather more readily. Benches of that origin make possible the agricultural use of some valley sides, the average slopes of which would render the tillage of the soil impossible.

Owing to the alternation of resistant and nonresistant rock strata, some hillsides consist of sheer rises of a few feet separated by benches or gentle slopes (Fig. 16.7). Strong capping strata may protect weaker rocks beneath and erode into tabular mesa-like hills, even in humid climates. However, because of more rapid weathering and more active soil creep and slumping, the benches and rises developed in humid areas are less pronounced in appearance and less sharp in outline than those of arid lands.

Strong development of jointing in massive rocks can have as marked an effect upon detailed forms as does stratification. The exposed faces of gorge walls and of rocky crags and peaks often follow such joint planes very closely (Fig. 12.2).

16.10 *Form and Pattern of Major Features.* In most hill or mountain regions of complicated structure, differential weathering and erosion in unlike rocks are the cause of the principal features of relief. In some it is the structural features, such as extensive faults, which dominate the scene.

Some great mountain ranges, and many smaller ones, appear to have been formed principally by faulting. The 400-mile-long range of the Sierra Nevada of California is carved by streams and glaciers in the scarp and upland of a tilted fault block. The escarpment of the block, in places more than 8,000 ft. high, faces eastward and the upland inclines less steeply westward (Fig. 12.5). The bold west-facing front of the Wasatch Mountains in Utah is likewise the result of displacement along a fault zone, the gentler slopes being generally toward the east.

Many mountain systems which were originally folded and faulted by lateral compression are characterized by more or less parallel ranges. In some mountains of this type, the ridges may be raised blocks or anticlines and the valleys synclines or grabens, all somewhat modified by erosion. The parallel ranges and "trenches" of the Rocky Mountains in the United States–Canada boundary zone and the roughly parallel California Coast Ranges may owe their origin in considerable part to such structural factors.

More commonly, however, the linear pattern of ridges and valleys results from the differential erosion of elongated folds in rocks of unequal resistance to erosion. The original anticlines, synclines, and fault blocks may long since have been smoothed off by gradation, but the structure still remains. Renewed uplift permits deep differential erosion to occur, and in time the upturned edges, or bands of outcrop, of the more resistant rocks come to stand in relief as mountain ridges, while the weaker materials are excavated to form the valleys. If the patterns of outcrop are regular and the contrasts in resistance especially strong, the pattern of parallel ridges may be remarkably clear. Among the notable areas of that kind of surface configuration are the Appalachian ridge-and-valley region, which extends from northeastern Pennsylvania southward to Alabama; the Ouachita Mountains of Arkansas; and the Jura Mountains on the French-Swiss border (16.18).

In more irregular fashion, alternating masses of resistant and nonresistant crystalline rocks give rise to areas of interspersed hills and basins. Extensive fault scarps themselves produce ridges which are dissected by streams into hills, or their fault zones develop linear areas of weakness which streams find and degrade into valleys.

Many large ranges, exemplified by the Black Hills of South Dakota and the ranges of the Wyoming and Colorado Rockies, are immense anticlines or elongated domes. Deep erosion has exposed igneous and metamorphic rocks in the cores of the uplifts, the original sedimentary cover having been stripped away. These interior sections display little system in the form or arrangement of ridges and valleys. Around the margins, however, are linear foothills which mark the outcrops of the upturned sedimentary strata that still remain there. Along the eastern front of the Rocky Mountains in Colorado, for example, sedimentary rocks, bent upward by the mountain-building process, have been eroded into sharp cuestaform ridges and valleys which parallel the mountain front for many miles. Their escarpment slopes face toward the mountains, and their almost equally steep dip slopes incline toward the bordering plains (Fig. 16.8). Linear ridges of that type, wherever they occur, are called *hogback ridges*. Prominent hogbacks completely encircle the dome of the Black Hills.

Mountain masses that are of volcanic or laccolithic origin commonly have compact rather than linear forms, and a few are roughly circular in outline (Fig. 16.2). The eroded ridges and valleys of some of them have radial patterns or some modification of the radial arrangement. The Henry Mountains of Utah, and other smaller groups in the region, are examples of laccolithic mountains. The sediments, updomed by igneous intrusions, now are eroded away from the uplands and appear only as encircling cuestaform ridges. The San Juan Mountains of Colorado are the eroded remnants of a high upland composed of lavas and volcanic ash. Streams and glaciers have carved it into a mountain mass of great ruggedness and nearly radial pattern of drainage.

16.11 *Volcanic Cones.* In addition to the mountain masses caused by volcanic intrusion or extrusion, there are many notable examples of single volcanic mountains or cones, some of which are active and occasionally in violent eruption. Their general distribution has been noted previously (Fig. 12.15). Some of the great volcanoes are surrounded by lesser cones and also by mountain peaks carved by erosion in the massive uplifts of which the volcanoes are a part. Others stand alone.

In an earlier chapter the generalization was offered that cones built by the explosive erup-

Fig. 16.8 View northward along the eastern front of the Rocky Mountains near Denver, Colo., showing prominent hogback ridges. The mesa in the right background is capped by an old lava flow. (*Photograph by T. S. Lovering for U.S. Geological Survey.*)

tion of quick-hardening lavas are steeply sloping, while those formed by the effusion of slowly solidifying basaltic lavas are characterized by long, gentle slopes (12.13). As a generalization this statement is valid, though there are significant exceptions. Explosive cones which are composed of coarse, angular materials maintain slope angles of 35 to 40° without undue slumping or sliding. Those which are composed of fine ashy material that drifts readily in the wind, however, may be low and broad, as well as conspicuously asymmetrical.

Actually, most of the world's great volcanic cones are of structures that may be called *composite*. They are made up of layers of viscous lava interbedded among layers of ash, scoria, and other volcanic products erupted at different times. These layers are often penetrated by dikes of lava which branch from the central duct. Such cones are usually relatively steep-sided, though the lower slopes, upon which lava flows, ash, and alluvium have accumulated, are more gentle (Fig. 16.9).

Volcanic craters, the vents through which the volcanic products are erupted, are of great variety in form. Some are small and funnel-shaped, especially the vents of high, active, and perfect cones. Some, which are the craters of dormant and partially destroyed cones, are of great diameter and are believed to result either from the explosive destruction of the upper portion of the former cone or from its collapse through the withdrawal of lava from underneath. Such enlarged craters are known as *calderas*. Crater Lake, in the Cascade Mountains of Oregon, occupies a basin formed by the subsidence of an ancient cone. It is about 4 by 5 miles in diameter and has a newer but very small cone within it (Fig. 16.10). Other crater lakes of smaller size are not uncommon.

Fresh volcanic cones, especially the larger ones, are notable for their impressiveness and perfection of form. One of the most famous, Mount Fuji, in Japan, is a tall, almost perfectly symmetrical peak, especially striking because it stands alone and reaches its full height of more than 12,000 ft. within about 15 miles of the sea (Fig. 16.9).

Like other highlands, however, volcanic cones are soon attacked by the agents of erosion, and their smooth constructional forms become carved into the irregular features of erosional mountains. Streams, and in some instances glaciers, flow down their slopes in radial patterns, cutting ravines and etching into relief resistant dikes or lava flows. Mount Hood, Mount Rainier, and the other great cones of the Cascade Range in the northwestern United States have all been dissected and roughened in varying degree by the work of both streams and glaciers (Fig. 16.11). Some cones have been so reduced by erosion that little remains except the weathered stumps of the lava cores or plugs that led to the former volcanic outlets (Fig. 12.13).

In some areas volcanic cones are so closely grouped in clusters or alignments as to form

Fig. 16.9 The symmetrical cone of Mount Fuji rises more than 12,000 ft. above Suruga Bay and its bordering alluvial plains. (*Photograph by H. Suito.*)

Fig. 16.10 Crater Lake, Oregon, occupies a deep caldera formed by the collapse and destruction of the upper part of a great volcanic cone. Wizard Island (foreground) is a younger cone formed later. (*National Park Service, U.S. Department of the Interior.*)

Fig. 16.11 Mt. Hood, Oregon, is an extinct composite volcanic cone, deeply eroded by water and ice. (*U.S. Forest Service.*)

mountain ranges or groups by themselves. The high-peaked and almost continuous range that extends the entire length of the island of Java, for example, is made up almost entirely of volcanic cones. Much more commonly, however, the cones are built as individual features in association with complex mountains of partially diastrophic origin. The great cones of the Andes and those of the Cascade Range have developed in this way along the crests of elongated and deeply eroded mountain masses that came into being by a combination of diastrophism and the accumulation of lava and ash from earlier periods of volcanic activity.

16.12　Glacial Features of Hills and Mountains. Stream erosion is, without doubt, the major process involved in the primary carving of the great valleys, ranges, and peaks of most mountain and hill regions. However, many rough-land landscapes show clearly the marks of glacial modification. In some of these areas glaciers still exist, being themselves significant items in the landscape. Others have been abandoned by the ice, or else the ice has shrunk so that it now occupies but a small portion of the area it once covered and sculptured.

In most mountainous areas, especially the higher ones, the glaciers that have done the sculpturing have been the typical local ice masses confined to the mountain valleys. Some fairly extensive hill lands, however, and even a few low mountain areas show signs of having been completely overridden by the great continental ice sheets of the Pleistocene period.

Fig. 16.12　A mountain glacier and its snow fields. Crevasses are visible in the nearer ice. Lateral moraines flank the ice tongue, and a medial moraine streaks its surface. (*Photograph by Ewing Galloway.*)

16.13 *Mountain snowfields and glaciers* are themselves important relief features, apart from the forms produced by glacial erosion and deposition. Snows are common to all high mountains. In middle and high latitudes the winter mantle of white settles even over the lower slopes, save where exposed flanks are cleared by the sweep of the wind. The seasonal alternation from winter white to the variety of warm-season colors produced by rock and vegetation works a profound change in the landscape.

The snows of many mountains are, however, permanent. They owe their preservation to the decrease of temperature with altitude. Consequently, the lower limit of permanent snow is high in the tropics, but in the subpolar regions it approaches sea level. In regions of similar temperature the snow line is lower where snowfall is abundant and higher where it is not abundant. In the same locality it is higher on mountain sides exposed to strong insolation and lower on the shaded sides. If these many variations are allowed for, it may be said that the lower limit of permanent snow in the tropics is 14,000 to 20,000 ft. above sea level. In middle latitudes it is at elevations of 5,000 to 14,000 ft.; and on the margins of the polar regions it varies from 2,000 ft. down to sea level.

From their broad, snow-covered areas of accumulation on the mountain slopes and especially in the valley heads, mountain glaciers extend down the valleys in the form of elongated tongues that may reach many miles in length (Fig. 16.12). The tiny, almost extinct glaciers of the western United States rarely exceed a mile in length, but in the Rocky Mountains of Canada and in the Alps, glacial tongues 5 to 10 miles long are common. Some of the largest valley glaciers are in southern Alaska and in the Himalayas, where lengths of 20 to more than 50 miles are recorded.

Below the zone of snow accumulation, the surface of the ice is in many places deeply corrugated by open cracks or crevasses, especially at sharp turns in the valleys or at places where the gradient abruptly increases. Upon the sides of the ice tongue there accumulate ridges of earth and rocks obtained from the valley walls. Others, derived from tributary glaciers or from projecting spurs, sometimes streak the center of an ice tongue. These, which are called *lateral moraines* and *medial moraines,* respectively, are conspicuous surface features of many valley glaciers (Figs. 16.12 and 16.13). At the lower end of the glacier, wastage by melting and evaporation is rapid, and the load of earth and rock debris increases in proportion as the ice mass shrinks, and may bury it entirely.

16.14 *Features Produced by Mountain Glaciers.* It is difficult to generalize about the nature of mountains that have been subjected to valley glaciation, for there is much variety. There are, however, a number of characteristics that are encountered so frequently in glaciated mountains as to warrant being considered typical. Similar characteristics may often be found in mountains that have never been glaciated, but rarely are they as clearly defined, and almost never are so many present in the same area.

Glaciated mountain valleys are most often conspicuously open and free from projecting spurs. Their walls are commonly somewhat oversteepened, especially near the base, sometimes contrasting rather sharply with gentler slopes above and with the open valley floors. If the glaciers still exist or have existed quite recently, there is much exposure of bare rock and a relative absence of regolith on the walls. Polishing and grooving may be seen on some rock exposures. Valley heads are abrupt and steep-walled, looking as though they had been scooped out of the mountain side by a gigantic power shovel. These features, especially when they are half round and have vertical walls, are called *cirques* (Fig. 16.14).

The lengthwise profiles of glaciated valleys are rarely smooth. Instead they are usually more or less steplike, with steep drops or falls separating relatively flat or even basinlike segments. Where basins do occur, they are usually shallow and may contain small lakes. In a few mountain valleys, unusually large and deep lakes occur,

Fig. 16.13 Several tributary glaciers, descending from high snowfields, join to form a large glacial tongue in the foreground. Note the many cirques at the glacier heads, the crevasses at sharp turns and in steeper sections of the glaciers, and the prominent medial and lateral moraines in the foreground. Head of Susitna Glacier in southern Alaska. (*Photo by Bradford Washburn.*)

Fig. 16.14 The head of a glaciated mountain valley. A large cirque in background, with precipitous rock walls and a small remnant glacier. Characteristic stepped-down valley profile with lakes and waterfalls. (*Photo by Hileman, from Glacier National Park.*)

forming features of striking beauty. Lake Chelan in Washington, Lake Louise in the Canadian Rockies, Lake Como in northern Italy, and Lake Lucerne in Switzerland are but a few of the more familiar examples of this type.

Tributary valleys often enter the main valley in a discordant fashion, their mouths appearing as notches far up the side of the main valley wall. The streams issuing from them must plunge in rapids or sheer falls to reach the main valley floor. Such *hanging valleys* are most convenient places for the development of water power because of the great drop involved, even though the volume of water may be quite small (Fig. 16.15).

Where continued weathering and erosion have brought the steep walls of opposing cirques or of adjacent valleys close together, the divides between them are narrowed and finally sharp-ened into knife-edged ridges of great ruggedness. Mountain peaks, their bases hewn by quarrying ice erosion in several flanking cirques, are reduced to sharpened pyramids with angular ridges and precipitous faces. Some of the larger peaks of this type, such as the famous Matterhorn (Fig. 16.16), are among the most awe-inspiring and spectacular of all natural features.

The characteristics discussed above are all the product of the erosional activity of the ice. Regolith has been cleared and kept cleared from the valley walls. Blocks have been removed from the cirque walls and from jointed sections of the valley floor by plucking. Spurs and projecting knobs have been plucked and scoured away. Mechanical weathering, especially frost wedging, has attacked the rock faces, driving them back and sending the weathered debris onto the ice below. The basins, steps, and

Fig. 16.15 Glaciated mountains in the Canadian Rockies. At the right is a cirque lake. Its drainage falls to the next lake below and from there far down to Lake Louise, which may be seen at the left in the main valley. (*Photograph by De Cou. From Ewing Galloway.*)

hanging valleys indicate that the ice has eroded differentially, accomplishing most where it was thickest, most rapidly moving, or best equipped with grinding tools, or where the rock was weakest or most broken. Many of the forms probably existed in general outline before the glaciers formed. The ice has, in varying degree, modified and accentuated what the streams had left.

Like their larger relatives, mountain glaciers also produce depositional features of considerable importance. Indeed, because of the quantities of material that are carried onto the moving ice from the valley walls above, mountain glaciers are often very heavily loaded with debris, building, in consequence, moraines that sometimes reach startling size (Fig. 16.12). At the sides of the ice tongue, bouldery lateral moraines are strewn along the slopes, and curved end moraines are built like dams across the valley floors, sometimes impounding lakes behind them. Eskers, outwash deltas, and valley trains are also found, in all respects similar to those associated with continental glaciers.

16.15 *Features Produced by Continental Glaciers.* Within the areas of continental glaciation there were hill regions also in which the relief of the original features, caused by an earlier stream erosion, did not greatly exceed the thickness of the continental ice sheets. Except for occasional rock masses which may have projected through the glaciers, they were engulfed and overridden.

The effect of ice scour upon the hill features is pronounced, whether the original features were stream-eroded portions of ancient crystalline highlands or of maturely dissected sedimentary uplands. The intricate patterns caused by gullying were erased, and there were substituted rounded features generally devoid of pinnacled promontories or sharp contours (Fig. 16.17). Mantles of regolith were swept away,

Fig. 16.16 The Matterhorn, a roughly quadrangular peak resulting from the headward encroachment of four cirques. (*Photograph by Ewing Galloway.*)

Fig. 16.17 The flowing contours of an ice-scoured hill region in Vermont. The hill features are subdued, and the valleys are drift-mantled. (*Photograph by Underwood and Underwood.*)

and their place taken by thin stony soils or bare rock. Some of the ice-shaped hills show steepened and rocky lee slopes on a scale that produces landscapes of scenic grandeur in spite of relatively small actual relief. Associated with the scoured and rounded hills are broad open valleys, usually thin-soiled and boulder strewn.

The drainage of ice-scoured hills, like that of ice-scoured plains, shows abundant evidence of glacial disturbance. Waterfalls and rapids, small and great, interrupt the courses of streams the valleys of which, remade by ice, trend across the grain of rocks of unequal resistance to erosion. Lakes and swamps also abound, even amid the highlands. Some are small morainic ponds or marshes of temporary nature. Others lie in portions of preglacial valleys, now blocked by morainic dams, while still others occupy ice-eroded rock basins and are beautifully set amid forested hills.

It happens that the more noted of the ice-scoured hill regions are situated in areas of ancient crystalline rocks that yield relatively

small amounts of drift. These include the more rugged portions of the Canadian Shield, the Adirondack Mountains, parts of New England, the Highlands of Scotland, and parts of the ancient highland of Scandinavia. They have many features in common. Agricultural land is scant and poor. Indeed, some ice-scoured hills have no agricultural use but are given over wholly to timber. In others, meadows and pastures occupy the greater part of the area, and the slopes and uplands bear only poor timber or shrubby heath.

In the Pennine Hills of northern England, the Green Mountains of Vermont, and the hills of southern New York, less resistant rock has provided more abundant glacial drift, and although the hills resulting from ice scour are equally rounded, they generally are less bare than are those in the ancient crystalline highlands. The valleys have more abundant drift, and although the drift is stony, they offer better agricultural possibilities than those in which crystalline rocks predominate (Fig. 16.18).

Fig. 16.18 Keuka Lake, one of the Finger Lakes, rests among the smooth-sloped glaciated hills of the Allegheny-Cumberland region in western New York. Contrast with Fig. 16.5. (*Photograph from NYSPIX-Commerce, Albany, N.Y.*)

16.16 The Appalachian region of the eastern United States affords an excellent example of the development and diversification of a major rough-land area. For purposes of study, the rather indefinitely bounded area may be considered to extend from the Hudson and Mohawk Valleys, in New York, southwestward to Tuscaloosa and Montgomery, Ala., a distance of approximately 1,000 miles. The width of the belt, between the locally obscured eastern foot of the Blue Ridge and the even more indefinite western margin of the Allegheny-Cumberland Hills, varies from about 250 miles in the north to 150 miles in the south (Fig. 16.19).

Appalachian terrain assumes a striking variety of hill and low mountain forms, most of which are the product of stream erosion upon several contrasting types of rock structures. Only in the extreme north and northwest did continental glaciation also play a significant part in the sculpturing of the land. There was no mountain glaciation.

On the basis of its terrain, the Appalachian system can be divided longitudinally into three distinct belts, each of which corresponds also to a particular type of rock structure. The westernmost and broadest belt, the Allegheny-Cumberland section, is largely a dendritically dissected hill land developed on horizontal or gently warped sedimentary strata. The middle belt, the ridge-and-valley section, is a zone of remarkably long, parallel features carved in strongly folded strata. The easternmost, and through much of its length the narrowest belt, the Blue Ridge section, is composed of hills and low mountains eroded in complex crystalline rocks.

Taken as a whole, the region has had a long and complex history, most of which need not be reviewed here. The original uplift and folding occurred over a long period of time during the Paleozoic era, more than 250 million years ago. Mountain making involved not only the present Appalachians but also a considerable area extending to the eastward. The intensity of the folding that occurred increased from west to east, the Blue Ridge and eastern ridge-and-valley sections having suffered profound jamming of the crust, with intense folding and considerable faulting.

Since the time of this first strong tectonic activity there has been a series of alternating periods of erosion and renewed uplift of which little is known and nothing need be said. At a fairly recent time, however, perhaps only a few million years ago, the area existed in the form of a low old-age erosional plain which cut across or beveled the diverse structure without significant regard to the hardness of the rocks. This plain was then uplifted in the form of a broad, low arch, into which streams cut with renewed vigor. Because of the sharp contrasts in resistance of the exposed rocks, the erosion was strongly differential, and it is this selectivity that has produced the diverse landforms that exist today.

16.17 *The Allegheny-Cumberland hill region,* called by geologists the Appalachian Plateau, is deeply and maturely dissected in dendritic pattern, and displays a local relief which, in general, is between 500 and 2,000 ft. Over most of the area streams are closely spaced, the interfluves having been reduced to sharp-crested and sometimes peaked ridges

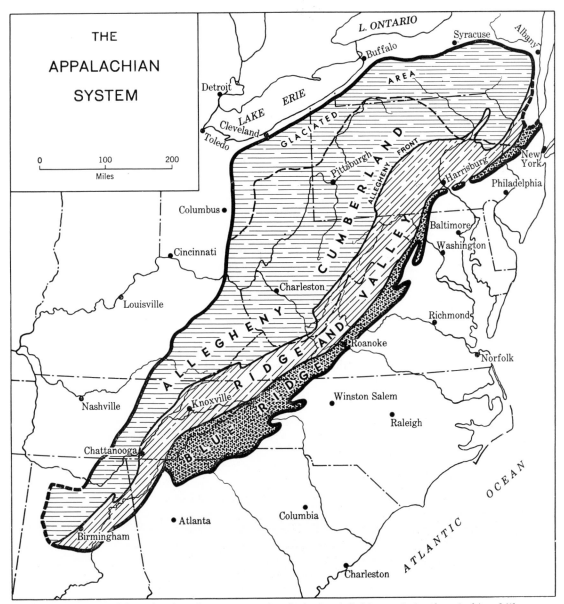

Fig. 16.19 Map showing the extent and principal subdivisions of the Appalachian hill and mountain system.

Fig. 16.20 A narrow valley in the Allegheny hill region of southern West Virginia.

(Fig. 16.5). Over broad areas there is little variation in the elevation of the major ridge crests. Valleys are usually narrow and V-shaped; only along the major streams has valley widening produced narrow bottomlands. The steepness of valley sides is rarely extreme except in a few areas of unusually resistant rocks (Fig. 16.20).

In several sections, notably along the northern and eastern margins and in the Cumberland Plateau of Tennessee, resistant cap rocks, chiefly sandstones and conglomerates, have preserved some of the upland, giving the landscape the character of a tableland. The eastern edge of the Allegheny-Cumberland section is marked through most of its length by a high east-facing escarpment, the Allegheny Front, which is basically a cuesta upheld by the resistant cap rock, here gently inclined toward the west (Fig. 16.21).

In northeastern Ohio and southern New York the relatively low and tabular upland was overridden by the continental ice sheets. Glaciation, by a combination of scour and drift deposition, produced here a much smoother, more gently sloping topography than may be encountered anywhere else in the region (Fig. 16.18). Strong erosion in several north-south valleys in southern New York led to the formation of a group of elongated basins in which are now found the remarkable and beautiful Finger Lakes (Fig. 16.22).

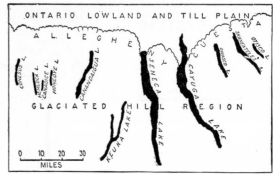

Fig. 16.22 The Finger Lakes in the glaciated hill region of western New York.

In the more subdued relief of the lower western part of the Allegheny-Cumberland region, especially near the Ohio River, good roads and well-developed farms occupy the spacious valleys and some of the broader uplands. Many of the hills are pastured, and only the steeper slopes

Fig. 16.21 The high and continuous east-facing escarpment of the Allegheny Front, shown here in Pennsylvania, marks the eastern border of the Allegheny-Cumberland Hills. (*Photograph by Pennsylvania Department of Labor & Industry, Harrisburgh, Pa.*)

remain in woodland. In the maturely dissected districts, however, crop land is limited in extent, since both bottomlands and flat uplands are nearly lacking. Most of the slopes are wooded, but some of surprising steepness are cultivated. Roads, railroads, and settlements are in the narrow valleys. Many of the region's settlements, largely coal-mining camps, are strung along the valleys in linear pattern. In some of the more tabular sections, roads, farms, and villages are found on the uplands, although the gorgelike valleys serve as the avenues of railway transportation. Most favorable agriculturally is the glaciated northern section, where uplands, valleys, and smooth slopes are all farmed.

16.18 *The Appalachian ridge-and-valley region* is the most notable example in the world of parallel ridges and valleys. In the time since the erosional plain was re-elevated, the principal streams have cut down along the courses in which they previously flowed, and their tributaries have adjusted themselves to the structural

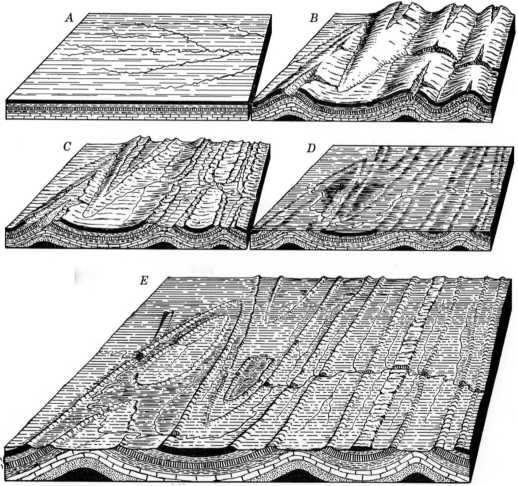

Fig. 16.23 A series of diagrams in chronological sequence to illustrate the erosional development of linear ridges, parallel valleys, enclosed valleys, and water gaps in the Appalachian ridge-and-valley section. *A,* horizontal strata; *B,* anticlinal and synclinal folding, with pitching anticlines; *C,* erosional mountains carved from the folded structures; *D,* the region eroded to old age; *E,* the peneplain slightly elevated and re-eroded.

conditions by etching out new valleys in the less resistant strata. There are several important results of the progress of this second cycle of erosion.

Broad valleys with rolling floors have been carved in the less resistant rocks, mainly limestones and shales. The upturned edges of the resistant members of the folds, usually sandstones and conglomerates, are left standing in relief in the form of long, even-crested ridges, the summits of which are probably not far below the level of the old peneplain (Fig. 16.23). The major ridges range in height from 500 to 1,500 ft. above the adjacent valleys. They seldom are more than 3 miles wide, but some of them extend almost unbroken, and with remarkably uniform height, to lengths of 25 to 100 miles or more (Fig. 16.24).

Not all the ridges of the Appalachian ridge-and-valley region are parallel. The anticlines and synclines of which they are the eroded stumps sometimes terminate abruptly, pitch gently beneath the valley level, or merge with one another. Such structures are the causes of great variation in the shapes, sizes, and continuity of the valleys and, consequently, in the patterns of settlement and the routes of transportation that follow them. Figure 16.23 shows two enclosed, canoe-shaped valleys which result from the erosion of anticlinal structures.

Narrow notches, called *water gaps,* have been cut through the ridges where the major streams run across their trend (Fig. 16.25). Other notches, begun by streams that changed their courses and abandoned the notches, are called *wind gaps.* These gaps are the gateways between adjacent valleys. The streams in accomplishing their erosion have adjusted their courses to the trend of the rock structure with the result that a somewhat rectangular pattern of drainage, called *trellis drainage,* has evolved (Fig. 13.14).

Some of the valleys of this region are noted for their great continuity, and a few for their agricultural productivity. The most famed is the "Great Valley," which, under several local

Fig. 16.24 A view across the parallel ridges and valleys in one section of the folded Appalachians. Water gaps cut two of the ridges at the extreme right. In many parts of the ridge-and-valley section the valleys are much wider than those shown here and contain large areas of farm land (see Fig. 16.25). (*Photograph by Fairchild Aerial Surveys, Inc.*)

Fig. 16.25 Looking from the air along the crest of a hogback ridge in the ridge-and-valley section in Pennsylvania. The Susquehanna River here cuts the ridge at right angles and has made a water gap. The fields of the cultivated valleys are snow-covered, while the wooded ridge appears dark. (*Photograph by Fairchild Aerial Surveys, Inc.*)

names, extends from New York to Alabama. The ridges, because of their steep slopes and thin infertile soils, remain principally in woodlands. A general view "across the grain" of the region includes wooded ridge beyond wooded ridge, with intervening valleys upon whose undulating to rolling bottoms are the fields and patchy woodlands of farms, together with highways and villages.

16.19 *The Blue Ridge section,* or crystalline Appalachians, is comprised of igneous and metamorphic rocks of great age and structural complexity. Through much of its length the section is no more than 5 to 20 miles wide and rises 500 to 2,000 ft. above the Piedmont to the east and the Great Valley to the west (Fig. 16.26). Towards its southern end, however,

especially in North Carolina and Tennessee, it broadens to more than 50 miles and achieves a local relief of 2,000 to 3,000 ft., forming one of the most truly mountainous areas in the eastern United States. There is reason to believe that parts of this higher southern section were not reduced to a plain during the formation of the broad general erosion surface.

The absence of extreme contrasts in rock strength has permitted the development of dendritic drainage in most of the Blue Ridge area. In the high southern section, however, differences in valley width may be in part attributable to minor differences in resistance. Especially toward the western margin of the region, some rocks of great resistance stand out as ranges of mountains and have steep bare

Fig. 16.26 In northern Virginia the Blue Ridge rises about 2,000 ft. above its base and is only a few miles wide. View near Luray, Va. (*Photograph from Library of Congress Collections.*)

Fig. 16.27 Massive granite bedrock exposed on a steep valley side in the southern Blue Ridge in North Carolina. (*U.S. Geological Survey photograph.*)

Fig. 16.28 The irregular, peaked ridges and eroded basins of the southern Blue Ridge in western North Carolina. (*Photograph by Cline.*)

slopes (Fig. 16.27). A much larger part is eroded into hills of rounded summits and moderate slopes, the flowing contours of which are well mantled with regolith and clothed with forest (Fig. 16.28).

In the narrow northern section, the major streams coming from the west cross the range in water gaps, precisely as in the ridge-and-valley section. The southern section, however, forms a divide from which streams flow eastward toward the Atlantic and southwestward toward the Gulf of Mexico.

In utility to man, the Blue Ridge section somewhat resembles the Allegheny-Cumberland area. The scarcity of gently sloping land limits the agricultural potentialities, although some remarkably steeply inclined fields and pastures may be seen. Most favorable are some of the broad, rolling valleys and basins of the southern section, especially about Asheville, N.C. The water gaps of the northern section provide easy crossing of the Blue Ridge, but in the south, absence of low gaps creates a barrier of some significance.

17

The Continental Margins and the Sea Floor

17.1 The Continental Shelf. To say that the continents end and the oceans begin at the shoreline seems a most obvious truism. But if the statement is changed to read, "the continental masses end and the ocean basins begin at the shoreline," it is no longer true. A generalized profile of the continents and ocean floors shows the continental surfaces as platforms which at the edges drop off with surprising abruptness to the deep-sea floors. The remarkable thing is, however, that the abrupt edge of the continental platform rarely coincides with the coastline. Instead, it usually is found well to seaward of the coast, at a depth of 400 to 600 ft. below sea level. It is as though the seas were overfull and had spread beyond the rims of their basins to inundate the rim of the land (Fig. 17.1).

This concept has a considerable degree of geological validity. The shallowly submerged edges of the platforms are composed of sediments and other continental types of rock, which in many places differ sharply from the materials beneath the adjacent deep-sea floor. It is entirely reasonable, and for certain purposes highly valuable, to consider the submerged margin of the platform as a part of the continent, called the *continental shelf*. The relatively steep *continental slope* that falls from the edge of the shelf to the deep-sea floor then becomes the true edge of the continent.

17.2 Sea-level Changes and the Present Shoreline. If the margin of a continent is raised or lowered diastrophically, if the volume of the ocean basins is tectonically altered, or if there is a change in the amount of water in the seas, the position of the shoreline will change. If the land rises or the sea level declines, the shoreline will migrate seaward across the continental shelf. If the land sinks or the sea level rises, the shoreline will move landward. During late geological time, changes in sea level and vertical movements of the land have both occurred often and with considerable magnitude, which means that the positions of the world's shorelines have been altered repeatedly and in large amount.

Especially significant for the earth as a whole were the changes in sea level that accompanied the formation and disappearance of the great Pleistocene ice sheets. Since the water that formed the glaciers came ultimately from the sea and was returned to the sea when the ice melted, it follows that the sea level declined as each ice sheet grew, and rose again as the ice melted. When the last glaciation was at its maximum, the sea level is believed to have been 300 ft. or more lower than it is now, thus exposing as dry land vast areas of what is now continental shelf. Thereafter the water surface rose irregularly, probably reaching its present level no more than a few thousand years ago. Some coastal lands, especially in the far north, have been diastrophically active even more recently.

As a result of these events, the present position of the shoreline has been only recently attained, and in some places the shore is still shifting. The effects of these movements of the shoreline may be clearly seen in the present outlines of certain coasts and in various features repeatedly encountered in the coastal zones.

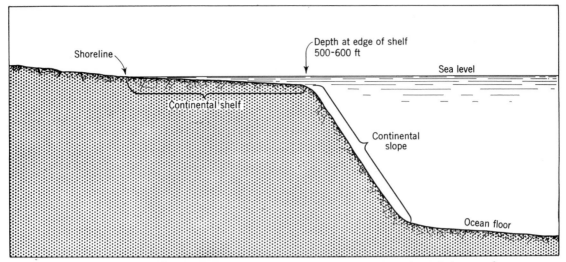

Fig. 17.1 Diagram to illustrate relation of continental shelf and continental slope to shoreline and ocean floor.

Features of the Shoreline

17.3 Coastal features are the result of the operation of many different agents and processes. Changes of sea level, erosion and deposition by waves and currents, deposition by agents working on the adjacent lands, diastrophic happenings, and several types of organic accumulations have all left their mark upon the coastal belt. Nearly all coasts are complex in their formation, representing the combined action of several of the agencies named. Marine erosion and marine deposition may both be active at different points along the same stretch of coast. A stream delta, a lava flow, or a coral reef may complicate a shoreline on which marine processes have produced most of the features. A given coast may show evidence of both a fall and a rise in sea level, because both may have occurred, successively, at a rather recent date. These factors make it extremely difficult, and of questionable value, to classify coasts according to their mode of origin. It will be worthwhile, however, to consider the more commonly encountered coastal features and associations of features and to inquire into the combinations of events that have produced them.

17.4 Bays are, in general, formed by marine erosion, by depositional building-out of the shore on either side, or by the drowning of valleys or depressions by a rising sea level or a subsidence of the land.

On exposed coasts inlets or coves are sometimes developed as a result of differential erosion in rocks of varying resistance. However, such re-entrants are usually small. Wave attack is strongest on projecting headlands and least in bays, thus tending to straighten the coast line rather than to make it more irregular. Continued erosion on a coast where coves have been developed would be more likely to obliterate the inlets than to continue to enlarge them.

Bays or lagoons formed by deposition about them may be considered as merely incidental to the formation of the depositional features, and will be mentioned briefly in that connection.

Most of the larger indentations of the coasts owe their existence to the third cause, that is, the submergence that results from rising of the sea or sinking of the land. Some very large, steep-sided and elongated gulfs or seas, such as the Gulf of California, the Red Sea, and the Persian Gulf, are believed to have originated through the foundering of a portion of the land as a graben or syncline (Fig. 17.2). Most of the lesser bays, however, have been formed by the inundation of erosional valleys or minor depressions. Since the large postglacial rise of sea level was world-wide in its effects, it is not

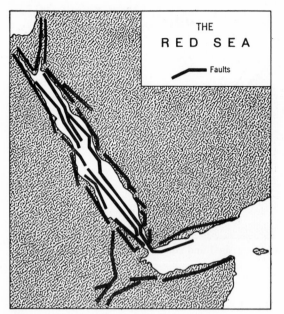

Fig. 17.2 Map of the Red Sea and its surroundings, showing the relation of its outline to major fault lines. (*After Machatschek.*)

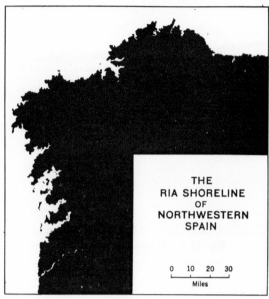

Fig. 17.3 Large estuaries or *rias* on the Spanish coast.

surprising to find bays produced by drowning so widely distributed.

17.5 *Estuaries.* A general rise of sea level or a broad diastrophic depression of the land permits landward encroachment of the sea and the establishment of a new shoreline upon what was previously the land surface. The new shoreline will assume a position which is that of a contour line upon the former land surface. Its outline will, when first established, follow all of the wanderings of that contour line, and will thus reflect the form of the drowned surface.

If the submerged surface was a smooth alluvial slope, its contours will be regular, and the new shoreline will be similarly regular. But if, as is more often true, the surface was an erosional surface, its contours will be highly irregular, and the shoreline resulting from its drowning will also be irregular. The sea will penetrate into the valleys, forming bays, while the higher interfluves remain above water as peninsulas or headlands. Individual embayments resulting from submergence are called "drowned valleys" or *estuaries,* and shorelines characterized by

Fig. 17.4 The middle Atlantic coast of the United States exhibits a remarkably fine development of estuaries.

358

many of them are called *ria shorelines* (Fig. 17.3).

If the gradients of the valleys being drowned are very gentle, the resulting estuaries will reach far into the land, while the drowning of steeply pitching valleys will produce only relatively short indentations. The form and pattern of the bays will follow the form and pattern of the valleys that have been drowned. Thus some estuarine patterns are dendritic, others are simple and parallel, and others are highly irregular. Some estuaries, developed by the drowning of plains, have gently sloping low banks, while others, formed in hilly and mountainous country, are flanked by high, steep walls and are strikingly picturesque.

An excellent example of a ria shoreline is provided by the Atlantic Coast of the United States. In the section between Delaware and South Carolina the development of dendritically branching estuaries is unusually fine (Fig. 17.4). Farther south, estuaries are present, though less prominent, some possibly having been reduced in size through deposition of sediment. The shorelines of northern New England and eastern Canada are of great irregularity, owing to the submergence of plains of ancient crystalline and sedimentary rocks of complicated structures and varying degrees of resistance to erosion. However, the present shorelines in that section are not merely those of stream erosion and submergence but have also many details of outline and profile given them by ice scour and deposition during the period of their complete coverage by the continental glaciers (Fig. 17.5).

The shorelines of Great Britain, northwestern Europe, and northern Siberia offer other examples of estuarine development resulting from the drowning of gently sloping erosional plains. Highlands with ria shores have many examples. They are particularly extensive and varied as to detail in western Europe and the Mediterranean borders. They include the shore of northwestern Spain, the Gulf of Corinth and other deep indentations upon the shores of Greece, and the highly irregular shores of the Aegean and Adriatic Seas. It is from the many parallel bays (called *rias*) on the hill-land coast of

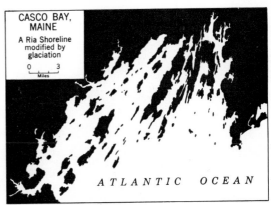

Fig. 17.5 The glaciated shoreline of Casco Bay has many islands, rocky peninsulas, and narrow inlets.

northwestern Spain that the term "ria shoreline" is derived (Fig. 17.3). Other examples of highlands with ria shorelines are found on the coast of Japan and the long hilly coast of South China.

17.6 *Fiords.* Several mountainous coasts of the world are distinctive because of the presence of large numbers of narrow, deep, and sheer-walled bays, some of which penetrate unusually far into the land. To these long narrow arms of the sea the Norwegian name *fiord* is applied. Fiorded coasts provide some of the finest scenery in the world. High mountain uplands are there, their summits seldom visible from the narrow fiord below. High and rocky walls, mist shrouded, rise on either hand, and occasional cascades plunge from the mouths of hanging valleys. Sharp bends and rocky islands obstruct the view, and a narrow horizon seems to shut out the world and create complete isolation. Yet the quiet waters of the fiord are easily accessible, since they are so deep that they may be navigated in safety, even by ocean-going ships (Fig. 17.6).

The dimensions of some of the largest fiords are truly remarkable. Portland Canal, a fiord that forms part of the boundary between Alaska and British Columbia, is 90 miles long, $\frac{1}{2}$ mile to 2 miles wide, and, in mid-channel, has water ranging from 90 to 1,250 ft. in depth. The Sogne Fiord, the longest in Norway, has a length of 112 miles, an average width of 4

Fig. 17.6 A view from the head of a fiord in Norway. The village occupies a small delta, but the rocky island, the steep walls, and the presence of the large ship suggest deep water. (*Photograph by Ewing Galloway.*)

miles, and its water reaches a maximum depth of 4,000 ft. It is probable that fiords are ice-scoured mountain valleys which have been submerged by a relative rise of sea level since the time of their formation. It is probable also that mountain-valley glaciers discharging into the sea are able, by reason of the great depth or thickness of the ice tongues, to erode their valley floors well below sea level. After the disappearance of the ice the valley floor is occupied by sea water, sometimes deeply and far inland. Some fiords are continued inland by troughlike valleys and end in cirque valley heads, a few of which still contain glaciers (Fig. 17.7). Many fiords, perhaps because of the greater vigor of ice erosion near the glacier head, are deeper near their landward than toward their seaward ends. Submerged morainic deposits near the outer ends of the fiords tend further to shallow the water there.

Especially near the seaward margins of some fiorded areas, the ice-scoured channels are so numerous and so varied in direction that the rocky coast is dissected into thousands of island blocks, some large and mountainous, others mere rocky points of great menace to navigation. Many of the cross fiords are so arranged as to form channels that parallel the coast for long distances and are sheltered on the seaward side by an almost unbroken succession of rocky islands (Fig. 17.8).

The principal regions of fiorded mountain coasts are in the higher middle latitudes where, during the glacial period, many valley glaciers descended to sea level. Coasts having deep fiords and intricate pattern are (*a*) the west coast of Norway, (*b*) the west coast of North America from Puget Sound to Alaska, (*c*) the coast of southern Chile, and (*d*) the west coast of South Island, New Zealand (Fig. 17.8). Others of lower altitude and less grandeur are parts of the coasts of Scotland, Iceland, Greenland,

Labrador, and the Arctic islands. Between fiords on the one hand and ice-scoured rias of the type seen on the coast of Maine on the other, there are intermediate features of endless variety in size and shape.

17.7 Benches, Cliffs, and Terraces. On exposed coasts where the water deepens to seaward rapidly enough to permit waves to break directly against the shore, marine erosion is usually actively at work, driving back the shoreline. During the erosional process certain characteristic features appear.

Wave erosion is most effective near average sea level and cuts a notch in the shore profile there. This it enlarges by undercutting and, on strongly eroding shores, produces steep cliffs

and bold headlands. The erosion of cliffs in unconsolidated material or weak rock is likely to proceed with comparative evenness, but in resistant rocks, inequalities in rock hardness or the presence of numerous joints and other lines of weakness sometimes cause it to proceed unequally. Some of the results of differential erosion are the formation of eroded coves, detached chimneylike pinnacles of rock, and half-submerged projections upon the sea floor (Fig. 17.9).

As the sea cliff retreats landward under erosion, it leaves behind an eroded base which inclines gently seaward a little below sea level. It is called a *wave-cut terrace*. Some shorelines are bordered by marine terraces of that origin

Fig. 17.7 A view down the troughlike Vidde Valley, Norway. Note the hanging valley at left and the absence of projecting spurs. In the foreground is a mountain dairy farm or *saeter*. (*Underwood and Underwood*.)

many hundreds or even several thousands of feet wide (Fig. 17.10). The shallowness of the water, especially on the newer landward margins of these features, and the presence of submerged rock projections cause them to be a menace to navigation.

The materials dislodged by erosion are moved offshore by the undertow and are deposited beyond the margin of the wave-cut terrace in a form which may be called a *wave-built terrace*. To the construction of this embankment, which forms simply a seaward extension of the wave-cut terrace, may be added some sediments carried into the sea by streams and then distributed by waves and currents.

Sea cliffs and marine terraces have often been either submerged or left high and dry by

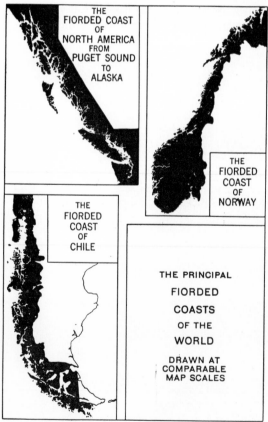

Fig. 17.8 The fiorded coasts of Norway, south Chile, and British Columbia–southern Alaska are similar in pattern.

relative changes of sea level subsequent to their formation. If they are submerged, they are likely to be soon rendered inconspicuous by the deposition of sediment over them. Terraces and cliffs that have been brought above the sea by a raising of the land or a lowering of sea level are, on the other hand, very common features of coastal lands throughout the world. Some coasts display a whole series of such terraces, forming giant steps in the profile of the land as it rises from the present shore. Most of the individual terraces were not continuous at the time of their formation, and they have usually been further broken by stream gullying since the time of their uplift. However, their gently sloping platforms provide many acres of tillable land on coastal slopes that would otherwise be too steep for cultivation (Fig. 17.11).

Along coast lines that have been diastrophically active in recent time, raised terraces usually are more or less warped, and are sometimes found many hundreds of feet above the present level of the sea. Along parts of the California coast, much of which follows known or suspected fault lines, terrace remnants are found at elevations of as much as 1,500 feet. Along stable coasts, however, where there has been little tectonic disturbance, the terraces are nearly horizontal, and are usually confined to elevations of less than 300 ft. Some of these terraces have been attributed to the high stands of sea level that occurred during times of glacial disappearance in the Pleistocene period.

It should be emphasized that elevated terraces are found along coasts which also display estuaries indicating a late rise of sea level. This is true even on such a remarkably estuarine coast as that of Virginia and North Carolina. Most coasts show evidence of both fall and rise of the sea, evidence which is entirely compatible with the idea of an oscillating sea level during glacial times.

17.8 Beaches and Spits. Sandy and gravelly debris that has been loosened from the shore or from the shallow bottom, or that has been washed into the sea by streams, is reworked and redistributed by wave action and by longshore currents generated by obliquely striking

Fig. 17.9 A wave-cut cliff and detached rocky islets on the exposed coast of Cornwall, England. (*Photograph by Burton Holmes. From Ewing Galloway.*)

waves (13.46). Some of this material is moved seaward and laid down on the wave-built terrace or on the bottom beyond the terrace. The remainder is deposited on or near the shore in various forms of beaches and bars.

On protected sections of the coast, or even on exposed coasts that are not too frequently swept by destructive storm waves, relatively gentle wave action tends to move sand or gravel onto the shore, forming beaches. Along a smooth and low coast, the beaches may form a continuous strip many miles in length. On irregular coasts, however, the sediment is concentrated in the re-entrants, the headlands often being swept clear and subjected to active erosion. Such beaches deposited in bays commonly assume a curved, crescentic shape.

Through the erosion of headlands and the accumulation of beaches in the re-entrants, an irregular shoreline is gradually straightened by wave action (Fig. 17.12).

Debris that is moved parallel to the shore by obliquely striking waves and longshore currents continues to shift until it comes to an angle in the shoreline, to the sheltered or deeper waters of a bay, or to a protected position between a close-in island and the shore. At these places it is dropped, making a ridge or embankment upon the bottom. With the aid of waves that occasionally strike them from seaward, these deposits may in time be built up to or above the water surface, forming a point of sand or gravel that prolongs the line of the shore to seaward or across the mouth of a bay.

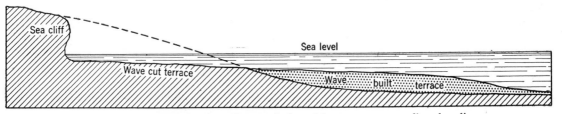

Fig. 17.10 A profile to show the association of features on an eroding shoreline.

Fig. 17.11 Marine terraces on the coast of California, near Los Angeles. The steplike profiles of cliffs and terraces may be seen in the distance, the surface of one of the terraces in the foreground.

Such features are called *bars* or *spits*. In a narrow or shallow bay a spit may grow entirely across the entrance, or a pair of them may grow, one from either side toward the middle, forming a *bay bar* (Fig. 17.13). In the mouth of a broad bay the shoreward movement of waves and currents past the projecting point of a spit may cause it to grow with a shoreward

Fig. 17.12 A sandy beach has been deposited in this sheltered bay, while the headland beyond has been swept clear by wave action. Cape Sebastian, Ore. (*Oregon State Highway Commission photograph.*)

curve, whence it is called a *recurved spit* or hook. Such features are exemplified in the shapes of Sandy Hook, at the entrance to New York Bay, and the curved tip of Cape Cod.

Where deposition occurs between an island and the shore, a bar may be formed connecting the island with the mainland.

17.9   Offshore Bars. Along coasts where shallow water causes the waves to break far from shore, long *offshore bars* are developed just inside the line of breakers (13.45). As such a bar grows in height it appears first above sea level as a series of narrow islands (Fig. 17.14). Further deposition by waves and the drift of longshore currents fills gaps between some of the portions and connects them.

Between offshore bars and their mainland shorelines are long shallow lagoons. Because the bars usually touch the mainland at intervals, especially at projecting points, the continuity of the lagoons is interrupted. Drainage from the land discharges into the lagoon and seeks an outlet through the bar, and in the lagoon the water level rises and falls periodically with the tide, which flows in and out through gaps, or *tidal inlets*, between sections of the bar. This tends to keep some of the gaps scoured open. The development of an interrupted bar and of segmented lagoons tends to complicate a previously simple shoreline and greatly to lengthen it.

The formation of an offshore bar is followed by its slow migration landward and its eventual disappearance. This process narrows the lagoon, and river sediment does its part also by aggrading that shallow body of water. After partial filling by sand and silt the lagoon acquires a

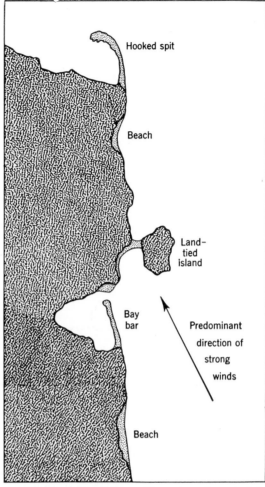

Fig. 17.13   Map-diagram illustrating characteristic types of bars, spits, and beaches and the typical sites in which they develop.

fringe of salt-water vegetation and, at low tide, may be only an expanse of featureless marshland. Eventually the shoreward migration of the bar carries it to the mainland, the lagoon dis-

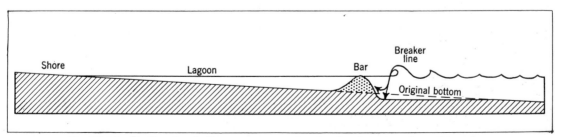

Fig. 17.14   Profile of a shallow-water coast, showing development of an offshore bar.

365

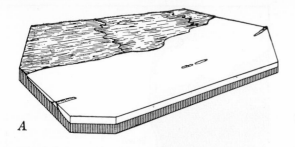

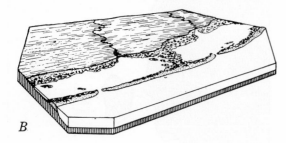

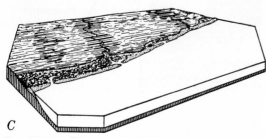

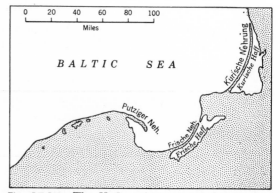

bays. Indian River, on the east coast of Florida, is a long narrow lagoon. Beyond it lies an offshore bar which extends coastwise for more than 100 miles, interrupted only by narrow tidal inlets. The Carolina shoreline shows similar features (Fig. 17.16). The long bars developed there are made up of segments that meet at

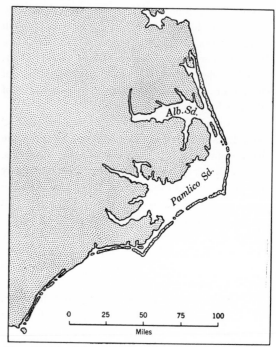

Fig. 17.15 Diagrams illustrating stages in the development of an offshore bar. *A,* bar begins to form at the breaker line, locally reaching the surface; *B,* bar has become almost continuous, enclosing shallow lagoons; *C,* bar has been driven shoreward by wave pounding, and lagoon has disappeared through narrowing and filling.

Fig. 17.16 Wave-modified offshore bars on the Carolina coast.

appears, and the bar becomes merely a beach upon a shore of simple outline (Fig. 17.15). The time required for a transformation of the type described is long, but the shallow coastal waters of the world show numerous examples of offshore bars and lagoons in various stages of progress from youth to old age and extinction.

The Atlantic and Gulf Coasts of the United States show generally the estuarine features resulting from submergence, and numerous offshore bars which indicate shallow coastal waters. Padre and Matagorda Islands, on the Texas coast, are offshore bars, and behind them are extensive lagoons and broad, shallow estuarine

Fig. 17.17 The *Haffs* or lagoons and their enclosing *Nehrungs* or bars on the Baltic coast of Poland. Each *Haff* has a narrow outlet to the sea.

sharp angles. These appear to result from the influence of various shore currents. They enclose not only lagoons but such broad bodies of water as Pamlico, Albemarle, and Currituck Sounds, which are in part estuarine. The bars on the New Jersey shore, on the other hand, are nearly straight, and they enclose only narrow lagoons.

Similar features are found on many other lowland coasts. The North Sea Coast from the Netherlands to Denmark is fringed by the long chain of the Frisian Islands, which are separated from the mainland by narrow lagoons. The large lakes on the coast of eastern Germany are cut off from the Baltic by long, curving bars that appear to be intermediate in nature and manner of formation between bay bars and offshore bars (Fig. 17.17).

17.10 Shoreline Features Resulting from Land Deposits. Portions of certain shorelines are characterized not so much by the deposits of waves and currents as by those of rivers, glaciers, and the wind. Among these are the shorelines of the great deltas and delta fans of the world and of innumerable smaller ones. Usually these features present broadly convex fronts to the sea, and their simple outlines are sometimes interrupted by the fingerlike projections of distributary levees (Figs. 14.21 and 14.22).

Glacial deposits likewise modify the details of shorelines in some localities. For example, the great embayment which includes New York harbor is estuarine, but the shoreline features of the Long Island Sound portion of it result from the submergence of the irregular deposits of a till plain, while the more regular south shore of Long Island is the submerged margin of a great glacial outwash plain. The projecting base of Cape Cod is a partially submerged marginal moraine, while the complicated shoreline of Boston Bay results from the submergence of a till plain on which isolated drumlins create several of the adjacent islands. In Antarctica and parts of Greenland and Alaska portions of the shorelines are created by glacial ice itself (Fig. 14.59).

Wind-blown sand is in many places an accompaniment of shoreline development, although it does not often modify the shore outline notably. As soon as beach sands begin to be thrown up by the waves, they are readily dried and are then slowly moved by the wind and

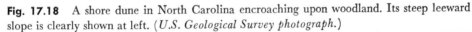

Fig. 17.18 A shore dune in North Carolina encroaching upon woodland. Its steep leeward slope is clearly shown at left. (*U.S. Geological Survey photograph.*)

collect in the form of dunes. On low shores with abundant sand and onshore winds, the dunes may be closely spaced and of considerable size. In profile they are like those of the desert (14.41), and they move in similar manner. They may migrate some thousands of feet or even a very few miles; but generally they move inland, and in humid climates they tend to become stagnant and overgrown with vegetation before they have traveled far (Fig. 17.18).

17.11   Features Produced by Organic Agencies. Several types of organisms that thrive in shallow waters are able to effect changes in shorelines, largely through the accumulation of remnants of their own structures. Most of these are only locally important, because their growth is restricted to small areas of protected waters. Only the corals, which can survive even on exposed coasts, achieve great significance.

Various kinds of plants grow in the shallow, sheltered waters of lagoons and bays. Some, like water hyacinths, are floating plants which sometimes, in vast numbers, completely cover the surface of large bodies of water. Others, like the marsh grasses and reeds, are rooted in the bottom. In either case, the remains of the dead plants sink to the bottom and contribute to the filling and obliterating of the lagoons and bays. Somewhat more aggressive, though more restricted in area of occurrence, are the mangroves, a group of tropical shrubs or small trees that root in shallow salt water. Their branching roots unite at or above the water line, so that below the surface they form a fantastic tangle that serves as a trap for leaves, twigs, and sediments. Mangroves have in some places aided in building the shore seaward for short distances. Sections of the west coast of southern Florida are bordered by mangrove swamps.

The shallow waters of many tropical coasts are characterized by reefs of limestone comprised principally of the crumbled skeletal structures of minute marine animals called corals. Under certain conditions corals grow abundantly in shallow waters some distance from shore, and their deposits form a *barrier reef* which is separated from the mainland by a broad lagoon. Of this nature is the great reef which for 1,000 miles parallels the northeast coast of Australia. Other coral reefs form about islands. Fringing reefs grow with such rapidity

Fig. 17.19 Bikini, an atoll of the Marshall Islands group in the central Pacific. The line of reefs and low sandy islands encloses a lagoon measuring about 20 miles in length. (*Official U.S. Navy Photograph.*)

in some clear, shallow, warm waters as to build a shoreline seaward in spite of wave and current erosion.

Some small reef-encircled islands, perhaps volcanic, seem to have undergone slow submergence, possibly that resulting from the general post-glacial rise in sea level, while the coral fringe about them has continued to grow. Such encircling reefs now appear at the surface as low, and more or less complete, coral rings, called *atolls,* which enclose circular lagoons (Figs. 17.19 and 17.20).

17.12   Coasts and Harbors. Between coastal characteristics and human activities there exist many relationships, chief among which are those involving navigation and the development of harbors. Clearly the configuration of the shoreline and of the bottom close to shore are significant factors that must be taken into account in locating or improving ports or channels.

It must be kept in mind, however, that a port is a feature of human, rather than physical, geography. The value of a harbor depends not simply upon its own physical characteristics, but even more upon whether it is located where a harbor is needed. Some of the most commodious and sheltered bays are of almost no value as harbors, because the land behind them is unproductive, sparsely populated, or inaccessible. An example is provided by the magnificent fiords of southern Chile, backed as they are by a wild, storm-swept, mountainous and almost uninhabited land. On the other hand, some of the world's busiest ports have been developed where no natural harbor existed, because the hinterland required a shipping and receiving point for its products and imports. The harbor of Los Angeles and to an even greater degree that of Callao (the port for Lima, Peru) are largely man-made, long breakwaters having been built to protect an otherwise exposed section of coast.

Where the need for a port exists, the character of the coast may go far to determine the amount of work and money that must be expended in order to develop the necessary shelter, depth of channel, and docking facilities. Major

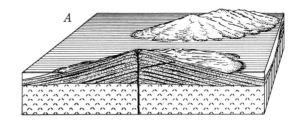

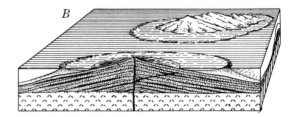

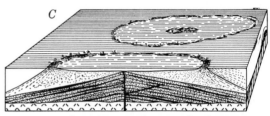

Fig. 17.20   Diagrams to illustrate the development of atolls. *A,* fringing coral reefs about mountainous islands; *B,* growing coral deposits keep pace with submergence of islands; *C,* mountainous islands submerged. Only rings of coral remain.

coastal indentations such as fiords, estuaries, and the lagoons behind offshore bars may afford entirely adequate shelter from wind and sea, but the last two often require extensive dredging in order to provide sufficient depth for ocean-going vessels.

Along smooth coasts that are devoid of sizable inlets it is necessary to create an artificial harbor by partially enclosing a section of water by breakwaters, or by dredging channels and docking basins out of river mouths or coastal flats. Along some coasts excessive rise and fall of the tides create serious problems to harbor development (18.5 and 18.10).

No major harbor is entirely "natural." Even such spacious and well-protected bays as those of New York, San Francisco, Rio de Janeiro, or Sydney have required some dredging and reshaping to provide sufficient deep-water docking space to handle their immense traffic. Those without such excellent natural endowments, however, have required even longer years of planning and work, as well as tremendous expense, to bring them to their present state of capacity and efficiency. The existence of a deep and well-protected bay in a place that is well connected with a productive or populous hinterland represents a resource of incalculable value.

The Sea Floor

17.13   Configuration of the Sea Bottom. A detailed discussion of the features of the ocean floors lies beyond the scope of an introductory textbook in geography. A brief sketch of the topic, however, may serve not only to arouse interest in a fascinating and as yet little-known field of investigation but also to suggest comparisons between the forms and processes of the sea floor and those of the land surfaces and to give some understanding of the nature and occurrence of certain types of islands.

It has been noted that the margins of the seas are generally quite shallow, being underlain by the continental shelf. From the outer edge of the continental shelf, the bottom slopes off relatively steeply to the great depths that are characteristic of the major portion of the ocean floor. But the deep-sea floors that extend outward from the foot of the continental slopes are not to be thought of as featureless plains. While large areas probably are quite smooth, there are also numerous broad swells and depressions, great ridges, scarps, mountains, and troughs of extreme depth that give to the submerged surface a surprising degree of variety. Realization of this remarkable irregularity has grown rapidly in recent years with the use of the echo-sounding method of depth determination. This technique permits much more accurate and detailed survey of the sea bottom than was possible with the sounding line.

17.14   Features of the Shelf and Slope. The continental shelf is in places entirely absent, and in places it reaches the extreme breadth of more than 600 miles. Most commonly widths of 10 to 100 miles are encountered. Generally widths are greatest off glaciated coasts and those with many large rivers, while steep, mountainous coasts are often associated with conspicuously narrow shelves or even none at all (Fig. 17.21).

Generally the surface of the continental shelf is a relatively smooth plain, gently inclined to

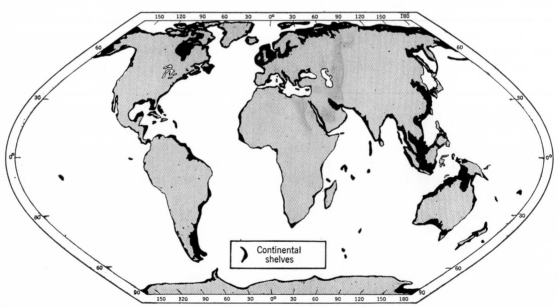

Fig. 17.21   World map of continental shelves.

seaward. Shallow depressions and inconspicuous swells and terraces do little to detract from the essential smoothness. Increasing familiarity with the details of shelf topography, however, has brought with it a realization that many sections of the shelf are much rougher than the idealized picture would suggest.

Especially noteworthy are certain shelf areas that were invaded by continental ice sheets during the late Pleistocene period. The broad shelves off New England, for example, show the same minutely irregular morainic and scoured terrain that may be found on the adjacent mainland. Long Island, Martha's Vineyard, and Cape Cod are in considerable part made up of marginal moraine deposits and outwash. Off the Norwegian coast the shelf is furrowed by tremendous trenches that prolong to seaward the lines of some of the great fiords and presumably represent the erosional work of the same glacial tongues.

A number of shelf areas, such as that off southern California, show gross irregularities in the form of scarps, blocklike ridges, and troughlike depressions. The simplest explanation of these features is that they have been produced by the same block-faulting phenomena that have produced similar topography in the neighboring coastal ranges.

Among the most intriguing features of the continental shelf and slope are the *submarine canyons*. These are deep, seaward-sloping valleys that have their heads on the continental shelf and their lower ends on the continental slope. Some have depths measurable in thousands of feet, with sides that are comparable in steepness to large canyons on the land surfaces. They are very numerous and widespread. The heads of some lie within the mouths, or a short distance to seaward of the mouths, of major rivers. Both the Hudson and the Congo Rivers have large submarine canyons associated with them. Other canyons, however, appear to be quite unrelated to river mouths.

The origin of these huge valleys has aroused much interest and speculation. Various theories have been advanced, but so little is known of the processes that actually affect the sea bottom

that none of the hypotheses can be solidly substantiated. The weight of present opinion favors the theory that the canyons are erosional features, cut by currents of denser, sediment-laden water that pour over the edge of the shelf. The sediment may be carried onto the shelf by streams, or it may be stirred up from the shelf by storm waves. In a few instances, widening and lengthening of the canyons have been observed to occur by slumping of the steep sides.

17.15 The Deep-sea Floors. The average depth of the sea is slightly less than 13,000 ft., a figure that may be compared with the average elevation of the land, which is only about 2,000 ft. The greater part of the sea floor lies between 10,000 and 20,000 ft., a range of values that suggests that even at these great depths the sea bottom is not devoid of major relief features. Relatively smooth plains probably do cover large areas on the floors of broad basins. However, important irregularities have been found to exist on the floors of all the oceans, and in those areas that have been most carefully mapped, the degree and detail of roughness that has been revealed are truly remarkable.

The largest of the irregularities are the massive ridges or swells that rise thousands of feet above the depths on either side, measure hundreds of miles in width, and extend for immense distances. The best known is the Mid-Atlantic Ridge, which follows closely the median line of the Atlantic Ocean from Iceland southward almost to Antarctica (Fig. 17.22). It is roughly 1,000 miles broad, and its crest is generally 5,000 to 10,000 ft. above its base. In only a few places does it approach the surface. However, several small islands do occur along it, the largest group being the Azores. To the extent that the topography of the ridge is known, it is distinctly mountainous. Somewhat similar rises occur in the southeast Pacific and central Indian Oceans, and shorter and narrower ridges are numerous. The Hawaiian Islands are volcanic peaks built upon the crest of a moderately large ridge.

Much smaller are the *seamounts,* isolated peaks or short ridges that occur in considerable numbers upon the ocean floors. The western

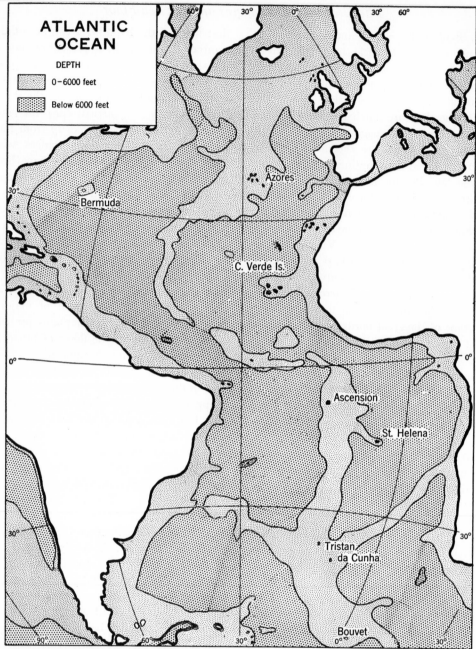

Fig. 17.22 Map showing depths in the Atlantic Ocean. The Mid-Atlantic Ridge and several lesser ridges may be clearly distinguished.

part of the Pacific Basin is dotted with dozens of them, some of which reach the surface to form islands, although most are not that high (Fig. 17.23).

Concerning the origin of these sea-bottom features, little can be definitely determined. It may be inferred, however, that the dominant agencies shaping the floor are tectonic processes, mass movements, and sedimentation. The great ridges and seamounts are probably tectonically produced, in similar manner to the cordilleras, mountain systems and peaks on the land masses. Many of the seamounts are clearly volcanic cones, and some of the ridges are crowned bf volcanoes. The Mid-Atlantic Ridge is known to be a focus of earthquake activity, and some of the islands upon it are volcanic. Certain seamounts, such as those off southern California, have the form of fault blocks.

The important contrast with the development of continental landforms is that these upraised masses on the sea bottom are not attacked by most forms of erosion. Only slumping and similar types of mass movement can serve to reduce or alter the tectonically produced features. Therefore the prominences, once developed, are likely to persist much longer and to be less intricately sculptured than corresponding forms on the lands.

17.16 Troughs and Island Arcs. The greatest depths in the seas are not found in the middle of the broad ocean basins as might be expected. Instead, they occur in the bottoms of remarkable narrow and elongated troughs near the margins of the seas. Practically all of these trenches are located along the convex seaward sides of long, curving chains of islands. From their pattern such chains are known as *island arcs* (Fig. 17.24). Among the arcs that have prominent troughs associated with them are the Aleutian, Kuril, Marianas, and Indonesian arcs in the Pacific, and the eastern loop of the West Indies in the Atlantic. The greatest known depth of the sea, nearly 36,000 ft., has been

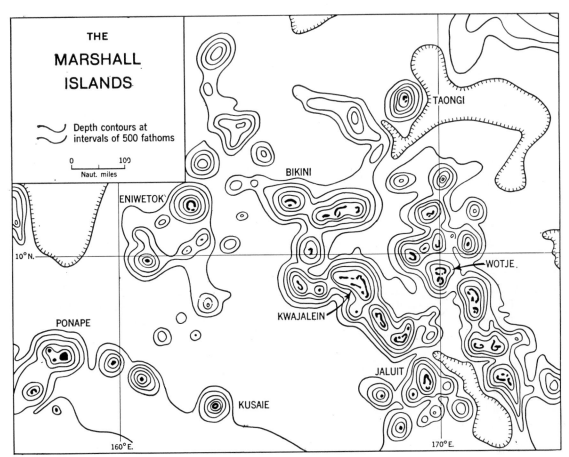

Fig. 17.23 Volcanic seamounts are thickly clustered in the Western Pacific. The Marshall Islands are coral atolls which have formed in association with a group of these great peaks that rise from the ocean floor. (*Modified from "Depth Curve Chart of the Adjacent Seas of Japan," Maritime Safety Agency, Tokyo, 1952.*)

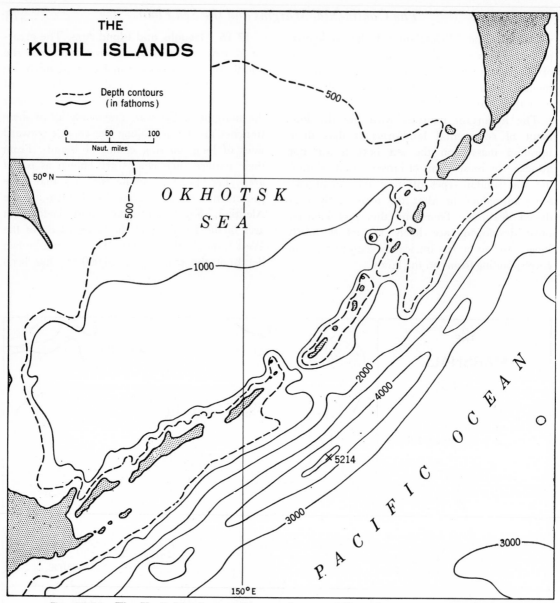

Fig. 17.24 The Kuril Islands, stretching northeastward from Japan, are a typical island arc, with an associated trough or "deep." (*Modified from "Depth Curve Chart of the Adjacent Seas of Japan," Maritime Safety Agency, Tokyo, 1952.*)

recorded in the Marianas Trench southwest of the island of Guam.

The nature and origin of troughs and island arcs have excited much curiosity among geophysicists. Intensive study has been carried on, especially in the Indonesian area. The resulting theories are complex and somewhat conflicting in detail. There is, however, general agreement that the island arcs are complex anticlinal belts and the troughs associated synclines of great size, both produced by the same large-scale lateral compression of the crust. Vulcanism commonly occurs in the anticlinal zone, usually on the concave side. Some island arcs, such as the Lesser Antilles (smaller West Indian islands), actually form a double line, the inner being volcanic, the outer not.

Map Section

AVERAGE ANNUAL PRECIPITATION

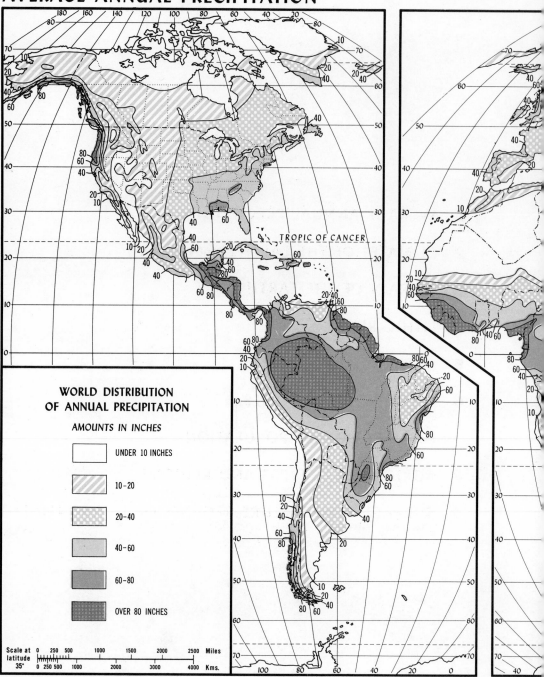

TROPIC OF CANCER

WORLD DISTRIBUTION
OF ANNUAL PRECIPITATION

AMOUNTS IN INCHES

	UNDER 10 INCHES
	10-20
	20-40
	40-60
	60-80
	OVER 80 INCHES

Scale at latitude 35°

0 250 500 1000 1500 2000 2500 Miles

0 250 500 1000 2000 3000 4000 Kms.

1

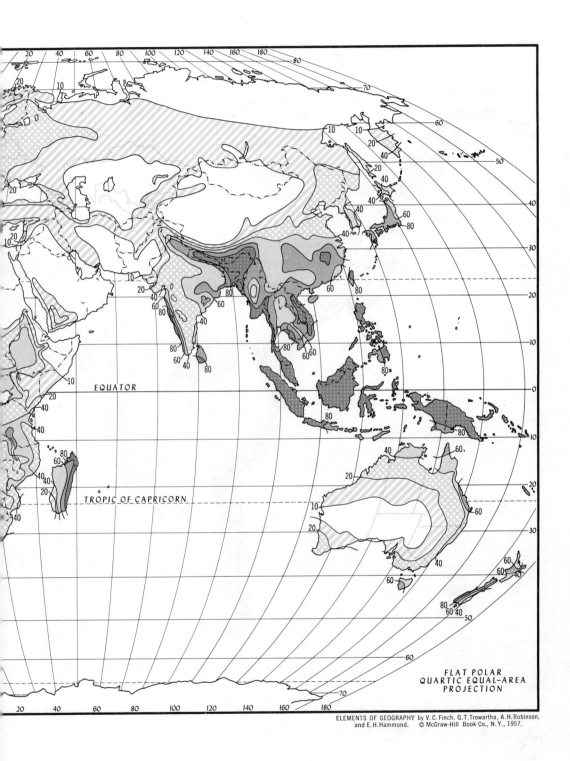

EQUATOR

TROPIC OF CAPRICORN

FLAT POLAR
QUARTIC EQUAL-AREA
PROJECTION

ELEMENTS OF GEOGRAPHY by V.C. Finch, G.T. Trewartha, A.H. Robinson, and E.H. Hammond.   © McGraw-Hill Book Co., N.Y., 1957.

TERRAIN OF THE EARTH

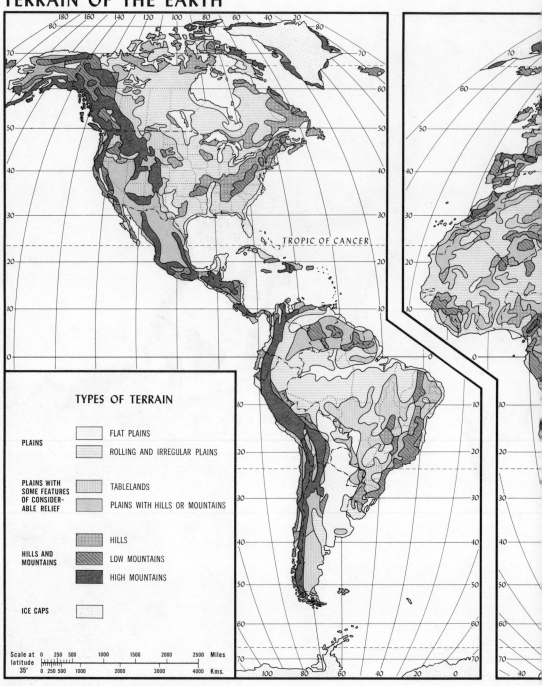

TROPIC OF CANCER

TYPES OF TERRAIN

PLAINS
FLAT PLAINS
ROLLING AND IRREGULAR PLAINS

PLAINS WITH
SOME FEATURES
OF CONSIDER-
ABLE RELIEF
TABLELANDS
PLAINS WITH HILLS OR MOUNTAINS

HILLS AND
MOUNTAINS
HILLS
LOW MOUNTAINS
HIGH MOUNTAINS

ICE CAPS

Scale at latitude 35°
0 250 500   1000   1500   2000   2500 Miles
0 250 500   1000   2000   3000   4000 Kms.

3

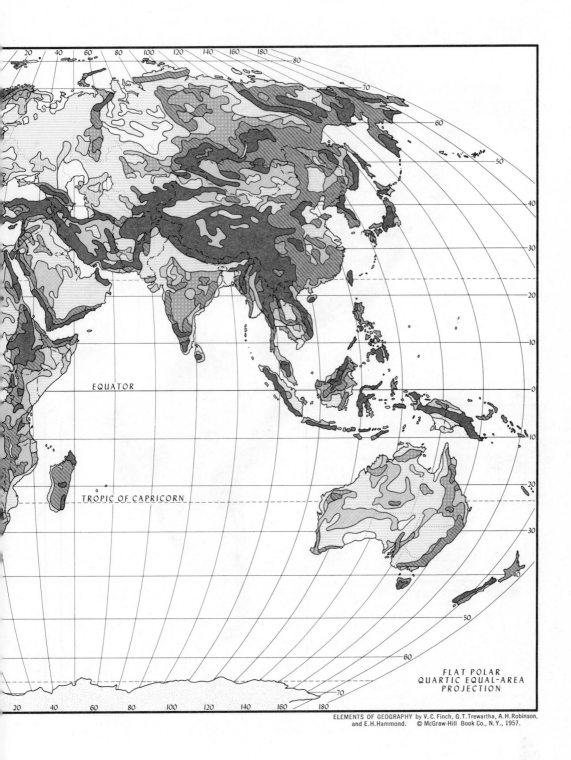

EQUATOR

TROPIC OF CAPRICORN

FLAT POLAR
QUARTIC EQUAL-AREA
PROJECTION

ELEMENTS OF GEOGRAPHY by V.C. Finch, G.T. Trewartha, A.H. Robinson,
and E.H. Hammond.   © McGraw-Hill Book Co., N.Y., 1957.

LITHIC REGIONS

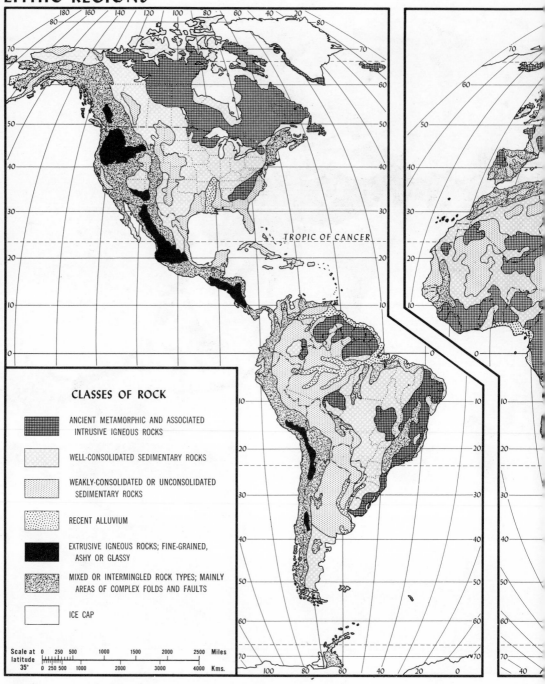

TROPIC OF CANCER

CLASSES OF ROCK

ANCIENT METAMORPHIC AND ASSOCIATED INTRUSIVE IGNEOUS ROCKS

WELL-CONSOLIDATED SEDIMENTARY ROCKS

WEAKLY-CONSOLIDATED OR UNCONSOLIDATED SEDIMENTARY ROCKS

RECENT ALLUVIUM

EXTRUSIVE IGNEOUS ROCKS; FINE-GRAINED, ASHY OR GLASSY

MIXED OR INTERMINGLED ROCK TYPES; MAINLY AREAS OF COMPLEX FOLDS AND FAULTS

ICE CAP

Scale at latitude 35°

0   250 500   1000   1500   2000   2500   Miles

0 250 500   1000   2000   3000   4000   Kms.

4

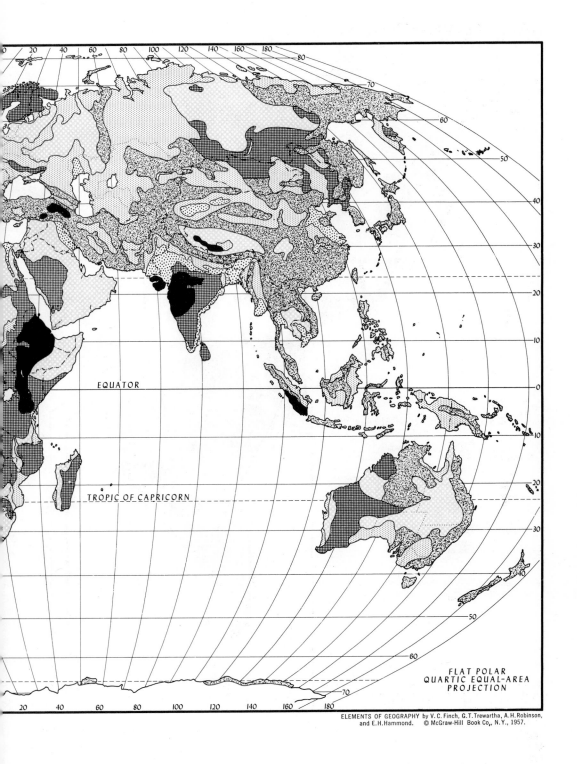

EQUATOR

TROPIC OF CAPRICORN

FLAT POLAR
QUARTIC EQUAL-AREA
PROJECTION

ELEMENTS OF GEOGRAPHY by V. C. Finch, G.T. Trewartha, A.H. Robinson,
and E.H. Hammond.   © McGraw-Hill Book Co,, N.Y., 1957.

NATURAL VEGETATION

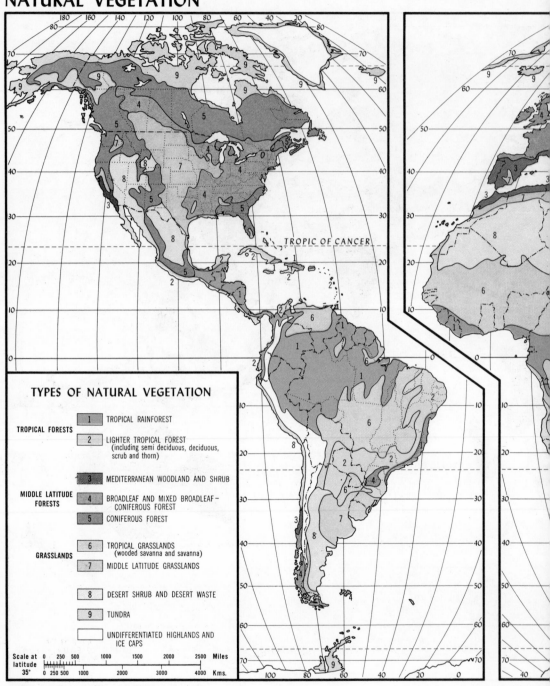

TYPES OF NATURAL VEGETATION

TROPICAL FORESTS

| 1 | TROPICAL RAINFOREST |
| 2 | LIGHTER TROPICAL FOREST (including semi deciduous, deciduous, scrub and thorn) |

MIDDLE LATITUDE FORESTS

3	MEDITERRANEAN WOODLAND AND SHRUB
4	BROADLEAF AND MIXED BROADLEAF-CONIFEROUS FOREST
5	CONIFEROUS FOREST

GRASSLANDS

| 6 | TROPICAL GRASSLANDS (wooded savanna and savanna) |
| 7 | MIDDLE LATITUDE GRASSLANDS |

8	DESERT SHRUB AND DESERT WASTE
9	TUNDRA
	UNDIFFERENTIATED HIGHLANDS AND ICE CAPS

Scale at latitude 35°
0   250 500   1000   1500   2000   2500 Miles
0 250 500 1000   2000   3000   4000 Kms.

TROPIC OF CANCER

5

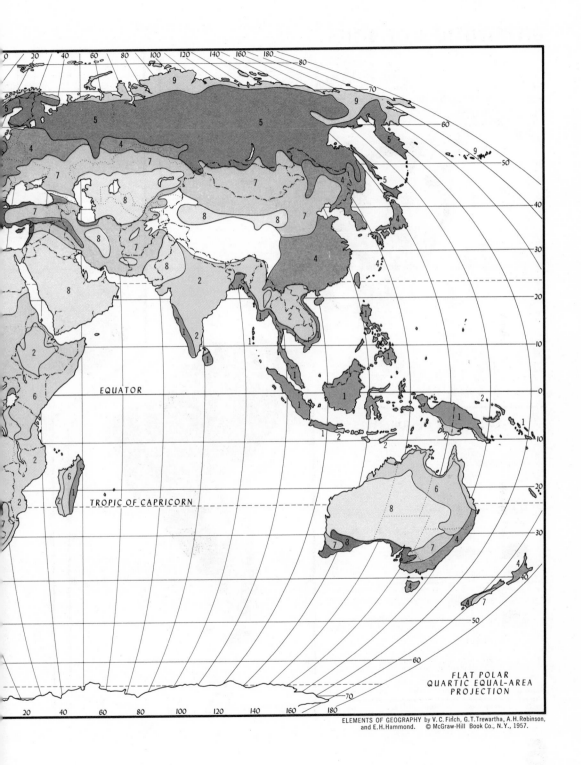

FLAT POLAR
QUARTIC EQUAL-AREA
PROJECTION

EQUATOR

TROPIC OF CAPRICORN

ELEMENTS OF GEOGRAPHY by V.C. Finch, G.T. Trewartha, A.H. Robinson, and E.H. Hammond.   © McGraw-Hill Book Co., N.Y., 1957.

DISTRIBUTION OF SOILS

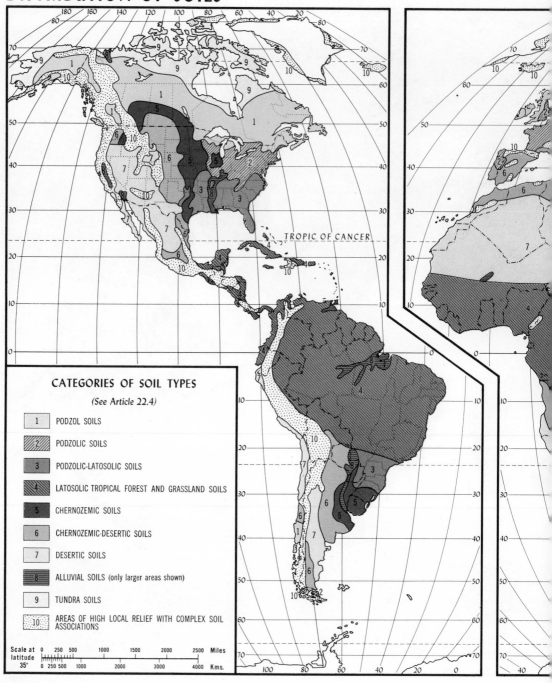

TROPIC OF CANCER

CATEGORIES OF SOIL TYPES

(See Article 22.4)

1	PODZOL SOILS
2	PODZOLIC SOILS
3	PODZOLIC-LATOSOLIC SOILS
4	LATOSOLIC TROPICAL FOREST AND GRASSLAND SOILS
5	CHERNOZEMIC SOILS
6	CHERNOZEMIC-DESERTIC SOILS
7	DESERTIC SOILS
8	ALLUVIAL SOILS (only larger areas shown)
9	TUNDRA SOILS
10	AREAS OF HIGH LOCAL RELIEF WITH COMPLEX SOIL ASSOCIATIONS

Scale at latitude 35°

0 250 500 1000 1500 2000 2500 Miles

0 250 500 1000 2000 3000 4000 Kms.

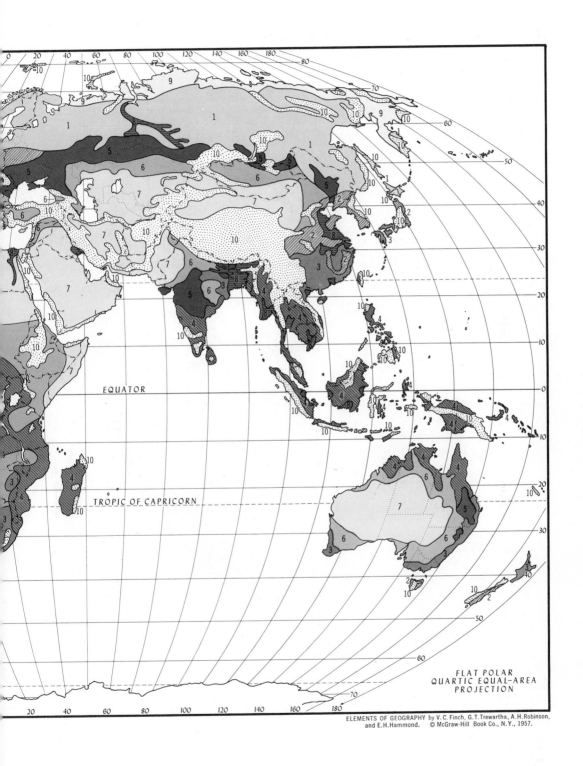

EQUATOR

TROPIC OF CAPRICORN

FLAT POLAR
QUARTIC EQUAL–AREA
PROJECTION

ELEMENTS OF GEOGRAPHY by V.C. Finch, G.T. Trewartha, A.H. Robinson,
and E.H. Hammond.   © McGraw-Hill Book Co., N.Y., 1957.

DISTRIBUTION OF POPULATION

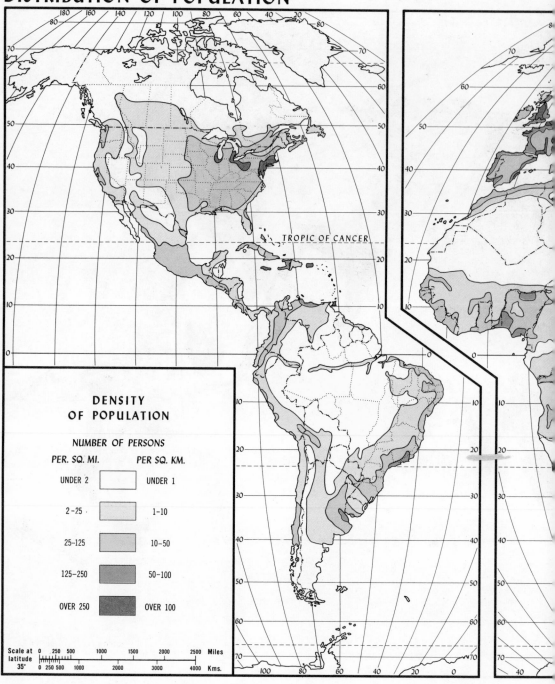

TROPIC OF CANCER

DENSITY OF POPULATION

NUMBER OF PERSONS

PER. SQ. MI.		PER SQ. KM.
UNDER 2		UNDER 1
2–25		1–10
25–125		10–50
125–250		50–100
OVER 250		OVER 100

Scale at latitude 35°

0	250	500	1000	1500	2000	2500	Miles
0	250 500	1000	2000	3000	4000		Kms.

7

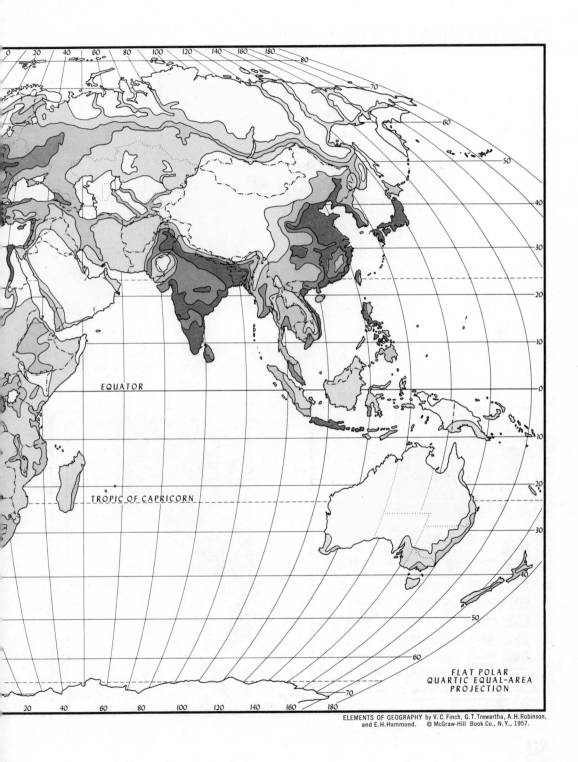

EQUATOR

TROPIC OF CAPRICORN

FLAT POLAR
QUARTIC EQUAL-AREA
PROJECTION

ELEMENTS OF GEOGRAPHY by V.C.Finch, G.T.Trewartha, A.H.Robinson,
and E.H.Hammond.   © McGraw-Hill Book Co., N.Y., 1957.

AGRICULTURAL TYPES AND REGIONS

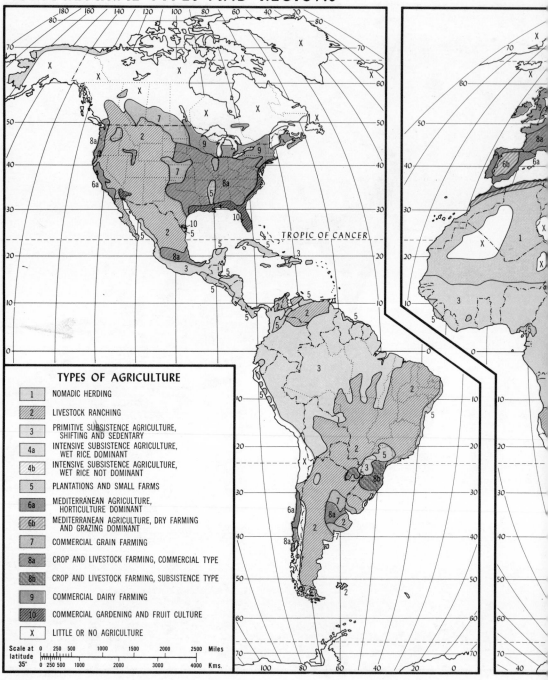

TROPIC OF CANCER

TYPES OF AGRICULTURE

1	NOMADIC HERDING
2	LIVESTOCK RANCHING
3	PRIMITIVE SUBSISTENCE AGRICULTURE, SHIFTING AND SEDENTARY
4a	INTENSIVE SUBSISTENCE AGRICULTURE, WET RICE DOMINANT
4b	INTENSIVE SUBSISTENCE AGRICULTURE, WET RICE NOT DOMINANT
5	PLANTATIONS AND SMALL FARMS
6a	MEDITERRANEAN AGRICULTURE, HORTICULTURE DOMINANT
6b	MEDITERRANEAN AGRICULTURE, DRY FARMING AND GRAZING DOMINANT
7	COMMERCIAL GRAIN FARMING
8a	CROP AND LIVESTOCK FARMING, COMMERCIAL TYPE
8b	CROP AND LIVESTOCK FARMING, SUBSISTENCE TYPE
9	COMMERCIAL DAIRY FARMING
10	COMMERCIAL GARDENING AND FRUIT CULTURE
X	LITTLE OR NO AGRICULTURE

Scale at latitude 35°

| Miles | 0 | 250 | 500 | 1000 | 1500 | 2000 | 2500 |
| Kms. | 0 | 250 | 500 | 1000 | 2000 | 3000 | 4000 |

8

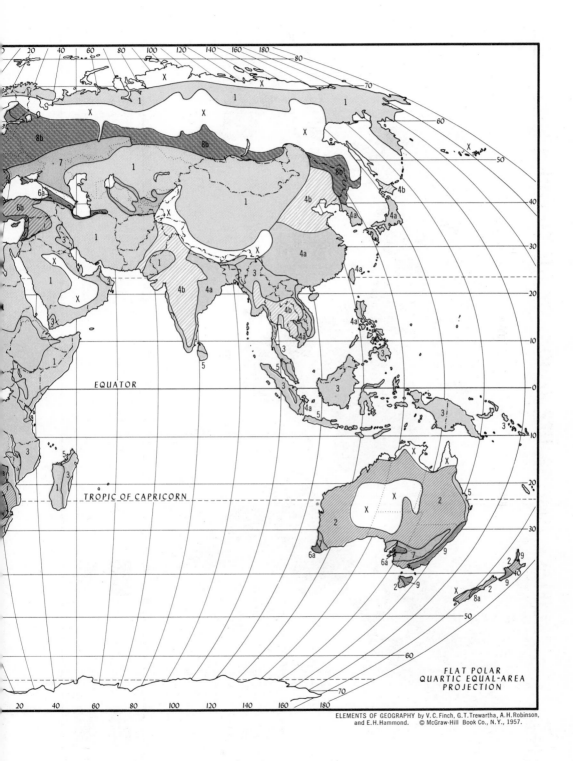

EQUATOR

TROPIC OF CAPRICORN

FLAT POLAR
QUARTIC EQUAL-AREA
PROJECTION

ELEMENTS OF GEOGRAPHY by V.C.Finch, G.T.Trewartha, A.H.Robinson,
and E.H.Hammond.   © McGraw-Hill Book Co., N.Y., 1957.

SURFACE TEMPERATURE REGIONS OF THE CONTINENTS

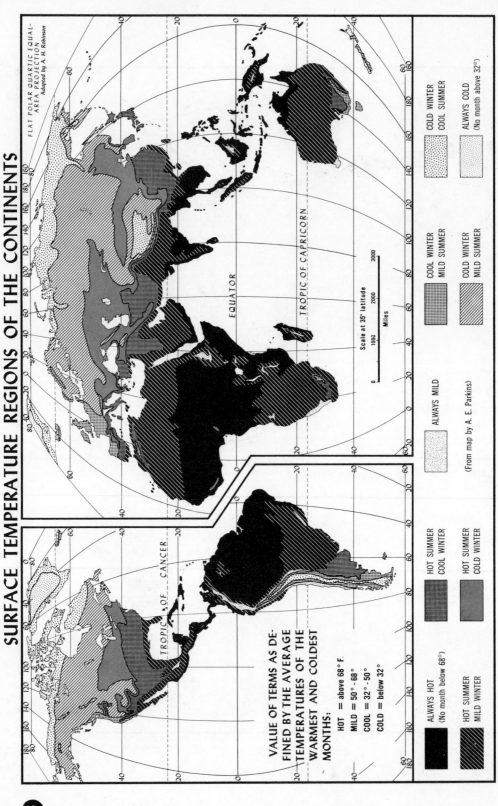

FLAT POLAR QUARTIC EQUAL-
AREA PROJECTION
Adapted by A. H. Robinson

EQUATOR

TROPIC OF CAPRICORN

TROPIC OF CANCER

Scale at 35° latitude

Miles

0   1000   2000   3000

VALUE OF TERMS AS DE-
FINED BY THE AVERAGE
TEMPERATURES OF THE
WARMEST AND COLDEST
MONTHS:

HOT = above 68° F.
MILD = 50° - 68°
COOL = 32° - 50°
COLD = below 32°

ALWAYS HOT
(No month below 68°)

HOT SUMMER
MILD WINTER

HOT SUMMER
COOL WINTER

HOT SUMMER
COLD WINTER

ALWAYS MILD

(From map by A. E. Parkins)

COOL WINTER
MILD SUMMER

COLD WINTER
MILD SUMMER

COLD WINTER
COOL SUMMER

ALWAYS COLD
(No month above 32°)

9

18

The Seas

18.1 The Seas. The land surfaces upon which man lives and from which he derives the greater part of his sustenance in reality occupy what may seem a surprisingly small fraction of the whole surface of the globe. Nearly 71 per cent of the earth is covered by the oceans, and all of the land masses are completely surrounded by water, forming huge islands in the continuous sea. Not only is the sea wide; it is also deep, its volume being many times as great as that of the portions of the continents that lie above sea level. It is the sea, not the land, that is the prevalent environment on the earth, foreign though it seems to the human point of view. Though man does not live in the sea, he has much to do with it, for it serves him as a route of transport, as a source of food and, increasingly, of minerals, as a modifier of his climate, and a partitioner of his lands. A study of the earth as the home of man cannot properly neglect so great and so significant a part of that earth.

18.2 Sea water is a substance of highly complex composition. To be sure, only 3.5 per cent of the substance, by weight, is anything but pure water, and most of this small amount of impurity is accounted for by common salt (sodium chloride) which is present in solution. Most of the small remainder is supplied by dissolved salts of magnesium, calcium, and potassium. Beyond this, however, there are minute quantities of an immense number of other substances, such that a complete listing here is impossible. Most of these impurities have probably been brought into the sea at a very slow rate by streams, though some may be derived from other sources. Continued evaporation, which leaves the salts behind, thus permits a gradual concentration of the soluble materials.

The degree of concentration of dissolved salts, called the *salinity* of the water, varies somewhat from place to place. In the open sea, the variations are small, generally less than 5 per cent on either side of the mean value. The principal factor affecting salinity is the relative rate of precipitation and evaporation. Heavy rainfall lowers the surface salinity by dilution. Strong evaporation raises the salinity by removal of water and concentration of salts.

The highest salinities in the open sea are found in the dry, hot subtropics, where evaporation is great. Nearer the equator salinities decrease because of heavier rainfall. In the cooler middle latitudes salinities are relatively low because of the decrease in evaporation, together with considerable rainfall.

In coastal waters and nearly enclosed seas, the salinity often departs greatly from the mean. In hot, dry, nearly isolated seas, such as the Red Sea and Persian Gulf, the salinities reach very high figures, because this water is subject to strong evaporation but cannot mix freely with less saline waters from the depths of the open sea. On the other hand, in the neighborhood of the mouths of large rivers, or in nearly enclosed seas into which large rivers flow, such as the Black Sea and the Baltic Sea, the dilution by fresh water reduces the salinity to relatively low figures.

The mean density of sea water is slightly higher than that of pure fresh water, because of the presence of the dissolved salts. The den-

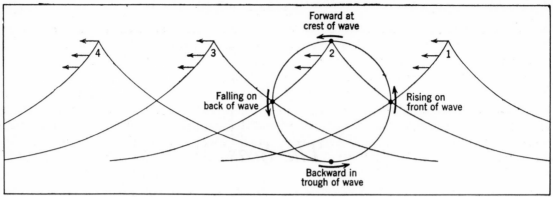

Fig. 18.1 Diagram to illustrate the circular motion of a water particle during the passage of a wave in the open sea.

sity becomes greater with increasing salinity and with decreasing temperature. Thus excessively saline or excessively cold surface water will tend to sink, being replaced by water from beneath. Where warm and cold waters meet, the colder sinks beneath the warmer. In middle-latitude waters, where winter cooling of the surface is extreme, there commonly occurs during the winter an "overturning," with the chilled surface waters becoming cold enough to sink, while slightly warmer waters from below come to the top.

Movements of the Ocean Waters

18.3   Waves are the smallest and most localized of the several kinds of movements in which the ocean waters are involved. Most waves are originated by the wind, though they may continue to travel beyond the area stirred by the wind and long after the wind has ceased to blow. The importance of waves lies chiefly in their effect upon the operation of seagoing ships and, more pertinent to the present discussion, in their function as an erosional and transportational agent along the coasts.

In deep waters, with low or moderate wind velocities, wave movements are smoothly progressive, each water particle describing essentially a circle as the wave impulse passes. The particle rises on the front of the wave, moves forward as the crest passes, drops down the rearward slope, and moves backward in the succeeding trough (Fig. 18.1). However, with high wind velocities the crest of the wave is tipped forward and breaks, forming a whitecap.

The height of waves in the open sea appears to depend upon the velocity of the wind, the length of time the wind has blown, and the distance the wind has driven the waves across the surface. Up to a certain point, the height becomes greater with increasing values of each of these controls.

Near the shore, where the depth of water decreases, an approaching wave is slowed by friction from below, the crest rising, steepening, and finally crashing forward as a breaker, which may hurl tons of water against the bottom or, if close enough inshore, against the land (Fig. 13.31). It is here that the erosional effect of the waves is greatest.

18.4   The Tides and Their Causes. The tides have become a virtual symbol of the certainty and inflexibility of natural processes. Nearly all shores of the open seas experience these distinct periodic rises and falls of sea level. The amount of change is usually of the order of a few feet, and the cycle of change is, in most localities, passed through twice a day. Like most familiar natural phenomena, the tides have been known and studied from very early times, but understanding of how and why they vary from place to place has been slow in coming, and even now it is not securely grasped. The basic factors that produce the tides are not especially obscure, but the actual mechanism of tidal activity on the earth is exceedingly complex.

The principal forces that produce the tides

are (*a*) the gravitational attraction of the moon and (*b*) the centrifugal force of the earth's revolution about the center of gravity of the earth-moon system. The gravitational attraction between any two bodies decreases very rapidly as the distance between the bodies increases. In the present example, the attractive force is directed toward the moon, and is considerably greater on the side of the earth nearest the moon than on the side opposite. The second force is less familiar and somewhat less obvious. In a system such as the earth and moon, one body does not revolve about the other while the other remains stationary. Instead, both revolve around the center of gravity of the pair. Since the earth is much the heavier of the two, the center of gravity of the earth-moon pair is actually just within the earth. The moon swings in a large circle around this point and the earth in a small circle. Though the demonstration is beyond the scope of this book, it may

be shown that the resulting centrifugal force on the earth is always directed away from the moon and is the same everywhere on the earth.

Since the earth neither falls toward the moon because of gravitational attraction nor flies away from it because of centrifugal force, it follows that at the center of the earth these forces must precisely balance one another. On the side toward the moon, however, the gravitational force exceeds the centrifugal, producing a net pull toward the moon. On the side away from the moon, the centrifugal force exceeds the gravitational, producing a net pull away from the moon (Fig. 18.2).

The effect upon the fluid oceans is to draw a flow of water toward the moonward side and toward the opposite side, raising the water level there, while lowering the level on the sides at right angles to the moon. Ideally the resulting pairs of bulges and of lowered water levels would, as the earth rotates on its axis,

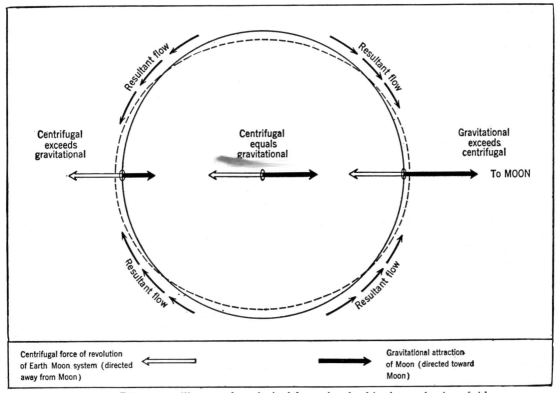

Fig. 18.2   Diagram to illustrate the principal forces involved in the production of tides.

circle the earth in a westward direction, producing at any given point two rises and two falls of sea level during each rotation. Because the moon advances in its 28-day orbit about the earth at a rate that would delay the tidal recurrence somewhat, the true period between successive high tides would, therefore, be approximately 12 hr., 25 min., rather than 12 hr.

The sun also sets up tides, in precisely the same manner as the moon. However, the distance between the sun and earth is so many times greater than that between earth and moon that the tide-producing forces are much smaller, and the resulting tides are less than one-half as high as those caused by the moon. In fact, the effects of the sun do not appear as separate tides, but simply as modifications of the lunar tides.

At times of new moon and of full moon the earth, moon, and sun are nearly in line, the lunar tides and the solar tides occur in the same places, and the height of the solar tides is added to that of those caused by the moon. This causes the high tides of those periods to be unusually high and the intervening low tides of the same periods to be unusually low. They are the periods of *spring tide,* which recur every two weeks. When the moon is at its first and third quarters, the earth-sun line is nearly at right angles with the earth-moon line. The solar tides then fall between, and detract from, the lunar tides. That causes the difference between low and high tide at that time to be less pronounced than usual. They are the periods of *neap tide,* which also recur every two weeks (Fig. 18.3).

18.5 *The Occurrence of Tides.* Because the seas are not continuous, but form a series of interconnected basins of many shapes and sizes, the tides do not actually behave as simple progressive bulges moving westward about the earth. Instead, that type of movement appears to be combined with various oscillatory or swashing movements such as may be produced by tilting or swinging a basin full of water. Each major ocean basin and bordering sea has its own pattern and style of tidal movement, and movements set up in each of two adjacent seas may, in the zone between them, interfere with and affect one another. The result is extreme variety from place to place in height of successive tides, in intervals between tides, in amount of rise and fall, and various associated phenomena.

In general, the tides of the Atlantic Ocean conform most nearly to the ideal type. This may be illustrated by a curve showing the actual rise and fall of the tide at New York (Fig. 18.4). On some shores, notably parts of southern Asia and the Caribbean and Gulf shores of America, there is but one high tide per day.[1] The shores of the Pacific Ocean gen-

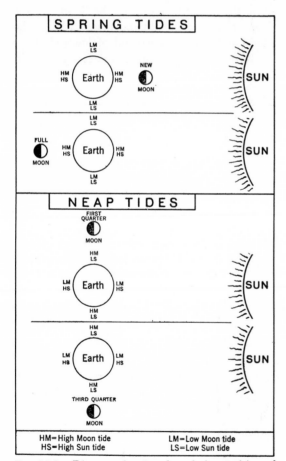

Fig. 18.3 Diagram showing the relative position of sun, moon, and earth during spring tides and neap tides.

[1] H. A. Bauer. A World Map of the Tides. *Geog. Rev.,* Vol. 23, pp. 259–270, 1933.

erally are characterized by what may be called mixed tides. In them each alternate high tide is much lower than the preceding one. This condition may be illustrated by a curve showing the actual tidal rise and fall at Honolulu (Fig. 18.5).

The average difference in water level between low and high tide at any place is called its *tidal range*. The amount of the range is determined by a number of factors. The tides of nearly enclosed bodies of water, such as the Mediterranean and Baltic Seas, are so slight as to be negligible. In sheltered waters, such as the Gulf of Mexico and the Caribbean Sea, the range is small, usually less than 2 ft. Common tidal ranges on exposed coasts are between 5 and 10 ft., though in some places less and in others more. In a few localities, some of them the sites of important commercial ports, the tidal range is so great that it is a distinct handicap to the use of the shore. Some harbors, notably Liverpool, England, have required expensive improvements to offset the disadvantages of the continuous rise and fall of the water level while ships are loading and unloading cargo at the wharves.

Places of great tidal range mainly are situated upon funnel-shaped bays or estuaries, where the range increases with distance from the bay mouth toward its head. Cherbourg, France, has an average tidal range of 17 ft., and Liverpool has a range of 29 ft. The head of the Bay of Fundy, Nova Scotia, has 42 ft. and, at time of spring tide, sometimes as much as 50 ft. of extreme tidal range. Even in the rivers and harbors tributary to the Bay of Fundy ships are temporarily stranded at low tide only to be afloat again a few hours later when the tide sets landward.

18.6 Ocean Drifts and Currents. The waters of the oceans, even if wave movements be neglected, are not stationary, but take part in a broad system of continuous circulation that involves practically the entire water mass. The pattern of movement is three-dimensional, but the deeper parts of the system will not be considered here.

Much the larger part of the surface move-

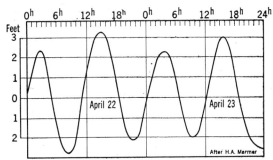

Fig. 18.4 The intervals and amounts of tidal rise and fall at New York during a 48-hr. period (*After H. A. Marmer.*)

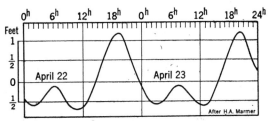

Fig. 18.5 The intervals and amounts of rise and fall of a tide of mixed type at Honolulu during a 48-hr. period. (*After H. A. Marmer.*)

ment of ocean waters is in the nature of a slow, relatively inconspicuous transfer (average rate $2\frac{1}{4}$ miles per hour) that affects only shallow depths. This is more correctly spoken of as a *drift,* in contrast to the deeper and more rapidly flowing *currents* that attain velocities two or three times the foregoing average. Currents are usually confined to localities where discharge takes place through narrow channels. An example is the Florida Current, which, in making its exit from the Gulf of Mexico through the narrow strait between Florida and Cuba, achieves velocities of 4 to 6 miles per hour.

18.7 *General Scheme of Surface Drifts and Currents.* Except in the polar seas, there is a tendency for all the other great oceans to exhibit general patterns of surface currents and drifts which, in many of their broader aspects, greatly resemble each other (Fig. 18.6). Fundamentally, surface ocean currents are related to the direction of the prevailing wind (18.9).

The most conspicuous elements of the cir-

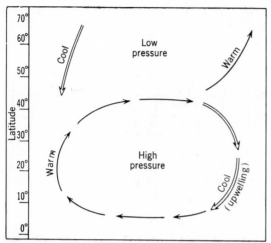

Fig. 18.6 Generalized scheme of ocean currents in a Northern Hemisphere ocean.

culation are the great, closed elliptical whirls about the subtropical oceanic high-pressure cells. The trade winds on the equatorward sides of the subtropical highs in both hemispheres tend to drift the surface waters westward before them across the oceans. This is the *Equatorial Current*. (There are really two equatorial currents, separated in the eastern part of the oceans by a minor countercurrent setting toward the east.) Checked in its westward progress by the continent, the Equatorial Current is divided, part of it flowing northward and part of it southward. Because of deflection (earth rotation) and trend of the coast line, and because of the wind direction around the western end of the subtropical high, the warm poleward-moving current gradually is bent more and more to the east.

At about latitude 40° westerly winds and deflection cause the warm surface waters to turn slowly eastward across the ocean in the form of a *west-wind drift*. In the eastern part of the sea the drift divides, a part of it being carried by the winds equatorward along the coast until it again joins the Equatorial Current and thus completes the low-latitude circuit. In the Northern Hemisphere, however, a considerable portion of the west-wind drift is carried poleward by the stormy southwesterlies, its rela-

tively warm waters washing the west coasts of the continents and eventually entering the Arctic Ocean. The Arctic, compensating for this receipt of warm water, produces an outward surge of cold water that passes down the western side of the ocean into the middle latitudes. In the Southern Hemisphere much of the west-wind drift continues as such clear around the earth in the unbroken belt of ocean that occupies the southern middle latitudes.

It should be emphasized that the picture given above is greatly simplified. Superimposed upon this generalized average pattern are numerous eddies and surges, together with changes in direction and strength of currents following the seasonal shifts and reversals of winds.

If, however, the idealized pattern is compared with a somewhat generalized map of actual currents, it will be seen that the concept has validity (Fig. 18.7). In the Atlantic and Pacific Oceans the subtropical whirls, west-wind drifts, and arctic currents are clearly distinguishable. In the Indian Ocean only the Southern Hemisphere pattern is well developed.

18.8 *Warm and Cool Currents.* If it is kept in mind that poleward-drifting surface waters, since they come from lower latitudes, are inclined to be *relatively* warm, while those from higher latitudes are likely to be cooler *than the surrounding waters,* the following generalizations may be made. In the lower latitudes (equatorward from about 40°) warm ocean currents tend to parallel the eastern sides of continents, while cool ocean currents parallel the western sides of continents (Fig. 18.6). In the middle and higher latitudes the reverse is more often the case, warm ocean currents affecting the western sides of land masses, and cool ones the eastern sides. Along east coasts (western sides of oceans), therefore, there is likely to be a *convergence* of contrasting currents, while along west coasts they tend to *diverge.*

It should be added that a part of the cool water along west coasts in lower latitudes (Peru and northern Chile, northwest and southwest Africa, southern California, and others) is the

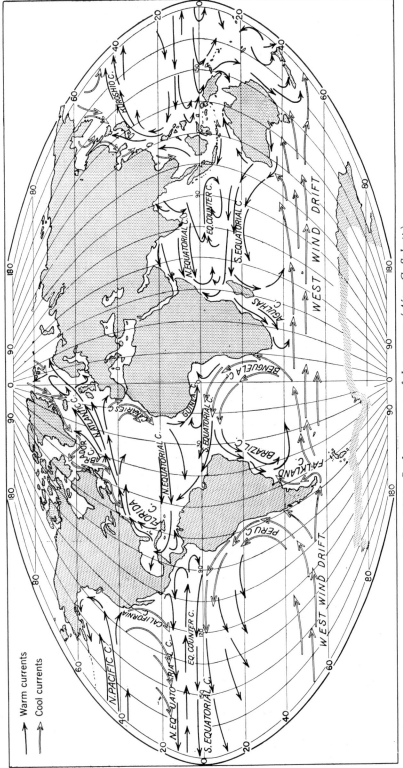

Fig. 18.7 Surface currents of the oceans. (*After G. Schott.*)

381

result of upwelling from depths of several hundred feet along the coast. These regions occupy positions along the eastern margins of well-developed subtropical high-pressure centers and their associated wind whirls, which are conspicuous features over oceans in these latitudes. Along their coasts, equatorward-moving winds from the subtropical whirls drive the surface waters toward lower latitudes. Owing to the deflective force of earth rotation, the ocean currents along these cool-water coasts have a component of movement away from the land. Colder water from below, therefore, rises to replace the surface water (Fig. 18.6).

18.9 *Origin of Surface Currents.* The system of water movement as we know it is largely the resultant of the combined forces of wind friction against the surface and of density contrasts associated with differences in temperature and salinity. The specific pattern of surface movement is determined principally by the winds. But although there is a general agreement between prevailing winds and ocean currents, the flow patterns of the two fluids are not identical. Temperature and salinity differences, shape, depth, and degree of enclosure of the basins of the oceans and marginal seas all affect the pattern of circulation.

18.10 Tidal Currents. Quite local in their occurrence but highly important to coastal development and to man's use of the coasts are the inshore currents initiated by the tides. These are phenomena of the coastal waters, and especially of those places where lagoons, sounds, or extensive bays communicate with the open sea through relatively narrow openings.

In order to raise or lower the water level in a semienclosed bay, there must be a horizontal flow of water inward or outward through the opening. If the tidal range is large and the area of the bay is large, the volume of water pouring through a narrow entrance will also be great. The resulting current velocities through the opening may become sufficiently high (not infrequently 5 to 10 miles per hour) to have an erosional effect, tending to maintain the opening against bar development and to deepen the channel. This is why many bay bars and most offshore bars have openings in them.

Such strong tidal currents also affect the navigability of harbor entrance channels. A ship entering or leaving against the current must expend much power in order to make headway. A ship moving with the current is difficult to control, in much the same manner as an aircraft making a downwind landing. Especially difficult is the docking of a large ship across the direction of a tidal current, where sidewise drift occurs. Although these difficulties are somewhat less severe for powerful modern steam vessels than for sailing craft in earlier times, the difference is only one of degree.

Surface Temperatures

18.11 Surface temperatures of the seas range from about 28.4°F., which is the approximate freezing point of sea water, to about 86°F. This is a much smaller range of values than is experienced on the lands, very low temperatures not being present in the seas (unless temperatures of the polar ice be included). Changes in the temperature of the sea surface during the year are remarkably small, amounting to no more than 2 to 7°F. in tropical waters and 9 to 15°F. in the upper middle latitudes. Variation in the surface temperature between day and night is no more than a fraction of a degree. Thus, while the sea exhibits a considerable variety of temperatures, these values change little from day to day and only in modest degree during the entire course of the year, a fact of great importance to the earth's climatic characteristics.

The chief process by which the sea is heated is absorption of radiation from the sun and the atmosphere. Cooling of the sea is accomplished largely by radiation from the surface and by evaporation of water from the surface. Since incoming radiation decreases from the tropics toward the poles, and since the greatest cooling of the seas occurs in the higher latitudes, especially during the winter, it is not surprising to find that the ocean temperatures follow essentially a latitudinal pattern (Fig. 18.8). The tropical seas are warm, and variations from place to place are small. Poleward of the tropics, however, temperatures fall off rapidly with increasing latitude.

The fact that the sea-surface isotherms do not strictly follow the parallels of latitude indicates clearly that radiation is not the only control. Prevailing air temperatures have an effect also, particularly in lowering sea temperatures near the eastern coasts of the continents in the middle latitudes during the winter.

Much more important, however, is the circulation of ocean water in the great surface current systems. By this means, warm water is brought into the middle latitudes by the poleward-moving currents on the western sides of the oceans and is moved across to the eastern sides in the west-wind drifts. Cool water is brought equatorward by the currents on the east sides of the subtropical oceans and by the arctic currents on the opposite sides in the high latitudes.

The effects of these movements of the ocean waters may be seen in Fig. 18.8. The average sea temperature on the coast of southern Japan, washed by a warm current, is nearly 10° warmer than that in southern California, in the same latitude but washed by a cool current. Between Labrador, flanked by a cold arctic current, and northern Ireland, in the path of the warm west-wind drift, the difference is more than 15° in August. During the winter, it is nearly twice that.

A reinforcement of the cooling effect of the equatorward-moving currents along the subtropical west coasts of the continents is provided by the rising of cool water to the surface where the currents turn offshore (18.8). This effect may be demonstrated by the fact that during the summer the water temperature along the coast of central California, where such upwelling occurs, is actually lower than the temperature much farther north along the coast of Oregon and Washington.

18.12 Ocean Temperatures and Climate. While the relationships between the oceans and the various climatic elements are discussed in the appropriate sections of the chapters dealing with climates, certain of the more significant connections may conveniently be recalled here.

Because of the great width of the oceans, air masses passing across them are in contact with the water surface for considerable periods of time. This gives the surface layers of the atmos-

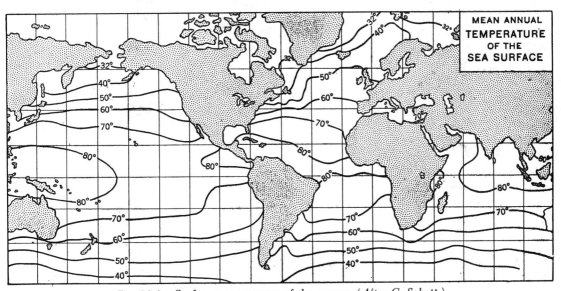

Fig. 18.8 Surface temperatures of the oceans. (*After G. Schott.*)

phere a good opportunity to assume temperatures that are approximately those of the sea surface itself. At least, the temperature of the air will change toward that goal. If this same air is then transported onto an adjacent continent, it carries with it the sea temperatures.

Since the ocean temperatures tend to be relatively mild and to change but little from winter to summer, a corresponding mildness is a distinguishing characteristic of the temperatures of those land areas into which sea air is regularly carried. The effect is especially noticeable on the west coasts in the middle latitudes, where the prevailing onshore movement of marine air imparts much warmer winter and cooler summer temperatures than are characteristic of the interiors or eastern sides of the continents. Thus at San Francisco, the mean temperature of the warmest month is only 60°, and that of the coldest no lower than 49°.

The more or less "foreign" temperatures for any given latitude that are brought about by ocean currents are variously reflected in coastal climates. The effect upon temperature is straightforward. Thus, for example, in northwestern Europe, where westerly winds carry the effects of the warm North Atlantic Drift far into the continent, coastal temperatures in January are 30 to 40° warmer than the average for these latitudes. Where currents of contrasting temperatures converge, as along the middle-latitude east coasts in Asia and North America, the sharp gradient in sea temperature is to a small degree reflected in a similarly abrupt gradient in air temperature along the coast. Cool-water coasts in the subtropics are often foggy, the fog being the result of warm air from over the ocean proper being chilled to below the condensation point by passing over the cool current near the shore.

Biotic Resources of the Sea

18.13   Major Classes of Sea Life. The myriads of forms of life that exist in the sea may, for present purposes, be divided into three major groups according to their mobility. Most

familiar are the *free-swimming forms,* which include the larger fish, Crustacea, and sea mammals that are able to move about over considerable distances in search of food. A second group is made up of the *sessile forms,* those plants, shellfish, corals, etc., that are more or less permanently attached to the bottom. The third, and perhaps least familiar group, comprises the *plankton.* These are small, sometimes microscopic organisms, both plant and animal, that either because they have no means of locomotion or because they are so very small, are incapable of self-determined movements of any significant scale. Instead, they drift with the water in which they live.

18.14   *Plankton.* The plant plankton may be said to represent the most fundamental source of food for sea life in general. All forms of sea creatures, including the animal plankton, feed either directly upon these tiny plants or upon other sea animals, many of which, in turn, do feed upon the plants. Remove the plant plankton from the sea, and all other forms of life would soon perish.

Where the plant plankton are concentrated, there also will be found the greatest numbers of sea animals, feeding upon the plants or upon one another. Any localized conditions favoring the concentration of plant plankton will tend to concentrate fish, shellfish, and sea mammals as well.

The needs of plant plankton are the same as those of plants in general: light, and certain mineral and organic nutrients. The first requirement confines them to the surface layers of the sea, into which light can penetrate. The second is manifested chiefly in a need for constant replenishment of the nutrients, to make up for those which have been removed from the waters by the existing generations of plankton. This renewal must come largely from the waters below. Hence any process that brings deeper water to the surface will favor the maintenance of a dense plankton growth. Significant means for accomplishing this are (*a*) turbulent mixing of water by wave action in shallow coastal waters, (*b*) upwelling of cold waters along subtropical west coasts, and (*c*) winter overturning of waters in the higher middle latitudes (18.2). The surface waters in areas where one or more of these processes occur appear to be the centers of plankton concentration and therefore of sea life generally.

18.15 Fish and Fisheries. The greatest resource of the oceans is edible fish, and yet the value of the world's annual catch ordinarily does not equal that of the American corn, cotton, hay, or wheat crop. Although seas cover approximately three-quarters of the earth's surface, the areas frequented by edible fish in large numbers, and in which they are most easily caught, are very much restricted. Most of the world's fishing is done along the margins of continents in continental shelf waters whose depths are less than 200 fathoms (1,200 ft.).

The commercial fishing grounds of world importance are, in general, outside the tropics and in the Northern Hemisphere. It is often stated that tropical waters contain fewer edible fish than those farther poleward, because there is a greater concentration of plankton in cooler waters. This belief that both plankton and fish are less abundant in tropical seas is somewhat open to question. Certain it is that in the low-latitude seas the number of fish species is greater than it is in middle and higher latitudes. On the other hand, it is apparently true that there are no such regional concentrations of a few valuable and better known species as there are in the cooler seas. Tropical fish suffer the further handicap of being softer and inclined to spoil more readily, so that they are commercially less valuable. Locally, the fish resource of tropical coastal waters may be of highest importance to the native inhabitants. The outstanding significance of Northern Hemisphere fisheries, in all probability, is associated with the presence there of large areas of shallow water along the margins of the more populous continents.

18.16 *Fishing Regions of World Importance.* Organized commercial fishing on a large scale is concentrated in four regions: (*a*) the coastal waters of Japan, Sakhalin, and eastern Siberia, (*b*) those of New England, Maritime Canada, and Newfoundland, (*c*) the coasts of northwestern Europe, and (*d*) the Pacific coasts of northwestern United States, Canada, and Alaska (Fig. 18.9).

Not only is the continental shelf around

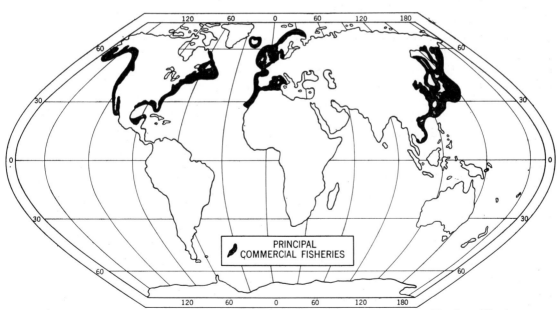

PRINCIPAL COMMERCIAL FISHERIES

Fig. 18.9 The principal commercial fisheries are in the cool seas of the Northern Hemisphere, especially along the broader continental shelves.

Japan and off eastern Siberia one of the world's most important fishing grounds, but Japan is also the world's most important fishing nation, her catch making up approximately one-quarter of the world's total. The annual catch of Japan is three to four times that of the United States or Great Britain, which are her closest rivals. Cool and warm currents are both present, herring being the principal food fish of the former, and sardines, bonito, tunny, and mackerel, of the latter. More than in most countries fish is a staple article of diet in Japan; in fact it is the main source of animal foodstuffs. Large quantities of fish are also used as fertilizer in this land of ultraintensive agriculture.

The life of New England, Newfoundland, and Maritime Canada is closely associated with the development of the fish resource. Fishing here is carried on both in the shallow inshore coastal waters and in the region of the banks, the latter being more important. The North Atlantic Banks, extending as broad submarine elevations from Nantucket to the eastern coast of Newfoundland, are the world's greatest cod fisheries. Herring, mackerel, haddock, and halibut are a few of the other commercially valuable species of this western North Atlantic region. Fish such as herring and mackerel, which live relatively near the surface, are caught mainly by drift nets and lines. Other fish, represented by cod, halibut, and haddock, travel and feed in deeper waters (200 ft. or more below the surface) and are more difficult to catch. These are taken (a) by hand lines operated from the decks of fishing boats, (b) by long trawl lines buoyed up at both ends, to which are attached several hundred shorter perpendicular lines, and (c) by trawl nets. The latter are in the form of huge cone-shaped bags, and, because of their size and weight and the depth at which they are operated, they must be hauled by steam-powered vessels called trawlers. Shell fish, especially oysters, obtained from the coastal waters of the Middle Atlantic States, are another important element of the western North Atlantic fisheries. Chesapeake Bay is the principal focus of this development.

Along the Pacific Coast of North America

salmon is by far the most important fish, and from that region comes practically all the world's canned salmon. The habits of this fish make it particularly easy to catch, and this fact greatly increases the danger of salmon extermination. Each spring and summer millions of adult salmon, driven by the urge to spawn, leave the ocean and ascend the streams emptying into the Pacific from northern California to the Bering Sea. Before winter sets in, each salmon reaches the river or lake of its birth and there in the sand the female deposits its eggs. This fact that, when life is about spent, the adult salmon returns to the spot of its birth, makes it particularly easy to catch these fish in nets as they ascend the coastal rivers. The result has been a rapid rise of the salmon industry on a particular river and then a serious decline. By 1920 the salmon industry of North America was threatened with depletion. As a result of conservation measures established since that date, salmon runs have increased again in some of the streams.

More than 200,000 men, drawn chiefly from Great Britain, Norway, Holland, and France, annually engage in fishing in the stormy waters of the eastern North Atlantic. In this region weather is characteristically bad and the seas rough, so that the loss of life among fishermen is high. Fishing goes on throughout the year, although spring, when plankton is most abundant along the coasts, is the season of greatest activity. Herring, cod, and mackerel are the principal fish. Northwest Europe is the greatest fish-exporting region of the world, the annual shipments often exceeding 1,000,000 tons.

18.17 Sea Mammals. In addition to edible fish, there are other sea animals, such as seal, walrus, and whale, which are valuable for their skins, oil, bone, ivory, or flesh. Without exception, each of these animals has been the object of such ruthless slaughter that it has led to serious depletion of its numbers, and in some instances near extermination has been the result.

The fur seal is an inhabitant of the waters and coasts of the North Pacific, more especially the Bering Sea, and those bordering the Antarctic Continent. Desire for profits led to such reckless killing of these valuable animals that the industry has been practically ruined. To prevent complete extinction fur seals are now protected by international agreement. Arctic seals, valuable principally for their oil and skins, are caught off the northeast of North America as they drift southward on the ice floes in early spring. Their numbers, too, have been greatly reduced. A native of shallow coastal arctic waters and sought for its ivory and tough hide, the walrus has suffered the same fate as the seal. Formerly all these animals furnished one of the principal sources of food for the natives who occupied the arctic coasts.

Whales inhabit both Arctic (North Atlantic Arctic and North Pacific Arctic) and Antarctic seas. Their particular value is for oil. In the Arctic seas whales have been so greatly reduced in numbers that the whaling industry has all but disappeared. It is now at high tide in Antarctic waters, but without strong international regulatory measures taken to conserve the whales of those regions the history of the Arctic industry could be repeated.

References for Section B

General

Lake, Philip. "Physical Geography." Cambridge University Press, London and New York, 1949.

Martonne, Emmanuel de. "A Shorter Physical Geography." Alfred A. Knopf, Inc., New York, 1927.

Passarge, S. "Beschreibende Landschaftskunde." Friederichsen, de Gruyter & Co., Hamburg, 1929.

Strahler, A. N. "Physical Geography." John Wiley & Sons, Inc., New York, 1951.

Supan, A. G. "Grundzüge der physische Erdkunde." Walter De Gruyter & Co., Berlin, 1927–1930.

Landforms and Their Development

Bagnold, R. A. "The Physics of Blown Sand and Desert Dunes." William Morrow & Company, Inc., New York, 1941.

Bowman, Isaiah. "Forest Physiography." John Wiley & Sons, Inc., New York, 1911.

Byerly, Perry. "Seismology." Prentice-Hall, Inc., New York, 1942.

Cotton, C. A. "Landscape, as Developed by the Processes of Normal Erosion." John Wiley & Sons, Inc., New York, 1948.

———. "Climatic Accidents in Landscape-making." Whitcombe & Tombs, Ltd., Wellington, N. Z., 1942.

———. "Volcanoes as Landscape Forms." John Wiley & Sons, Inc., New York, 1952.

Davis, W. M. "Geographical Essays." Ginn & Company, Boston, 1909.

Fenneman, N. M. "Physiography of Western United States." McGraw-Hill Book Company, Inc., New York, 1931.

———. "Physiography of Eastern United States." McGraw-Hill Book Company, Inc., New York, 1938.

Flint, R. F. "Glacial Geology and the Pleistocene Epoch." John Wiley & Sons, Inc., New York, 1947.

Gautier, E. F. "Sahara: The Great Desert." English translation by D. F. Mayhew. Columbia University Press, New York, 1935.

Gilluly, J., A. C. Waters, and A. O. Woodford. "Principles of Geology." W. H. Freeman & Company, San Francisco, 1954.

Gutenberg, B. (editor). "Internal Constitution of the Earth." Physics of the Earth-VII. McGraw-Hill Book Company, Inc., New York, 1939.

Heck, N. H. "Earthquakes." Princeton University Press, Princeton, N.J., 1936.

Hinds, N. E. A. "Geomorphology." Prentice-Hall, Inc., New York, 1943.

Kemp, J. F. "A Handbook of Rocks." D. Van Nostrand Company, Inc., New York, 1940.

Lahee, F. H. "Field Geology." 5th ed. McGraw-Hill Book Company, Inc., New York, 1952.

Leet, L. D., and S. Judson. "Physical Geology." Prentice-Hall, Inc., New York, 1954.

Lobeck, A. K. "Atlas of American Geology." Geographical Press, Columbia University, New York, 1932.

———. "Geomorphology: An Introduction to the Study of Landscapes." McGraw-Hill Book Company, Inc., New York, 1939.

Longwell, C. R., and R. F. Flint. "Introduction to Physical Geology." John Wiley & Sons, Inc., New York, 1955.

Nevin, C. M. "Principles of Structural Geology." John Wiley & Sons, Inc., New York, 1949.

Penck, Walther. "Morphological Analysis of Land Forms; a Contribution to Physical Geology." English translation by H. Czech and K. C. Boswell. The Macmillan Company, London, 1953.

Sharpe, C. F. S. "Landslides and Related Phenomena." Columbia University Press, New York, 1934.

Thwaites, F. T. "Outlines of Glacial Geology." Edwards Bros., Inc., Ann Arbor, Mich., 1934.

Thornbury, W. D. "Principles of Geomorphology." John Wiley & Sons, Inc., New York, 1954.

Tolman, C. F. "Ground Water." McGraw-Hill Book Company, Inc., New York, 1937.

Umbgrove, J. H. F. "The Pulse of the Earth." Martinus Nijhoff, The Hague, 1947.

von Engeln, O. D. "Geomorphology, Systematic and Regional." The Macmillan Company, New York, 1942.

Wooldridge, S. W., and R. S. Morgan. "Outlines of Geomorphology." Longmans, Green & Co., Inc., New York, 1937.

Worcester, P. G. "A Textbook of Geomorphology." D. Van Nostrand Company, Inc., New York, 1939.

Zeuner, F. E. "The Pleistocene Period, Its Climate, Chronology and Faunal Successions." Printed for the Ray Society, London, 1945.

SEE ALSO THE LIST OF GENERAL REFERENCES, ABOVE.

The Continental Margins and the Sea

Coker, R. E. "This Great and Wide Sea." The University of North Carolina Press, Chapel Hill, N.C., 1947.

Daly, R. A. "The Floor of the Ocean: New Light on Old Mysteries." The University of North Carolina Press, Chapel Hill, N.C., 1942.

Johnson, D. W. "Shore Processes and Shoreline Development." John Wiley & Sons, Inc., New York, 1919.

Kuenen, Ph. H. "Marine Geology." John Wiley & Sons, Inc., New York, 1950.

Lake, Philip. "Physical Geography." Cambridge University Press, London and New York, 1949.

Shepard, F. P. "Submarine Geology." Harper & Brothers, New York, 1948.

Steers, J. A. "The Coastline of England and Wales." Cambridge University Press, London and New York, 1946.

Sverdrup, H. V. "Oceanography for Meterologists." Prentice-Hall, Inc., New York, 1942.

————, M. W. Johnson, and R. H. Fleming. "The Oceans: Their Physics, Chemistry, and General Biology." Prentice-Hall, Inc., New York, 1942.

Thornbury, W. D. "Principles of Geomorphology." John Wiley & Sons, Inc., New York, 1954.

Wooldridge, S. W., and R. S. Morgan. "Outlines of Geomorphology." Longmans, Green & Co., Inc., New York, 1937.

Zeuner, F. E. "The Pleistocene Period, Its Climate, Chronology and Faunal Successions." Printed for the Ray Society, London, 1945.

Section C EARTH RESOURCES

Human Dependence upon Earth Resources.
Man lives upon the earth's surface; from the atmosphere and from the upper portion of the earth's crust he obtains his foods and the things out of which he fashions his material culture. All natural elements which he uses can thus properly be called resources. This list is long and even includes conditions of climate and the terrain features of the land surface which already have been discussed at length. In addition, however, there are other elements for which he finds use, such as some of the materials of the earth's composition or its natural vegetable and animal life. These are not grown or manufactured by human enterprise but exist as parts of the natural earth. Unlike climate and landforms, they actually are consumed or fashioned into more useful forms by man. Because they either are obtained from the natural earth or exist in or upon it, they are called natural resources, or *earth resources.*

Since the beginning of human existence man has directed his activities with reference to such earth elements as he has learned how to use for his own benefit. Among primitive peoples the list was not long. Water, fibers, roots, seeds, fruits, fish, and game supplied food and clothing. Wood and carefully chosen stones yielded shelter, weapons, and implements. A little earth and some native metals were used in making other utensils and articles of personal adornment. The advance of material culture has been accompanied by a steady increase in the number of earth substances required and in the degree and the variety of human dependence upon them. For example, modern society requires water, as did the old, but in such quantities as never before. The natural supplies of plants and animals long since have proved inadequate, and cultivated or domesticated species have supplemented or replaced them. Yet those provided by nature still are in demand. New requirements for woods and metals in modern industry have increased the demand for them a thousandfold and have woven them into combinations whose patterns are constantly changing. The dependence of present civilization upon certain earth resources has grown so rapidly in recent decades that few people realize how different the present is, in that respect, from even the recent past. This is well illustrated by the use of energy resources, such as coal, petroleum, natural gas and water power, which are required for the ever-increasing processing of other resources. In the first fifty years of the present century the utilization of energy resources quadrupled in the United States.[1]

It should be borne in mind that a resource does not just exist, but in a real sense is created by man. For example, natural gas or the radioactive minerals have existed much longer than man has; yet they became natural resources only when man learned to use them. His ability to utilize the natural elements is increasing at a kind of geometric rate so that each year that passes sees many new adaptations or the creation of new things from the natural endowment of the earth. His increased knowledge helps him to find new supplies or to use more efficiently those he now has. Consequently, the supply of earth resources is increasing. Because of their vital importance in modern affairs, an understanding of the occurrence and distribution of the natural, or earth-given, resources is as fundamental to an appreciation of the broader problems of geography as is a knowledge of climate or landforms.

[1]Estimate by the U.S. Bureau of Mines. Annual Report of Resources for the Future, Incorporated, Washington, D.C., 1955.

Classes of Earth Resources. The natural resources available for the use of man are of two principal classes: inorganic and organic. In the former class are found those gaseous, liquid, or solid earth components that have value for direct human use or as bases for the production of other necessary goods. Such are water, the mineral fuels, the metalliferous ores, building stones, and the valuable chemical raw materials of earth or air. Organic resources are such as are derived from the natural plant and animal life of various parts of the earth. Among them are wood, natural pasture, wild game, and fish. The soil, a resource of fundamental importance, is made up of both inorganic and organic components. With the inorganic rock fragments, which are the bases of soils, are mingled variable quantities of plant and animal remains and a world of microscopic organisms. Some organic forms in the natural environment of man can hardly be called resources. Worthless or poisonous plants and certain forms of insect or of microscopic life are parts of the natural equipment of areas, but they constitute hazards to life and the ability to make a living just as, for example, certain aspects of weather and climate do. However, comment upon that phase of the subject of earth resources falls beyond the scope of this textbook. The resources to be considered in the following chapters of this section of the book are (*a*) water, (*b*) natural vegetation, (*c*) soil, (*d*) the mineral fuels, and (*e*) ores and other economic minerals.

There are some natural resources, both organic and inorganic, of which man may use as much as he desires without fear that the supply will ever be exhausted. Such may be called the *inexhaustible resources,* and air, sand, or common clay are examples of the class. Others, although the supply may be limited in quantity, tend to replenish themselves when they are used. These may be called the *renewable re-sources,* and water, wood, and natural pasture illustrate the class. Still others, such as coal, iron, or chemical salts, have required the operation of natural processes through the geologic ages for their accumulation. When once they are used, they are gone forever. Such may be called *nonrenewable resources.*

The Conservation of Earth Resources. The dependence of modern society upon a variety of critically important earth resources is well known. There is nothing to indicate that future generations will not need most of these resources and perhaps others that are not now thought valuable. Consequently, it is clear that present generations are charged with a responsibility toward the future, particularly with respect to the nonrenewable resources which now are being produced in unusually large quantities. *It is, in fact, the responsibility of the present generation to secure to society, both now and in the future, the maximum benefit from the use of those materials provided by nature.* The discharge of that responsibility calls for much knowledge and a careful balancing of the earth conditions with the human factors involved. Information is needed upon the following matters: (*a*) What kinds and how much of the various resources are available? (*b*) To what extent may the more abundant and the renewable resources be substituted for the less abundant and the nonrenewable? (*c*) How may resources be used with the least waste, and how may new methods of production and use reduce waste? (*d*) In how far is it wise to sacrifice human energy and risk human life to save resources? (*e*) How may the rights of present generations be properly balanced against those of the future? Efforts to gather information and solve problems concerning any phase of this complicated matter may be considered a part of the field of *the conservation of natural re-sources.*

References for Section C

Water Resources

"A Water Policy for the American People, Vol. I." "Ten Rivers in America's Future, Vol. II." Reprint of the President's Water Resources Policy Commission, U.S. Government Printing Office, Washington, D.C., 1950.

Borchert, John R. The Surface Water Supply of American Municipalities. *Ann. Assoc. Amer. Geographers*, Vol. 44, pp. 15–32, 1954.

Carrier, E. H. "The Thirsty Earth: A Study in Irrigation." Christophers, London, 1928.

"Developed and Potential Water Power of the United States and Other Countries of the World—December 1954." *U.S. Geol. Survey Circ.* 367, Washington, D.C., 1955.

Dixey, Frank. "A Practical Handbook of Water Supply." Thomas Murby and Co., London, 1931.

Langbein, Walter B. *et al.* "Annual Runoff in the United States." *U.S. Geol. Survey Circ.* 52, Washington, D.C., 1949.

MacKichan, Kenneth A. "Estimated Use of Water in the United States–1950." *U.S. Geol. Survey Circ.* 115, Washington, D.C. 1951.

McGuinness, C. L. "The Water Situation in the United States with Special Reference to Ground Water." *U.S. Geol. Survey Circ.* 114, Washington, D.C., 1951.

Newell, F. H. "Water Resources: Present and Future Uses." Yale University Press, New Haven, 1920.

Smith, Guy-Harold (editor). "Conservation of Natural Resources," John Wiley & Sons, Inc., New York, 1950.

Thoman, John R. "Statistical Summary of Water Supply and Treatment Practices in the United States," *Public Health Service Publ.* 301, U.S. Government Printing Office, Washington, D.C. 1953.

Thomas, H. E. "The Conservation of Ground Water." McGraw-Hill Book Company, Inc., New York, 1951.

Voskuil, W. H. "Economics of Water Power Development." McGraw-Hill Book Company, Inc., New York, 1928.

Natural Vegetation

"Atlas of American Agriculture." Sec. E, Natural Vegetation. U.S. Government Printing Office, Washington, D. C., 1924.

Beard, J. S. The Savanna Vegetation of Northern Tropical America. *Ecol. Monographs*, Vol. 23, pp. 149–215, 1953.

Borchert, John. The Climate of the Central North American Grassland, *Ann. Assoc. Amer. Geographers*, Vol. 40, pp. 1–39, 1950.

Cain, Stanley A. "Foundations of Plant Geography." Harper & Brothers, New York, 1944.

Carpenter, J. Richard. The Grassland Biome. *Ecol. Monographs*, Vol. 10, pp. 618–684, 1940.

Clements, Frederic E., and Victor E. Shelford. "Bio-Ecology." John Wiley & Sons, Inc., New York, 1939.

"Climate and Man." The Yearbook of Agriculture, 1941. U.S. Department of Agriculture, Washington, D.C., 1941.

"Grass." The Yearbook of Agriculture, 1948. U.S. Department of Agriculture, Washington, D.C., 1948.

Haden-Guest, Stephen, John K. Wright, and Eileen M. Teclaff (editors). "A World Geography of Forest Resources." The Ronald Press Company, New York, 1956.

Hardy, M. E. "The Geography of Plants." Oxford University Press, New York, 1920.

Haviland, Maud D. "Forest, Steppe, and Tundra." Cambridge University Press, London, 1926.

Hayek, August. "Allgemeine Pflanzengeographie." Verlagsbuchhandlung Gebrüder Borntraeger, Berlin, 1926. Contains a world vegetation map.

Küchler, A. W. A Geographic System of Vegetation. *Geog. Rev.,* Vol. 37, pp. 233–240, 1947.

"Plant Geography." "American Geography, Inventory and Prospect." Preston E. James and Clarence F. Jones (editors). Syracuse University Press, Syracuse, N.Y., 1954.

———. World-Natural Vegetation. Colored map in "Goode's School Atlas." Pp. 16–17. Rand McNally & Company, Chicago, 1949.

Lillard, Richard G. "The Great Forest." Alfred A. Knopf, Inc., New York, 1948..

Livingston, Burton E., and Forrest Shreve. "The Distribution of Vegetation in the United States as Related to the Climatic Conditions." *Carnegie Inst. Wash. Publication* 284, 1921.

Martonne, Emmanuel de. "A Shorter Physical Geography." Alfred A. Knopf, Inc., New York, 1927.

———. "Traité de géographie physique." Vol. 3, Biogeographie. Armand Colin, Paris, 1927.

Newbigin, Marion I. "Plant and Animal Geography." Methuen & Co., Ltd., London, 1936..

Richards, P. W. "The Tropical Rainforest; an Ecological Study." Cambridge University Press, New York, 1952.

Roseveare, G. M. The Grasslands of Latin America. *Bull.* 36, Imperial Bureau of Pastures and Field Crops, Aberystwyth, Great Britain, 1948.

Schimper, A. F. W. "Plant Geography upon a Physiological Basis." English translation. Oxford University Press, New York, 1903.

———— and F. C. von Faber. "Pflanzengeographie auf physiologischer Grundlage." 3d ed. Gustav Fischer Verlagsbuchhandlung, Jena, 1935. Contains world vegetation map in color.

Shantz, H. L., and C. F. Marbut. The Vegetation and Soils of Africa. *Research Series* No. 13, American Geographical Society, New York, 1923.

Supan, Alexander. "Grundzüge der physichen Erdkunde." 7th ed. Vol. 2, Part 2, Pflanzen und Tiergeographie. Walter De Gruyter & Co., Berlin, 1930. Contains world vegetation map in color.

Transeau, Edgar N. The Pattern of Vegetation. "Global Geography," Chap. 8. George T. Renner (editor). Thomas Y. Crowell Company, New York, 1944.

"Trees." The Yearbook of Agriculture, 1949. U.S. Department of Agriculture, Washington, D.C., 1949.

Waibel, Leo. Vegetation and Land Use in the Planalto Central of Brazil. *Geog. Rev.,* Vol. 38, pp. 553–554, October, 1948.

Weaver, John E., and Frederic E. Clements. "Plant Ecology." 2d ed. McGraw-Hill Book Company, Inc., New York, 1938.

Weaver, J. E. "The North American Prairie." Johnsen Publishing Company, Lincoln, Neb., 1954.

Zon, Raphael, and William N. Sparhawk. "Forest Resources of the World." 2 vols., McGraw-Hill Book Company, Inc., New York, 1923.

Soil Resources

Bennett, Hugh H. "Elements of Soil Conservation." 2d ed. McGraw-Hill Book Company, Inc., New York, 1955.

Blanck, E. "Handbuch der Bodenlehre." Vol. 3. Springer-Verlag OHG, Berlin, 1930.

Bushnell, T. M. The Story of Indiana Soils. *Purdue Univ., Agr. Expt. Sta., Special Circular* 1, June, 1944.

————. Some Aspects of the Soil Catena Concept. *Proc. Soil Sci. Soc. Amer.* Vol. 7, pp. 469–476, 1943.

Cline, Marlin G., Basic Principles of Soil Classification. *Soil Sci.,* Vol. 67, pp. 81–91, 1949.

Glinka, K. D. "The Great Soils Groups of the World and Their Development." English translation by C. F. Marbut. Edwards Bros., Inc., Ann Arbor, Mich., 1927.

Harper, Horace J. Problems and Progress of Soil Conservation. *Advances in Agron.,* Vol. 3, pp. 265–322, 1951.

Hole, F. D. Suggested Terminology for Describing Soils as Three-dimensional Bodies. *Proc. Soil. Sci. Soc. Amer.* Vol. 17, pp. 131–135, 1953.

Joffe, Jacob S. "Pedology." Rutgers University Press, New Brunswick, N.J., 1936.

Kellogg, C. E. Climate and Soil. "Climate and Man." Yearbook of Agriculture, 1941. U.S. Department of Agriculture, Washington, D.C.

————. "The Soils That Support Us." The Macmillan Company, New York, 1941.

————, and Fidelia D. Davol. An Exploratory Study of Soil Groups in the Belgian Congo. *Inst. natl. l'étude agron. du Congo Belge (I.N.E.A.C.)* Sci. Ser. No. 46, 1949, Brussels.

Krische, Paul. "Bodenkarten." Paul Parey, Berlin, 1928.

Marbut, C. F. Soils of the United States. "Atlas of American Agriculture." Part 3, U.S. Government Printing Office, Washington, D.C., 1935.

Muckenhirn, R. J., E. P. Whiteside, E. H. Templin, R. F. Chandler, Jr., and L. T. Alexander. Soil Classification and the Genetic Factors in Soil Formation. *Soil Sci.* Vol. 67, pp. 93–105, 1949.

Orvedal, A. C., J. Kubota, and Howard M. Smith. Major Soil Profiles and Their Relationship with Climate. "Frost Action in Soils." *Highway Research Board (National Research Council) Rept.* 2, pp. 1–10, Washington, D.C., 1952.

Robinson, Gilbert W. "Soils: Their Origin, Constitution, and Classification." 2d ed. Thomas Murby and Co., London, 1936.

Sigmond, Alexius A. J. de. "The Principles of Soil Science." English translation from the Hungarian by A. B. Yolland. Thomas Murby and Co., London, 1938.

Simonson, Roy W. Changing Place of Soils in Agricultural Production. *Scientific Monthly,* Vol. 81, pp. 173–182, 1955.

Soils. "Science in Farming." Yearbook of Agriculture, 1943–1947, pp. 485–612. U.S. Department of Agriculture, Washington, D.C., 1947.

"Soils and Men." Yearbook of Agriculture, 1938. U.S. Department of Agriculture, Washington, D.C.

Thorp, James, and Guy D. Smith. Higher Categories of Soil Classification: Order, Suborder and Great Soil Groups. *Soil Sci.,* Vol. 67, pp. 117–126, 1949.

Wilde, S. A. "Forest Soils and Forest Growth." Chronica Botanica Co., Waltham, Mass., 1946.

Winters, E., and R. W. Simonson. The Subsoil. *Advances in Agron.,* Vol. 3, pp. 31–45, 1951.

Wolfanger, L. A. "The Major Soil Divisions of the United States." John Wiley & Sons, Inc., New York, 1930.

Mineral Resources

Bayley, W. S. "A Guide to the Study of Nonmetallic Mineral Products." Henry Holt and Company, Inc., New York, 1930.

DeMille, J. B. "Strategic Minerals." McGraw-Hill Book Company, Inc., New York, 1947.

Emmons, W. H. "Geology of Petroleum." McGraw-Hill Book Company, Inc., New York, 1931.

Fox, Cyril S. "Bauxite and Aluminous Laterite." Crosby Lockwoood & Son, London, 1932.

Hotchkiss, W. O. "Minerals of Might." The Jaques Cattell Press, Lancaster, Pa., 1945.

Leith, C. K., *et al.* "Elements of a National Mineral Policy." The Mineral Inquiry, American Institute of Mining and Metallurgical Engineers, New York, 1933.

————. "The Economic Aspects of Geology." Henry Holt and Company, Inc., New York, 1921.

————. "World Minerals and World Politics." Mc-Graw-Hill Book Company, Inc., New York, 1931.

Lovering, T. S. "Minerals in World Affairs." Prentice-Hall, Inc., New York, 1943.

Moore, Elwood S. "Coal." 2d ed. John Wiley & Sons, Inc., New York, 1940.

Pratt, Wallace E., and Dorothy Good. "World Geography of Petroleum." American Geographical Society and Princeton University Press, New York, 1950.

Read, Thomas T. "Our Mineral Civilization." The Williams & Wilkins Company, Baltimore, 1932.

Ries, H. "Economic Geology." John Wiley & Sons, Inc., New York, 1930.

Schackne, Stewart, and N. D'Arcy Drake. "Oil for the World." Harper & Brothers, New York, 1950.

Smith, J. Russell, M. Ogden Phillips, and Thomas R. Smith. "Industrial and Commercial Geography." 4th ed., Henry Holt and Company, Inc., New York, 1955.

Tryon, F. G., and E. C. Eckel (editor). "Mineral Economics." McGraw-Hill Book Company, Inc., New York, 1932.

Van Royen, W., and Oliver Bowles. "The Mineral Resources of the World." "Atlas of the World's Resources," Vol. II, Prentice-Hall, Inc., New York, 1952.

Voskuil, W. H. "Minerals in World Industry." McGraw-Hill Book Company, New York, 1955.

"World Oil." Gulf Publishing Company, Vol. 142, No. 3, Houston, Texas, February, 1956.

Zimmerman, E. W. "World Resources and Industries." Rev. ed., Harper & Brothers, New York, 1951.

19

Water Resources of the Land

19.1 The Variety of Uses of Water. Water exceeds any other nonuniversal earth resource in the urgency of its need and in the quantity used. The water of the earth never varies in total amount but it is in perpetual motion and is constantly changing from one to another of its forms—gas, ice, and liquid. The most significant of these changes and movements is the never-ending distilling process wherein moist maritime air masses move over the land and discharge some of their water as precipitation. The major part is evaporated, but the water remaining on the land moves downward toward the sea as streams and into the ground water. It is from these two sources that most of the withdrawal water requirements of man are met. Consequently, regions of abundant precipitation usually, but not always, have abundant supplies of water, and their inhabitants are able to use it lavishly. In arid regions water is the element of first importance in restricting the settlement and use of land, and the supply of it is used with utmost economy.

There are several ways to classify the use of water but the easiest categories to visualize and apply are the withdrawal and nonwithdrawal uses. When water is diverted from its source, be it well, spring, or stream, it is called withdrawal; when it is used in place (*e.g.,* for navigation or recreation) it is a nonwithdrawal use. Figure 19.1 shows for the United States the comparative volume of the major withdrawal uses of water and the relative importance of ground water and surface water as suppliers. The withdrawal use of water for water power is not included because of its tremendous volume compared to the other uses. More than six times as much water is used for water power than for all other withdrawal uses combined.

The use of water is increasing rapidly as the population grows and as industrial and irrigation needs multiply. Figure 19.2 shows that the estimated requirements for water have increased more than five times since the beginning of the present century.

Water supplies and water bodies are useful in many different ways, some of the more important of which are (*a*) in domestic supply, (*b*) for industrial processes, (*c*) for the irrigation of crops, (*d*) for the production of mechanical power, (*e*) as routes of inland transportation, and (*f*) in the added attractiveness that they give to scenic or recreational areas. The use of water for drinking and household supply ranges from a small daily ration among the nomadic people of arid lands to the daily per capita allowance of more than 100 gal. which is provided in American cities. That use certainly is the most important to mankind, but there are other important urban requirements. Modern manufacturing establishments such as steel mills, textile dyeing-and-finishing plants, and paper mills are large users of water. A steel mill, for example, is estimated to use in its various processes about 65,000 gal. of water for each ton of finished steel it produces.[1] A choice of site for such an establishment often is made because of the availability there of an abundant supply of water having the requisite chemical properties or degree of pureness. For

[1] S. T. Powell and H. E. Bacon. *J. Am. Water Works Ass.,* Vol. 42, p. 782, 1950.

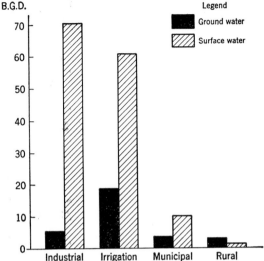

Fig. 19.1 Estimated withdrawal use of water in the United States, 1950, in billions of gallons per day (B.G.D.) Water used for hydroelectric power is not included. The municipal value includes that supplied to industry from municipal water works; the industrial value is that obtained from private sources only. (*From Geological Survey Circ. 115, 1951.*)

these uses great manufacturing cities must supply much more water per capita of their population than is used in the homes. The average total consumption of water for all kinds of uses in 90 cities of more than 100,000 population in the United States is the equivalent of about 125 gal. per day per inhabitant. Per capita consumption in the principal European cities averages hardly one-half that amount. On the other hand the municipal system of Chicago supplies each day to its homes and factories an amount of water equivalent to about 235 gal. for each of its residents.[2] That industrial city has the highest per capita rate of consumption of any in the United States.

19.2 Sources of Water Supply. The large quantities of water required for withdrawal use by modern urban and industrial centers are obtained from wells, springs, large lakes, and large rivers, but even more generally from small streams the drainage of which is stored behind

[2] W. W. De Berard. "Chicago Water System Serves Growing Population. . . ." *Civil Eng.,* Vol. 20, pp. 699–703, 1950.

dams to create municipal reservoirs. Only about one out of four of the principal American cities obtains its water supply from wells. Most of the remainder, and especially the large cities, use surface waters. However, about 60 per cent of the total population of the country lives in cities of less than 25,000 population, in villages, and on farms where ground water, obtained from wells and springs, is the principal source of supply. For the irrigation of crops, surface waters are much more important than ground water, since the latter source supplies only about one-fourth of the irrigation water used in the arid sections of the United States. Although the conditions found in the United States with respect to water supply are not representative of those to be found in all parts of the world, they give an indication of the required volume of this essential resource and some measure of the relative importance of the sources from which it is obtained.

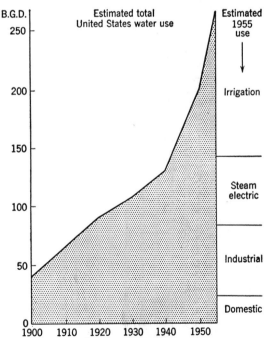

Fig. 19.2 Estimated total United States water use, 1900 to 1955, in billions of gallons per day (B.G.D.). (*Based upon estimates of the U.S. Department of Commerce in the 1955 Annual Report of Resources for the Future, Washington, D.C., 1955.*)

The Ground-water Supply

19.3 The Availability of Ground Water. It has been noted previously that a part of the precipitation percolates downward into the pore spaces and crevices of the regolith and the underlying rocks. Under ordinary conditions, the lower levels of these pore spaces are filled with water and the top of the saturated zone is called the *ground-water table*. The water stored below the ground-water table is the source of supply for springs and wells.

The availability of ground water is obviously not everywhere the same. In regions of abundant and well-distributed precipitation the pore space in the earth is likely to be well filled, but in arid regions the rapid evaporation of moisture and the high percentage of runoff following the infrequent, but often heavy, rains do not permit of a deep penetration of ground water. The supplies in arid regions are, therefore, mainly such as move slowly, deep underground, from more humid regions. Frequently they are limited in quantity and are to be had only in a few localities, and those places take on critical importance in the migration and settlement of people.

Even in humid regions ground water is not everywhere abundant. A copious supply depends not only upon abundant precipitation but also upon (*a*) earth materials of sufficient *porosity* to absorb and store a large quantity of water and (*b*) the existence of pore space, bedding planes, fracture planes, or other avenues providing sufficient *permeability* to permit a relatively free underground movement of water from a large storage area to the well or spring from which it is being removed. Beds of gravel, sand, loosely compacted sediments, porous sandstones, and thinly bedded or cavernous limestones provide these conditions. Such water-bearing formations are called *aquifers*. Compact clays and shales, massive and little-fractured igneous rocks, and some other formations provide but little storage capacity for water and but little facility for its underground flow. Springs in such rocks seldom are abundant, and wells are difficult to construct and limited in flow.

19.4 *Pore Space for Ground Water.* In sandstones the pore space capable of being filled by water commonly exceeds 20 per cent and sometimes reaches 40 per cent of the volume of the rock. In unconsolidated earth or glacial gravels the figure is much greater. In massive crystalline limestones there often is 5 to 10 per cent of pore space; and in chalky or cavernous limestones there is much more than that amount. In dense igneous and metamorphic rocks the pore space is much less. In solid granites it seldom is more than 1 per cent; and in some metamorphic rocks it is said to be less than one-half of 1 per cent. In such rocks the pores are so small they do not readily yield the little water that they contain. Numerous joint cracks or structural planes in dense rocks greatly increase both their water-holding and water-yielding capacities.

Figure 19.3 shows the ground-water areas of the United States and illustrates the complexity of occurrence of aquifers capable of yielding adequate supplies of water. It should be borne in mind that the map is only a partial picture due to lack of adequate surveys in some areas.

19.5 The Qualities of Ground Water. No ground water is free from dissolved mineral, but the nature and quantity of the chemical salts carried in solution differ widely from region to region. A few dissolved minerals, such as sulphur or iron, impart to water a disagreeable taste or render it unfit for certain industrial processes. Some minerals give tonic, laxative, or other medicinal qualities to the water. Among the most abundant of the soluble salts found in ground water are compounds of calcium (lime), sodium, and magnesium. In desert regions seepage waters commonly are charged with compounds of these and other salts to a degree that retards or prevents their use. In the United States these are known as *alkali waters*. In humid regions most of the readily soluble sodium compounds have long since been removed from the upper portion of the ground. However, limestones, lime-ce-

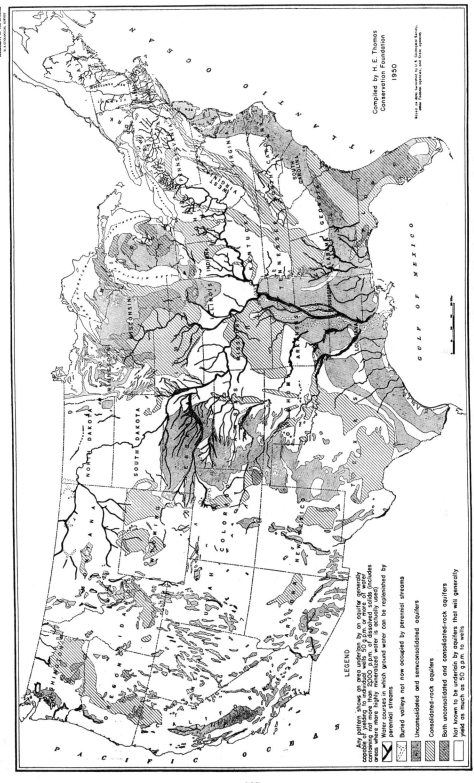

Fig. 19.3 Ground-water areas of the United States. Map by H. E. Thomas of the Geological Survey. (*Reprinted by permission of the Conservation Foundation, New York.*)

397

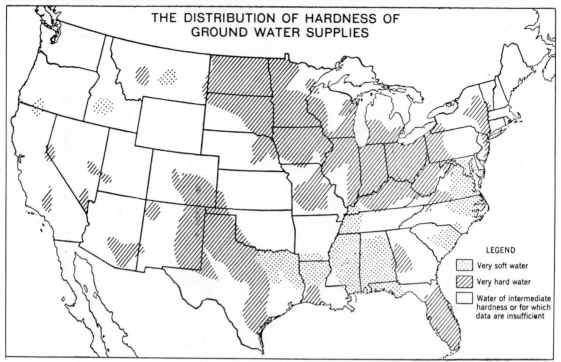

Fig. 19.4 *(After U.S. National Resources Board.)*

mented sediments, and dolomites furnish supplies of calcium and magnesium which, although they do not much affect the taste of water, give it the quality called *hardness* which does affect its domestic and industrial utility.

Ground water ordinarily has been filtered through the earth, sometimes for many years, before it is used. It is, therefore, relatively free from mud and other suspended materials.

19.6 *The Hardness of Water.* The amount or degree of hardness in water usually is expressed in terms of parts of dissolved mineral per million parts of water. Regions underlain mainly by ancient crystalline rocks or by highly siliceous sands or sandstones usually have not much available lime, and their waters may contain as little as 5 or 10 parts of hardness per million. These are the naturally "soft" waters. Water containing as much as 60 parts still is considered soft, but if it contains more than 120 to 180 parts per million it is considered "hard" water. In regions of lime-containing sedimentary rocks, well waters in common use contain 300 to 500 parts and, in a few places,

as much as 700 to 800 parts per million (Fig. 19.4). Many wells in arid regions, and some even in humid regions, tap supplies of ground water so hard as to be unfit for use. Hard waters require "softening" when they are used with soap and present serious problems in certain industrial processes or in the supply of steam boilers. This is because of their chemical reactions and the undesirable precipitates that they form.

19.7 Springs. A spring is a concentrated natural outflow of water from underground. It may flow either continuously or intermittently and its water may be either cold or warm, hard or soft. Springs result from a variety of conditions involving the position of the ground-water table, the configuration of the land surface, and the nature and structure of the rocks.

Figure 19.5*A* illustrates the occurrence of a spring on the side of a valley which has been eroded below the usual level of the local ground-water table. Springs of that type are common in glacial drift and often are the main sources of supply of small brooks at the headwaters of rivers. After a period of protracted drought the level of the ground water that supplies such a spring may be lowered, and it will cease to flow until the water level is raised by the downward seepage of further rains. Figure 19.5*B* illustrates the site of a spring caused by the movement of water downward through porous formations and then horizontally along the top of an impervious rock layer. Sands, sandstones, or porous limestones, underlain by compact clays or shales, supply conditions of that kind and often produce many springs, all at about the same level. Figure 19.5*C* illustrates the manner in which water from a wide area of rocks, even those of low water-holding capacity, may be converged upon a spring by means of joint and fault planes. In some regions water thus collected is conveyed deep underground where it comes under the influence of hot igneous rocks and finally issues as hot, or "thermal," springs or even as geysers. The latter add to the scenic attractiveness of several regions in which they occur, such as Yellowstone National Park; Ice-

land; and North Island, New Zealand. In those regions, geysers, the name of which is derived from that of one of the intermittent hot springs of Iceland, are resources of considerable value, because of the tourist business they bring. Hot water and steam from underground are used in a few localities as sources of heat and power. Such localities are found in Italy, Iceland, and California.

Some springs drain water from far beyond the immediate localities in which they are found. Because they are outlets for considerable areas and draw upon large ground-water supplies some of them have large volumes and are perennial in flow.

19.8 *Large Springs.* Under certain conditions of underground drainage, springs attain the proportions of considerable rivers. That is notably true in regions of cavernous limestones or of porous lavas. In such rocks, ground water descends from the surface through numerous openings and ultimately converges upon an underground channel in some volume. There are in the United States about 60 springs with sufficient flow so that each would supply all the water required by a city of $\frac{1}{2}$ million inhabitants. There are at least a half dozen that flow with sufficient volume so that any one of them would supply a city of 1 million inhabitants.[3] Most of the large springs of the country are included in four regions. They are the limestone areas of (*a*) the northern Florida karst and (*b*) the Ozark region of southern Missouri; and the permeable-lava regions of (*c*) the Snake River Valley of Idaho and (*d*) western Oregon and northern California.

19.9 The Use of Spring Waters. In the United States are thousands of farmhouses and not a few villages that are located upon sites originally chosen because spring water was found there by a pioneer settler. Large numbers of those springs, most of them on valley slopes, still are flowing and still supply water for farm families.

The drilling of many wells has drawn heavily

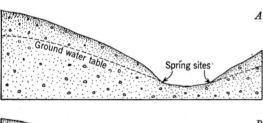

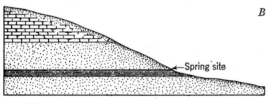

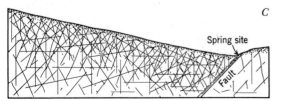

Fig. 19.5 Diagrams to illustrate some of the many possible conditions of surface, material, and structure that are related to the occurrence of springs.

[3] O. E. Meinzer. Large Springs in the United States. *U.S. Geol. Survey, Water Supply Paper* 557, 1927.

upon the ground-water supply. The substitution of tilled crops for forest and grassland has tended to increase the rate of runoff and to decrease correspondingly the proportion of the precipitation that enters the ground. Both these changes have diminished the ground-water supply and have resulted in the lowering of the water table in many localities. This has had the effect of rendering the supply of spring water less dependable, while at the same time the growth of population has tended to make it less adequate and more subject to pollution. There are many relatively small springs which have acquired local or even wider fame for the purity or reputed medical properties of their waters. In some localities the bottling and shipment of these is a considerable industry. Moreover, thermal and medicinal springs of special properties or great renown serve in various parts of the world as a reason for population concentration. About them have grown, in both Europe and America, several widely known health resorts and cities of considerable size.

19.10 Wells penetrate the saturated zone below the water table in order that ground water may be collected from an aquifer in sufficient quantity and lifted to the surface. Formerly wells were made only by digging a hole to the ground-water level, and they seldom were many feet deep. Millions of such *dug* wells still are in daily use in nearly all parts of the world, although their shallow and open construction makes them particularly subject

to pollution (Fig. 19.6). Many dug wells have only temporary supplies of water, while others are permanent. Figure 19.6 shows also the relation of three wells to a fluctuating ground-water table and indicates the reason for their varying degrees of permanence of water supply; the well numbered 1 is a modern *drilled* well which reaches far below the lowest position of the water table and has never run dry; that numbered 2 is a dug well which reaches below the ordinary water table and has water at all times, except after periods of protracted drought; that numbered 3 is dry most of the time except after a long period of rains.

A modern deep well, like that numbered 1 above, is made by drilling a small hole scores or hundreds of feet, through surface formations and the upper part of the ground-water zone, into the deeper waters of some known aquifer, such as a porous sandstone. From a drilled well water must be lifted by a pump through a pipe which is carefully encased to prevent the surface waters from seeping into the drill hole and thus contaminating the deep water supply.

Many wells are located badly because of ignorance of the nature of ground-water movement and of the structure and permeability of the rocks that govern ground-water movement in the locality in which they are constructed. Figure 19.6 shows that, while well 2 is situated higher up the slope than No. 1 and appears to be in a safer position with respect to pollution,

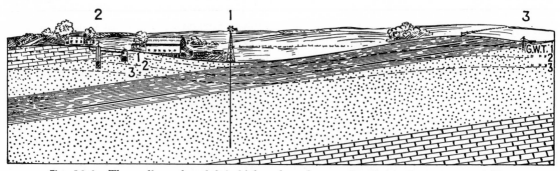

Fig. 19.6 The well numbered 2 is higher than that numbered 1 and appears to yield a safer water supply but, in fact, it does not because of the rock structures concerned. The stippled layers indicate porous, water-bearing formations. The numbered dashed lines show depths of the ground-water tables: 1, in wet seasons; 2, ordinary level; 3, in dry seasons.

it is in fact not so. The porous rock formation below the surface carries seepage from barns and cesspool directly toward the house well rather than away from it, as the surface slope would indicate.

The quantity of water from deep wells, as well as the quality, depends upon the nature of the underlying rock and its structure. If the well hole terminates in a thick porous aquifer of great areal extent and broad outcrop, it may yield an abundant and continuous supply of water. If the only rock beneath a locality is of the massive crystalline type, the water yield may be continuous but not abundant. The rock has so little pore and crevice space that its water content is small. The rate of flow into a well in dense rock is sometimes increased by using explosives at the bottom of the hole to shatter the surrounding rock and make numerous crevices through which the water of a larger area may flow in. However, some hard crystalline rocks are so low in water content that no device can bring about a sufficient flow to justify the very high cost of drilling deep wells in them. Shale rocks, although not hard, also commonly are compact, impervious, and "dry," but usually they are closely associated with other sedimentary rocks which are porous. Wells in regions of cavernous limestones sometimes tap underground *streams* of water. Such wells may yield abundant supplies, but since the water has entered the underground channel directly from the surface drainage, some of it

through sinkholes, it has had little natural filtering and is subject to pollution. It is likely to be little safer than the river waters of the same region, since the latter have at least been exposed to the bacteria-destroying power of sunlight.

19.11 *Artesian Wells.* Common use applies the term *artesian* to any deep drilled well from which water flows or in which the water level rises so near to the surface as to require little pumping. Originally the term was restricted to such wells as flow freely without pumping. Artesian wells are possible under any one of several sets of conditions of underground structure, one of which is illustrated in Fig. 19.7. The favorable situation must include the following conditions: (*a*) a water-bearing formation of some pervious material; (*b*) the aquifer must outcrop or be exposed at the surface in a region of sufficient precipitation to fill it with water; (*c*) the formation must disappear at a low angle of inclination beneath a capping layer of some impervious rock, such as shale; (*d*) it must lead toward a region where the land surface is lower than it is at the exposed end of the pervious formation; and (*e*) there must be no free exit from the pervious rock at an elevation lower than the region of the wells. A well drilled through the impervious layer and into the water-bearing formation taps a supply that is under pressure owing to the weight of the water that is backed up in the higher end of the aquifer. Water will rise in the well bore

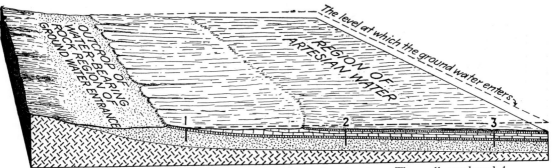

Fig. 19.7 A diagram to illustrate one type of artesian structure. The well numbered 1 (left) reaches the water-bearing formation, but its top is as high as the level of ground-water entrance, and it would require pumping. Wells numbered 2 and 3 should provide flowing water.

or flow from the opening as long as the rate of addition in the outcropping area exceeds the rate of loss through wells and seepage. In a few regions saucerlike structural basins of concentric relief contain water-bearing formations which outcrop about the edges of the basin and incline from all sides, underneath other rocks, toward its center, where artesian water may be had in abundance. A structure of that kind is found in the Paris Basin. (The term artesian, applied to wells of this class, is derived from Artois, the name of a district in northern France.)

19.12 *Notable Artesian Structures.* Artesian water is obtained from favorable structures, which occur locally in a great many places, and from a few that cover areas of truly great extent. One of the latter is the northern Great Plains region of the United States. There a series of water-bearing formations, especially the Dakota sandstone, outcrop at considerable elevation near the Rocky Mountains and incline eastward, under suitable capping layers, toward the lower plains. They yield artesian

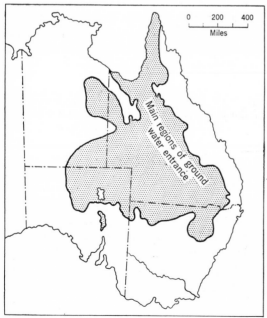

Fig. 19.8   The Great Artesian Basin of Australia. (*After James E. Collier.*)

waters far out in the eastern part of the Dakotas.

The dry lands of Australia also are blessed with artesian waters obtained from more than a half dozen favorable structures. One of these deserves its name, the Great Artesian Basin (Fig. 19.8). This is a broad synclinal structure, having a total extent equal to about one-fifth the area of the United States. In it aquifers, mainly sandstones, outcrop about the margins, while its interior portion is buried beneath impervious clays and shales. The principal intake area lies in a large region of moderate rainfall west of the Great Dividing Range in eastern Queensland. The center of the basin lies beneath that arid region which includes southwestern Queensland and parts of the adjacent states. Some of its waters flow from natural springs, some from shallow wells, and some from deep wells; the deepest is more than a mile. Some of the nearly 9,000 wells flow freely and others require pumping, some yield cool waters and others hot, some fresh and others saline.[4] Few yield enough to irrigate significant areas of crops, but they are most important in providing water for livestock and the pastoral occupants of these dry plains. Artesian structures are found also over large areas in northern Africa and central Argentina. There are many limited artesian structures and spring sites in American dry lands and those of other countries that furnish water for the irrigation of a few acres of crops in addition to that required for other uses.

Unfortunately, the flow of water in an artesian basin cannot be maintained at a higher amount than that absorbed in the catchment area where an aquifer outcrops. It is, therefore, capable of depletion. Thousands of flowing wells in the Dakotas and hundreds in Australia, because of careless waste of water through them, have decreased the pressures in both regions until many wells now require pumping, and the flow of others is much reduced.

[4] James E. Collier. Artesian Water and Australia's Pastoral Industry. *Scientific Monthly,* Vol. 40, pp. 117–129, 1945.

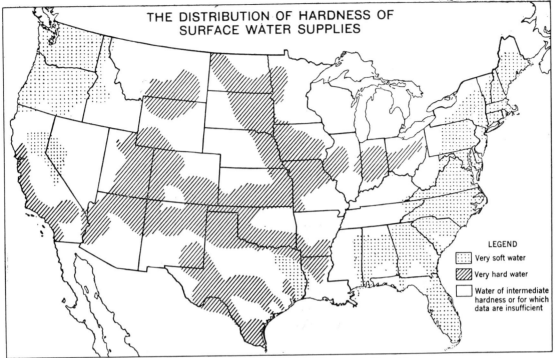

THE DISTRIBUTION OF HARDNESS OF
SURFACE WATER SUPPLIES

LEGEND

::::: Very soft water

/// Very hard water

☐ Water of intermediate
hardness or for which
data are insufficient

Fig. 19.9 (*After U.S. National Resources Board.*)

The Surface-water Supply

19.13 The Occurrence and Resource Qualities of Surface Water. It has been noted from Fig. 19.1 that surface water (runoff) constitutes by far the major source for the withdrawal uses of water save for rural domestic and stock supply. The most important nonwithdrawal uses such as navigation, waste disposal, recreation, and conservation of wildlife depend entirely upon surface-water supplies. The amount available for use varies from place to place on the earth depending upon a number of interrelated factors, among the more important of which are precipitation, temperature, vegetation cover, and regolith. The expected relationships between these individual factors and runoff hardly need cataloging, for example, high temperatures promote rapid evaporation which in turn diminishes runoff. On the other hand the recognition of the exact situation which obtains relative to surface-water supply in all parts of the earth is a difficult task, for, in general, few helpful detailed surveys have been made. The

following small table shows a recent estimate of the annual runoff in inches from each of the continents:[5]

Continent	Annual Runoff, Inches
South America	17.7
North America	12.4
Europe	10.3
Africa	8.0
Asia	6.7
Australia	3.0

The figures are derived by dividing the estimated total discharge of the streams by the area of the continent, thus providing a mean depth of water which is a kind of index of relative dryness or wetness. It will be seen that South and North America are the most favored and that Australia is the driest of the continents.

Surface water differs from ground water in a number of important respects as a resource. Generally, the surface waters are less mineralized than the ground water of the same region, because they are derived in part from

[5] Estimate by M. I. L'vovich, in Walter B. Langbein *et al. Geological Survey Circ.* 52, Washington, D.C., 1949.

the immediate runoff of rain water (Fig. 19.9). In periods of drought the surface supply fails, and the streams, fed mainly by springs, have increased hardness. However, surface waters are likely to contain larger quantities of sediment and organic matter, including bacteria, than ground water. For that reason many cities find it necessary to treat their water supplies (*a*) by chlorination or other means of disinfection for the destruction of bacteria, (*b*) for the coagulation and flocculation of very fine sediment and colloidal matter, and (*c*) by filtration, to remove sediment. For example, nearly half the population of the United States uses water that has been treated in some way in almost 7,000 treatment plants.[6] Water used for irrigation must not have too high a mineral content and many industrial uses, ranging from boilers to canning, require water having various mineral specifications. The large industrial and municipal withdrawal uses of water occasion problems of pollution when the effluent is returned to surface drainage. This affects recreation and wildlife, as well as communities downstream who may also use the surface water. Surface drainage through streams and lakes is also related to matters of great economic concern such as soil erosion, flood control, and inland navigation as well as those uses previously mentioned.

Out of these varied uses grow conflicts of human interest which lie beyond the scope of the elements of geography. However, the natural-resource qualities of surface waters may be examined briefly in their relation to some of these uses.

19.14   Surface Water for Municipal Supply. Surface water is the major supply source for large communities because of the tremendous volume used and the inability of most aquifers to supply such volume at such a rapid rate. For example, over half of the communities in the United States having more than 10,000 inhabitants are supplied from surface water. The proportion so supplied increases with size

and four out of five cities with more than 50,000 inhabitants use surface water.[7] Water for municipal supply, as previously pointed out, must usually be treated in a number of ways both before and after its use, the latter treatment being to reduce the amount of pollution resulting from the effluent. In many areas surface water is by no means available in constant supply. Consequently, in addition to treatment plants and disposal facilities, various kinds of dams and impounding reservoirs are necessary to maintain a uniform supply.

In many areas of the world large cities have grown up without an adequate, easily obtainable, surface (or ground) water supply and it has been necessary to bring water great distances by aqueduct. In some areas sea water is distilled, but because the unit cost of distilling is related to the mineralization of the source water this is costly since sea water has from 32,000 to 36,000 parts per million of total dissolved solids. It appears that, even with atomic energy providing the power requirement, for some time to come it will be cheaper to transport fresh water great distances than to distill sea water.

19.15   Waters Used for Irrigation. The soils of arid lands generally are abundantly supplied with the mineral elements of soil fertility and require only water and sometimes organic fertilizers to make them productive. Adequate supplies of water are not easy to obtain, for the actual water requirement of crops is large, and inevitably much is lost by seepage and evaporation in the course of getting it to the crops. In American irrigation practice, although the amount of water required varies with the region and the crop, it is customary to provide annually the equivalent of a layer 2 to 3 ft. deep over the entire area to be irrigated. To secure so much water every type of source is drawn upon, but, the world over, surface runoff supplies most of it. Except for the paddy rice-growing countries of southeastern Asia, irrigation is most practiced in lands that have less than 20 in. of average annual precipitation. Since the water requirement of the crops grown

[6] Statistical Summary of Water Supply and Treatment Practices in the United States. *Public Health Service Publ.* 301, 1953, p. 4.

[7] *Ibid.*, p. 8.

is generally much more than that quantity, and since always there are losses in the process of capture, storage, and transportation, it follows that the rainfall of a large area is required to provide water to irrigate a small area. From that fact it is necessary to conclude that only a small part of the dry lands of the earth ever can be irrigated.

19.16 *The quality of irrigation waters* is not everywhere the same. Some, particularly that obtained from underground sources, is heavily charged with dissolved salts, certain of which are harmful to cultivated plants or to the structure of the soil. Such water when applied to the land sometimes leaves more soluble material in the soil, as a result of surface evaporation, than is removed through the drainage channels. This tends to increase the alkali content of irrigated soils and gradually to render them unfit for crops. Waters derived directly from mountain precipitation and the melting of mountain snows are particularly free from this defect and are much employed in the irrigation of alluvial fans upon the mountain borders. Some part of the irrigation water applied to the land, supplemented by a part of the natural rainfall, soaks into the ground, joins the ground-water supply, and then commonly is recovered by pumping or by other means. It is then reused for irrigation unless, or until, the quantity of harmful salts dissolved during its stay underground renders it unfit for the watering of crops.

19.17 Physical Conditions Favorable to Water-power Production. Water has no inherent ability to develop energy. Its capacity to do work is attained by virtue of the solar energy which evaporates it and causes the wind to transport it onto the land, whence it returns toward the sea under the force of gravity. The essential conditions required to produce water power are *water* and *fall,* and within limits one of them may substitute for the other. A small volume of water falling a great distance may have the same capacity to do work as a great volume of water falling a short distance. Moreover, the former usually is capable of being more economically harnessed than is

the great stream on a low gradient. Water power is, therefore, obtained at less cost from small mountain streams than from the great rivers of plains regions.

Several conditions of physical environment combine to furnish great water power and to make it economical to use. An ideal physical situation for water-power production might well include the following conditions: (*a*) *a large stream,* and (*b*) a *precipitous fall* in the lower course of the stream where the entire weight of the falling water may be harnessed at low cost. It is further desirable that the stream be the drainage of a region (*a*) of large size and (*b*) of abundant precipitation. It is also desirable (*c*) that the precipitation be uniformly distributed throughout the year and (*d*) that the runoff of the stream be further regularized by the natural storage of rain water in great areas of spongy forest floor, numerous swamps, or lakes.

19.18 *Stream Flow and Potential Power Development.* A regular stream flow is desirable for water-power development because fluctuation in flow produces irregular power capacity. Ordinarily, it is not economical to build a power plant capable of utilizing the maximum flow of an erratic stream. Many power plants have capacity to use only the minimum flow, since otherwise a large financial investment in power plant would be unproductive of returns during much of the year. The construction of dams and other works for the storage of water tends to unify stream flow by capturing flood waters and holding them for use in the season of low water, as has been done for example, in the Tennessee Valley (Fig. 19.10) and in many other river basins throughout the world.

19.19 *Land Relief and Potential Water-power Sites.* Formerly, when downward-moving water was used solely for mechanical power, usable sites were limited to those available in regions where power was wanted. The power had to be used at the place of its production. The development of electric power transmission has, to a degree, made the place of power production independent of the place of its use, but

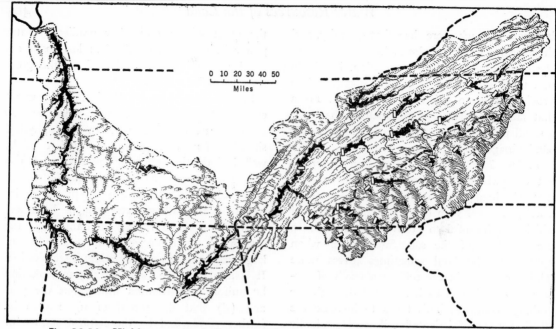

Fig. 19.10 Highly generalized diagram of the Tennessee River drainage basin showing the numerous Federal and non-Federal reservoirs which aid in power production and flood control.

not entirely. It is not yet economically feasible, in most regions, to send power by wire more than 300 to 400 miles. Moreover, it is not always possible to use all the power potential of a great stream, even near a power market, because the cost of control and storage works on large streams is high. Therefore, certain power sites of great possibility go unused while others, which are physically less desirable, are developed. Most power sites are chosen because of the benefit of some natural advantage. Such are found in plains regions where a stream crosses an outcrop of resistant rock which increases the stream gradient or causes a narrows, which makes an economical site for a dam.

The disturbed drainageways of glaciated plains, both ice-scoured and ice-deposited, furnish more numerous power sites than are provided on the drainageways of stream-eroded plains. The steep gradients and diversity of rocks found in mountain valleys furnish more frequent and valuable power sites than are common to plains regions. This is particularly true of recently glaciated mountains. In them snow-fed streams descend through narrow lake-filled valleys of highly irregular gradient or plunge over the steep walls that terminate hanging valleys. Although potential water-power sites are numerous in glaciated mountain regions many of them are far from any feasible market for power and cannot now be economically utilized.

19.20 *The World Distribution of Potential Water Power.* Because of the conditions indicated above, the potential water power of the world shows very uneven distribution (Fig. 19.11). In North America the western mountain cordillera has the greatest power possibilities, because of its heavy precipitation, great relief, ice-eroded mountain features, and forested slopes. That region is followed by the Laurentian Shield, which combines the numerous falls and rapids of its ice-scoured surface, a moderate elevation, vast area, a fairly abundant precipitation, and natural water storage in myriad lakes and extensive forests. In Europe the glaciated highland regions of Scandinavia and the Alpine countries hold the largest water-power possibilities. In Asia the conditions are most fully met on the rainy southern front of the Himalayas and in China. In South America there are three significant districts: eastern

Brazil, the eastern slopes of the northern and central Andes, and southern Chile. Australia, being generally low and dry, has but little to offer in potential water power. However, Africa exceeds any other continent in this respect. Although much of its area is desert, several great rivers originate in the rainy tropical region, and each of them, on its way to the sea, descends in falls over escarpments from the uplands of this continent.

19.21 The Value of Streams for Inland Navigation. In nearly all parts of the world, except deserts and mountains, streams are used as avenues of interior transportation. Prior to the development of railways they were used for navigation much more than they are now. Even yet, there are large areas of several continents, including North America, where streams and lakes are the principal highways. Waterways attained early importance as routes of travel because of several advantages that they afforded over primitive land routes. Although they seldom are more direct than land routes, they are, by their nature, reduced to fairly uniform grade and eliminate most of the vertical irregularities common to land routes. Even primitive water craft carry easily burdens too heavy for man or pack animals. On routes from continental interiors outward, heavy loads may be moved on well-graded streams with little expenditure of energy, when aided by the river current.

Certain great rivers offer such advantages for transport, in regions of delayed economic development, that they still carry the major part of the traffic. The Yangtze is the principal means of moving goods to and from the far interior of central China. The Congo provides a means of carriage in equatorial Africa, although falls cause several interruptions to navigation and prevent direct connection by boat with the coast. The Amazon drains a large area of heavy rainfall over a gradient so low and so free from obstruction as to provide ample depth and width even for any modern craft that are likely to enter there.

However, in the world as a whole, and especially in those countries better provided with roads and railways, river navigation is of decreasing importance. That river transportation has not been able to compete more effectively with that by rail and motor truck is due to important defects in the natural qualities of rivers as major thoroughfares. Some of these defects are indicated in the following statements: (*a*) The depth of most rivers fluctuates greatly with the seasons of maximum and minimum rainfall. This is notably true in arid and semiarid lands where watercourses so seldom are navigable that they never have had significance in that connection, except under special conditions, such as are found in the Nile. Even great rivers, like the Missouri, in regions of seasonal and highly variable rainfall, often are so shallow as to become incapable of use. (*b*) Young streams, which have fairly direct courses, commonly are interrupted by falls and rapids, while old streams of low and uniform gradients usually meander and provide long and indirect routes of transport. (*c*) Old streams constantly shift their channels and deposit sand bars which are a menace to navigation. (*d*) In severe climates rivers are closed to navigation several months each year by ice. (*e*) It is difficult to provide upon the banks of a river having a variable depth and shifting channel adequate facilities for the transfer of heavy cargo between bank and boat. (*f*) Many places from which goods must be moved are not reached by

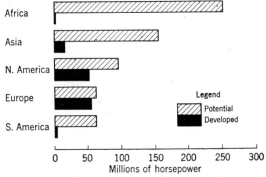

Fig. 19.11 Estimated potential and developed water power of the continents, 1954. Potential estimate based on ordinary minimum flow. Australia is not included because it has so little of either. (*Data from U.S. Geological Survey.*)

navigable streams, and other kinds of transport facilities must be provided. (*g*) The movement of river craft is comparatively slow and especially so against the stream current. Because of these problems, river transportation may be costly. The channel must be maintained, terminals provided, and locks and bridges operated; but these costs, and others, are usually borne by the governmental authority from taxes. If costs are properly allocated, rail or truck transportation may be cheaper.

In spite of these defects rivers are used even in modern industrial areas, especially for the movement of heavy goods of great bulk. The Rhine is heavily used in Europe and the major rivers of the United States provide the means for the annual movement of tens of millions of ton-miles of commerce. Nevertheless, the total is small compared to that moved by rail and truck.

19.22   The Value of Lakes for Inland Navigation. The use of the large lakes or inland seas of the world for navigation presents less difficult problems than does the use of rivers. Some are closed by ice part of the time, but not many are troubled by variable depths or obstructed channels. Owing to their fortunate position between important iron-ore and coal regions of the continent, the Great Lakes of North America have been provided with special craft and organized into one of the most effective routes of transportation in the world. They have played a large part in the historical and industrial development of the region in which they lie. An indication of their utility is the fact that each year the locks between Lake Superior and the other lakes carry more tonnage than either the Suez or Panama Canal. Although there is not the same opportunity for special service in other regions, some of the lakes of other continents serve the transportational needs of their regions well. Among the most used of them are the three great lakes

Victoria, Tanganyika, and Nyasa in eastern Africa; the Caspian Sea and Lake Baikal in Asia; and others of smaller size.

19.23   The Value of Lakes and Streams as Centers of Recreation. The exhilarating sports found in swimming, fishing, and various forms of boating serve as an attraction so strong that large numbers of people make at least a brief annual trip to some body of inland water for purposes of recreation. In recent years the building of good roads and the mobility afforded by the automobile have permitted a widespread gratification of this desire, with the result that large amounts of money are spent by vacationists, and the lakes and streams that attract them have become physical assets of great value to the regions in which they lie.

The greatest number of attractive lakes is found in regions of glaciation. Some of them are the morainic lakes of regions of glacial deposition, but the larger number is found in regions of ice scour or of ice scour with associated morainic damming. It often happens also that the conditions of ice scour which are responsible for the lakes have conspired with other factors to render the surrounding land of low agricultural value. This in turn has tended to keep the region in a forested or wild condition, which increases the attractiveness of the lakes and their recreational value. Lake-dotted areas are found in mountain, hill, and plain lands alike. The glacial lakes of the Alpine countries, Rocky Mountain regions, high Sierras, or southern Andes add mountain scenery to their attractiveness. The more accessible lakes of the hill lands of New England, the Adirondacks, or the English Lake District and Scotland and the numberless lakes in the plains of the Great Lakes region, eastern Canada, Scandinavia, Finland, or the borders of the Alps draw ever larger numbers of people to their shores. They constitute a resource worthy of studied conservation and development.

20

Natural Vegetation and Associated Animal Life

20.1 Natural Vegetation as a Geographic Element. One of the most striking features of the earth's land surfaces is the plant cover which varies greatly in kind and in density from region to region. This vegetation cover has geographical significance in a variety of ways. Ranking high in importance is the esthetic contribution which it makes to the variety in appearance and the attractiveness of the earth's land surfaces, for the visual landscape is to a significant degree the product of the vegetation mantle. Forested areas stand in marked contrast to grasslands; the green woodland in leaf gives a totally different scenic effect to that provided by the somber grove which has shed its leaves; while during the period of rich and varied autumn colors some deciduous woods of middle latitudes are spectacular in their beauty. Since how a region "looks"—its visual appearance—is a feature of great geographic importance, it must follow that natural vegetation takes high rank among those elements which serve to differentiate regions in appearance.

In addition to its esthetic qualities, native vegetation and animal life have important resource value. In the preagricultural stage of human development they were the exclusive sources providing the essentials for food and clothing. As civilization advanced and population multiplied and spread, the original vegetation over areas of subcontinental extent has been consumed or destroyed, leaving behind a greatly altered landscape consisting of modified natural plant formations as well as human settlements, tilled fields, and other features of land utilization. Nevertheless, even in this twentieth century, forest products in the form of lumber, fuel, and pulp, and natural pasturelands for animal grazing, continue to make an important contribution to economic well-being. As a resource in another form, it is the enduring attraction of woods, forest, and wildlife which gives many of the most popular summer and winter playgrounds their special lure for tourists.

Since the natural vegetation is an expression of the composite physical environment, and is the integration of all factors, past as well as present, it likewise serves as an indicator of the potentialities of an environment for human use. The suitability of a soil for certain types of farming is often clearly indicated by the density and composition of the vegetation cover. Thus, even in those parts of the earth where the original vegetation has long since disappeared, and agriculture is of long standing, the soil continues to bear the imprint of the type of plant cover under which it developed.

20.2 Causes of Regional Variations in the Plant Cover. The character of the natural vegetation is determined by the physical environment whose principal conditioning elements are climate, soils, and organisms. Unlike animals, plants do not have the power of locomotion, cannot construct shelters, and do not generate heat, so that they are unable to escape the effects of the surrounding environment to the same degree. All the factors of the environment act collectively and simultaneously upon plants and the action of any one element is conditioned by all the others. Nevertheless certain elements of the environment are more important than others in influencing the nature of the plant cover.

In its broader aspects the distribution of natural vegetation over the earth reflects present climatic conditions more than any other single element. Plant geographers have long recognized this fundamental principle which is evidenced by the general parallelism which exists between temperature and precipitation characteristics on the one hand and vegetation characteristics on the other. Whether it is the means or the extremes of the climatic factors which are more important in controlling vegetation patterns is not so clear. But the world pattern of natural vegetation has not always existed in its present form. It is a product of evolution, for vegetation is dynamic, not static, and as climate has changed in the past so has the vegetation.

A noteworthy example of vegetation change is the succession of flora that occupied what had been the ice-covered parts of northwestern Europe following the retreat of the glaciers and the associated modification of the climates. The denuded land surface first developed a mantle of lowly plants somewhat similar to those which comprise the present tundra. As the climate became less severe, these plants were replaced by coniferous or needle trees and at a later stage these in turn gave way to a broadleaf and mixed broadleaf–needleleaf forrest in the less severe continental climates. Such an evolution of the vegetation cover is spoken of as a *plant succession*. With the stabilization of climate the last stage in such a succession is known as a *climax* or *plant formation*. The climaxes consequently are the extensive vegetational types which correspond to the major types of climate. "The climax communities are considered to be the highest types of vegetation that can develop under the different aspects of climate, and are in dynamic equilibrium with the climate."[1] The visible unity within the climax is due primarily to the dominants or the controlling species. Illustrations of extensive and important climaxes are the tun-

dra of the poleward margins of North America and Eurasia, the coniferous forest of the subarctic climates of the same continents, and the tropical rainforest of the constantly wet lands of the low latitudes.

Modifications and variety within the climatically induced larger plant communities are usually the result of secondary factors, chiefly soil and biotic elements, and these are associated with exposure, drainage, local climates, and the effects of burning and human exploitation. Thus while climatic control is primary in plant distribution, the edaphic or soil control is usually secondary. But soil and climate are not completely independent factors, for soil character in its broader features is greatly influenced by climate and natural vegetation. Nevertheless, there are many local variations in soils which are the result of nonclimatic factors such as the parent soil material and bed rock, drainage conditions, and angle of slope. Thus soils may vary almost from spot to spot and as a consequence produce local variation in the vegetation cover.

In addition to the climatic and edaphic factors there is a third which warrants comment, *viz.*, the biotic factor. It operates in a variety of ways. Thus overgrazing may operate to change the native vegetation of a region, as it has, in all probability, on the North American Great Plains. Other types of biotic influence are associated with obligatory pollinating insects, the relations that exist between hosts and parasites, and obligatory food dependency.

The classification and brief description of the original vegetation cover here presented is plant geography in its broadest aspects—an attempt to describe the principal plant associations, show their relationships to the environmental complex, and indicate their world distribution (Plate 5). Over considerable parts of the earth, man, through his use of the land, has so greatly modified the original vegetation that at present it bears little resemblance to what it was in its native state.

20.3   *Animals*. It is nearly impossible to classify animals in terms of environment as one classifies plants. Since the latter are immobile,

[1]Stanley A. Cain. "Foundations of Plant Geography," p. 11.

they must adapt themselves to their environment by their forms and structures. Animals, on the other hand, being mobile, can, within certain limits, change or circumvent their environment, by migrating or burrowing. The plant is a captive of its environment and is compelled to wear the evidences of its captivity in the form of structural adaptations where everyone may see them. Animals, on the other hand, adjust themselves to their physical surroundings by what they *do*, rather than through their structures and forms. As a consequence no attempt is here made to classify animals into great associations or communities, as is done for plants. Since, however, the type of animal life is sometimes closely related to vegetation characteristics, brief comments occasionally are added concerning the representative animal life associated with certain vegetation groups.

How Physical Conditions Affect Plant Life

20.4   Plant Associations. One does not have to be either a botanist or widely traveled to be aware of the effects of physical environment upon the characteristics and distribution of plants. Even the layman quickly observes that poorly drained locations, such as swamps, or the periodically inundated margins of rivers and lakes, have a distinctive association of plants that differs markedly from the vegetation cover of higher and drier sites. Certain plants, such as mosses and ferns, are found characteristically in shady, damp locations, while others such as juniper thrive best in sunlight.

The above illustrations, to be sure, apply to relatively restricted areas, but in a more general way vegetation cover may have a considerable degree of similarity even over very extensive areas of scores of thousands of square miles, provided the physical environment remains relatively uniform. Moreover, similar environments in widely separated parts of the earth are likely to have plant covers that are much alike in general aspect, even though they are not composed of identical species. Thus the tropical rainforests of the Amazon Basin and the Congo,

separated by wide expanses of ocean, are, nevertheless, relatively similar in general appearance and type of plants. So also are the grasslands of Argentina, the United States, and Hungary.

Based upon common physical needs, therefore, certain plants, although unrelated to one another, are repeatedly found growing side by side in similar environments. It is with these *plant associations* over relatively *extensive areas,* occupying as they do characteristic physical environments, that the geographer is chiefly concerned. These extensive associations comprise the large-scale or first-order pattern of the earth's vegetation cover. In order to appreciate the significance of the great plant associations and their distribution, some explanation is necessary of the ways in which various elements of the physical environment influence vegetation.

20.5   Temperature and Light. Unlike many animals, plants do not generate heat. As a consequence their very existence as well as their characteristics are greatly influenced by the temperatures of air and soil. For every species of plant there appear to be three critical temperatures: (*a*) lower and (*b*) upper limits beyond which it cannot exist and (*c*) an optimum temperature in which it grows most vigorously. The lower limit is sometimes called its *specific zero.* This minimum temperature is not necessarily associated with 32°, for many tropical plants perish before the freezing point is reached, while certain forms of arctic vegetation thrive in subfreezing temperatures.

Different species resist cold in different ways. Some make the adjustment by retarding growth and arresting certain functions, such as assimilation and respiration, during the period of low temperatures. This may result in a marked external change such as takes place with leaf fall in middle-latitude deciduous trees. Certain other plants, such as coniferous trees or the evergreen shrubs of Mediterranean climates, lapse into a dormant period without any apparent outward   change. In some species the plant completes its entire life cycle during the warm period, so that the vegetative portions disappear entirely throughout the season of cold and it is only by means of a seed, which is capable of greater and more prolonged resistance to low temperatures, that the plant is perpetuated. These are the *annuals,* of which, for instance, rice and corn are representative. They stand in contrast to *perennials,* the vegetative parts of which live on year after year.

The length of the vegetative period is not alike for the same plant in contrasting climates. In regions of short summers, such as Siberia, the growth period is reduced to 3 or 4 months, but at the same time the rapidity of growth during the shortened summer is great. For example, the beech, which completes its seasonal growth in 3 months in the latitude of Yakutsk, Siberia, requires 6 months in central Germany.

Not only heat but also light affects the characteristic development of plants. Reproductive functions, for instance, are favored by light. This is shown by the fact that flowers can be prevented from opening by being grown in semidarkness. Those plants which grow in shade usually are characterized by greater development of their vegetative parts, such as stems and leaves, at the expense of flowers which contain the reproductive organs. On the other hand, light tends to produce large, brightly colored flowers but thicker and shorter leaves and stems.

20.6 Water. (Hygrophytes, Xerophytes, and Tropophytes.) No plants can live entirely without water. Taken in at the roots it is the principal ingredient of sap, in which mineral matter in solution is carried to all parts of the plant. Transpiration of water takes place through the leaves, the process being associated with chemical changes by which the sap is prepared for assimilation by tissues.

Plants that exist in water or in very damp and humid regions are designated as *hygrophytes.* In these the stems are usually long and relatively fragile, containing a minimum of woody fiber, while leaves are large and usually thin. Roots are likely to be shallow. The banana tree, characteristic of the wet tropics, is an example of hygrophytes. At the opposite extreme are the *xerophytes,* which are adapted to drought conditions. In these, roots are long or widespread in order to increase the depth or

area from which water is obtained, while stems are likely to be shorter and stronger. Leaves are smaller and thicker, their stomata (openings for transpiration) fewer, and a hairy undercover is common. A thick corky bark or a coating of wax may further protect against rapid transpiration. Leaves may even be replaced by thorns. Certain desert species adapt themselves in a different way, *viz.,* by accumulating supplies of water within their vegetative structures. Such a one is the fleshy-stemmed cactus.

In climates that have a wet and a dry period, or in those in which there is a distinct period of cold, many plants are hygrophytic in one season and xerophytic in the other. These are called *tropophytes.* In tropical wet-and-dry climates, for instance, most trees drop their leaves during the period of drought and temporarily become xerophytes, for the woody stems and branches and the shiny wax-covered buds are highly conservative of water. With the coming of the rains again the buds open, and hygrophytic leaves and reproductive organs are formed. In middle latitudes the season of cold has a similar effect to that of the season of drought in the tropics, for the rise of sap is checked by low temperature as well as by low rainfall. Thus winter is a period of physiological drought during which deciduous plants lose their leaves and become xerophytic in character.

20.7 Soil. Although temperature and water are the two principal physical elements determining the general character of the earth's natural vegetation, modifications within the great climatically induced groups are due principally to soil contrasts (the *edaphic factor*). Thus within the northeastern pine forests of the upper Great Lakes states, the composition of the original stand depended largely on the character of the soil. On the poorest sandy soils jack pine was almost the exclusive tree. On the somewhat better sandy soils Norway pine was intermingled with jack pine; while in regions of higher fertility Norway pine occurred in mixtures with white pine and northern hardwoods. Throughout the hardwood forests of New York white pine occupied the sandy plains.

In its modifying effects upon plant life the

soil environment makes itself felt in a number of ways, especially through its temperature, chemical composition, and water retentiveness. Sandy or stony soils, which are very porous, may induce a xerophytic vegetation even in regions of moderate rainfall. Shallow soils are likewise inclined to be droughty. Where a high percentage of salt is present, as in parts of deserts or along seacoasts, most plants will not grow. Vegetation in such areas of salt concentration has distinctive characteristics, being xerophytic in many respects. A proportion of over 3 per cent of lime in soil is likewise injurious to most vegetation. In cool, damp, subarctic regions, the barren soils of which are covered with raw and highly acid humus, such xerophytic plants as heather and furze are characteristic.

The Great Plant Associations

20.8 Types of Natural Vegetation. No widely accepted geographical classification of the earth's plant cover has as yet been evolved. In part this results from an actual lack of reliable information concerning the nature of the vegetation mantle over extensive areas. An additional factor complicating the problem of classification is the fact that trees, grass, and shrubs exist in such a variety of combinations as to make a simple classification difficult. Lack of agreement on what constitutes the essential geographical elements in the plant cover has been a further retarding factor. The classification here presented is therefore tentative in character. While it has the merit of being simple, it can be objected to on grounds that it is not wholly consistent and that its types are too generalized.

THE GREAT PLANT ASSOCIATIONS
Types of Natural Vegetation

1. Forest associations
   a. Tropical forests
      a^1. Tropical rainforest
      a^2. Lighter tropical forest (including semideciduous, deciduous, scrub, and thorn forest)
   b. Middle-latitude forests
      b^1. Mediterranean woodland and shrub
      b^2. Broadleaf forest
         (1) Deciduous
         (2) Evergreen

b^3. Needle-leaf or coniferous forest
b^4. Mixed broadleaf–needle-leaf forest
2. Grassland associations
   a. Tropical grasslands (wooded savanna and savanna)
   b. Middle-latitude grasslands
3. Desert shrub
4. Tundra

20.9 Four Principal Classes of Vegetation. Plant geographers are inclined to recognize four principal classes of natural vegetation: (*a*) forests, (*b*) grasslands, (*c*) desert shrub, and (*d*) tundra, the latter composed chiefly of herbaceous plants other than grass. Without doubt the distribution of these major classes of vegetation over the earth's land areas is environmentally controlled, largely the result of climate, but it is by no means easy to make broad generalizations regarding the specific qualities of the environment of each class. Tundra, to be sure, is largely confined to climates in which the summers are so short and so cool as to largely exclude other plant forms, and desert shrub is a product of climates very deficient in rainfall. But on the other hand, some arid regions are characterized by a sparse cover which is more grass than shrub, so that it is not true that shrub always indicates greater aridity than grassland. It is probably true as a general rule that forests occupy the rainier regions while grasslands are more frequently to be found in subhumid and semiarid climates. But there are important exceptions which are not easily explained. The above generalization, while largely true in the middle latitudes, is scarcely valid in the tropics where both grassland and woodlands occupy a wide range of climates. The origin of tropical grasslands is a highly controversial question. With our present limited knowledge, therefore, it is impossible to establish very clear and definite environmental relationships between forest, grassland, and shrub over the earth as a whole.

20.10 Woodland or Forest Associations. Within this group the tree is the essential element. Other woody plants such as bushes and shrubs, together with grasses and parasitic forms, may be present as well, but these are usually only accessory parts of the forest. When trees grow in a closed formation and are so close together that their crowns touch, the result is a genuine forest. But there are many instances, especially in the tropics, of plant covers in which the trees are widely spaced and grass or shrubs are abundant so that it is difficult to know whether the whole should be classified as predominantly woodland, grassland, or shrub. Woodland associations dispute the possession of the land with grassland associations, the forests more often than not occupying the rainier regions and becoming more luxuriant with increasing precipitation and temperature.

20.11 *The Woodland-Forest Environment.* It does not seem unusual that genuine forest should be more demanding in its environmental requirements than either grass or shrubs. Therefore, it is principally where physical conditions are so adverse as to discourage luxuriant tree growth that grass and shrub become dominant. In general, the tree has a larger transpiring surface, compared with the area of ground covered, than have other plants and its transpiring surface is farther removed from the water supply in the soil. Moreover, by reason of its height the tree suffers more from wind and evaporation. On the other hand, because of its deep and extensive root system the tree is able to tap deeper-lying supplies of water and is capable of withstanding drought, even during the vegetative or warm season, provided there is a continuous supply of water at the roots. In other words, the *season of rainfall* is of less significance to trees.

The limiting factors in forest growth may be summarized as follows: (*a*) Low temperatures limit forest range both in high latitudes and in high altitudes. Since a large amount of permanent plant tissue is required to form a tree, and moreover, since the new shoots formed each season have to be matured sufficiently to be able to endure the following drought or cold period, it follows that forests require a fairly long growing period. Even the hardiest conifers require a mean warm-month temperature of not less than 50°F. The isotherm of 50° for the warmest month, therefore, approximately marks the poleward limit of forests.

(*b*) The subsoils must be permanently moist, and the moisture must be present in a form that is readily available. Climates with highly variable rainfall are not well suited to forests for there is danger of exhaustion of soil-moisture reserves. Demands upon soil moisture are greatest in the growing season, so that other things being equal, a climate with a warm-season rainfall maximum is more favorable for forest growth than one where summers are dry and winters wet. Since a tree absorbs some moisture even in the dormant period, a climate whose rainfall is excessively seasonal in character tends to inhibit tree growth.

(*c*) In climates with very low winter temperatures, the prevalence of strong or continuous wind is injurious to trees. Wind is directly related to the rate of transpiration, and strong dry winds during the cold season when the soil moisture is locked up through freezing are particularly bad. Thus winds are a limiting factor to forest growth both in high altitudes and high latitudes. A good forest climate, therefore, is one with a warm rainy vegetative season, a continuously moist subsoil, and a low wind velocity, especially in the dormant season.

From what has been said above it is possible to make certain generalizations regarding the distribution of forests over the earth. They are excluded from high latitudes, poleward of about the 50° isotherms for the warmest month, by the absence of a period of sufficient warmth and by the cold dry winds of winter. On this frontier, forests give way to tundra. In the middle latitudes they occupy both the humid eastern and western portions of the continents, but are excluded from the deep interiors because of the prevailingly dry climates in those locations.

In tropical latitudes the distribution pattern is not so clear. Luxuriant forests usually prevail in the rainy equatorial regions and extend farther poleward along some eastern margins of the land areas where precipitation is abundant. Farther removed from the equator, as rainfall declines in amount and becomes more seasonal in character, the dense evergreen forest gives way to a lighter woodland composed of shorter trees, more widely spaced, many of which are deciduous in character. In this transition zone between constantly wet climate and dry climate, grasses and shrubs are intermingled in complex patterns with trees, so that it becomes difficult to know whether the plant cover should be classified as a woodland containing much grass and shrub or, on the other hand, as a wooded grassland. In recent years there has been an increasing tendency to doubt the existence of climatically induced grasslands in the tropics, although savannas (grasslands) in which trees are the dominant form may be a climax.[2]

20.12 Grassland Associations. The vegetation cover here consists principally of perennial grasses, although other herbaceous plants may be present in considerable numbers, and in the grasslands of the tropics clumps of trees and shrubs are prominent features.

Grasslands in the low latitudes are known as *savannas*. They exist in bewilderingly complex combinations with trees and shrubs, in some places with trees dominant so that they may better be classed as woodland. Open grasslands which are devoid of trees exist, but they are in the minority. More common are the open savannas with trees growing scattered or in clumps. Formerly it was widely believed that savannas were a product of the tropical wet-and-dry climate in which most of them do exist. It was this coincidence that led to the name "savanna climate." More recently doubts have grown relative to whether the open tropical grasslands are climatically induced and there are numerous plant geographers who support the idea that they were either originally wooded areas which have been modified by cultivation and frequent burnings, or are the result of soil or seasonal drainage conditions unfavorable to the growth of trees. There is greater likelihood that the savannas in which trees predominate may represent a true climax. It is not unusual for the climatic transition from tropical wet climate to desert to be

[2] P. W. Richards. "The Tropical Rain Forest, An Ecological Study." Pp. 338–345. Cambridge University Press, New York, 1952.

paralleled by a vegetation transition in which forest and woodland of various densities and species remain dominant throughout and genuine grasslands are absent.

Middle-latitude grasslands, unlike those of the tropics, are characteristically without trees except along water courses or close to the forest margins. Tall-grass or mid-grass prairie is characteristic of the more humid parts of the grassland, while combinations of mid-grass and short-grass prairies represent the drier forms.

20.13 *Grassland Climate.* The presence of natural grassland is proof that the physical conditions, at least, are unfavorable to the growth of trees. On the other hand, it is not unfavorable climatic and soil conditions which prevent the development of grasses in the present forested areas, but only the competition of trees. Thus there are few if any forest areas where grasses cannot thrive, but the converse of this is not true. In this sense there is no such thing as a true grassland climate. Through cutting off the light which reaches the ground by their heavy foliage, and even more by the taking up of large amounts of both water and nutritive salts by their roots, trees may starve out the grasses.

It was formerly thought that grasslands in all latitudes characteristically developed under climates where the annual rainfall is modest in amount and seasonal in its distribution. In other words, grasslands were thought to occupy subhumid and semiarid lands and therefore intermediate locations between forests and desert shrub.

For the middle latitudes, at least, the above statement seems reasonably accurate. There the grasslands appear to occupy locations which are too dry for forests and yet at the same time are not so deficient in rainfall as to preclude plant growth other than desert shrub or cactus. There is still much controversy concerning the origin of grasslands in the tropics, but increasing support, too, for the idea that they are a consequence of soil and drainage conditions which discourage tree growth or that they owe their origin to the burnings and clearings of the forest associated with native agricultural operations.[3]

Since most grasses are relatively shallow rooted, they suffer from prolonged drought if it coincides with the warm period or growing season. Climates with winter rains and summer drought, therefore, are not ideal for grasses. Moisture in the deep subsoil is of little value; it is the surficial layers that are critical. Since this top moisture is quickly lost by evaporation, frequent, even if weak, precipitation is essential during the growing season. During the resting period (winter in middle latitudes) grasses can endure great drought without injury. Winds are of little significance, since grass does not grow tall enough to be greatly affected by any but the slower-moving surface currents. Most hostile to grass is drought during the growing season.

20.14   Desert shrub, characteristic of arid regions, consists of woody xerophytic plants usually only a few feet in height. They are broadleaf in character and may be either evergreen or deciduous in their habits. Growth may be in the form of single isolated plants widely spaced or they may exist in groups or patches.

20.15   Tundra vegetation consists largely of herbaceous or nonwoody plants other than grass, although the latter may not be absent. Sedges, mosses, and lichens predominate. This lowly plant cover is typical of those high-latitude portions of the continents where summers are too short and cool for even the hardy conifers to thrive. For much of the year the ground remains frozen so that while there may be adequate water in the soil, it exists in the solid form which is inaccessible to plants. The environment consequently is deficient both in heat and in water, these deficiencies being reflected in the lowly, widely spaced, xerophytic plant life resembling in many ways the vegetation of deserts.

[3] O. F. Cook. Milpa Agriculture, a Primitive Tropical System. *Smithsonian Inst. Ann. Rept.,* 1919, pp. 307–326; Leo Waibel. Vegetation and Land Use in the Planalto Central of Brazil. *Geog. Rev.,* Vol. 38, pp. 553–554, October, 1948; J. S. Beard. The Savanna Vegetation of Northern Tropical America. *Ecol. Monographs,* Vol. 23, pp. 149–215, 1953.

Rarely are there sharp boundaries separating woodland, grassland, desert shrub, and tundra but almost always gradual transitions from one to the other. As a consequence there are transitional belts where trees and grass, grass and shrub, and trees and tundra plants intermingle.

Types of Forests and Their Distribution[4]

LOW-LATITUDE FORESTS

20.16   Tropical Rainforest. This most luxuriant type of woodland community is the climax vegetation of tropical lowlands and slopes where rainfall is heavy and well distributed throughout the year, there being no marked dry season. Distribution of the tropical rainforest is imperfectly known. Certainly the Amazon Basin, in northern South America, and West Central Africa are the two largest areas of tropical rainforest, although it is found along many rainy coasts and on numerous islands in the tropics as well (Plate 5).

Three principal characteristics feature this forest type: (*a*) There is a great variety of different species of trees present. Seldom are there fewer than 15 tree species per acre and there may be as many as 40. This is in contrast to most middle-latitude forests, where one, or at most a few, species may form almost solid stands. But although species are numerous, rainforest trees are relatively uniform in appearance. (*b*) There is developed to an unusual degree a vertical stratification in the forest, this feature arising from the fact that the multiple species arrange themselves in several groups, each having a particular height limit. The result is a forest with a number of tree tiers, each with its own height level and each lower one reflecting an increasing tolerance for shade as

[4] Trees are classified as either (*a*) broadleaf or (*b*) needle leaf (conifers); (*a*) deciduous or (*b*) evergreen. Evergreens are those which retain some foliage throughout the year, while deciduous trees periodically lose their leaves and are therefore bare for a portion of the year. Broadleaf trees are both evergreen and deciduous; conifers are predominantly evergreen.

Fig. 20.1 Tropical rainforest in the Amazon Basin of Brazil. Note the density of stand, variability in size of trees, and irregularity of the forest crown. (*Courtesy of Hamilton Rice Expedition of 1924–1925.*)

imposed by the canopy above. (*c*) The number of climbers, lianas, and epiphytes is unusually large. The giant lianas have the appearance of great cables interlacing the branches of the forest crown and binding the individual trees together.

20.17 *External Aspect.* Luxuriant, complex, exuberant—such is the character of tropical rainforest (Fig. 20.1). In external aspect it presents a richly varied mosaic of many shades. The mature leaves are a deep green, but young leaves, on the other hand, are highly colored, resembling autumn foliage in middle latitudes. The result is a forest in which the fresh green of middle-latitude woodlands is absent. Leaves are large and often leathery in texture.

The skyline, too, is different, the crown of the tropical forest being irregular and jagged with many crests and furrows. This comes from the great variety of trees of varying heights which comprise it. No other forest equals it in richness of species, and these are intricately intermingled. Pure stands of a species are practically unknown.

Tropical rainforest is evergreen broadleaf in character, there being no general dormant period when the forest as a whole is bare and without foliage. On the other hand, the leaves are, as a rule, renewed each year, but different species drop their leaves at different times. For the whole forest, leaf shedding is a sporadic thing rather than seasonal for all the species. Individual trees without leaves may be observed at any time in the rainforest, but the new crop is not long in appearing. Just as the climate is without a marked seasonal rhythm, the vegetation is likewise.

20.18 *Internal Aspect.* An internal view shows the tropical rainforest to be composed of trees which vary greatly in height and diameter growing close together. The average height of the tall trees comprising the upper story of the forest is seldom over 150 to 180 ft. Trunks are relatively slender and without branches until near the top. The bark is thin and smooth.

417

Fig. 20.2 Interior view of the tropical rainforest in the Belgian Congo of Africa. The time required for this photograph was 20,000 times the normal exposure in the open. Undergrowth appears to be dense. (*Courtesy of American Geographical Society.*)

The result of its being a multistoried forest is a dense canopy of shade with very subdued light underneath (Fig. 20.2). In the Congo forest Shantz found that the time required for a photograph was twenty thousand times the normal exposure in the open. Lianas, climbing plants, epiphytes, and parasites are relatively abundant.[5] This mass of vines and creepers appears almost to suffocate the trees that are its supports. Within the forest the tall, branchless trunks resemble gigantic dark columns supporting an almost impenetrable canopy, composed of the interlocking crowns of the trees and the vines and creepers that cover them.

In the virgin forest, because of deep shade, undergrowth is not unusually dense although often sufficient to obstruct distant views. In regions of deepest shade only a thick mat of

herbs or ferns covers the floor, so that one can proceed in all directions without following paths or even chopping new ones. Typical *jungle* conditions, with a thick and impenetrable undergrowth, are characteristic chiefly of sections where light reaches the forest floor, for example, along rivers and coasts, on precipitous wet slopes, and in abandoned agricultural clearings (Fig. 20.2).

Reflecting the abundant moisture in the surface soil, tropical rainforest trees are relatively shallow rooted and consequently weak in holding power. Their great trunks commonly are supported by giant buttress roots in the form of winglike outgrowths which extend 10 to 25 ft. up the stems.

Of the Amazon forest, Haviland writes:

If the approach is by boat up one of the great rivers, which are still the only highways through the greater part of the forest region, the sight is one of unforgettable grandeur. On either side the banks are veiled by a wall of green foliage between 100 and 200 ft. high, towering above its own inverted image in the water. . . . This profusion of flowering climbers, which in some places hides the out-

[5] Lianas are ropelike plants which entwine themselves around trunks and branches. Epiphytes, of which orchids are a common example, characteristically grow on the branches of tropical trees and spread their roots among the cracks in the bark. They frequently have hanging roots. Parasites are plants that feed from the sap of the tree on which they grow.

lines of the trees themselves, is characteristic of the South American forest. The creepers cover the whole roof of the forest as with a canopy and fall to its foot at the water side like a curtain. . . . This mass of creepers is not altogether the suffocating burden or host of parasites that it appears to be. In exchange for support, it affords shade which is essential to the well-being of the forest; and it has been shown that when the veil has been torn aside so that the sun can beat down on the roots, the giant trees perish. For this reason an artificial clearing is usually fringed with dead trees.

Here and there dark caverns yawn in the wall of foliage at the water side. These are the mouths of creeks and streams shut in by overarching branches from which long aerial roots hang down like stalactites. To enter these caves by boat is like passing from the open air into a vast dim hall, supported by immense columns. The trunks of the trees rise up for 70 or 80 ft. without a branch, and the undergrowth is thin and straggling. The ground is strewn with dead leaves, though it may be remarked that the accumulation of leaf mold is not very great, owing to the rapidity of bacterial action.[6]

There is reason to believe that the tropical rainforest has persisted relatively unchanged from very remote times. Recently it has been rudely disturbed by the spread of Western civilization to the tropics with associated clearing of the forest for plantations and an expanding native agriculture. It is estimated that tropical rainforest may still comprise as much as half of the earth's forest area, but at the accelerated rate at which it is being destroyed much of it may disappear within the lifetime of those now living.

20.19 *Animal life* of the tropical rainforest is not so conspicuous as is the vegetation, although it varies in kind and abundance from one region to another. In the crown of the forest, where there is an abundance of food, a great variety of birds and some climbing animals such as monkeys and apes exist. On the darkened floor below, large animals usually are not numerous, although in Africa the hippopotamus inhabits the river margins, and elephants, giraffes, and the big catlike animals may

[6] Maud D. Haviland. "Forest, Steppe and Tundra." Pp. 42–43. Cambridge University Press, London, 1926.

penetrate the forest for some distance. Reptiles and amphibians are relatively abundant. It is chiefly in insect life, however, that the tropical forest abounds. Although not conspicuous, and very elusive, the hum and sing of insect life are ever present. Ants are among the most numerous forms, and termites, a kind of destructive woodworm, are likewise abundant. Not only in the tropical forest, but throughout most poorly drained areas in the low latitudes, are to be found parasitic, disease-carrying insects, some of them dangerous alike to man and animals. Yellow fever, sleeping sickness, and malaria are examples of diseases which are propagated through the bites of insects.

20.20 Lighter Tropical Forest. Under this heading are included a considerable variety of woodland types—semideciduous, deciduous, scrub, and thorn—whose distinctive characteristics and precise distributions are not sufficiently well known to permit localizing the individual types on a small-scale, generalized vegetation map such as Plate 5. As a general rule, and where soils and drainage do not interfere, tropical rainforest at its climatic limits gives way to semideciduous and deciduous forest and with declining rainfall this in turn passes over to savanna woodland and finally to thorn woodland and desert shrub.

Characteristically these woodlands of the tropics, other than the rainforest, are composed of smaller trees more widely spaced and with a denser undergrowth of shrubs or grass (Fig. 20.3). More of the trees also are deciduous in character, although not all species are leafless during the drier dormant season. It is during the season of drought, nevertheless, that contrast with the rainforest is most marked. Scrub and thorn forest varies in density from an open parklike growth of low stunted trees and thorny plants to dense thickets of the same (Fig. 20.4). The trees composing the dry scrub forest are small in diameter, rarely exceeding 1 ft. No other tropical forest type equals it in tolerance of physical conditions.

20.21 *Utilization of Tropical Forests.* Although tropical forests occupy nearly 50 per cent of the earth's total forest area, at the

Fig. 20.3 Lighter tropical forest (semideciduous) in the Belgian Congo. The large trees are sufficiently far apart so that they do not create a dense shade. Coarse grass mantles much of the forest floor. (*Courtesy of American Geographical Society.*)

present time they supply only the limited needs of local populations and furnish to world commerce small quantities of special-quality woods, such as dyewoods and cabinet woods. Nevertheless these low-latitude forests, especially the tropical rainforest, represent one of the world's great potential timber supplies. The problems involved in their utilization are serious—labor

supply, sanitation, requirement of new logging technologies, how to utilize the great variety of species composing the tropical forest—but none of them appears to be insurmountable.

MIDDLE-LATITUDE FORESTS

20.22 Mediterranean Broadleaf Evergreen Scrub Forest. Mediterranean woodland and shrub is a relatively rare type, for seldom are trees broadleaf evergreen and at the same time adapted to regions with long, hot periods of summer drought. In those parts of the humid tropics where pronounced dry seasons are characteristic, trees protect themselves by shedding their leaves and thereby becoming xerophytic during the dry season, although they are hygrophytic during the periods of rains. In Mediterranean woodlands, on the other hand, adjustment is made in other ways, protective devices against rapid transpiration permitting the trees to retain their foliage, and consequently their evergreen characteristics, during the period of aridity. But although evergreen in character, there is more of a seasonal

Fig. 20.4 Scrub forest in Senegal, West Africa. (*Courtesy of Field Museum of Natural History.*)

rhythm in vegetative and reproductive processes than is true of the tropical rainforest.

This unique Mediterranean woodland is found in subtropical regions with mild, rainy winters and long, dry, hot summers. The climate as well as the vegetation is unusual, for the times of maximum temperature and maximum rainfall do not coincide. The largest representative area is the Mediterranean Sea borderlands, with smaller areas in California, middle Chile, southern Australia, and the Cape Town region of Africa.

Mediterranean woodland is predominantly a mixed forest of low, or even stunted, trees and woody shrubs (Fig. 20.5). Tall trees are rare. Where climatic and soil conditions are most favorable the virgin forest is composed of low, widely spaced trees with massive trunks and gnarled branches. Between the trees the ground is completely or partially covered by a pale, dusty, bush vegetation, which very much resembles the soil in color. From a distance, therefore, it may appear as though the ground were almost bare of small plants. In all of them woody parts are more prominent than foliage. As a protection against evaporation the tree trunks are encased in a thick, deeply fissured bark, this feature being perfectly exemplified by the cork oak. Leaves, too, which are small, stiff, thick, and leathery, with hard, shiny surfaces, are designed to prevent rapid losses of water.[7] The olive tree with its massive trunk, gnarled branches, thick fissured bark, and small, stiff, leathery leaves is very representative of Mediterranean sclerophyll woodland in regions of hot (*Csa*) summers.

Even more common than the woodland composed of low trees and shrubs described above is a vegetation mantle consisting principally of shrubs and bushes in which there may be some

[7] It is this leaf characteristic which has given the Mediterranean woodland the name *sclerophyll*.

Fig. 20.5 Mediterranean sclerophyll woodland in California. An open stand of dwarf oak merging with grassland. (*Courtesy of U.S. Forest Service.*)

Fig. 20.6 Mediterranean chaparral or maqui in Cape Province, South Africa. (*Courtesy of American Geographical Society.*)

Fig. 20.7 A mixed broadleaf deciduous forest (oak-hickory) in northern Indiana. Much of this type of forest occupied good agricultural land and as a consequence was destroyed in the process of settlement. (*Courtesy of U.S. Department of Agriculture.*)

stunted trees (Fig. 20.6). This bush thicket is known as *chaparral* in California and *maqui* in lands bordering the Mediterranean Basin. In places the woody shrubs form a thick and relatively tall cover; in others it is short and sparse. Chaparral in some regions may represent the original vegetation cover. In other sections it is the underwood remaining after the low trees of the original woodland have been destroyed. The chief economic importance of chaparral usually lies in its watershed protection.

20.23   Broadleaf Forests. Within the more humid parts of the middle latitudes are found two great forest groups: (*a*) the broadleaf trees, and (*b*) the needle-leaf conifers. Over large areas they exist as mixed conifer-broadleaf forests. As a general rule, but with important exceptions, the coniferous forests occupy the colder continental locations and thus are usually on the poleward side of the broadleaves. In regions of porous, and therefore water-deficient, sandy soils, such as the Atlantic and Gulf Coastal Plain of the United States, or on steep mountain slopes where soils are thin or rocky and temperatures lower, conifers may supplant broadleaves even in the lower middle latitudes. The latter condition is illustrated in the case of the southern Appalachians, which carry a long tongue of coniferous and mixed forest southward into the broadleaf belt.

Temperate broadleaf forests vary widely in composition, the dominant tree species differing from one region to another. In parts, especially along their poleward margins, there are numerous conifers among them, so many, in fact, that some plant geographers designate such forests as *mixed* rather than broadleaf (Fig. 20.7). In eastern United States two general broadleaf-forest areas are distinguished: (*a*) a northeastern one (northern Wisconsin and Michigan, New York, and southern New England) in which birch, beech, and maple predominate but with a large infusion of hemlock and other conifers; and (*b*) a central and southern one lying south of the first and terminating at the northern and western boundary of the sandy Coastal Plain (Fig. 20.8). In this

latter forest, which was originally the finest and most extensive area of broadleaves anywhere in the world, oak, chestnut, hickory, and poplar predominate but with pines prominent toward the Coastal Plain margins.

The greater part of the original American broadleaf-forest belt, lying as it does in an environment eminently suited for agriculture, has now been cleared and turned into farmland. Poorer cutover lands often have a brush cover. The remaining stands are chiefly in the rougher Appalachian country and in Tennessee, Kentucky, Missouri, and Arkansas. Outside the United States, other relatively large areas of temperate broadleaf or mixed forest are to be found in Japan, Korea, southeastern China, central Russia, Rumania, southwestern Siberia, western Europe, southern Chile, southeastern Australia, and New Zealand (Plate 5).

20.24   *Deciduous Broadleaves.* By far the greater part of the temperate broadleaf forest is *deciduous* in character, the trees dropping their leaves during the winter season (Fig. 20.7). Except in the dormant season this forest is rather uniformly bright green in color, and its profile is regular. The amount of underwood varies with density of tree stand, being much greater where an appreciable amount of light reaches the ground. Trunks of the deciduous trees are xerophytic in character, having a relatively thick bark which protects against transpiration during winter. On the other hand, the leaves are thin and delicate, requiring no protective devices, since they remain on the tree only during the warmer part of the year. As a result of seasonal leaf fall, for the year as a whole, considerable sunlight reaches the soil under deciduous forests.

20.25   *Evergreen Broadleaves.* Only along the humid subtropical margins of the middle latitudes are there important *evergreen* broadleaf forests, but these are not nearly so extensive as the deciduous variety. Their principal regions are in southern Japan, southern and southeastern China, New Zealand, and southeastern Australia. In many respects these subtropical forests are akin to those of the wet tropics. Lack of seasonal leaf fall, density of under-

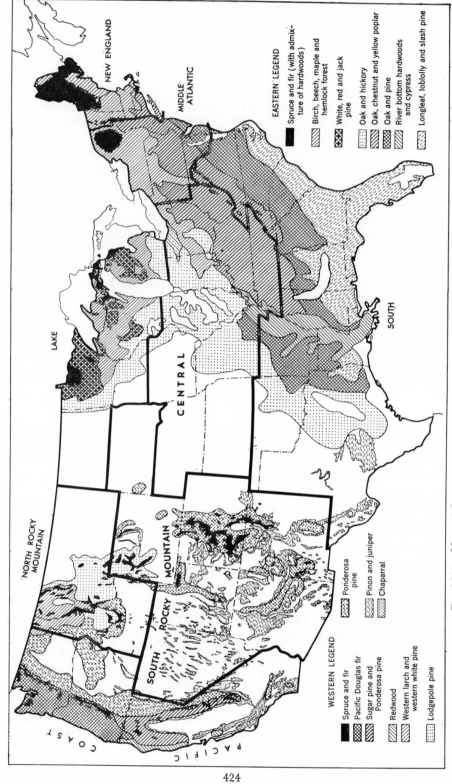

Fig. 20.8 Natural forest types of the United States. (*Courtesy of U.S. Forest Service.*)

EASTERN LEGEND

Spruce and fir (with admixture of hardwoods)

Birch, beech, maple and hemlock forest

White, red and jack pine

Oak and hickory

Oak, chestnut and yellow poplar

Oak and pine

River bottom hardwoods and cypress

Longleaf, loblolly and slash pine

WESTERN LEGEND

Spruce and fir

Pacific Douglas fir

Sugar pine and Ponderosa pine

Redwood

Western larch and western white pine

Lodgepole pine

Ponderosa pine

Pinon and juniper

Chaparral

NEW ENGLAND

MIDDLE ATLANTIC

LAKE

CENTRAL

SOUTH

NORTH ROCKY MOUNTAIN

SOUTH ROCKY MOUNTAIN

PACIFIC COAST

growth, the prevalence of lianas and other climbing plants, all are suggestive of the resemblance. The number of species composing the forest is likewise considerable. Oaks of various kinds are among the commonest trees. Eucalyptus and acacia are important elements of the Southern Hemisphere forests.

20.26 Needle-leaf or Coniferous Forests. Coniferous trees are predominantly *evergreen,* the addition and fall of the needles being a continuous process and not confined to any particular period or season. In some species the leaves may remain on the trees for 5 years or more. Unlike broadleaves, however, the needles of conifers are xerophytic in character so that shedding is not necessary to protect against a cold or drought season. On the whole, the crown of a coniferous forest does not intercept so much sunlight as does that of the broadleaf woodland, but (*a*) since the former lies predominantly in higher latitudes where there are longer periods of low sun, and (*b*) since it is never without foliage, less sun reaches the earth. As a result there is usually less surficial

vegetation, a minimum of bacterial activity, and smaller accumulations of humus in the soil.

20.27 *Subarctic Conifers.* Conifers reach their maximum development, as far as areal extent is concerned, in the severe subarctic regions of North America and Eurasia, where they form wide and continuous east-west forest belts stretching from coast to coast (Figs. 20.9 and 20.10). To the subarctic coniferous forests have been given the name *taiga.* On their northern frontiers they make contact with the treeless tundra, a region thoroughly hostile to trees. The Eurasian taiga forms the single largest continuous forest area on the earth. Conifers (larch, spruce, fir, pine) predominate, although broadleaf trees (alder, willow, aspen, birch, mountain ash) are scattered throughout, individually as well as in thickets or clusters. The latter are characteristic of low swampy areas and of regions bearing a second growth. Species are few in number.

Xerophytic character is conspicuous, for taiga soils are physiologically dry much of the year, water being freely accessible at the roots only

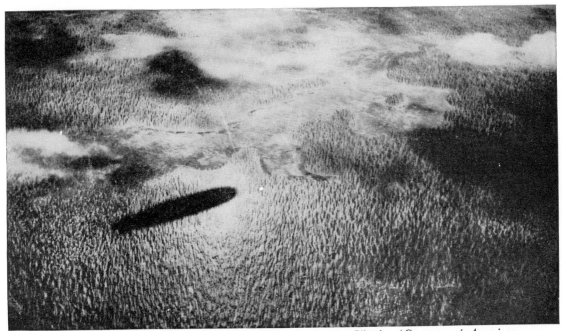

Fig. 20.9 An air view of the swamp taiga of western Siberia. (*Courtesy of American Geographical Society.*)

Fig. 20.10 Thin stands of conifers in the ice-scoured region of Canada. Compare with Fig. 20.9. (*Royal Canadian Air Force Photograph.*)

during the short warm season of 3 to 5 months. Even in summer absorption of water is retarded by the coolness of the soil and the acidity of the humus which accumulates in the deep, cool shade. In these regions of long, cold, dry winters and short cool summers, trees are relatively small in size, usually not over $1\frac{1}{2}$ ft. in diameter, and growth is slow (Fig. 20.11). Wet swampy areas covered with sphagnum moss, and containing such trees as spruce and balsam, are numerous, these spots being designated as *muskeg* in North America.

On the shaded forest floor vegetation is meager, mosses and lichens being the most common plant forms, and sometimes even these are stifled by the thick blanket of slowly decomposing needles. Little organic matter is made available to the soil, for needle leaves are a poor source of humus to begin with, while the low temperatures and deep shade act to retard decomposition and discourage the activity of soil fauna. Animal life is not so abundant as in the middle-latitude forests farther south, although trapping is an important occupation, and the taiga is one of the principal sources of natural furs. The long-continued cold tends to make for heavy pelts. Wolf, bear, fox, otter, mink, ermine, squirrel, lynx, and sable are representative animals.

20.28 *Conifers in Lower Middle Latitudes.* South of the great belts of subarctic conifers are other areas of needle trees which, although less extensive, are nevertheless more valuable forest regions. This comes about as a result of their being composed of larger trees and superior timber species and at the same time being more easily accessible.

In western North America broken belts of conifers extend southward from the taiga following the rainier highland chains (Pacific Coast Mountains and Rocky Mountains) to beyond the Mexican border (Fig. 20.12). The forests of the American Pacific Coast states, western Canada, and Alaska constitute the most extensive area of fine coniferous forest anywhere in the world. Large trees, dense stand, good-quality timber, all contribute to this high rank. Most valuable of its trees is the Douglas fir, which reaches a diameter of 6 ft. or more and a height exceeding 250 ft.

Fig. 20.11   Side view of subarctic coniferous forest in Yukon, Canada. Note the small size of the trees. (*Courtesy of U.S. Forest Service.*)

East of the Rockies conifers extend southward from the taiga into southeastern Canada and the northern portions of the northeastern tier of American states—Minnesota, Wisconsin, Michigan, the Adirondacks in New York, and much of Maine. The most valuable timber trees from this eastern forest have been removed, leaving behind extensive areas of waste and cutover land of little value. South of the taiga in Eurasia valuable coniferous forests occupy the slopes of the Alps, Carpathians, and other highland regions as well as certain sandy areas of coastal plains.

Separated from this northern belt of conifers, in the United States, by extensive broadleaf forests is the *southern pine forest,* which occupies the Atlantic and Gulf Coastal Plain (Plate 5). It is composed of 10 different species of pine of which the longleaf pine is most abun-

dant (Fig. 20.13). Climatically this needle-tree forest seems somewhat out of place, for rainfall is abundant, and the growing season long. However, the poor, sandy, droughty soil and high evaporation are offsetting factors, creating an environment that is generally hostile to broadleaf varieties. Open parklike character, with the ground covered by a mantle of coarse grasses or low shrubs, is typical. This southern pine forest has, during the last few decades, been one of the principal sources for American lumber, although the peak of its production has been passed. Extensive areas of nearly worthless cutover land are now one of the most conspicuous features of the southern pine region. On the poorly drained floodplains of the Atlantic and Gulf Coastal Plain pines give way to a contrasting forest type composed of such trees as tupelo, red gum, and cypress (Fig. 20.14).

The principal regions of forest utilization in the middle latitudes are the United States and Canada in the Western Hemisphere and northern Europe in the Old World. In the United States it is the forests of the Pacific Coast states

Fig. 20.12   Interior view of the Douglas fir forest in the United States Pacific Northwest. Trees are of large size and the stand is dense. (*Courtesy of U.S. Forest Service.*)

Fig. 20.13 The southern pine forest (longleaf, loblolly, slash pines) of the United States, typical of the Atlantic and Gulf Coastal Plain. (*Courtesy of U.S. Forest Service.*)

Fig. 20.14 River-bottom forest in the Gulf Coastal Plain of the United States; principally cypress, tupelo, and red gum. (*Courtesy of U.S. Forest Service.*)

and those of the Atlantic and Gulf Coastal Plain that provide a large proportion of the American lumber supply (Fig. 20.15). In Europe, northern Russia, Finland, Sweden, and Poland are the large lumber producers. In all the regions named, by far the largest cut is from conifers. Compared with the temperate forests of the Northern Hemisphere, those of the Southern Hemisphere are unimportant, although, to be sure, they are of some significance in providing local supplies of timber.

Types of Grassland and Their Distribution

20.29 Tropical Grasslands; Wooded Savanna and Savanna. There is at present too little reliable information available concerning the various types and gradations of tropical grasslands and their distribution to permit a satisfactory classification and mapping. For this reason the considerable variety of low-latitude grasslands are grouped together under one general heading. The reader should be forewarned, however, that this must not be interpreted to mean uniformity of species and appearance. There are open savannas with only occasional trees and there are others in which trees or shrubs are so numerous that it is difficult to decide whether the vegetation is more properly classified as grassland or woodland. There is also regional variety in the height of the grasses.

Until recently the tropical grasslands were interpreted as representing the climax vegetation of areas where precipitation was intermediate in amount between the heavy year-round rainfall of tropical rainforest and the constant drought of the desert. This climatic explanation in recent years has been seriously questioned. It now seems doubtful whether tropical grasslands are a climax formation in equilibrium with a tropical grassland climate. It actually appears as though a tropical grassland climate is nonexistent, for with declining rainfall tropical rainforest gives way to semideciduous and deciduous forest and finally to scrub and thorn forest. It has been fairly well established for Latin America that the tropical grasslands of that continent are relatively co-

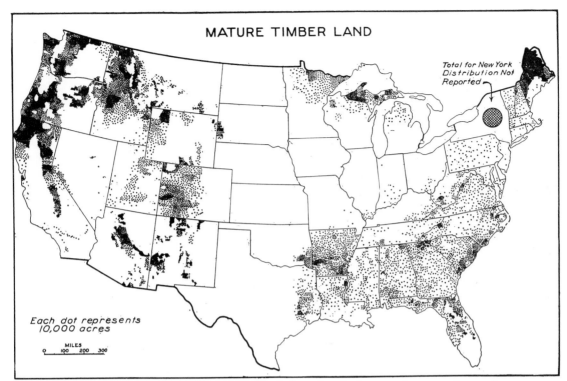

Fig. 20.15 The distribution of land with timber of such size as to be currently merchantable with respect to the major products of the area. It does not include second growth cut primarily for chemical distillation, firewood, mine props, posts, and ties. (*Courtesy of U.S. Forest Service.*)

incident with areas of flattish or slightly rolling terrain where, because of the mild relief and an impermeable subsoil, drainage is poor. In such areas the vegetation may be subjected to standing water in the rainy season and a parched soil at other times. Repeated burnings may help in establishing and expanding the grasslands.[8]

20.30 Vegetation Character. Savannas of both the wooded and the open variety are common. In places the trees are few and widely scattered while in others they are so numerous as to form thickets. Patches or clumps of trees intermingling with patches of grass seem the most common. Tall trees are not absent, to be sure, but low and dwarf varieties are more common. As a usual thing they have twisted and gnarled trunks, a thick corky bark, and leathery leaves (Figs. 20.16 and 20.17).

Savanna grasses are variable in height. In

Africa there are high savannas where the grasses range from 5 to 15 ft. in height, but these do not seem to exist in Latin America. Much more common are the tall bunch grass (1 to 2 ft. high) and the short bunch grass (under 1 ft. high). Both exist in the form of slender tufts with much bare earth between individual tufts so that the grass may occupy not more than 60 per cent of the soil surface. As a consequence a sod is absent. The leaves of savanna grasses are stiff and leathery so that only fresh young shoots are palatable to grazing animals. Among the natives it is a common practice to burn off the grasses in the dry season in order to make room for new growth at the beginning of the rains. Throughout the tropical grasslands dense *galeria*[9] forests usually occupy the river floodplains.

20.31 Middle-latitude Grasslands. The grasslands of middle latitudes appear to be the

[8] J. S. Beard. The Savanna Vegetation of Northern Tropical America. *Ecol. Monographs*, Vol. 23, pp. 149–215, 1953.

[9] From the Italian word *galeria,* meaning "tunnel" and referring to the arch of trees over the river.

Fig. 20.16 Tall coarse grass with low trees in the wooded savanna of Africa north of the equator. The height of the grasses is about 8 ft. so that they reach into the lower branches of the short trees. (*Courtesy of American Geographical Society.*)

Fig. 20.17 Wooded savanna in Kenya, East Africa. (*Courtesy of American Geographical Society.*)

climax vegetation of subhumid and semiarid regions. In this respect they stand in contrast to the savannas of the tropics. An additional item of contrast is the general absence of trees in the grasslands of middle latitudes except along their contact zones with forest and in the vicinity of streams.

In the grasslands of interior North America east of the Rocky Mountains three large subdivisions are recognized: (*a*) the short grass occupying much of the semiarid Great Plains, (*b*) the mixed prairie occupying a somewhat more humid belt to the east of the short grass, and (*c*) the tall-grass prairie, or true prairie, typical of the better-watered lands between the mixed prairie and the eastern forest (Fig. 20.18). The tall-grass prairie extends eastward as far as western Indiana in the form of a wedge driven into the forest. West of the Rockies extensive areas of short bunch grass characterize parts of Washington, Oregon, Idaho, and California.

The tall-grass prairie in North America was dominated by tall, luxuriant, and deep-rooted grasses which formed a deep and tough sod. In the humid eastern prairie grasses 5 to 8 ft. in height prevailed, and under the most favorable conditions they reached heights of 10 to 12 ft. The early settlers stated that cattle on such prairie could be located by a man on horseback only by standing up in the saddle. Farther westward in the drier prairie, mid-grasses 2 to 4 ft. in height prevailed. Usually there was a large variety of showy flowery plants intermingled with the grasses, so that in spring and early summer the original American prairies had the appearance of a colorful flower garden. The border between the prairie and the mixed prairie approximately coincided with the 30 in.

rainfall line in the south, 25 in. in Nebraska, and 20 in. in North Dakota.

The mixed-prairie area is in the nature of a transition zone with the vegetation somewhat more xeric in character than is that of the true prairie.[10] The characteristic vegetation consists of both mid-grasses, 2 to 4 ft. in height, and short grasses, usually under 1 ft., these two typically forming an upper and a lower story.[11]

Still farther west where rainfall is less and the depth of moist soil is usually under 2 ft. the short grasses prevail. In unusually dry years the short-grass area moves eastward, while in humid years the mid-grasses may be relatively conspicuous on the Great Plains. Moreover the short grasses and mid-grasses may be somewhat intermingled within any general area, with the

[10] J. Richard Carpenter. The Grassland Biome. *Ecol. Monographs*, Vol. 10, pp. 618–684, 1940.

[11] J. E. Weaver. "North American Prairie." P. 247. Johnsen Publishing Company, Lincoln, Neb., 1954.

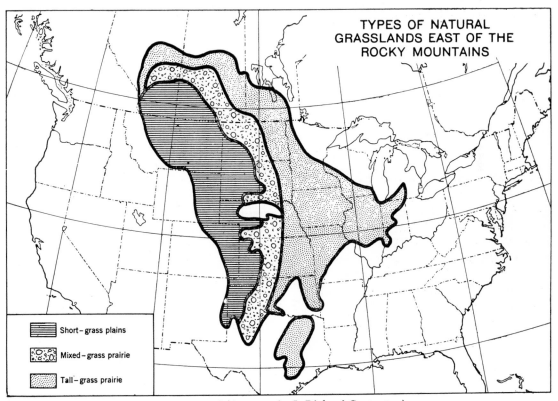

TYPES OF NATURAL GRASSLANDS EAST OF THE ROCKY MOUNTAINS

Short-grass plains
Mixed-grass prairie
Tall-grass prairie

Fig. 20.18 (*After map by J. Richard Carpenter.*)

Fig. 20.19 Bunch grass in Oregon. (*Courtesy of U.S. Department of Agriculture.*)

Fig. 20.20 Desert shrub, chiefly sagebrush, in Nevada. This type of vegetation cover is of little value for grazing. (*Photograph by John C. Weaver.*)

mid-grasses occupying the more favorable sites from the standpoint of moisture. In all the grasslands east of the Rockies rainfall is concentrated in the late spring and summer season. Bunch grass occupies regions with about the same amount of rainfall as the short grass but it is either less concentrated in the warm season or has an emphatic winter maximum (Fig. 20.19).

Although North American grasslands have been subdivided into several groups and their distributions shown (Fig. 20.18), this same degree of detail has not been possible for the remainder of the earth's middle-latitude grasslands. On Plate 5 all middle-latitude grasslands have the same legend. This should be interpreted to mean that insufficient information is available to permit a more detailed system of classification and of distribution similar to that for North America. There seems to be some evidence that short grass such as characterizes much of the American Great Plains is unique to North America and is rare on the other continents. If this is true, the conclusion might be drawn that the semiarid grasslands of the other continents resemble somewhat the mixed prairie of North America, while the subhumid ones show similarities to North American prairie, both mid-grass and tall grass.

Because of the high quality of the soils which develop under middle-latitude grasslands, together with the fact that they are usually regions of low relief, wherever there is sufficient rainfall for the growing of crops the natural grasslands outside the tropics have been converted into tilled land. Very little of the original prairie remains as natural grassland. Even parts of the semiarid grassland have been brought under cultivation, although much of it still serves as natural grazing land. Some of the earth's most prized and most productive agricultural land was formerly natural prairie.

Plant Cover of Deserts and Tundra

20.32 Deserts. Some few deserts or parts of deserts are extensive areas of rocky plain or sand and almost wholly without plant life. This is the exception rather than the rule, however, for most arid regions of both low and middle latitudes have some vegetation even though it is sparse. It may be low bunch grass, widely spaced with bushes, or in places fleshy water-storing plants such as cacti; but much more commonly it is perennial xerophytic shrub. In the United States this latter type of vegetation predominates over a large part of the area west of the Rockies, interrupted here and there by bunch grass, or by forests at higher elevations. Rainfall over much of this region is under 12 in.

The perennial shrubs of desert areas grow far apart, with much bare soil showing between (Figs. 20.20 and 20.21). This wide spacing is a response to low rainfall. Growth is very slow. Desert shrubs, exemplified by such American types as sagebrush and creosote bush, are physiologically equipped through special forms of roots, stems, and leaves to withstand drought. Some are deciduous, others evergreen in character.

Another class of desert plants, in contrast to the perennial shrubs, depends entirely upon the erratic rainfall, germinating with a rain, ripening seeds when the moisture is gone, and dying forthwith. Such *annuals* do not appear xerophytic, their adaption to drought being through a very rapid development and a short duration of life. Their stems and leaves are delicate, roots are thin and relatively shallow, and flowers are of considerable size. In contrast to the scanty, low, pale-green vegetation of the desert proper is the verdant color of luxuriant vegetation around oases where water is abundant. Almost knife-edge boundaries frequently separate the two. In wet or subirrigated land containing a high percentage of alkali, green, fleshy-leaved, salt-tolerant plants are characteristic.

20.33   Tundra. Genuine tundra is composed largely of such lowly forms as mosses, lichens, and sedges, the whole incompletely covering the ground. In places there is much bare, stony soil with only the most meager plant life. On the southern margins of the tundra, where it

Fig. 20.21   Desert shrub with scattered tufts of desert grass in Cape of Good Hope Province, South Africa. (*Courtesy of American Geographical Society.*)

merges into the taiga or coniferous forest, the vegetation cover is more complete, and stunted and creeping forms of trees and bushes are conspicuous. Grasslands exist on the marine margins of the tundra. Owing to the coldness and acid character of the soil, which retards water absorption, as well as to the long winter period of physiological drought when the soil moisture is locked up in solid form, most tundra plants appear xerophytic, having stiff, hard, leathery leaves, with thick cuticle. As a result of the short period between frosts the vegetative period in the tundra is reduced to 2 months or less. For this reason plants are compelled to hurry through their vegetative cycle, and even then many of them are frozen while still in flower or fruit. "An Arctic landscape at the approach of winter most resembles a southern country that has been ravaged by a severe night frost before winter was expected. Many plants are put to rest while still in full development. Whilst the plants were in full activity they were paralyzed by the benumbing cold." (Schimper.) Schimper cites an example of plants in the tundra of northeastern Siberia which pass through their complete vegetative cycle in 3 weeks.

Dry tundra is composed principally of lichens interspersed with coarse grasslike sedges. The predominance of lichens results in a dull, gray landscape tone. Wetter flooded areas along streams, or shallow basins on higher ground, are often moss swamps. The southward-facing drier slopes or declivities are the flower oases, where in summer a great variety of brilliant colors are characteristic.

20.34 *Tundra Animals.* To animals as well as to plants tundra is inhospitable. Bird life is largely migratory, inhabiting these regions principally in summer and wintering farther south. Large, predatory carnivores such as bears, wolves, and foxes fare badly in winter, being usually in the extremity of famine and reaching spring in an emaciated condition. Reindeer or caribou and musk ox are the two largest and most valuable of the herbivorous tundra animals. Siberian tribes never feed their reindeer but compel them to forage for their food even in winter. Mosquitoes and stinging flies are thick in summer, these being among the principal torments of man and animals, forcing them to seek higher and drier sites. Most mammals of the tundra do not hibernate, all the smaller forms such as hares, foxes, wolves, and lemmings making their winter quarters underneath the snow, where temperatures are not so severe. Seal, walrus, and polar bears inhabit the coastal margins or the drift ice, where they feed chiefly on marine life.

21

Soils

21.1   The Soil Resource. It is, of course, impossible to single out any one resource and state that it is more important than any other; for a number of resources, like water or the air we breathe, are indispensable. One such is the soil. All our food, even sea food indirectly, comes from the soil either as plants we eat or by way of animals whose meat and products we eat. The great variety of minerals and other critical substances by which human life is maintained come in one way or another almost entirely from the soil. Consequently, everyone should have a general understanding of the nature and distribution of this resource upon which his life depends. Like most resources soil is not everywhere of the same utility; in some areas the soil is deficient in one respect or another; in other areas there is no soil at all.

Where soil exists, it is a dynamic natural complex of mineral and organic substances which can support the life of plants. It is the product of a continuing process of development or evolution which takes place in a parent material such as the residual mantle rock. It is formed by slow processes, which include various kinds of physical and chemical weathering and, in addition, others that go on only under the influence of living organisms. The organisms concerned include higher animals, earthworms, abundant forms of microscopic life such as bacteria, and especially the remains of vegetation which have been deposited upon and within the surface soils for thousands of years. For this reason the soil is considered to extend downward only so far as abundant organic life penetrates, generally not more than

5 to 8 ft. Below the soil, whatever its thickness, is the parent material of the soil, and below that is solid rock.

21.2   The Parent Material of Soil. The regolith, or the broken and weathered accumulation of rock fragments overlying the bedrock of the earth, is the parent material from and in which the soil develops. There are many kinds of regolith, such as the sediments of old lake bottoms, the accumulation of glacial drift, the new alluvium on floodplains and deltas, the sands and gravels of dry areas, and especially the mantle rock weathered in place from bedrock. Each kind of parent material has a unique combination of minerals (in which certain elements exist) which have weathered to a particular array of fragment sizes. It might be expected, then, that since there is such a variety of parent materials, each with its unique set of elements and particle sizes, that the parent material would in all cases be the critical factor in soil development. This is true of many young soils. This is not so, however, for most older soils because the complex of climate and its associated pattern of vegetation commonly plays a more important role. This fact serves to emphasize that the soil is a living thing and that the organically derived characteristics are no less significant (and frequently more so) than the physical characteristics derived from the parent material. Nevertheless, the bulk of most soils is made up of earth materials. They are the same minerals as those discussed previously under the head of earth materials; they are composed of the chemical elements of the earth's crust; and in the case of any given soil its mineral components originally were the same as those of its parent material. From these mineral components the soil derives not only a considerable part of its mass but also some of its elements of fertility and some of its peculiarities of physical constitution.

The parent material may be thought of, then, as a kind of limiting factor in the development of soil. Its mineral characteristics are particularly significant, for it is only from those minerals that the chemical elements can be derived that are the sources of soil fertility. If a critical element is missing in the parent material, it will be missing in the soil.

21.3 Soil Elements. It was noted previously that of the great array of chemical elements found in the earth's crust, only a few are abundant. The same is true with respect to soil constituents. The most abundant soil components are the elements oxygen, silicon, aluminum, and iron, and they are combined in the common minerals, or their weathered derivatives, which give bulk to the soil. They are not, however, necessarily the most important elements from the standpoint of the things that grow in the soil or the uses man makes of them. Plants are known to require for their proper development quite a number of different elements, and still others are being discovered that seem to play an essential part in plant growth and human nutrition. Some are supplied as gases directly from the air or as gases dissolved in the water of the soil; some, including nitrogen and the necessary mineral elements, such as calcium, potash, and phosphorus, are taken in solution from the soil itself.

21.4 *Supply and Removal of the Mineral Elements.* The mineral elements in the regolith can be absorbed by plants only when they are included in the soil solutions. They are reduced to this state by weathering processes which disintegrate and decompose them into smaller and smaller particles. These pass through the stage of fineness called *clay* and ultimately they reach a submicroscopic size and undergo chemical change. In this state they combine with water and become gluelike and are known as *colloids*. Much of the nature of a

soil, its fertility, and its agricultural character reside in its colloidal portion. The body of the soil will normally contain, therefore, particles of fresh and unweathered mineral, partially decomposed particles, and others grading down into the colloidal state. The larger particles furnish a reserve of mineral elements which are slowly made available for plant use by a continuation of the weathering processes.

Since plants absorb part of their sustenance in the form of dissolved minerals, it follows that, upon their death and oxidation, these soluble mineral substances also are returned to the soil in the form of ash. Some part of that supply is used again by other plants, but some is removed in solution by percolating ground water, by a process called *leaching,* and, in humid regions, is carried away in the drainage waters. In arid regions, where there is little downward movement of ground water, the rate of removal of soluble salts is low, and there may be appreciable—in spots even a harmful —accumulation of soluble minerals in the soil. In humid regions, however, the loss by leaching is heavy.

The slowness with which the new supply is made available often leaves humid-land soils that are continuously cropped deficient in one or more of the critical elements. The deficiency may, of course, be made up by the application of mineral fertilizers. Alternative means are commonly employed. One of the methods is called *fallowing.* That is the practice of allowing land to lie idle during one or more years in order that mineral decomposition may make available a sufficient amount of the critical elements to grow a crop. Other means include processes by which a part of the minerals removed from the land in the form of crops is returned to it in the form of animal manures mingled with straw and other plant refuse.

21.5 Organic Matter in the Soil. Although it is true that the bulk of most soil is made up of minerals, it is the presence of organisms and of organic matter that makes soil essentially different from regolith. The organic matter is derived from plant and animal substances which, in addition to their small amounts of mineral ash, are made up largely of carbon, nitrogen, and water.

Nitrogen is essential to plant growth. There is an inexhaustible supply of it in the air, but that is not available to plants, which must take it from the soil in solution. It is made available in the soil in the soluble form of nitrates largely through the work of microorganisms, some of which are able to take nitrogen gas from the soil air and transform it. The leguminous and some other plants play an important role in this connection since their roots act as hosts to these nitrogen-transforming bacteria. Other soil organisms make nitrogen available through their ability to decompose the complicated organic remains of plants and animals which are then incorporated in the soil.

In the early stages of the decomposition of plant remains one may recognize in the soil some fragments of plant tissue, but later these are reduced to a state of division so fine that they assume a jellylike consistency and are of highly complex physical and chemical properties. Finally, this material also reaches the colloidal state and is taken into solution. Partially decomposed plant remains are called *humus*. The organic matter of the soil is constantly drawn upon by plants, but if a proper amount of raw organic matter is added to the soil each year the humus supply is maintained. Some soils have by nature very small amounts of humus, but others are richly supplied with it. Some, like peat soils, are made up largely of raw or little-decomposed organic matter which has not yet reached the condition of humus.

The part played by the organic material of the soil in maintaining soil fertility is exceedingly complicated, but it includes the following: (*a*) The organic material, when finally it is taken into solution, furnishes food to plants, not only nitrogen but also some quantities of phosphorus, potassium, calcium, and such other elements as remain from the plant and animal tissues from which it is derived. (*b*) The processes of decomposition yield organic acids which aid in the solution of soil materials. (*c*) Organic material is necessary to the existence of the microorganisms of the soil, those which break down the organic compounds, and also others which are beneficial to plants. (*d*) The porous nature of the humus causes it to have a high capacity for the absorption of water and of substances dissolved in water. This tends not only to maintain a supply of soil water for plants but also to retard the removal, or leaching, of dissolved minerals until plants can use them. (*e*) The presence of humus promotes an arrangement, or structure, of the soil particles which is favorable to cultivation and plant growth.

21.6 Acid Soils and Alkaline Soils. Soil water, through the solution of carbon dioxide from the air and the addition of the acid products of organic and mineral decomposition, tends to become a weak acid. Many soil constituents, such as lime, sodium, and others, have basic reactions. In the processes of chemical weathering, the acid-soil waters attack these alkaline minerals, neutralize or dissolve them, and are themselves neutralized. In localities where ground water and organic acids are abundant, they tend to neutralize and remove all the readily available alkaline substances, and thereafter the soil solutions have generally acid reactions. In dry regions the weathering of rocks furnishes alkaline earths, but supplies of both soil water and organic acids are limited. Consequently the soluble alkaline substances are not all leached out but tend to accumulate in the soil and give it an alkaline reaction. In some instances the soil may become strongly charged with saline matter, including common salt. In some regions the supply of soil acids is just sufficient to balance, or neutralize, the alkaline substances as they are supplied from the soil minerals. The soils of such regions give neutral reactions.

Most agricultural plants grow best in soils that have a neutral or a near-neutral reaction. The availability of calcium is one of the more essential factors in plant, animal, and human nutrition and consequently much soil acidity is undesirable. Too much alkaline, or especially saline, content in the soil is likewise undesirable for plant growth. The problem is not entirely simple, since there are various kinds and conditions of soil acidity and alkalinity. In general, however, the acidity of a soil may be reduced or corrected by the addition of an alkaline substance, especially pulverized limestone. The excess of alkaline or saline substance, which is found in the soils of some arid lands, usually is capable of removal by the application of abundant irrigation water and the provision of good drainage. This practice tends to dissolve the excess and to carry it away in the drainage waters.

From the above it is apparent that the factor which more than any other determines the acidity or alkalinity of the soil is the degree of leaching. This in turn depends largely upon the rainfall but also on temperature, vegetation, and other factors. Humid regions have in general acid soils, whereas those of dry regions tend to be alkaline or saline.

21.7   Important Physical Properties of Soils. The agricultural utility of soils is not determined by their chemical properties alone. Certain physical characteristics have quite as much to do with their ability to produce crops abundantly. The more important among the various physical properties are (*a*) the size distribution of soil particles, called the *texture*, (*b*) the quantity of water included in the soil and the manner of its retention, (*c*) the manner of arrangement of the soil particles with respect to each other, called the soil *structure*, and the volume of the pore space included, called the soil *porosity*.

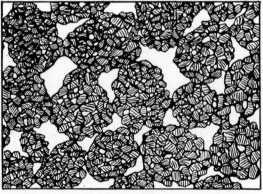

Fig. 21.1 A diagram to illustrate structure and pore space in a flocculated soil.

21.8   Soil Texture. The mineral particles of which soils are largely composed vary greatly in size from one locality to another and often from the surface downward also. In some soils coarse particles are predominant; in others, exceedingly fine ones; in most there is an intimate intermingling of particles of various sizes. Some of the commonly recognized textural classes, from the largest to the smallest, are sand, silt, and clay. The clays include the finest particles capable of being seen, even with a microscope. However, other still smaller particles exist—the inorganic colloids, or colloidal clays. Soils may, therefore, include in their composition visible particles of mineral matter, visible particles of organic matter, colloidal clays, organic colloids, and material in solution. The colloidal substance appears to exist in part independently of the soil particles but mainly as a gelatinous coating upon them. Fine soils have larger total surface areas than do soils of coarser texture. It is from the surface areas of soil particles and from the films of soil solution and colloids upon them that plant roots draw much of their nourishment. Therefore, fine soils, having large surface areas, provide large feeding areas for plant roots.

21.9   Soil Structure. Not all the important physical conditions of the soil may be explained in terms of soil texture. If that were true, fine-grained soils would always be compact and impervious to water, but such is not the case. Instead, it is found that many clayey and silty soils have an arrangement of particles that is permeable to water, admits abundant soil air, and prevents the soil from being heavy, tough, or cold. This property of a soil is called its *structure*. A good soil structure is attained by the association of soil particles into groups or granules, which then behave as individuals. These groups, which are sometimes called *floccules,* may themselves be arranged into larger compound groups and thus build up a structure in which there are pore spaces between the particles in the floccules and larger spaces between the floccules (Fig. 21.1).

Soils of fine texture, in which the particles are well flocculated, build up internal structures in which the pore space available for air, water, and root penetration is much greater than in most structureless soils. In the latter the actual amount of pore space is believed to be sometimes less than 20 per cent of the soil volume. In highly flocculated clays it may exceed 60 per cent. Most agricultural soils include amounts of pore space ranging between 35 and 50 per cent of the soil volume.

A good structural arrangement of soil particles, with ample pore space, is promoted by the presence of lime and by the growth and decay of plant roots or the addition of organic fertilizers. These form films of colloidal and limy material which coagulate into waxy cements that attach the soil particles together, without filling the pore spaces, and thus keep the floccules from falling apart. Structures of this kind are not present in all soils. They may be produced in certain soils by proper management, and they may be destroyed by improper treatment. They commonly are found in soils of fine texture and good colloidal content, but sandy soils are essentially without structure, each sand particle acting as an individual.

21.10 Water and Air in the Soil. Plants absorb their food from the soil solutions, but only a few crop plants are able to thrive in soils in which the pore space between the soil particles is completely filled with water all the time. Most of them require soils containing both air and water. However, the yearly water requirement of plants is large. It has been shown by experiments to be, for various crops, as much as three hundred to one thousand times the dry weight of the mature plant. Water exists in the soil in various relationships.

The water of the soil is supplied from the atmosphere. Even in regions that are nearly rainless, the soil may not be absolutely dry, for it is capable of taking from the air that penetrates it a minute quantity of water vapor. This is held as a microscopic film of water molecules upon the outsides of the individual soil particles and especially by the soil colloids. It is known as *hygroscopic water* (Fig. 21.21). It is more abundant in humid regions than in dry ones, in fine soils of large surface area than

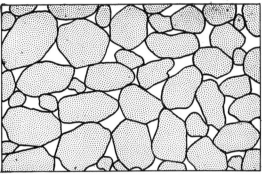

Hygroscopic

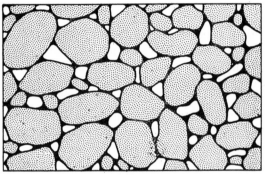

Capillary

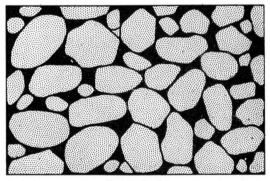

Gravitational

Fig. 21.2 Forms of soil water. The stippled areas indicate soil grains, the blackened margins, water, and the white areas, air spaces.

in those of coarse texture, and in soils of high colloidal content than in those low in colloids. Hygroscopic water adheres firmly to the soil particles, does not move from one part of the soil to another, and is very resistant to evaporation.

Soils that are moistened frequently have

thicker films of water about their particles. This is called *capillary water* (Fig. 21.2). It is held upon the soil particles by surface tension and is absorbed by the soil colloids in great quantity, causing them to swell and giving them their jellylike consistency. The capillary film upon ordinary soil particles does not fill the pore spaces between them but exists together with soil air (Fig. 21.2). It is, however, with its dissolved materials, readily available to plants.

Immediately following protracted rains the pore spaces of soils may be completely filled with water, displacing the air. In this condition there is water in excess of that which can attach itself to the soil particles, and the surplus will move downward into the zone of ground water. This may be called *free* or *gravitational water*.

When the supply of capillary water is abundant, it moves slowly downward under the pull of gravity. When the supply is diminished by plant use or surface evaporation, it may move horizontally, or even creep upward, under the pull of its own surface tension. In fine-textured soil, water may be drawn upward in this manner from depths of several feet, although in periods of extreme drought it may not rise fast enough to furnish plants a sufficient supply. In soils of coarse texture, both the amount and the upward movement of capillary water are limited.

In many low sites, where the ground-water table coincides with the land surface, or in localities where water is prevented from downward movement by an impervious layer in the subsoil, there may be a permanent supply of gravitational water at the surface. That will create a waterlogged or swampy soil in which most cultivated plants will not grow. Where good underdrainage exists, the gravitational water moves downward, quickly in soils of coarse texture or open structure and slowly in those which are fine and compact.

It will be seen, therefore, that in all except coarse soils water moves both downward and upward. In humid regions the supply of surface moisture is sufficient to keep the downward movement in excess of that in the upward direction. In arid regions, however, the supply of precipitation is insufficient to provide enough water to cause a gravitational movement down to the level of a deep ground-water table. Surplus gravitational water may distribute itself downward for a few feet, but later it creeps upward as capillary water bringing with it salts dissolved below. It is by this means that lime and other salts accumulate in the upper portions of dry-land soils, while in humid-land soils they are leached out and carried away in the underdrainage.

21.11   Factors in Soil Formation. A number of major factors are involved in the development of the soils in various parts of the earth. The original parent material is acted upon by climate and by certain biologic factors; it exists in particular kinds of terrain and under particular drainage conditions which have obtained for considerable periods of time. It should not be inferred that these environmental factors are constant in any place and that, therefore, a static soil condition will ultimately result. The soil is dynamic and is continually changing, sometimes even rather rapidly as, for example, when man upsets the natural balance of soil-forming factors by clearing and cultivating in a way detrimental to a particular type of soil.

21.12   *Parent Material.* It has already been noted that the parent material in which the soil develops is an important limiting factor. Although the processes of development, when carried to completion, impart new characteristics to the soil complex, they do not in all soils erase completely the distinctive effects that may result from great differences among parent materials. Some parent materials may change rapidly, whereas others may be highly resistant to change. Some are highly complex mineral compounds; others are simple. Some are high in lime, others low. The parent material at any particular place may or may not be an important factor in the development of the physical characteristics of the soil. It is, however, in all instances important in terms of the chemical elements it contains. If the parent material lacks the elements required for plant, animal, and human nutrition, it will remain a resource of questionable utility until such time as these are made available by catastrophic (floods, volcanic eruptions, dust storms) or artificial means.

21.13 *Climate* influences soil formation both directly and indirectly. Directly it affects the weathering of rocks, the percolation of water through the soil, and the work of the gradational agents. The soils of humid regions are more leached than those of dry lands. They are commonly more acid also and usually have little available lime, whereas those of arid lands are little leached and usually contain lime or soluble salts. Climate also affects the development of the soil through its seasonal variations in temperature and rainfall. Prevailingly high temperatures promote rapid chemical change in the soil, and cold slows it down. Alternating seasons of rain and drought cause soils to develop color and composition different from those of soils of continuously rainy regions.

21.14 *Plants and animals* play important parts in soil formation. Microorganisms (bacteria, fungi, protozoa, etc.) cause the decay of plant and animal remains and aid in their transformation into humus. Some kinds transform atmospheric nitrogen into soil nitrogen, as previously noted. These minute organisms live and die in such vast numbers (billions per gram of soil) that their own bodies also make an important contribution to the organic content of the soil. The roots of higher plants, such as grasses and trees, penetrate the soil and help to make it porous. When they die, they add organic matter within the soil. Deep-rooted plants bring mineral solutions up from the subsoil and build them into their tissues. When these die and decay, the minerals are added to the upper soil layers. However, the organic acids provided by plant decay in humid regions hasten the soil-leaching process. The work of worms is surprisingly important in mixing organic remains with the mineral soil constituents and in bringing subsoil minerals to the surface. Burrowing animals perform a similar service on a smaller scale, and all animals aid in soil formation since plant prod-

ucts pass through their digestive tracts and are returned to the soil for further transformation.

21.15 *Physical Site.* In addition to the other factors mentioned, the development of the soil is influenced by its physical site. This is because differences in surface slope may greatly affect the moisture and air conditions within the soil and the rate of its surface erosion. Maximum development is most likely to take place on rolling and well-drained uplands where there is free underdrainage and moderate surface erosion. On such sites the removal of old and leached surface material by erosion just about keeps pace with the downward progress of the soil-forming processes. Soils developing under such conditions are called mature soils. The soils of steep slopes, on the contrary, generally fail to develop to such a degree of maturity because much rain water runs off the surface instead of percolating into the ground. This produces less leaching, and it accelerates surface erosion, exposing the less developed lower layers. Lack of soil water and increased erosion reduce the density of the vegetative cover and thus lessen the organic contribution to the soil development. In poorly drained or marshy areas soils do not develop to maturity either, but in this case it is due to the slowness of leaching and to the fact that air cannot penetrate. Hence some of the organic and chemical processes are not carried out.

The various factors involved in soil formation require time for the completion of their several processes. Hence, time is itself a factor. It is not a constant, however, since the other factors in combination do not progress at the same rates under different total environments. It is not possible to say how long it takes for a soil to develop. Some may reach a condition of balance with their environments in comparatively short periods, possibly in a few hundreds of years or less; others may require thousands of years.

21.16 The Soil Color. One of the more obvious effects of the complex of soil-forming factors is the color of the soil. Although the soil color may be a conspicuous feature of the landscape in some regions, it is far more significant as an indicator of physical or chemical conditions. Consequently, soil color is commonly an important part of the description of a soil, and many soil groups have colors as parts of their names.

Soils range in color through a wide variation of shades or tints. Among the commonest colors are shades of red, brown, or yellow. These are due to the different forms, degrees of hydration, and concentrations of the oxides of iron and aluminum which exist as thin coatings or stains upon the soil grains. In some humid regions a whitish color commonly results from a lack of iron oxides. In arid regions the same color may denote a harmful concentration of soluble salts. Black and dark-brown colors in soils usually, but not always, denote a considerable content of organic matter. In many soils two or more color-forming elements are present, giving rise to intermediate colors, such as yellowish brown or grayish brown. It is commonly assumed, with good reason, that dark soils are generally productive and that the light-colored ones (red to white) are, by comparison, relatively unpro-

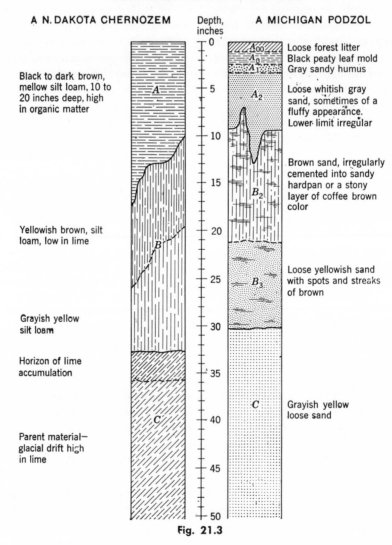

CONTRASTING SOIL PROFILES

A N. DAKOTA CHERNOZEM   Depth, inches   A MICHIGAN PODZOL

Black to dark brown, mellow silt loam, 10 to 20 inches deep, high in organic matter

Yellowish brown, silt loam, low in lime

Grayish yellow silt loam

Horizon of lime accumulation

Parent material— glacial drift high in lime

Loose forest litter
Black peaty leaf mold
Gray sandy humus

Loose whitish gray sand, sometimes of a fluffy appearance. Lower limit irregular

Brown sand, irregularly cemented into sandy hardpan or a stony layer of coffee brown color

Loose yellowish sand with spots and streaks of brown

Grayish yellow loose sand

Fig. 21.3

ductive. Although this is true of many soils, it is not always so. Surface soils, in some regions, are prevailingly unlike their subsoils in color, and wet soils generally are darker in color than the same soils when dry. The color of soil changes, not only from place to place but also from the surface downward and from one time to another.

21.17 The Soil Profile. In soils that have been subjected for a long time to the soil-forming processes, the qualities acquired through development are made evident by an arrangement of the soil into layers, or *horizons*, of different thicknesses and different chemical and physical properties. The succession of these layers, from the surface down to the underlying parent material, is called the *soil profile*.

Three horizons are commonly recognized: an upper, or A, horizon; an intermediate, or B, horizon; and a lower, or C, horizon (Fig. 21.3). In most soils the A horizon is distinguished from the others in color, texture, and structure. It is that part in which organic life and debris is most abundant, and in grassland soils it may consist almost wholly of organic material. Forest soil may have a thin surface layer of organic material, while its lower portion has lost some of its mineral constituents. In humid regions, generally, its development has involved the loss of something from its original composition. Through the work of percolating water some soluble material has been leached out, and some finely divided material has been carried downward in suspension, or *eluviated*. The A horizon is, therefore, in most humid-land soils a horizon of leaching and eluviation and is left poorer in soluble substances and coarser in texture as a result. The B horizon may be, in contrast, one of *illuviation*. In it may be deposited some of the materials carried in suspension from above and some parts of those carried in solution either from above or from below. It may become a zone of enrichment; in some soils it becomes dense and impenetrable by these additions. The C horizon is the little-changed parent material from which the soil was derived. The thickness of each of these horizons varies greatly with the type of

soil. In some they are thin, and in others so thick that, for purposes of minute description, each horizon is further subdivided, as may be seen in Fig. 21.3.

21.18 Pan Layers. Some soils develop a dense or compact horizon or layer known as a *pan layer*. Sometimes these layers are almost impenetrable, but in any case they interfere with root and, in some instances, water penetration and are thus unfavorable from the point of view of soil use and management. Pan layers develop as a result of a variety of factors, the commoner being (a) excessive water in humid regions and (b) precipitation of carbonates in dry regions, both of which result in a strongly illuviated or cemented horizon. There are many kinds of pan layers which have been grouped into several general types; only the most important can be mentioned here.[1]

The name *claypan* applies to those compact layers of uncemented clay which may result either from a high concentration of clay in the original subsoil or by its movement from the overlying A horizon. Claypans are relatively widespread, commonly occurring in very smooth or flat lands, either in the humid nontropics or in the subhumid and arid regions in any latitude. The nutrients in claypans do not differ much from those of the soils in which they occur, and the difficulties they occasion are mostly those due to poor permeability and unfavorable properties. Another kind of pan layer occurs where there has been actual cementation by iron oxide, calcium carbonate, silica, and even organic matter. These are called *hardpans*.[2] The most common kind of hardpan is the iron crust or laterite (see Art. 22.8) which occurs widely in humid tropical soils in a variety of physical forms. Other hardpans occur in humid areas of the middle and high latitudes (Fig. 21.3), but they are not so widespread as in the tropics. Hardpans also occur in dry regions through cementation, commonly by calcium carbonate. These hardpans, sometimes called *caliche*, occur mostly in the warmer dry

[1] Eric Winters and Roy W. Simonson. The Subsoil. *Advances in Agron.*, Vol. III, pp. 31–45, 1951.
[2] *Ibid.*

areas. Generally, hardpans are poor for plant growth, sometimes because of their relatively low nutrient qualities, but primarily because of their physical hardness.

21.19 Soil Maturity. It was indicated above that a mature soil is the result of the slow evolution of a soil in its given environment. Such a soil if developed in a well-drained location is said to have a *mature profile* and to represent the climax of development under the given conditions. The mature profile does not develop if the soil-making forces have been modified due to rapid erosion, rapid aggradation, or poor drainage. Instead, the horizons show the effects of these modifications; therefore many soils do not have mature profiles. Consequently, it cannot be expected that all the soils of a district will have the profile typical of the mature soil of that district. In fact, in some considerable areas little if any mature soil is to be found. The normal processes of agriculture, such as deforestation, plowing, and heavy grazing, tend to increase the rate of erosion and to intermingle and otherwise destroy soil horizons. Indeed, the typical profiles

of mature soils probably are nearly, if not quite, restricted to the untouched soils of a region, whether they are the soils of forest or those of prairie. Many regions of high agricultural development have remaining only a few scattered remnants of their virgin soils. Yet, when mature soils are present, they show significant similarities of profile over large areas, even when they are derived from widely different parent materials. Moreover, even the soils with immature profiles in a region commonly have qualities that indicate they are related to the mature regional type.

Classification of Soils

21.20 Soil Regions. A particular soil with uniform profile characteristics occurring over a contiguous area is called a *soil body* (Fig. 21.4). The soil body may be thought of as being somewhat like an organism, in that it has some qualities derived from its ancestry, such as its parent material, as well as some that come as a result of growing up in a particular way because of a   given set of environmental

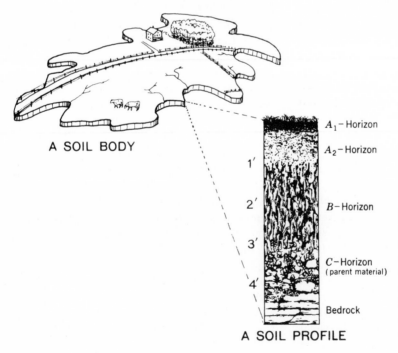

A SOIL BODY

A_1 – Horizon

A_2 – Horizon

1′

2′

B – Horizon

3′

C – Horizon
(parent material)

4′

Bedrock

A SOIL PROFILE

Fig. 21.4 The soil body has a relatively uniform profile development. Adjacent soil bodies will have different profile developments as a result of some difference in the soil-forming factors. (*Courtesy F. D. Hole, Soil Survey, Wisc. Geol. and Nat. Hist. Survey.*)

conditions, such as climate and vegetation. Generally, as a soil body advances in age some of the qualities inherited from its ancestry tend to become less important in its make-up, whereas those acquired through development tend to assume greater importance. There is, therefore, a tremendous variety of kinds of soils, for the number of forming factors, *i.e.,* ancestries and environments, can exist in a bewildering number of combinations. On the other hand each soil body has some distinguishing characteristics similar to those of some other soils. As was found to be the case with the climatic elements, it is therefore possible, on the basis of these characteristics, to prepare a system of classification of soils which will enable them to be studied on several levels of generalization.

21.21 Soil Classification. The highest order of generalization recognized by the soil scientist is that of the soil orders, of which there are three, *zonal soils, intrazonal soils,* and *azonal soils.* Zonal soils include those mature soil types which have well-developed characteristics based largely upon the dominance of climate and vegetation among the soil-forming processes. Intrazonal soils include those types which have more or less well-developed soil characteristics but in which some factors other than climate and vegetation were dominant in their formation, such as excessive or poor drainage, unusual parent material, or excessive evaporation. Azonal soils, such as sand areas or recent alluvium, are those that do not have well-developed soil profiles. These three orders include all soil types.

The system of soil classification proceeds from the three orders to the *suborders,* which divide all soils into 10 or 12 categories. The suborders are in turn further divided into the *great soil groups,* of which approximately 40 are found in the United States alone. A classification of soil types which ended with the great soil groups would be wholly inadequate for most purposes. The soil scientist, therefore, proceeds to further refinement. He divides each great soil group into *families,* the families into *series,* and the series into *types.* There are thousands of soil types. They distinguish the soil differences of small areas, parts of farms, or even parts of fields. The families, series, and types, in the United States, commonly are given names derived from geographical localities where they were first recognized and defined. The classificational process of the soil scientist goes even farther. Some soil types, which would be much alike otherwise, have agriculturally significant differences related to the texture or slope. These differences are recognized by the term *phase,* and include such terms as stony phase or steep phase. The ultimate unit in soil classification is the individual soil phase body, which is related to the landscape as an individual tree is related to the forest of which it is a part. Figure 21.5 illustrates for portions of the United States how the use of various degrees of generalization in the classification system results in more or less detail in the soil map.

Another way of considering the relationships among soils is by the associations of diverse soils that occur within a single region. These result from variations in drainage, exposure, and vegetation due to variations in parent material, relief, and slope. It is not unusual to find repetitive patterns of single soil-forming factors, such as parent material or slope. Sometimes such patterns are characteristic of large areas. For example, much of the plains area of northern North America is made up of rocky hills, usually barren or thinly covered with drift, associated with thicker drift deposits on valley sides and in valley bottoms. On this pattern of terrain features develop three of the major soil groups, *viz., lithosols* (rocky soils) on the relatively barren areas, *podzols* (see Art. 22.5) on the better-drained drift accumulations, and *bog* or *half-bog* soils (peat, muck, etc.) in the bottom lands. This is an association of one zonal soil type, one intrazonal, and one azonal. Similarly a uniform parent material in a climatic region may well give rise to soil types that belong to more than one of the orders and to several of the great soil groups in the general system of soil classification. Thus the development of differences in profile, the degree of

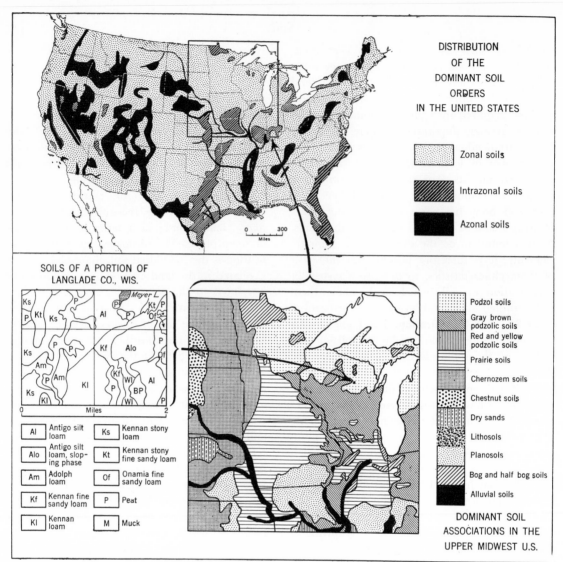

Fig. 21.5 Soils maps of different scales can show different degrees of detail in the classification of soils. Note the area covered on one map in relation to the scale on the adjacent map. (*Generalized from maps of the United States and Wisconsin Soil Surveys.*)

humus incorporation, the soil reaction, and others of importance can also occur within a local area. The particular local sequence of related soil types in a region is sometimes called a soil *catena*.

Since repetitive patterns of soil-forming factors (parent material, vegetation, drainage, etc.) frequently occur over wide areas, it may be that the distinctive associations of soils or of catenas in these areas would be a more logical method for the geographic consideration of

soils. On the other hand, the recognition and description of such associations throughout the world are not well enough known at present to enable one to generalize sufficiently.[3]

21.22 A World View of Soils. Any attempt to secure a *world* view of the function of the soil as an element of earth environment requires that the vast number of types as now

[3] Francis D. Hole. Suggested Terminology for Describing Soils as Three-dimensional Bodies. *Proc. Soil Sci. Soc. Amer.*, Vol. 17, pp. 131–135, 1953.

recognized by the soil scientist be grouped in a manner suited to brief and convenient description so that the general pattern of their world distribution may be readily understood. For this purpose the more distinctive and areally significant categories of *great soil groups* is used. Categorization on that basis rests upon the essential properties of all the soil horizons, and it recognizes the effects of all the soil-making forces, especially those due to climate. It should be emphasized, however, that most of the characteristics selected for description are those of the well-drained, upland, zonal soils. These are not the only soils in the regions, and they are not everywhere the most productive soils from the agricultural viewpoint. The distribution of soils over the earth, organized on the above bases, is shown in Plate 6.

22

The World Distribution of Soils

22.1 Soil Zones. A particular kind of soil belonging to either the intrazonal or azonal orders of the soil classification may occur anywhere in the world. For example, new alluvium (an azonal soil) is found in any latitude but its basic characteristics, wherever it is, are those of relatively unmodified alluvium, *i.e.*, the primary soil-forming factors of climate and vegetation have had little effect upon it. On the other hand, the soil types which belong to the zonal order are the result of considerable modification through the agencies of climate and vegetation. Consequently, the map of zonal soils shows a well-developed regionalization which corresponds more or less to the regionalization found in the maps of climate and vegetation. Thus one might expect to find a particular category of zonal soils recurring on the world map where similar complexes of climate and vegetation recur. Although, broadly stated, this relationship appears to exist, the student should bear in mind that in some areas this may be an oversimplification bordering on the erroneous, since (*a*) climate and vegetation regions are by no means always coincident, (*b*) because of terrain characteristics the mature upland zonal soils may well be in the minority in many areas, and (*c*) other factors, particularly parent material, may cause significant departures from the zonal pattern. Especially important, and not recognized in the pattern of zonal soils, are the associations of soils, zonal or otherwise, which may occur over large areas. Nevertheless, in spite of these deficiencies, certain broad generalizations as to the relation between soils, climate, and vegetation can be made. One of the most significant is that fundamental differences develop between the soils of the humid lands and the soils of the dry lands.

22.2 *The mature soils of humid regions* especially in the subtropics and higher latitudes have generally, although not in all cases, developed under natural vegetations of *forest or woodland*. There the organic matter is incorporated in the soil rather slowly and there is a net downward movement of soil water. Therefore, the upland soils of humid regions as a whole are much leached, prevailingly light in color, usually acid, and characterized by a comparatively low content of both organic matter and mineral plant foods. However, the chemical phases of the soil-forming processes, and the results produced by them in terms of soil profiles, are notably different in warm humid regions from those which operate in cool humid regions. The dominant soil-making process of the more humid tropical and subtropical regions is called *latozation* and produces a *latosol*.[1] In this process solution is dominant; the basic soil minerals and even silica are dissolved and leached away, leaving a concentration of reddish iron and aluminum oxides in both the A and B horizons. In the humid lands of the higher latitudes, on the contrary, the dominant soil-making process is called *podzolization* and produces a *podzol*. In this process organic compounds appear to combine with iron and aluminum compounds so as to permit the

[1] The terms *latosol, latosolic,* and *latozation* are now used by the soil scientist to refer to the soils and soil-making processes of the tropical and subtropical areas. The terms *laterite* and *laterization* are reserved for certain extreme clayey concentrations rich in iron and aluminum oxides and the processes of their formation.

leaching of iron and aluminum from the A horizon and their deposition in the B horizon. Silica is left behind in the A, which shows as a white or light gray horizon beneath the black layer of humus and above the dark brown B horizon. Thus, generally stated, many of the soils of the tropics are latosols and those of the high latitudes are podzols. Intermediate between the tropical and subarctic areas there exist many soils that show some of the effects of both latosolic and podzolic development.

22.3 *The mature soils of subhumid and dry regions,* on the other hand, generally have developed under natural vegetations of *grass* or *shrub* which may in some instances have a thin stand of trees. Because of the relatively low precipitation they are not greatly leached, but are characterized by a considerable, and in some places excessive, content of soluble mineral matter. Calcium especially may be plentiful in these soils and they are likely to be neutral or basic in reaction. Because there is in many of the areas of dry climate an upward movement of capillary water in the soil, there can be accumulated at some level an actual *horizon of lime accumulation.* The process by which the calcium content of the surface soil is kept high is known as *calcification* and is characteristic of dry-land soils although not necessarily limited to them. It should be noted that the less-rainy tropical wet climates have developed a mixed tree and grass vegetation even though there is considerable precipitation. The wet and dry seasons of the savanna climate in some places have combined with vegetation to produce a kind of tropical transition soil having some characteristics of both dry and humid soils. Although there are thus some significant differences between the soils of the warm dry regions and those of the cool dry regions they are not so marked as are those between the tropical soils and the podzols in the humid regions. Instead, there is a greater difference between the soils of the very arid or desert regions and those of the subhumid grassland regions, whether they lie in low latitudes or farther poleward. The typical mature *desertic* soil of a dry region is light in color, high in saline or alkaline minerals, and low in organic matter, while the *chernozemic* soil of the subhumid grassland region is neutral or moderately alkaline, black or dark brown in color, and high in organic matter.

22.4 Broad Descriptive Soil Categories. As was previously stated, there are so many of the zonal great soil groups that it is necessary to combine some of them in order that their general pattern of distribution can be readily grasped. The following outline shows the broad descriptive categories and those of the major zonal great soil groups included in each. To these have been added the alluvial soils from the azonal order since these are geographically very significant areas in the world. Because the mountain areas of the earth show tremendous internal variety in soils, as they do in climate, these areas have not been internally differentiated.

Broad Descriptive Soil Categories (1 to 9) Based upon Zonal Soils and Dominant Great Soil Groups

Great soil groups	Descriptive soil categories
Podzol	1. PODZOL SOILS
Gray-Wooded Gray Podzolic Brown Podzolic Gray-Brown Podzolic	2. PODZOLIC SOILS
Red-Yellow Podzolic	3. PODZOLIC-LATOSOLIC SOILS
Reddish latosols and a variety of imperfectly known latosolic, latosolic-podzolic, latosolic-chernozemic, and other soil groups	4. LATOSOLIC TROPICAL FOREST AND GRASSLAND SOILS
Prairie Chernozem Degraded Chernozem Reddish Prairie Noncalcic Brown Rendzina	5. CHERNOZEMIC SOILS
Brown Reddish-Brown Chestnut Reddish Chestnut Terra Rossa	6. CHERNOZEMIC-DESERTIC SOILS
Desert Red Desert Sierozem	7. DESERTIC SOILS
Alluvial	8. ALLUVIAL SOILS
Tundra	9. TUNDRA SOILS
	10. SOILS OF AREAS WITH HIGH LOCAL RELIEF WITH COMPLEX SOIL ASSOCIATIONS.

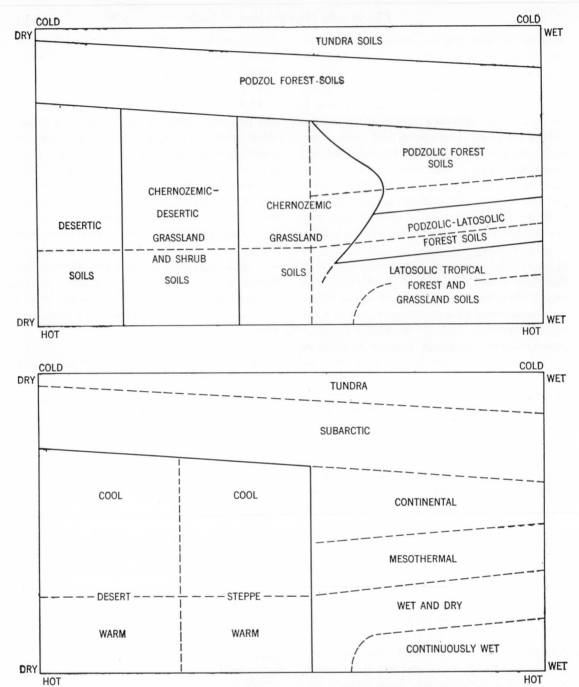

Fig. 22.1 Highly generalized relationship between major climatic zones and the broad descriptive soil categories.

To introduce the discussion of the climates of the world, the several types were shown on a hypothetical continent in order to clarify their typical positions and arrangements. Simi-

larly Fig. 22.1 is intended to show in a highly schematic manner the relation between climate (and its usual associated vegetative cover) and the broad categories of soils listed above and

450

shown on Plate 6. The diagram may be thought of as being a land mass extending northward from the equator to the high latitudes and grading from a humid east to an arid west.

A brief survey may now be made of each of these several broad categories of soil with respect to its profile characteristics and its inherent capacity for human use. Attention should also be directed to the major pattern of their world distribution as shown in a generalized way on Plate 6. The fact that this map of the world distribution of soil groups leaves much to be desired is due to several conditions: (*a*) *Soil types,* like climatic types, do not ordinarily change abruptly from one to another but rather by continuous gradation. Consequently, boundary lines on the map are drawn through zones of transition. (*b*) The small scale of this map requires that it be very general, but the facts of soil distribution are highly detailed (Fig. 21.5). (*c*) Large areas of some of the continents, especially in the lower latitudes, are incompletely surveyed as to soil, and information about them is inadequate or almost entirely lacking. (*d*) The categories are made up largely of great soil groups in the zonal order with the addition of one azonal soil, *viz.,* alluvium. In many areas of the world intrazonal and azonal soils abound and are intimately linked with the zonal soils (Fig. 21.5).

Soils of the Humid Lands

It was noted above that the mature soils of the humid lands are of two extreme groups, with several of intermediate character. These may be considered in the following order: (*a*) podzolic soils which are found principally in the regions of subarctic coniferous forest and higher middle-latitude mixed forest; (*b*) the latosolic soils of the tropical rainforest and other areas of tropical climate and vegetation; (*c*) the podzolic-latosolic soils which ideally occur in some of the areas midway between the first two.

22.5 Podzols. Podzols are the typical mature soils of regions having humid subarctic climate. Although occurring in the humid tropics and subtropics, podzolization is much more favored by long winters and short summers. Podzolic soils are different from latosolic soils in structure, profile, and color.

The mature podzol is developed under a natural vegetation mainly of coniferous forest. Conifers do not require abundant basic soil elements for their growth, and since they are mainly shallow-rooted trees, they draw only small supplies of the soil bases to the surface, even where such are available in the parent material beneath. Thus, there is little chemical reaction to oppose the tendency toward soil acidity. The effects of the long cold winter, moderate summer temperatures, and a forest litter of resinous pine needles are to retard bacterial action and to permit the formation of a brown layer of raw humus or half-decomposed organic remains, which represent the accumulation of many years. This spongy material on the forest floor retains water, becomes highly acid as the result of fermentation, and the downward-moving soil solutions are made acid by it. The strong acidity is unfavorable to the existence of earthworms, and they are few. Consequently their customary work of mingling the decaying vegetation with the upper soil layers is not accomplished, and the line of separation between raw surface humus and the mineral soil is sharp. Moreover, the effect of the strongly acid solutions upon minerals is to render soluble and to remove from the surface soil the iron and aluminum. Consequently, underneath the layer of raw humus the A horizon of a mature podzol is leached of its iron and readily soluble minerals, and by eluviation, it has lost most of its clay and colloidal constituents also. It is, therefore, poor in the mineral elements of soil fertility and nearly structureless. Through loss of iron it is bleached to a grayish-white color (the name podzol is derived from Russian words meaning "ashes underneath"). Beneath a bleached A horizon of variable thickness there is typically a brown, acid B horizon which is strongly illuviated. In some localities a pan layer has developed. The C horizon is composed of the glacial drift or other parent material of the soil (Fig. 22.2).

Fig. 22.2 Podzolic forest soils. Profiles of two podzolic soils. Both show the effects of the typical heavy leaching of the A horizon and the strongly illuviated B horizon. The one on the right is from Ontario. (*Photograph by G. A. Hills, Ontario Department of Lands and Forests.*) The left-hand profile is a poorly drained podzolic soil on lacustrine sands and silts in Minnesota. (*Photograph by William M. Johnson, Soil Conservation Service, U.S. Department of Agriculture.*)

Acid podzols, without improvement, are poor soils for most farm crops. Under cultivation, the surface layer of organic matter soon is lost, and the grayish surface soil requires lime, fertilizer, and good management to keep it productive and to prevent its poor structure from becoming a hindrance to tillage. Although a few food plants, such as the blueberry, grow wild on light sandy podzols, the podzols used for general agriculture are of finer texture. On such soils, after fertilization, potatoes are widely grown. They are acid tolerant. Good yields of grass, oats, rye, and numerous vegetables are obtained from podzols after lime and fertilizers are applied.

The main regions of podzol development, as is shown in Plate 6, are in the higher middle latitudes. However, they are not strictly confined to those latitudes. Partially podzolized soils are abundant in the humid lower middle latitudes and are to some extent found in the red-soil regions, or even in the humid tropics where unusual conditions have permitted the accumulation of coverings of acid organic matter.

22.6 Podzolic soils are a group of soils which usually are found in those regions of the world that have broadleaf deciduous forests and humid microthermal climates (Plate 6). Under these vegetational and climatic conditions there is a surface accumulation of organic material which forms a dark layer 1 to 3 in. deep. It is not so abundant, so poorly decomposed, or so acid as that associated with the podzols. Moreover, the organic material derived from broadleaf forest contains more lime, potash, and other basic elements than does that from coniferous forest, and these are easily mixed by earthworms with the mineral components of the soil. The A horizon of the podzolic forest soil is leached but not impoverished or greatly bleached. It generally is stained with a brown hydroxide of iron. The admixture of organic matter into the brown surface material

gives it a grayish-brown color. The quantity of organic material decreases downward, and the B horizon is commonly yellowish brown and of heavier texture than the A horizon, because it has been illuviated from above. As in the podzols, the C horizon is the little changed parent material of the soil, much of it glacial drift. The podzolic forest soils have generally better structures than the other forest-land soils, keep their structures better under cultivation, and respond more readily to the application of lime and organic fertilizers. The humus of forest origin is better distributed in the upper soil horizons than in the podzols, because of

Fig. 22.3 Podzolic forest soils. Profiles of two podzolic forest soils. Compare these with Fig. 22.2. Note that in the gray-brown podzolic soil on the right the organic matter is better mixed and the effect of leaching in the A horizon is not so marked. (*Photograph by G. A. Hills, Ontario Department of Lands and Forests.*) The gray-wooded podzolic soil on the left is intermediate between the gray-brown and a podzol. It is developed on glacial till in Minnesota. (*Photograph by William M. Johnson, Soil Conservation Service, U.S. Department of Agriculture.*)

the work of earthworms and other soil organisms which thrive under less acid conditions (Fig. 22.3). This reserve of humus, together with some quantities of the critical soil minerals, causes newly cleared podzolic forest soils to be productive. However, they presently lose their strength under continuous cropping unless they are carefully managed and well fertilized.

Not all podzolic soils have developed under forest vegetation. For example, the soils of eastern South Island, New Zealand, show no evidence of forest association; yet they are acid in reaction and are podzolized. Their formation is not completely understood.

Plate 6 shows the mature podzolic soils to be typical of some of the intensively cultivated agricultural lands of the world, such as northeastern United States, northwestern Europe, and several other regions of smaller size. The North American region is a large and important one. It includes much of that area originally covered by mixed hardwood forests, and it extends from Maryland and southern New England westward to southern Wisconsin and southern Illinois. This is the most densely populated part of the continent. It is also an area of great agricultural diversity. Indeed, one of the distinctive characteristics of the podzolic soils is their suitability to a wide variety of crops: hay and pasture, small grains and corn, vegetables, root crops, and many others. Each great soil group in this category includes soil families, series, types, and phases in great number and of complex distributional patterns. They are derived from many kinds of parent materials: rocks of many classes, the several types of glacial and glaciofluvial deposits and others on these rolling glaciated plains. From most of them the once extensive forest has been removed to make place for farms, and erosion has set in.

22.7 *Soils Associated with the Podzols and Podzolic Soils.* Included in the areal patchwork made by the various series and types of the normal podzol and podzolic soils are others which are not zonal. Among these are such azonal soils as fertile river alluvium and infertile sands and gravels, the latter resulting from sandy glacial outwash or from the abandoned shore deposits of temporary glacial lakes, etc. Even more widespread are types of intrazonal soils that have resulted from poor drainage. Among these are dark-colored soils formed in the depressions of glaciated plains or in other marshy or boggy places. In them the surface soils are high in organic matter derived from the remains of grasses, sedges, and other marsh plants. They commonly are underlain by sticky compact clays. If drained, these soils are productive. Also included, and often in larger areas, are the intrazonal soils of extensive drift-covered glacial uplands so flat that, under their natural vegetation of forest, little erosion took place for centuries. In them (planosols) the soil-making processes and poor drainage have resulted in the formation of a leached and acid A horizon underlain by a pan layer. The capacity of these soils for producing crops varies greatly with local conditions, but generally they are less productive than the zonal soils with which they are associated (Fig. 21.5).

In connection with the podzols, as with the other groups, there are soils of immature or imperfectly developed profiles. Recent alluvial deposits, ice-scoured and stream-eroded slopes, glacial marshes, and other areas of high water table comprise large total areas of structureless soils or such as have abnormal or immature podzolic profiles. Podzolization proceeds most rapidly and extends deepest on light permeable materials that are low in lime, such as sand. However, there are, in the region of the podzols, considerable areas of tight glaciolacustrine clays, such as those of the Ontario Clay Belt. In some of these the compactness of the clay has impeded the underdrainage, creating wet lands or even muskeg. Consequently, there are large areas of bog and half-bog soils of the intrazonal order. In the glaciated regions of North America and northern Europe there are also considerable areas of rocky ground providing what is called a lithosol, a stony, azonal soil with few soil characteristics.

22.8 Soils of the Tropical Areas. Not enough is known about the character and distribution of the variety of soils in tropical areas to make very valid generalizations or to map them adequately on a small world map. Vegetation distributions are somewhat more complex in the tropical regions, *i.e.*, the vegetative cover has more internal variety, and changes from one kind to another within relatively small areas seem to be more common there than elsewhere. The soils also show great variety, ranging from darker grassland soils to forest-land soils which show latosolic development, and even some podzolization takes place under the proper vegetative cover. Because our knowledge is insufficient at present to differentiate clearly or generalize properly about the distribution of soils in the tropics, these areas are treated differently from the other areas shown on Plate 6.

The soil scientist gives the term *latosol* to those tropical soils in which high temperatures and relatively abundant precipitation are the dominant soil-forming factors. Weathering commonly extends deeply in these areas and the combination of intense weathering and chemical activity sometimes changes the surface materials so much that there may be little similarity between the chemical nature of the soil and that of the parent material from which it was formed (Fig. 22.4). Many tropical soils are granular, very porous, and have great permeability to water. Consequently, they are capable of being tilled immediately after heavy rains but are subject to drought. Being highly leached, latosols and other, though not all, tropical soils are low in plant foods, both mineral and organic, and are usually not capable of sustained cropping without fertilization; and, since they are porous, some require irrigation in dry seasons. The profiles of many tropical soils are unusually deep, sometimes extending downward more than 10 ft. Latosols are low in silica, high in oxides of iron and aluminum, and have a relatively high clay content. Most of them are red or reddish. Some of them have developed within the profile a material called *laterite* which is a claylike material rich in the oxides of iron and aluminum that develops into hardpans or crusts.

It seems remarkable that some leached tropical soils should, in their natural state, be able to support such abundant vegetation as tropical rainforest and yet decline in productivity so rapidly upon cultivation. It may be that this results from the interrelation between forest and soil. The roots of the broadleaf trees of the rainforest continuously bring to the surface at least small amounts of the critical mineral elements from underlying sources. When the forest trees die and decay, the minerals and some of the organic material contained in them

Fig. 22.4 Latosolic soil. Profile of yellowish red latosol formed from gneiss northwest of Rio de Janeiro, Brazil. Latosol profiles are typically deep and commonly do not have as much horizon differentiation as podzols. There is some darkening of the thick A horizon by organic matter. Plant roots extend to depths below 5 ft. in this soil. (*Photograph by Roy W. Simonson, Soil Conservation Service, U.S. Department of Agriculture.*)

are returned to the surface soils and are in part reabsorbed by the roots of other trees, thus providing a sufficient supply as long as the forest exists. Following the destruction of the forest and the planting of shallow-rooted crops, this cyclic movement of minerals and organic nutrients is interrupted, and the surface reserves are quickly depleted. Some of the latosolic tropical soils are not well suited to crops such as corn or tobacco that draw heavily on soil fertility. They are better adapted to the growth of crops such as oil palms which utilize the intense tropical sunlight and abundant rains for the production and storage of fats, starches, sugar, and other carbohydrates.

Tropical soils developed under grass are commonly also more deeply weathered and less fertile than mid-latitude soils developed under grass. Like many other tropical soils they are likely to be reddish at least beneath the surface.

It was noted previously that mature soils attain their best development upon undulating surfaces where underdrainage is free and erosion is small but not entirely absent. From that it may properly be inferred that there are many localities, within the large areas shown as tropical soils on Plate 6, that do not have mature soils. The soils of some of these are intrazonal, and those of others are azonal in character. Among the former are the soils of boglands or other areas of poor drainage, and those that have an unusual lime content, owing to the limy nature of their parent materials. The azonal types include the rapidly eroding surfaces of steep slopes, where the soils are thin, stony, and immature. They also include porous sands without profile development, recent deposits of volcanic ash, and especially the recent alluvial deposits of floodplains and deltas. In these latter the rate of accumulation is too rapid to permit the slow development of normal profile characteristics. Yet in many instances they are, where adequately drained, more productive agricultural land than the mature soils with which they are associated.

22.9 Podzolic-Latosolic Soils. These soils which have some characteristics of both latoza-

tion and podzolization occur in association with others in many areas of the tropical and subtropical regions. They are, however, the dominant soil in only a few areas, as shown on Plate 6. Their occurrence in areas of considerable agricultural importance such as the Cotton Belt of the United States and southern China renders them significant geographically. They have been subjected to the process of latozation, but either the process has not been so complete as in the case of a true latosol, or it has taken place under slightly different conditions of rainfall and drainage. The upper horizons of these soils generally are brown, friable clays and loams. The B horizons usually are deep and more compact than in the latosol, and their colors vary from red to yellow or mottled. The lighter colors result from a less complete oxidation of the iron content, and this in turn is believed to indicate more abundant soil moisture resulting from either greater rainfall or less thorough underdrainage. Many of the red and yellow soils have also been more or less affected by podzolization. In such soils, a thin upper layer of organic material is underlain by an acid B horizon of red or yellow material.

The agricultural capacity of these soils is not high, but with careful management they are productive. Although, as a class, they are low in calcium and other alkaline substances, they still contain some reserves of unweathered rock minerals and considerable colloidal materials from which these plant foods may be made available. Their generally finer textures cause them to be more retentive of moisture, but permit adequate drainage. However, their supplies of organic matter seldom are abundant. Under cultivation the colors of the red and yellow subsoils usually predominate. That is because cropping quickly uses the small surface reserve of organic matter, plowing tends to intermingle the A and B horizons, and the less granular structure makes them subject to erosion. Although they presently become exhausted under continuous cropping, they respond well to fertilizers because of their fine textures. In some regions they are kept in continuous productivity by heavy fertilization, but in others worn-out lands are abandoned for periods of years to permit the accumulation of new reserves of plant food.

Soils of the Subhumid Grasslands and Deserts

22.10 Soils of Subhumid Areas. It was previously pointed out that there is considerable coincidence between humid climates and forests on the one hand and between subhumid climates and grassland and shrub on the other. It is not possible, however, to draw a clearly defined climatic line that will everywhere coincide with the zone that lies between forests and grasslands. Neither is it possible to find an abrupt change in zonal soils from those which are developed under forest to those developed under grass. Nevertheless the usual effect of limited soil moisture, and the presence of grass cover, is to cause the development of soils very different from those of the humid forest lands.

In regions where the moisture supply normally is sufficient to support a dense and luxuriant growth of grasses, growth and annual death of a part of the thick sod produce organic matter *in* the soil which gives rise to a large supply of humus.

Because the humus is largely of grass-root origin, it is not confined to the surface but extends to depths of several inches to 3 or 4 ft. Slow leaching leaves sufficient lime to combine with the large amount of organic colloids and colloidal clays in these dark soils, thus promoting excellent structural conditions, which are found in all the soil horizons. The abundant and deep organic material is the source of their prevailing dark colors.

Because most grassland soils develop under comparative dryness, they are less leached than any of the soils previously considered. Consequently, most of these soils are relatively high in available calcium compared to soils developed under more humid conditions. There is normally a redistribution in the soil profile of the lime contained in the parent material. Frequent periods of drought cause upward movements of capillary water. This movement brings up lime, dissolved from the parent material of the soil, and the evaporation of water from the soil surface causes its deposition. Subsequent rains tend to carry the lime down again, but ultimately a position of balance is established. As a result there is in most of these soils a *horizon of lime accumulation*. It is nearer the surface in regions of abundant lime and low rainfall and farther down in soils that are better supplied with moisture or are derived from parent materials poor in lime.

As one moves from the subhumid to the semiarid and finally to the arid sections, a change occurs in the character of the soils (Fig. 22.1). Less moisture means less leaching and more calcification. It also means less vegetative cover and therefore less humus and a lighter soil color. The horizon of lime accumulation rises until in some desert regions it coincides with the surface. Although there are no abrupt lines along which boundaries can be readily drawn, there is sufficient difference between the soils of the subhumid and the arid extremes that at least three groups can be recognized: (*a*) the chernozemic soils of the relatively humid portions of the dry lands and the dry-humid transition zone; (*b*) the desertic soils of the shrub-covered arid regions; and (*c*) the chernozemic-desertic soils lying between the first two.

22.11 Chernozemic Soils. The chernozemic category includes several well-recognized zonal soils such as the Prairie, the Chernozem, and variants of these.

Adjacent to some of the forest-soil regions, but on their drier margins, are very dark brown soils which are known as Prairie soils. They are widely developed in the United States, Russia, and South America. They appear to have formed under a natural vegetation of tall grasses, yet in climates having sufficient moisture so that leaching has lowered the available calcium to the point where they are neutral or even moderately acid. They have fine granular textures and dark color. Both these qualities are derived from abundant and deep accumulations of the organic matter from grass roots. They have no horizon of lime accumulation.

The Prairie soils are excellent agricultural soils. Because of their high humus content, their good structure, and the more abundant soil moisture associated with them they are among the most productive soils of the world. The rich Corn Belt chernozemic soils of central Illinois, Iowa, and Missouri are Prairie soils (Plate 6). The typical mature soil is found on rolling interfluves where the natural vegetation of prairie grasses was best established. In the United States they are developed mainly in

Fig. 22.5 Chernozemic soil. Profile of a Chernozem formed from glacial till in South Dakota. The A horizon extends to a depth of a little over a foot, while the B horizon extends to a depth of nearly 2½ ft. The white spots in the bottom of the B and in the C horizon are carbonate accumulations. (*Photograph by Roy W. Simonson, Soil Conservation Service, U.S. Department of Agriculture.*)

regions of older glacial drift in which are considerable admixtures of loess. On steeper slopes, especially river bluffs, fingers of woodland originally projected into the prairies. On such sites the gray-brown podzolic soils were developed.

Chernozem (a Russian word meaning black earth) is the name applied to a zonal soil that is naturally one of the most fertile, although perhaps not the most adaptable, of the chernozemic category. It is formed under a dense vegetation of prairie and steppe grasses and under average annual precipitation sufficiently low (about 20 in. in the United States) so that, while some of the most soluble soil minerals are leached out, an abundance of lime and the less soluble alkaline minerals remain. The low precipitation also results in a lack of eluviation, and the soil has a large component of clay and colloids. In true Chernozem soils the horizon of lime accumulation lies generally between 3 and 5 ft. beneath the surface and is still within reach of the grass roots, which find in it an inexhaustible source of calcium. The surface material of the Chernozem is high in humus and of a black or very dark-brown color (Fig. 22.5). The soil structure is well flocculated, granular, and porous. Upon tillage it crumbles into a fine seedbed, and it has a large capacity for holding water. Reserves of both organic and mineral plant food in the Chernozems are so abundant that the soils will stand cropping for long periods without fertilization. The high colloidal content of Chernozems causes them to be extremely plastic and sticky when they are wet and, on slopes, to suffer badly from surface erosion when they are cultivated. In general, however, there are no better soils than Chernozems for grain, cotton, and other extensive field crops that draw heavily upon soil fertility.

Plate 6 shows the probable world distribution of the chernozemic soils. These highly fertile soils reach their most excellent development in the middle latitudes, especially on the gently undulating uplands along the prairie-steppe margin in the United States and in southern Russia. However, even in North America there are differences between the chernozemic soils of the northern end of the belt, in Canada and the Dakotas, and those of Texas. The latter were developed under grass and shrub vegetation less dense than the northern sod and under higher temperatures. They have, in consequence, a lower humus content and a more brownish-black color and a redder subsoil.

In regions of subhumid tropical grassland also there are some dark soils which are classed as chernozemic. These soils have not been studied so widely as those of higher latitudes. They contain abundant organic matter and a horizon of lime accumulation. However, long-continued high temperatures hasten the decomposition of organic matter, even under subhumid conditions. It is probable that a large part of the tropical chernozemic soils are neither so deep nor so black as those of the Dakotas. The black soils of central India, classed as chernozemic in Plate 6, are derived from the weathering of basic igneous rocks, and they owe their black color to their peculiar mineral content rather than to abundant organic matter.

In several humid regions there is a dark-colored intrazonal soil, high in humus, which is found in association with podzolic and latosolic forest soils. It is similar to Prairie soil in character and yet significantly different in origin. The soil type is called Rendzina. It is developed from parent material containing lime in such abundance that the supply continues to exceed the rate of loss through leaching. Hard limestones break down too slowly to form Rendzinas. In soft chalky limestones, however, or in beds of glacial or lacustrine marl, the rate of physical disintegration is more rapid than the rate at which leaching can remove the lime. Consequently, the resulting soils are high in lime in spite of heavy leaching. High lime content apparently encouraged an original vegetation of tall prairie grasses rather than forest. This, in turn, produced a dark soil of the chernozemic type, but being intrazonal they are not shown on Plate 6 except where they have been included with adjacent zonal chernozemic soils. Examples of Rendzinas are found in the soils of the Black Prairies of Alabama and Texas, in certain dark soils of eastern Cuba, and in some of the chalk lands and glacial marls of Europe.

22.12 Desertic soils develop under sparse vegetations composed of widely spaced desert shrubs and, therefore, lack the abundant organic matter of the chernozemic soils. Because they are low in organic matter the lighter colors predominate in these soils, and the reds, browns, yellows, and grays of weathered rock minerals are widely exposed. This characteristic is accentuated by the accumulation of lime and

Fig. 22.6 Desertic soil. Profile of a Sierozem ("near-desert") soil formed on alluvial sediments in Nevada. Although the regolith is deep, horizon differentiation is low. Carbonate accumulation occurs at depths below 14 to 16 in. (*Photograph by Roy W. Simonson, Soil Conservation Service, U.S. Department of Agriculture.*)

other whitish substances near to, or even upon, the soil surface. The alkaline and saline materials usually are present in such abundance that commonly the surface materials, or those immediately below the surface, are cemented by them into crusts or hardpan layers. The desertic soils are characteristically low in nitrogen but have large supplies of soluble minerals. In such soils as are of medium to coarse texture, the concentration of alkaline materials is not generally sufficient to be harmful to plants. In some areas, however, the surface accumulation of salt and alkali is so great that cultivated plants cannot grow in it. It is, however, not only the quantity but also the quality of the salts that determine the agricultural utility of desert soils. It is commonly held that soils in which the compounds of calcium predominate maintain better structures under irrigation, whereas a predominance of sodium salts tends to destroy the soil structure and eventually to render irrigated land unfit for use.

It is probable that the larger parts of the great deserts are not covered with mature soils. Instead there are patches of bare rock, expanses of desert gravels covered with the pebbles remaining after deflation, tracts of dune sand, and areas of immature soil resulting from the recent and rapid growth of alluvial fans. Alluvial soils are the most widely cultivated in arid lands partly because of their suitability for irrigation. But even desert sands contain so many undecomposed rock fragments that they are well supplied with soluble minerals, and if abundant water is available for irrigation they may be made agriculturally productive.

22.13   Chernozemic-desertic soils constitute a category of soils that are neither so dark colored nor so rich in humus as the chernozemic, nor do they have the high concentration of alkaline materials or the light color characteristic of desertic soils. The prevailing color is brown or reddish brown. These soils show the influence of decreased moisture in several ways. They have developed under a grass cover less luxuriant and deep rooted than

that associated with the chernozemic soils. In general, it is a continuous sod cover of various species of "short grass," but it includes also areas of grass with intermingled shrub. The roots of the grasses provide an abundant but less penetrating source of humus than those of the taller grasses. The dryness of the earth has promoted the formation of brown rather than black humus, which is intermingled with a powdery surface soil and lies above a subsoil of a somewhat coarse and lumpy structure. These soils have a zone of accumulated lime or other alkaline substances deposited beneath the surface by the movement of soil moisture. Because the precipitation of these regions is slight, the horizon of alkaline accumulation is relatively near the surface (1 to 2 ft.), and in some localities, the lime is so abundant that it forms a tough hardpan layer in the soil. In general, however, chernozemic-desertic soils are easily tilled and are found, upon the undulating to rolling land, well adapted to cultivation. The fact that these soil regions, the world over, are predominantly regions of livestock grazing rather than of soil cultivation is due to a deficiency of rainfall rather than to deficiencies in their soils.

Tundra and Alluvial Soils

22.14   Tundra Soils. In the treeless regions of the Arctic fringe the soil profiles show evidence of excessive rather than deficient moisture. This is due to the low rate of surface evaporation and to the presence of permanently frozen subsoil. The better drained sites of the Arctic-fringe regions have soils somewhat like podzols, but the usual horizons include a brown peaty surface layer which is underlain by grayish horizons, one of them characteristically plastic or even fluid. A large part of the tundra is poorly drained and the prevailing soil conditions are those of bog and hummocky marshland. The soils are in several respects similar to the glacial marsh and bog soils found in middle latitudes, many of which are drained and cultivated. In the Arctic region large areas cannot be drained, are unsuited to tillage, and support a natural vegetation useful only as pasture. Better drained slopes and those most exposed to sunlight offer possibilities for the growth of a few short-season agricultural crops.

22.15 Alluvial Soils. It is probably more difficult to generalize about the characteristics of alluvial soils than any of the other great soil groups. On the other hand they have been grouped together and, where their extent makes it possible, shown on the map of soil categories (Plate 6), because alluvial soils probably support a larger proportion of the world's population than any other great soil group. The character of alluvial soils is largely derived from the source materials from which the specific alluvial products originated. Consequently, the textures may range from sands, through silts, to clays; they may range in color from the light-colored alluvium derived from desertic soils to the dark-colored derived from chernozemic soils; and they may be more or less rich in plant nutrients. They are, generally, free of stones and easily cultivated, but in many areas are poorly drained. Because of the fact that the parent material, when deposited, is already weathered and relatively loose they quickly acquire some of the characteristics of the zonal soils associated with the same vegetation and drainage. If not disturbed, they will ultimately develop from the azonal alluvial soil to another of the zonal group characteristic of the region where they occur. Most of the great soil categories mentioned above have alluvial soils associated with the mature zonal soils and in many instances they constitute the most prized land.

Not all alluvial soils are productive; for in many areas they are too wet or too dry, or occur where the growing season is too short, or are too subject to flood to be much utilized. On the other hand, in Far Eastern areas where rice growing in alluvial paddy lands is widespread, the alluvial soils are probably more generally utilized than elsewhere in the world. Most of Japan's productive land, for example, is of alluvial origin but in units so small they cannot be shown on the world map. Mention should also be made of the fact that Egypt's dense agricultural population has, almost entirely, subsisted on the production from alluvial soils. On the other hand, the tropical alluvial soils of some parts of central Africa are at present little used because they are infested with the tsetse fly.

Soil Conservation

22.16 Destructive Soil Erosion. There has been already abundant opportunity to observe that erosion is one of the most powerful and widespread of the processes involved in the modification of the earth's surface. The fact that, in the geologic past, soil has been removed during the slow processes of land degradation is not now a matter of great concern. On the other hand, the fact that present erosion is doing the same thing is a matter of vital concern, because human disturbance of the balance of nature has greatly *accelerated* the process, and it is now removing the upper horizons of developed soils much faster than natural processes can replace them. In some localities soils are fast being removed down to the parent materials of the soil or even to bare rock. This is destructive soil erosion, since there is lost in a few years or in a few generations a resource which has required thousands of years for development, a resource which cannot be replaced.

Not all kinds of soil are equally subject to destructive erosion. It may be appreciated from foregoing descriptions that some soils, such as some latosols or eluviated sandy soils, might even benefit by the uniform removal of some depth of surface soil. This would expose less weathered minerals and less leached materials underneath. But those soils, because of their high porosity, are among those least subject to rapid erosion. On the other hand, the dark-colored soils, with the organic accumulations of the ages in their upper horizons, are highly subject to erosion, as are also certain of the forest soils of high clay content.

22.17   The Causes of Destructive Soil Erosion. The principal cause of destructive soil erosion, both by rain water and by wind, is human disturbance of the natural conditions by the removal of the natural vegetation and the loosening of the soil by cultivation. The natural vegetation is destroyed by land clearing, burning, excessive grazing by livestock, and plowing. The rate at which the soil is destroyed after these changes depends upon the textural and structural conditions of the soil, the conditions of climate, particularly the number of intense rainstorms per year, and the degree of land slope. Under natural conditions a cover of forest vegetation tends to decrease the rate of runoff because of the many small pits and irregularities of the forest floor and because the litter and humus collected there are highly absorptive of moisture, tending to hold rain water until it can escape slowly. Dense growths of prairie grasses have much the same effect. When the natural vegetation is removed and the tilled soil is alternately beaten by rain and dried by sun and wind, the erosive influence of both wind and water has full effect.

22.18   Kinds of Destructive Soil Erosion. The manner in which soils are eroded and the kind and degree of their destruction also depend much upon the texture and structure of the soil, conditions of climate and land slope, nature of tillage, and other matters. One of the most widespread and least noticed kinds of erosion on tilled land is *sheet wash*. This may be accomplished by the removal of a uniform thin layer of soil, but more commonly it results from the formation of myriads of minute gullies (Fig. 22.7). These gullies are so small that they may be erased by the next cultivation of the field, but others soon form, and the stripping process continues. This phase of soil erosion is the more harmful because it removes the finer and more nutritionally useful of the soil particles first.

In some kinds of soil, especially in compact

Fig. 22.7   Incipient gullies in a tilled field and serious erosion of topsoil resulting from a single rain. In the foreground is sand from which the finer and more fertile soil constituents have been removed. (*Courtesy of U.S. Soil Conservation Service.*)

Fig. 22.8 Soil completely destroyed for agricultural use by unchecked gullying. (*Photograph by H. H. Bennett. Courtesy of the Geographical Review, published by the American Geographical Society of New York.*)

and poorly flocculated clays and silts underlain by softer materials, *gullying* rapidly becomes deep and extends itself by headward erosion of the dendritic type. On the rolling surfaces this process, if left unchecked, quickly destroys both soil and subsoil beyond all hope of repair (Fig. 22.8). Under such conditions the whole damage does not result from the erosion of the upland soils. Adjacent lowland soils sometimes are ruined at the same time by being buried under accumulations of the coarser and less fertile alluvial products of the erosion.

In the subhumid plains of the United States great damage has resulted from wind erosion on surfaces laid bare by plowing or by overgrazing on the part of livestock. In some localities the powdery soil thus exposed has been removed to a depth of several inches. As more land in this region is cultivated, dust storms increase in number and severity. During the prolonged drought of the mid 1930's, millions of tons of fertile topsoil were drifted about like snow by storms or were lifted so high into the air that quantities settled far to the eastward, as has happened many times before.

22.19 The Reduction of Destructive Soil Erosion. The seriousness of the soil-erosion menace is barely beginning to be realized in America, and too little is being done to reduce the loss (Fig. 22.9). It certainly is not possible to stop entirely losses by solution and erosion, which have gone on since the world began. However, some things may be done to reduce the rate of destructive erosion brought about by human disturbances of the natural balance of forces. To that end a program of planned soil conservation should be supported. Such a program must include a slow return to permanent forest or permanent grass of those lands in which erosion has progressed so far as to destroy the value of the land for tillage. It must include also means of protecting, by conservative methods of tillage and management, those areas which are best suited to, and are required for, crop production, so that they may continue to be productive for hundreds or thousands of years to come. Among the methods having this latter end in view, the specialists in erosion control recommend (*a*) the construction of dams or obstructions to erosion in gullies already

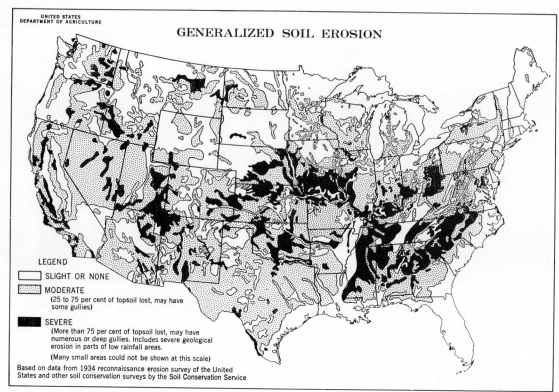

Fig. 22.9 Generalized distribution of the extent of soil erosion by wind and water in the United States. (*From a map by Soil Conservation Service, U.S. Department of Agriculture.*)

formed, (*b*) the plowing and tilling of land along contour levels in order to cause furrows to run across the land slope and thus reduce the rate of sheet wash, and (*c*) the adoption of crop rotations which include 2 to 6 years of continuous hay. Above all is required an awakened consciousness of the need for soil protection and of the disastrous consequences to an increasing population that may arise from the ruthless waste of this fundamental resource.

23

The Mineral Fuels

23.1 Industrial Civilization and the Mineral Fuels. One of the most indispensable of the many abilities which have enabled man to develop a modern industrial civilization is the ability to harness power. Thus he can accomplish tasks well beyond his relatively feeble muscular potential. His major sources for such power are the mineral fuels, coal and petroleum (including gas). To be sure man uses such other sources as falling water, wood, or the movement of the atmosphere, but he depends primarily on coal and petroleum. The likelihood that atomic and solar energy will supplant the mineral fuels as major power sources seems to be steadily increasing, but in spite of urgent and continuing experimentation to that end, the time has not yet come when dependence on the mineral fuels can be decreased. Therefore, no full appreciation of the potentialities of regions or countries for human use, or of their industrial development and economic problems, is possible without knowing their relation to these earth resources. For that reason it is essential that the student of geography have a clear understanding of the nature of these substances, the comparative supplies available in the world's greatest deposits, and the major patterns of their world distribution.

Both coal and petroleum are fossil fuels in the sense that solar energy was in times past "locked up" in plant and animal tissue which in turn has been preserved to some extent during the geologic past. Coal and petroleum are, therefore, parts of the earth's crustal structure, and their origin and present distribution are explainable only in terms of the processes and events of earth history. When these conditions are grasped, it becomes apparent that we may expect that large parts of the world will be deficient in deposits of these substances. It becomes equally clear why it is possible for certain other regions to have large supplies of one or even both of them.

Coal

23.2 The Structural Associations of Coal. Coal is a form of sedimentary rock derived largely from the unoxidized carbon of plant tissues. Even thin beds of coal represent long periods of accumulation, during which the remains of luxuriant vegetation were preserved from the ordinary processes of complete decay as a consequence of being buried beneath swamp waters and, subsequently, layers of clay, sand, or lime.

The origin of coal, mainly vegetative deposits in ancient swamps, raises several points of geographic significance. First, it may be noted that the original position of swamp deposits is nearly horizontal. This may be observed in modern swamps. When such deposits are buried underneath other sediments, they become members of a series of horizontal sedimentary rocks. The coal beds of some of the greatest coal fields of the world have still an essentially horizontal position, a condition that simplifies the problems of mining. In other coal fields the beds are not horizontal but, together with associated rocks, show evidence of subsequent disturbance, through warping, folding, or faulting. In some places this has involved the metamorphism of the coal. A second point of significance is that modern swamps seldom are of vast extent. A few, such as those on the Atlantic Coastal Plain, contain many square miles or even some hundreds of square miles of area, and it is probable that larger ones have existed in the past. Nevertheless, it is not surprising, considering their swamp origin, that individual beds of coal are not of great extent. Only a few are large enough that the same bed may be traced underground for many miles.

Although most of the individual coal beds are of relatively small areal extent, the same is not necessarily true of the great coal fields. In some of the larger fields, conditions favorable to the growth of luxuriant swamp vegetation and the accumulation of plant remains must have existed widely and for long periods of time. In such regions individual swamps flourished, disappeared, and were then buried underneath accumulated earthy sediments while, at the same time, other swamps grew near by. Subsidence of the land took place, and another swamp formed above the remains of the older one but separated from it by layers of sediment. All degrees of variations in the circumstances of deposition are recorded in the present formations of some coal fields. Large and small, thick and thin, the beds are widely distributed in area and in vertical sequence. In some localities they so far overlap each other that a mine shaft may pass through several thin and unprofitable coal strata before reaching one of desirable thickness and quality. In certain localities a half dozen or more coal beds are known to lie one above another, separated by various thicknesses of sedimentary rock.

Since coal is known to occur with the rocks belonging to a fairly well-defined range of geological time, it is possible, by studying the rock outcrops, to determine the general extent of a coal region and, by means of test borings, to discover the number and relative thickness of the coal beds in its various parts. Consequently, it is possible for geologists to approximate with fair accuracy the reserves of coal available for future use in a field, a country, or in the world, in so far as the structures have been examined.

23.3 Varieties of coal differ greatly from region to region, and even within the same field a considerable number of market classes and grades of coal may be produced. Several standard classes are recognized, each of which marks a stage in the evolution of swamp deposits into high-grade coal. Only four of them will be mentioned here.

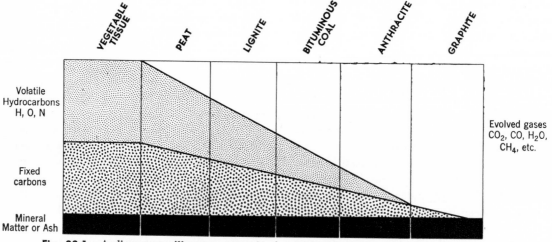

Fig. 23.1 A diagram to illustrate stages in the slow metamorphosis of vegetable material into coal of various types. (*After Newberry.*)

It may be assumed that all coal began as *peat,* preserved but crumbled and blackened organic remains, similar to that which may be seen underlying present swamps and bogs. The higher forms of coal represent successive stages in the transformation of peat as a result of the weight of the overlying rocks, through diastrophism, or by any other process of metamorphism that involves compression and the loss of water and gases (Fig. 23.1). A form somewhat older and more compact than peat is the crumbly brown coal called *lignite.*

Additional changes produced the soft black coals of the general class called *bituminous.* Of bituminous coal there is an almost endless list of slightly different grades and qualities. Important fields, and even different parts of the same field or different beds in the same locality, have their own recognized grades.

Further compression of coal beds, especially if it was accompanied by warping of the formations together with faulting and sometimes heating, produced the class of hard coal called *anthracite.* The transformation was accompanied by a great loss of volatile constituents, and the resulting anthracite is low in gas and high in carbon, which makes it a nearly smokeless fuel.

One of the most significant distinctions among the various classes of coal is that based upon its suitability for the manufacture of *coke* to be used in the extraction of the metal iron from its ore. There is presently no other way of recovering iron in large quantities. This fuel for use in the blast furnace is prepared by roasting certain classes of bituminous coal in special ovens to drive off the volatile matter, leaving a product of usable quality. The metallurgical requirements of coke are relatively stringent, and only a small proportion of the world's coal deposits can be so used. Consequently, this seriously restricts the areas where iron can be produced economically. Estimates of coking coal reserves give the greater share by far to the United States and the U.S.S.R. in that order and considerably lesser amounts to Germany, the United Kingdom, and China.

23.4 Coal Classes and Their Relation to Geologic Age. Since coal is formed mainly from the accumulation of vegetation in swamps, it follows that no coal could be formed until there was abundant land vegetation. It is, therefore, not logical to expect that coal will occur in significant quantity in rocks that belong to those periods of earth history before land plants were abundant. The time sequence in which the major additions of plant and animal life were made to the earth is shown in Appendix E. From that table it will be seen that the rocks of all the vast extent of time earlier than the Paleozoic bear little evidence of extensive land vegetation. Even the early Paleozoic periods seem not to have had vegetation of sufficiently high order of development to produce the bog deposits necessary to the abundant formation of coal. It was not until the Carboniferous period that conditions became suitable for the widespread and abundant growth and accumulation of a coal-forming vegetation.

The coal fields of the world represent periods of accumulation from the early Carboniferous down to the Tertiary period and, if peat deposits be included, down to the present. In a general way, there may be recognized among the many classes of coal represented in these fields a general order of quality which is highest in the older coals and lowest or poorest in those of more recent origin. This order is not without its notable exceptions, yet the general relationship is logical in view of the fact that time is an important element in the transformation of raw peat into good coal.

23.5 The accessibility of coal is, in part, a matter of where the coal beds are located with respect to markets, but here its meaning is restricted to the subject of their structural and situational relations to the earth's surface. In some localities of little-disturbed sedimentary rocks coal beds are found so close to the surface that they may be mined in open pits after the removal of only a few feet of overburden (covering earth or rock) (Fig. 23.2). In others the beds are so far underground as to be reached only by mine shafts of great depth. In still other

Fig. 23.2 Giant furrows turned by power shovels in the process of strip mining in southern Illinois. The 4-ft.-thick bed of coal exposed in the bottom of the deep trench is mined out before the next furrow is turned.

areas, although originally the beds were deeply buried, they are now made readily accessible by deep stream dissection which exposes outcrops of coal among the rocks of the valley walls (Figs. 23.3a and 23.4). In regions of complicated rock structure, coal beds, once horizontal but now greatly folded, present various degrees of accessibility. In some such localities erosion exposes parts of coal beds at the surface. In others the same beds are bent downward to great depths or are displaced or shattered by faulting. In such structures the difficulties of mining are greatly increased (Fig. 23.3b).

THE COAL REGIONS OF THE CONTINENTS

Because coal still is the principal source of power in manufactural industry and also is necessary for the smelting of iron, its distribution is a matter of critical importance in relation to the world centers of heavy manufacture, present and future. Although there are coal

THE APPALACHIAN BITUMINOUS FIELD

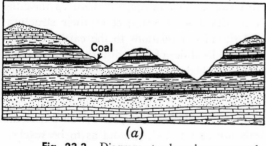

(a)

THE PENNSYLVANIA ANTHRACITE FIELD

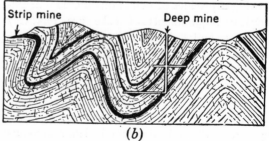

(b)

Fig. 23.3 Diagrams to show in contrast the common relationships of surface and structure in the bituminous and anthracite fields of the Appalachian coal regions.

reserves in all the continents and in most of the countries of the world, the distribution of the great ones is most uneven. They are, in fact, grouped in three principal regions: (*a*) central and eastern North America, (*b*) from northwestern Europe eastward, and (*c*) eastern Asia.

23.6 North America is credited with the greatest of all coal reserves. These have been appraised at about 45 per cent of the total estimated supply of the world. The North American coals include representatives of every class from high-grade anthracite to the lowest grades of lignite. They are contained in several fields, the location and extent of which are shown in Fig. 23.5.

It will be observed that certain areas of the continent are without coal. Notable among them are the ancient rocks of the Laurentian Shield of Canada and the Appalachian Piedmont and also the young sediments of the Atlantic and Gulf coastal margins. In the complicated structures and partly igneous rocks of Mexico and the regions west of the Rocky Mountains coal fields are small and scattered

and, with a few notable exceptions, yield coals of low grade.

23.7 *The Appalachian Province.* Not the most extensive, but much the most important, among the coal fields of the continent is that of the Appalachian hill region. It is comprised of two principal subdivisions: (*a*) a small highly folded section containing anthracite coal in the Appalachian ridge-and-valley region of northeastern Pennsylvania and (*b*) a large region of little-folded rocks which contain numerous beds of bituminous coal, some of them thick and of high quality. This latter region extends from northwestern Pennsylvania through Ohio, West Virginia, Kentucky, and Tennessee into northwestern Alabama.

The anthracite region is noted for the high carbon and low gas content of its coals and for their smokeless quality. This region is the source of most of the anthracite used in America. The extreme folding to which the region has been subjected has inclined many of the coal formations at high angles underground, and associated faulting has dislocated

Fig. 23.4 A stratum of bituminous coal outcropping, along with other sedimentary strata, in a road cut on a West Virginia hillside.

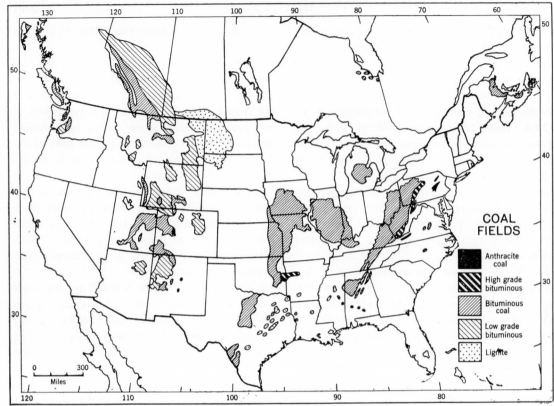

Fig. 23.5 The principal coal fields of the United States and Canada distinguished as to location, extent, and principal types of coal.

them. This has greatly increased the cost and difficulty of mining, thus making anthracite an expensive fuel (Fig. 23.3b).

The bituminous region contains workable beds of coal which, in total, represent a period of accumulation which was long, even from the geological viewpoint. Mainly, they are of Carboniferous age and of good quality. Some of them are of the character required for the manufacture of blast-furnace coke. One such coal bed of great thickness and large extent in western Pennsylvania was the basis of Pittsburgh's early supremacy in iron and steel manufacture, and it still furnishes coke for that and several other smelting centers. Additional supplies of coking coal are now obtained from other sources, especially from fields in West Virginia and Alabama.

More than three-fourths of the high-grade coal output of the continent, some of which has special uses other than for coking, is obtained

from the Appalachian bituminous field. The coal of that field is noted also for the ease with which it is mined. The coal-bearing rocks largely are included within the limits of the maturely dissected Appalachian hill country. Being traversed by innumerable deeply incised stream valleys, the coal beds often are exposed along the valley walls, and mining is relatively simple. It is accomplished in large part by means of "drifts," or horizontal tunnels driven into the hillside outcrops of nearly horizontal coal seams (Fig. 23.3a). In many mines the dip of the coal bed permits the mine workings to slope gently downward toward the mine mouth, and the removal of both coal and drainage waters is aided, or may be wholly accomplished, by gravity. In western Pennsylvania, at least, some of the nearly horizontal coal seams are strip-mined on the hillsides where they outcrop. A power shovel turns a gigantic furrow exposing unweathered coal at the bottom of a trench which follows a contour level more or less around a hill, leaving the more deeply buried part of the seam under the core of the hill to be recovered by future drift mining.

The abundance, accessibility, and high quality of these bituminous coals give the Appalachian fields first importance in America and perhaps in the world. They supply the coal used in the eastern and northeastern industrial districts and also most of the American export coal.

23.8 *The Interior Province.* The interior region of the United States also is abundantly provided with coal fields. Generally the coal is Carboniferous in age and bituminous in quality. The several areas are known, respectively, as (*a*) the *Eastern region* (Illinois, Indiana, and Kentucky), (*b*), the *Northern region* (Michigan), (*c*) the *Western region* (Iowa, Missouri, Kansas, Oklahoma, and Arkansas), and (*d*) the *Southwestern region* (Texas). In the Eastern and Northern regions the coal-bearing rocks have broad synclinal structures, and in the former, the coal beds of the middle portion are so deeply buried under younger rocks that they are difficult to reach. Therefore, mining is practiced mainly about the margins of the field (Figs. 23.6 and 23.2). In the Western and Southwestern regions the coal beds are inclined gently downward toward the west and pass beneath increasing thicknesses of rock. The coal is mined along the more shallow eastern edges of the fields, where it provides abundant supplies of lower rank bituminous coal for limited local markets.

23.9 *The Rocky Mountain province* is made up of many relatively small fields ranging from southern Montana to New Mexico, and includes deposits in Wyoming, Colorado, and Utah. Coal of all qualities occurs because of the great variety of structural changes which have taken place in this area, but most of the coal is subbituminous quality. Although relatively of only local importance in so far as marketing is concerned, the reserves are large and capable of being used to produce synthetic products.

23.10 *The Great Plains province* includes some of the Canadian Rocky Mountains and extends from Wyoming and the Dakotas into southern Alberta and Saskatchewan. In the mountainous areas diastrophic forces have converted the coal to subbituminous and bituminous grades, but in the eastern sections where such forces have not been so active the coal is of lower grade.

As was previously pointed out with respect to the coal of the Rocky Mountain area, the Great Plains region is locally important, but ranks far below the eastern fields. Even the small fields in the Maritime Provinces of Canada produce more coal than the Canadian Great Plains region. Nevertheless, Great Plains coals have been extremely important in that they have supplied a local source for fuel which has enabled transcontinental rail transportation to be relatively cheap.

23.11 *Pacific Coast Fields.* Although much of the Pacific Coast region has no valuable coal regions there are a few deposits of considerable local significance. Important among

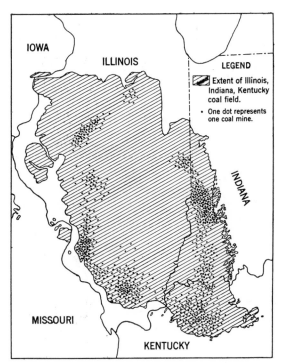

Fig. 23.6 Most of the coal mines in the synclinal Eastern region are located upon its more shallow margins.

them are those of Alaska, Vancouver Island, and the Puget Sound region. The Alaskan deposits have more future than present value, but those of Vancouver Island, though limited in quantity, have enjoyed considerable importance because they are near the North American terminals of some of the major transpacific steamship routes.

23.12 *Coal in eastern Canada* is not abundant, because the larger part of eastern Canada is comprised of pre-Paleozoic rocks. Several small inclusions of Carboniferous rocks occur in the Maritime Provinces, and they yield limited quantities of coal. The best and most used deposits, including some coking coal, are found near Sydney on the northern coast of Nova Scotia. These supply a local iron and steel industry, but already they have been exploited until some of the mines extend out beneath the

sea; the working of them has become more and more dangerous and costly. It is a matter of great concern to Canada that its most populous and industrially developed region, which lies between Lake Huron and the city of Quebec, is practically devoid of coal.

23.13 **Western Europe** ranks first in coal production if the output of all its components is totaled and compared with the outputs of the other two major coal areas, North America and eastern Asia. In total coal reserves Europe ranks third among the continents, and hardly more than one-twentieth of its supply is below bituminous grade. The average quality is, therefore, good. However, it is estimated that the total European coal resource, of bituminous grade or better, is little more than one-half as great as that available in North America, and North America has also nearly seventy-

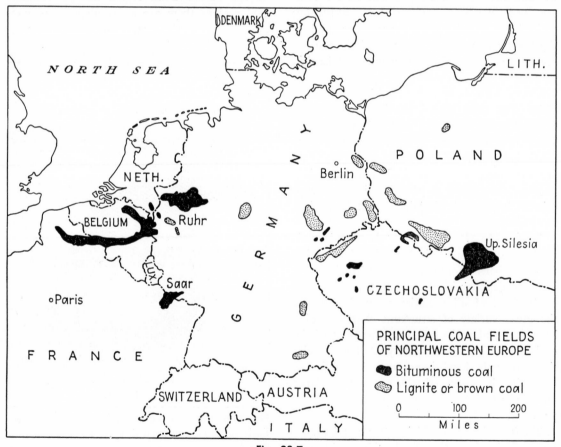

Fig. 23.7

five times as much subbituminous coal, brown coal, and lignite. The present value of European coal is increased by the fact that the principal fields are so distributed that they fall within the territorial boundaries of several European countries, the industrial advancement of which may be attributed in part to these sources of fuel. The leading nations in order of production as well as in availability of proved reserves of good-quality coal are the United Kingdom, Germany, and Poland. Czechoslovakia, the Low Countries, France, and Spain are second-rank producers far below the first three named. An indication of the wide availability of coal in Europe is the fact that coal is produced in more than twenty countries, but only the United Kingdom and Germany have large deposits of coking-quality coal required for the production of pig iron.

Figures 23.7 to 23.9 show the coal fields of Europe including the important deposits in the Ukraine of western U.S.S.R. This deposit ranks fourth behind the United Kingdom, Germany, and Poland in reserves of good-quality coal.

23.14 *British coal fields* occupy no less than six distinct regions in England, Scotland, and Wales. Mainly the coal beds are of Carboniferous age and contain coal of bituminous quality or better. So well distributed are they that only two parts of the island are more than a few miles removed from one or more of them (Fig. 23.8). Those two parts are the ancient crystalline rock region of the Highlands of Scotland and the plain of southeastern England, in which London is situated. It is probable that all the coal-bearing rocks of Scotland would have been removed by erosion had not a section of them been preserved in the rift, or graben, valley of the Scottish Lowlands. Associated with each of the major British coal fields is an important industrial district, and some of them, especially that of South Wales, are close to the sea and well situated for the export of coal.

Although the quality of British coal generally is superior, it is not always easily mined. The rocks of some of the fields have been sub-

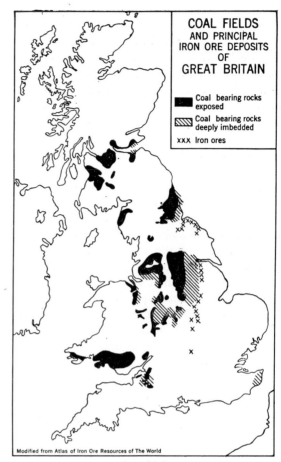

Modified from Atlas of Iron Ore Resources of The World

Fig. 23.8

jected to severe deformation or are buried beneath thick sediments. In the South Wales field, where the highest grades of coal are found, rock folding brought some parts of the coal beds to the surface, where stream erosion exposed them and made mining simple. However, most of the easily accessible coal has been mined, and some of the workings now have followed the coal structures deep and far underground, greatly increasing the cost of production. The total quantity remaining in Great Britain is estimated at an amount nearly one-half as great as that in the Appalachian field of the United States. It is sufficient for many years to come.

23.15 *The coal fields of western continental Europe* are numerous, but none covers so much area as the greater ones of North America. Moreover, some of them contain

473

much thin coal or coal at great depths, and a few yield only low-grade coals. The more important fields and most of the better grades of coal lie in the east-west belt through the center of the continent. The ancient crystalline rocks of Scandinavia and Finland to the north of that belt and the much disturbed rocks of the Mediterranean Basin on the south of it contain either no coal or but small and unimportant fields.

The central coal belt of Europe extends from northern France through Belgium, Germany, and Czechoslovakia, into Poland (Fig. 23.7). Several of the fields lie wholly or in part in what, prior to 1945, was Germany, and they were fundamental to the great industrial strength and military power of that nation. The various fields include coals of many types: coking coal, bituminous, subbituminous, and lignite. Low grades of coal and even peat are much more used in continental Europe than in Great Britain or the United States.

Coal of good quality is mined at several points along a band of Carboniferous rocks in the western end of the central European belt. This important zone extends from northern France, across central Belgium, and into Germany. Its most productive portion lies in the Ruhr Valley of Westphalia, east of the Rhine. That field is of particular importance because it has long been the center of the heavy iron and steel industries of Germany and because it contains a reserve of coking coal reputed to be larger than any other in continental Europe. Nearby is the coal field of the politically famous Saar Basin. Another highly important district is that of the middle eastern region. Its richest coal deposits lie in Poland, Upper Silesia, and adjacent portions of Czechoslovakia.

23.16   The U.S.S.R. The coal fields of Soviet Russia are numerous and widely distributed, but most of the large reserve of good-grade coal is in Siberia (Fig. 23.9). The district of first industrial importance is the Donets Basin in southern European Russia. This greatly folded area yields some anthracite and much bi-

tuminous fuel coal, but it is valued especially for its coking coal, which is not abundant in the U.S.S.R. Donets coals supply the heavy industry of the southern region, and some is shipped to the Moscow industrial centers. Second in importance at present is the Kuznetsk Basin of southern central Siberia. It is the source of fuel for a growing industrial district, and its coal (supplemented from Karaganda) moves more than 1,400 miles west to the iron and steel center of Magnitogorsk in the southern Ural Mountain region. The Kuznetsk region is estimated to be tremendously rich in high-quality reserves, and is considered to be second only to the Appalachian coal fields in the United States.[1] Third in importance, and most recently developed, is the Karaganda field located midway between the Kuznetsk and Ural areas. There are smaller coal fields on the flanks of the Ural Mountains, in the region west of Lake Baikal, and in far-eastern Siberia. In the isolated forest areas of northern Siberia are extensive coal deposits whose boundaries and reserves are imperfectly known.

The great industrial regions in and about Moscow and Leningrad do not have local supplies of good coal. There is lignite near Leningrad, and the Moscow region has a large area with coals of subbituminous and lignite grades.

23.17   Eastern and southern Asia have some widely distributed deposits of coal in addition to those in the central Siberian section of the U.S.S.R. (Fig. 23.10). Although estimates are insufficiently based upon good evidence in some cases, China seems to have by far the greatest amount. Coal is found in many parts of China, but the greatest deposits are in North China and Manchuria. The North China area in the provinces of Shansi and Shensi have the largest reserves of good quality, although their distance from markets has retarded their development. As China grows industrially, they will assume greater importance. The coal fields of Manchuria

[1] Walter H. Voskuil. "Minerals in World Industry." P. 132. McGraw-Hill Book Company, Inc., New York, 1955.

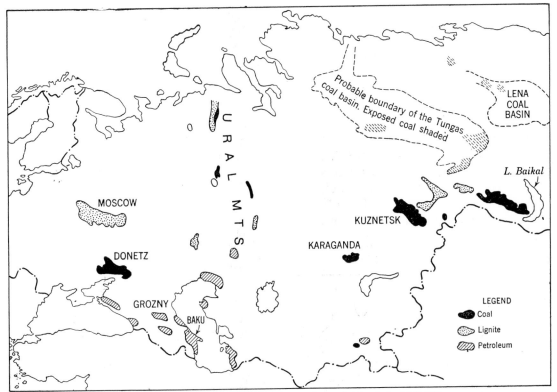

Fig. 23.9   The principal coal and petroleum fields of the U.S.S.R.

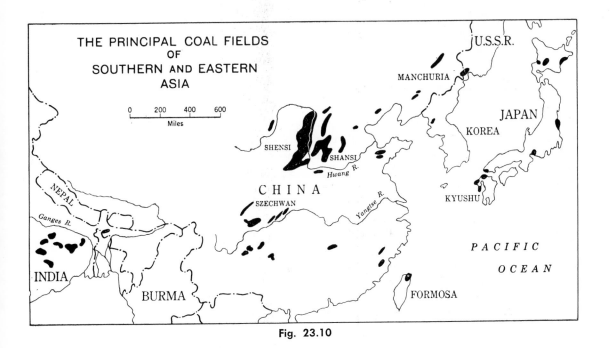

Fig. 23.10

support a considerable industrial development and are especially valuable because they contain good coking coal.

Other Asiatic countries that have important coal supplies are India and Japan. Those of India are located in the northeastern part of the Deccan, about 150 miles inland west of Calcutta, and are now being much used in connection with the iron ores of the same region. The reserves are apparently large but the supply of coking coal is limited. Unfortunately for industrial Japan the reserves of coal in that country are relatively small and scattered, and many of the beds are badly faulted. The most productive field is that of northern Kyushu.

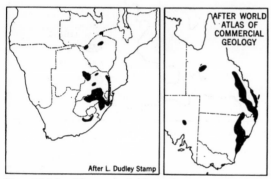

Fig. 23.11 The principal coal fields of South Africa and Australia.

23.18 Africa and Australasia. Australia, although it is a much smaller continent than Africa, has a larger coal reserve (Fig. 23.11). Fortunately, the principal field is located near the humid east coast of New South Wales, in or near the principal centers of population. Because of its abundance, good quality, and accessibility, Australian coal is the leading source of supply in the Southern Hemisphere, but the total reserve supply is not comparable with that of the larger fields of the Northern Hemisphere. The African coal reserve is not great, but the present production is considerable. It is obtained mainly from fields in the southeastern part of the continent, especially in the Transvaal and Natal.

23.19 South America has the misfortune to be, of all the continents, least well endowed with coal. There are in its entire extent only a few areas of coal-bearing rocks. The extensive highlands of the east and northeast are, in large part, of pre-Paleozoic rocks, and the sediments that flank the long eastern front of the Andes are very young. In the Andes of Colombia and Peru and on the coast of central Chile there are small deposits of valuable coal, and there is some of low grade in southern Brazil. Their total reserve is believed to be less than 1 per cent of the quantity available in North America.

Petroleum

23.20 Petroleum and natural gas have not only been important additions to man's energy resources, but the large variety of fuels and lubricants available from petroleum has enabled man to reduce the significance of space a hundredfold since the first well was drilled a century or so ago. The importance of petroleum as an energy resource is increased by the fact that it is a liquid that can be transported easily, in or out of pipes, and that its energy equivalent is greater than that of coal. Its present significance can be gauged by the fact that the amount of energy produced by the supply of petroleum and natural gas in the United States has increased phenomenally in the last half century and now accounts for almost two-thirds of the total production of energy in the United States (Fig. 23.12). Petroleum and natural gas are important in the other industrial areas of the world, although to a somewhat lesser degree than in the United States.

The cleanliness, compactness, and convenience of petroleum as a fuel and the fact that new machines are continually being devised for using the products which can be derived from it have made petroleum a critical item in the resource inventories of modern nations.

23.21 The Structural Associations of Petroleum. Petroleum (rock oil) and its related substances natural gas and asphalt are earth materials, presumably of organic origin. They have been so long included in the rocks that no trace of any organic antecedents is clearly discernible in them, and the very nature of the hydrocarbons of which they are composed is unlike that of the oils and other analogous compounds found in plants and animals.

Petroleum and its related substances are found in quantity in sedimentary rocks only, perhaps because they may have had their origin in small marine organisms whose remains were intermingled with marine deposits. Generally they are held in permeable rocks, especially sandstones, where they saturate the pore space of the rock just as it is filled elsewhere by ground water. Petroleum is found in limestones also, and some porous or slightly cavernous limestones yield it in large quantities.

Oil- and gas-bearing rocks are found in a considerable variety of physical associations and are of different geological ages. Like coal, however, they are not found among ancient crystalline rocks of pre-Paleozoic age. Some oil sands are found at great depths, where they are buried underneath hundreds or thousands of feet of younger rocks. In some localities there are two or more oil-bearing formations, one above the other but separated by great thicknesses of intervening strata, and they may be of widely different geological ages. The oil and gas accumulations usually are overlain by rocks that contain abundant ground water, and many are underlain by them also. The oil and gas seldom are distributed uniformly throughout the total extent of the rock in which they occur but are gathered together in limited areas, called *pools*. The pools are accumulations of oil trapped in the porous rock in some form of structural pocket from which they cannot escape. Some of these "structures" are the tops of anticlines which are capped by shales, clays, or other impervious rocks that prevent the upward escape of the oil or gas. Other pools are found in pockets, domes, or lenses of many shapes and origins into which the oil or gas has migrated from surrounding areas and there collected. Migration into these

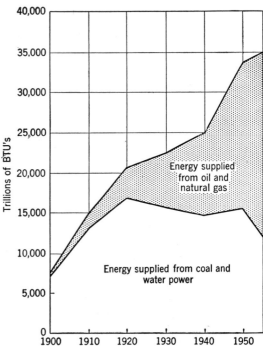

Fig. 23.12 Division of energy production in the United States in the years 1900 to 1954, showing the relative share contributed by petroleum and other energy resources. (*Generalized from Annual Report of Resources for the Future, Washington, D.C., 1955, based upon data from U.S. Bureau of Mines.*)

structural traps has taken place, in the long geological past, because the oil and gas are lighter than the ground water and tend to rise until they are caught and held beneath some impervious formation.

From such traps the oil and gas are recovered by drilling through the impervious capping rocks (Fig. 23.13). Through some drill holes oil is forced upward violently by the expansive force of the associated gas. Such wells are called "gushers." From others, and from most of them eventually, the oil must be brought up by pumping. Since the oil is contained in the small pore spaces in the pervious rock, not all of it can be recovered by pumping. Much of it remains as a film of oil clinging to the rock particles, or its flow is impeded by the collection of tarry substances. Even with the most improved methods a considerable portion of the original oil remains in the ground when pumping becomes unprofitable and the

477

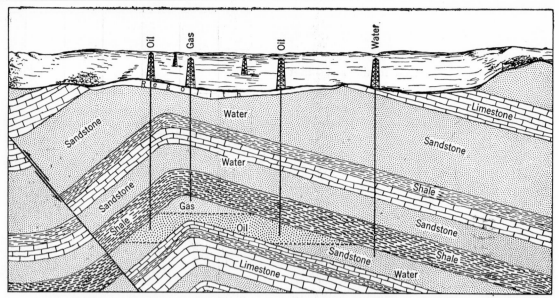

Fig. 23.13 A diagram to illustrate one of many types of geological structures in which petroleum is entrapped. It shows also the relation between the locations of several wells and the nature of their products. The existence of this buried anticlinal structure is not evident from the surface relief.

wells are abandoned. With poor methods, no more than 15 or 20 per cent of the oil may be recovered.

The manner of occurrence of oil and gas has an important geographic consequence. Because the structures suitable for petroleum collection commonly are small and deeply buried (some of them more than 2 miles below the surface), it often is impossible accurately to predict their exact location and extent or even their presence. When one structure is found in a region, it seldom is possible to predict how many others may be found nearby and still less possible to estimate the volume or value of their contents. Confident appraisal of the petroleum reserves of the nation or of the world is, therefore, not so readily made as in the case of coal resources. It must suffice, in the evaluation of the importance of petroleum and gas as elements of regional equipment, for the student to become acquainted with those fields which have either present importance or proved resources for the near future.

Of the sedimentary basin areas of the world that are possible sources of oil, four are considered especially likely to contain large oil reserves. These are (a) the Middle East, *i.e.*, the region enclosed by the eastern Mediterranean, the Red, Black, and Caspian Seas, and the Persian Gulf; (b) the regions bordering the Gulf of Mexico and the Caribbean Sea; (c) Indonesia and other nearby areas in the Far East; and (d) the areas surrounding the Arctic Sea. The first three are important oil producers, and exploration is increasing in the last area. If the world be divided into the conventional Western and Eastern Hemispheres, the estimated reserves of each are unequally divided in the approximate proportion of two to one, the larger being in the Eastern Hemisphere.

WESTERN HEMISPHERE OIL AND GAS FIELDS

23.22 Fields in the United States. Nature has endowed the United States with several regions in which petroleum and gas are found, and the production and consumption of those fuels in the United States far exceed that of any other country. This country produces nearly 50 per cent of the world's oil, but unfortunately it is credited with a much smaller percentage of the world's reserves. Each of the regions includes a number of subdivisions, or

478

fields, and many localities in which are found individual oil structures, the total number of which is great. In some of the structures both oil and gas are found together; some yield oil but not much gas, and others yield gas alone. In every productive field also are structures that already have yielded all that they are capable of producing economically, and they have been abandoned. There are some that have passed the maximum of production, and still others that are now at the peak of their productive lives. Doubtless there are, in most of the fields, additional pools which remain undiscovered and hold a reserve for the future. The active life of most pools is relatively short, and already some of the fields have declined in production until they are but minor factors in the national output. The question of how long the United States can maintain its present abundant petroleum production is not capable of assured answer. A feverish search goes on for new pools or for new structures at greater depths, or even for new fields in relatively unproductive areas such as Alabama and Florida. More than 40,000 new wells are drilled annually, and the proven reserves of the country have been increasing a little each year. In 1947, for the first time, United States imports of petroleum and its products exceeded exports, and the demand continues to increase rapidly. The need for conservative practices in the production and use of these essential products is evident.

The several principal regions of oil and gas

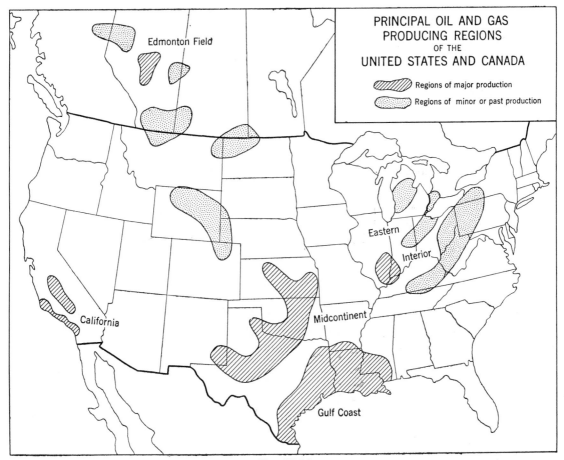

Fig. 23.14

production are indicated in Fig. 23.14. They are, from east to west, the Appalachian, Eastern Interior, Mid-Continent, Gulf Coast, Rocky Mountain, and California regions. The states in the Mid-Continent and Gulf Coast regions have long been the most productive and contain the greatest proven reserves. They are followed by California. The Gulf Coast region is estimated to have the largest proportion of the nation's total.

23.23 *The Appalachian Region.* The first oil and gas field to be developed on a modern scale was in the Allegheny region of America. That region was for many years the most productive in the world. The fuels are obtained from many fields, and pools are found in the early Paleozoic rocks (mainly sandstones) which incline gently westward from the highlands. They extend intermittently from western New York to Tennessee, and the region, as a whole, is of greater extent than the important coal field which includes younger and higher rocks that are found in the same general area. Petroleum from the Appalachian field is noted for its superior quality as a source of lubricating oils, which involves low sulphur content, ease of refining, and the fact that it leaves a residue of paraffin rather than asphalt. Some gas is found in association with oil in most of the pools of this field, but also there are many pools of gas with which no oil is found. The most productive part of the field is its central portion, located in southwestern New York, western Pennsylvania, and northern West Virginia. Although its yields of oil still are considerable, it has passed, many years since, the peak of its productivity. Much natural gas remains, however—a resource of vital importance for household and industrial use in the region— and it is closely related to the growth of certain types of manufacture there.

23.24 *The Eastern Interior Region.* Fields of importance are located in Ohio, Indiana, Illinois, and Michigan. The Michigan fields are new but relatively small, while the others, formerly of great importance, have declined. The greatest of them is that which lies in southeastern Illinois and adjacent Indiana. Formerly

it yielded oil of high quality and a large quantity of gas, but the latter resource has dwindled also.

23.25 *The Mid-Continent region* includes several widely scattered fields and hundreds of pools in Kansas, Oklahoma, central and western Texas, southeastern New Mexico, southern Arkansas, and northern Louisiana. Petroleum, of both paraffin and asphaltic types, is found in abundance through a series of rocks covering a wide range of geologic time. This region has been producing for many years. Many of its pools have been exhausted, but new ones have been discovered, and the practice of deeper drilling has reached oil in older rocks at lower horizons. Gas is abundant in this region also. However, owing to small urban population and slight industrial development, there is but limited local market for gas, and much of it has been wasted. Pipe lines now carry gas from west Texas to industrial consumers far to the north and east (Fig. 29.9).

23.26 *The Gulf Coast region* includes numerous pools found in the young rocks of eastern Texas, southern Arkansas, Louisiana, and Mississippi. In some areas the deposits are associated with a large number of salt domes, or mounds underlain by rock salt. The deposits also extend out into the continental shelf and considerable offshore development is likely, although the cost of such recovery is of course much greater than on land. The Gulf Coast area is becoming increasingly important as a United States producer.

23.27 *The Rocky Mountain region* is comprised of many fields distributed over a large area which is mainly in Wyoming, although it extends northward into Montana, south into Colorado, and eastward into North Dakota.

On the far northern coast of Alaska there are indications of petroleum also. The United States government has created there a reservation, 35,000 square miles in extent, whose future production is to be held for the use of the naval forces. Some wells have been drilled, but the oil reserves of the region are unknown.

23.28 *The California Region.* The oil and gas fields of California are distributed over a belt that extends from the environs of Los Angeles northward toward San Francisco. Some of the fields are located in the plains and hills of the southern California piedmont district, some in the San Joaquin Valley and the Coast Ranges, and others on the very shoreline itself. As a whole, the California region is highly productive and as a state it ranks second only to Texas in importance. Its oils mainly are heavy and of the asphaltic type.

23.29 Canadian Oil Fields. Until recently oil production in Canada was restricted to small amounts produced in Ontario in the section north of Lake Erie, in southern Alberta, and in the Mackenzie River basin west of Great Bear Lake. With the discovery of the Leduc field south of Edmonton in 1947, Canada began to increase her production and reserves. Recent estimates place Canadian reserves and production ahead of Indonesia and Mexico and exceeded only by the United States, Venezuela, the U.S.S.R., and the Middle Eastern countries. Most of the production is in Alberta and

extends into British Columbia to the northwest and into Saskatchewan and Manitoba to the southeast. There is every reason to believe that Canadian status in the world oil situation will rise.

23.30 Caribbean Region. Bordering the Caribbean Sea are two productive oil regions (Fig. 23.15). One of them, on the coast of Mexico, includes fields near Tampico and Túxpam. These began to yield abundantly early in the present century and for some years gave Mexico second rank among the oil-producing countries of the world. They now have passed the peak of their productivity, and although the output still is considerable, Mexico has only about 1 per cent of the world's proven reserves.

A second, and much more important, region includes several fields distributed along the northern coast of South America, mainly in the Maracaibo and Orinoco basins of Venezuela, with smaller regions in Colombia and the island of Trinidad. Venezuela has perhaps 8 per

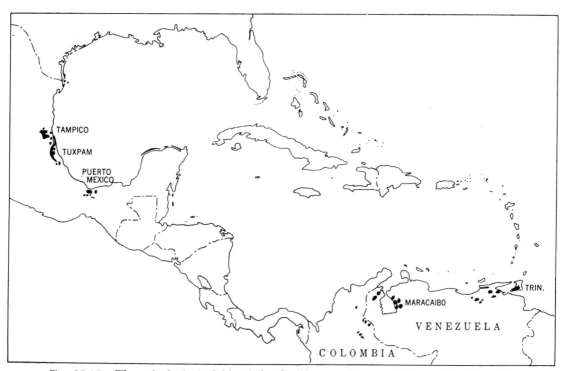

Fig. 23.15 The principal oil fields of the Caribbean region are in Venezuela, Colombia, and eastern Mexico.

cent of the world's known reserves and ranks
next after the United States among the countries of the world in production. Seepage and
evaporation of volatile constituents from an
ancient pool in Trinidad gave rise to the famous asphalt lake of that island, where hardened asphalt, removed from the surface, is replaced by the slow upwelling of new supplies
from beneath.

23.31   South America, beyond the Caribbean borders, gives some evidence of widespread occurrence of petroleum. Of the several
countries, only Argentina and Peru now have
important production. However, their combined output is less than that of Mexico.

EASTERN HEMISPHERE
OIL AND GAS FIELDS

23.32   General Distribution. The presence
of oil and gas is known in many localities in
Europe, Asia, Africa, and Australia through
producing wells or natural seepages of gas, oil,
or tar. However, Africa and Australia have no
proven reserves of significance. Fields of large
present output or such as give assurance of
great future importance are confined to Europe
or to Asia and its bordering islands.

It is of great significance that although the
financial interests of the leading west-European
countries control supplies of petroleum elsewhere, not one of those countries contains within its own borders any significant petroleum
supply, and the same seems to be true of China
and Japan. The largest present output and the
greatest known reserves lie in three regions:
(*a*) southeastern Europe, especially southern
Russia; (*b*) the Persian Gulf region; and (*c*)
the East Indies.

**23.33   The Oil Fields of Southeastern Eu-
rope and Southern U.S.S.R.** New but relatively
small production has been developed in France,
the Netherlands, Hungary, Austria, and West
Germany, and some oil has been produced for
many years in Poland, but it has declined in
importance. The Ploesti fields of Rumania
achieved great fame during the Second World
War because of the struggle for their control
as a source of supply for Germany. Rumania

is still the leading producer in Europe outside
the U.S.S.R., but its production has declined
greatly and its reserves are small.

The oldest, most persistent, and most productive fields in Europe are in southeastern
Russia adjacent to the Ural and Caucasus
Mountains and the Caspian Sea. Of several
fields in this region those near Baku (on the
peninsula of Apsheron), Grozny (north of the
Caucasus), the middle Volga, and Turkistan
are most productive (Fig. 23.16). Oil from
the first two of those fields enabled Russia to
lead the world in production until the opening of the present century. Although its output is about one-fifth that of the United States,
Russia produces more than 75 per cent of all
the oil of Europe and is the largest single oil
producer among the political divisions of the
Eastern Hemisphere. Its potential reserves are
extensive and range from the Caucasus region
to the Far Eastern island of Sakhalin, north
of Japan. The proven reserves of the U.S.S.R.
total less than 8 per cent of those of the world,
but estimates of potential reserves run as high
as 24 per cent.

23.34   The Oil Fields of Southern Asia. The
oil fields of southwestern Asia, or the Middle
East, are located mainly in Iran, Iraq, Saudi
Arabia, Kuwait, and smaller political subdivisions near the Persian Gulf (Fig. 23.16). These
areas, taken together, produce less than one-
half as much oil as the United States but considerably more than the U.S.S.R. However, the
proven reserves of the region are large, nearly
50 per cent of the world's known supply. That
is more than the proven reserves of the United States and the U.S.S.R. together. These
facts help to explain why so many problems
of world politics and economic strategy originate in or near this part of Asia.

The known petroleum reserves of southeastern Asia are smaller in size but by no means
unimportant. They are widely scattered, the
more important being in the Indonesian region, especially Sumatra, British Borneo, Burma, and New Guinea. These have total proven
reserves of less than 2 per cent of the world's
known supply.

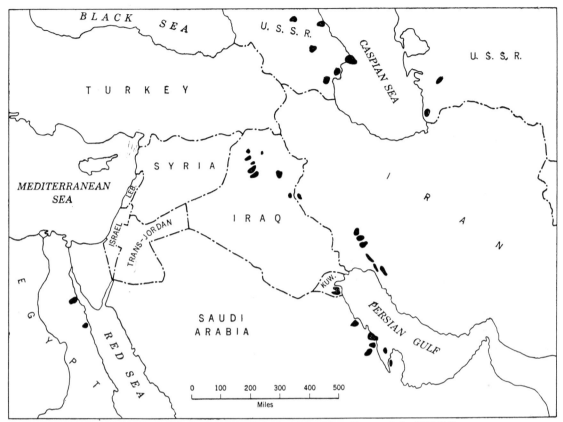

Fig. 23.16 The principal oil fields of the Near East and the U.S.S.R.

SUPPLEMENTARY OIL RESOURCES

23.35 Oil Shales and Sands. The recovery of petroleum from underground ceases when the flow has decreased to the point where the cost of pumping exceeds the value of the oil recovered. It has already been noted that when wells are abandoned much oil still remains underground but it cannot now be economically recovered. This stage has already been reached in so many pools in the United States that, although new discoveries maintain the supply at a high level, fears are expressed concerning the future. The sources from which synthetic oils could be obtained are oil shales, sands, and coal.

In the United States and elsewhere, large supplies of oil-yielding organic matter are contained in compact shales and loose sands. The material does not flow and hence cannot be removed by pumping. Petroleum has been obtained from such sources in the United States and elsewhere. However, the cost of production is high, because the material must first be quarried or mined and then treated, before the crude oil, such as now flows from wells, can be obtained. For the future, there are large supplies of oil shale in the western United States, especially in Wyoming and Colorado, and tar sands in the Athabaska region of Canada. Oil and gasoline substitutes can be produced also from coal by subjecting it to various chemical processes. This was done in Germany on a large scale during the Second World War, but it also is relatively costly. In any case, these sources will be expedients adopted only to supplement a failing oil supply.

24

Ores and Other Economic Minerals

24.1 Classes of Mineral Resources. In addition to water and the mineral fuels, the earth provides many inorganic substances for human use. In the list are the raw materials of a wide array of industries. The substances are of great diversity and include some as different from each other as the crude rocks and sand used in road construction are different from the fine metals and gems that enter into the making of an expensive watch. The mineral resources drawn upon to supply these needs may be grouped, according to the purpose for which they are produced and the manner of their treatment, into (*a*) the ores of the metallic minerals and (*b*) the solid, nonmetallic, nonfuel minerals. Those of the first group are prepared for use by treating with one of several processes of mechanical concentration or chemical reduction, and from them the metals are obtained. Those of the second group sometimes are used practically as they come from the earth. The list of the metals is a long one, but that of the nonmetals is longer. In the latter are rocks, sand and gravel, clays, lime, salines, fertilizers, abrasives, gems, and many others.

The Metallic Minerals

24.2 The Importance of Metalliferous Ores. Before the beginning of written history men knew the value of certain metals and sought the materials from which they might be obtained. Copper and tin were alloyed to produce bronze, which was harder than either of its components. Gold and silver also were highly prized, as they are now. Later came the use of iron and other metals such as manganese, chromium, nickel, tungsten, molybdenum, and vanadium. Some of these are used separately in the arts and specific industries, while others are combined with each other, and especially with iron, in a number of industrially important alloys. Without these alloy steels modern high-speed metalworking machines and efficient technological processes would be impossible.

Of the many metals concerned, a considerable number may be classed as precious or semiprecious. These are used in relatively small quantities. While the existence of a supply of one of them, such as gold, silver, chromium, or tungsten, is important to many industries, and economically important to the region in which it occurs, it can hardly be called a basic mineral resource. The very smallness of the volume of output of each of them and the limited quantity required, coupled with high specific value, enable these and similar metals to move freely in the channels of international trade, unless tariffs and restrictive trade regulations are imposed to prevent it. In a sense, the whole world draws upon the same sources of supply. Even a distant country enjoys almost the same advantage from such a resource, except in time of war, as does the country in which it is produced. A few metals that are used in large quantities, especially iron, may be thought of as fundamental resources. This is particularly true if they occur in close proximity to supplies of the fuel needed to smelt them. So much of iron and its ores is required, and they are of such comparatively low specific value, that they do not move in the channels of international trade with the same ease as do those of the other class. They do, indeed, move to some extent, but the possession of a domestic supply of iron ore is considered always, next to a supply of coal or petroleum, a matter of major economic importance by the great nations.

In the world of modern industry, therefore, ores of the metals, precious and nonprecious, are elements of great significance in the complex of things that go to make up the natural equipment of regions. Because of that fact, it is necessary for the student of geography to grasp at least the fundamentals of those earth conditions upon which the presence or absence of valuable ores is likely to depend, and to know the broad features of the world distribution of the most important of these substances.

24.3 The Common Physical Associations of Ore Deposits. An ore deposit is a concentration of a metallic mineral, or one of its chemical compounds, sufficiently rich in the metal so that it is profitable to use it. Some metals, *e.g.,* gold and copper, are found sometimes in a metallic, or "native," state. More commonly the metallic elements occur in chemical combination with other elements in the form of sulphides, sulphates, oxides, carbonates, and other compounds, from which they must be set free by processes of reduction called *smelting.* Usually, also, the valuable compounds are intermingled with some quantity of rock or earthy material, called *gangue,* from which they must be separated by mechanical means.

The local concentration of minerals by natural processes into ores of profitable quality is believed to have come about in several different ways, which may be touched upon here only because they have to do with the distribution of regions of mineral occurrence. Some, for example, appear to have originated at the same time as the igneous rocks in which they are found, but to have separated from them while yet in the liquid molten state because they were heavier or for various other reasons. Others seem to have been thinly distributed in the original rocks and to have separated out later through some process of concentration, especially by the slow chemical work of ground water.

Traces of metallic minerals are found in many rocks, both igneous and sedimentary. In liquid igneous intrusions it is possible, as has been stated, for molecules of like kind to come together and separate from the parent mass during the slow process of cooling. However, when valuable minerals are distributed through solid rocks, they are more likely to be concentrated by the work of solutions. This may come about as a result of several processes which, in general, do either one of two things: (*a*) Some solutions may contain molecules of a valuable mineral, and perhaps others as well, bring them together, and deposit them in greatly enriched zones. The deposition may take place in cavities, thus forming such features as mineral veins, or it may take place by a process of replacement, similar to that of petrification. (*b*) The work of solution may largely remove the rock minerals associated with those having valuable properties, leaving the latter behind in greatly concentrated or enriched form. While these processes may be accomplished by the ordinary cold waters of the ground, it is likely that the result has commonly been brought about by the steam and hot waters associated with igneous intrusions. Hot water is active chemically, and such water is likely to contain gases and solutions derived from the molten masses, which themselves may contain some of the valuable minerals or may bring about chemical changes in the rocks with which they come in contact.

It is not surprising, in view of the foregoing facts, that rich mineral ores are more often found (*a*) in regions that have at some time been affected by igneous intrusions, (*b*) in regions of crystalline rock where the processes of metamorphism have been accompanied by great pressure and the development of heat, or (*c*) in regions where both igneous activity and metamorphism have operated together. This association of conditions clearly has an important relation to the world patterns of distribution of the metallic mineral resources. Although there are some notable exceptions, it is broadly true that the great areas of undisturbed sedimentary rocks are poor in the ores of metals.

This is exactly the opposite of the relationship found to exist in connection with coal and petroleum. Conversely, it is true that the principal areas of ancient crystalline rocks, the bases of old worn-down mountains, and regions of young complex mountains are likely to have localities in which mineral ores may be found. Ore deposits are more often discovered in mountain regions not merely because of the existence there of more of the conditions favorable to their formation but also because of conditions favorable to their discovery. The vigorous erosion characteristic of mountains tends to dissect the rock structures and to lay open to view those associations of physical features and rock composition by which the prospector for minerals learns to recognize the existence of ores.

IRON ORES AND THEIR DISTRIBUTION

24.4 The Physical Associations of Iron Ores. With the exception of aluminum, iron is the most abundant of the metallic minerals in the rocks of the earth. Because it is so easily oxidized, or rusted, it is seldom found in metallic form but in some chemical combination. The more important of these are the oxides named hematite, magnetite, and limonite, and the carbonate named siderite. The oxides are particularly abundant, and they are scattered widely but thinly through a large part of the regolith and give the common red, brown, or yellow colors to it. Ordinary earth has not enough iron in it to make it profitable for use as an ore. Pure hematite and magnetite contain as much as 70 per cent of metallic iron, but large deposits of ore seldom are pure, since they contain admixtures of gangue minerals, especially silica. Some are known, however, that yield large amounts of ore containing 55 or more per cent of its weight in iron. Most of the ore used in the world must, in order to be profitable under present economic conditions, contain more than 30 or 35 per cent of iron. Some iron ores contain objectionable elements, for example, phosphorus or sulphur, which if chemically combined with the ore are difficult to remove in the smelting process.

Although iron is a very abundant metal, the distribution of usable ores of iron is somewhat limited and is a matter of national concern. Those deposits of largest present value are (*a*) high in metallic iron, (*b*) low in objectionable impurities, (*c*) capable of being inexpensively mined, and (*d*) situated so that they may be transported cheaply to regions where the other necessary ingredients of iron manufacture are easily assembled near a large market for iron and steel. Few iron-ore deposits meet all those requirements. Some, which meet enough of them, have attained international importance and should be known. Among the outstanding deposits, measured by their present contributions to the world's iron industries, are those of the United States, Canada, Venezuela, the western European countries of France, Great Britain, Sweden, and Germany, and those of the U.S.S.R. Others of smaller present or large potential importance require consideration also.

24.5 The Iron Ores of the United States. In the United States much more iron ore is mined and used than in any other country in the world. This is in part made possible by the high quality, ease of mining, and convenient location of some of the ores of the Lake Superior region. There are in that region, which includes parts of northern Minnesota, Wisconsin, and Michigan, several bodies of ore (Fig. 24.1). All of them, however, are found in the ancient crystalline rocks of the Laurentian Shield, which in that region extends southward from the principal area of those rocks in Canada. Furthermore, there are several other bodies of usable ore in the United States besides those of the Lake Superior district.

24.6 *The Lake Superior ores* are hematite of a desirable grade. Although the region contains large quantities of low-grade ore in which the proportions of silica and other gangue minerals are high, those mined up until recent years were very rich, the average iron content being about 55 per cent. Quite as important in the development of the American steel industry is the fact that these ores are unusually low in phosphorus. Because of their relative purity

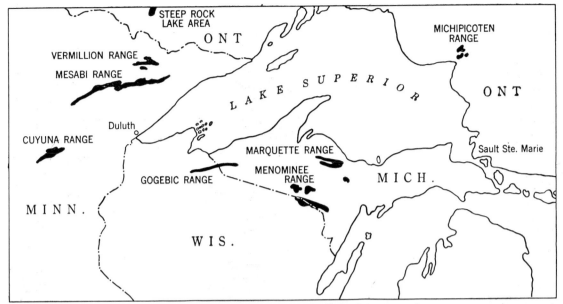

Fig. 24.1   The iron-ore ranges of the Lake Superior region.

in this respect they could be used in the manufacture of steel by the rapid and cheap bessemer process, which played an important part in the development of the American industry. It has largely been supplanted now by other processes which are able to deal with ores of higher phosphorous content.

The physical situation of the Lake Superior ores is as great an advantage as is their chemical composition. They have been concentrated in the ancient rocks by the work of ground waters and lie in pockets which, in general, are near the surface. Particularly in that district of northern Minnesota called the Mesabi Range, the most accessible and highest-grade ores were included in a broad and shallow structural trough covered only by an overburden of glacial drift. When the overburden was stripped away, the ore could be removed from open pits by power shovels loading directly into railway cars (Fig. 24.2). This has been the most productive iron-ore body in the world. Open-pit mining has been possible in limited parts of some of the other Lake Superior ranges also. However, rapidly increasing requirements and the hurried demands of two world wars have drawn so heavily upon these sources that it is realized that the reserves of

rich open-pit ores are clearly exhaustible. In the other Lake Superior ranges considerable good ore is mined underground from deposits broken and displaced by faults, but underground mining is a much slower and more difficult process. It should not be inferred that the ores of present commercial quality are likely to be depleted in a decade or less. On the contrary, they will continue to be produced for several decades. It is desirable, however, that alternative sources be utilized as much as possible in order to conserve the unusually accessible and convenient Lake Superior ores. One alternative source is the mineral called taconite.

There are in the Lake Superior region enormous tonnages of taconite. This is the parent rock from which the richer ores were derived by natural processes of enrichment through the removal of silica by the solvent action of underground waters. Taconite yields both hematite and magnetite, but its iron content is only about 25 to 35 per cent as compared with the 50 to 60 per cent found in the rich ores now nearing exhaustion. These low-grade ores are not suitable for direct shipment. The rock must first be quarried and crushed and then put through processes of concentration to separate

Fig. 24.2 Mining iron ore in an open pit in northern Minnesota. Open-pit ore of high quality is no longer abundant in the Lake Superior region. (*Courtesy of the Oliver Iron Mining Company.*)

the iron-bearing material from the silica before it can be transported economically. The processes by which the taconite is beneficiated into concentrates containing some 60 per cent iron have been perfected, and this enormous reserve is beginning to be used on more than an experimental scale.

The relation of the Lake Superior ores to regions of manufacture and market is fortunate. The construction of canals connecting Lakes Superior and Huron, at Sault Sainte Marie, provided a deep waterway for the transportation of ore almost from the mine to the very margin of the Appalachian coal field and the heart of the American industrial region (Fig. 29.12). Special devices and carriers for handling the ore have reduced the cost of transportation to a very low figure. For many years more than three-fourths of the iron ores mined in the United States have come from the several districts of the Lake Superior region.

24.7 *Other United States ores* are available in many localities, but mainly the deposits

contain only limited reserves. Those now most in use are located in Alabama and New York. Among the sedimentary rocks of the Folded Appalachians are discontinuous beds of iron ore which are found in localities from New York to central Alabama. These ores are most used in Alabama, where they are mined in the same district with the coal and limestone required in smelting them (Fig. 24.3). They are of relatively low grade, since they yield only about 35 per cent iron. Other considerable deposits of ore, hematite and magnetite, are known in the Adirondack Mountains of New York and at various places in the interior states, the Rocky Mountain and other western localities, especially Utah and California.

24.8 **Other Western Hemisphere Reserves of Iron Ore.** Iron ore moves so cheaply by water that even the ample United States supply has not prevented some foreign ores from moving to meet abundant coal upon the eastern seaboard for smelting there. Most of these limited imports come from other North or South

American sources, chiefly from Venezuela, Canada, Peru, and Chile in that order.

Canada has the larger part of the ice-scoured rocks of the Laurentian Shield, but until recently it was not known to contain such large and easily mined ore deposits as those in Minnesota. Some of considerable value have been mined in districts both west and east of Lake Superior, but a more productive deposit is that mined underground on a small island near St. John's, Newfoundland. The reserve in this deposit is hematite and is large, and the ore yields over 50 per cent iron, but it is high in phosphorus. However, it has easy access to water transportation, has been smelted near the coal deposits at Sydney, Nova Scotia, and some has been shipped to British and European markets.

A most important ore deposit, recently discovered, lies in the region on the boundary between eastern Quebec and Labrador. This seems to be one of the world's great reserves. Much of it is hematite with an iron content exceeding 60 per cent and so situated that open-pit mining may be practiced. However, the region is far inland, and to get ore from it to the United States coal and established smelting centers requires a journey of 360 miles by railroad to the north shore of the Gulf of St. Lawrence and then by water and rail transport inland or to the centers on the east coast.

Venezuela supplies nearly a third of the increasing iron-ore imports into the United States. The deposits of high-grade ore are located near the Orinoco River, and it is sent by ocean-going ore carriers to the eastern United States.

Other South American deposits are located in Peru about 300 miles south of Lima and in north central Chile, both of which produce several million tons per year. Some ore is also produced in Brazil, Mexico, Argentina, and Cuba. Although Brazil does not now compete with Peru and Chile in the export of ore, it has a remarkable supply which, for several physical and economic reasons, is not now producing much commercially. The ore fields lie more than 200 miles north of Rio de Janeiro in the ancient crystalline rocks of the Brazilian plateau. They include a number of localities which contain ore bodies of the highest quality, some hematite, some magnetite, and they comprise one of the great and rich reserves of iron ore in the world.

24.9 Western European Iron-ore Deposits. The iron industries of western Europe depend mainly upon European sources of ore. Like those of North America, the greatest centers of iron manufacture are located in, or close to, the principal coal fields. In only a few places are the ore and coal found together; hence, one or the other must usually be transported. In the United States they move freely by water over the Great Lakes, and generally, the ore moves to, or toward, the coal. In one particular respect the European situation is different. Although some of the countries contain both iron ore and coking coal, the numerous political boundaries of western Europe have separated some of the more important deposits, and much of the ore, especially the high-grade ore, has had to move in international trade to reach the principal smelting centers. The large iron resources are in France, Great Britain, and Sweden. That of Sweden is less in quantity

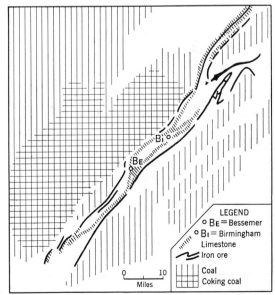

Fig. 24.3 Distribution of essential minerals in the Birmingham, Ala., industrial region.

than those of the other two but superior in quality. Other important sources of ore are found in Germany and Spain. Those of Germany are not adequate to the large needs of the country, but those of northern Spain, a country of little coal, have provided ore for export to England and other countries until some of the deposits are nearly exhausted.

The iron ores of France include the largest single iron reserve in Europe and one of the large ones in the world. They are found in the northeastern part of the country in the province of Lorraine and extend across the boundary into Luxembourg and slightly into Belgium (Fig. 24.4). At various times part of this area has been under German political control. But whether under French or German control, these ores have contributed in some degree to the development of the German iron and steel industry. The Lorraine ores are mainly limonite and of relatively low grade, since they average only about 30 to 40 per cent of iron. However, they lie near the German, Belgian, and French coal fields and the great industrial mar-

ket of Europe. They are high in phosphorus, but a special process of steel manufacture extracts that undesirable element and makes from it a valuable by-product fertilizer.

The iron ores of Great Britain are fairly abundant but are scattered, of different kinds, and mainly of low grade. It has long been the practice of British smelters to supplement the domestic supply with other ores, especially the better grades imported from Sweden, Spain, North Africa, Newfoundland, and elsewhere. However, of domestic low-grade ores Britain has a supply sufficient for many years, and economy is enforcing a greater dependence upon them. They are distributed in several localities, the larger reserves being in eastern England (Fig. 23.8). They are closely associated with supplies of coal and limestone.

The iron ores of Sweden are only moderately abundant, but the principal deposits are noted for their high quality. They are mainly magnetite and average 55 to 65 per cent iron. The largest and best deposits are situated in the crystalline rocks of the far-northen part of the country. Since there is almost no coal and but little iron manufacture in Sweden, the ores are exported, in normal times, to Germany, Britain, and other European countries.

24.10   Iron-ore Deposits in the U.S.S.R. The U.S.S.R. has large reserves of good iron ore, the more important of which are found in three localities. These are Krivoi Rog, in the southern Ukraine, the Kerch peninsula in the Crimea, and Magnitogorsk, at the southern end of the Ural Mountains. The first named is the richest deposit and normally the most productive. It is located about 300 miles west of the Donets coal basin, with which it is associated in the development of the Ukrainian region of heavy industry. The ores at Magnitogorsk are not well associated with local coal, but a great expansion of industry there was enforced during the Second World War, coal being supplied from the several small deposits farther north in the Ural region and from the distant Kuznetsk and Karaganda fields in Siberia (Fig. 23.9). Smaller iron-ore deposits in eastern

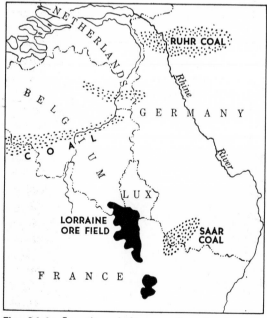

Fig. 24.4 Location of the great Lorraine iron-ore field of France with respect to coal fields.

Asiatic Russia are used locally in the development of an independent industrial economy there.

24.11 Other Significant Iron-ore Deposits. Through the vast expanses of Africa, Asia, and Australia iron-ore deposits are known to exist in many places. Some of them now produce in sufficient quantity to provide abundantly for local industry, as do those of southern Australia, for example. It is probable that in localities as yet imperfectly explored other, and perhaps significant, resources may be found. However, of all the many iron-ore deposits known, only one appears so great as to rank among the major sources of iron in the world. That one is in India. It lies adjacent to the principal, but not highly productive, coal field of the country in a district about 150 miles west of Calcutta. The ores are hematite of high iron content; they are of great extent and are so near the surface that some at least are capable of being mined in open pits.

24.12 Significant Facts about the Iron Resource. Iron is the most important metal in the present-day world, and it is the second most abundant. Moreover, scattered over the earth are many places where there are ores of some present or future significance as sources of the metal. Of these many deposits only a few have now any great importance. Much the larger number have little present value because they are (*a*) small, (*b*) remote, (*c*) low in iron content, (*d*) far from a source of coke, or (*e*) combined with substances that increase the difficulty and cost of smelting them. Which of the deposits of present low importance may achieve future prominence cannot be predicted, because of the possibility that new methods of manufacture of iron may be developed in the future.

However, since iron at present must be reduced from the ore by the use of certain grades of coal in the form of coke, it is important to consider in what parts of the world these two ingredients are found close together. The distribution of the world's plains is such that they contribute to the commercial supremacy of the Atlantic Ocean. One reason for that supremacy may be noted here. The only world regions in which abundant deposits of iron ore and of coking coal are known to be closely associated lie on the borders of the North Atlantic Basin. These include eastern United States, the countries of northwestern Europe, and the U.S.S.R. In them are the present world centers of heavy iron and steel manufacture and of many other industries that depend on cheap iron and steel. There seems good geographic basis for believing that those centers will long continue, because no others appear to have better natural endowment or more advantageous situation. Some of the world's greatest reserves of ore are in Brazil and India, but the former has little, and the latter has only a limited supply of, coking coal. China has large reserves of excellent coal but no known supply of ore of comparable importance. Also, it may be noted, Japan, which strove to be a progressive industrial nation and a first-class military power, has but limited domestic supplies of coal and even less iron ore of usable grade. With respect to the basic raw materials for iron and steel manufacture the situation of the United States has indeed been fortunate.

OTHER METALLIC MINERALS

24.13 Important Nonferrous Metals. The list of metals that have importance in modern arts and industries is so long that adequate descriptions of their several uses and regions of occurrence might well produce more confusion than enlightenment. In any case it would require more space than is available here. Instead, comment will be restricted to a few of the more important metals and to the locations of the major world regions that are noted for their important productions and possible reserves of the precious and semiprecious metals. Of these the most significant are copper, aluminum, magnesium, the ferroalloys, and the metals used as sources of atomic energy.

A great variety of earth conditions is favorable to the occurrence and discovery of the ores of the several metals here included. The generally favorable conditions have been discussed (24.3), and it needs only to be reiterated that the principal world regions of mineralization are those of ancient crystalline rocks, or of more recent crustal disturbances, or of igneous activity. Although this is true in a general way, it is a rule that has notable exceptions. One type of exception is found in the deposits of lead and zinc ores associated with sedimentary rocks. Examples of these are the lead and zinc deposits of southwestern Missouri, southwestern Wisconsin, and adjacent Illinois, or those of Belgium and Poland. Other exceptions of great importance are the ores of aluminum and magnesium.

24.14 Copper and Its Ores. Copper is the basis of the modern electrical world and is employed also as an alloying metal with several others. The uses of electricity are continually growing, and it is to be expected that the significance of copper will continue to grow.

Copper ores, although of great variety, are not widely distributed in commercially usable quantities, and none of the great industrial nations is self-sufficient in copper resources. In general, the ores are very low in metallic content and thus require considerable treatment. Their occurrence conforms to the generalization repeated above, namely, they occur in regions of crystalline rock or in areas of recent tectonic activity. The major known reserves are located in North America, South America, and Africa in that order, and among them they account for some three-quarters of the known copper resource.

North American copper reserves are located primarily in parts of the western cordilleran area of the United States and Canada. Major producing areas are Arizona, Utah, New Mexico, Montana, and Nevada. Other deposits are known in the Laurentian Shield area of northern United States and southern Canada. The United States produces approximately a third of the world's copper.

South American copper is concentrated in Chile and southern Peru with the former having perhaps the greatest single known deposit. In Africa copper is located in the Katanga region of Northern Rhodesia and in the adjacent southern Belgian Congo. Copper reserves elsewhere in the world are small, although those of the U.S.S.R. are estimated to be perhaps one-fourth as great as those of North America.

24.15 Aluminum and Magnesium. Aluminum, even more abundant than iron, is like iron in that it is a constituent of earthy minerals which are widely distributed in the regolith. It is a component of common clay and other substances, most of which are too low in grade to be utilized profitably. Only in a few places are there rich deposits of the earthy ore of aluminum, called *bauxite*. Varieties of this substance are of different origins, but it seems clear that some are derived from sedimentary clays that have been changed through long-continued leaching by ground water, whereas others are known to have been derived by a process of natural beneficiation of igneous rocks that originally were low in iron and silica. The notable deposits of the Ouachita Mountain region of Arkansas are of the latter type, whereas those of France are of sedimentary origin. Large reserves of bauxite available in Hungary, Yugoslavia, and France provide abundantly for European consumption, but the domestic reserves of the United States are not great, and much of the ore now consumed is imported from Surinam and Jamaica. Other deposits of bauxite are known in many parts of the world: British Guiana, Brazil, the Gold Coast in equatorial Africa, the East Indian region, China, and the U.S.S.R. It is significant that so little high-grade aluminum ore is known to exist in either the United States or Canada.

Magnesium, another of the light metals, and its alloys have been produced in quantity only in recent years. Fortunately its sources are many. They include magnesium-bearing rocks such as dolomite, brines obtained from vast underground salt beds, and even sea water. These sources are widely distributed over the earth, and the problems which concern magnesium production are mainly those of large-scale industrial organization rather than of possession of raw materials.

24.16 The Ferroalloys and Sources of Atomic Energy. The modern industrial world depends upon steel of various kinds made by alloying certain metals with iron. The list of iron alloys is long, containing such metals as nickel, tungsten, vanadium, and molybdenum, but the two in greatest demand are manganese and chromium. About 13 pounds of manganese are used in making each ton of steel in the United States, and since manganese ore of commercial quality is lacking in the United States, it must be imported. Deposits of manganese ore are found in the U.S.S.R., India, Union of South Africa, Gold Coast, Brazil, French Morocco, and a number of other areas. Chromium is also vital to the steel industry, and the United States is also lacking in commercial chromium ores. The largest reserves are in southern Africa, Turkey, the U.S.S.R., and the Philippines.

The opening of the age of atomic energy, in 1945, directed public attention toward the world distribution of uranium and thorium, the principal minerals from which fissionable materials are obtained. This is of the greatest concern. Both minerals are known to have fairly wide distribution in nature, but the rich deposits at present known are restricted in area. The critical deposits of uranium are located in the Belgian Congo, the region near Great Bear Lake in northern Canda, Czechoslovakia, and several localities in southwestern United States. Numerous other deposits, now believed secondary, may prove to be of major order. Thorium is derived from certain sands, the best of which are found in Brazil and India. However, lower-grade materials are widely distributed, some occurring in the United States.

24.17 Other Source Regions of Industrial Metals. Actual and potential resources of the precious and semiprecious industrial metals are only imperfectly known. Many have been discovered, worked out, and exhausted. Some have produced steadily for long periods of years. Many of the deposits of great value that have been discovered are of small areal extent, and their existence is not marked by obvious surface features. In some cases their discovery has been a matter of chance. Whether others like them exist and, if so, their number and future productiveness cannot be said. Changes in methods of ore reduction may, in the future, change centers of production and increase the available supply of metals. Large quantities are known of substances bearing copper, gold, and other metals which it is not now profitable to mine because the cost of mining and smelting them is greater than the present values of their products. That may not always be true. In any case, the areas in which new discoveries are likely to be made are of the type previously described (24.3). Some of these and the bases of their world importance are noted below.

The Laurentian Shield. One of the world regions highly productive of the metals, and one having large possibilities of future discoveries, is the Laurentian Shield. From the ancient crystalline rocks beneath its ice-scoured surface are obtained not only the rich iron ores of the several Lake Superior districts, Labrador, and Newfoundland, but also a wealth of other metals. These include most of the world's supply of nickel and large amounts of gold, silver, cobalt, copper, uranium, and others. Important discoveries are made in this extensive region each year, and the exploitation of mineral resources is one of the principal industries which have attracted the settlement of people there.

The American cordilleran region, from Alaska to Cape Horn, is one of the world regions noted for the abundance and variety of its mineral products. These include widely distributed bodies of ore, some of which have been practically exhausted while others still are in full production. Doubtless many others remain to be discovered or are reserved for a future time when new processes shall make them profitable. Valuable deposits of copper are found in the region in localties as far separated as Chile, Peru, Arizona, Montana, and Alaska and in many intermediate places. Gold, silver, lead, and zinc are sufficiently abundant so that Mexico, the United States, and Canada hold high rank in the production of each of them. The Andean countries of South America are important producers not only of copper but also of platinum, tin, and tungsten besides having an appreciable output of other metals. It was the gold of this region that gave impetus to its conquest by Spain.

Central and South Africa. The crystalline rocks of central and southern Africa include several productive mineral regions. Within that vast area are the Rand, the world's leading gold-producing district, and such important centers in the production of copper as those of the Katanga in Northern Rhodesia and the Belgian Congo. There are also districts producing chromium, manganese, and uranium, not to mention the leading localities from which diamonds are mined.

Other mineral regions of world renown may only be mentioned. Among them are the following: (*a*) Areas of igneous and crystalline metamorphic rocks in southern and western Australia which have yielded gold, silver, lead, zinc, and minor quantities of other metals. The exploitation of those mineral ores had much to do with the progress of exploration and settlement in Australia. (*b*) The crystalline rocks of the highlands of eastern South America, in Brazil and the Guianas. In addition to the large deposits of iron ore and bauxite, previously mentioned, these highlands yield important quantities of manganese, gold, and precious stones. They are known also to contain deposits of several other metals which are as yet little developed. (*c*) A large region of crystalline rocks in eastern Asia. They extend from Korea, on the south, to the shores of the Okhotsk Sea on the north and thence westward in southern Siberia through the regions of the Yablonoi Mountains, Lake Baikal, and the Sayan and Altai Mountains. From this region is obtained a large part of the gold that makes the U.S.S.R. one of the leading producers of that metal. It contains large areas that are as yet little explored geologically. (*d*) The highlands of southeastern Asia. From them are now obtained the larger part of the world's tin, tungsten, and several other metals. (*e*) The cordilleran region of southern Europe and the Mediterranean borders. In it are included important centers in the production of several metals. They are located in Spain, North Africa, Italy, Czechoslovakia, and the Caucasus district of southern Soviet Russia.

24.18   Summary. From the foregoing it may be concluded that the world's principal centers of actual and potential production of the precious and semiprecious metals are those of complex mountain structures or such as are associated with igneous or crystalline rocks. In contrast with those regions are several, the surfaces of which are comprised mainly of sedimentary rocks, which may be buried deeply beneath thick mantles of alluvium. Despite the fact that the regions of sedimentary rocks contain the world's supplies of mineral fuels and certain of the ores of iron, aluminum, lead, and zinc, they are, in general, poor in the ores of the precious and semiprecious metals.

Although the larger part of the ores of the metals are found in regions of ancient rocks or of mountain structures, it may not be safely concluded that all such regions are so endowed. It is probable that lack of detailed exploration in certain of those regions may explain their present lack of known ore deposits, but that is not true of all. For example, the crystalline Highlands of Scotland and the large areas of similar rocks in Scandinavia and Finland are known by geologists in much greater detail than are those of Canada or Africa. Similarly, the geology of the Alps is known in more minute detail than that of any other mountains of the world. Yet in neither of these regions are there many oustanding deposits of the precious and semiprecious metals.

The Nonmetallic, Nonfuel Minerals

24.19   Minerals for Many Uses. In addition to the mineral fuels there are produced from the earth more than 50 other nonmetallic minerals. Some of them are used in their natural states, while others pass through processes of industrial manufacture and appear as components in goods having hundreds of essential uses. Rocks, sands, clays, salts, abrasives, fertilizers, gems, and many others make up the list. Most of them are found in a variety of grades or qualities which have equally varied uses. They are essential parts of the natural equipment of regions, but no limited portion of the earth contains all of them. Indeed, there are few regions, if any, that contain all of even the most essential.

Because of the great number of these substances, many must be omitted from this brief treatment. Others, the more essential or those required in greater quantity, may be grouped for consideration under two major headings: (a) those used as raw materials in the chemical industries and (b) minerals used in making utensils or in construction. A few minerals, such as lime, belong in both classes.

MINERAL RAW MATERIALS FOR THE CHEMICAL INDUSTRIES

24.20 Salt is one of the common rock minerals of the earth. Owing to its solubility in water, it is not abundant in the zone of free ground-water circulation. Inexhaustible supplies are available for human use, however, from the following sources: (a) the sea, which contains $2\frac{2}{3}$ lb. of salt for every 100 lb. of water; (b) natural brines, which are the waters of ancient seas trapped in sediments, now deep underground, and cut off from ground-water circulation; (c) deposits of rock salt, which probably are precipitates from the evaporation of water in the arms of ancient seas or in former arid interior drainage basins. Those deposits now are sedimentary rocks deep underground, where they are protected by the other sediments from the solvent action of ground water. (d) Another limited source of supply is found in the surface encrustations of salt in the playa and similar deposits of the interior drainage basins of deserts.

Salt is used not only as a food and a preservative of food but also in large quantities in chemical industries. It is the basic raw material from which a number of the compounds of sodium are made. For industrial uses it is obtained largely by mining rock salt or by the pumping of brines, either natural brines or those produced by pumping water down to bodies of rock salt.

Primitive peoples in many regions have found it difficult to procure sufficient salt, even for their limited requirements. Yet salt is now so readily obtained and is found in so many places that few parts of the world are without some local supply. Industrial salt, however, comes mainly from a few sources.

Salt-producing Regions. The industrial regions of North America are supplied with salt, both rock salt and brine, from abundant reserves. Thick beds of rock salt underlie large areas in central and western New York, northeastern Ohio, southeastern Michigan, and peninsular Ontario. Other large reserves are found in the buried "salt domes" of the Louisiana-Texas Gulf Coast, in deposits in central Kansas, and at various places in the southwestern states.

The industrial centers of Europe likewise are well provided with salt. There are large deposits in western England, central Germany, Austria, and southern Soviet Russia. Other populous countries, especially China and India, also are large producers of salt.

24.21 Sulphur has many uses in modern industry, especially in the form of sulphuric acid and for various uses in connection with the manufacture of steel, oil, paper, rayon, rubber, explosives, and in other chemical industries. It has long been obtained from deposits associated with recent volcanic activity. Some still is mined from these sources in Italy, Spain, Japan, and Chile. In the United States, which now produces more than four-fifths of the world's supply, the principal deposits have no immediate volcanic connection. Instead, they are found in association with petroleum and the rock-salt deposits of the Louisiana-Texas coast. There native sulphur is recovered by means of wells through which superheated steam is pumped underground to the sulphur beds and molten sulphur is returned to the surface. This supply of easily obtained native sulphur is not unlimited, and alternative sources are being utilized to forestall what could be a critical shortage. Such sources are the recovery of sulphur from oil-refinery operations, and additional supplies are obtained as by-products from the smelting of certain mineral ores in which the metals are chemically combined with sulphur. Such are certain ores of iron, copper, and zinc.

24.22 The Mineral Fertilizers. Certain elements of soil fertility have been mentioned previously as being especially subject to depletion by crop production and by the leaching action of ground water. They are calcium, potash, phosphorus, and nitrogen. For each of these there are known sources of mineral supply which are drawn upon in the manufacture of commercial fertilizers. Some sulphur also is employed for the purpose. Soil lime, in the form of calcium carbonate, is readily available in the local limestones of many regions, and the location of supplies is not a matter of national concern. The other three are much less abundant, and notable deposits of them are items of earth resource of great importance.

Nitrogen is the most abundant element in the atmosphere, but it is inert and largely unavailable to plants in that form. It must be combined with some other element to form a soluble salt. This may be accomplished in a number of ways, and synthetic nitrogen production exceeds the production from natural sources. Until recently, however, the principal world supply was from mineral sources. Most important of these were the surface deposits of the desert of Atacama, in northern Chile. There, in areas of the salt-pan or playa type, are accumulations from ages of seepage and surface evaporation. The valuable mineral nitrate of soda is intermingled with sand, common salt, and other substances from which it is separated by a simple manufacturing process. So much in world demand was this mineral that, for many years, taxation upon its export was the principal financial resource of the Chilean government, and the business of its extraction and shipment supported a considerable population in the midst of a desert and in several seaports.

Potash[1] is a component of many plant tissues and is obtained in small quantities from

the ashes of wood, seaweed, and other substances. The principal commercial sources are complex minerals containing potash which are found in beds like rock salt, with which they are in some places associated. Large deposits are located in western Europe, mainly in central Germany and Alsace in northeastern France, where the greater part of the world's supply has, until recently, been obtained from mines 1,000 ft. or more beneath the surface. Deposits of potash minerals are known to exist in many areas. In the United States a very large reserve in New Mexico remained practically undeveloped until the Second World War cut off imports from Europe.

Phosphorus is present in certain rock minerals and from them is supplied to the soil. It is an indispensable constituent of all living cells. It must be supplied to all soils which are deficient in it, through the use of animal manures and mineral fertilizers. The principal mineral sources of phosphorus occur as calcium phosphates, mainly in rock form. This rock is believed to have been formed from the alteration of limestone by the chemical action of ground water which had passed through ancient accumulations of bird and fish remains.

Valuable beds of phosphate rock usually occur as local pockets in limestone strata and are known to exist in several parts of the world. The location of those most used is as much related to the regions of consumption as to the extent and richness of the deposits. The principal sources of supply for the European market are located near the Mediterranean coast of Africa in Tunisia, Algeria, and Morocco. The United States is largely supplied from extensive beds in western Florida and also from central Tennessee (Fig. 24.5). Other great reserves are known to exist in the northern Rocky Mountain region of the United States, in Russia, Siberia, and some of the islands of the Pacific Ocean.

CRUDE MINERALS FOR CONSTRUCTION AND UTENSILS

24.23 Rock for Construction. Many kinds of rock and large quantities of it are used in architectural and engineering structures. In

[1] *Potash* is a general term referring to primary potassium-bearing materials, but specifically refers to potassium oxide (K_2O).

Fig. 24.5 Mining phosphatic limestone for its phosphorous content, in central western Florida.

the form of cut stone, crushed rock, or gravels of stream or glacial origin, some material that will serve these purposes is found in most parts of the earth. It may seem that rock, in this broad sense, is one of the universal items of regional equipment, like the air. That, however, is not true. Some regions are endowed with rocks having unusual qualities of structure, strength, beauty of color, or ease of working. Others have none at all.

Because crude rock is heavy and of low value, it seldom moves far from its place of origin unless it has some particular quality to recommend it to a wider market. Regions in which rocks of special quality abound have, therefore, a valuable resource, especially if they also are near a large market for stone. Such a region is New England. There a vast quantity of crude rock, glacial boulders, and gravel is supplemented by special rocks in a region of igneous intrusion and metamorphosed sediments. Beautiful and massive granites, slates of parallel cleavage, and excellent marbles all are produced. The even-textured and easily worked gray limestones of southern Indiana have a national market, and some other stones of unique quality have practically world markets, such as the statuary marble of Italy.

A few regions of considerable size are practically devoid of rock. Among these are the great deltas of the world, where silt covers hundreds of square miles and rock is buried to great depths. Much larger are certain of the plains of older alluvium or the regions of deep loess accumulation. Among these is the loess- and alluvium-covered Pampa of Argentina and similar areas in the American Corn Belt, where older glacial drift and loess cover the rock strata deeply. In these regions are localities that do not even have any crude rock or gravel with which to surface roads.

24.24 Sands, Limes, and Clays for Industry. Sand, in crude form, enters largely into construction as an ingredient of concrete, mortar, and plaster. Also it shares with lime and clay a place of importance as a raw material of industry. Lime and clay are required in the manufacture of cement; clay is basic to the brick, tile, and pottery industries; and sand is the chief raw material in the manufacture of glass. These three substances are of common occurrence. There are, for example, river sands, beach sands, wind-blown sands, glaciofluvial sands, and pure sandstones. There are unconsolidated marls, soft chalks, and hard limestones. There are river clays, lacustrine clays, marine clays, residual clays, and shale rocks. Not many regions are without one or more of these minerals. However, qualities differ. Glacial lake clays may be good enough for the manufacture of ordinary brick and tile, but other uses have more particular requirements. Pottery clay, especially, must be pure and burn white in the kiln. It usually is found in residual deposits where it has weathered from coarsely crystalline feldspars. Good grades of glass sand, free from iron or clay, may be sought hundreds of miles from the centers of glass manufacture. Therefore, some regions gain advantage from natural endowments of sands, limes, or clays suited to particular requirements. Some, indeed, have achieved international fame through their products, such as that which attaches to the regions of pottery clays in southern England, northern France, or Bavaria.

PART TWO

Population

25

Population

25.1 The Place of Population in Geography. Population is neither a physical element of geography nor yet a cultural element, but instead occupies a unique position which sets it apart from all others. Geography, consequently, may be thought of having three primary groupings of its elements: (*a*) man who utilizes the resources of the physical earth and from them creates the cultural earth, (*b*) the physical earth which provides the natural environment in which a population operates and the resources which it uses, and (*c*) the cultural earth which is the product of man's creation out of the natural stuff.

In geographical science, whose central theme is the variety which characterizes the earth's surface, population is the pivotal element, for geography, to a large degree, is man-centered. Population is the point of reference from which the other elements are observed and from which they derive significance and meaning. It is population which furnishes the focus.

There are a number of sciences, such as geology, botany, zoology, meteorology, and soil science, each of whose specialized fields is responsible for one segment of the natural earth. Clearly, geography has no monopoly on the study of the physical earth. A uniqueness of physical geography is that it views the physical earth as the home of man and, to an important degree, selects its materials for study with man or population in mind. Stated somewhat differently, it is the *resource concept* which is to the forefront in physical geography. Here a distinction is being drawn between physical earth and natural resources, for the latter is always an expression of appraisal in terms of human usefulness. An earth without population lacks resources, for resources imply human wants. They are the physical earth in the service of man. Moreover, while the physical earth changes only very slowly, resources change as civilization changes. Coal is only a black rock to the native of Amazonia while to the west European it is a source of industrial power. It bears repeating, then, that even physical geography is man-oriented and hence closely related to population.

But if physical geography is somewhat humanistic in outlook because of the connection between the physical earth and population by means of the resource concept, the connection is even closer between the cultural earth and population. From the cultural features which embellish the earth's surface in almost limitless combinations can be read the chronicle of population, its ebb and flow, its accomplishments and defeats, for culture reflects the numbers, and even more precisely, the qualities of its creators. Thus the total culture within an area develops its unique and distinctive characteristics partly as a result of population numbers, which suggests intensity of use, but even more it reflects the socioeconomic qualities of the population. Quality of population, or stage of civilization, counts for more than mere numbers, and culture is more a product of men's minds than of their bodies.

The geographer's goal in any or all analyses of population is an understanding of the regional variations in the earth's covering of people. It is with their spatial or distributional aspects that he has particular concern. But this involves not only regional variations in numbers of people, including density and distribution patterns, but also the movements and migrations of population and its areal variations in quality as expressed through such attributes as health, race and nativity, age composition, literacy, religion, occupational status, stage of economic development, and the like.

Population Numbers

25.2 Numbers of People. That there are on the earth at present approximately 2.6 billion people probably is the most basic of all statistical facts. Compared with it data on area of cultivated land, tons of coal mined, or number of automobiles manufactured are in the nature of embroideries. Yet in spite of the unusual importance of the figure for total population it is nevertheless true that human life is not a very conspicuous element, for the total portion of the earth's surface actually occupied by the bodies of men is insignificantly small. In terms of mass and areal extensiveness, his material culture is ever so much more dominant in the geographic scene than is the creator of the culture. Van Loon, in his popular book on geography, emphasizes this relative insignificance of the quantity aspect of human life when he shows that the earth's more than 2,600,000,000 inhabitants could all be put into a single large cubical box measuring slightly more than $\frac{1}{2}$ mile on a side. Or, allowing each person 6 sq. ft. to stand on, the planet's total population would not occupy more than 450 square miles, which is about two-thirds the size of an average Wisconsin county. But in spite of the fact that human beings cover such a microscopic portion of the earth's surface, it still is true that outstanding in importance among all maps of earth features is that of men or population.

Yet numbers alone are an inadequate gauge of the capacity of a population to utilize natural resources, to enjoy the fruits of its labors,

and to create a material culture. Numbers are principally a count of men's bodies, the capacities of which do not vary so widely over the earth. The variable element in population lies chiefly in people's mental skills and equipment, their degrees of technological advancement, their social and economic institutions—all of which are features of population not revealed by a mere count of heads.

25.3 Population Numbers in the Past.[1] For at least 100,000 years, and possibly for 1,000,000 years, men using tools have been living on the earth. During the long Paleolithic period, when man was exclusively a gatherer of food provided by nature, the number of people must have been very few. In the hunting-gathering regions of North America the estimate is 16 persons per 100 square kilometers, or 42 per 100 square miles.

The first significant acceleration in population increase was coincident with the Neolithic revolution which followed the termination of the last ice age, perhaps under 15,000 years ago. It was during this period that man first began to plant and cultivate and to domesticate animals. By thus improving upon nature our ancestors increased and made more secure their food supply thereby creating a base for a much enlarged population. Small scattered agricultural villages, which shifted frequently in location, constituted Neolithic society.

A second early period of accelerated population growth resulted when the village dwellers learned to cooperate as groups in regulating and controlling water and soil resources. This beginning of group activity seems to date from around 4000 B.C. in the Lower Nile region and in Mesopotamia, and a millennium or more later in the Indus valley of northwestern India and Pakistan and the Hwang, or Yellow, River valley of northern China (Fig. 25.1). A series of epoch-making inventions—among them the plow, wheeled cart, sailing

---

[1] Historical Outline of World Population Growth. "The Determinants and Consequences of Population Trends," Chap. II. *United Nations Population Studies,* No. 17, pp. 5–20, 1953.

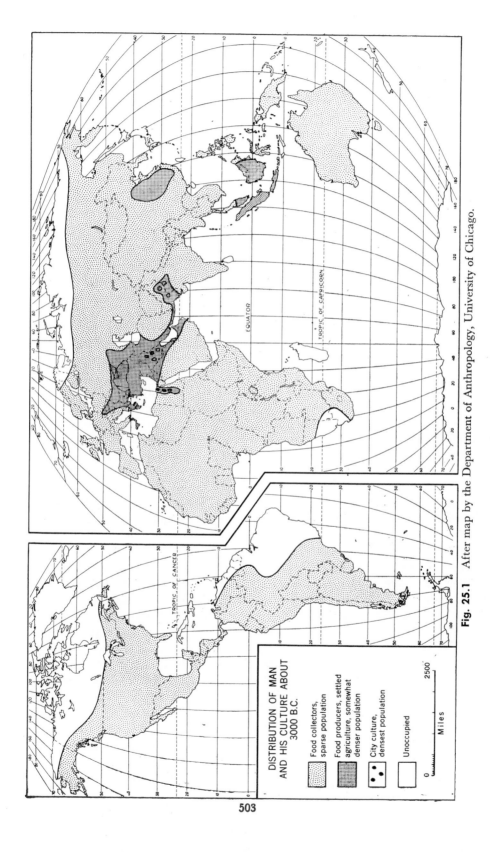

DISTRIBUTION OF MAN
AND HIS CULTURE ABOUT
3000 B.C.

Food collectors,
sparse population

Food producers, settled
agriculture, somewhat
denser population

City culture,
densest population

Unoccupied

Miles
0   2500

Fig. 25.1   After map by the Department of Anthropology, University of Chicago.

boat, and the smelting of metals—coming with great rapidity were preparatory to the development of urban living. Subsequently there evolved in favored areas cities which were dependent for food upon the primitive farming society in the midst of which they existed.

By early historic times there had developed three principal types of population regions:

1. A series of city-centered agricultural-commercial civilizations concentrated around the margins of the Mediterranean Sea, and in southwestern, southern, and eastern Asia. A similar, but isolated, center existed in Middle America. In these areas population was relatively dense for this early period.

2. Frontier areas of agricultural-village and tribal economies in northern Europe and Asia, Africa south of the Sahara, most of North and South America, and Oceania. Here population densities were intermediate in character.

3. Nomadic areas of mounted horsemen, notably in central and western Asia. These were regions of relatively sparse population.

Throughout this period, beginning with the emergence of prehistoric village agriculture and terminating with the establishment of great ancient urban civilizations, the earth's human life multiplied slowly but there were frequent interruptions caused by recurrent conflicts.

Accurate counts of population in the ancient world are nonexistent. Estimates of the number of inhabitants of the earth as of the beginning of the Christian era range from 200 to 300 million. Within the Roman Empire, as of about this date, the population may have been 50 to 80 million (23 million in the European sections, 19+ million in the Asiatic parts, and 11+ million in the African subdivisions). China may have accounted for 60 to 70 million and India for 100 to 140 million.[2]

During the medieval period the pattern was one of a slow general population increase, but with wide fluctuations from region to region and from one period to another. Most estimates place the earth's number of people at 500 to 550 million by about the middle of the seventeenth century or the beginning of the

[2] *Ibid.,* pp. 7–8.

modern period. The net increase was probably small in the ancient centers and in southern and western Europe, and more pronounced in the frontier areas of central and eastern Europe.

25.4 Regional Rates of Population Growth in Modern Times. Although population growth for the world as a whole has been markedly accelerated during the past 200 years, the rates have shown striking differences for various peoples and regions. Europe, for example, where the Industrial Revolution and the demographic change which followed originated, felt its effects first, so that it was the European peoples who increased at a much more rapid rate than the others. Within three centuries population in areas of European settlement multiplied over eight times while the rest of the world's population by contrast increased only three to four times. In 1650 Europeans represented 20 to 25 per cent of the earth's population; in 1933, 39 per cent.

One writer has compared the growth of the earth's population to a long thin powder fuse that burns slowly and haltingly until it finally reaches the charge and then explodes. Throughout 99 per cent of human history population remained sparse and grew slowly. The first real burst in population growth, the explosion at the end of the fuse, was coincident with the latest epoch in human progress—the Industrial Revolution (Fig. 25.2). This involved not merely technological advances but associated economic, social, and political changes as well. Three centuries ago the world witnessed what, by present rates of growth, appears almost a stationary population. This was the result of a high death rate nearly canceling out the effects of a high birth rate. Probably half the children died before reaching ten; 50 per cent of the population was under twenty; old people were few; the waste of life was colossal.

The Industrial Revolution began in Europe, and from there its influence spread round the world. The effects upon population growth were almost phenomenal, for it initiated an acceleration of population growth that, considering the earth as a whole, has continued for three centuries and down to the present time.

The average annual rate of growth was only 0.29 per cent in 1750; but 0.44 by 1800; 0.51 in 1850; 0.63 in 1900; 0.75 in 1940; and 0.9 in 1950. Because the growth of world population is determined only by two factors, births and deaths, the unprecedented acceleration contemporaneous with the Industrial Revolution must be explainable in terms of these two factors. All evidence points to declining mortality as the principal cause. This began, at first slowly and gradually, as a result of a more abundant, regular, and varied food supply, which resulted, in part, from improved agricultural techniques, but even more, probably, from better transportion, which in turn stimulated commerce and small-scale industry. From this, commercial agriculture had its beginnings. Expanding ocean transportation carried the new agricultural techniques of Europe to new lands and fertile soils overseas, whose surplus produce shortly began to stream back to Europe. Each improvement in one part of the system reacted to improve all other parts, and the total effect was to reduce famine, undernourishment, and susceptibility to disease, and with these the death rate. The effects of scientific medicine and public sanitation were not felt until a later date, largely after the mid-nineteenth century, but these safeguards, when they did arrive, had a remarkable effect on lowering still further a mortality rate already greatly reduced.

25.5 *Expansion of European Peoples.* This numerical expansion was accompanied by a vast geographical expansion as European settlers moved into new and sparsely populated lands which they discovered. Between 1846 and 1932 more than 50 million emigrated to frontier lands overseas. Thus, European stock, and with it European culture, were transplanted to the far corners of the earth—North and South America, Australia, New Zealand, North and South Africa, Siberia. Applying their advanced techniques to new and fertile soils, the European settlers were able to produce such an abundance of food and agricultural raw materials that huge export surpluses became available for the mother countries.

In regions already densely populated, such as eastern and southeastern Asia, the emigrating Europeans were able to achieve political and economic domination even though their own numbers remained relatively small. Using their own skills and their own capital, and exploiting the abundant native labor, they set up commercial plantation agriculture in fertile and strategic areas. The products as well as the profits from these plantation ventures went largely to Europe. The native peoples reaped relatively little economic advantage from being associated with the world economy, although certain elements of European culture such as medical science, public sanitation, improved transportation, and scientific agriculture had the effect of reducing mortality rates.

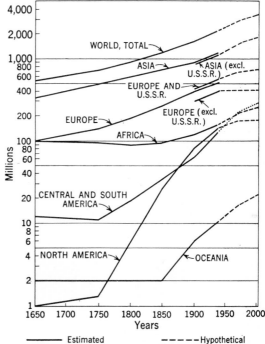

Fig. 25.2 Estimated population of the earth and its continental subdivisions from about A.D. 160 to 2000. The earth's population grew very slowly up until about two centuries ago; since that time there has been a greatly accelerated growth, especially among European peoples. (*From Annals of the American Academy of Political and Social Science. Chart prepared by the Office of Population Research, Princeton University.*)

Estimates of World Population by Regions, 1650–1950

Estimated Population in Millions

Series of Estimates and Date	World Total	Africa	Northern America	Latin America	Asia (excl. U.S.S.R.)	Europe and Asiatic U.S.S.R.	Oceania	Area of European settlement
Willcox's estimates: *								
1650.....................	470	100	1	7	257	103	2	113
1750.....................	694	100	1	10	437	144	2	157
1800.....................	919	100	6	23	595	193	2	224
1850.....................	1,091	100	26	33	656	274	2	335
1900.....................	1,571	141	81	63	857	423	6	573
Unted Nations estimates:								
1920.....................	1,834	136	115	92	997	485	9	701
1930.....................	2,008	155	134	110	1,069	530	10	784
1940.....................	2,216	177	144	132	1,173	579	11	866
1950.....................	2,406	199	166	162	1,272	594	13	935

* W. F. Willcox. "Studies in American Demography." P. 45. Cornell University Press, Ithaca, New York, 1940.

The total result is that within three centuries the earth's population has multiplied approximately five times and the rate of acceleration continues to increase. Recently population growth has slowed down in large parts of the European culture area but it has at the same time gathered momentum elsewhere.

There are some who believe that a continuing rapid increase of the earth's population will so tax the resource base which supports human life that disastrous results are likely to be the case. Others are less pessimistic and consider that with improved technologies the resource base is capable of being expanded sufficiently rapidly to provide for the growing population for some time to come. It is some-thing of an awesome fact nevertheless that if the present rate of population increase were to continue, the earth's inhabitants might number nearly 4 billion by 1980.

25.6 *Population Change.* The two tables above and below and Figs. 25.2 and 25.3 illustrate the gross regional pattern of population change over the past three centuries. The reader should be warned that all the figures for the earlier dates are only estimates, and those for Asia and Africa are based upon very slim evidence. If the figures for Africa may be considered sufficiently accurate to warrant making comparisons, it appears as though that continent has not held its own in population growth, for while it may have supported a fifth of the earth's people in 1650, this had been reduced to 8 per cent by 1950. Asia's and Europe's proportions, together representing three-quarters of the world's population, have not changed markedly since 1650. The most striking proportional increase is indicated for Anglo-America and Latin-America, both settled by Europeans, and it is their increase which partly accounts for the remarkable expansion indicated for the Area of European Settlement (see table below).

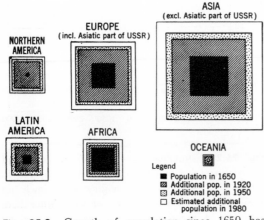

Fig. 25.3 Growth of population since 1650 has been *relatively* most rapid in Europe and the Americas although the largest *absolute* increase has been in Asia. (*After chart prepared by the United Nations.*)

Percentage of World Population by Regions

Region	1650	1800	1950
Africa	21	10	8
Anglo-America	0.2	0.7	7
Latin America	1.4	2.1	7
Asia (excl. U.S.S.R.)	55	66+	53
Europe and Asiatic U.S.S.R.	22	21+	24
Oceania	0.4	0.2	0.5
Area of European settlement	23	24+	39

25.7 The Present Demographic Characteristics of the Earth's Population. The earth's population varies widely in its demographic characteristics and therefore in its potential rates of population growth. Birth rates and death rates, which measure factors which are basic to population change, are greatly in contrast in different earth regions. There are some where the birth rate is high, over 35 to 40 per 1,000, but where the people constantly suffer ill health and where the expectation of life at birth is below 30 years. In such areas the death rate is so very high that it tends to cancel out the effects of the high fertility and consequently the rate of population growth is small to moderate, and variable. At the other extreme are areas where the expectancy of life at birth is 65 years, so that the death rate is low. But if the birth rate is also low, as it commonly is, this population may also be one of small or only moderate growth. Between these two extremes are regions with different combinations of fertility and mortality rates, producing contrasting growth rates in the immediate future.

On the basis of the fundamental demographic factors of fertility and mortality, three population groupings, with their implications for population change, are distinguished.[3]

Group 1 includes areas where fertility and mortality rates are both relatively low (Fig. 25.4). Characteristically, birth rates are below 25 per 1,000 and death rates below 15 per 1,000 so that population growth is likely to be relatively slow or moderate. The regions of low fertility and mortality include most of Europe except the U.S.S.R., the United States and Canada, Australia, New Zealand, Japan, and the *European* population of South Africa. On the whole these are regions which are in an advanced stage of economic development.

Group 2 is represented by regions now ex-

[3] The Identification of Population Types for Studies of the Inter-relationships between Economic, Social and Population Changes. United Nation's Economic and Social Council, 1949, pp. 151–162. See also, Framework for Future Population Estimates, 1950–1980, by World Regions, Prepared by the Population Division of the United Nations, 1954.

periencing rapid population growth which, barring catastrophes, should continue for several decades. In them the death rate has dropped markedly, while the birth rate is still high, but where recently it has shown some tendency to decline. Included in Group 2 are the U.S.S.R., the Balkan countries of southeastern Europe, and Latin America.

Group 3 consists of countries where fertility is high and not declining and where the death rate is likewise high and variable. Neither fertility nor mortality has shown a consistent downward trend. The rate of population increase is erratic and the growth over long periods is slow or moderate. When technical developments reduce the death rates, steady and rapid population growth will occur. Included in this group are most of the countries of eastern, southern, and western Asia and most of Africa. In general, Group 3 includes the economically least developed areas of the earth, where agriculture still is the dominant economy.

25.8 Regional Differentials in Natural Rates of Population Growth. From the previous discussion and from Fig. 25.4 it becomes clear that just as there have been large regional differences in population growth in the past, so there are at the present and probably will continue to be in the future. In other words, the relative distribution of people over the earth is constantly changing. In the past few centuries it is the European peoples that have grown most rapidly but that is unlikely in the future, for in most of the areas of European settlement population has now become fairly stable and future growth will be slow to moderate, and in places even a static condition may come to prevail.

By contrast certain other regions are undergoing an acceleration of population growth which will continue for some time while still others are on the threshold of large-scale population increase. The U.S.S.R. is one of the regions where the present rate of increase is large and so also is Latin America. During the past three decades India has shown an accelerated rate of population increase and China

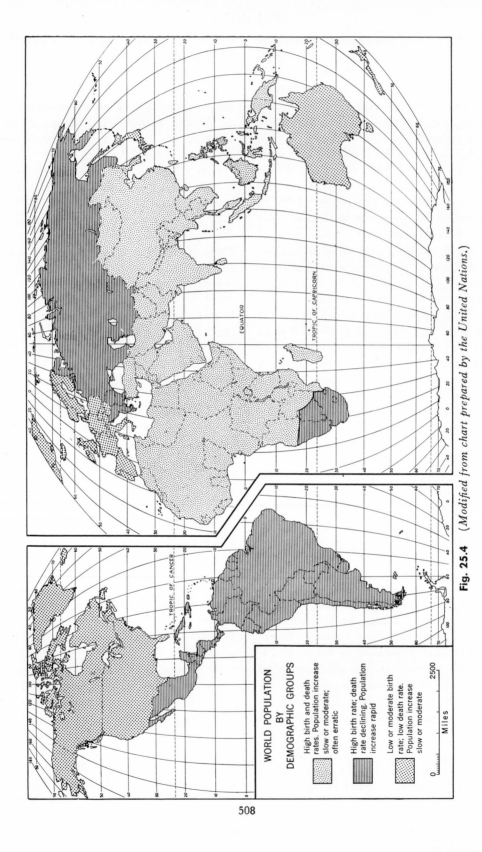

WORLD POPULATION
BY
DEMOGRAPHIC GROUPS

High birth and death rates. Population increase slow or moderate; often erratic

High birth rate; death rate declining. Population increase rapid

Low or moderate birth rate; low death rate. Population increase slow or moderate

0   2500
Miles

Fig. 25.4 (Modified from chart prepared by the United Nations.)

may be on the threshold of increased growth just as soon as the high mortality rates are slightly reduced.

Of world importance is the fact that eastern and southern Asia, which at present supports one-half of the earth's population and represents some of the highest rural population densities, is also a region of high potential population growth. Here fertility rates are high and are likely to change only slowly. At the same time improved public sanitation, better medical facilities, and a more reliable food supply are resulting in lowered mortality rates, so that the rate of natural growth will increase. Moreover, as this region enters a period of accelerated population growth, it starts from a base representing half the earth's population so that the actual numerical increase may be unbelievably large. The case of India may be cited, where in one decade alone 50 million were added to the population. This is nearly a third of the population of the United States and larger than the total number of people in Britain, France, or Italy. What seems reasonably clear is that the period of rapid expansion of European peoples has nearly ended and that a large part of the world's population increase in the next half century probably will take place in the economically retarded areas of eastern and southern Asia and to a lesser extent in the U.S.S.R. and probably tropical Africa and South America.

Differential rates of population growth in the past, as between regions and nations, have carried in their train serious dislocations and consequences of an economic and political character. There seems no reason to believe that similar differential rates of growth in the future, resulting in unequal pressures of men upon resources, can escape producing similar dislocations and tensions.[4] The actual lack, or even *felt* lack, of adequate resources for supporting a rapidly expanding population at a desired standard of living may cause a nation to try to right what it considers to be inequalities by resorting to armed force. The upward surge of population in eastern and southern Asia, combined with an expansion of industrial and military potential, is likely to make that part of the world more conscious of its low standards of living and the excessive pressure of men upon resources. In the process of adjusting to increased population pressure and to intensified demands for economic improvement, tensions are likely to develop which have in them the seeds of conflict.

25.9 Recent Population Change in the United States. Until recently the course of population development was thought to be well charted and understood in the United States and Canada, but recent developments have compelled a revision of current notions. In the United States there had been an almost unbroken decline in the birth rate since about 1800 down to the Second World War and all available evidence pointed to a continuation of that decline to a point where a near-static condition of population numbers would prevail in the near future. From 1860 until the outbreak of the First World War the rate of growth decreased in spite of an increasing volume of immigration. After the First World War the decline continued at a more rapid rate and in the decade 1930–1940 growth reached an all-time low of 7.2 per cent. Then the unexpected occurred. From a depression low in 1933 when the birth rate was only 16.6 and the annual number of births only 2.3 million, these figures soared to 25.7 and 3.9 million in 1947. By 1952 the comparable figures were nearly as high, 24.5 and 3.8 million. It is still not clear what the motivating forces are which produced this accelerated fertility and growth pattern. In the beginning it was considered to be a temporary feature following the depression of the 1930s and the occurrence of the Second World War. The continued high growth, however, has confounded the experts so that they are timid about forecasting future

[4] Fergus Chalmers Wright. "Population and Peace." International Institute of Intellectual Cooperation, League of Nations, Paris, 1939.

Warren S. Thompson. "Population and Peace in the Pacific." University of Chicago Press, Chicago, 1946.

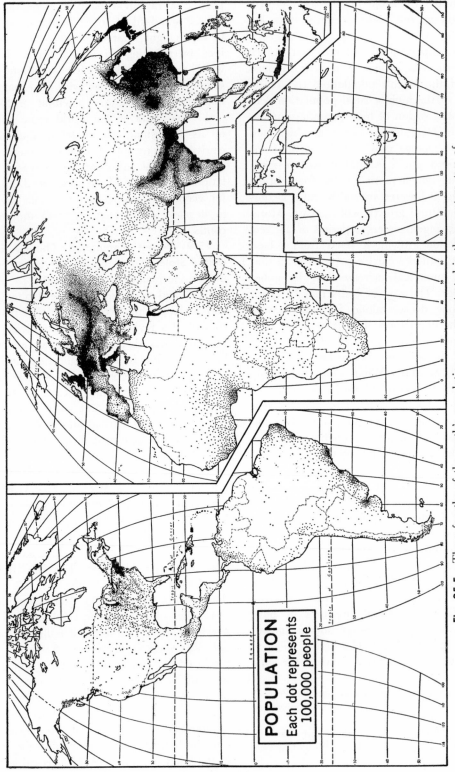

Fig. 25.5 Three-fourths of the earth's population are concentrated in three centers, two of them in eastern and southern Asia and a third in Europe.

POPULATION
Each dot represents
100,000 people

trends. Canada's population history has closely paralleled that of the United States except that its birth rate has been consistently higher (28.7 in 1947; 27.4 in 1952).

Population Distribution

25.10 *Population Distribution Uneven.* The present distribution of the earth's people is probably only a temporary point in a process of change that has gone on since the beginning of human history. The present, therefore, is in the nature of a photographic snapshot. It is hard to believe that population distribution will not change in the future as it has continued to do in the past, but what the changes will be it is not given us to know.

The most characteristic feature of the present-day distribution of people is its extreme unevenness (Fig. 25.5). It has been estimated that nearly one-half of the world's people is contained within about 5 per cent of the earth's land area while, by contrast, 57 per cent of the land area contains less than 5 per cent of the population. The ratio of men to area not only shows a wide range of variability, but what is more, there is no easy explanation for this variability. The highest densities of population are to be found in very different kinds of areas. Some, like those of Java and Puerto Rico, are in the wet tropics; others, of which western Europe is an example, are in the higher middle latitudes. High population densities also are to be found both in regions of simple subsistence agriculture (China and India) and also in countries which are characterized by advanced technical civilizations such as the countries of western Europe. Areas of low density show similar contrasts both in physical environment and in stage of economic development (Fig. 25.6).

The reasons for the present distribution of the earth's peoples are both numerous and complicated. In part the distribution reflects the productivity of the land as determined by combinations of such environmental features as climate, soil, terrain, and mineral resources. In part it results from cultural contrasts in the people themselves, including such features as stage of economic development, technological equipment, social organization, and geographical location. Characteristically these factors do not operate singly but rather in combinations, so that it is usually difficult to weigh the effect of a single factor. As a general rule it may be stated that in simple agrarian societies where population depends more largely upon the direct food-producing potential of the land, the physical factors such as climate and soil exercise a greater influence. As civilization becomes more advanced and local food production less significant in determining population numbers, the cultural factors commonly increase in significance.[5]

25.11 Ecumene and Nonecumene. In its broadest aspect, distribution of people consists of dividing the earth into its inhabited and uninhabited parts (Fig. 25.5). The term *ecumene* has been applied to those parts of the earth where people live, in order to differentiate them from the unoccupied portions, the *nonecumene*. The ability of the human animal to occupy different environments and to push out the boundaries of the ecumene increased with advances in civilization. The development of clothing and of fire made possible the occupying of colder climates. Taming the wild horse and camel opened up the semiarid grasslands and the deserts. When man was capable of navigating the oceans, his victory over space was substantially increased and the horizons of the ecumene were much widened. The strongest incentive for an ever-widening of the occupied lands has always been the search for new living space. A probing of the uninhabited and unknown areas continues, driven by the urge to discover valuable economic materials and by the love of adventure or for sport or mere exhilaration. In very recent times the airplane has almost annihilated the unknown space of the earth's surface.

On first thought it may seem a simple matter to describe and represent on a map the

[5] The Determinants and Consequences of Population Growth. *United Nations Population Studies,* No. 17, pp. 163–177, United Nations, New York, 1953.

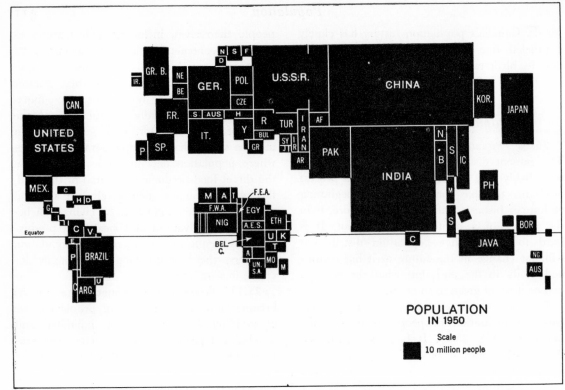

Fig. 25.6 How the world map would appear when the countries are drawn as rectangles whose areas are proportional to their populations. Note that China and India dwarf all other countries. Compare with an atlas map showing the areas of the several continents and countries. (*After a sketch by Pierre George.*)

so-called ecumene. Actually it is very difficult. No extensive areas of the earth's surface at present remain completely unexplored. The areas over which man currently moves are considerably more limited, however, for within the net of his communication systems there still remain areas of high mountains, deserts, and polar ice caps which are largely untraveled and certainly unoccupied. Nevertheless, the ecumene is not a compact closed area. Of the earth's nearly 56 million square miles a German geographer estimates that approximately 18 million represent barren land, chiefly dry deserts and cold deserts. He would further reduce the ecumene to 30 to 35 million square miles by subtracting extensive unoccupied island-like areas of forest, desert, and highland, embedded within the general ecumene. Certainly the most extensive and the most contiguous areas of non-ecumene are the ice caps of Antarctica and

Greenland, while the largest enclosed "islands" of unoccupied territory exist within the deserts, the South American tropical rainforest, portions of the tundra and subarctic forests, and certain high altitudes.

The last few centuries have witnessed a spread of European agricultural settlement within the ecumene on a scale never equaled previously. This did not so much represent an absolute expansion of the ecumene as it did the filling in with permanent settlement areas either thinly or periodically occupied by aboriginal peoples. This phenomenal spread of Western culture with its associated upsurge in population of European origin has resulted in the land areas of the earth being brought into use, to an extent never realized before. Rapid filling in of the ecumene in recent centuries has been associated with (*a*) the discovery and utilization of minerals on an enormous scale, (*b*) the substitution of power machinery for human labor, (*c*) the spread of Old World grains into the grasslands of the middle latitudes, (*d*) the diffusion of Old World garden crops (sugar cane, plantains, rice, and coffee) and of New World crops (potatoes, manioc, maize, tobacco, and upland cotton) as well, and (*e*) the extension of irrigation and drainage by agricultural engineering methods.[6] Down to the first half of the nineteenth century the world's grasslands were pretty much the domain of the nomad and as a consequence were relatively empty of population. Railroads, the steel plow, well drills, windmills, and harvesting machinery made their conquest possible. From these newly cultivated fertile soils of the prairie steppes of the middle latitudes came a flood of food and raw materials which made possible the remarkable growth of urban population and hence the full realization of the Industrial Revolution.

25.12 *Boundaries of the Ecumene.* Considering the rapid expansion of population and the diligent search for new settlement areas that have occurred during recent centuries, it would appear that the remaining unoccupied, or only periodically occupied, lands must be those which present serious obstacles to settlement. These obstacles are principally climatic in character, for it is the cold lands, the dry lands, and the humid tropical lands which comprise most of the nonecumene, as well as the transition lands of sparse population (compare Plate 2 and Fig. 25.5).

25.13 *The Cold Lands.* Here the principal climatic handicaps are (*a*) the short frost-free season, (*b*) the cool summers, and (*c*) a long season without direct sunlight. Additional nonclimatic obstacles are the permafrost, the low-grade soils, and the large areas of poorly drained land. Completely barren of settlement are the extensive ice plateaus of Antarctica and Greenland, as well as some of the northernmost island tundra lands of both North America and Eurasia. Such lands seem hopeless as potential

settlement areas. Farther south, the more extensive continental tundra lands and subarctic lands of Eurasia and North America represent the genuine transition zone between ecumene and nonecumene. Here thinly populated favorable sites break the continuity of the nonecumene so that the whole area consists of a mosaic of thinly settled and completely unpopulated areas.

In so far as it is possible to foresee at present, it seems unlikely that there will be a significant free migration of agricultural settlers to the remaining nonecumene of these northern lands. The expansion of the ecumene on the cold frontier is bound to be slow.

25.14 *The Dry Lands.* On this frontier of the ecumene the single major handicap is the meagerness and unreliability of water, although plant life is also sparse. Over extensive areas these are obstacles which cannot be overcome or improved, so that a significant reduction of the dry nonecumene seems unlikely. Modern engineering techniques applied to irrigation have been successful in somewhat expanding the dry frontier during the past half century but the opportunities for a continuing and large expansion of the irrigated area are not great. Moreover, the less costly type of expansion is in the past; that ahead will require greater outlays of capital for a smaller reward.

Two other possibilities for reclaiming dry lands for agriculture are occasionally mentioned. One of these is artificial rain making through the seeding of supercooled clouds with dry ice or silver iodide crystals. Among experts there are strong differences of opinion relative to the possible economic significance of artificial rain making in general. As a means of significantly shrinking the dry nonecumene it seems hopeless. The other suggestion is related to the possibility of adding greatly to the volume of water available for irrigation by converting salty ocean water into fresh water. Up to the present the cost of such conversion has been prohibitive and the future possibilities are far from bright.[7]

---

[6] Carl O. Sauer. The Prospect for Redistribution of Population. "Limits of Land Settlement," Isaiah Bowman (editor)., Chap. I. Council on Foreign Relations, New York, 1937.

[7] Cecil B. Ellis. "Fresh Water from the Ocean for Cities, Industry, and Irrigation." The Ronald Press Company, New York, 1954.

25.15 *The Wet Tropical Lands.* Unlike the other two types of unoccupied, or sparsely occupied, nonecumene the wet tropics lack in neither heat nor precipitation. In fact it is the superabundance of climatic energy, together with the features of vegetation, soils, and drainage associated with it, which seems to have retarded settlement in extensive tropical areas. Nowhere on the earth do plants grow so quickly and abundantly, and since plant life is the ultimate source of food, it would appear as though the wet tropics are potentially capable of supporting a large population. There are offsetting factors, however, among them relatively infertile soils, periodically flooded lowlands, an excessive growth of weedy vegetation, the prevalence of numerous debilitating and killing diseases, and the discomforts associated with the constantly high temperature and humidity.

Actually the wet tropics present something of a population conumdrum as regards population distribution, for some parts are nearly population voids, while others have an extremely dense population. As a general rule tropical regions in the Old World are far better populated than those of the New. Just why this is the case is not known. It does suggest, however, that the potentialities for supporting a larger population are far greater in the wet tropics than they are in either the cold or the dry lands.

25.16 **Future Population and an Expanding Ecumene.** In terms of man's present productive skills it may appear that human life as it is now spread over the earth fairly well reflects the economic potentialities of the various areas. Of all the nonecumene only parts of the wet tropics would seem to offer opportunities for new settlement on a large scale.

In the man-resource relationship it should be emphasized, nevertheless, there are two factors which are constantly changing, for the resource factor is dynamic as is the population. The resource base changes as men's science and technology advance. Ideas are more important than things. Thus the earth's potentialities for supporting population will no doubt change in the future as they have done in the past, although it is not possible for us at present to see what these changes will be.

DISTRIBUTION OF POPULATION WITHIN THE ECUMENE

25.17 **Patterns of the First Order.** Roughly four-fifths of the earth's population is concentrated in three clusters of subcontinental size (Fig. 25.5). On a map of world population the largest and most conspicuous cluster is the one in eastern and southern Asia which contains approximately half the world's people, or 1.3 billion. More correctly this Asiatic cluster is composed of two centers, one in eastern Asia (China, Japan, and Korea) and the other in southern Asia (India and Pakistan). The most populous units within the Asiatic cluster are China with 500 to 600 million; India, 387 million; Japan, 90 million; Pakistan, 81 million; Java, 55 million; and Korea, 30 million (Fig. 25.6).

The Earth's Four Principal Population Regions†

Continuous habitable region	Area in millions of square miles	Population		Central latitude
		In millions	Per square mile	
Eastern Asia	1.7	620–720	360–420	35°N.
India and Pakistan	1.0	470	470	25°N.
Europe	2.8	623	223	50°N.
Eastern North America	1.9	150	79	40°N.

† See C. B. Fawcett. The Numbers and Distribution of Mankind. *Smithsonian Institution Rept.*, p. 338, 1948.

The second major cluster of world population is in Europe which includes about a quarter of the earth's people, or over 600 million. Thus over three-quarters of the earth's inhabitants are concentrated on one continent, Eurasia, one on the Atlantic side and the other along the eastern and southeastern margins fronting on the Pacific and Indian Oceans. The two great Eurasian centers are separated by the extensive dry lands of the interior of the continent.

Central and eastern Anglo-America (United States and Canada) comprise the third world cluster of population. This is of considerably smaller magnitude than the other two, so that it is strikingly less conspicuous on the map of world population (Fig. 25.5). An unusually large proportion of the 175 million people of Canada and the United States comprise this cluster so that it represents 6 to 7 per cent of the world total.

It is worth noting the contrasting latitudinal locations of the four population clusters. That in Europe, at about 50°N., is farthest poleward. The North American cluster is centered about 10° farther equatorward at about 40°N. Both of these are emphatically middle latitude in location. By contrast the two Asiatic centers are subtropical and tropical in location, one being centered at about 35°N. and the other at 25°N. Two of the population clusters front upon the Atlantic Ocean, one on the Pacific Ocean, and one upon the Indian Ocean.

25.18 *The Population Clusters Compared.* The four population concentrations pair off in other important respects as well. Thus, the American center developed as a result of a budding off from Europe and consequently bears the stamp of European culture and its features of economic development. Commercial and regionally specialized agriculture, factory industry, large foreign and domestic trade, and efficient transportation systems are characteristics of the Atlantic Basin centers. These two are far advanced in a machine-age civilization; the Industrial Revolution, construed broadly as involving economic, social, and political as well as technological changes, has here transformed the ways of living. On the whole, and of course relatively, individual wealth is great; living standards are high; regional specialization is well developed; cities, the offspring of industry and commerce, are numerous; and human life is valued highly as evidenced by the relatively low mortality rates and the fertility rates as well.

By contrast, the ancient world still exists to a large degree in the two Asiatic centers. These are regions of poor peasant farmers engaged in intensive subsistence agriculture. Population presses closely upon the food supply; poverty and disease are omnipresent; depressingly high birth rates and high death rates manifest a people wasteful of energy in the eternal chain of reproduction. Sickness, malnutrition, and preoccupation with death further exhaust vitality. The Industrial Revolution has only modestly affected most of the people in these two regions; factory industry and trade are meagerly developed; cities are *relatively* few; communications are in places crude and inefficient. Both in forms of culture and in stage of economic development the Asiatic peoples are strikingly in contrast to those comprising the two centers bordering the Atlantic Basin. Japan is the single unit within the Asiatic clusters which has westernized its economy to an important degree, and yet even there the large rural population has not been greatly affected. Nevertheless, throughout the whole region of eastern and southeastern Asia there are evidences of a widespread discontent of these peoples with their lot, which suggests that they may be on the eve of a period characterized by important economic changes. But such changes will have but small effect upon the well-being of the large Asiatic population unless at the same time growth in numbers is limited.

25.19 Distribution Patterns of the Second Order. *Asia.* If the focus is sharpened somewhat, it is evident that within any large area of the earth there are patterns of population distribution of a second order which are also conspicuous and distinctive. Thus in eastern and southern Asia, which supports such a large percentage of the world's people, the spread of population is very uneven. Here it is a much fragmented or *clustered* pattern that is conspicuous, with a relatively small part of the total land area supporting a great majority of the people (Fig. 25.7). Almost knife-edge boundaries frequently appear to separate areas containing several hundred, or even thousand, persons per square mile from others which are almost barren of settlement. This markedly clustered pattern of population is closely associated with surface configuration and soil characteristics, for southeastern Asia is, in general, a hilly region with restricted lowlands composed of river alluvium. Moreover, the residual soils of the uplands are characteristically badly leached and of low fertility so that the fertile alluvial lowlands stand out by contrast. The peasant farmers have tended to gravitate toward these alluvial lowlands, where soils are fertile and gentle slopes and abundant water, two items relatively necessary for the inundated rice crop, are easily available. The more difficult slope sites with thinner less fertile soils are avoided. In hilly Japan only 14 to 15 per cent of the land surface is actually cultivated. One might with great fitness describe the Orient as having an "alluvial civilization."

This concentration of agricultural effort on only the best land is explained in part by the large dependence upon hand labor and hand tools. It requires approximately 15 man-days to spade an acre of land by hand, so that the farmer who depends entirely on his own muscles can cultivate only an acre or two of ground. Even those who have an ox or horse can plow at most only a few acres. Since it takes just as long to dig up and cultivate poor land as good land, the oriental farmer is obliged, in order to feed his family, to put his efforts on the most

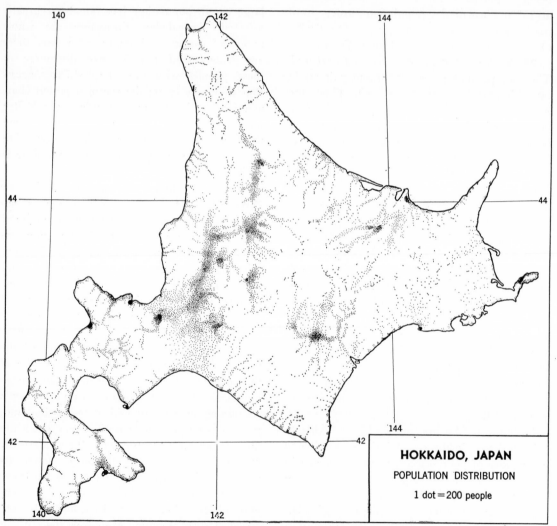

HOKKAIDO, JAPAN

POPULATION DISTRIBUTION

1 dot = 200 people

Fig. 25.7   As in most of eastern and southern Asia, population in Hokkaido, the northern island of Japan, is highly concentrated upon the fertile plains of new alluvium.

productive soil. On anything else he would starve. In the United States on less productive lands the farm area is increased, and this greater area is operated through the use of more animal or motor power and the use of labor-saving machinery. But this adaptation the oriental farmer is incapable of making.

In Japan, which is much more highly industrialized and urbanized than the other political units of the Orient, the coincidence of population with fertile alluvial lowlands is unusually marked. In 1950 urban population amounted to about half the total. But the great metropolises have developed on the most extensive alluvial plains so that city and country people alike overcrowd the level lands. Since the lowlands are predominantly coastal in location, the result is a population which closely hugs the seaboard. It is not surprising that the Japanese are closely bound to the sea. For a people whose mode of living is closely adjusted to a subtropical environment the colder climates of the higher middle latitudes are less attractive, so that a great majority, of the nation's population is in that part of the country which lies south of the 37° parallel. Within this subtropical part of Japan there is a marked concentration of people in a long, thin irregular zone, more than 600 miles long, extending from Tokyo and Yokohama on the northeast, southwestward along the Pacific Coast to the Nagoya area, and thence along the shores of the Inland Sea to northern Kyushu. Within this populous belt lie 50 per cent of the country's cities and three-quarters of its industrial workers, and in it are produced over 80 per cent of the manufactures. Within the hilly interior of the country, population clusters in a number of basin-like areas or exists in the form of long thin lines, dendritic in pattern, coincident with the river valleys.

China, with a fifth to a fourth of the earth's people, 70 to 80 per cent of them rural, exhibits a very uneven distribution. If a line trending northeast-southwest is drawn from Yunnan in the southwest to northern Manchuria, it divides China into two very unlike population regions. Dry highland China to the west of the line with 2.2 million square miles of territory contains an estimated 15 to 20 million people, while humid China to the east with 1.8 million square miles probably has 500 to 560 million. Within humid eastern China the great concentrations are coincident with the North China Plain, the Yangtze Plain, and the Basin of Szechwan. A dendritic pattern of distribution is very conspicuous in the hill lands of South China.

The 470 million people of India and Pakistan, likewise, are crowded onto the fertile alluvium of the river valleys (Fig. 25.5). It is estimated that in the neighborhood of one-half the total are in the Indus-Ganges valley of northern India. Since the western part of this lowland is dry, densities are much higher in the humid Ganges part of the plain than in that portion drained by the Indus River. With increase in rainfall eastward, population likewise increases in the same direction, and reaches over 600 per square mile in the Ganges Delta. Hilly peninsular India shows fewer people, the very high densities being coincident with the coastal deltas, particularly those of the east side.

By contrast with eastern Asia (China, Japan, Korea) and southern Asia (India and Pakistan), the peninsular and insular area between (Burma, Thailand, Indo-China, Malaya, Indonesia, and the Philippines) has many fewer peoples (Fig. 25.5). Here the general over-all density of population is much less than in the rest of the Orient. Why this should be is not so clear. In part it is attributable to the lower stage of agricultural technology which characterizes many of these peoples, who have become intensive cultivators of paddy rice only within the last century. When Europeans first made contact with this region they found many of the extensive delta lands only meagerly settled. At the present time, however, the population is highly concentrated on the fertile plains of new alluvium as it is elsewhere in eastern and southern Asia.

Among the islands of the East Indian archipelago only Java is densely populated. The Indonesian islands other than Java have populations which are well below the average of the Far East. Thus Java and Madura, which have only 7 per cent of the area of Indonesia, contain nearly 70 per cent of the total population. This unusual concentration of people in Java is related in part to the high fertility of the volcanic soils of that island. In part, also, it was the result of the Dutch finding in Java a large and tractable native labor supply for their plantation agriculture. The Javanese for centuries have been sedentary farmers versed in husbandry, while the other islands until recently were largely peopled by tribal groups still in the gathering-economy stage. Without doubt the fact that Java early became the center of Dutch civil and military control, and thus was the first to benefit from European agricultural methods and sanitation, had much to do with the disproportionate growth of population in that island.

Over dry central and western Asia population is concentrated in or near the highlands, or along rivers, where water for irrigation is more abundant. In Siberia there is a marked focusing of the agricultural population on the east-west belt of fertile dark soils in western Siberia, lying between the subarctic taiga region on the north and the dry lands of the Aral-Caspian region to the south.

25.20 *Europe.* In western Europe as well, even on the lowlands, the clustered population pattern is conspicuous, although the boundaries of the clusters are usually not so sharp as in eastern Asia. This clotted pattern is particularly evident in Great Britain, where only 8 per cent of the population are farmers and 80 per cent are classed as urban. In that island six of the seven most conspicuous population clusters are industrial urban concentrations which are fairly coincident with important coal fields (Fig. 23.7). Three of these are in central England flanking the Pennine uplands: the Lancashire node to the west with the two great metropolises of Manchester and Liverpool; the Yorkshire node to the east of the highlands containing Leeds, Bradford, and Sheffield; and the Midlands industrial center at the south end of the Pennines supporting Birmingham and Stoke. The Northumberland-Durham population node in

northeastern coastal England, along the Tyne and Tees rivers, is supported by resources of both coal and iron. Here Newcastle, the most northerly of the great English cities, has developed. The Scottish population node, relatively coincident with the Scottish Lowland and its coal field, contains the great cities of Glasgow and Edinburgh. South Wales and its coal support the population clot of which Swansea and Cardiff are a part.

The London center, the greatest of all, and containing about one-fifth the total population of Great Britain, is the striking exception to the general coincidence of population centers with coal, for the immediate London area lacks coal. Greater London, to be sure, is a manufacturing area of first rank, but its factories turn out goods of a kind which require less power and more labor and which are attracted by the great London market. Throughout its history London has been more famed as a port than as a factory town, while it is the political and financial capital of the nation as well. Most of Britain's industrial regions have their own ports which serve them more or less locally, but London, on the other hand, is the port for almost the whole of Britain and an entrepôt port for a more extensive area.

On the continent of Europe there is a continuous belt of extremely dense population oriented east-west along the fiftieth parallel from the North Sea and English Channel to the lower Dnieper in Soviet Russia. This might be called the *European population axis,* and it is highly coincident with the urbanized industrial regions (Figs. 25.8 and 25.14). The belt broadens from east to west, and the density of population likewise increases in the same direction. It reaches its greatest density in the general vicinity of the industrialized lower Rhineland, coincident with important coal and iron deposits and lying near the mouth of one of the world's great natural waterways (Fig. 25.8). This maximum concentration of people in the general region of northwestern Germany, Holland, Belgium, and northern France is continued eastward in somewhat less intense form through southern and eastern Germany; north-

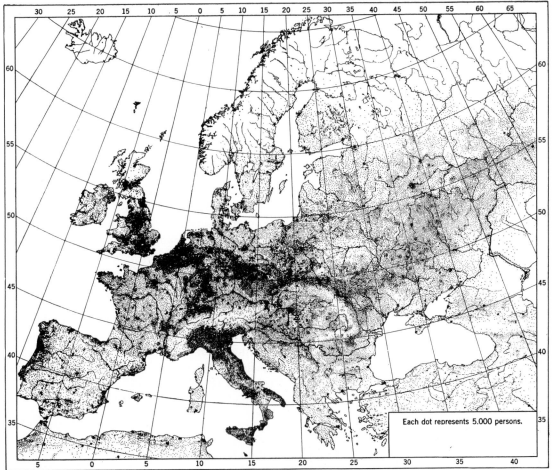

Fig. 25.8 Distribution of population in Europe. (*Adapted from "Sydow-Wagners Methodischer Schulatlas." Previously published in Dudley Kirk, "Europe's Population in the Interwar Years."*)

ern Bohemia and Moravia in Czechoslovakia, southern Poland, and into the Ukraine of southern Soviet Russia.

The more than 200 million inhabitants of the U.S.S.R. are concentrated largely within the European part of the country west of the Ural Mountains. More precisely, it is within a long thin triangle, oriented east-west, the apexes of whose angles are at approximately Odessa and Leningrad in the southwest and northwest, and at Tomsk east of the Urals, that a very large part of the country's population, agricultural land, and industrial production is contained. This is the Soviet coreland. Throughout the length of the European population axis, which contains more than a fourth of the people of the continent, lie the most im-

portant coal basins of Europe, the power resources of which have aided the growth of numerous industrial cities (Fig. 25.8).

In Mediterranean Europe high population densities are found on a number of small isolated basins or delta plains, but these populations are based chiefly upon agriculture. Chief among these "islands" of population is the one occupying the large and relatively fertile Po Valley in Italy. Here both rural and urban populations are present in great numbers, for this is Italy's most highly industralized region and her focus of agricultural production as well.

It thus becomes obvious that, although eastern Asia's population concentrations are composed of peasant agricultural peoples focused upon fertile alluvial plains, to a much larger degree western and central Europe's population is concentrated in commercial and industrial towns and cities grouped with respect to basic mineral resources, important routes of trade, or fertile plains producing raw materials and food.

25.21 *Anglo-America.* In the United States the most striking feature of population distribution is the contrast between the well-occupied eastern half, on the one hand, where the climate is humid and lowlands predominate, and the thinly peopled West, a region of general rainfall deficiency and one where highlands and rugged terrain are abundant (Fig. 25.9). The better-watered sections of the Pacific Coast states west of the Cascade and Sierra Nevada Mountains are of course the important exception to a generally sparse population in the western half of the country.

Approximately 85 per cent of the country's inhabitants are located east of the 100th meridian. Over much of the eastern half of the country population is widely spread, and while there are contrasts in density, to be sure, a marked clotting or clustering is not so conspicuous. It is chiefly in the northeastern portion of the United States, north of the Ohio River and east of the Mississippi, which includes the nation's manufacturing belt with its large city population, that clots of above-normal population density become more prominent (Fig. 25.9). Most conspicuous is the almost continuous belt of high density stretching along the Atlantic seaboard states from southern Maine to Maryland. This is coincident with the country's greatest manufacturing concentration, and the same region includes a large percentage of the great foreign-trade ports such as New York, Boston, Philadelphia, and Baltimore.

West of the Appalachians the clots of highest population density are fairly coincident with the industrial nodes along (*a*) the southern and southwestern shore of Lake Michigan, which includes Chicago and Milwaukee, (*b*) the western and southern shore of Lake Erie, containing Detroit, Cleveland, Toledo, Buffalo, and

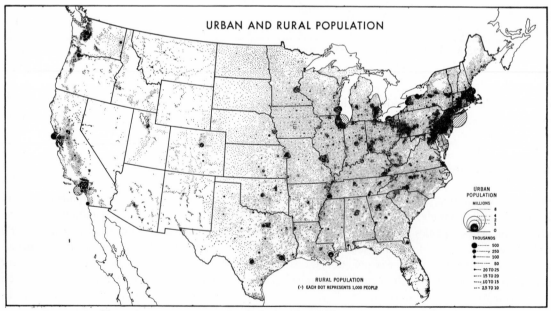

Fig. 25.9 Note the concentration of population in the humid central and eastern part of the country and in the lowlands of the Pacific Coast states. The dry and mountainous West has relatively few people. The densest population is in the most urbanized areas. (*Courtesy of U.S. Department of Agriculture.*)

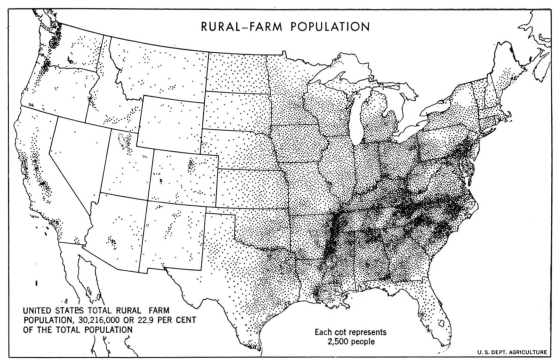

RURAL–FARM POPULATION

UNITED STATES TOTAL RURAL FARM
POPULATION, 30,216,000 OR 22.9 PER CENT
OF THE TOTAL POPULATION

Each cot represents
2,500 people

U. S. DEPT. AGRICULTURE

Fig. 25.10 The rural-farm population is chiefly concentrated in the humid East and especially in the southeastern part of the country. (*Courtesy of U.S. Department of Agriculture.*)

Akron, (*c*) the southern margins of Lake Ontario and the Mohawk Valley, where Rochester, Syracuse, Utica, and Schenectady are located, and (*d*) the upper Ohio Valley in western Pennsylvania and eastern Ohio, where Pittsburgh is the chief metropolis. Over eastern United States rural-farm population is highest in the South where the two principal crops, cotton and corn, require large amounts of human as well as animal labor (Fig. 25.10).

West of about the 100th meridian population rapidly thins out as a result of increasing aridity. Thus the dry mountain states comprising almost 30 per cent of the nation's area have an average population density of only 6 per square mile. This is to be compared with a density of 45 for the Pacific Coast states, 148 for New England, 300 for the Middle Atlantic states, and 51 for the country as a whole. In the dry West, also, the population distribution pattern in one in which a few spots or linear strips of relatively high density are separated by extensive areas of very sparse settlement. Usually the spots of high density are associated with areas having supplies of water for irrigation—river valleys, piedmont alluvial plains, mountain basins—or localities of important mineral exploitation.

Within the generally dry West it is the Pacific Coast states with their more humid and therefore productive climates, and their larger industrial and port cities, that show the largest population figures. Thus, in 1950 the three Pacific Coast states had a combined population of 14,487,000, while the eight mountain states to the east of these and including the territory east to the Great Plains had only 5,075,000 people. Moreover, the Pacific Coast states showed the largest percentage population increase (49 per cent) for the period 1940 to 1950 of any regional subdivisions of the country. Within the Pacific Coast states there are three principal groupings of population: (*a*) the Puget Sound–Willamette Valley center in Washington and Oregon, which supports such cities as Seattle, Portland, and Tacoma; (*b*) the Great California Valley and San Francisco Bay node with San Francisco and Oakland: and (*c*) a southern center occupying the smaller lowlands around and back of Los Angeles and San Diego.

Canada's 15 million people are markedly concentrated along the southern margin of the country, where the available agricultural lands are located. But the east-west belt of population along the international boundary is far from continuous, large areas of barren country tending to isolate the people into four or five distinct clusters. Chief of these is the one occupying the Ontario Peninsula and the St. Lawrence Valley. Other less important ones are (*a*) in the Maritime Provinces facing the Atlantic, (*b*) in the Prairie Provinces, and (*c*) in maritime southwestern British Columbia.

25.22 *Latin America, Australia, Africa.* In tropical Latin America, more especially Middle America, and South America north of the equator, population is markedly concentrated in the cooler uplands. Nearly two-thirds of Mexico's people live in the higher, cooler, and more humid southern portion of that country's central plateau. Mountain and plateau location

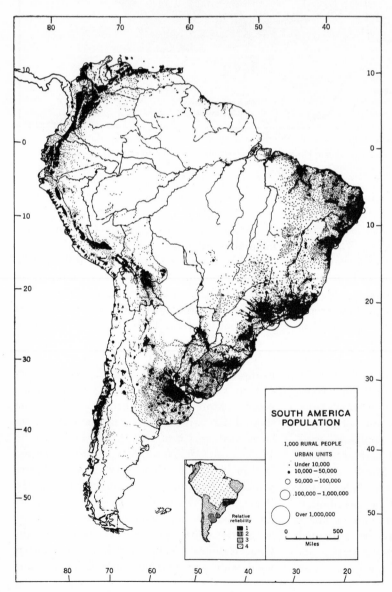

Fig. 25.11 Population in South America is concentrated in relatively isolated clusters around the perimeter of the continent. (*From Preston E. James, "Latin America," 2d ed., The Odyssey Press.*)

tends to isolate the individual population clusters from each other so that anything like a national consciousness is difficult of achievement.

Throughout South America the people tend to concentrate along the margins of the continent, leaving the interior relatively empty of settlement (Fig. 25.11). Dry southern Argentina and the interior wet tropical lowlands of the expanded northern part of the continent contain only a sprinkling of people. The margins of the continent are more attractive for settlement where the highlands provide an escape from tropical heat, as they do in Venezuela, Colombia, Ecuador, and eastern Brazil. Moreover, the ocean serves as a highway and provides what is the only efficient means of intercommunication for many important settlement areas. A pattern consisting of several distinct and relatively isolated centers of population is characteristic of eastern South America. In northeast Brazil the high density reflects the early importance of tropical agriculture when African slaves were used in great numbers. Farther south, the centers of population around Rio de Janeiro and Santos, and including the upland metropolis of São Paulo, reflect an agricultural economy based upon such commercial crops as coffee and cotton. The middle-latitude settlement cluster on the plains of the Rio de la Plata in Argentina and Uruguay is associated with one of the world's great regions of surplus agricultural production and the ports of Buenos Aires, Montevideo, and Rosario that serve it.

Australia's 9 million people are likewise marginal in location and concentrated chiefly along the subtropical southeastern seaboard. Much of interior and western Australia is too dry for agricultural land use, and the humid tropical climate of the northern part has likewise been a deterrent to settlement.

The Sahara, which is one of the earth's largest empty spaces, effectively divides Africa into two very unequal parts. Strangely, it is in the eastern Sahara that Africa's highest population densities are encountered, for in Egypt, on the delta and floodplain of the Nile, the ratio of people to land rises to 1,500 per square mile. Thus the Nile oasis stands out sharply by contrast with the adjoining barrenness of the great desert. To the north of the Sahara in northwest Africa bordering the Mediterranean Sea, the increased rainfall has permitted the development of a moderately dense population based largely upon agriculture.

South of the Sahara the spread of population is very uneven. Least well occupied is the dry region of southwestern Africa, but there are large areas in central tropical Africa as well where densities are relatively low. In other parts of tropical Africa, however, especially the western Sudan and the Guinea Coast lands, the ratio of people to land is relatively high. Nigeria, one of the populous states, is estimated to have a population of nearly 25 million. The reasons for these wide variations within tropical Africa are not clear. Other areas of population concentration are the East African uplands, including the Abyssinian Highlands, and the humid southern and southeastern margins of the continent, including both lowland and upland areas.

Density of Population

25.23 The Simple Man-Land Ratio. How much land there is to how many people is a fundamental consideration in the life of any society. This relationship of number of men to area of land is called the *man-land ratio,* which, in its simplest form, may be expressed as the number of persons per unit of area (square mile or square kilometer). This is sometimes known as the simple *arithmetic density* of population. In 1955, the earth's population was estimated to be about 2.6 billion, which, expressed in terms of the man-land ratio, was 45 persons per square mile of land surface. But this figure fails to provide a very realistic picture of actual conditions, since human life is by no means evenly distributed over the continents. It appears, then, that the idea of density is almost inextricably tied up with that of distribution. Only where people are dispersed rather widely and evenly over an area is the figure for average arithmetic density alone highly significant (Plate 7).

25.24 Other Forms of Population Density. Even in regions where human beings are widely and evenly dispersed, the simple ratio of people to area is usually not a very satisfactory measure of *real* density, or the pressure of population on the resource base. This is because equal areas vary greatly in their potentialities for supporting populations. Contrasts in climate, terrain, soil, and economic minerals provide one variable, while populations in different stages of development and with contrasting abilities to use what the physical earth has to offer provide still another. If, for example, the ice-covered continent of Antarctica, with an estimated area of 5 million square miles, and without any permanent settlements, were to receive 100 inhabitants, it probably could be called overpopulated, since it has so few resources for supporting human life. On the other hand, the fertile Nile and Yangtze plains can support 500 persons on 1 square mile—twenty-five million times the previous density—and still not be considered greatly overpopulated. It becomes obvious that simple arithmetic density, or total population divided by total area, is not adequate to measure population pressure.

If in the denominator of the man-land ratio one were able to substitute for total area a figure which represented *productive capacity*, a much better representation of real density could be obtained. This is known as the general *economic density* of population. The figure for productive capacity of land is not so easily arrived at, however, since the natural equipment of a region is not one but a variety of items. The geographer, trained as he is in the various aspects of natural earth, appears to be best equipped to make this contribution relative to the total natural potentialities of regions.

A more realistic measure of population concentration is *physiological density* which substitutes cultivated area for total area in the denominator of the man-land ratio. It is more realistic because it omits that part of the land area which is agriculturally unproductive, although to be sure such land may have some economic value for recreational purposes or as

a source for fuel or lumber. As an example, in Japan where only about 15 per cent of the land is cultivated, the arithmetic density of population in 1956 is 600 per square mile but the physiological density approaches 4,000 per square mile.

A somewhat different concept is provided by *agricultural density* which is simply the number of agricultural people per square mile or kilometer of cultivated land. It is the countries with relatively high arithmetic densities of population, large percentages of which are engaged in agriculture, that show high agricultural densities (Fig. 25.12). Thus in highly industrialized and urbanized Britain where only 5 per cent of the active population is employed in agriculture the agricultural density is low, while in a country like China where the farming population constitutes a large percentage of the total the agricultural density is high. Using Japan as a specific example. Here the arithmetic density is 600 and the physiological density is around 4,000 but the agricultural density in this country, where 45 per cent of the population is on farms, is nearly 1,800 persons per square mile.

Density of Population for Continents, Subcontinents, and Selected Countries for about 1950

	Persons per Square Mile	Persons per Square Mile of Cultivated Land
WORLD TOTAL	45.5	500
North America	22.5	230
United States	49.0	215
Canada	27.5	102
Puerto Rico	628.0	1,600
South America	15.5	335
Brazil	14.5	640
Paraguay	7.5	215
Europe	207.0	685
Belgium	720.0	2,150
United Kingdom	531.0	1,600
France	193.0	495
Italy	396.5	710
Germany	500.0	1,285
U.S.S.R.	23.0	230
Asia	123.0	1,000
Japan	547.5	3,500
China	121.5	1,285
India	298.0	800
Africa	17.0	295
Belgian Congo	11.5	70
Sudan	12.5	3,200
Egypt	49.5	2,150
Oceania	4.0	180

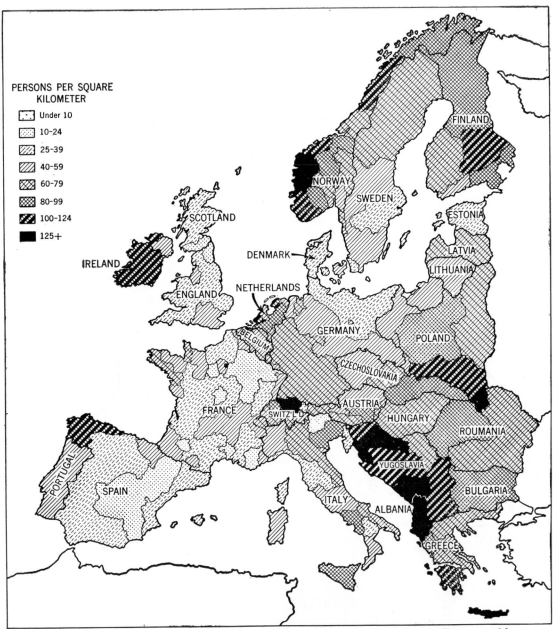

Fig. 25.12 Density of agricultural population in western and central Europe. Compare with Fig. 25.13 showing general density. Some areas with very high general arithmetic density, such as England, do not have a high agricultural density, while other regions, such as Yugoslavia and parts of Norway with relatively low general density, have very high agricultural density. (*From Wilbert E. Moore, "Economic Demography of Eastern and Southern Europe." Map prepared by the Office of Population Research, Princeton University.*)

25.25 The General Economic Density of Population in Complex Civilizations. The problem of comparing population density and productive capacity of land becomes further complicated in those regions where men do not live directly from the soil. There is no *simple* way of expressing the potential capacity of areas for supporting population in a complex industrial and commercial civilization. In order to evaluate the general economic density of a country it is necessary to consider, in addition to the agricultural productivity, the various natural resources independent of the soil, such as minerals, timber, fish, and scenery. Additional items to be evaluated are the degree of actual exploitation of these resources and the proportional use of other factors such as capital, quantity and quality of labor, and degree of technical development. For example, the United Kingdom's 50,000,000 people draw only a small part of their economic livelihood directly from the soil of the 94,000 square miles on which they live. Of prime importance in evaluating that country's capacity for supporting human life is its supply of mineral resources, especially coal. With coal as the principal source of industrial power Britain draws

raw materials and food from all parts of the world, processes the raw materials in British factories utilizing her accumulated capital and her abundance of high-quality labor, and returns the finished materials again to the far corners of the earth. On the other hand, in simple rural civilizations that are composed of self-sufficient peasant families, the direct relationship between number of people and productive capacity of land is not so difficult to observe. So difficult is it to evaluate the general economic density for the various regions of the world that comparative data are as yet not available.

25.26 Density Distribution. In the preceding discussion concerned with the distribution of *numbers* of people and the patterns result-

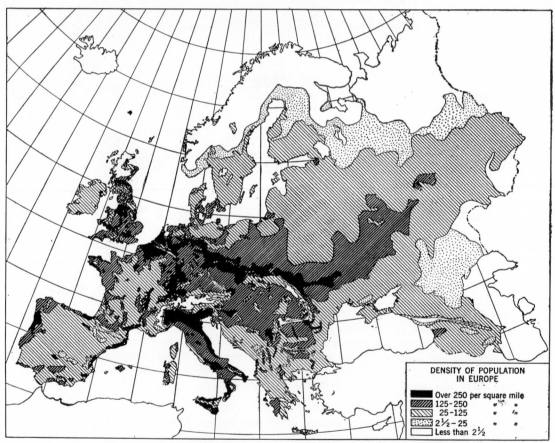

Fig. 25.13 Over most of Europe high density of population is relatively coincident with strongly industrialized and urbanized areas. (*Map by Weise. Reproduced by Mark Jefferson and published in The Geographical Review.*)

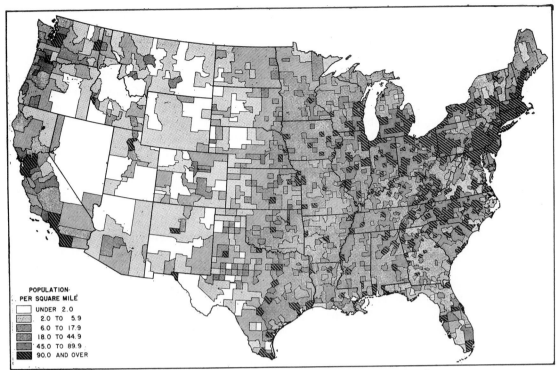

Fig. 25.14 (*Courtesy of U.S. Department of Commerce.*)

POPULATION·
PER SQUARE MILE
UNDER 2.0
2.0 TO 5.9
6.0 TO 17.9
18.0 TO 44.9
45.0 TO 89.9
90.0 AND OVER

ing, for the world as a whole and for the individual continents and even for a few countries, impressions concerning *relative* densities of different regions have been obtained from the dot maps employed. From such maps, however, numerical density readings are impossible. A more precise and quantitative expression of arithmetic population density can be observed from Plate 7 and Figs. 25.13 and 25.14. Admittedly arithmetic density is far from being a satisfactory index of actual population pressure upon the resource base, but its use is made necessary since figures for more refined ratios are not at present available for much of the earth.

On the world map (Plate 7) the most extensive areas of high arithmetic densities, where population exceeds 250 per square mile, are in (*a*) eastern and southeastern Asia, (*b*) western and central Europe, and (*c*) northeastern United States. Within the Orient, which contains the largest areas with high densities, it is eastern China, the Ganges lowland in northern India and Pakistan, and the coastal lowlands of peninsular India, Japan, Java, and southern and western Korea that show extensive areas with over 250 persons per square mile.

In Europe it is the east-west population axis previously described, reaching from southern Britain, Belgium, and Holland on the west to the Ukraine in the U.S.S.R. on the east, that forms the conspicuous belt of high density (Fig. 25.13). This is the continent's industrial belt as well. A southward projection from the east-west axis follows along the industrialized middle Rhine Valley as far as the Alps. The Po Valley and other plains in peninsular Italy, Sicily, and the lowlands of southern France and eastern Spain are smaller but still important areas of high population density. In the United States it is the urban industrialized northeastern part, more especially the Atlantic Seaboard states from southern New England to Maryland and the areas bordering the lower Great Lakes, that have densities exceeding 250 per square mile.

Within the three extensive world regions

showing high population densities there are a number of striking contrasts. Chief of these is the fact that in Asia the high densities are those of rural peoples, while in Europe and the United States they are to a larger degree urban populations supported by trade and manufacturing. Moreover, within any of the regions shown in Plate 7 where *average* densities exceed 250 per square mile, there are great variations within different localities, with some districts far exceeding the general average. Such variations can be shown only on a much more detailed map. For example, on the Yangtze lowlands of China the population density is nearly 900 per square mile, on the North China Plain close to 650, and on the plains of Bengal in northeastern India over 600. In several fairly extensive urban areas in Europe and northeastern United States the density figure is several thousand per square mile.

The unusually high rural population densities characteristic of eastern and southern Asia are made possible by the type of agriculture practiced there. Almost exclusively it is an agricultural technology based upon the exploitation of the vegetable kingdom. Animal products are little used for either food or clothing. Several times more food calories can be produced on an acre of land in rice or wheat than on a similar area devoted to grazing milk animals. It follows, therefore, that a much larger farm population can be supported by a type of agriculture emphasizing crops than by a mixed agriculture involving animals as well as crops.

Very low densities of less than two per square mile are characteristic of the subarctic and tundra areas of the Northern Hemisphere continents, most of the deserts, and large parts of the wet tropics in South America. Although it is true that the general lineaments of the world pattern of population densities are directly related to the productive capacities of the lands, the details of the pattern show many exceptions. Not only the natural productivity of regions, but also many social, historical, and political factors are involved in understanding the details of population densities in the various parts of the world.

25.27 Population Migration. Throughout history the distribution of population has changed from period to period as a result of (a) differential rates of natural increase in the various earth regions as determined by fertility and mortality rates and (b) the migration of peoples. Some of the most important events in world history are associated with large-scale movements of human beings in the process of abandoning their former homeland for some more or less permanent new domicile. Such a migration occurred when the Aryan ancestors of the present Hindus left the desert and oasis environment of Turkistan, crossed the mountain barriers of northwestern India, and occupied the better-watered lands of the plains of Hindustan. The populating of Anglo-America by floods of immigrants from Europe is a more recent example of a migration of gigantic proportions which changed the course of world history. Some migrations have been of long duration extending over centuries; others were much more restricted in time.

Wherever large-scale movements of people occur, important modifications result both in the emigrating group and in the original inhabitants of the land being occupied. Thus the European invasion of North America resulted in a near extermination of the aboriginal peoples of that region, and there was very little mingling of the cultures of the resident and immigrant groups. In Latin America, on the other hand, where the Indian civilization was more advanced than it was farther north, there resulted a much greater fusion of native and European cultures and the very large mestizo element in the present population is the result.

25.28 *The Causes of Large-scale Migrations.* There are migrations which are the result of *physical* causes, while others have been of *socioeconomic* origin. Among the physical causes of migration may be mentioned such items as gradual climatic changes or great cataclysms such as floods or famine. Such causes were probably more important in motivating primitive migrations than they are in those in more advanced societies. Some scholars are of the opinion that the outpourings of the nomadic peoples of dry inner Asia on several occasions during the Middle Ages, and their invasion of the more humid lands of China to the east and of Europe to the west, were associated with long periods of serious drought in the homeland of the invaders.

Of greater importance in motivating large-scale movements of peoples are the socioeconomic causes. Many of the earlier migrations of great magnitude or of great consequence were associated with (*a*) *invasion* in which primitive and more virile peoples forced their way into the domain of a culturally more advanced state or (*b*) *conquest* in which an advanced state attacked more backward peoples and subsequently incorporated them and their domain into its own politically controlled area. The barbarian invasions which led to the fall of the Roman Empire belong to the first class, while the earlier conquests of the Roman legions leading to the expanded Roman Empire were of the second variety.

Large-scale movements of people also may be state initiated and take the form of (*c*) *colonization,* of either the exploitive or free type, and (*d*) forced or free migration. Exploitive colonization characteristically involved a movement of only small numbers of residents from the mother country, chiefly administrators, soldiers, and businessmen. Settlement colonization, by contrast, involved much larger numbers of subjects. Forced migration in the past took the form of slave trading and the deportation of undesirables, such as convicts and religious and political dissenters. Modern forced migration reached flood tide during the Second World War as refugees fled before the invading armies and Nazi Germany developed its slave-labor program involving the transfer of millions of conquered peoples to work in German war industries. It is estimated that some 20 million people were uprooted from their homes by the war and forced to migrate. Perhaps half of this number represented foreigners who were recruited or forced to work in Germany. About 2 million alien fugitives, chiefly Poles, migrated to the U.S.S.R., while over 1 million Jews left Europe just prior to and during the war. Free migration, whose motive is the prospect for economic better-

ment, is chiefly a product of the nineteenth and twentieth centuries. To an unusual degree it involved Europeans seeking to establish new homes in other continents.

25.29 *Intercontinental Migrations.* By far the greatest of the intercontinental migrations was that which occurred during the seventeenth to the twentieth centuries as European peoples spread to the new lands of the Americas and to Australia, New Zealand, and South Africa. The flood tide of this movement occurred in the nineteenth century and early twentieth, when between the years 1846 and 1932 more than 50 milllion emigrated from Europe, thereby not only populating the new lands in which they settled, but carrying to them as well the elements of European culture. In the new soil of the Americas, Australia, and South Africa the seeds of European civilization produced sturdy plants which, while they strongly resembled the parent stock, bore earmarks of the new environment as well.

The first European emigration, that of the seventeenth and eighteenth centuries, was associated with the colonial policies of the several European countries, most of which were interested in those regions capable of being exploited for their precious minerals or stones or for such rare products as spices. Great Britain was the only European power at that time whose demographic and economic conditions permitted the sending abroad of large numbers of immigrants qualified to establish productive settlements. It was that country, therefore, which eventually acquired political control of most of the new lands lying within the middle latitudes. The total number of emigrants leaving the British Isles for the New World in the seventeenth century was about 500,000 and in the eighteenth century, 1,500,000. The total German intercontinental migration up until the beginning of the nineteenth century is estimated to have been about 200,000.

The nineteenth century saw a decline in European emigration associated with government-sponsored colonization and a gigantic expansion in free emigration. By the middle of the century the annual departures from the British Isles reached 300,000; in 1854, 240,000

Germans left the homeland, of whom 215,000 went to the United States. Between 1840 and 1880, a total of 9,500,000 immigrants, 90 per cent of them from Europe, entered the United States. In the decade following the American Civil War, the annual emigration from Europe averaged around 350,000 to 375,000.

25.30 *Intracontinental and Intranational Migrations.* Of the above types, the one of most outstanding importance to American students has been the westward movement of population in the United States contemporaneous with advance of the frontier. The West was settled from the East. It was this migration westward of population and the frontier that brought about the agricultural development of the country. Up until about the time of the Revolutionary War population was concentrated in the Atlantic Seaboard colonies, and to the east of the Appalachian barrier. By 1860 the westward migration was so far advanced that states as far west as Ohio, Kentucky, and Tennessee were losing more people than they were gaining by migration. The great westward movement of population continued until 1920, after which year the great flow into California was its only manifestation.

In the period just preceding the Second World War some of the largest streams of population movement existed in eastern Asia. From North China there went annually over 1 million people into the frontier lands of northern Manchuria. Another stream of Chinese emigrants, chiefly from South China, moved toward the less well-populated regions of Malaya, Siam, Indo-China, and the East Indies, omitting Java. From the densely populated delta lands of Bengal there was an important trek toward the less completely settled Assam Valley.

Another type of international migration has been that associated with a movement from rural to urban areas, a type which accompanies industrialization and urbanization. In the United States agricultural settlement had extended over the entire country by 1930, for during the decade 1920–1930 almost all the agricultural states were giving up population

to the industrial areas. The increasing mechanization of agriculture, especially after 1920, which decreased the amount of farm labor necessary, and the great industrial expansion in the northeastern part of the country, has tended somewhat to reverse the earlier westward flow of population in the United States. As early as 1890 New Jersey, Massachusetts, and Rhode Island were gaining population by migration from other states. It was not until the decade 1920–1930 that Illinois and Indiana had a net gain of migrant population because of enlarged industrial activity. During the decade 1920–1930 the rate of increase in urban population for the entire country was more than six times the rural rate, indicating a very large rural-urban migration. The result was a net migration from farms to cities of more than 8 million people, 75 per cent of them 25 years of age or younger.

Similar rural-urban migrations have occurred in other rapidly industrializing countries. In Japan during the two decades 1920–1940, urban population increased from 32 to 50 per cent of the nation's total, while rural population declined in the same proportion. During this same period, population outside communities of 30,000 or more remained almost static, so that the total national increase of over 17 million must have been absorbed by the cities.

25.31 *Daily and seasonal migrations* of labor comprise still another phase of population movement. Between 1907 and 1913, Argentina annually recruited about 60,000 laborers from Italy and Spain to work in her harvest fields. Following the harvest season they returned again to their homelands. A few decades ago, before laborsaving machinery was so common on American farms, 250,000 transient laborers were required for the grain harvest. They began their work at the southern margins of the winter grain region in early summer and moved northward with the harvest season. Before the First World War 5 to 7 million Russians made periodic journeys to work on farms and in factories. In California alone some 150,-000 transient laborers are employed in fruit picking.

Large-scale daily migrations of people are characteristic chiefly of large cities. The downtown section of any large city is an area of extraordinarily high population densities by day but, on the other hand, is relatively depopulated at night. This inward surge of people toward the heart of a metropolis in the morning, and toward the peripheral and suburban residential areas in late afternoon, is a recognized feature of almost all urban areas. Such large-scale commuting is made possible only by efficient communication systems.

Population Characteristics and Their Distribution

25.32 As suggested in an earlier section, analyses of numbers of people, their distribution patterns, and their densities are not an adequate geographical treatment of population. This is because numbers represent essentially a count of men's bodies whose energy potentials are not radically different from one part of the earth to another. More fundamental population contrasts are to be discovered in the acquired qualities of men's minds, their training, and their cultural heritage. Certain it is that how, and the degree to which, man uses the earth and how he modifies its surface, how much he produces and consumes, as well as his physical well-being, in fact the sum total of his cultural accomplishments as expressed in the inclusive term civilization is related not alone to mere numbers of people, but even much more to their characteristics or qualities. The 7 per cent of the world's population living in Anglo-America, trained to use inanimate power and machines, is said to accomplish one-half of the world's work. Clearly a map showing distribution of population by the dot method, on which identically the same number of points or dots is made to represent 1,000 illiterate and primitive natives of Amazonia and also 1,000 highly civilized inhabitants of Sweden, is totally inadequate as a representation of the potentialities of these two groups as either producers or consumers.

The various characteristics which cause the population of the earth to differ markedly from one part to another are numerous. Unfortunately many of these qualities have never been enumerated or mapped so that an accurate description of world distribution of most population qualities is impossible at the present time. Two main classes of population quality may be recognized: (*a*) those which are physical in character and are chiefly the attributes of the bodies of men and (*b*) those which are cultural in their origins, socioeconomic in character, and hence indexes of civilization.

25.33 Physical Characteristics. Among the physical qualities are such items as skull size and shape, body weight and height, and color of hair and skin. But none of these, except possibly skin color, appear to have much functional significance in affecting man as either a producer or consumer. Modern censuses usually tabulate three physical characteristics of population which are of considerable value in a comparative regional analysis of population quality. They are (*a*) race and nativity, (*b*) balance between the sexes, and (*c*) age composition. While race or nationality is not indicative of inherent potentialities, it is, nevertheless, often suggestive of cultural backgrounds, economic status, and differentials in terms of birth rates, death rates, intelligence quotients, and other important social indexes. In such countries as the United States, Malaya, and Brazil where the population is composed of two or more racial groups unequally distributed, there is little value in regional comparisons of population unless the data have first been segregated by race and nativity.

25.34 *Age composition* of population is one of its most significant qualities. For one thing it is an index of future population growth, for young populations have higher fertility potentials. It is an indication, also, of (*a*) the actual and potential labor force in a nation, (*b*) the potential magnitude of the reservoir of military man power, (*c*) and the future size of the groups for which educational opportunities must be planned. Welfare organizations, planning boards, government bureaus, employers of labor—all are in need of such data. The stage which a region or country has reached in the aging process is indicated by the proportion of people in the population who are under 15 or over 65 years of age. In the United States the aging process has gone a long way, for in 1950 only 27.5 per cent of the population was under 15, in contrast to 32 per cent in 1910, 38 per cent in 1880, and 42 per cent in 1850. The larger areas of the earth where there has been a marked aging of the population are northwestern and central Europe, the United States, Canada, Australia, and New Zealand (Fig. 25.15). By contrast the people of the U.S.S.R., southern Europe, Central and South America, Africa, and Asia are much younger. In these regions the indications are that 35 to 40 per cent of the population are under 15 years of age while the comparable figure for western Europe is 20 to 25 per cent. It will be noted that the older populations are characteristic of highly industrialized and ur-

banized countries where birth and death rates are relatively low, while nations which are predominantly agrarian in their economies are likely to have younger populations.

25.35 *The sex balance,* or the relative proportions of men and women in a population, is likewise a physical quality of importance. Unfortunately data relating to the proportion of men and women in the population are not available for large parts of the earth. Since women tend to live longer than men, in those regions of the world with aging populations, women are likely to be in excess of men in the total population. Thus in England there are 1,088 women for every 1,000 men. In addition, war casualties are usually more serious for the male population which is further reason why women strongly predominate in most of the countries of western Europe. Migrations are likely to involve men to a greater extent than women so that countries and regions of strong emigration, such as Italy, Norway, and Georgia, have a predominance of females, while by contrast in regions characterized by strong immigration, such as Canada, Australia, and California, males are more numerous. Many of the characteristics of the social, political, and economic life of regions and communities are related to this aspect of population, as are the magnitude and quality of the labor force.

25.36 *Health.* Probably the single most important physical quality of a population is its state of physical well-being or its health. That health is not identical with the absence of disease is obvious; still there is a relationship. Unfortunately medical science has paid little attention to people who are healthy so that much of the information that is available is concerned with one negative aspect of health, *viz.,* disease, and with individual diseases at that. Whole populations in large areas of the wet tropics are so infested with malaria, hookworm, dysentery, and other debilitating diseases as to make the people unfit for vigorous physical or mental effort. Still another oblique way of gauging the health of different populations is through their diets. Large parts of the world's population live at substandard levels of physical

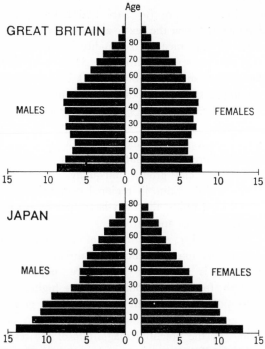

Fig. 25.15 Age pyramids for an aging population (Great Britain) and for a relatively young population (Japan). Where a large percentage of the population is contained in the younger age groups, a relatively rapid future growth is more likely.

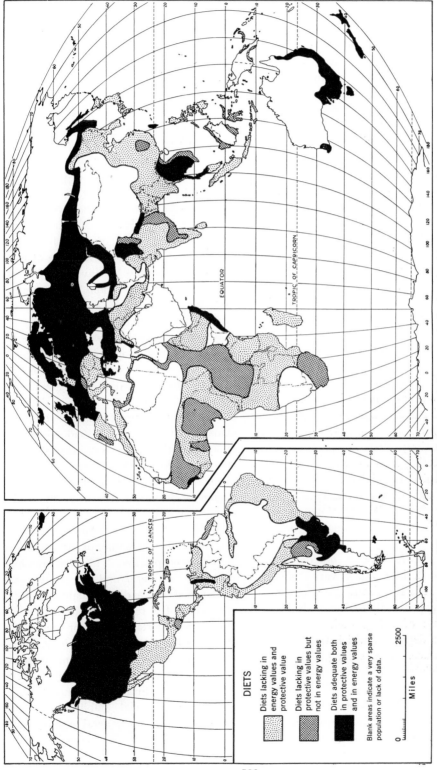

Fig. 25.16 Diet is one indirect measure of the general physical health of a population. As a rule a superior diet is characteristic of those parts of the world that have experienced the greatest technological advances. (*Generalized from map by Jacques May, published by the American Geographical Society.*)

DIETS

Diets lacking in energy values and protective value

Diets lacking in protective values but not in energy values

Diets adequate both in protective values and in energy values

Blank areas indicate a very sparse population or lack of data.

0   Miles   2500

well-being because their diets do not provide the essential ingredients for good health (Fig. 25.16).

As a rule, the general population health, as measured by such indices as average length of life, increase in human stature, and number of doctors and hospital beds per unit of population, is highest in regions of advanced industrial civilization (western Europe, the United States, Canada, Australia, and New Zealand) and lowest in the underdeveloped and industrially backward areas.

25.37   The cultural or socioeconomic qualities of populations likewise show great regional variations and from this fact arise many of the earth's greatest geographical contrasts of an economic and political nature. These cultural qualities of population are very numerous. They include among others, religious beliefs, educational status, marital status, occupational status, place of residence (rural or urban), and stage of economic development, this latter quality including a people's technological skills. Less tangible qualities of a population, but perhaps no less significant, are such features as prejudices, customs and habits, and different kinds of loyalties and allegiances. Some of these qualities greatly affect man as an agent of economic production; others are of more consequence in affecting man as a consumer and enjoyer of the fruits of his labors. Most of these qualities are of a kind not revealed in census enumerations so that their general world patterns of distribution are only vaguely understood.

25.38   *Religious belief* and practice is a population characteristic which varies widely over the earth. It is likewise a powerful motivating agent which directly or indirectly influences men's ways of living, their use of resources, and the degree to which they modify the earth's surface. The stifling effects of authoritarian religion which was more concerned with appeasing an angry and whimsical god than improving the well-being of humanity resulted in the Middle Ages being literally the Dark Ages. The less religious ancient Greeks appear to have been happier and accustomed to good living on a much higher plane than were religion-suffocated Europeans of the Middle Ages. On the other hand, where religion has been relatively more interested in men and their earthly welfare then in dogma, creed, and ritual it has had a greatly beneficial effect on population. Education, holidays and festivals, landholding systems, literature and the arts, and diet are only a few of the human enterprises which are affected one way or another, and to a greater or less degree, by religious beliefs.

25.39   *Educational status*, without doubt, is one of the best indicators of population quality, for the amount and quality of schooling received by children are a measure of the extent to which a society is investing in the well-being of future generations. Unfortunately data on educational status are available only for restricted areas of the earth. Until recently the only index available was the percentage of literacy, or the proportion of the population that could read or write. And for 40 per cent of the earth's population even literacy data are not available. Lowest rates of illiteracy are characteristic of western Europe, United States, Canada, Australia, New Zealand, and Japan. It appears that there is a correlation between regions of low illiteracy and those with low death rates, low or moderate birth rates, a high degree of technical advancement, and representative government.

25.40   *Residence* is a quality of population which refers to the nature of the settlement units in which people live. The two principal divisions are (*a*) *rural* and (*b*) *urban*. Actually, residence is less a direct quality of population and more of a recognition that as a result of residence important traits or qualities develop. Thus rural society stands in sharp contrast to urban society in such items as population density, size of settlement clusters, degree of ethnic and cultural homogeneity, and occupational and social stability. Unfortunately there has been no general agreement among nations relative to what constitutes a city so that the boundary between rural and urban is indefinite and variable. As a consequence comparative studies of residence for different parts of the earth are made very difficult.

The earth as a whole is still predominantly rural in character with about 70 per cent of its population living in places with fewer than 5,000 people. Three-quarters of the earth's population is still to be found in countries that are characterized by peasant agricultural economies. The four regions that are most highly urbanized—northwestern Europe, the United States and Canada, Australia, and southern South America—contain only 21 per cent of the earth's total population but at the same time 45 per cent of those living in cities of over 100,000. This uneven distribution of urban intensity to a considerable degree reflects the effects of the Industrial Revolution which began in Europe and subsequently spread to many other parts of the earth. Characteristically, urbanism has gone hand in hand with the spread of the European industrial civilization. It is not always coincident with over-all dense populations, for some regions, like those in the Southern Hemisphere, became urbanized without acquiring dense populations (Figs. 26.12, 25.17, and 25.18).

25.41 *Occupational status* as a quality of population ranks among those of the very highest importance, for the nature of a man's work largely determines the physical and cultural environment in which he works. These in turn influence his personality traits and are closely associated with such phenomena as health, longevity, educational status, and birth rates. In a modern census, data on occupational status are relatively abundant, for this is rceognized as being one of the most significant qualities of population. Of high rank among the items listed under the general heading of occupational status is that which differentiates between those who are gainfully employed (the labor force) and those who are not. The size, quality, and variations in the labor force and the proportion of it in the several occupational groups and in particular industries are refine-

ments of the primary data which geographers find of great usefulness.

25.42 One final quality of population should be mentioned, *viz.,* the degree to which a people is advanced in *technological skills* as evidenced by their use of inanimate energy and machines. It has been suggested that all cultural history can be interpreted as an increasing and improved control over energy. This is not to imply that physical equipment is all that is essential for the efficient use of mechanical energy; equally as much it involves efficient social, political, and economic institutions. The industrial economy often appears in disguised forms. Its most obvious form is represented by the central power station, the locomotive, or the tractor. In less obvious form it assumes the guise of the mathematical formula, banking systems, and efficient government. The aim of the energy economy is more bountiful living and greater economic security.

In terms of total energy consumed the United States leads the world. The *per capita* en-

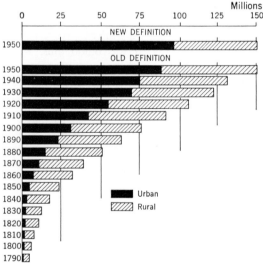

Fig. 25.17 Over the past century the population of the United States has become increasingly urban in character, with a relatively smaller proportion of the people continuing to live outside of cities.

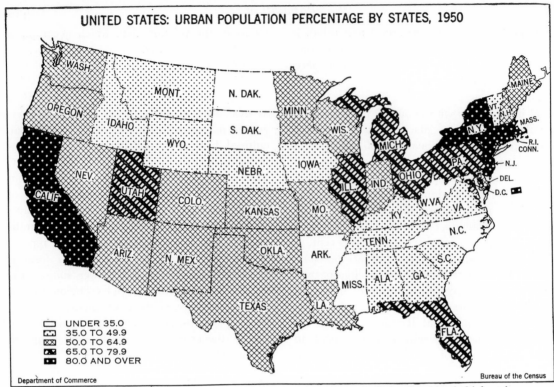

Fig. 25.18 Within the United States the proportion of people living in cities is highest in the industrialized northeast and in California and Florida. The least urbanized sections are the agricultural areas of the southeast and northwest.

ergy consumption in 1950 was nearly 8,000 metric tons of coal equivalent. In Canada, holding second rank, it was 6,300 tons, while in a group of countries in western Europe and in Australia and South Africa it varied between one-fourth and one-half of the consumption in the United States. By contrast the consumption in most parts of Latin America, Asia, and Africa is very low. The per capita consumption of power in the United States is seventy-two times that in India, fifty-three times that in Egypt, and thirty-six times that in Brazil. To an overwhelming degree that quality of population represented by an advanced stage of technological development and the use of machine power is concentrated in Anglo-America and Europe.

Selected References on Population

Beaujeu-Garnier, Jacqueline. "Geographie de la Population." Librairie de Médicis, Paris, 1956.

Bowman, Isaiah (editor). "Limits of Land Settlement: A Report on Present-day Possibilities." Council on Foreign Relations, New York, 1937.

Broek, Jan O. M. Climate and Future Settlement.

Yearbook of Agriculture, 1941. Pp. 227–236. U.S. Department of Agriculture, Washington, D.C., 1941.

Davis, Kingsley, and Hilda Hertz. The World Distribution of Urbanization, *Bull. Intern. Statist. Inst.,* Vol. 35, pp. 227–241, 1952.

Demographic Studies of Selected Areas of Rapid Growth. Milbank Memorial Fund, New York, 1944.

The Demographic Yearbook, United Nations, New York. Published annually. The single most important source for current statistics on population.

The Determinants and Consequences of Population Growth. *Population Studies,* No. 17, United Nations, New York, 1953. A rich compendium of information on various aspects of population.

Fawcett, C. B. The Numbers and Distribution of Mankind. *Smithsonian Rept.* 1948, pp. 383–392.

George, Pierre. "Introduction a l'étude géographique de la population du monde." Presses Universitaries de France, Paris, 1951.

Hankins, Frank H. Pressure of Population as a Cause of War. *Ann. Amer. Acad. Pol. Soc. Sci.,* Vol. 198, pp. 101–108, 1938.

Huxley, Julian. World Population. *Scientific American,* Vol. 194, pp. 64–76, March, 1956.

Price, A. Grenfell. "White Settlers in the Tropics." *American Geographical Society Special Publication* 23, New York, 1939.

Taeuber, Irene B. Migration and Population Potential of Monsoon Asia. *The Milbank Memorial Fund Quarterly,* Vol. XXV, pp. 21–43, January, 1947.

Taracouzio, Timothy Andrew. "Soviets in the Arctic: An Historical, Economic, and Political Study of the Soviet Advance into the Arctic." The Macmillan Company, New York, 1938.

Thompson, Warren S. "Population and Peace in the Pacific." University of Chicago Press, Chicago, 1946.

Thornthwaite, C. Warren. "Internal Migration in the United States." Pp. 5–18. University of Pennsylvania Press, Philadelphia, 1934.

World Population in Transition. *Ann. Amer. Acad. Pol. Soc. Sci.,* Vol. 237, January, 1945.

PART THREE

Cultural Elements of Geography

FEATURES RESULTING FROM MAN'S USE OF THE PHYSICAL EARTH

Introduction

Thus far two great groups of geographic elements have been analyzed and their distributions described: (*a*) the natural or physical elements and (*b*) population. It now remains to treat those elements which are the consequence of population occupying the physical earth and making use of its resources. These are termed the cultural elements. Among the most important of the cultural elements are those which are associated with the efforts of human beings to make a living, *i.e.,* the facts of land utilization, including agriculture, manufacturing, and trade.

Unfortunately there does not exist any such careful and systematic ordering and classification of the earth's man-made or culture features, their characteristics and origins, as there is for its natural features. This, in part, may reflect the greater difficulty in classifying the less orderly array of man-induced features, as compared with those resulting from natural forces, since human beings are not governed by natural laws as are rivers and winds but by minds through which they are able to frustrate environment or adapt it to their needs. Man's acts are not entirely the result even of reason, for what he does is often influenced by whims and prejudices as well, so that the works of his hands may lack that orderliness and system characteristic of natural forms. This may help to explain why human geographies, unlike physical geographies, are rarely a classification and analysis of the elements of the subject, but rather are topical and regional treatments of associated cultural features.

A second reason for the more complete analysis and classification now available for the natural features as compared with the cultural is that a number of specialized earth sciences have been at work on the problem of analyzing and classifying physical phenomena: geology and geomorphology on the nature and distribution of earth materials and landforms, pedology on soils, meteorology and climatology on atmospheric conditions, biology on plant and animal distributions. Each of these sciences has aided geography by providing it with basic materials on a particular phase of the natural earth. There has been no equivalent contribution to human geography from the various social sciences.

It is immediately noticeable that the size of Part Three of this book dealing with the cultural elements is by no means equal to that of Part One which sets forth the natural elements. *This discrepancy between the sizes of Parts One and Three in no way indicates the authors' concept of the relative importance of the natural and cultural elements in geography.* It chiefly reflects a fundamental contrast in the nature of the two groups of elements and of the materials bearing on the genesis and distribution of them. There are clearly defined world patterns in *types* of climate, soil, and native vegetation, and it is this fact that makes possible a relatively complete analysis of the distributional aspects of those natural elements. But world patterns are not so clear for types of settlements, trade, manufacturing, or even of agriculture. In these elements there is much greater regional individuality, and as a consequence less in the way of generalized types which are repeated on the several continents. Any discussion of the cultural elements, therefore, is compelled to deal more with particular instances and regions than with types that are world wide in scope. Such a discussion does not warrant the same elaboration as one that is focused upon world types.

The discussion of the more important elements of human geography, included within the following chapters, attempts to introduce the beginner in geography to the general content of that field. In brief fashion it brings to his attention the more important groups of features inscribed by human beings upon the regions that they occupy. It is suggestive of the kinds of things, along with others of a physical nature, that one would observe and record on a map or in a notebook if he were making a geographic study of a region. No attempt is made to describe the human geography for the whole earth or for any part of it. The emphasis is upon *types* of land use and of material culture rather than upon a complete covering of the field of human geography. Nor has it been felt necessary to be consistent and logical in treating all the various forms of land use and their associated cultural features. For example, the extractive economies such as mining, hunting, fishing, trapping, and logging are not analyzed in separate chapters of Part Three as are agriculture and manufacturing. Significant comments on these less important economies, however, are included in certain chapters of Part One.

26

Settlements

26.1 Definition. The term settlement, here used as a noun, refers to the characteristic groupings of population into occupance units, together with the facilities in the form of houses and streets which serve the inhabitants. These units vary in size and complexity from the simple isolated one-family farmstead of the Iowa prairies on one hand to the great urban metropolis such as New York or Chicago on the other. In either case, however, the farmstead or the metropolis, the settlement unit represents an organized colony of human beings together with the buildings in which they live or that they otherwise use and the paths and streets over which they travel.

Settlement geography is closely related to population geography, for the ultimate detail of population distribution is revealed in the size, spacing, and arrangement of the settlement units. Moreover, since settlements and their facilities are designed to serve specific purposes, settlements have functional meaning. Their exterior features are consequently a reflection of the numbers and characteristics of population at the time they were constructed—their economy, their architectural fashions, and their culture in general. For the historical geographer, interested as he is in a study of past geography, settlements provide a wealth of important and readily observable data.

It is unfortunately true that there does not exist at the present time sufficient reliable information to permit the writing of a satisfactory discussion of settlement types in terms of their world distributions and the principles involved in these distributions. Important as this geographic element is, therefore, the fol-

lowing brief analysis is obliged to be more in the nature of comments on the classification and characteristics of settlements in a few particular regions. Any world classification into types, with accompanying maps showing distribution of these types, like those provided in this book for some other geographic elements such as climate, vegetation, soils, and agriculture, is still impossible.

Settlement Types

26.2 Two Primary Types of Settlements. Based upon form and function, two great subdivisions of settlements may be recognized: (a) the *isolated,* or *dispersed,* type in which the single-family residence unit is the distinctive nucleus, as it is, for instance, on an American farmstead; (b) the *nucleated type* in which there is a collection of several or many family residences, together with other types of buildings (Fig. 26.1). Nucleated settlements are designated by various names according to their size and the complexity of their functions, *i.e.,* hamlets, villages, towns, and cities. In all of them, however, the two most visually conspicuous features are always the *buildings* and the *streets*. Nevertheless, it is the human beings who developed the buildings and the streets to serve their needs, and who function as a social and economic unit, that are the dynamic element within the settlement.

DISPERSED SETTLEMENTS

26.3 Character and Advantages of Dispersed Settlements. For the most part, dispersed settlement, where the one-family resi-

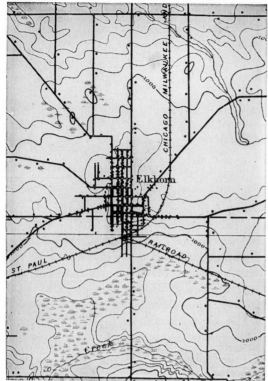

Fig. 26.1 Illustrating clustered and dispersed settlements. A market town in Wisconsin surrounded by isolated farmsteads. The latter are indicated by tiny black squares. (*Elkhorn Sheet.*)

dence stands isolated and apart from others, is characteristic of agricultural areas. In some parts of the world hunters, trappers, fishers, and miners may live in open-country dwellings, and, in the United States at least, there are fairly numerous nonfarm residences scattered throughout the rural areas. Nevertheless, for the world as a whole, the farmer is by far the most numerous open-country dweller. To such a degree is this true that the dispersed settlement unit is often taken to be synonymous with the farmstead.

The outstanding characteristic of dispersed settlement is the minute size of the settlement unit, *viz.*, the family, and the isolation and privacy in which it exists. Such isolated living tends to separate men psychologically as well as economically. Admittedly there are both advantages and disadvantages to this system of open-country living, the advantages being

chiefly economic and the disadvantages social. Economically the isolated farmstead, located on a compact and unified farm, has the advantage of keeping the farm family at its place of work and near the fields and animals that it cultivates and rears. There is not required the time-consuming movement between home and fields that is necessary when the farmer is a village dweller, with his scattered fields located at some distance from the residence. Freed from the restrictions associated with living in a village with other farmers and working the surrounding fields along lines developed for the village as a whole, the isolated farmer is much more independent as far as his methods of farm management are concerned. He is less obliged to conform to any pattern as set by others, and therefore the energetic, resourceful farmer is able to forge ahead of his less ambitious neighbors. Freer reign is given to individual initiative and enterprise so that there is less of a dead level in the farming population, and stagnation is less likely.

Many would argue that the offsetting social disadvantages of open-country dwelling more than counterbalance these economic advantages. They consider that whatever economic progress has been attained by the change from the farm village to the system of dispersed settlement has been at the expense of important losses in terms of social values. The sense of neighborly interdependence and the solidarity and strength fostered by the village communal agriculture are greatly weakened when farm families live isolated and alone on widely dispersed farmsteads.

The close, warm, communal life of the farm village, the feeling of being an integral part of the life of many men, is lacking. Moreover, the only neighbors of an American farmer are other farmers and they are at some distance, and this prevalence of men of his own vocation tends to weaken his sense of economic and social interdependence. The division of labor between different classes in a farm village serves as a constant reminder to its residents of neighborhood interdependence.

An additional social handicap in open-country

living is that the farmer labors much of the time alone. It is a lonesome labor unrelieved during long hours by association with his fellow men. Much of the farm work in rural villages, on the other hand, is done in groups or gangs, and this fellowship in labor introduces an element of the play spirit into even the most arduous work and relieves it of its boring qualities. This lightening of the load when men work together is experienced on an American farm chiefly on such occasions as silo filling and at threshing time.

26.4 Origin and Distribution. The historical record is not entirely clear as to the origin of dispersed settlement, but evidence seems to indicate that the rural village was by far the most common type of agricultural settlement prior to the enclosure of English open fields. Certainly before that event the prevailing custom was for farmers to live in rural villages. The movement for enclosures and the associated disintegration of the English farm village falls into two periods, 1485–1560 and 1760–1820. It grew out of a need for a more efficient and economical system of cultivation than was possible under the village type of agricultural settlement with its characteristic pattern of scattered fields with much land held in common. These same needs have caused the dispersed type of settlement to spread to other parts of the world as well.

At the present time the open-country type of rural settlement, with the individual farmstead set down in the midst of its fields, is almost universally characteristic of rural United States and of the agricultural sections of Canada. In the United States almost the only clear-cut example of the agglomerated farm-village type of rural settlement is to be found in the Mormon regions of Utah.

Outside Anglo-America dispersed rural settlement appears to be strongly characteristic of Australia and New Zealand, of the Scandinavian countries, the small Baltic States, and the British Isles in Europe, and of Argentina and Uruguay in South America. Smaller regions of dispersion, or regions where that form of rural settlement is less dominant, are the high-

land regions of Mexico, Costa Rica, and western Panama, the Orinoco Lowlands of Venezuela and Colombia, the Lake Maracaibo Lowland in Venezuela, southern Portugal, western France, the highland areas of central Europe, northern Japan, northern Manchuria, Szechwan province in China, and scattered areas in South Africa and in the East African Highlands.

26.5 Reasons for Dispersed Settlement. Numerous attempts have been made to find a logical explanation for the world distribution pattern of dispersed settlement described in the preceding paragraph, but without a great deal of success. The reasons for this type of settlement appear to be different in different regions. In more recently settled areas such as the United States, Canada, Australia, and Argentina, the abundance of cheap land, resulting in large farms, has probably been the principal factor fostering separate farmsteads. Where the unit of cultivation is several score, or even several hundred acres, all in one single holding, village type of settlement would have resulted in much loss of time and energy going back and forth between residence and fields. Nevertheless, the Russian colonists in the spring-wheat belt of Siberia characteristically live in villages, this tendency to live together even in a region of new and abundant land perhaps reflecting the dominance of nucleated settlement in European Russia.

26.6 *Natural Factors.* In certain parts of the world there appears to be some relationship between natural factors, particularly surface configuration, and settlement type. A number of European writers have observed that dispersion appears to increase in direct proportion to the ruggednesss of the land surface. In other words, isolated farmsteads are more characteristic of hilly land, while compact rural villages reach their maximum development on plains. In Japan this is strikingly true. The relationship has been noted likewise for Switzerland, Germany, southwestern Poland, Austria, Hungary, and Slovakia. In southern Europe, the Dinaric Alps and the Carpathians stand out as marked centers of open-country dwelling.

The explanation, in part, may lie in the physical character of such locations, the whole aspect of which leads to a diffusion of resources—arable land, water, and natural sites with pleasant exposures. Vidal de la Blache writes: "The scattered manner of grouping suits localities where, as a result of the dissection of relief, soil, and hydrography, the arable land is itself divided up. The clustered village is indigenous, on the other hand, in districts where the arable area is continuous, admitting of uniform and extensive exploitation."[1] In regions of dissection and abundant slope, the scattered fragments of cultivable land are often too small to support more than a few isolated farmsteads. The inhabitants are compelled to utilize other resources, such as pastures and woodland, which in turn require larger landholdings.

It should be pointed out, however, that the foregoing generalization concerning type of rural settlement and associated relief does not have universal application, for there are numerous hilly regions of the world where the farm village is characteristic. In regions where both types of rural settlement are common, however, there is often a tendency for the isolated farmstead to be more characteristic of the hilly portions.

Certain other natural factors are believed to act in a manner similar to relief in restricting the amount of contiguous arable land and thereby favoring dispersed settlement. Scarcity of water, marshes, forests, stony moraines, and poor soils are some of these adverse elements. In Poland, for example, areas of poor soil, marshes, and dunes are considered to be sites of ancient open-country living. In Shropshire, England, villages prevail except in the heavily wooded country without fertile alluvium. In Germany and Finland there appears to be some correlation between areas of poor soil and dispersion. Dispersion is said to be possible in Flanders because of the abundant ground water, whereas in parts of Russia and in southern Belgium the restricted number of places where

[1] P. Vidal de la Blache. "Principles of Human Geography." P. 316. Henry Holt and Company, Inc., New York, 1926.

water is available handicaps widespread open-country living.

26.7 *Cultural Factors.* Type of economy and historical changes also have been instrumental in affecting the present pattern of world settlement types. In Europe dispersed dwellings are common in regions where pastoralism and transhumance are important. The moorlands of Wales and Yorkshire, used chiefly for grazing, are islands of dispersion within larger regions of village dominance. In Switzerland, Austria, and Norway the highlands are seasonally occupied by herders who live in dispersed chalets, *Almhütte*, or saeter huts. The pastoral Lapps appear to live in dispersed fashion except in winter, when they gather in hamlets or take lodging with some peasant.

During those periods when farmers had need of defense against hostile neighbors, there was good reason for their congregating in villages, where better protection of life and property could be had. As defense needs became less significant, open-country isolated living became more prevalent. The decline of feudalism with the associated freeing of the serfs and the change from communal to private land tenure likewise favored the decline of the farm village and an associated increase in the number of separate farmsteads. The Industrial Revolution, improved transportation, and the rise of commercial agriculture had much the same effect. Recent agrarian movements in Poland, Czechoslovakia, Hungary, and other countries, where estates have been dissolved and the land divided among the peasants, has led to further dispersion.

The rapid increase in population in Europe since the Industrial Revolution has been a factor leading to colonization of available agricultural land by single families. Thus on the Danube Plains, which has been one of Europe's most exclusive regions of farm villages, there is an increased number of isolated farmsteads on the open flattish grasslands (*puszta*) which separate the older agricultural villages and their surrounding plowed land. At first this took the form of summer occupance of isolated dwellings in the midst of the fields, but with a return to the villages in winter. Recently, there has been a growing tendency to continue residence away from the villages in winter as well as in summer, so that genuine dispersion is developing.

In summary, it may be repeated that no very valid generalizations having world-wide significance can be made explaining the present distribution of open-country dwelling over the earth. Most of the explanations given in the preceding paragraphs have chiefly local significance. At the present time the drift appears to be away from the farm-village type of settlement and toward open-country living.

26.8 American Farmsteads. The farmstead is the center of operations on an American farm. It contains the operator's residence; barns and sheds for the shelter of animals, the storage of feeds and the protection of machinery and tools; together with adjoining feeding pens and yards, a home garden, and possibly an orchard. Usually it varies in size from a fraction of an acre to a few acres in extent. But although it is the heart of the farm, the farm-

stead is its unproductive part, in so far as primary goods are concerned. The fields are the sources of the raw materials from which salable or consumable agricultural products are made. It is at the farmstead that these raw materials from the fields are collected, processed, stored or fed, and made ready for sale. To a geographer farmsteads are one element of a region's settlement fabric. Not only their spacing and distribution as units, which in a real sense is a measure of farm population, but also their areas, dimensions, locations, numbers of buildings, and the sizes, functions, and arrangements of their buildings, are essential ingredients of a region's settlement geography (Figs. 26.2, 26.3).

American farmsteads vary markedly in character from one agricultural region to another.[2] Most pretentious and attractive are those of the specialized dairy regions and the Corn Belt.

[2] Glenn T. Trewartha. The Regional Characteristics of American Farmsteads. *Ann. Assoc. Amer. Geographers*, Vol. 38, No. 3, pp. 169–225, 1948.

Fig. 26.2 Aerial view of a farmstead in Illinois. (*United Photo Shop.*)

Here substantial well-painted houses, large barns, numerous machine sheds, and other outbuildings, with these buildings also painted, are conspicuous. Least pretentious and attractive are the farmsteads of the Cotton Belt and of the range livestock region. In the cash-grain regions they are distinctive by reason of their large size and the relatively large number that have windmills and granaries.

It needs to be emphasized that the farmstead is not, however, just an agglomeration of buildings and yards; it is, rather, the focus or nucleus of a "culture structure with functional significance," a structure composed of human beings, the buildings that they occupy and use, the fields that they cultivate, and the livestock that they raise. Unlike the medieval manor, the American farmstead is not a self-sufficient unit, for many of the farm family's needs are supplied from the shops of nearby market towns and paid for with cash received from the sale of vegetable or animal products raised on the farm. The isolated farmstead is, nevertheless, the individual cell out of which America's rural settlement structure is composed. It is such a tiny focus, however, that it is incapable of exerting an important centralizing influence as does the rural village, for instance.

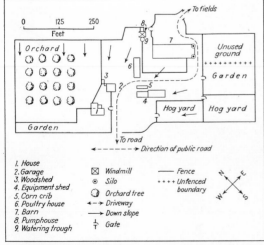

Fig. 26.3 Plat of a farmstead on a Wisconsin dairy farm. Note the large barn with twin silos and the numerous other outbuildings.

NUCLEATED OR COMPACT SETTLEMENTS

26.9 As stated earlier, houses and streets in various combinations of number and pattern, and the people who occupy and use them, comprise the essential elements of all types of compact or collective settlements, from the rural village to the largest metropolitan center. As soon as houses become grouped the necessity is immediately created for intercommunication between them, so that more or less clearly defined streets become necessary, and the spaces between the buildings become relatively regular.

Not only is the street system within the settlement a conspicuous and essential element, but beyond the boundaries of the town proper its centripetal influence is clearly marked by the road pattern. Each agglomerated settlement becomes a focus of transport lines, for one of the prime functions of towns and cities is their market services. In fact, highways (roads, canals, rivers, railroads, steamship and air lines) together with the things that flow over them—human beings as well as goods—have very likely created a majority of the towns and cities now in existence.

26.10 Two Classes of Compact Settlements. Two principal classes of compact settlements are here recognized: (*a*) those which are essentially rural in aspect and function and (*b*) those the functions of which are largely nonagricultural or urban. In the first group are agricultural *villages,* the residents of which are chiefly tillers of the soil. Such a settlement primarily is concerned with the production of agricultural goods. Within the second, or urban, group are *cities,* the inhabitants of which "have no immediate interest in the production of the materials for their food or clothing but are engaged in transporting, manufacturing, buying, and selling these materials or in educating the people or in managing the affairs of the state or in merely 'living in town'" (Aurousseau). As a usual thing also, urban settlements are more closely built up, so that there is a denser population per unit area than in the rural villages. Included within the large and diverse group of urban settlements, here designated under the general title of cities, are such small ones as hamlets and villages, those of intermediate size commonly spoken of as towns, as well as the cities proper.

The Agricultural Village

26.11 Nature and Development. In the rural hamlet or village type of settlement, which is the commonest form over a large part of the earth's surface, farmsteads, instead of being isolated as they are in the United States, are grouped together into relatively compact communities. In such villages the predominant, sometimes almost exclusive, group is farmers. To be sure there may be some artisans, tradesmen, and professional men, but usually they are greatly in the minority. The agricultural village therefore is principally a place of residence and not primarily a business center. It is composed chiefly of farm dwellings and their associated outbuildings.

Community living probably is as ancient as the human race and represents an instinctive drawing together of peoples for cooperative efforts in defense, work, or some other activity. Some sort of locality groups existed even among nonagricultural tribes. Genuine village life arose, however, with the beginnings of agriculture, and there is abundant evidence that men have lived in village groups in Europe and Asia since early Neolithic times. Among primitive agricultural peoples the village was not fixed at one site, for agriculture was often of the shifting type, with moves sometimes as frequent as every two or three years. In these shifting communities the women did most of the work in the fields, with the use of only hand implements and without the aid of domestic animals. Commonly the primitive village was composed of a group of kinsmen.

At a later stage, when agriculture became more permanent, the village became fixed in its location. A definite area of land with fixed boundaries was recognized as belonging to the village. Domesticated animals were employed in conjunction with the plow and the cart, which resulted in men instead of women doing the larger part of the work. Irrigation, manur-

ing, and the feeding of livestock became common practices. Control of the land was at first vested in the village group, or, as in the manorial villages of England, in the lord of the manor. Personal ownership of land was a matter of gradual evolution. The arable land was cultivated by individuals, while the pasture, forest, and waste land was held in common by the village and was used in common.

In modern agricultural villages the land is permanently owned by families or individuals, and common land is rare. The individual farms, however, are still composed of numerous small unfenced parcels scattered in various directions and at various distances around the village. Unlike an American farm, which is usually composed of a contiguous block of land, the farm of a villager in Europe or Asia is composed of several small, unfenced, noncontiguous plots. The latter is known as the *open-field system* of agriculture. It is usually associated with the village type of rural settlement.

26.12 *The Latifundium Type of Rural Village (Hacienda, Plantation, Finca, Estate).* Throughout certain parts of the world there is a type of compact rural settlement that differs in certain fundamentals from the typical farm village. This type of clustered settlement, designated here as *latifundium,* is associated with extensive agricultural estates, often of thousands of acres, where large numbers of hired laborers are necessary to carry on the ordinary work of the estate. The tea and rubber plantations in various parts of tropical southeastern Asia (Malaya, Ceylon, Burma, India, Java, Sumatra, and others) and the haciendas of Latin America are of this type. In the United States the larger sugar-cane plantations of Louisiana have a village type of settlement. On such extensive farms there is usually a central core area that contains the more pretentious homes of the owner and his overseers, together with the more numerous and modest huts or cabins of the native laborers.[3] In ad-

[3] Some plantations are operated by sharecroppers or tenants rather than by hired laborers under an overseer, and under such an organization no central community is required.

dition there may be a commissary or store and perhaps a school, hospital, and church.

Such a settlement is not composed of a group of independent farmers, owning their own homes and cultivating their own land, as is true of the modern agricultural village. The plantation is like a factory, being organized to produce commercially a particular product or crop. As a result the plantation settlement is composed of buildings owned by the estate and rented to the laborers. The latter usually are not closely attached to the land so that they may not stay long at one place. Such a settlement therefore usually lacks the permanency and close social bonds characteristic of the genuine agricultural village. The latter has its life and institutions developed by the people in the village; in the plantation, settlement life is closely regulated by the estate owner. The following description is of a coffee plantation community in the state of São Paulo, Brazil:

A characteristic group of estate buildings is associated with the cultivation of coffee. The most important building is the manager's dwelling, surrounded, at least in the older part of the state, by well-kept lawns and shrubs. Near by are the stables for the estate animals, the sheds for storage, and the extensive tile or concrete platforms on which the crop is spread to dry in the sun. And also near by are the rows of laborers' cottages which betray in their untidy and cheerless appearance the temporary nature of the relationship between owner and tenants. This group of buildings constitutes the *fazenda* and amounts to a rural hamlet in an area of agglomerated population.[4]

26.13 Distribution of the Village Type of Rural Settlement. The farm village is the characteristic type of rural settlement throughout most of Latin America, Africa, and Asia. Certain exceptions to this generalization have already been pointed out in the discussion on dispersed farmsteads. Europe shows a complicated intermingling of the dispersed and nucleated types, with Soviet Russia being the largest contiguous area where the village type

strongly prevails. In somewhat less dominant form it is also characteristic of Mediterranean, central, and northwestern Europe, except in the regions mentioned in Art. 26.4. Aboriginal settlements on the arctic plains of North America are chiefly agglomerated.

26.14 *The Agricultural Village of Colonial New England.*[5] Although in the United States at the present time the farm village is a rare exception within the standard pattern of isolated farmsteads, this situation was not true during the early history of the country. For the first hundred years and more of its history rural New England was a land of village-dwelling farmers (Fig. 26.4). In part this compact type of rural settlement had its origins in the need for protection against the Indian menace. In part it reflects the nature of New England's colonization, which was by organized communities and not by individuals. Often the colonizing group had previously existed in England as a church congregation or neighborhood, so that the colonists arrived in their new home motivated by common aims and ambitions and relatively homogeneous in political and social character. Moreover, it was the policy of the New England colonizing companies to make grants of land to groups rather than to individuals. Land was not sold, but instead was awarded to responsible groups desirous of establishing a home in the wilderness. Once the community was established, Puritan ideals of religion and education tended to hold it together. The school and the meetinghouse were the standard focal centers of the New England farm village.

The New England town or township was a grant of land 4 to 10 miles square in extent. Usually somewhere near the geographical center of the town the village was established, with a *common* or *green* as its nucleus. Fronting upon the common and upon the main street were the church, school, and burying ground, together

[4] Preston E. James. The Coffee Lands of Southeastern Brazil. *Geog. Rev.*, Vol. 22, pp. 225–244 (236), 1932.

[5] Glenn T. Trewartha. Types of Rural Settlement in Colonial America. *Geog. Rev.*, Vol. 36, No. 4, pp. 568–596, 1946. Edna Scofield. The Origin of Settlement Patterns in Rural New England. *Geog. Rev.*, Vol. 28, pp. 652–663, 1938.

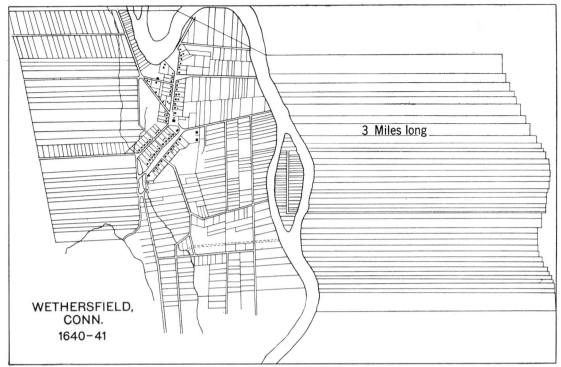

Fig. 26.4 Plat showing the layout of home lots and fields of a rural village in colonial New England. The farm homes are indicated by small black squares.

with the home lots of the original settlers. The home lots contained not only the farmhouse but in addition barns and other outbuildings, a garden, and enclosures for feeding livestock and raising corn. The compactness of the village depended to a large degree upon the size of the home lots. Usually they varied between 1 and 5 acres in extent. The farm of each villager was composed of several small tracts of land lying in different quarters of the town.

Although Puritan New England was the arch stronghold of the community type of rural settlement in Colonial America, it was not unknown in other sections. For the first decade or two in Virginia stockaded communities were almost the exclusive form of settlement. In Georgia experimentation with carefully planned farm villages continued for even a longer period. In the course of a relatively short time, however, the community type of settlement in the South disintegrated and was absorbed into the plantation system, which became the dominant form of agricultural organization. Be-

yond the Appalachians in what is now Kentucky and Tennessee the first settlements were by groups occupying stockaded posts called *stations.*

26.15 The Modern American Village Not Rural. In the United States the counterpart of the European and Asiatic agricultural village of a few score or hundred farm residences can scarcely be said to exist. Since most of America's rural population is in isolated farmsteads, even a small compact settlement of a few hundred inhabitants is likely to be composed largely of shopkeepers, artisans, and professional men, with very few farmers among them. They are chiefly places of business. Most American "villages," then, as far as function is concerned, are urban, not rural. Thus in Montfort, Wis., a village of about 600 inhabitants set down in the heart of an important agricultural area in southwestern Wisconsin, more than one-half of the population is dependent upon income from retail merchandising. Most of the others are supported by the professions, by the railway, and by other types of transportational and communicational services. Hardly a score of the 125 families may be classified as retired farmers, and certainly less than half a dozen are active farmers.[6] Such a community is fundamentally a service and trading center for the farmsteads of the surrounding countryside. Even an American crossroads hamlet of only a score of dwellings is largely made up of nonfarm families, although it is not unusual for such a settlement to have a few farmsteads. The hamlet, therefore, is relatively more rural than the somewhat larger village.

26.16 *Some Examples of Agricultural Villages in the United States and Canada.* The best example of a community type of rural settlement in Anglo-America is the Mormon farm villages in Utah.[7] Most of the Mormon farmers of Utah do not live on their farms, but within villages from which they commute to one or several fields outside the village. This community form of living resulted from a planned mode of agricultural settlement established by the Mormon Church during the middle decades of the last century. It was admirably suited for defense against the Indians and for the social and religious contacts that the church desired. The farm villages are laid out in rectangular pattern, most of them having a central square on which is located the church or tabernacle. In a representative village such as Escalante (1,000+ population), the usual 5-acre blocks are divided into four home lots of $1\frac{1}{4}$ acres each on which are located the farm home, together with barns, corrals, pens, and sheds. Farms are usually small, their average size in the Wasatch Oasis being only 37 acres. The average distance from the farmsteads to the scattered parcels of land composing the farms is 2.3 miles. It is significant to note that in the newly developed irrigated areas in Utah the iso-

lated farmstead is more common than the farm village, and even in the longer settled areas dispersion is the newer mode of settlement.

At Amana in eastern Iowa is a group of seven farm villages housing nearly 1,500 persons who comprise the Amana settlements.[8] Like the Mormon villages, those of Iowa are the product of a planned mode of settlement by a religious sect. Each village has its own fields, supervised by a farm manager who allocates the labor for the village and decides on the crops to be grown in given fields. Community barns, sheds, and silos serve to store crops and farm machinery and to house livestock.

Somewhat intermediate between genuine dispersion and agglomeration is a type of rural settlement associated with long-lot farms. Under this arrangement, because of the narrowness of the farms, the closely spaced farmsteads along a single street or highway give the appearance of a loose village organization. French settlement in the Lake St. John Lowland in Canada[9] and in the Mississippi Delta is prevailingly of this type. In the Lake St. John Lowland farm lots are $\frac{1}{8}$ mile wide and 1 mile long with the narrow side facing the highway. In certain parts of New England likewise, farmsteads are so close together along highways as to give the appearance of community settlement.[10]

26.17 Agricultural Villages of the Far East. The compact farm village is the basic unit of settlement in eastern and southern Asia, where one-half of the earth's population is concentrated. Thus in China, where 70 to 80 per cent of the 580,000,000 people are dependent upon the land, 88 per cent live in settlements having fewer than 10,000 residents, while the most fundamental unit is the farm village of 250 to 2,500 people (Fig. 26.5). In Japan, where nearly 45 per cent of the 90,000,000 inhabitants are dependent upon agriculture, over 44 per cent of the total reside in the 9,600 rural

[6] V. C. Finch. Montfort: A Study in Landscape Types in Southwestern Wisconsin. *Geog. Soc. Chicago, Bull.* 9, pp. 15–44, 1933.

[7] Chauncey D. Harris. Salt Lake City: A Regional Capital. Ph.D. Dissertation, University of Chicago, 1940, pp. 42, 117–121. Lowry Nelson. The Mormon Village: A Study on Social Origins. *Proc. Utah Acad. Sci.,* Vol. 7, pp. 11–37, 1930.

[8] Darrell H. Davis. Amana: A Study of Occupance. *Econ. Geog.,* Vol. 12, pp. 217–230, July, 1936.

[9] Robert M. Glendenning. The Distribution of Population in the Lake St. John Lowland, Quebec. *Geog. Rev.,* Vol. 24, pp. 232–237, 1934.

[10] Edna Scofield, *op. cit.,* pp. 652–663.

settlements having fewer than 5,000 citizens. Nearly 20 per cent more live in villages or towns having between 5,000 and 10,000 inhabitants, and these are predominantly rural as well.

The basis of Chinese civilization is the village community (Fig. 26.6). Many of these villages are family villages, being composed of families all bearing the same surname and tracing their descent from a single ancestor. The units of the village are not individuals but families. Each member lives and works not for himself but for the family to which he belongs. Each family owns its own lands, possesses certain rights in the common land, and shares rights and responsibilities connected with the upkeep of the ancestral temple and the burial ground. Sometimes the village proper is separated from its fields by a wall as a protection against bands of plunderers. A Chinese village is a physical and cultural feature. Thoughout 500 years of modern history it has changed little. The houses are like those occupied by the ancestors of the present villagers half a millennium ago. The descendants are doing what their ancestors did, cultivating the same fields in the same way,

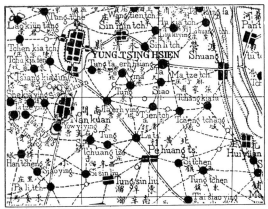

Fig. 26.5 Rural hamlets and villages (solid black circles), together with market towns, on the North China Plain. (*From Carte de la Chine, Sheet 202. Scale about 1 in. = 2½ miles*).

going to the same markets, following the same customs and habits. The Chinese farm village has few shops, and those that do exist carry a very limited supply of goods. Trading is done chiefly at the market towns. In the smaller farming villages there are practically no artisans, for the farmer is blacksmith, carpenter, and architect as well. Since the communist revolution some modifications of the Chinese farm

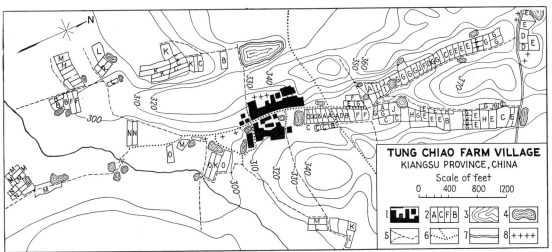

Fig. 26.6 A Chinese rural village and its associated fields, ponds, temples, etc. 1, the village; 2, field plots (all marked *A* are tilled by Farmer A, those marked *B* by farmer B, etc.); 3, hill lands, usually in grass and graves (contour figures are in feet); 4, ponds for irrigation and fish; 5, earth paths; 6, paths paved with stone; 7, paved road 7 ft. wide; 8, Buddhist temples. (*Original map by J. L. Buck. From Jones and Darkenwald, "Economic Geography," by permission of The Macmillan Company.*)

village, as described above, have been in progress.

In Japan the ubiquitous farm village[11] is striking in two respects: (*a*) it is a social unit to a degree unknown in the Occident, and (*b*) the well-being of the villager is not primarily expressed in money. Tiny shops, each specializing in a single class of goods such as fish, tobacco, cakes, cloth, etc., occupy the front rooms of a few residences. These goods cost money, but they are bought not so often with cash as with rice. In other words the village still exists to a considerable degree in the rice-money economy of the fourteenth to sixteenth centuries. An almost unbelievable frugality characterizes the living of the villagers, but this keeping alive on the very cheese rind of existence is made endurable by the close communal life of the village unit. They play and work together so that life in the village is attractive and warm in spite of its incredible meagerness. It is this accepted frugality of living on the part of Japan's large agricultural population that is one of the country's greatest bulwarks, keeping industrial wages at a low level and thereby permitting the Japanese exporter to compete with those of nations with greater natural resources.

26.18 Agricultural Village Patterns. Villages differ greatly from one another in shape and pattern by reason of contrasts in the arrangement of streets and their houses. These contrasts are sometimes the result of the physical character of the land on which the settlement is built (its site), but equally often they are associated with historical causes. For example, a river levee or a beach ridge along a coast may induce an elongated, or "shoestring," type of settlement with the houses laid out on either side of a single principal road or street which follows the crest of the ridge. This type of village is very common in Japan on the wet inundated lowlands where floods are frequent and consequently elevated dry sites offer some protection. On the other hand, when a settlement originates at the crossing of two main

highways on a plain, the village is likely to be more compact in form with its streets laid out in rectangular pattern conforming to that of the main highways. In hilly regions of uneven surface configuration, winding roads following stream divides or valley bottoms may induce very irregular and complicated street arrangements. Sometimes it happens that the original houses of a settlement were built before any road pattern developed, each house occupying what seemed to the owner a favorable site. Later, when a street system emerged, it was of necessity irregular and almost without plan. In South China, where animal-drawn vehicles are absent, village streets are narrow, crooked lanes. In North China, on the other hand, where animal-drawn carts are common, streets are fairly wide and straight and have a rectangular pattern.

URBAN SETTLEMENTS (HAMLET, VILLAGE, TOWN, AND CITY)

26.19 Definition. Although rural settlements may be either dispersed, such as isolated farmsteads, or compact like farm villages, urban settlements, on the other hand, are always compact or nodal in character. In the rural settlements the concern is chiefly with primary production, most commonly agriculture. In urban settlements, on the contrary, the primary goods produced by the farmer, miner, or lumberman are processed in manufacturing plants, transported, bought and sold, and financed. These are secondary forms of production. In addition towns perform functions of a political, educational, social and religious character. Urban settlements in ascending order of size and complexity are hamlet, village, town, and city. There are no very precise definitions differentiating these four types of urban settlements.

26.20 The Unincorporated Hamlet.[12] Of the compact nucleated settlements in the United States having significant urban functions, the unincorporated hamlet is the smallest

[11] John F. Embree. "Suye Mura, A Japanese Village." University of Chicago Press, Chicago, 1939.

[12] Glenn T. Trewartha. The Unincorporated Hamlet. *Ann. Assoc. Amer. Geographers*, Vol. 33, No. 1, pp. 32–81, March, 1943.

and least conspicuous. It is neither purely rural nor purely urban, but a combination of both, with the urban functions predominating. In population the American hamlet usually ranges from 20 to 150 inhabitants. The founding of these tiny settlements was almost contemporaneous with the coming of settlers into a region. They developed as service and social centers for the surrounding farm areas. Rarely are they purely residential settlements and commonly they contain one or more of the following other functional units: post office, church, school, general store, cheese factory, feed mill, tavern, filling station, garage. It is a usual thing to have several of these functions combined in one establishment. Where the total volume of business is small, as it must be in a hamlet, it seems a natural thing for several types of business to be integrated under one proprietor and housed under one roof. Moreover, the residence also may incorporate a place of business. In a study of 167 hamlets in southwestern Wisconsin it was found that over 9 per cent of the residences have some sort of business enterprise connected with them. The fundamental function of the American hamlet, the tiniest of compact settlements, is that of a commercial service center for the buying and selling operations of the surrounding farm population (Fig. 26.7).

The families who reside in an American hamlet are largely nonfarmers. On the other

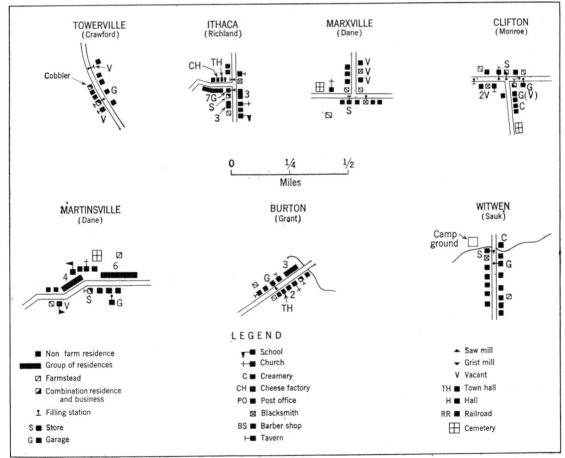

Fig. 26.7 Samples of hamlet types in Wisconsin. The hamlet is the smallest type of nucleated settlement. The population is composed principally of nonfarmers.

Fig. 26.8 Aerial view of a small Illinois market town with isolated farmsteads in the background. (*United Photo Shop.*)

hand, it is by no means uncommon for a hamlet to contain one or more farmsteads, each with its collection of barns, sheds, windmill, silo, and cattle and hog yards. In Wisconsin some 12 per cent of the residences in hamlets are farmstead dwellings. This is not to be wondered at when one considers how near to being rural these little settlements are. Urban squeamishness to barnyard odors has not developed to the point where these things seem particularly objectionable. It is probably good for the hamlets to number active farmers among their citizens and to be in close physical proximity to farmsteads. The result will be to keep hamlets rural-minded, a feature which is not true of the larger villages and towns which tend to face away from the country and to envy and imitate the city.

26.21 Functional Areas in the Market Village and Town. In the agricultural village composition is relatively uniform throughout,

the settlement being composed of farm residences and associated shelter and storage sheds. Usually no "business section" exists, although there are often scattered shops. In the market village and town, on the other hand, where urban functions usually predominate, there are almost certain to develop distinct and specialized *functional areas*. The two that stand out prominently in almost any market town are (*a*) the commercial core, or business district, and (*b*) the residential portion (Figs. 26.8 to 26.10). It is in the former, where shops and stores predominate, that urban functions are concentrated. The commercial core may be distinguished from the residential area, not only by the *kind* of buildings but also by their *spacing*. In the former the structures often abut against one another, while the residences are likely to be farther apart. Other functions, such as manufacturing, government, education, and recreation, may be represented in the market town, but usually they are not segregated into distinct areas of conspicuous size.

Like the rural village, the town may be cast in a variety of shapes and patterns, both externally and internally. One of the commonest arrangements is that in which the commercial core lies somewhat near the geographical center of the town with residential areas surrounding it on all sides. Thus while the rural village has no distinct nucleus or center, this becomes a characteristic feature of cities and towns.

The City

26.22   Cities, the Focal Points in Man's Utilization of the Earth. The city represents the most complete modification of a portion of the earth's surface that man, through his constructive and destructive contacts with that surface, has been able to make. There human beings are crowded together in greatest numbers and density, and, partly as a result of this concentration and intensive occupying of the surface, man has there brought together his mightiest assemblage of material-culture features. So complete is the culture cover that it tends to mask, and at the same time greatly modify or possibly obliterate, the original natural features of the site. Even beyond the margins of the city

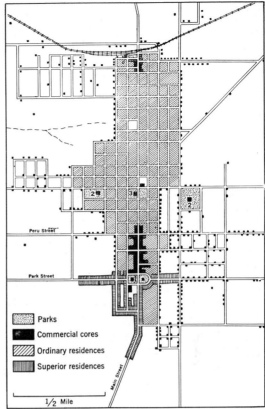

Fig. 26.9   Arrangement of functional areas within a market town. The town has grown northward toward the railroad where a secondary business core has developed. (*Map by Stanley Dodge.*)

Fig. 26.10   Business section of an American town, Rawlins, Wyo. (*Ewing Galloway.*)

557

proper, the settlement makes itself felt in an intricate network of communications, for these routes represent the necessary lines of contact with the countryside that it serves and that supports it. Through these channels pass tremendous quantities of food and raw material to be consumed or otherwise used by the city organization, and it is along these same routes that the city's products feed back to the surrounding countryside. "The city creates the road; the road in its turn creates the city, or recreates it. . . . "

While each city is unique and has individuality in the details of its arrangement and form, it has, on the other hand, much in common with other cities in many aspects of its appearance and development. Thus cities of similar size and function and in the same general regional setting tend to resemble each other in over-all internal structure. This makes possible certain broad generalizations about cities.

26.23 What Supports Cities? Cities do not grow by themselves; they are not parasites living off the surrounding countryside. They are created by society in order to perform functions that are incapable of being performed in the open countryside, but rather must be con-

centrated in central places. They are the head offices in a region's organization. In regions of primitive or self-sufficient economies the need for city services is slight, so that urban centers are few. By contrast, in modern industrial societies where regional specialization and economic interdependence are characteristic, there is great need for the services performed by cities and hence their numbers are large.

The activities in which a city engages and by which it is supported are of two general kinds. First, there are those which tie it to the outside area or areas. In larger cities this is not just a local or adjacent area, but includes more distant regions as well, possibly the whole country and even foreign nations. Much of the manufacturing, wholesaling, and banking that go on within a city are closely related to the needs of surrounding areas. The city's life depends upon these outside connections, for it is the services which it performs for these regions which bring money *into* the city. These are sometimes designated as the *basic* activities of a city.

The second group of activities characteristic of urban communities are those which are developed in order to fulfill the needs of the

Classification of Urban Groups According to Dominant Functions
(After Aurousseau)

Class I Adminis- tration	Class II Defense	Class III Culture	Class IV Production (Manufacturing)	Class V Communication (Commerce)			Class VI Recreation
				Group A Collection	Group B Transfer	Group C Distribution	
Capital cities Revenue cities	Fortress cities Garrison towns Naval bases	University towns Cathedral towns Art centers Pilgrimage towns Religious towns	Manufacturing cities Craft towns	Mining towns Fishing towns Forest towns Depot towns	Market towns Fall-line towns Break-of-bulk towns Bridgehead towns Tidal-limit towns Navigation-head towns	Export cities Import cities Supply cities	Health resorts Tourist resorts Holiday resorts
					Entrepôt cities		

people living within the city itself. Much of the retail business, the activities of barbers, bakers, and newspaper publishers, the theaters, and the local systems of transportation may cater largely to the local population. These activities associated with serving the city's own population may be termed *nonbasic* in character. This is not to suggest that these are any less significant than the basic activities. Both are essential. Clearly cities do much more than just serve the agricultural areas, as is obvious from the fact that in a recent year the farm income in the United States was only 5 per cent of the total national income.

The table preceding attempts to classify cities and towns according to their dominant functions. The descriptive terms used in the table are self-explanatory. Illustrations of each type can easily be called to mind. Of the several classes of cities listed, some were more important in ancient civilizations, while others, such as Class IV, manufacturing, and Class V, commercial, are characteristic of modern industrial economies.

26.24 Cities of the Past. Cities are very ancient in their origins, almost as ancient as civilization itself, for the earliest urban developments go back to the fourth millennium B.C. In order for population to be able to concentrate in cities two conditions are required: (*a*) there must be a surplus of food over that required to feed the food producers and (*b*) there must be means of transportation for concentrating the surplus food at chosen spots. Significantly the earth's first cities developed in the valleys of the Nile, of the Tigris and Euphrates, and somewhat later in those of the Indus and the Hwang, or Yellow, rivers. In these locations the combination of fertile alluvial soils and seasonal river floods permitted a maximum food production so that a surplus was available. Nevertheless, the primitive means of transport obliged these earliest cities to be dependent upon a food surplus produced very locally. This in turn limited the size to which cities could grow so that probably they did not exceed 20,000 in population. As transport im-

proved, larger cities were possible, but even classical Athens may have been a city of only 60,000 to 70,000 people.[13]

The oldest city of which we have any record is Memphis, the walled capital of ancient Egypt, which was in existence as early as 2500 B.C. Somewhat later the capital cities of Babylon and Nineveh flourished in the valley of the Tigris and Euphrates Rivers. For ten centuries, and up to about A.D. 500, city life outside of Asia followed the shores of the Mediterranean Sea. Tyre and Sidon, capitals of ancient Phoenicia, were especially famous as port cities. The Greek cities of Athens, Corinth, and Syracuse were not only local capitals and defense towns, but they were urban centers in the modern sense as well, with a high degree of economic vitality. Carthage and Rome, likewise capitals, were hives of industry and trade.

Following the collapse of Rome and with the invasion of the barbarian tribes, cities were sacked and pillaged and for five centuries or more urban life in Europe declined. Those which continued to exist were much reduced in population and eked out a miserable and isolated existence. From about the eleventh century on cities began to revive in Europe. This in part was stimulated by the Crusades. Italian cities, such as Florence, Genoa, Venice, and Pisa, were among the first to feel the effects of the revived trade. The medieval Hanseatic cities of Germany similarly were supported chiefly by trade.

Cities in China, although not so ancient as some of those in the Mediterranean Basin, may antedate by a millennium the beginning of the Christian era. To an unusual degree ancient Chinese cities were political centers although, to be sure, they performed economic functions as well. The Chinese concept of a city was not that of a large number of people residing within a restricted area, but rather it was the official residence of a public officer and the visible evidence of a city was the encircling

[13] A. E. Smailes. "The Geography of Towns." P. 15. Hutchinson's University Library, Hutchinson & Co., Ltd., London, 1953.

wall. The rank of a city was determined not by size but by the rank of the public official residing there. This rank was conspicuous in the name of the city. If the name ended in *fu* the city was of high rank; if it ended in *ting* or *chow* it was of lower rank.

Both in the Mediterranean Basin and in the Far East, then, it is evident that original location and subsequent growth of cities were frequently associated with political and defense considerations. In modern times, however, these items have had little to do with the location and growth of great urban communities. Only a few of the world's great cities are political capitals, and probably none of them has defense value. In the nineteenth and twentieth centuries city development has been largely dependent upon industry and trade.

26.25 Modern Cities: Functions and Locations. In regions where a relatively large proportion of the population lives in cities, it is usually indicative of a relatively advanced stage of material civilization—a stage that many regions of the world have not yet reached. In all periods of world history the city has represented the vanguard of intellectual progress and culture. With the city came division of labor and the necessity for economic surplus, and out of this came leisure, wealth, development of the arts and sciences, and general intellectual advance. It has been said that steam, steel, and credit have made the modern large city possible. Transportation and storage made it feasible to keep a million and more people fed with perishable foods. Credit allows one generation to build and the next generation to pay its share of the cost. The modern metropolis, with one main business nucleus, is a product of fast transportation which permits the shuttling of large numbers of people in and out of the downtown section each day. Old cities in Europe and the Far East characteristically had several nuclei.

Most cities have located and developed as a result of more than one causative factor, and the functions they perform are likewise seldom singular. Nevertheless the support of modern cities and the functions they perform can be classified into three principal subdivisions: (*a*) Cities as central places performing multiple services, often of a marketing nature, for the surrounding area. (*b*) Transport cities located frequently at break-of-cargo points along transport routes and performing the services associated with such a location. (*c*) Manufactural cities and others of specialized function type.

26.26 *Cities as central places* are likely to be distributed rather widely and uniformly throughout a productive area. Where resources are unevenly spaced, the cities are likely to be as well. They are the marketing and social centers for tributary areas of variable size. Such cities vary greatly in size and in the extent of the tributary areas they serve. They are the standard type and are found widespread throughout most of the nonindustrialized regions of the earth. In the Middle Western agricultural region of the United States cities as central places exist as retail and wholesale trade centers. The downtown shopping sections and wholesale districts of such cities contain imposing stores supported in part by the trade of the tributary area. Many central cities and towns combine political and social functions with those of marketing. Thus many state capitals and county seats are likewise central places. In some parts of the world, also, these central places are partly supported by temples, shrines, and churches which attract large numbers to religious and social events.

26.27 *Transport cities* are a specialized type of urban development, and unlike central places are likely to have an uneven distribution inasmuch as lines of communication, because of terrain and other causes, are not symmetrically developed. Most cities with specialized functions appear to be associated with certain types of strategic locations favorable to urban development, which cause "the seed to spring to life and guarantee its growth." Such cities appear to have had their inception and growth in considerable numbers in at least two kinds of locations: (*a*) adjacent to some obstacle which hindered the further movement of men or goods and made it necessary to halt transport, break cargo, and perhaps find some different means of travel from there on; and (*b*) the convergence or crossing of important trade routes. If a break of bulk is necessary, such a transport focus becomes a desirable place at which to process goods. Especially where the form of transport changes, such as changing from rail to ship or vice versa, a break in bulk is unavoidable. At such points storing, sorting, packaging, and reassembling become necessary.

One of the commonest forms of transport city is, therefore, the port which is located at the line of contact between land and water. The great ports of New York, London, and Hamburg are representative of this type of location. Buffalo at the eastern end of Lake Erie is an excellent example of a break-in-bulk city, for there the lake boats carrying wheat transfer their cargoes to rail lines which take them east. Duluth and Superior at the western end of Lake Superior, where iron ore and wheat arriving by rail are transferred to lake boat, have a similar function. Some ports such as Singapore and Hongkong act as middlemen and are known as entrepôts. At such points goods are transshipped from small to large ships, or vice versa.

Some transport centers are located so as to serve as gateways to contrasting regions. Minneapolis–St. Paul, Omaha, and Kansas City function as gateway cities between the humid east and the dry west. St. Louis similarly is a gateway to the southwest and Louisville, Cincinnati, and Baltimore to the Cotton Belt. Mountains are still another type of obstacle, the barrier effects of which have nurtured the growth of transport cities. Thus, along the base of the Alps from Vienna to Lyon on the north and from Trieste to Turin on the south are perfect girdles of cities, many of them located at the plain ends of mountain passes.

Arid lands are likewise effective barriers to communication, so that the margins of deserts have their "ports" as do the margins of oceans. After a difficult crossing of these dry waste spaces, caravansaries are needed, where men and animals may rest, obtain food and water, and business may be transacted. Bukhara in Russian Turkistan and Timbuktu on the equatorward margins of the Sahara are representative of this type of commercial city.[14]

At the *end* of a barrier, where routes of travel converge as they are forced to go around the obstacle, are to be found especially favorable conditions for the growth of great trade centers. Chicago, at the southern end of Lake Michigan, is strategically situated, not only because it is at the junction of land and water routes, but even more because the lake barrier converges a large number of important land routes toward its southern extremity. Atlanta, Ga., at the southern end of the Blue Ridge Mountains, profits by a similar concentration of land routes.

Istanbul (Constantinople) is a classical example of a city that has prospered as a result of its strategic location at the *crossing* of important trade routes. There the most important land route between Europe and Asia intersects at the narrow Bosporus, the equally important water route leading from southern Soviet Russia and the Black Sea to the Mediterranean.

In the United States, so much of whose commercial development has taken place within the last century or since the advent of the railroad, city development has been more closely associated with the "civilizing rails" than it has in most parts of the world. St. Louis, Kansas City, Omaha, Indianapolis, and scores of other American cities owe their principal growth to the convergence and crossing of numerous rail routes.

26.28 *Manufactural Cities and Others with Specialized Functions.* Like transport cities, those supported by a specialized service such as manufacturing, mining, or recreation are not likely to be evenly spread as are central places. Specialized functions are likely to be associated with a highly localized resource. Sometimes it is a physical resource such as a mineral deposit which localizes a city. Scranton in the anthracite coal field of northeastern Pennsylvania illustrates the point. Long Beach, Miami, and Nice (France) are resort cities which have benefited from their climates, beaches, and

[14] Vidal de la Blache. *Op. cit.* Pp. 473–474.

ocean views. Once a city has gained fame for a certain specialization, it tends to attract similar and related industries. Thus a specialized automobile-manufacturing city like Detroit attracts other industries which process parts for cars.

Industrial cities not infrequently are also great commercial cities, for they find in those items of location favorable to the *movement* of men and goods, features that favor the *processing* of goods as well. Great commercial centers obviously are able to facilitate the assembling of raw materials and the dispersal of finished products, both of which are necessary for factory growth, and the local market and labor supply are additional factors attractive to industrial concentration. New York City, Chicago, London, and Osaka (Japan) are representative of a large group of cities that are specialized both in the *movement* and in the *processing* of goods.

There are many others, to be sure, which are more exclusively manufactural in their functions, whose development has not been so closely associated with transport advantages. Without doubt, coal, the principal source of industrial power, has been an item of first importance in the location and development of industrial cities. This relationship between mineral fuel and manufactural centers is nowhere better illustrated than in western Europe, where a high degree of coincidence is evident between coal fields and industrial cities. This is particularly true of urban clusters specializing in heavy industries, such as metals, in which large amounts of heat and power are required. In central and western Europe there is a marked concentration of cities within an irregular belt extending from the Silesian coal field in Poland and Czechoslovakia on the east to that of Wales on the west and including the other coal fields of the British Isles, the Westphalian–Belgian–north France field, and important lignite beds in central Germany. Birmingham, Manchester, Newcastle, Essen, Lille, Liége, Leipzig, and Katowice are only a few of the many manufactural cities within the great European coal belt.

Where cheap and easy transport of coal is

available, the manufactural city depending upon that source of power may not be located immediately upon the field. Belfast, in northern Ireland, receiving Glasgow and Carlisle coal by boat; Cincinnati with cheap river transport of coal from the Appalachian field; and Gary, Milwaukee, Cleveland, and Detroit enjoying economical lake transport from the same region, all are examples of the point in question. The numerous cities of the manufactural belt of the United States (Fig. 28.5), located in the northeastern part of the country north of the Ohio and east of the Mississippi River, for the most part lie outside any coal field. They have, however, easy access to the coal from the extensive Appalachian Field. Other localizing factors are the Great Lakes which bring iron ore and coal together, productive agriculture, and cheap ocean transportation to the North Atlantic Seaboard.

In the last decade or two the increasing use of electric power in industry has had a significant effect upon urban development. Where electricity is generated from coal the generating plants may be located at the coal pits and the power sent wherever needed within a radius of a few hundred miles. The outsanding fact of post–First World War industrial development in England was the rapid expansion of the London center so that, although it is removed from any coal field, it has been, nevertheless, the fastest growing of Britain's large industrial areas.

26.29 Distinguishing Features of a City. Mere size, expressed in terms either of number of people or of area occupied, is scarcely sufficient clearly to distinguish the city from the market town, although, to be sure, cities are characteristically larger than towns. A much more precise distinction may be made, however, in terms of (*a*) the number of urban functions and (*b*) the number of functional areas (Fig. 26.11). The small central-place market town usually has only *one* distinct primary *urban* function (commonly market service), which serves more than just the local settlement. If what has been a market town increases its functions, so that in addition to market services it adds those of manufacturing, government,

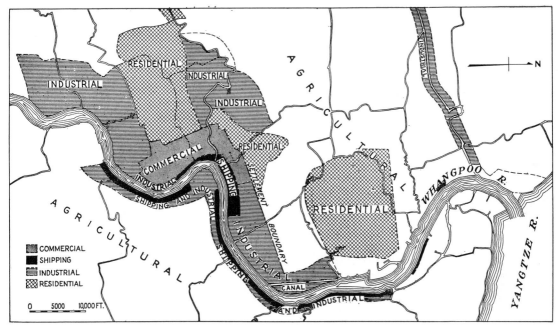

Fig. 26.11 Functional areas of Shanghai, China.

recreation, and others, then it is multifunctional and so may be characterized as a city.

Very obviously, along with the expanding urban functions or services, there is a parallel growth in complexity of the city structure, with a more complete segregation of particular functions within definite areas. Thus, although the town may have, in addition to its residential areas, a definite business core, the city will have these two and also specialized areas where factories are concentrated or perhaps where warehousing services are developed. As a consequence of the several contrasting functional areas, the city *looks* different in its different parts.

Functional Areas. Within the downtown business district, tall, closely spaced, substantial buildings of brick, stone, and concrete occupied by retail shops and professional offices prevail. This emphatically is the hub, or the nucleus. Upon it the street system converges so that within it traffic is usually congested. Land is so expensive that buildings tend to be relatively tall. It is this portion of the city which usually provides the characteristic urban skyline. Beyond the business core there may be a number of small, scattered, local business areas and in addition, numerous single streets given over

in large part to shops and office buildings.

Wholesale, heavy-retail (lumber, feed, and fuel), and storage functions are concentrated outside the business core, where land is less in demand and cheaper. Very definitely this type of business is attracted by rail or water transport facilities which make easy the movement of heavy, bulky commodities. Spur railroad tracks and freight cars usually are conspicuous. Such business requires much ground space for shelter and storage, while the buildings that it occupies are relatively low and widely spaced. There is a feeling of openness about it which is absent in the business core, and congestion of traffic is less conspicuous.

Exclusively manufactural areas are likewise regions of cheaper land and widely spaced buildings surrounded by storage yards and served by spur railroad tracks and canals. Water towers and tall smoking chimneys are characteristic features. Industrial areas have the reputation of being dirty and unattractive.

Residential districts within large cities vary more in quality and appearance than do those of smaller market towns, *i.e.*, greater extremes of poverty and luxury are represented. Some of the least desirable residential districts are those which have been encroached upon by expanding manufactural or business areas so that they have become decadent. The finest and most exclusive residential districts usually occupy attractive physical sites well removed from industrial and business concentrations, as, for instance, along a river or lake or on an elevated spot that provides extensive and attractive views.

26.30   Distribution of Cities and of Urban Population. The degree to which city residence prevails in different parts of the earth is imperfectly known. The regions where a very small proportion of the population (under 20 per cent) reside in cities are eastern (except Japan), southern, and southwestern Asia, and most of Africa except parts of the northern and southern extremities of that continent. These are largely areas of subsistence agriculture and a very low per capita trade and output of manufactured goods. A moderate (20 to 40 per cent) concentration in urban places is characteristic of most of tropical Latin America, parts of extreme northern and southern Africa, Spain, Norway, Finland, Poland, and most of the Balkan peninsula omitting Yugoslavia. A relatively well-balanced condition between urban and rural (40 to 60 per cent urban) is characteristic of the United States and Canada, Soviet Russia, Czechoslovakia, France, Sweden, Italy, the Netherlands, and Chile. Strong urbanization (60 to 80 per cent) is represented by Germany, Belgium, Switzerland, Austria, and somewhat oddly, by two agricultural nations in the Southern Hemisphere, Argentina and Australia. The highest degree of urban concentration is reached in Great Britain where over 80 per cent of the population is in cities.

The geographical reality of the city is expressed in a more concrete manner by noting the actual distribution of the larger (100,000 population and over) cities of the earth. As of about 1950 there were approximately 800 such cities; 365 of them are in Europe, 232 in Asia, and 132 in North America. At first glance it might appear as though Asia were highly urbanized. Considering its large population this is not the case. Actually Australia with only 6

large cities is the most urbanized, with 60 per cent of the total population living in cities over 100,000.

Among the nations the United States ranks first in number of cities with over 100,000 people, followed by Soviet Russia, the United Kingdom, Japan, India, Germany, and China.

On the world map (Fig. 26.12) are six separate regions of outstanding urbanization, where more than one-fifth of the people live in *large* cities of over 100,000. These are (*a*) most of the United States and adjacent small sections of southern Canada, (*b*) northwest Europe (Britain, Germany, Netherlands, Denmark, and Sweden), (*c*) Japan, (*d*) the La Plata River region in South America, (*e*) Australia and New Zealand, and (*f*) South Africa. Two kinds of regions are represented: (*a*) those specializing in industry and commerce as well as in agriculture such as the United States, northwestern Europe, and Japan and (*b*) those that are predominantly agricultural such as the three Southern Hemisphere regions. In the latter, agriculture is of such an extensive type as to require only a small amount of human labor. For this reason an undue proportion of the population resides in port cities supported by trade in agricultural products from the hinterland.

Distribution of Cities with More than 100,000 Population

Europe (Including all of U.S.S.R.)		365
U.S.S.R. (1939)	89	
United Kingdom	66	
Germany	55	
France	22	
Italy	25	
Spain	24	
Asia (Excluding U.S.S.R.)		232
Japan	64	
India	57	
China	33	
North America		132
United States	106	
Canada	10	
South America		47
Argentina	15	
Brazil	14	
Africa		14
Australia and New Zealand		9

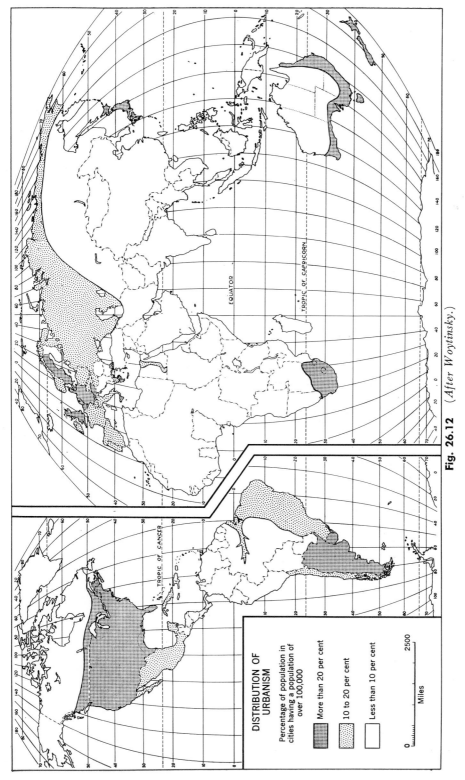

Fig. 26.12 (*After Woytinsky.*)

DISTRIBUTION OF URBANISM

Percentage of population in cities having a population of over 100,000

More than 20 per cent

10 to 20 per cent

Less than 10 per cent

Miles

0   2500

565

References for Chapter 26

Ahlmann, H. W. The Geographical Study of Settlements. *Geog. Rev.,* Vol. 18, pp. 93–128, 1928.

American Journal of Sociology. Symposium issue on World Urbanism, March, 1925.

Aurousseau, M. The Arrangement of Rural Populations. *Geog. Rev.,* Vol. 10, pp. 223–240, 1920.

———. The Distribution of Population: A Constructive Problem. *Geog. Rev.,* Vol. 11, pp. 563–592, 1921.

Brunhes, Jean. "Human Geography." Pp. 74–110. Rand McNally & Company, Chicago, 1920.

Davis, Kingsley, and Hilda Hertz. The World Distribution of Urbanization. *Bull. International Statistical Institute,* Vol. 33, Part 4, pp. 227–241, 1951.

Dickinson, Robert E. "City, Region and Regionalism." Routledge and Kegan Paul, Ltd., London, 1947.

"Encyclopedia of the Social Sciences." The Macmillan Company, New York, 1933. See sections on cities and urbanism.

Geddes, Joseph. "Farm versus Village Living in Utah." *Utah Expt. Sta. Bulls.* 249 and 269, 1934–1936.

Jefferson, Mark. Distribution of the World's City Folks: A Study in Comparative Civilization. *Geog. Rev.,* Vol. 21, pp. 446–465, July, 1931.

Mumford, Lewis. "The Culture of Cities." Harcourt, Brace and Company, Inc., New York, 1938.

Nelson, Lowry. The Mormon Village: A Study in Social Origins. *Proc. Utah Acad. Sci.,* Vol. 7, pp. 11–37, 1930.

Publications of the International Geographical Union on Types of Rural Settlement, 1st Report, Newton, Montgomeryshire, England, 1928; 2d Report, Florence, 1930; 3d Report, Paris, 1931. For the complete papers abstracted in the 3d report noted above, see *Compt. rend. congrès. intern. de géographie,* 1931, pp. 8–314.

Sanderson, Dwight. "The Rural Community." Ginn & Company, Boston, 1932.

Scofield, Edna. The Origin of Settlement Patterns in Rural New England. *Geog. Rev.,* Vol. 28, pp. 652–663, 1928.

Smailes, A. E. "The Geography of Towns." Hutchinson's University Library, Hutchinson & Co., Ltd., London, 1953.

Terpenning, Walter A. "Village and Open-country Neighborhoods." Appleton-Century-Crofts, Inc., New York, 1931.

Trewartha, Glenn T. Types of Rural Settlement in Colonial America. *Geog. Rev.,* Vol. 28, pp. 652–663, 1938.

———. Some Regional Characteristics of American Farmsteads. *Ann. Assoc. Amer. Geographers,* Vol. 38, No. 3, pp. 169–225, 1948.

———. Chinese Cities. *Ann. Assoc. Amer. Geographers,* Vol. 41, pp. 331–347, 1951; Vol. 42, pp. 69–93, 1952.

27

Agriculture and Its Associated Features

27.1 In its broad sense, agriculture is the most necessary of the world's principal forms of production, and it certainly is by far the most widespread. It is closer to being a global activity than any other enterprise. Agricultural land is likewise the most basic and fundamental of the world's resources. It is from the land that man is fed and clothed, since the manufacturer who processes food and clothing is dependent upon the farmer for the larger part of his raw materials. The agricultural population is also one of the world's principal consumers of manufactured products. So it is that even much of the industrial and commercial development of regions is based at least indirectly upon the land.

Between one-half and two-thirds of the earth's population live on farms. This agricultural population may be divided into two groups of unequal size. The larger group lives in those parts of the world which, as yet, have been little affected by the mechanical revolution. These are chiefly subsistence farmers who are engaged in producing food for their own families. By contrast, a smaller group of the earth's farmers live in those parts of the world which have been profoundly influenced by the mechanical revolution. These people are engaged in commercial agriculture, for they produce for a market and they exchange farm products for industrial goods. Machine industry cannot live without commercial agriculture.

Dependence upon nature is the most fundamental characteristic of agriculture, even that which is commercial in character. In this respect agriculture stands in contrast to manufacturing, for in the latter man has largely gained the upper hand over Nature. The farmer, however, remains only Nature's helper in the growth of plants and animals, and to a large extent is helpless in the face of uncontrolled natural forces. An additional weakness of agriculture when yoked with modern industry is the fact that the former is still largely a small one-family enterprise, often operated at only modest efficiency, in which the farmer is in a weak position in the market both as a seller and a buyer. Because of these inherent weaknesses it is difficult to integrate agriculture smoothly and efficiently into an industrial economy and many of the so-called farm problems in technically advanced countries derive from this incompatibility.[1]

27.2 Agricultural Land. Agriculture requires land, but not all land is suited to agriculture. In fact, natural land seldom is capable of more than the most primitive of agricultural uses such as grazing or the collection of wild grains or hay. To prepare it for more intensive uses requires the investment of labor and money to clear, drain, fence, survey, or otherwise improve or allot it for tillage. Therefore, land as a factor in production is not, like the air, a free gift of nature. It must be won, and hence it has value.

Since agricultural land must be produced through the investment of capital and labor, it follows that much of the land of the world is

[1] On the topic of the place of agriculture in an industrial world, see Eric Zimmermann, "World Resources and Industries," rev. ed., pp. 147–175, Harper & Brothers, New York, 1951.

incapable of becoming economically agricultural, since it could never be made sufficiently productive to pay adequate returns on the investment. Handicaps of one kind or another inherent in its conditions of climate, soil, or surface configuration impose limits on its utility. It was the purpose of Part One of this book to state in some detail the complex of natural elements, some of which govern the quality of land, and there is no need to review them here. However, there are factors other than those of physical nature that are concerned with the value of land. Included among these are economic location, *i.e.*, an advantageous position with respect to other lands or to centers of population. Because the inherently fertile lands of the earth cannot be moved to advantageous locations, provided they do not have them, some that are inherently less productive have

higher sales values because of better situation. A supply of good agricultural land is, however, one of the critical elements in the environmental complexes with which the regions of the world are unequally endowed.

Significant Agricultural Elements and Their Classification

The distinguishable elements of culture that are associated with agricultural production are both numerous and varied. Only a few of them are noted here, and principally those which have material form and are visually observable. The following paragraphs comment upon those which are considered particularly significant as giving character to the various types of agriculture in the world and in making it possible to distinguish one type from another.

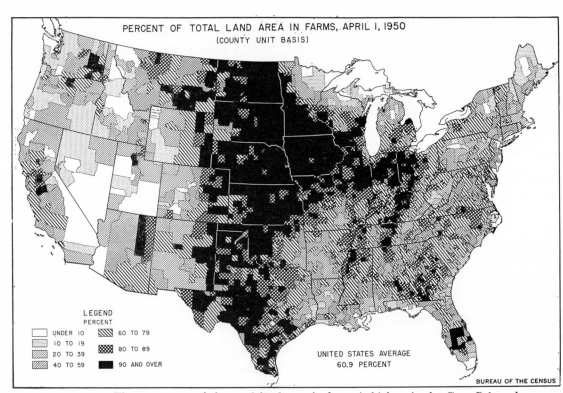

Fig. 27.1 The percentage of the total land area in farms is highest in the Corn Belt and much of the Great Plains. It is lowest in the dry and mountainous West and in the poor cutover lands of northern Minnesota, Wisconsin, and Michigan.

The farm population, their houses, and farmstead arrangements and structures have been discussed previously.

27.3 Percentage of the Total Land Area of a Region Agriculturally Utilized. Certainly one of the most fundamental geographic items concerning any region has to do with the percentage of its area that is agriculturally productive, *i.e.*, is utilized for the *raising of crops* or the *pasturing of animals.* For the world as a whole there is a marked concentration of farmed land in the humid sections of the middle latitudes. Throughout the polar lands, the deserts and the subarctic forests the land is only meagerly utilized, mainly because of obvious climatic handicaps. Large parts of the wet tropics also have only sparse agricultural development, although the reasons for this are more complicated and less obvious. But even in the humid sections of the middle latitudes, where the world's agricultural lands are concentrated, there are wide variations in the percentages that are in farms. This comes about chiefly as a result of differences in climate, surface configuration, soil quality, drainage condition, location with respect to the great industrial markets of the world, and the intensity of the need for land. The last named depends in part upon the history of settlement, the cultural inheritance, and the standard of living.

In the United States, where about 61 per cent of the total land area is held in farms, the percentage varies locally from less than 10, in parts of the sandy and swampy Coastal Plain, the ice-scoured crystalline rocks of the northeast, and the arid West, to more than 90 per cent in the level and fertile plains of the central Mississippi Valley region (Fig. 27.1). In Japan, largely because of the rugged nature of its land surface, only about 15 per cent of the country is agriculturally productive. In Norway, where the rugged surface is severely ice scoured, the comparable figure is 5 per cent or less.

27.4 Distributional Pattern of Agricultural Land. Not only the amount, but also the distributional aspect of farm land is geographically significant (Fig. 27.2). In the Laurentian Up-

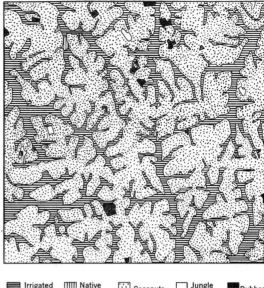

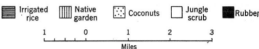

Fig. 27.2 Pattern of agricultural land in humid southwestern Ceylon. Rice occupies the river floodplains and coconut groves the interfluves. (*Ceylon Survey, Avisawella sheet.*)

land of Canada, for example, the distributional pattern of cultivated land is an exceedingly patchy and fragmented one, concentration being upon isolated areas of glacial till and glaciofluvial plains separated from each other by barren hill lands, swamps, and forests. This is quite in contrast with the distribution pattern typical of much of the Mississippi Valley, where deep soils and the general absence of rugged terrain permit farms to occupy almost the entire surface in contiguous blocks as far as the eye can reach. That is not true of all parts of the United States or even of much of the highly tilled plains of western Europe or of many other parts of the world where there are interruptions to the continuity of farm lands. Areas of unproductive sand or swamplands and hill lands in forest, owned by governmental or corporate bodies, separate certain tracts of farm land from each other, create patterns of great irregularity, and provide the nonagricultural spots in the utilization fabric.

27.5 Plowed or Cropped Land and Permanent Pasture. Agricultural lands in general yield valuable products of several different classes such as crops, pasture, wood, and others. Undoubtedly crop land and pasture land occupy the larger areas and are much the most important. It should be emphasized that, in creating a picture of the use of farm land within a region, two elements are significant with respect to each of these uses of land: (*a*) the quantity aspect, expressed in terms of percentage of the whole area so utilized, and (*b*) the distribution pattern of each type of land use. Unfortunately the information available from statistical sources and from field surveys is not uniformly adequate for the creation of such a picture, and if it were, the details of quantity and distribution would far exceed the limits of the present space. It is possible, therefore, to present only the most general of pictures in terms of contrast and for large areas.

In the United States, where about 61 per cent of the total national area is in farms and ranches, only about 25 per cent of the total area, or 41 per cent of the farm-land area, is in tilled crops, and this is very unequally distributed. In arid parts of the western states, for example, there are many counties in which no more than a small fraction of 1 per cent of the total area is under tillage, while in certain sections of the Corn Belt nearly all the farm land and more than three-fourths of the entire land area are tilled (Fig. 27.3). In the United States as a whole, nearly three-fifths of the farm lands are in permanent pastures, woodlands, idle or fallow lands, and other uses.

In Japan and China proper, on the other hand, tilled land occupies a much more significant place in the land-use system. The human populations of these countries are dense, and most of the tillable lands are used to produce food for direct human consumption, the animal

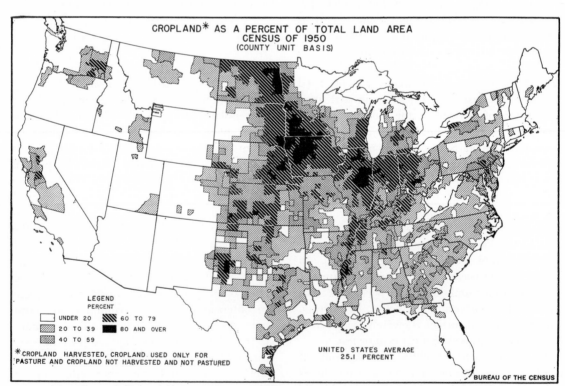

Fig. 27.3 Only one-quarter of the nation's land area is used for tilled crops. Highest percentages are chiefly in the Corn Belt where terrain, soils, and climate combine to provide a favorable environment for agriculture.

industries are only meagerly developed, and grazing lands do not occupy a significant area. In New Zealand the situation is quite the opposite. It is a newly settled country with a small population, a large livestock-grazing industry, and a small requirement for the kinds of food crops that must be raised at home. Consequently, a large area of potentially tillable land is devoted to pasture, and only about 3 per cent of the total area of the country is under the plow.

27.6 The Proportions of the Plowed Land in Various Crops. A further refinement in the analysis of the uses of farm land, following the distinction of plowed land from that in other uses, would show the subdivision of the plowed land into the kinds and amounts of the various crops raised (Fig. 27.4). In the United States, for example, of the farm-land area cropped, approximately 24 per cent is planted to corn, 19 per cent to hay, 20 per cent to wheat, 8 per cent to cotton, 11 per cent to oats, 3 per cent to sorghums, 3 per cent to barley, and 3 per cent to soybeans. Five crops represent about 81 per cent of the acreage in all crops. But within the country are regions of agricultural specialization, the percentages for which are greatly different from the average figures for the country as a whole. For example, one county in North Dakota, representative of the spring wheat belt, has 40 per cent of its cropped land in wheat, about 12 per cent in hay and forage crops, 19 per cent in barley, 13 per cent in oats, and only 5 per cent in corn. A county in the Iowa Corn Belt, on the other hand, has 52 per cent of its crop area in corn, 18 per cent in oats, 12 per cent in hay, 10 per cent in barley, and only 2 per cent in wheat. These percentages show remarkable contrasts in crop emphasis and differences between the agricultural systems of the two regions, although the percentages of the total areas in harvested crops in the two areas are not greatly different.

27.7 The Amount Produced per Unit Area. Although areal spread or acreage certainly is the most fundamental geographic fact concerning agricultural land utilization, the crop yield

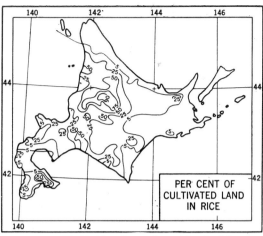

Fig. 27.4 Hokkaido, the nothern island of Japan.

per unit area is important supplementary information. It is an indication of the quality of the land and of the intensity of the farming practices as well. An acre of corn in terms of space occupied is identical in Iowa or Georgia, and yet the average per acre yield of corn in bushels is about 50 in the first state and only 10 in the second. This is in large part an expression of differences in the fertility of the dark prairie soils of Iowa and the leached red and yellow soils of Georgia. An average acre of rice land in Japan produces approximately 70 bushels of rice; in the United States, 48 bushels; and in the Philippine Islands, only about 22 bushels. The rice lands of the United States have, in the main, new dark Prairie soils which certainly are not inferior to the much cropped alluvial lands of Japan. Their lower yields are indicative of much more extensive farming methods, where yield is sacrificed to save on cost of production; whereas in Japan the soils are heavily fertilized and vast amounts of human labor are expended to bring the yield of rice up to a high level. In the Philippine Islands primitive methods result in lower average yields than those obtained by extensive farming on good lands in the United States.

27.8 Cropping Systems and Practices; Seasonal Landscapes. Depending largely upon climatic conditions, the seasons of planting and harvesting vary greatly from one part of the earth to another. In the constantly wet tropics, where there is no generally dormant season for

571

vegetation by reason of a deficiency of either heat or precipitation, definite seasons for planting or harvesting are not conspicuous. Seeds may be put into the soil at any time with assurance that conditions are satisfactory for their growth and maturing. In the tropical wet-and-dry (savanna) lands, on the other hand, where a dormant season is imposed by the drought of the low-sun period, there is a definite seasonal rhythm to agricultural practices. Except where irrigation is developed, crops are normally planted at the beginning of the rains and harvested during the dry season. Fields commonly lie fallow during the period of low sun.

Throughout the middle latitudes a seasonal rhythm of agricultural operations is usually imposed by a period of cold, although in some parts a drought season may have the same effect. But over the middle latitudes as a whole, winter, or the period of low sun, is the dormant season for agriculture, whereas spring is

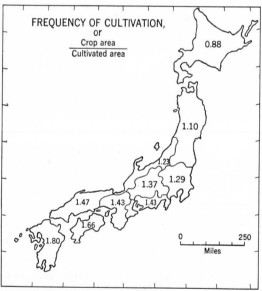

Fig. 27.5 Over much of subtropical eastern Asia it is a common practice to plant a field in more than one crop during the year. In the southernmost island of Japan 80 per cent of the agricultural land bears more than one crop. Toward the north, as the growing season shortens, the practice of multiple cropping becomes less common, and in Hokkaido, the northernmost island, the ratio of the area of crops to the cultivated area drops below 100, some land lying fallow.

the season of planting, summer of growth, and autumn of harvesting. This characteristic cycle is so well recognized that it has impressed itself upon the customs, habits, recreations, and literature of the inhabitants.

There are important departures from the previously noted cycle. On the tropical margins of the middle latitudes the mild winters permit some crops to flourish throughout the cool season. Thus the American Gulf Coast region, southern California, and Mediterranean Africa are important producers of winter fruits and vegetables for the markets farther north. Although oranges are picked throughout the year, the principal season is winter, when other fruits are scarce and expensive. In the dry-summer subtropical, or Mediterranean, regions where the periods of maximum heat and maximum rainfall do not coincide, the cereal crops commonly are planted in the fall at the beginning of the rains and harvested in late spring. In those regions of mild Mediterranean climate, grains grow more or less continuously throughout the winter. Even in the warm-summer phase of the humid continental climates, hardy cereals such as wheat and rye are fall-sown, although growth practically ceases during the winter. Most of the wheat grown in, and to the south of, the American Corn Belt, as well as that of western and central Europe, is designated as winter wheat, meaning that it is sown in the autumn. In the higher middle latitudes (subarctic, and humid continental climates with cool summers), however, the winters are severe, and practically all crops are spring-sown, the fields being free of crops in winter.

27.9 *Multiple Cropping and Interculture.* It is customary in the United States to raise only one crop in a field at a time and to plant a field only once during the course of a year. After the single crop has been harvested, the field is then usually allowed to lie fallow until the next year's planting season arrives. But in countries of dense population and restricted agricultural land areas, and especially in those where the growing season is relatively long, such practices as *multiple cropping* and *interculture* are common. By multiple cropping is meant the practice of replanting a field to a second crop after the first has been harvested, so that two and occasionally three harvests are obtained from the same land during the course of a year (Fig. 27.5). In Japan, for example, nearly 40 per cent of the rice fields are replanted in autumn to unirrigated crops such as wheat or barley.

Interculture is a kind of simultaneous rotation of crops in alternate rows, by which two or more different crops, planted at different times, are grown together in the same field. By this "close dovetailing rotation of crops in point of time, space, and labor" two or three harvests may be obtained in one year. In Japan summer vegetables frequently are intercultured. Four-fifths of the Italian vineyard acreage represents mixed crops, the rows of grapes being alternated with fruit trees which serve as their supports, with grain and vegetables frequently planted between the vine rows. Hay or grain crops are sometimes grown in American orchards.

27.10 Livestock Production as a Phase of Agriculture. Two large divisions of specialized agriculture may be recognized: (*a*) the growing of crops and (*b*) the raising of animals, although frequently the two types of economy are combined, even on the same farm. Certain crops, to be sure, such as rice, wheat, flax, cotton, and tobacco, are converted directly into forms useful to human beings. Others like corn, oats, hay, and mulberry are principally used as feed for domestic animals, which in turn furnish products or services for human use. However, many of the world's economically important domestic animals are grazers, and certain types of animal industry are found in regions where natural grass pastures, hay, and forage crops are abundant, whereas others are more sharply restricted to areas producing grain and other concentrated feeds. Since the earliest times the natural grasslands have been regions of extensive livestock production.

27.11 Uses of Animals and Animal Products. Under modern farming conditions the raising of livestock is done in such a variety of ways, and for such diverse purposes, that classification is not easy. Most animals, however, serve one or more of three general uses: (*a*)

as sources of food, such as meat, milk, eggs, or honey; (*b*) as sources of industrial products, such as fibers (wool, hair, silk) or leather (hides); (*c*) as beasts of draft or burden. The kinds and quantity of animal products emanating from a region are important geographic data.

27.12 Systems of Livestock Production. The systems of economy under which livestock are raised are several. At one extreme is the *nomadic herding* practiced by the tribal peoples of dry Africa, inner Asia, and the Asiatic tundra. A somewhat more advanced stage in animal industry is represented by *livestock ranching,* a commercial form of livestock grazing such as that practiced in western United States, the steppe lands of South Africa, or the grasslands of South America and Australia. A still more intensive stage of animal raising is to be found in those humid lands of general agriculture where there is an abundance of good pasture and, in addition, a plentiful supply of grain and forage crops for feeding. In part the animals forage for their food, even though their movements are limited by fences, but heavy feeding from the crops produced on the farm is also practiced. This type of commercial *livestock farming* is well developed in western and central Europe, the American Corn Belt, and parts of the Argentine Pampa.

27.13 Number of Livestock per Unit of Area. Primary in determining the importance of any region in animal production, no matter of what kind, is information relative to the number of animals per unit of area (square mile, acre, or other unit). To obtain this in comparable terms it is necessary to reduce the various kinds of animals to a common denominator, which may be called a *livestock unit.* This may be considered to be the equivalent of one horse, one mule, one cow, seven sheep, seven goats, or five swine. On this basis one may compare the relative numbers of livestock per square mile in different regions.

27.14 Livestock Units in Relation to Area of Cropped Land. Important as the above data are, however, they are not sufficient to give a clear notion of the importance of livestock in the regional economy. As an illustration, Na-

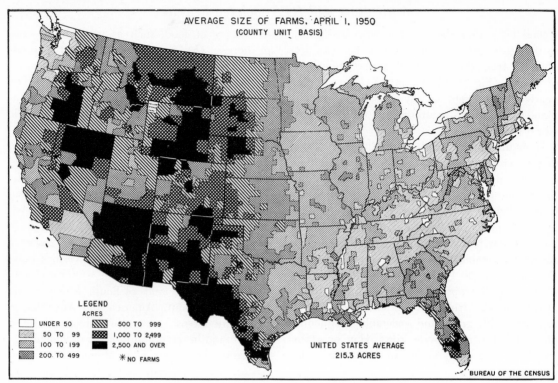

Fig. 27.6 Farms are largest in the dry-farming and livestock-ranching areas of the West. They are relatively small in parts of the South and in certain horticultural districts.

trona County in east central Wyoming and Fond du Lac County in southeastern Wisconsin have, respectively, about 14 and 140 livestock units per square mile. On the basis of these quantity data alone, one might conclude that Fond du Lac County is highly specialized in livestock production, and that Natrona County is not. But this is not the case, since relatively the Wyoming county is more dependent upon livestock than is the Wisconsin one. The difference lies in the contrasting types of animal industry, for in semiarid Wyoming it is sheep and cattle ranching, whereas on the more productive lands of eastern Wisconsin dairy farming is the principal industry. This contrast can be brought out clearly by comparing the

Comparative Data for Three Counties, Each Representative of a Type of Livestock Industry*

	Livestock Ranching, Natrona County, East Central Wyoming	Dairy Farming, Fond du Lac County, Southeastern Wisconsin	Commercial Livestock Farming, Carrol County, West Central Iowa
1. Percentage of total land area in all crops	0.6 (very low)	57.1 (high)	63.1 (very high)
2. Total livestock units per square mile	13.8 (very low)	137.9 (very high)	116.1 (very high)
3. Total livestock units per 100 acres in all crops	340 (very high)	37.6 (medium)	28.7 (medium)
4. Percentage of total livestock units in:			
Horses and mules	6.0 (very low)	11.7 (low)	12.5 (low)
Cattle	37.5 (medium)	83.1 (very high)	70.8 (very high)
Sheep, goats	56.2 (high)	1.2 (very low)	1.6 (very low)
Swine	0.5 (very low)	4.9 (low)	14.9 (high)
5. Gallons of milk produced annually per acre of land in all crops	27.6 (low)	142.5 (very high)	27.9 (low)

* After Wellington D. Jones. Ratios and Isopleth Maps in Regional Investigation of Agricultural Land Occupance. *Ann. Assoc. Amer. Geographers*, Vol. 20, pp. 177–195, December, 1930. Data modified in agreement with a later U.S. Agricultural Census.

total number of livestock units per 100 acres in all crops for each region. The figures representing the above ratio are 340 for Natrona and only 37 for Fond du Lac County.

27.15 Kinds and Number of Animals. A further important kind of data useful to a clear understanding of a region's livestock industry has to do with the particular *kind of livestock* raised. This can best be expressed as the percentage of the total livestock units in horses or cattle, or sheep and goats, etc. These data applied to Natrona and Fond du Lac counties tend further to differentiate the two regions, for although the former has 56 per cent of its livestock units in sheep and 37 per cent in cattle, the latter has 82 per cent in cattle and only 1¼ per cent in sheep. Further differentiation should be made between regions in which the cattle are being raised primarily for milk or for beef. This can be determined by data showing the quantity of milk produced annually per unit of area, per acre of land in farms, or per

acre in all crops. This is clearly brought out by the last item in the preceding table which compares a ranching area, a dairy area; and a beef-cattle and swine-raising area in the Corn Belt.

27.16 The Farm—Size and Shape; Number and Size of Fields. A farm is defined by the United States Census as all the land that is directly farmed by one person. Thus a large plantation operated by several tenant farmers would be considered not one but several farms. The size of this operating unit varies greatly from place to place depending upon the productivity of the land, density of rural population, and several other factors. In the livestock ranching region of Wyoming and Montana, for example, the average ranch size is 1,000 to 2,000 acres, but in drier and rougher southwest Texas there are several counties in which it reaches 10,000 acres or more. In the North Dakota spring wheat region the average operating unit is about 500 acres, in the Corn Belt

Fig. 27.7 An aerial view showing the rectangular field pattern on the flattish Illinois prairie. This pattern likewise reflects the rectangular land-survey system. Farmsteads can be identified by the clusters of trees. (*United Photo Shop.*)

it is about 160 acres, and in the rich cotton lands of the Mississippi floodplain and in certain irrigated horticultural districts, such as the southern California citrus belt, it is 50 acres or less (Fig. 27.6). In Europe, where population is denser and land more scarce, farms are naturally smaller, 85 per cent of the holdings in France containing less than 25 acres. In Switzerland they average about 20 acres. Japan, representing one of the world's most densely populated rural areas, far surpasses most of Europe in the smallness of farms, the size being under 2 acres.

27.17 Shape and Composition. A large part of the farms in the United States are roughly rectangular in shape and are composed of a single contiguous block of land. The farm is further divided into several individual fields of a variety of shapes and sizes but with a tendency toward rectangularity, especially where the land is not too rough (Fig. 27.7). The prevalence of right angles in the landholding pattern of the United States is largely the result of the original land surveys by which most of the country, excepting the eastern and southern states, was subdivided by north-south

and east-west lines coinciding with meridians and parallels (see Appendix C for a discussion of the American system of rectangular land survey). The section, 1 mile on a side, became the basic land-subdivision unit. Usually the American farms, as well as the individual fields, are enclosed by fences, although this is not always the case. In the flat lands of the Argentine Pampa rectangular land subdivision prevails also. It is not, however, systematically oriented with respect to compass directions (Fig. 27.8).

Quite in contrast with the foregoing picture are the farms of many European countries or those of the Orient. The Japanese or Chinese farm, instead of being one contiguous plot, usually is composed of several small, unfenced parcels of land of different sizes and shapes (Fig. 27.9). The parcels are scattered in various directions and distances about the rural village where the farmer dwells. For North China, where farms average 4 to 7 acres in size, there is an average of about six separate plots per farm. The plots average not far from an acre in size, and their usual distance from the farmstead is slightly over half a mile. This open-field system with noncontiguous plots is also typical of many parts of continental Europe (Fig. 27.10). The representative Swiss farm, with a total area of about 21 acres, is composed of over 14 unfenced parcels.

27.18 Regional Classification. The foregoing paragraphs of this chapter have attempted to outline the more significant elements in the agricultural complex of a region. The definition of an agricultural region would therefore rest upon the ability to recognize some distinctive association of these major elements. Unfortunately for the ease and clarity with which such regions may be delimited, the elements are many, some are capable of census enumeration or statistical computation, and others are not. Moreover, some parts of the world are covered by adequate and detailed agricultural census enumerations. Others have but general enumerations or none at all. From this it may be concluded that, although agricultural regions may be delimited for some

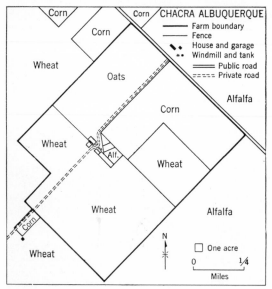

Fig. 27.8 Arrangement of fields, cropland, and farmstead on an Argentine farm of 554 acres. (*Map by Robert S. Platt.*)

Fig. 27.9 Irregular pattern of irrigated rice fields on an alluvial plain in Japan. The individual fields, separated by narrow dikes, are only a fraction of an acre in area.

parts of the world with fair precision, it is not possible for the world as a whole. Regions for the world as a whole must be general, and for some of them many of the desirable facts are entirely lacking. For none of them is it possible to proceed systematically through the entire list of even the known elements, since the present purpose and space do not permit so great detail. Moreover, a map to accompany such a world subdivision as is here proposed must be at a small scale and therefore general. The regional types outlined on this map may appear simple but are in fact mere generalizations of complex associations. Within each of the areas mapped as units are many variations which could be brought out only by means of a much more thorough analysis than the present purpose warrants.

Fig. 27.10 In many parts of the world a farm is not one contiguous plot, but is composed of several scattered parcels of land. The average Swiss farm has an area of 21 acres in 14 separate plots. (*Courtesy of U.S. Department of Agriculture.*)

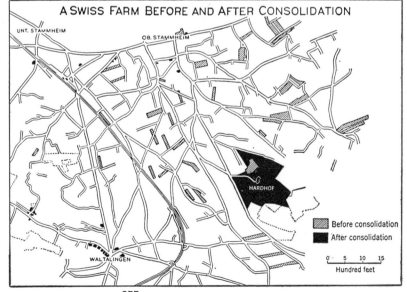

A SWISS FARM BEFORE AND AFTER CONSOLIDATION

UNT. STAMMHEIM

OB. STAMMHEIM

HARDHOF

Before consolidation

After consolidation

0 5 10 15
Hundred feet

WALTALINGEN

The following classification and the map of agricultural regions (Plate 8) are therefore limited to a subdivision of the world into approximately a dozen agricultural types. In this it is in accord with the general classifications of climates, landforms, soils, etc., that have been employed in this book. In the classification here employed[2] the regional distinctions rest primarily upon a brief list of features that have recognized functions and have been noticed either in the foregoing part of this chapter or in earlier chapters of Part Three. They are:

1. The crop and livestock association.

2. The methods used to grow the crops and produce the stock.

3. The intensity of application to the land of labor, capital, and organization, and the output of products that results.

4. The disposal of the products for consumption (*i.e.*, whether used for subsistence on the farm, fed to livestock, or sold for cash or other goods).

5. The ensemble of structures used to house and facilitate the farming operations.

Major Agricultural Types and Regions

27.19 Types of Regions.[3] Even the most casual survey of world agriculture shows strongly contrasting groups of regions: (*a*) those in which the major emphasis is upon the raising of animals, (*b*) those in which crop production is dominant, and (*c*) those in which

[2] Derwent Whittlesey. Major Agricultural Regions of the Earth. *Ann. Assoc. Amer. Geographers,* Vol. 26, pp. 199–240 and plate, 1936. See also Whittlesey's revised map contained in "Goode's World Atlas," pp. 24–25, Rand McNally & Company, Chicago, 1953.

[3] NOTE: A more comprehensive treatment of the topic, types of agriculture, may be found in the following textbooks:

Darrell Haug Davis. "The Earth and Man." Rev. ed. The Macmillan Company, New York, 1948.

Samuel Newton Dicken. "Economic Geography." D. C. Heath and Company, Boston, 1955.

Clarence Fielden Jones and Gordon Gerald Darkenwald. "Economic Geography." Rev. ed. The Macmillan Company, New York, 1954.

these basic functions share about equally in the attention of the farmer. Each of these, however, is capable of further subdivision, and the various resulting types are of different degrees of economic intensity, some requiring a high concentration of labor, capital, and organization upon the land, and others requiring but little. In the following types it is not possible to say precisely in all cases which is a more and which is a less intensive form of agriculture. However, the general arrangement is intended to present first the most primitive and least intensive forms of agricultural and pastoral enterprise and to reserve until last those of more advanced and intensive nature.

27.20 Nomadic Herding. Nomadic herding is a primitive form of livestock industry. Those who live by means of it have no fixed habitations, but migrate with their flocks and herds in search of water and forage. They are but a step removed from the hunting stage of human economy. The animals kept by nomadic herdsmen include most of the domesticated herbivorous species such as horses, cattle, camels, sheep, goats, and reindeer. These supply their owners with most of their wants in foods and raw materials: meat, milk, wool, hair, skins, and utensils. They supply transportation also to those who live in sparsely peopled districts. This is a subsistence type of animal raising.

Nomadic herding once was widespread in Eurasia and Africa, where it evolved with primitive civilizations, but it has suffered encroachment there by higher forms of land use. This encroachment still is in progress in Asia, where Chinese farmers slowly crowd the nomads from the more humid margins of Inner Mongolia. In recent years also the agricultural revolution in the U.S.S.R. has forced some of the inhabitants of the Siberian steppes to settle upon the land over which they and their ancestors have roamed for centuries. On the other hand, pastoral nomadism was not native to the American continents or Australia. In those continents the aboriginal inhabitants were either hunters of wild animals or tillers of the soil, having few domestic animals, and the later

Fig. 27.11 Slender fences of barbed wire divide western cattle ranches into large fields.

European immigrants had already developed beyond the nomadic stage. Only after the introduction of horses to the New World did the American Indians become, for a brief time, nomadic herdsmen, owning bands of ponies but little other stock. More recently the introduction of reindeer among the Eskimos of western Alaska and northwestern Canada has established a region of nomadic herding which may prove to be permanent.

The world regions that are characterized by nomadic herding (Plate 8) are mainly those which are dry, either actually or physiologically: steppe lands, desert margins, and tundra. The severely dry deserts of the Old World produce little forage and have few watering places. They are unable to support even sparse nomadic populations, although bordering tribes make temporary incursions upon them to utilize the short-lived forage that springs up following rains. The largest remaining regions of nomadic herding are those of central and western Asia and northern Africa.

27.21 Livestock Ranching. The steppe lands and desert margins of the Americas and Australia are regions of livestock grazing also, but the economic nature of the industry there differs from that of nomadic herding. In the United States it is called livestock ranching, and that name may be applied to it generally. It is, from one viewpoint, a retrograde form of settled agriculture. Farmers of European origin, accustomed to tilling the soil, occupied dry lands in the new continents and took up livestock grazing because aridity did not permit of satisfactory tillage. Although they adopted the means of existence of the pastoralist, they did not adopt the nomad's manner of life. Instead they retained the tradition of a settled habitation, the ranch house, and the idea of private ownership of the grazing lands, which were protected by patrol of their borders and by the ultimate building of fences to separate properties or even to divide individual holdings into great pasture fields (Figs. 27.11 and 27.6).

Livestock ranching, unlike pastoral nomadism, is a commercial form of land use. The livestock products are used by the ranchman to a limited extent only. Instead they are sold on local or world markets for a cash return, with which the ranchman buys his requirements. It is also a more intensive form of agriculture than pastoral nomadism, attention being given to the selection and breeding of stock, the artificial provision of water through wells, and even some tillage of the soil where a supply of irrigation water permits. Thus supplementary feed crops may be grown and some food for the ranch family. Although the ranch animals ordinarily are confined within the ranch limits, this is not always the case. In the North American cordilleran region, for example, cattle and sheep are driven from winter pastures on the lowland ranches to summer grazing on mountain pastures that are not a part of the ranch but are hired from governmental or other owners. This kind of seasonal migration of livestock is very ancient and belongs also to pastoral nomadism in the Old World and to other types of livestock management as well. It is called *transhumance*.

Within the several livestock ranching areas shown in Plate 8 are numerous modifications of the general type. The system of management and the kinds of livestock raised in the middle-latitude steppes of the United States and Argentina, for example, are not exactly like those of the tropical grasslands of Brazil or northern Australia. On the humid borders of the North American high plains, where good railway transportation permits of ready access to a large market, the ranches are smaller and the livestock industry more closely associated with crop tillage than in distant northern Australia. In the latter region in fact are some of the largest ranches, or "cattle stations," in the world, several of which reach an area of 5,000 square miles each, and at least one covers more than 12,000 square miles, or nearly as much as the states of Connecticut and Massachusetts combined. On the desert margins everywhere the capacity of the land to support livestock is limited by the sparsity of the forage, and the number of livestock units per square mile is small. In the good grasslands of western Nebraska, for example, 10 acres may be sufficient to support one animal unit, but in the drier lands of central Wyoming it may require 25 to 50 acres, and in the desert lands of Ari-

zona and Nevada more than 75 acres. Beyond a variable aridity limit, the area required to support livestock sufficient to maintain a commercial ranch unit becomes so great that it is no longer profitable to utilize it for ranching.

27.22 Primitive Subsistence Agriculture. In the wet tropics, on lowlands and in the hill lands and uplands, are vast areas of land which are used for agriculture in a rudimentary way. In the lowlands abundant heat and rainfall have given rise to a luxuriant vegetation, principally forest, but these same climate conditions also promote a luxuriant growth of weeds once the original vegetation is cleared away. These mainly are the regions of the latosolic soils whose store of fertility is quickly exhausted under continuous cultivation without skillful management. This type of management the primitive farmer may not be able to provide, and hence he is urged to adopt a system of cultivation that requires new lands for temporary cultivation.

Certain features are characteristic of nearly all types of primitive cultivation. As a rule the small patches of tilled land are scattered in their distribution so that they are surrounded and separated by areas of forest and bushland. Individual farms are small in area usually only a few acres. Kinds of crops vary from one region to another. Of the grains, maize or corn is the most important in the Americas, millet and sorghum in Africa, and upland rice in the Orient. Other common crops are yams, manioc, peanuts, taros, beans, peas, melons, and squash. To an overwhelming extent the crops are grown to provide food for the farm family. Raising crops for sale is uncommon. Farming methods and implements are crude. The labor is almost exclusively human labor. After planting the crops are largely left to the care of nature, for little time is spent on weeding and cultivating, although this varies among different peoples. Crops are grown without benefit of fertilizer.

Several subdivisions of primitive agriculture are recognized. Most extensively developed is that known as *shifting cultivation*. It involves the clearing of the fields in the forest and their tillage for two or three years in subsistence crops until weeds or soil exhaustion force their abandonment. This continues until all available field sites convenient to the settlement have been used. Then the entire group moves to a new site and establishes a new village settlement in a locality well removed from the earlier one. The old site of village and fields quickly reverts to forest, and after some decades it may again be cleared as new land in a process of slow rotation during which the soil recovers some of its elements of fertility and the troublesome weeds have been crowded out by forest growth. Where this simple system of shifting cultivation prevails, population of necessity is relatively sparse since at any one time most of the land is unused.

A second subdivision of primitive subsistence agriculture is one in which the fields are cleared of their original vegetation cover, cultivated briefly, and then abandoned as before, but by contrast the dwelling place of the cultivator is not moved. Here the practices are somewhat intermediate in character between the genuinely shifting and sedentary types of agriculture. Where the farm residence remains fixed in location, the farming system requires a more frequent reusing of abandoned fields and a considerable intensification of the agricultural practices. There is a more complete and intensive use of the land than is true in those areas where a shifting of residence as well as of fields occurs. Such an agricultural system requires more labor and is also capable of supporting a somewhat larger population.

A third and somewhat more advanced subdivision of primitive agriculture is that which is characterized by completely *sedentary* habits of living. Here groups of cultivators or individual farm families remain permanently in one area and till the same fields year after year. Under these conditions there is a more careful clearing and preparing the planted land and more attention is given to the growing crops as well as to their harvesting. Many times these farmers are located in close enough proximity to markets so that a portion of their produce is grown for sale.

A further modification of primitive agriculture is introduced when domesticated animals become an important part of the farming system. Poultry of various kinds is present in varying numbers throughout most of the areas of shifting and sedentary agriculture, but larger animals are uncommon except where sedentary habits of living have evolved. It is particularly in the tropical Andean highlands of South America that there has developed a form of primitive agriculture in which the raising of crops and the pasturing of animals (sheep, cattle, alpacas, llamas) are combined to an extent not characteristic of most other areas falling within this general type. The Andean peoples clear and till small fields on the slopes and uplands, and these, when the soils are depleted, are allowed to revert to pasture. However, the residences of the cultivators remain relatively fixed. At the cooler, higher altitudes the crops grown are different from those on the adjacent lowlands. Among some of the primitive agricultural peoples of Africa as well, especially those dwelling outside the densely forested areas, numerous cattle are raised, partly as a source of income and partly as a sign of wealth or social position.

With our present inadequate knowledge about the various world regions where primitive subsistence agriculture prevails it is impossible to show accurately on a small-scale map the world distribution of the several subdivisions of the agricultural system. Moreover, the subtypes are frequently intermingled within a general region, and there are gradations between the migratory and sedentary types, features which add to the difficulty of showing distribution on a world map. On Plate 8 no attempt has been made to distinguish between the several types of primitive subsistence agriculture. As a general rule shifting cultivation predominates to a greater degree in the wet tropical lowlands and hill country and especially where there is little contact with the outside world so that the most primitive conditions prevail. The more sedentary forms of cultivation are concentrated in highland areas of the tropics (Central America, the Andes, Ethiopia, East Africa) and in smaller scattered areas in tropical lowlands.

27.23 Intensive Subsistence Cultivation. In parts of eastern and southern Asia are ancient centers of civilization in which agricultural skills and implements long ago made it possible to support many more people per unit of area than is possible under rudimentary cultivation. The further growth of population required ever-increasing intensity in the use of agricultural resources and gave rise to distinctive systems of tillage. In the main they are of the subsistence type, only a small part of the farm produce being sold away from the locality of its production. Most of the readily tillable land is used, and additional areas are created at great labor through land drainage and the terracing of hillsides. Only the steepest slopes and the least productive soils remain in woodlands or pastures, but in some hilly districts woodlands occupy a significant part of the total area, nearly two-thirds in Japan, for example. Oriental agriculture is based very largely on the growing of cereals, tubers, and other vegetables. About 98 per cent of the caloric content of the Chinese diet is of vegetable origin. Such an agricultural system permits the feeding of a maximum number of people.

The animal industries are only modestly developed, since the major part of the land, and especially the cropland, is required to produce cereals and vegetables for direct human consumption. In this respect, however, parts of the Asiatic region differ because of contrasts in religious tolerance. In China and Japan there are relatively few cattle and sheep but many swine and poultry, scavenger animals that can be supported from agricultural and household wastes. Even ponds and streams are made to yield their maximum of food through the cultivation of fish and waterfowl. By contrast India and Pakistan have a dense cattle population but not many swine. Few of the numerous cattle are killed for their meat; most of them are used as draft animals on the farms or serve no particular economic use.

There is another significant agricultural contrast between parts of the general region of intensive subsistence cultivation. In the more rainy tropical and subtropical portions the cropping system is dominated by the growing of rice, and all other cultivated crops take places subordinate to this most productive of cereal grains. Rice occupies the irrigable deltas, floodplains, coastal lowlands, and terraces. Other grains occupy unirrigated lands or replace rice on the irrigated land in the cooler and drier season, after the rice harvest. In more tropical portions, where the growing season is long, multiple cropping enables two crops of rice to be harvested, which, together with beans, vegetables, and other crops, provides food for large numbers of people. These live in innumerable farm villages and till their tiny fields with endless patience and hard labor (Fig. 26.6), but seldom do they achieve more than a bare existence.

In contrast with these rice districts are the more northerly portions and interior highlands of China and Japan and the dry interior of India, where the summers are either too short or there is not sufficient irrigation water for the cultivation of rice. There various other cereal grains, especially wheat, corn, the grain sorghums, and millets, take its place. They are associated with beans, vegetables, and many other crops, such as cotton. The major areas of rice dominance are distinguished in the regional map (Plate 8). In addition to the major areas of intensive subsistence cultivation outlined on the map there are others too small to be shown at that scale. Mainly they are in the Old World, and most of them are the densely peopled oases or irrigation regions. Of these the oasis of the Nile Valley in Egypt is a conspicuous example large enough to be shown on the map.

27.24 Commercial Plantations and Small Farms. In restricted areas within the humid tropics and subtropics there has developed a type of agriculture whose purpose is the production of a single crop or limited group of crops for cash sale. Characteristically a plantation is a large unit of land so that it represents an extensive agricultural operation. In this respect, and in others as well, it stands in striking contrast to the small farms of the native agriculturists in the same general region. In some areas the extensive commercial plantations may occupy a large part of the total agricultural areas, as do the rubber estates in western Malaya. More commonly, however, the plantations are closely associated with subsistence and commercial tillage on small farms which is a type of agriculture of a very different character. In tropical southeastern Asia, one of the earth's most important regions of plantation agriculture, the large estates are decreasing in numbers. As one after another of the political units in this general region have severed colonial ties and acquired independence, the great plantations are being broken up into small farms and put into the hands of native agriculturists.

Plantation crops are produced on an extensive scale by efficient methods and in standard forms. The products most susceptible to this type of management are certain world staples that are required in large quantity, mainly in the industrial regions of the Northern Hemisphere. Such are bananas, tea, coconut oil, rubber, and certain tropical fibers. The choice of plantation site is made with reference to its ability to produce one of these commodities in large quantity and of superior quality, and hardly any other crops are grown. Not uncommonly the capital for plantation development, the skilled personnel for its management, the machinery for its operation, fertilizers for the crop, part of the food for the laborers, and sometimes even the laborers themselves are brought from outside the locality, and some of them from the farthest parts of the earth. On some plantations the laborers live in village settlements at the plantation center and work in gangs under supervision. This is notably true of rubber and tea plantations. Some kinds of plantation crops require also a preliminary

processing or elementary manufacture before they are shipped to their foreign destinations, and the plantation center is distinguished by an establishment for that purpose. Such are the large sugar mills, coconut-oil mills, and the factories required for curing and packing the freshly gathered tea leaves, rubber latex, and other crude plantation crops.

Like other agricultural staples, the products of plantation agriculture suffer from competition on the world market. There are few crops so restricted by nature that they cannot be raised in more than one region. Moreover, the great plantation establishments, once they have created a large market and have demonstrated efficient methods of production, begin to find competitors in the small farmers of their respective regions. Some crops such as sugar and cotton once were produced, and still are to some extent, under plantation systems of management but now are grown even more largely by a modified plantation system or by independent small farmers. The United States cotton region is an outstanding example of this change. The abolition of slavery, the breaking up of the great plantations, the lack of necessity for any expensive equipment in cotton growing, and the westward expansion of cotton into the subhumid districts have almost extinguished the true plantation system that once prevailed. Similar if less extensive changes have taken place in the Cuban sugar industry, the Brazilian coffee industry, and others. In fact, small commercial farms prevail over considerable parts of these regions, and an almost complete transition is to be found between the highly centralized plantation on the one hand and the small cash-product farm on the other. Those plantations tend to resist longest the effects of private competition whose products are of such a nature that they require some kind of special handling or expensive processing or standardizing between the field and the shipping point, things the small farmer is unable to provide.

Little attempt has been made in Plate 8 to distinguish between the areas of highly centralized plantation cultivation and those transitional forms noted above. The simple distinction provided does not do justice to the complication of the facts. Several of the areas are so small as to require special symbols to make them stand out, and none of them is marked in such a way as to distinguish the special product for which each locality is noted. Added detail regarding these, and the reasons for their locations, is a part of the subject matter of economic geography.

27.25 Mediterranean Agriculture. Although Mediterranean agriculture is not distinguished on quite the same basis as the other types noted here, it is an ancient association of cultural and natural features well recognized by geographers. The unique combination of dry subtropical climatic features together with hilly land or bordering plateau surface is, in each region of its occurrence, associated with a distinctive combination of crops and livestock industries, although the relative importance of the several component cultural elements is not everywhere the same. Cereal grains, especially wheat, grow during the mild, moist winter and mature with the coming of the dry summer. Certain other crops that are sensitive to low temperatures are native to the regions of Mediterranean climate and find there the freedom from severe frost necessary to their growth. Such are the olive tree and the grapevine. Xerophytic character or deep roots that seek underground water enable them to endure the summer aridity and produce their fruits at the end of the dry season. Still other crops of humid tropical or subtropical origin have been introduced into the Mediterranean regions by man. They find there the mild winters they require, but they are not naturally adapted to the summer aridity and are able to survive only where they are supplied with water by irrigation. The citrus fruits are the outstanding example of this exacting group of crops. However, where irrigation water is available, it is often supplied to other crops also, including some such as grapes and olives, which will survive without it but are much improved in yield and quality if they receive supplementary

irrigation. Other irrigated crops include vegetables, sugar beets, and alfalfa for hay and pasture. The irrigated land is used most intensively and is held in small farms that receive careful tillage and often represent a large investment of capital and labor per acre. Also it yields large returns.

However, only a comparatively small part of the total area of the land classified as having Mediterranean agriculture is capable of irrigation, either because it is rough land not physically suited to that use or, more commonly, because there is not sufficient irrigation water available. The larger part must produce cereals under dry-land culture, or the more hardy of the unirrigated tree crops, or it is used as pasture land for more or less migratory flocks and herds. Since most of the Mediterranean climatic regions include areas of hills and mountains, these are used mainly as grazing lands, and they occupy much the greater part of the total area but support only a small part of the population. The dry summer pastures do not supply forage adequate for many cattle or horses but are much better adapted to the use of sheep and goats, which are the most numerous of the livestock kept there.

Adjacent to some of the Mediterranean agricultural districts of Europe and southwestern Asia are plateau uplands in which the winters are more severe so that the less hardy subtropical crops of the Mediterranean type are largely excluded. Yet these areas are closely associated both physically and culturally with the true Mediterranean. In them the crop emphasis is more on dry-land cereals or on irrigated subsistence crops and less on horticultural crops such as vegetables and fruits for sale. In them also the seminomadic herder and his flocks occupy a more important position. The herdsman, having winter quarters in the Mediterranean lowland or in a plateau basin, tills little if any land and provides little in the way of tilled crops for the support of his animals. With the change of the seasons he moves from his winter quarters to the higher plateau uplands or the mountains where there is better forage. His flocks may include, in addition to his own, some animals that are the property of village farmers who remain at home to till the land and produce crops for human consumption. Some areas of each of these associated types are shown in Plate 8 and are distinguished by appropriate symbols.

27.26 *Regions of Mediterranean Agriculture; Horticulture Predominant.* The world regions of true Mediterranean agriculture are, of course, practically coincident with the climatic regions of that type (Plates 2 and 8). However, the agricultural emphasis varies considerably among the regions owing to differences in historical background, density of population, accessibility to markets, and other culture factors. In California citrus and deciduous tree fruits, vineyards, and vegetable crops are of paramount commercial importance. The industries that supply oranges, raisins, wines, peaches, figs, and other intensive crops are highly organized on a commercial basis, and they have a large national market available and the means of transportation with which to reach it. In the distant Mediterranean districts of Australia there is an even larger area of tillable land, but the supply of irrigation water is less abundant, the domestic markets are small, and the distances to outside markets great. Hence the more easily transported products of wheat farms and sheep ranches have a higher relative importance there. In fact, both the regions of Mediterranean agriculture in the Northern Hemisphere have large nearby markets, whereas those of Australia, Chile, and South Africa find no comparable outlets for their more perishable products. Notwithstanding these differences, the basic agricultural elements of all the Mediterranean regions have a striking similarity which warrants their inclusion in one of the major types of agricultural regions of the world.

27.27 *Regions of Mediterranean Agriculture; Dry Farming and Grazing Predominant.* It is especially in the area bordering the Mediterranean Basin that the line is most sharply drawn between areas in which horticulture is predominant and those in which dry farming and grazing are paramount. In these anciently settled lands the folkways of centuries are not easily disturbed. Moreover, it is in this region that the horticultural lowlands are marginal to tablelands and plateaus having more severe winter climates. One such area is the Iberian Peninsula. Its western, southern, and eastern lowlands are true Mediterranean, but the central plateau, 2,000 to 5,000 ft. higher, is devoted more largely to cereal culture and to the grazing of flocks of sheep which make their annual migrations from winter feeding grounds in the basins and lowlands to summer pastures in the uplands and mountains. The same is true of the Anatolian Plateau in Turkey and of the highlands of northwestern Iran. There increasing aridity and long-established custom put further emphasis on grazing, and this modified form of Mediterranean agriculture almost insensibly merges with the true pastoral nomadism of Arabia and Central Asia.

27.28 Commercial grain farming, like plantation culture, is a product of the modern industrial era. The two are alike in some respects but very different in others. The commercial grain farm, like the plantation, usually puts an emphasis on some one crop which it produces for cash sale. It is, however, unlike the plantation in its organization. It does not require a processing plant or even storage facilities, since the grain goes directly from the field to the market (Fig. 27.12). It does not have gang labor, outside management, or foreign capital. Except in the communal farms of Russia, it has no workers' village, but instead has dispersed farmsteads of rather small size and unimpressive type. The average size of commercial grain farms is large (320 to 640 or 1,000 acres in the wheat regions of the United States), and mainly they are operated by their owners or tenants upon an extensive basis, with a maximum of labor-saving machinery. The farmer supplies the management and, with his family and a hired hand or two, furnishes the labor, except for temporary help at harvest time. Wheat is usually the principal crop of commercial grain farms, but it is not the only one. In some districts corn, barley, rice, or flaxseed are raised for sale. Generally also there

Fig. 27.12 Commercial grain farming is found mainly in the steppe and prairie lands of the middle latitudes. Its success depends on cash markets and modern transportation. The market may be close, as is the case with this wheat field near a giant flour mill in Saskatoon, Saskatchewan, or it may be on the far side of the earth.

are secondary crops of hay, oats, and other feed crops for the farm animals. The number of animals kept is not great in proportion to the size of the farm. Most important are the horses used to pull the numerous and large tilling, seeding, and harvesting machines, but in many areas tractors have taken the place of these to a considerable extent. Other livestock includes a few cows and other animals, which are kept to furnish a domestic supply of milk and meat.

Commercial grain farming is found principally on the steppes and prairie margins of the middle latitudes, especially in the plains regions of chernozemic and steppe soils. Because of the low and erratic rainfall the yields of grain average low in spite of the fertile soils, but for the same reason the land is relatively cheap. The proportion of the average total area under the plow is high, exceeding 70 per cent in parts of North Dakota, Kansas, and eastern Washington. The farms being large, the farmsteads

are widely spaced. Having few livestock and little need for grain storage, they have few barns, and hence the farmsteads are unimpressive when compared with those associated with certain other types of middle-latitude farming. In fact, the whole landscape with its absence of woodlands, its large fields and widely spaced farmsteads, is one of peculiar openness.

On the semiarid margins of some of the commercial grain-farming regions part of the crop is raised by "dry-farming" methods. These are agricultural practices designed to conserve moisture by storing up in the soil part of the rainfall of more than one year, in order to produce a single crop. Thus the land is cultivated each year to make it permeable and retentive of moisture but is cropped only in alternate years. This type of farming is expensive in terms of labor, considering the possible returns, but it utilizes cheap land. It is particularly suited to grain farming because such crops as wheat and barley have relatively small water requirements.

The world regions of commercial grain·farming, shown in Plate 8, are, it will be seen, distinctive of regions of European rather than Asiatic type of civilization. They occupy the new and relatively cheap lands of the world, and most of them are bordered on their drier sides by regions of livestock ranching. In part they are regions of humid continental climate with warm summers, and these produce mainly fall-sown winter wheat, as in Kansas, Argentina, Australia, and the Ukraine. Some areas having the cool-summer type of continental climate raise mostly spring-sown wheat, as in southeastern Russia, western Siberia, the Prairie Provinces of Canada, and the Dakotas. Some specialize in grains other than wheat (Fig. 27.13). For example, corn is grown primarily for sale from the farm in a large district in eastern Illinois, also in the northern part of the Argentine grain region, and in the Transvaal and Orange Free State of South Africa. Rice, mainly a subsistence crop in the Old World, is grown

entirely for sale under the American system of culture found in California and Louisiana, but these and some other cash grain districts are too small to be shown on the accompanying world map.

27.29   Associated Crop and Livestock Farming. This name may be applied to a mixed type of agriculture in which some crops are grown as feed for livestock, some for cash sale, and some as food for local human consumption. The relative importance of these three functional elements varies from one region to another. In most of the regions the production of livestock is highly important, but in some it is practically the only source of cash income. The mixed farming regions may in fact be divided into two types: (*a*) those in which crops and livestock are raised mainly for sale, and (*b*) those in which they are produced mainly for local use. These may be called the commercial and subsistence types, respectively (Plate 8).

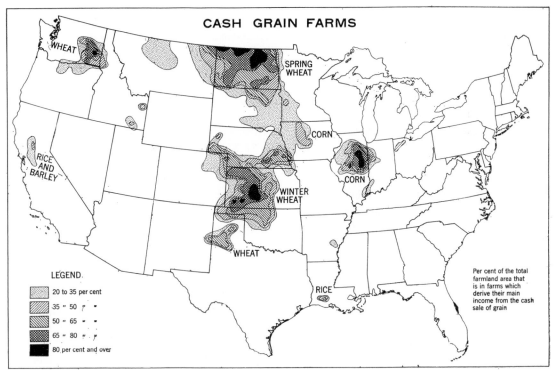

Fig. 27.13   Four principal areas in the United States, and several smaller ones, are characterized by a type of agriculture producing grains for cash sale.

27.30 *The commercial type* of crop and livestock farming is best exemplified by the American Corn Belt, where crops are raised mainly to feed hogs, cattle, and sheep, which are sold from the farm and are themselves the principal source of cash. Relatively little grain or other crops are sold from the farm and even less is used for direct human consumption. In the western European region the emphasis is more evenly divided. The significant feature of this type of farming, however, is that it is organized upon a commercial basis and that it has usually more than one source of cash income but with one of them commonly predominant. In general this type of farm is more versatile than the cash grain type, and this in turn implies regions of better climatic endowment, particularly more abundant precipitation.

The farming system of the commercial crop and livestock type varies considerably among the regions. It has, however, certain distinguishable features. Outstanding is some sort of rotation of crops that employs a succession involving (*a*) a tilled crop, (*b*) a small grain, (*c*) a hay crop, and (*d*) rotation pasture. Thus, in the American Corn Belt the principal tilled crop is corn, the small grain is likely to be oats or wheat, and the hay crop alfalfa, clover, soybeans, or grasses. In a succeeding year the former hay field may be used as pasture before it is plowed up and the land used again for corn. Such a rotation may run 3 to 5 years and sometimes more. In south central Europe the sequence may involve corn, but in those sections where the summers are too cool for corn, it is replaced in the rotation by such tilled crops as stock beets, turnips, or potatoes, all of which are much used in feeding animals. In the districts of poor soil and colder winters also, wheat may be replaced by rye. In the level, dark-colored, prairie soils of the American Corn Belt the percentage of land under tillage is high, 75 per cent in parts of Illinois, Iowa, and Nebraska. In these areas a minimum of land is held in permanent pasture, but in regions of rougher surface and poorer soils, parts of eastern United States or Europe especially, the ratio of pasture

land to crop land is much higher. However, the producing capacity of the land is high, and there normally is a surplus of feeds with which to fatten livestock in addition to those which are raised locally (Fig. 27.14). Additional animals usually are purchased from neighboring areas of lower rainfall or rougher surface. The American Corn Belt, the Argentine alfalfa belt, and various districts in France and Germany are noted as centers of livestock feeding.

The farms of these productive regions average smaller than those of the commercial grain-farming areas, 120 to 200 acres in the American Corn Belt, and much less in Europe, as compared with an average of 500 in the cash-grain region in North Dakota. The manner of tillage is much more intensive, involving more investment, more labor, and a larger use of fertilizer. It is more expensive land, and the typical farm has larger and more expensive buildings to house animals and crops. According to the 1950 Census the value of land and buildings per acre of farm property was $244 for the Corn Belt in central and eastern Illinois and only $26 in the spring wheat area of central and northern North Dakota. The farm buildings in the central European mixed farming region also are large, substantial, and some of them very old as compared with the small and often barnless cabins or sod houses that characterize the farm settlements of the Russian wheat belt.

27.31 *The subsistence type* of crop and livestock farming is restricted largely to less advanced middle-latitude regions and especially to those which are remote from modern transportation routes. The largest region of this type is in central and eastern European Russia, where distances are great, railways and roads few, and the farming system derived from a very old form of peasant agriculture. In that region rye and oats replace the wheat and barley that predominate in the commercial grain region of southern Russia. The rye and oats are mainly consumed locally rather than sold on the cash market. Other important subsistence crops include large quantities of

Fig. 27.14 The farmstead buildings of a corn and livestock farm in Illinois. The silo provides storage for part of the corn fodder. The feed yard of this farmstead contained about 50 head of fattening cattle and many hogs.

potatoes and cabbage and some other vegetables. The livestock density is not high, but cattle, swine, and sheep exist in moderate numbers and contribute to the local food supply. Horses are used for farm labor. Most of the Russian peasant farms have been collectivized under the Soviet regime, and doubtless the subsistence type of agriculture is being broken down, especially near the growing manufacturing towns of the Moscow and Ural industrial regions, which furnish new markets for farm produce. The farmers of this region live mainly in villages, their principal construction material is logs, and their barns and other farm buildings are fewer and simpler than those of the commercial mixed farming districts of western Europe. Subsistence farming produces very little cash income with which to buy improved equipment.

Other regions of subsistence crop and livestock farming are smaller and less clearly defined. The isolated Russian settlements of central and far eastern Siberia have borrowed their characteristics in part from old Russia and

may be considered similar in agricultural type. There are few such districts in Anglo-America, except possibly in parts of the southern Appalachian highland and Maritime Canada, and they are small. In the highlands of Mexico and in Central and South America subsistance agriculture of the ancient Indian type has been modified by the introduction of European animals, some of whose products are sold for cash.

27.32 Commercial Dairy Farming. Dairying is an intensive phase of commercial crop and livestock farming in which crops are raised to feed dairy cattle and other incidental livestock and in which milk and its products, rather than the animals themselves, furnish the principal source of cash income. Dairying is a more intensive use of land than beef production because a given quantity of feed will produce, through the medium of dairy cows, at least two or three times as much human food in the form of milk as it will in the form of beef. However, it requires more of the farmer's time and labor to produce it.

Commercial dairying prospers under varied

climatic conditions, and it does not demand soils of the highest fertility. Pasture, hay, silage crops, and grain concentrates are required, but the industry is sufficiently remunerative that the concentrates may be imported if the coarser feeds are available. One condition commercial dairying must have: access to large urban markets. Milk and cream are so perishable that they must be marketed within a few hours of their production. Butter and cheese can be held longer, up to several months, provided there are means of refrigeration in storage and transit. The major dairy regions of the world are, as shown in Plate 8, near the great industrial cities of northwestern Europe and northeastern United States and adjacent Canada. Dairying has not been traditional in the densely peopled subsistence farming regions of the Orient or in Mediterranean Europe with its poor summer pastures. Neither have the inhabitants of these regions the cash incomes that would enable them to support dairying on a large scale. Distant dairy regions such as those in Australia and New Zealand are of recent origin and have had the benefit of cheap land, efficient transportation, and protected access to the large British market.

The two major world regions of commercial dairy farming have advantages other than proximity to the great dairy markets. Relatively cool, moist summers are favorable to the production of pasture, hay, and other forage and fodder crops. They have also permitted the cultivation of oats and barley for grain and, in America, corn for silage. These are more suited to the feeding of dairy cows than to the fattening of beef and other meat animals. The average dairy farm in America is only slightly smaller (120 acres) than the crop and livestock farm, but its use is different. Less than half of it, on the average, is plow land, as against 50 to 75 per cent of the Corn Belt farm (Fig. 27.3).

The average value of land and buildings per acre of farm land in the two regions is about the same, but in the dairy farm the large barns and other buildings are worth more than those of the Corn Belt farm and the land somewhat less. The difference in land values may be attributed to differences in soil, surface, and drainage, the dairy region being mainly one of podzolic forest soils and recent glaciation, with areas of stony moraine and glacial marshes, which, however, are usable as pasture. The higher value of the dairy farm buildings is in consequence of the need for weatherproof structures for the protection of cows and forage crops and for the care of milk. Swine, poultry, and horses are necessary parts of the dairy farm livestock also and must be housed. Not all dairy regions require such elaborate structures. In New Zealand, especially, the winters are so mild that pasture is available all the year, no hay storage is necessary, and open milking sheds suffice for the protection of cows. There the benefits of cheaper land and lower housing costs are offset by high labor costs and especially by high freight charges to distant markets.

The form in which dairy produce is marketed varies within the parts of the great dairy regions also. Although there is no rigid separation, there is a tendency for those areas nearest the great cities to furnish the fluid milk while those farther removed furnish condensed milk and cheese, and the fringing areas supply butter. Thus, Great Britain, in normal times, is 100 per cent self-sufficient in fluid milk, about 30 per cent self-sufficient in cheese, but only 10 per cent self-sufficient in butter. The districts of New England, southern New York, and Pennsylvania supply the large eastern cities with milk, and southeastern Wisconsin and northern Illinois do the same for the Chicago metropolitan district. Northern New York State, the lower St. Lawrence Valley, and much of central and northern Wisconsin are noted for cheese manufacture, and Ontario, Minnesota, and other fringing districts are known for their butter output. In Europe, Denmark and the Baltic Sea margin are noted for butter production, but Netherlands and Switzerland, where dairy specialization is of long standing, have a large trade in cheese, for which they have become famous. Australia and New Zealand are noted for their production of butter, although the latter has a large cheese industry also.

27.33 Commercial Gardening and Fruit Culture. Another form of agriculture which depends upon the existence of the great urban markets is concerned with the supply of vegetables and fruits, both in and out of their usual season. These industries are a normal part of the Mediterranean agriculture, but they are found in other regions also (Plate 8). The greatest markets are those of industrial Europe and North America. In those regions are millions of people who have not time or land for gardening, but they have cash incomes with which to buy horticultural products. The great population centers of the Orient, being more largely agricultural, supply themselves during the usual season and go without during the

balance of the year, as did all the rest of the world only a few decades ago. The large cities of the Southern Hemisphere are not numerous and large enough to require either the great volume of produce that flows into the European and North American centers or so vast an industry to provide it.

The vegetable and fruit crops are the produce of highly intensive cultivation. The land area utilized is relatively small, but it is made to yield an astonishing quantity of food. It is heavily fertilized and tilled with a great expenditure of labor. The farms generally are small, and the nature of the farm operations does not require large or numerous buildings. In the typical horticultural district, therefore, neat houses with small barns and few outbuildings are spaced at short intervals in a landscape of intensive cultivation.

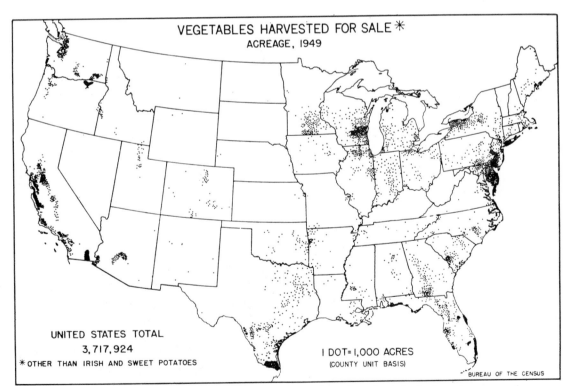

Fig. 27.15 The distribution of vegetables grown for sale reflects both the advantages of mild winters in the South and West and of special soils or closeness of city markets in the Northeast.

The great markets are supplied by two somewhat different types of industry. One is local and the other distant. The first takes advantage of nearness to the market. Often these small farms are located on the outskirts of the market cities or within truck-hauling distance. They supply vegetables and fruits of great variety, each in its own season, but they operate under whatever disadvantages of climate and soil the region may have. The second type operates under the disadvantage of distance from market but reaches out for localities of special advantage in climate, soil, or other environmental conditions, each according to its own requirements. The first is likely to be a general horticultural industry, growing a series of fruits and vegetables simultaneously or in sequence as the climate permits or the market requires. This type of industry is sometimes called market gardening. The second type is usually more specialized, growing one fruit or one or two vegetable specialties upon which the whole year's operations are based. Such industries commonly are called fruit farming or truck farming (Fig. 27.15).

In both Europe and America the great cities have their distinctive market-gardening districts. Near New York City are the extensive gardens of Long Island and the Jersey shore, areas of light permeable soils that are easily tilled. Similar industries are found northwest of Boston, in suburban Chicago, and about most other cities, roughly in proportion to their sizes. The truck-farming and fruit-growing areas, on the other hand, are farther away. Some take advantage of the temperature gradient from north to south to gain earliness of season. Beginning on the Gulf Coast or even in Cuba and Mexico, a wave of horticultural production sweeps northward through winter, spring, and summer, and finally merges with the garden products of the city environs. In Europe a similar zonal production begins in North Africa and creeps northward to areas on the channel coast of France, Belgium, Netherlands, and southern England. Many of the fruit-producing regions are highly specialized. Such are the irrigated apple districts of Washington, the peach region of Georgia, and the numerous wine districts of France. These in general are located with respect to some particular advantage of climatic condition which gives fruit of special and uniform quality year after year while that of less favored regions is variable in quality and quantity. Modern transportation has permitted even some Southern Hemisphere regions to compete in the northern markets. Apples, pears, and grapes from Argentina, South Africa, and Australia appear on United States and European markets in the season opposite to that of their normal production there, and thus they get prices that help to defray the high shipping costs. However, they are luxury items, and the trade is not large by comparison with that in wheat or some other agricultural staples.

References for Chapter 27

"Agricultural Geography of Europe and the Near East." *Miscellaneous Publication* 665, U.S. Department of Agriculture, Washington, D.C., 1948.

"Agriculture 1950, a Graphic Summary." U.S. Bureau of the Census, Washington, D.C., 1952.

Baker, O. E. Agricultural Regions of North America. *Econ. Geog.,* Vol. 2, No. 4, 1926; Vol. 3, Nos. 1, 3, 4, 1927; Vol. 4, Nos. 1, 4, 1928; Vol. 5, No. 1, 1929; Vol. 6, Nos. 2, 3, 1930; Vol. 9, No. 2, 1933.

Cook, O. F. Milpa Agriculture. *Smithsonian Inst. Ann. Rept., 1919,* pp. 307–326, Washington, 1921.

Jonasson, Olaf. The Agricultural Regions of Europe. *Econ. Geog.,* Vol. 1, No. 3, 1925; Vol. 2, No. 1, 1926.

Jones, C. F. Agricultural Regions of South America. *Econ. Geog.,* Vol. 4, Nos. 1, 2, 3, 1928; Vol. 5, Nos. 2, 3, 4, 1929; Vol. 6, No. 1, 1930.

Pioneer Settlement. *American Geographical Society, Special Publication* 14, 1932.

Shantz, Homer L. Agricultural Regions of Africa. *Econ. Geog.,* Vol. 16, Nos. 1, 2, 4, 1940; Vol. 17, Nos. 3, 4, 1941.

Taylor, Griffith. Agricultural Regions of Australia. *Econ. Geog.*, Vol. 6, Nos. 2, 3, 1930.

————. The Distribution of Pasture in Australia. *Geog. Rev.*, Vol. 27, pp. 291–294, 1927.

Van Royen, William. The Agricultural Resources of the World. Vol. 1, "Atlas of the World's Resources." Prentice-Hall, Inc., New York, 1954.

Van Valkenburg, Samuel, George B. Cressey, and Robert B. Hall. Agricultural Regions of Asia. *Econ. Geog.*, Vol. 7, No. 3, 1931; Vol. 8, No. 2, 1932; Vol. 9, Nos. 1, 2, 1933; Vol. 10, Nos. 1, 2, 4, 1934; Vol. 11, Nos. 1, 2, 3, 4, 1935; Vol. 12, Nos. 1, 3, 1936.

Whittlesey, D. S. Major Agricultural Regions of the Earth. *Ann. Assoc. Amer. Geographers*, Vol. 26, pp. 199–240, 1936.

————. Shifting Cultivation. *Econ. Geog.*, Vol. 13, pp. 35–52, 1937.

————. Fixation of Shifting Cultivation. *Econ. Geog.*, Vol. 13, pp. 139–154, 1937.

————. Major Agricultural Regions (World Map). "Goode's World Atlas." Pp. 24–25. Rand McNally & Company, Chicago, 1953.

Woytinski, W. S., and E. S. Woytinsky. "World Population and Production." Pp. 451–681. Twentieth Century Fund, Inc., New York, 1955.

Zimmerman, Eric W. "World Resources and Industries." Rev. ed. Pp. 147–397. Harper & Brothers, New York, 1951.

28

Manufacture and Its Associated Features

28.1 The Function of Manufacturing. The essential purpose of manufacturing processes is to change the form of materials in order to make them more useful or more valuable. The result is to give to the processed material what the economist calls *form utility*. For example, iron ore as it comes from the mine is practically useless; but after smelting, transformation into steel, and shaping into implements or machines, it attains considerable value. Likewise, cotton in the boll has little use; but after being ginned, spun into thread, woven into cloth, and the latter made into garments, it has acquired greatly increased usefulness and value through the application of energy and skill. It is so with a majority of the products of farm, forest, sea, and mine. Only a few, such as certain vegetables, fruits, coal, etc., are ready for human use in their primary state.

28.2 The Use of Land for Manufacturing. One of the features characteristic of complex modern industrial regions, such as western Europe and northeastern United States, is the fact that manufacturing in those regions overshadows both agriculture and the extractive industries, measured either in terms of the number of people employed or in the value of the output. In fact, in the United States, more persons are employed in manufacture than in agriculture and all the extractive industries, such as forestry, mining, and fishing, combined. On the other hand, the manufactural features cover much less area and are much less conspicuous than are those associated with agriculture. This results from the greater intensity of the manufactural processes and, therefore,

they need to occupy much smaller areas. One square mile of the American Corn Belt usually includes not less than four farms, and this means that 640 acres are operated by 6 to 8 workers and support 20 to 30 persons. This same area, however, could contain several large factories, employing thousands of workers, together with their fuel yards and storage facilities. For this reason it is difficult to construct such maps as Figs. 28.1 and 28.5, showing manufactured regions. The industrial areas shown on the maps accompanying this chapter include also much land used for agricultural, commercial, and residential purposes. Actually only a small part of the areas indicated is occupied by factories. It may well be true that all the land occupied by all the manufactural establishments of the world could be included within one of the smaller American states with plenty of room to spare. It is only locally, therefore, that the buildings and equipment of the manufactural industries are conspicuous elements of the landscape, but this fact is misleading with regard to the great importance of manufacturing.

28.3 Classes of Manufactural Industry. There are many hundreds of kinds of manufactural industries, and any attempt to compare the nature and significance of world regions of manufacture requires that the diverse industries be grouped according to some system of classification. Several such are in common use, each having its own point of view or purpose. One basic distinction commonly recognized is between the heavy and the light industries, the former manufacturing such items as iron, steel,

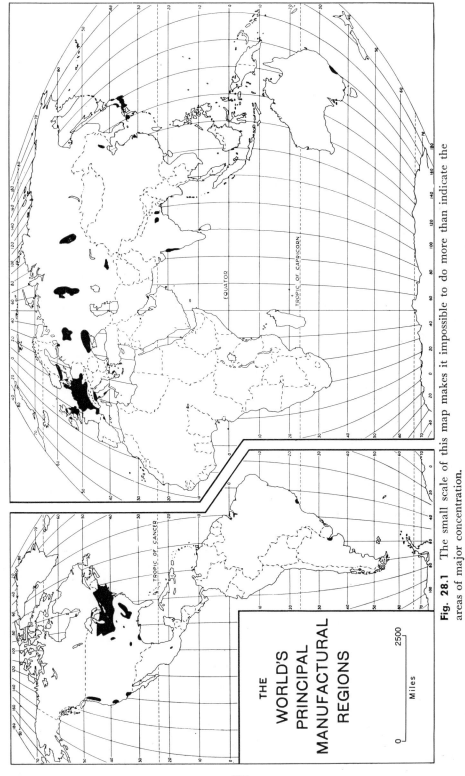

Fig. 28.1 The small scale of this map makes it impossible to do more than indicate the areas of major concentration.

THE
WORLD'S
PRINCIPAL
MANUFACTURAL
REGIONS

Miles

0   2500

clay products, and heavy machinery, the latter such as small metalwares, textiles, or garments. Some industries also are classed as primary or secondary. The former use only the crude products of the soil, forest, or mine as their raw materials. Many heavy industries are of the primary type. The secondary industries are those that employ the products of previous manufacture as their raw materials. The weaving of spun thread into cloth is thus a secondary industry, as is the manufacture of a watch or an automobile from metals.

The above broad subdivisions are useful as a starting point in classifying manufacturing activities as a whole, but they do not provide an adequate picture of the nature of regional industry. Many other facts are involved, such as the nature and source of the raw materials used, as well as the kinds of products and the uses to which they are put. Thus, some industries use mainly vegetable or animal products obtained from farms, while others use wood, metals, or chemicals drawn from forest or mines. A great many manufactured products include mixed materials drawn from various of these sources. Some manufactured products are finished and ready for the ultimate consumer, and some are unfinished and require further manufacture. The kind of use for which the manufactured products are intended is particularly important, and several distinctions can be made. Some of the more important are (*a*) goods for immediate consumption, such as foods, newspapers, automobile tires, etc.; (*b*) materials for construction, such as lumber, cement, and structural steel; and (*c*) capital goods, which include such machines and permanent equipment as are used by manufacturers in the production of other commodities.

28.4 Measures of Manufactural Character. The measurement of the industrial character of an area for purposes of regional comparison is usually based upon a variety of statistical facts, derived from published reports or from personal investigation. Fortunately, the great industrial nations issue statistical reports in great detail. These make possible several methods of measurement, each of which is use-

ful for a different type of comparison. Various classes of significant facts may be obtained from the statistics. Some of these are as follows: (1) Facts relating to the value of the things produced, such as (*a*) the value of the raw materials consumed, (*b*) the value added by the process of manufacture, and (*c*) the total quantity or value of the finished products. (2) Facts relating to the persons employed in the industry, such as (*a*) the number of wage earners and salaried employees, (*b*) the total number of man-hours of labor used in a month or year, and (*c*) the total amount of wages and salaries paid per month or year. (3) Facts relating to the capital invested in plant, equipment, and other necessary aspects of manufacture. (4) Facts relating to the quantity and sources of the energy or power used. By using several of these measurements in combination, industries may be compared as to their relative importance in a region, or regions may be compared as to the relative importance of the several industries in them.

28.5 Kinds of Manufactural Features. The factory or manufactural establishment is the point of convergence for the labor, capital goods, raw materials, and power and is the focus and heart of manufactural production, but it is only one of several important features associated with manufacturing. In addition to the factory are the homes of the workers, and daily the employees move back and forth between homes and places of work. Workers in transit are a conspicuous part of the industrial scene at certain times of the day. Likewise converging upon the factory, carried by boats, railroad cars, or trucks, are quantities of raw materials and fuel. These raw materials and fuels may not be very conspicuous at any one time, because they are a flowing rather than a stationary mass and do not remain in one place to be seen. Just as raw materials and power resources are converging upon the factory, so the industrial products are flowing from it toward local and distant markets. The magnitude of this outward flow is as difficult to see and appreciate as is the inflow, for this is a characteristic of all things under cover and in transit. For example, a worker may drive daily to and from his suburban home to a machine-tool factory in a Middle Western city; there he may operate a lathe, driven by electricity from a steam plant which uses coal mined in southern Illinois; on the lathe he may turn steel made from iron ore mined in Minnesota and smelted in Chicago; and the tool, when completed, may be transported by rail and ship to South America for use.

It should be clear, then, that the factory is only the focus, or hub, of a far more extensive series of features and processes which, in addition to (*a*) the manufacturing plant, includes (*b*) the workers, (*c*) the incoming raw materials and fuel, and (*d*) the outgoing factory products. These are the four principal groups, or classes, of material-culture features associated with manufactural production.

28.6 The Industrial Plant. Of major importance in a geographical analysis of a region's

manufactural character are facts concerning the numbers, kinds, and sizes of factories. Within the Chicago industrial district there are many thousands of manufacturing establishments, representing almost every kind of industry designed to meet human wants. Among the more important are machinery factories, meat-packing plants, iron and steel mills and their allied industries, agricultural-implement and electrical-equipment factories, foundries and machine shops, and printing and publishing establishments. All sizes of factories are represented, from the tremendous plants associated with iron and steel and meat packing to the small printing shops employing only a few workers. Chicago is, therefore, a manufacturing center of great diversity. Within the Pittsburgh industrial area, on the other hand, there is less diversity of industry, with greater specialization in iron and steel. Although, relatively, there are not many of these establishments most of them are large.

Fig. 28.2 The layout of a giant blast furnace and steel mill. The Carnegie-Illinois Steel Corporation plant of U.S. Steel in Gary, Ind., is located on the shore of Lake Michigan. Ample room for plant layout, water transportation, and an abundant fresh-water supply, together with a Middle Western location, are important factors in the growth of the iron and steel industries at this point. (*U.S. Steel Photograph.*)

Iron and steel plants account for only a small percentage of the number of factories in the Pittsburgh area, but they employ more than half the workers and account for more than half the value added by manufacture in the region.

28.7 Size of the Industrial Plant. Factories differ greatly in size and general appearance, depending upon the kind of industry they house and the part of the world in which they are located. Iron and steel plants nearly the world over are characteristically of large size, for only in large plants can the smelting of iron and the conversion of it into steel be done efficiently and economically (Fig. 28.2). They are distinctive also because of their typical features, such as the blast furnaces, piles of ore and coal, and the broad low buildings that house the rolling machines. Numerous tall chimneys pour forth smoke, and everywhere there is a dirty, grimy appearance. Cotton spinning, meat packing, and flour milling are other examples of the industries commonly housed in large plants,

which, however, are essentially different in appearance from steel mills and from each other (Fig. 28.3). It is more especially in western Europe and the United States, where industrial development has been greatest, that the large factory has become the characteristic manufacturing unit.

All industries are not housed in large factories. In many of the less industrialized areas of the world a large proportion of the manufacturing is carried on in small workshops, each having only a few workers. Even in highly organized industrial areas there are some industries which are characterized by small units of production. For example, most of the large cheese output of the United States is made in a few thousand cheese factories which together employ only a few thousand persons.

28.8 The Industrial Workers. In order to measure the relative importance of manufactural production as compared with other industries in a region, it is useful to have data showing what proportion of the employed popula-

Fig. 28.3 A multistoried cotton mill in New England. Space requirements for cotton manufacture are very different from those for the steel industry.

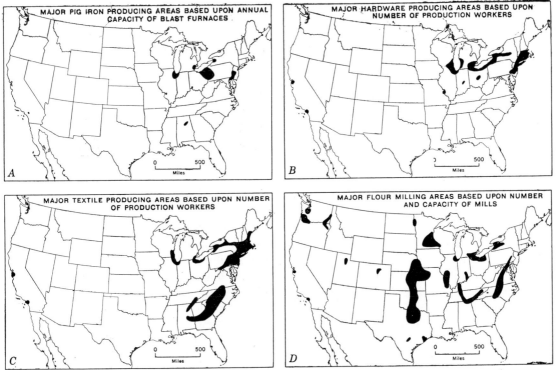

Fig. 28.4 Maps showing the generalized locations of certain industries. (*Based upon de-tailed maps by J. Alexander.*)

tion is engaged in manufacture. In the United States as a whole, for example, about one-quarter are so employed, but in Connecticut the comparable figure is almost a half; on the other hand in Nevada and New Mexico it is only about one twentieth. This is a clear indication of the much greater significance of manufacture in the regional complex of Connecticut than in that of Nevada or New Mexico.

In attempting to understand the industrial character of a region, it is desirable to know also the proportion of its factory workers that are employed in each of its principal types of manufacture. For example, Fall River and Lynn both are cities in eastern Massachusetts and might, without study, be assumed to be industrially similar. However, the relative importance of their principal industries shows them to be essentially different. In Lynn the three leading industries, measured by the number of persons they employ, are, in order of importance, the manufacture of electrical machinery, of shoes, and of leather. Fall River, on

the other hand, has only two important types of industry. They are the manufacture of textiles and the making of wearing apparel from textile materials.

Conditions Affecting the Location of Manufacturing

28.9 Locational Factors. An examination of Fig. 28.4 and a comparison of Maps *A, B, C,* and *D* show that individual industries are quite unlike in their locations. Map *A* shows the distribution of the major pig-iron-producing regions in the United States, and it will be seen that they are highly concentrated. Map *B*, showing the areas of hardware production including cutlery and hand tools, indicates that there is less concentration in that industry. The distribution of the textile-producing areas, Map *C*, shows two major areas of concentration, the South Atlantic and the New England–Middle Atlantic states; while Map *D*, flour-milling areas, reveals considerable spread throughout the United States. The factors involved in the location of any one of these industries are likely to be very complex. If one attempts to search out the various reasons why one particular group of plants has been located at a particular place or why they have all remained in that location, he is likely to find a confusing multitude of bases. Certain of these are inherent in the features of the earth, some others depend upon the economic structure of the existing social order, and still others are the result of vague historical beginnings or grow out of individual preferences, custom, or mere human whim. Nevertheless, it is possible to catalogue the factors having to do with the location of manufacturing and to indicate in a general way their relative importance.

28.10 Market. Of all the factors involved in the location of industry, the existence of a market for the manufactured goods seems to transcend all others. Great concentrations of people do not necessarily constitute a market; if that were so the heavily populated areas of Asia would be the world's greatest market. People plus purchasing power are required to constitute a market, and this combination is found in the industrialized areas of the world, especially in North America and Europe. In a sense, then, manufacturing breeds more manufacturing. There are several reasons for this. Per capita income is usually higher in manufacturing areas than in areas where income is largely derived from some other source. More people are required, on the average, to carry on manufacturing processes than other kinds of production, and hence manufacturing regions tend to be regions of population concentration. It is commonly cheaper to transport raw materials than it is to transport finished products; hence it often is advantageous to locate the processing plant nearer to the consumer of the goods than to the source of the raw materials.

Proximity of factory to market has other advantages also, such as those that stem from an intimate knowledge on the part of the manufacturer relative to the exact needs of his customers and of sudden changes therein. Thus, in the shoe industry, there are frequent changes

in style necessitating corresponding changes in the machines used in shoe manufacture. As a consequence, most of the American shoe-machine industry is located in or near the regions of shoe production. Similar advantages have been influential in the location of textile-machine production in the regions of textile manufacturing and the manufacture of automobile parts and accessories in southern Michigan. There are many illustrations of this principle, which is especially operative when the market is the general public. This is particularly true in the case of such food products as are either perishable or bulky or both. Bakery products furnish an excellent illustration of that type of manufactured goods. It is true also of such products as have particular application to the interests of only one locality, such as newspapers and job printing. Consequently, bakeries and printing establishments are found in nearly all cities and towns, and they belong to that group of manufacturing industries which has been called "ubiquitous." Such industries typically are decentralized.

28.11 Labor. A supply of labor is a factor in the localization of industrial establishments, but not to the extent it formerly was. Some types of manufacture still require skilled labor, trained to special operations, but even these laborers can be moved in time, or new ones may be trained if other advantages offset the labor element. On the other hand, the increasing mechanization and simplification of industrial processes tend to reduce the dependence of industry upon an established group of workers to which the industry must move rather than moving the labor to the industry. In spite of this change, some types of manufacture still tend to cluster or group themselves in districts where a supply of trained or adaptable labor is known to be available.

28.12 Power and Fuel. Modern industry differs from that of earlier times mainly as a result of the use of mechanical power. The consumption of such power in the United States, especially, is enormous. The problem of producing and transporting a large quantity of energy is tremendous, but obviously it cannot have the same industrial significance in all localities since not all have or use power of the same kinds or in the same quantities. The principal sources of mechanical energy the world over are coal, petroleum, and hydroelectric energy. One is sometimes more available but not always so satisfactory, since some industries, such as smelting, require a great deal of heat as well as mechanical power. How an industry may be located with respect to sources of power and fuel depends upon the nature of the industry and its energy and heat requirements and upon the relative costs of these elements from different sources. One extreme is represented by industries, such as the ferroalloy minerals, which are large users of fuel and power but whose products are compact and comparatively valuable. They find it advantageous to locate near the source of energy. The other extreme may be seen in industries such as shoe manufacture, which uses comparatively little mechanical energy and whose products are bulky. They are mainly located with respect not to sources of power but to a combination of other factors.

28.13 Raw Materials. The location of certain manufacturing establishments is sometimes influenced by the location of the raw materials that they use. Some of these materials are bulky, and their volume is much reduced by the processes of manufacture. It is therefore more economical to process them near their place of origin and to ship them to market in more condensed form. Such an industry is meat packing. On the average, only about 60 per cent of the live weight of market cattle dresses out as edible beef. Therefore, to ship live cattle from the great feeding grounds to the centers of consumption would be wasteful, although it formerly was done, before methods of refrigeration in transit made it possible to ship dressed beef from packing plants in central United States, Argentina, and Australia. The same conditions apply in the lumber industry. Rough sawn lumber contains only about 40 per cent of the wood in a log, 60 per cent having gone as waste or by-products. Because of that, sawmills usually locate near the forests and ship their rough lumber, rather than establishing themselves near their markets and receiving shipments of logs from distant sources.

Other industries require only compact and easily shipped raw materials, but their products are bulky and expensive to ship. They tend to locate with little regard to sources of raw materials. The manufacture of glass bottles, fruit jars, and similar containers is an illustration of this type. Sand is the principal raw material, but the products are bulky and fragile.

28.14 Capital. Local interest on the part of men who had money to invest in manufacturing enterprises over which they could exercise personal supervision was formerly a potent influence in the localization of industry. To some extent it still is. The growth of corporate finance has, however, much reduced the importance of this factor. The great manufacturing plants of modern times are located with little regard to the source of the money with which they are established. That may, in fact, come from distant and diverse origins. In some countries the money and capital goods necessary for the development of industry are supplied by government and derive from taxation. Under such conditions the location of industry follows governmental desire and may be in response to political or military discretion rather than to the operation of economic advantage. However, some parts of the world have much greater surpluses of capital savings than others, and these are likely to have greater industrial development, other conditions being favorable.

28.15 Transportation. The location of manufacturing establishments is greatly influenced by transportation facilities. Transportation affects location in numerous ways and actually is involved in most of the other factors already mentioned which influence location. The general situation of manufacturing concentrations, within a continent, country, state, or even a county, may well depend upon the availability of transportation facilities. Modern industries require raw materials in great volume from many sources, and they ship their products in large quantities to many destinations. For them good means of transportation are essential. Formerly, small home industries supplied most of the local needs, and little connection with distant places was necessary or possible. This gave rise to highly decentralized manufacturing industries. Even today a lack of transport facilities seems to be a strong factor in the maintenance of decentralized industry. Large industrial establishments, on the other hand, seek localities that are well provided with railroads, highways, and, if possible, water routes. The more efficient, cheap, and dependable these means of transportation become, the greater is the tendency for manufacturing to concentrate in areas providing an advantage in this respect. So potent is this factor that the great industrial centers are also the great railroad centers, and the growth of one promotes the development of the other. It is not accidental that the great manufacturing regions of America and Europe lie at the ends of the most used ocean route of the North Atlantic. As was pointed out previously, there commonly is a transportational advantage when a manufacturing establishment is located nearer the market than to the source of the raw materials. Arbitrary rules relating to costs of freight shipment are commonly in favor of unprocessed materials, *i.e.*, it is frequently cheaper ton for ton to ship the raw materials than the finished goods.

Transportation factors also affect the location of factories in an entirely different fashion. The precise position chosen for a plant to be established may be markedly influenced by the availability of spur tracks or nearness to a highway outlet. Ease of mobility with respect to the labor supply for its daily movement to and from the place of work is also a significant factor in the selection of the site for a factory. It may be seen, then, that the cost factor of transportation may affect the general *situation* of a factory and easy access to facilities may affect the choice of its actual *site*.

28.16 Secondary Factors Affecting Location. Numerous other factors influence both the situation and site of factories, especially new ones. For example, some communities attempt to attract the establishment of new plants or the movement of old ones by providing various kinds of subsidies. This may be in the form of preferential treatment with respect to taxes, utility costs, or even low-cost land. Recently many factories have been located beyond municipal boundaries to take advantage of lower property tax rates. The availability of adequate water supply has been an important factor in attracting industry in some parts of the United States. Still another factor can be the local labor situation with respect to the prevailing wage standards or the attitude toward labor-management relations. Some industries are located adjacent to factories of an entirely different type because they use waste products from other mills as their raw materials. Some are located near others of their kind largely because the city or region bears a name famous the world over for their particular kind of product. The locations of still other industries can be attributed to nothing more substantial than the merest chance or accident. Although it is impossible to make any regional generalizations with respect to the influence of such secondary factors, the potent effect of many of them upon the choice of a location for an individual plant is obvious.

The Great Manufactural Regions of the World

28.17 World Distribution of Manufacturing. So many conditions are involved in the location of manufactured industries, and they combine in so many different ways, that it might appear that industrial distributions would almost be haphazard. To some extent they are, but by no means entirely so. There is a recognizable grouping of the factory industries of the world into several major and some minor regional concentrations, and within these are districts of important specialization. The oldest and most highly developed of these is in northwestern Europe. Next most important is that of eastern North America. Newer and much less complex are the centers of eastern Europe, the Orient, India, and the Southern Hemisphere (Fig. 28.1).

MANUFACTURAL REGIONS OF NORTH AMERICA

28.18 The Northeastern Manufacturing Belt. Although the American manufactural regions are exceeded in world importance by those of Europe, they are remarkable for the diversity of their products, their rapid growth, and their areal concentration. Most of the cities and towns that are dominantly manufactural in type are located in a broad belt that lies in northeastern United States and southern Canada. Its boundaries reach from southern Maine southward along the Atlantic Coast to Baltimore; westward to Cincinnati, Ohio; northwestward to include Chicago and the industrial cities of southeastern Wisconsin; thence eastward across central southern Michigan, peninsular Ontario, and south of the Adirondack Mountains and the highlands of New England (Fig. 28.5). Within this area are concentrated more than two-thirds of the wage earners employed in manufacturing in the United States and Canada and like proportions of the industrial power used and of the value of manufactural output. Beyond the limits of this chief region are other centers of less significance in which the general-supply or "ubiquitous" industries hold a relatively more important place than in the major region. Of these, the southern Appalachian and the Pacific Coast are the most highly developed,

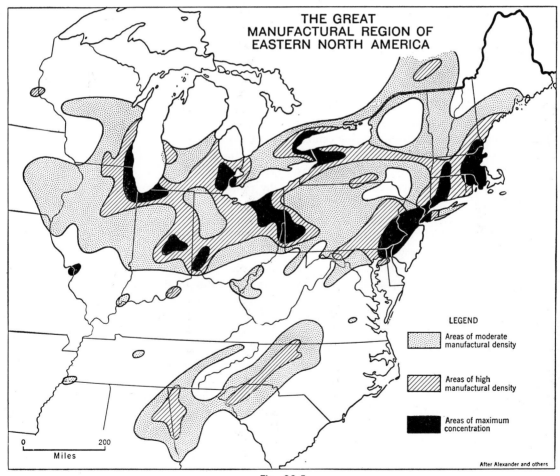

THE GREAT
MANUFACTURAL REGION OF
EASTERN NORTH AMERICA

LEGEND

Areas of moderate manufactural density

Areas of high manufactural density

Areas of maximum concentration

0   200
Miles

After Alexander and others

Fig. 28.5

whereas others in the central plains and on the western margins of the main belt are newer or more dispersed.

Many factors are concerned in the localization of these centers of manufacture, and their interaction has brought about regional specialization which, in many instances, is so striking as to give definite regional character. Even the major region is far from being a unit as to its type of development. It may in fact be subdivided into several areas of distinctive industrial character which differ in the nature of their principal industrial products and in the factors involved in their growth.

28.19 The Middle Atlantic Metropolitan Districts. The region that includes New York City, Philadelphia, Baltimore, and their immediate hinterlands has an unusual diversity of manufactures (Fig. 28.5). These reflect the interaction of many forces, among which the outstanding are the presence there of large centers of population, which furnish both local markets and abundant supplies of labor, the commercial or port influence, and the proximity of abundant coal in the northern Appalachian bituminous and anthracite fields. New York City itself is a great manufacturing center, but it is first of all a port. Its outstanding products are of the secondary type, employing as raw materials the manufactured products of other regions, domestic and foreign. The best illustration of this class of manufacture is the clothing industry, which uses cotton, woolen, and other textiles purchased from New England, the South Atlantic States, and other weaving centers. Other examples are found in such industries as the refining of sugar, vegetable oils, petroleum, and copper. Some of these industries are of great size and have large plants which are concentrated in one or another of the smaller cities of the New York metropolitan area, to which they give industrial character.

The secondary industries are important in Baltimore, Philadelphia, and other cities of southeastern Pennsylvania also, but relatively less important than in the New York area. This district has, on the other hand, a great industrial diversity since it includes many food-products industries, important textile, leather, and chemical manufactures, and also some of the heavy industries, such as blast furnaces, steel mills, and the building of ships, locomotives, and machinery. Some of the raw materials for these diverse industries come from foreign sources through the ports of the region since they, and especially Philadelphia, are outstanding ports of import. This is true, for example, of hides, tanning materials, certain chemical raw materials, and even iron ore and other mineral ores.

28.20 The New England Districts. American factory industries were established in New England at an early date: textile mills in eastern Massachusetts and metalworking in the Connecticut Valley. Glaciation had produced numerous water-power sites suitable for the initial stages of industrial development; there was an abundant labor supply available on the overpopulated farms of hilly New England and French Canada, and capital had accumulated among the merchants of the New England coastal cities. The water powers of the Merrimac, Connecticut, and other streams still are used to capacity, but they have long since ceased to be adequate. Coal is brought in from Appalachian sources by coastwise shipping and by rail, but its cost and the lack of iron ores have worked against the establishment of the heavy industries in New England; therefore the lighter forms of manufacture prevail. The early industries have been greatly elaborated and many new products introduced, but the original forms of manufacture still leave their impress in spite of growing competition from other parts of the country. Resulting from this heritage the eastern and southwestern sections of New England still show striking contrasts.

The eastern district, extending from Rhode Island to Maine, is dominantly one of machinery, textile, leather, and shoe manufacture. The machine trades represented there are especially electrical and those required as necessary adjuncts of textile and shoe manufacture. Southwestern New England, in contrast, is a region of light metalware manufactures. Its outstanding products are hardware, tools, electrical equipment, firearms, aircraft, and machines, the outgrowth of metal trades established there more than a century ago. There are also paper, textile, and many other manufactures, but they are of less importance. Both these districts enjoy the advantage of proximity to the great eastern centers of population that are markets for part of their products, the southwestern district having particularly close relationship with the metropolitan and port area of New York City.

Because of the rapid growth of manufacture in other parts of North America, the relative importance of the New England districts has decreased, even though the actual number of persons employed in all industries has steadily increased. A noticeable decrease has occurred in New England's oldest factory industry, cotton-textile manufacture, because of the fact that expansion of the industry finds many advantages in the southern Atlantic states.

28.21 The Central New York–Niagara–Ontario industrial belt extends from Albany to the eastern end of the Great Lakes waterway (Fig. 28.5). The section from Albany to Rochester occupies the natural thoroughfare of the Mohawk Valley and the Ontario plain. Its cities have grown up along the Erie Canal and the New York Central Railroad, which link the eastern industrial districts with the Great Lakes and interior regions. The area has no local resource of coal, but the rich resources of the Pennsylvania anthracite and bituminous coal fields lie only a short distance southward, and the adjacent highlands furnish water powers that supply part of its energy requirements. It also is a region of great industrial diversity. The primary iron and steel industries are but little in evidence, and the same is true of the primary textile trades. The secondary industries, however, are highly developed, and they include those which use many kinds of manufactures as their raw materials. Among the more important regional products are clothing, electrical and other machinery, optical instruments, chemical products, paper products, and printed matter. Some of these reflect a westward extension of

the industries found in southwestern New England, but others are closely allied to those of the New York City area or of the Niagara region. This belt is clearly transitional in its position.

Buffalo, Niagara Falls, and Toronto are the principal cities of the western portion of this belt and reflect the advantage of location at the eastern end of the Great Lakes waterway. Cheap lake transportation permits the assembling there of grain and other agricultural produce from the interior, iron ore from the Upper Lakes region, and coal from the adjacent Appalachian fields. Industry in this region benefits also from the hydroelectric power of Niagara Falls and from its position on a main route between the interior and the eastern seaboard. The Canadian portion has also the advantage of a tariff barrier at the international boundary, which protects certain industries that might otherwise not exist. The leading industries of the region are of the heavy type and include blast furnaces, steel works, and rolling mills and the manufacture of machinery and vehicles. Of great importance also are the chemical industries, the milling of grain, and others that use agricultural products. From this it will be seen that the industrial character of the region is more nearly like those of the regions to the westward than it is comparable with the New England or seaboard districts.

28.22 The Pittsburgh–Lake Erie Region. In the Appalachian coal fields of western Pennsylvania and West Virginia the best and most abundant coking coals of America are found together with great quantities of fuel coals, some petroleum, and some natural gas. These resources gave a great advantage to the establishment there of the heavy industries, particularly the blast furnaces and steel mills of the early period of abundant steel production. The iron ore of the Lake Superior mines was unloaded at the Lake Erie ports and moved inland to the smelting centers, of which Pittsburgh was most important. Later improvements in the processes of ore reduction and a gradual decrease in the quality of the iron ores made it less necessary to move the ore to the coal region and more profitable to move coal and coke toward the sources of ore, especially to the ore-unloading points on Lake Erie. For these reasons Cleveland, Lorain, and places between them and Pittsburgh, especially Youngstown, Ohio, developed large iron- and steel-making industries, and the area remains still the major center of such industries in America. In most of the cities of this region, one-eighth to one-half of all the workers are employed in these primary manufactures. Associated with them are other heavy industries, such as the heavy machine trades and the manufacture of steel pipe, structural steel, clay products, pottery, and glass. This major interest does not exclude other kinds of manufacture, such as the important clothing manufactures of Cleveland, rubber manufacture in Akron, and others, but it does give an industrial character to the region which the changes of half a century have not been able to erase.

Although the basic natural resources of this region are fuel and power, its development has been promoted also by a position near the center of the nation's population mass and a favorable location with respect to Great Lakes' transportation and the trans-Appalachian rail routes to the east.

28.23   The Detroit Region. Near the western end of Lake Erie is an industrial region whose center is Detroit, but it includes also a large section of southeastern Michigan, part of northwestern Ohio, and western Ontario (Fig. 28.5). Like the south shore of Lake Erie, it enjoys the advantages of a central position with respect to the main population belt and between the Appalachian coal fields and the northern iron mines on Great Lakes' transportation. It has also some of the basic industries of iron and steel production, but they are subordinated to those which use these metals and others as raw materials, especially in the manufacture of motor vehicles. In Detroit and its industrial satellites the production of motor vehicles and their engines, bodies, and parts is the dominant industry. However, the region has many associated manufactures which include tools, heating and refrigerating equipment, electrical machinery, glass, chemicals, and many others. In addition to the advantages of Great

Lakes' transportation for the assembling of power and of mineral, forest, and agricultural raw materials, this area profits immensely by having the advantage of immediate access to the great markets of the agricultural Middle West by rail and highway and also to the industrial East. The development of the Ontario section of the region has been further promoted by the tariff barrier at the international boundary.

28.24   The Cincinnati-Indianapolis Region. One of the important interior regions of manufacture includes the cities and towns of eastern Indiana and southwestern Ohio (Fig. 28.5). It lies at the eastern end of the rich lands of the Corn Belt and between the Appalachian and eastern interior coal fields. To the Appalachian coal and industrial area it has access not only by rail but also through water transport on the Ohio River. Its diversified manufactures reflect an abundance of fuel and a variety of industrial raw materials, such as the products of the blast furnaces and steel mills of the Pittsburgh region and the grains and animals of midwestern and southern farms. They reflect also the large markets of the interior. In fact this region lies closest of any to the center of population of the whole United States. Highly important are its machine trades, including automotive and electrical equipment, precision tools, scales, and many other types of mechanical products. Important also are the chemical and food-products industries, such as meat packing and the processing of grains, oil seeds, vegetables, and other agricultural raw materials.

28.25   The Lake Michigan Region. The western shore of southern Lake Michigan and its immediate hinterland comprise one of the major regions of manufacture in America. It is of great diversity, expresses the interaction of many factors, and is capable of division into several districts, which may not be considered here. Some of the principal factors include access to power resources by rail from the Illinois-Indiana coal fields and by lake transportation from those of the East. Other factors are access by lake to the northern iron-ore region, and the fact that it is a center of rail transportation from and toward the agricultural lands of the interior plains, the Rocky Mountains, and even the Pacific Coast, which are its largest markets and its sources of raw materials. Chicago and Milwaukee are its principal centers. In them and in some of their associated towns are manufactures of nearly all classes, but a few groups of them reflect the principal industrial character of the region. These include machinery, blast furnaces, and rolling mills (Fig. 28.2), which, like those of the Lake Erie shore, provide raw materials for many industries. Some of these latter supply the rural markets with automotive equipment, tractors, wire fencing, and a great variety of farm machines and implements. There too are large meat-packing plants, grain-processing mills, leather tanneries, shoe factories, and other establishments that draw their principal raw materials from the western farms and ranches and find their markets both locally and to the eastward. Also in this region are manufactories of furniture, paper, and other products whose raw materials come, at least in part, from the forests of the North and the West. Being central in position and the focus of many railroads, this region produces also large quantities of cars and other railroad equipment.

28.26 Other Centers of American Manufacture. Although the great industrial region of the Northeast contains, as has previously been noted, more than two-thirds of the manufacturing strength of the continent, there are others of great importance. They are scattered throughout the South and West, and among them are districts of specialized character, whose principal products reflect to some extent the resources and other advantages of the environs.

28.27 *The Southern Highland Borders.* The southern Appalachian region furnishes both water power and abundant coal; it also has access to cheap labor, forest resources, iron ores, raw cotton, and other essential materials. It is not surprising that it has undergone industrial development. The principal expressions of this development are seen in the cotton-textile district of the Piedmont, the blast furnaces and steel mills of northern Alabama,

and in wood products, machinery, and chemical industries. In general these localities are more specialized than those of the northern regions in the manufacture of primary products and have fewer of the secondary industries using these primary products as raw materials for further manufacture. This may be an expression of the lesser degree of industrial maturity of the southern region.

28.28 *Industrial Cities of the Central Plains.* East of the High Plains and extending from the Prairie Provinces of Canada southward to the Gulf of Mexico are widely spaced cities having considerable local importance in manufacture and not a small place in the whole industrial pattern of the continent. They include Winnipeg, Denver, Minneapolis–St. Paul, Omaha, Kansas City, St. Louis, Dallas–Fort Worth, and Houston. Most of them are first of all assembling points for regional produce, especially agricultural produce, and their leading manufactures are of the bulk-reducing type. Meat packing, grain milling, cotton compressing, oil refining, or similar industries take important places in them, and the more elaborate manufactures of secondary type are less developed. Of them all St. Louis is easternmost, largest, and most complex, since steel production, the machine trades, shoe manufacture, the chemical industries, and each of several others is important there, and some of them outrank meat packing, which is usually a leading industry in cities of the Central Plains.

28.29 *The Pacific Coast.* Manufacturing industries in the far-western regions of Anglo-America reflect the interplay of many factors, physical and economic. Among these are (*a*) large nodal groups of population which constitute local markets and reservoirs of labor, (*b*) the nature of the local raw materials, (*c*) a scarcity of coal but an abundance of petroleum and of newly developed hydroelectric energy, (*d*) great distance from the eastern centers of manufacture, and (*e*) access to the trade areas and transportation routes of the Pacific Ocean.

There are three distinct manufacturing areas in the coastal region: (*a*) the Los Angeles–San Diego group of cities, (*b*) the Puget

Sound–Willamette Valley group of cities, and (c) the San Francisco Bay group. In each of them are various industries which are concerned with the preserving, canning, and processing of perishable foodstuffs (fruits, vegetables, and fish) to prepare them for shipment to distant markets. Also there are many small industries designed to supply local demands, since the region is far removed from eastern factories which make similar products.

In the northern group, from Vancouver to Portland, sawmills and wood-using industries normally take first rank. The mountain forests provide the raw materials for these important industries, and the streams provide electric power. Also, mountain and dry-land pastures support a sheep industry which provides raw material for a woolen textile industry in the Willamette Valley. The power resource has been influential also in attracting other industries, such as the smelting and refining of aluminum and copper, the manufacture of aircraft, and the building of ships. All these are large consumers of electricity.

In the San Francisco area, petroleum refining, steel products, and shipbuilding rank high. Other industries, such as sugar refining, reflect the great importance of the port, into which come raw sugar and other products from Hawaii and the Philippines.

In the Los Angeles–San Diego region, the largest of the three, diversity is also characteristic. A large local market is served with much of its requirements in meat, clothing, furniture, machinery, and structural steel. Owing to advantages associated with climate, petroleum resource, and cultural and historical factors, four of the many industries take high rank. These are airplane and automotive assembly, the motion-picture industry, food processing, and petroleum refining.

28.30 The Pattern of Distribution. Changes took place in the distribution of American manufacturing during the decade 1940–1950, particularly as a result of a wartime economy. Yet, many of the changes are minor and others lack permanence or have already disappeared.

Under wartime stimulation new industries were firmly established in the Pacific Coast region and included blast furnaces, steel mills, and the manufacture of heavy machinery. Owing to these and to the enlargement of old industries, local labor supplies in some areas proved inadequate, and migrations of population took place. This was especially true of the Pacific Coast region. The number of persons employed in manufacturing industries in Washington, Oregon, and California doubled in the years 1939 to 1947. However, the number of persons employed in manufacturing in the Pacific Coast states was only 6 per cent of the United States total in 1947. That does not indicate that a revolutionary shift has taken place. It is true of course that some of these areas show a marked increase in number of production workers from 1939 to 1947, if the increase is expressed as a percentage. For example, both Los Angeles and Houston had an increase of over 100 per cent. Yet, of the 31 major industrial cities which experienced the *largest* increase in number of industrial workers, all but 4 are located in, or adjacent to, the main manufacturing belt of the northeastern United States. Moreover, there has been no radical change in the location of those factors of market, raw materials, fuel, power, and transportation facilities, which are the factors in response to which manufacturing industries are located or relocated. Therefore, there has not been any sweeping change in the general pattern of manufactural distribution in the United States.

MANUFACTURAL REGIONS
OF EUROPE AND ASIA

28.31 The continent of Europe is highly industrialized (Fig. 28.6). The Industrial Revolution of the eighteenth century found already there certain of the requisite cultural and physical conditions for a progressive and rapid development of factory manufacture. These included: (a) a large population having a fairly high standard of living, which provided a large potential market; (b) a high degree of technical skills, which had resulted from the perfection and specialization of household and

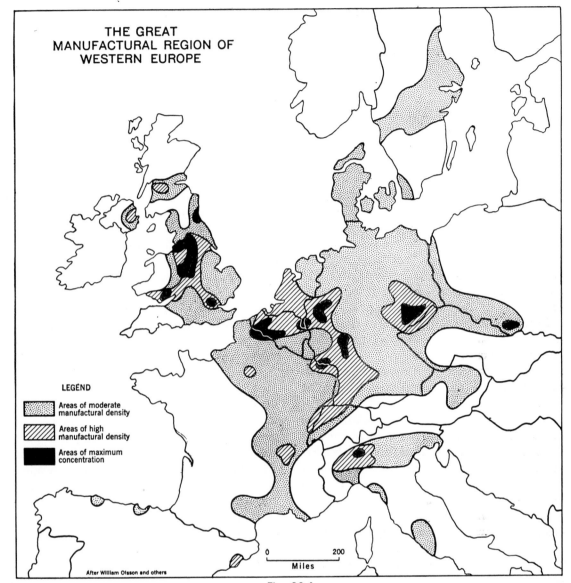

THE GREAT
MANUFACTURAL REGION OF
WESTERN EUROPE

LEGEND

Areas of moderate
manufactural density

Areas of high
manufactural density

Areas of maximum
concentration

0   200
Miles

After William Olsson and others

Fig. 28.6

small workshop manufacture; (c) inventive genius, which provided new machines and adapted them to the application of mechanical power; and (d) water power at first, and eventually steam engines driven by coal. There were many widely distributed sources of water power adequate for infant industries, and when these were outgrown, there were numerous coal deposits to replace them as primary sources of energy. Europe also had more highly developed routes of transportation than any other part of the world; good highways, canals and canalized rivers, and a deeply indented and estuarine coastline made large parts of Europe accessible from the sea. Under modern conditions coal is the primary source of mechanical energy for manufacturing, and water power takes second place. The near absence of petroleum in western Europe, significant as it may be from the standpoint of transportation and war needs, has little relation to the growth of industry since it is not, even in the United States where it is abundant, a major source of energy for manufacturing industries. It is not surprising, therefore, that the heavy and basic industries of Europe, which require great quantities of energy and fuel, are clustered about the richest coal fields (Figs. 23.7 and 23.8). There are commonly associated with them many other kinds of manufacture which find various advantages in being in the great centers of industry. However, there are also several lesser manufactural districts in which the lighter forms of industry predominate, especially such as do not require great quantities of fuel and power in proportion to their demands for labor and capital or to the value of their products. Some of these are associated with the smaller and poorer coal fields or are dependent upon modern hydroelectric or steam-electric power installations. They include especially the textile manufactures, chemical industries, and many others of the lighter type.

The manufacturing centers of Europe are by no means uniformly distributed. The major districts occur in a more or less continuous belt that extends east and west through the central portion of the continent. Northern Europe, on the one hand, and the Mediterranean borderlands, on the other, are much less well endowed and less industrialized. The principal belt includes Great Britain, on the west, and extends through northern France, Belgium, western and central Germany, Czechoslovakia, and southern Poland into central and southern Russia. Various portions of industrial Europe will be given further consideration.

28.32 British Centers of Manufacture. In Great Britain coal is abundant and other sources of power scarce. It is natural therefore that the great industrial centers of the nineteenth century grew up about the coal fields (Fig. 23.8). To a large degree this association still exists, although new factors have come into effect and shifts are taking place.

The early iron industries of England were located especially in the *Midlands* region near Birmingham, and this region remains highly important in the manufacture of machinery, vehicles, arms, hardware, glass, chemical products, and many other things. Although the region has less local coal than some of the others, it has the great advantage of central location and excellent railroad connections. Power brought by transmission lines from steam-electric plants in adjacent coal-producing districts is supplemented by hydroelectric power and both help to overcome the disadvantage of a declining local coal resource.

The same flexibility with respect to power supply that has been made possible by electric transmission has aided also in making *London* a great and diversified manufacturing center in recent decades, although it has no local coal whatever. Its coal supply must come from the northern fields by boat and train. It is the great commercial center and port of Britain, but its manufactures were formerly restricted and concerned mainly the processing and repackaging of a variety of products imported from abroad and designed for reexport to foreign markets. The vast labor supply of London, its connection by rail and water with the other British ports and centers of raw materials, and its ability to secure power have attracted to the city and its suburbs, in recent decades, many of the newer types of chemical and metal manufactures as well as shipbuilding and some other of the heavy mechanical trades.

In *northeastern England* is a principal region of heavy industry. It is located in association with the coal fields of Northumberland and Durham and one of the several principal domestic sources of iron ore in the Cleveland district of northern Yorkshire. Coastal location also favored manufactural development in this region since Swedish and Spanish iron ores came in through convenient ports, and many of the regional products were exported. Important centers of manufacture in this district are the great steelmaking towns such as Middlesbrough and Hartlepool. Newcastle-on-Tyne has long been a major shipbuilding port, but the region is also a producer of railroad and structural steel, locomotives, cars, and other heavy goods. It has also a variety of lighter manufactures, including chemical industries, which are based in part upon local salt deposits.

Associated with the productive coal fields of *Lancashire and Yorkshire,* which lie, respectively, to the west and east of the Pennine Hills, are industries of quite different types. These are the great centers of textile specialization. Sheep were numerous in the hilly uplands, and the manufacture of woolens was established there at an early date. When cotton spinning became important, and especially after the growth of large factories, American cotton was conveniently brought in through the west-facing port of Liverpool, and cotton textiles came to dominate the manufactures of Lancashire. For various reasons wool manufacture shifted to the eastern side of the Pennines and concentrated in western Yorkshire. A high degree of specialization grew up in both these textile regions, some towns spinning yarns of special kinds and others making only a limited class of fabrics. However, such extreme specialization was a disadvantage, and there is today more regional diversification. The metal trades have long been represented in this region also, especially in Sheffield, where charcoal steel and an excellent variety of grinding stone gave rise to the cutlery industry for which that city has long been famous. It remains so today, in spite of the fact that much iron ore is imported and synthetic abrasives are commonly utilized. The abundant coal and the iron ores of western Yorkshire and other deposits of eastern England have encouraged its expansion into one of the important steel-producing districts of the country.

Britain's most northern manufactural region lies in the *Scottish Lowlands,* between the River Clyde and the Firth of Forth. It is based upon the coal deposits of that area. It is a region of great industrial diversity but is noted particularly for its iron and steel products and its textiles. The former find particular expression in the shipbuilding of the River Clyde, near Glasgow, where the largest ocean liners are built and equipped. The region also includes famous centers of manufacture in cotton, wool, flax, and jute.

The industries of the *South Wales* coal field are more recent and specialized than those of the other coal regions. Metal refining and plating are the chief manufactures. Blast furnaces and rolling mills furnish raw materials for the manufacture of steel plates and tin plate, which are the most distinctive products of the area.

Prewar depression, wartime destruction of plants and facilities, and the ensuing reconstruction have combined to bring about numerous changes in British industrial locations. However, these are mainly changes of detail, involving a large number of small manufactures. Social planning and relocation in their broader aspects cannot overlook the areal distribution of those basic resources and conditions upon which British industry rests.

28.33 French and Belgian Centers of Manufacture. On the continent of Europe, the industrial districts of France and Belgium comprise the westernmost units in the great manufactural belt that extends eastward through central Germany and into Russia (Fig. 28.6). All the districts are related to the sources of power and minerals found in that part of the continent (Fig. 28.7).

The focus of French industrial development is in the northern and northeastern parts of the country. It comprises a broad belt that extends along the Belgian, German, and Swiss borders. France is not well supplied with large reserves of good coal, but there are large and well-integrated water powers. These are obtained from the bordering highlands of the Ardennes, Vosges, Jura, and Alps, and also from the Central Highland and the Pyrenees. Water powers are therefore available in many parts of France but especially in the northeast and east, where they are used in textile and other light manufactures. Water power is, however, inadequate for the support of heavy industry. The principal coal deposits of France are in the north, where they are continuous with those of Belgium. They supply fuel for the heavy industries in and near the coal fields, but

Fig. 28.7 The principal coal fields of France, Belgium, Holland, and western Germany in their geographical relation to the great iron-ore deposit of Lorraine (see also Fig. 24.4).

in recent times the fuel requirements of French industry have been met only by importing coal from the United States, Poland, and western Germany. In the north of France also are the great iron-ore deposits of Lorraine (Fig. 28.7). These, in combination with the coal, are the bases of the heavy industries. In part the ore moves to the coal, and steel mills are located in the north of France and in the heavy industrial belt of Belgium, which extends along the coal fields from Mons to Liége. This belt includes not only iron furnaces but also zinc smelters and other metallurgical industries together with machine manufactures, glass, clayworking, and chemical industries. In addition to its coal this region has a dense population from which to recruit an abundant labor supply. Not all the iron is smelted in this district, however, because much of the high-grade coal moves eastward to meet the ores of Lorraine, which are rather low grade and therefore bulky. This trade is the basis for the growth of heavy industry in the ore-producing region. The coal basin of the Saar is located closer to the iron ores of Lorraine than are the coal fields of northern France and Belgium. Here also are located iron and steel mills.

Paris, like London, is a great center of manufacture even though it has no local source of power. The fact that it is a transportation and market center and is able to furnish a large

labor supply is sufficient to attract industries to it, but mainly those of lighter type.

28.34 Western Germany has several highly important industrial districts, including those of the Saar coal basin and the upper Rhine Valley and Bavaria, but the most important are those of the lower Rhine region, which are associated with the productive coal fields of the *Ruhr River Valley* in Westphalia. This is the oldest and the largest center of German heavy industry. In the Westphalian district are more than a dozen industrial cities exceeding 100,000 population each and numerous towns of smaller size. Among them, as in parts of Great Britain, is much industrial specialization. The heavy industries are grouped on and to the east and southeast of the coal fields (Fig. 28.7). The hardware and lighter metal trades lie southward, and the textile districts have developed to the westward and northward. In some part of this great Rhenish-Westphalian region are plants producing nearly every class of manufactured goods.

The manufactural centers of western Europe have been for decades peculiarly subject to the fortunes of war. For example, during many years prior to 1918 Germany controlled, and its industry drew heavily upon, the iron ores of Lorraine. That control was lost in 1918, regained in 1940, and lost again in 1945. Moreover, the coal mines and industrial centers of northern France and Belgium have been repeatedly damaged by invading armies. During the Second World War the cities of the Ruhr-Westphalian region were frequent targets for Allied bombing raids, and the resulting devastation was widespread. However, the coal deposits still are there, some factories were little damaged, and others have been repaired.

28.35 Central European districts of manufacture include those of south-central Germany and Bohemia. They are associated with large deposits of lignite, scattered small deposits of coal, sources of water power, and various minerals, especially low-grade iron ores and the great German potash beds. Lignite is employed in the production of synthetic gasoline, and energy derived by various means from lignite, coal, and water power is integrated into a highly efficient power network. This central power resource and the exposed military position of the Westphalian region caused a shift of industry to this more distant interior. The iron ores served as a foundation for heavy industries, including some of the newest steel works. However, the low quality of the ores generally made it necessary to improve them by the use of high-grade ores, especially those imported from northern Sweden. Potash and the products of coal and lignite distillation formed the bases of highly developed chemical industries. The older products of the region are mainly of the lighter types, such as textiles, pottery, light machinery, optical goods, precision instruments, and the products of engraving and printing. These are the wares upon which the high industrial reputation of the region was made, and they remain important. A new political dispensation brought others which included armament, automotive, and airplane manufactures. All were knit together into a new kind of interdependent manufactural region. Much of the shift from the west appears to have been designed as a military precaution and seems uneconomic in view of the meager supply of coal and the low-grade iron ores. Now this industrial area is mainly within the zone of Russian control. How much of its former structure and importance may remain only the future can tell.

In Silesia there are coal, zinc ore, and some resources in iron and other minerals. These have permitted the growth of metallurgical industries around which other manufactures, including textiles and clothing, have gathered. This area, which between 1918 and 1939 was shared by Germany, Poland, and Czechoslovakia, was developed by all three countries. Now it is largely within the boundaries of Poland and also within the zone of Russian control. It has a most advantageous position on natural north-south corridors of central Europe, such as the Moravian Gate, at the western end of the Carpathian Mountains, and the Elbe Valley.

28.36 Other European Manufacturing Areas. There are many other manufacturing centers and activities in Europe but they do not compare in development with those which comprise the main belt. The only well-developed industrial section of northern Europe, outside of Russia, is in Sweden where perhaps a third of the population is engaged in manufacturing. The industries of Sweden are based upon highly developed skills, local high-grade iron ore, and the products of the forests. Swedish steel is known throughout the world for its quality. Sixty per cent of Sweden is covered with forests which supply the raw materials for many industries ranging from lumber and wood pulp to furniture and matches.

Lack of coal and other basic raw materials in southern Europe has not prevented manufactural development there but has notably affected its character. Spain has supplies of iron ore but little coal, and Switzerland, Italy, and the Balkan countries have no important reserves of either. However, the Alps and the Pyrenees furnish water power that is used intensively. For that reason the heavy industries are not highly developed, and those of that type which do exist depend largely upon imported coal and raw materials. In many areas manufacturing is operated under government promotion and for political or military reasons. The more typical industries are of the lighter kinds. These include food preparation, textiles, and the manufacture of fine metalwares. These industries and many others can utilize the hydroelectric power and the abundant skilled labor of the Swiss valleys, the Po Basin of Italy, and Catalonia in northeastern Spain. The Po River Valley is the location of much of the industry of Italy. Some iron and steel is manufactured, based upon imported ore, scrap, and coal. Textiles and light metalwares are the chief products. Northern Switzerland, although without much natural advantage except for water power potential, has developed a diversified manufactural character based upon skill and imported raw materials. The chief products are textiles and precision instruments such as watches and clocks. In central France the region centered on Lyon is an industrial area partially dependent upon the water power of adjacent highlands and coal from the St. Étienne region. Silk is the most famous product of the area, but chemicals, munitions, and iron and steel are also manufactured.

Manufacturing is poorly developed in the Balkan Peninsula. The area has little coal, its water power is much less than that of the more rainy and glaciated Pyrenees and Alps, and its peoples have long been troubled by political unrest that has not given manufacture the necessary condition of security.

28.37 Regions of Manufacture in the U.S.S.R. The vast expanses of Soviet Russia and its large population include many of the requisites of a large-scale manufactural development. Prior to the Soviet regime, however, they were but meagerly employed. Large reserves of coal exist and also petroleum, iron ore, manganese, and other raw materials such as metals, timber, and agricultural products. The intense effort to achieve industrial independence initiated by the Soviet government has brought about the use of these on a much larger scale than formerly, and several industrial districts have developed (Fig. 28.8): (*a*) the Moscow region, (*b*) the Leningrad region, (*c*) the southern region, (*d*) the southern Ural region, and (*e*) the central Siberian region.

Moscow is the center of an old region of manufacture, but it suffers from a lack of coking coal and iron ores close at hand. The region is spread out and consists of many separate industrial cities such as Gorki, Tula, Yaroslavl, and others, each specializing to some degree. The area is notable for its industrial diversity. Moscow itself is noted for textiles and other light manfactures, but because it is the chief city of the country, has a large labor supply, and is the principal rail center it has attracted a great variety of manufactures, some

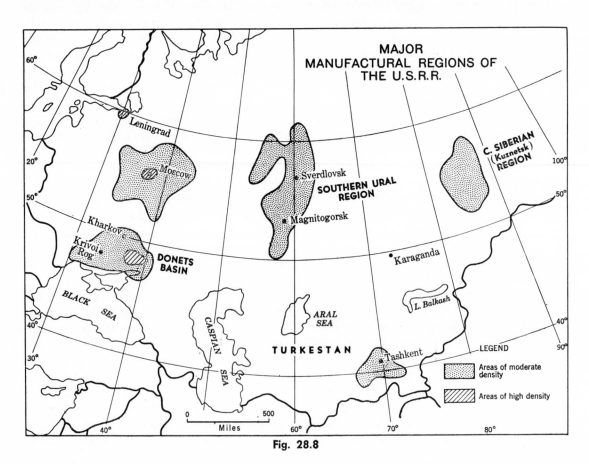

Fig. 28.8

of them of the heavier type. Its great size and diversity make the Moscow region the greatest industrial center in Russia.

The *Leningrad* region has no coal and must bring its supply at great cost from the south or from foreign sources. It has more water power than Moscow but few raw materials save timber and some agricultural products. Its great development as a manufacturing center has depended largely upon its strategic position as the gateway to the Baltic Sea, the only convenient seaport of all northern Russia opening toward the industrial countries of western Europe. Its main manufactures are textiles, wood products, and chemicals.

In the *Donets Basin,* the proximity of its great coal fields to the iron ores of Krivoi Rog led to the development of the heavy industries, and such cities as Kharkov, Lugansk, Rostov, and Stalingrad make up the southern industrial region. They specialize in machinery, tractors, farm equipment, and similar products. In the western section of the region is located the great Dnieper dam and a second point of industrial concentration. It is not nearly so developed as the Donetz basin.

Partly as a result of strategic considerations and partly due to the proximity of raw materials there has been considerable expansion of industry to the eastward, away from the major population centers. Two major areas of concentration exist. The larger is the *southern Ural* region, which has a variety of resources but none in great abundance. Some small deposits of coal and also high-grade iron ores, copper, lead, potash, salt, and other industrial minerals are found there. Ore reduction, machinery and arms manufacture, chemical industries, and many others supplement those of the Moscow and other western districts. The most critical shortage of materials in this region is of good coal, although some of the small deposits are of high quality. Its greatest surplus is of iron ore, mined near Magnitogorsk, and this is to some extent exchanged for coal with the Karaganda coal basin (Fig. 23.9) which has coal in abundance but little iron ore. The *Kuznetsk* industrial region lies 2,000 miles east

of Moscow (Fig. 28.8), and although its development is recent, it may prove of critical importance. Not only does it manufacture metal products using iron ore obtainable from the region to the south, but it has also at least the beginning of chemical, wood-products, paper, and general-supply industries. It has as its markets the growing population centers of central Siberia and the eastern Pacific maritime region.

There is some evidence of growing industrialization in some other areas of the U.S.S.R., notably in the Turkistan area south of the Aral Sea and Lake Balkhash. Great quantities of cotton from irrigated land are produced here, and based upon this raw material and the water power from adjacent highlands, a textile industry has developed. Various chemical, light metal, and wood industries have also been established. Far to the east, along the Trans-Siberian Railroad between Lake Baikal and the Pacific Ocean, some manufacturing has developed, also based upon local raw materials, notably wood from the forests and products of the seas.

28.38 Regions of Manufacture in Eastern and Southern Asia. The relation between coal deposits and the location of manufactural districts, so commonly observed in Europe and America, is less conspicuous in the Orient. The great coal fields of interior northern China have no associated manufactures, whereas the high industrial development of Japan has moderate reserves of coal to support it. For an explanation of these facts one must turn to the industrial history of the two countries and to their comparative accessibilities from the standpoint of transportation.

28.39 *China,* at the beginning of war with Japan in 1937, had barely passed the threshold of modern industrial development. Such modern factory industries as it possessed, largely textile mills, were concentrated in the densely peopled lower Yangtze Valley. They drew their coal from several small fields difficult of access. Only in Manchuria, under Japanese influence, had there developed a region of industrial concentration, based upon the local iron ore and coal. On the other hand, China is relatively well endowed with coal in the Shensi-Shansi area, one of the world's major coal reserves. In addition, China has adequate iron ore reserves, deposits of important nonferrous metals, such as tungsten, antimony, and tin, as well as salt and some petroleum. In the years since 1949 China's total industrial output has apparently quadrupled. The lack of an adequate transportation net is a handicap but the railroad system is being expanded. China, under the present government, is actively striving for industrial expansion, and from the point of view of resource endowment, it is to be expected that China will become increasingly important in the pattern of world industry.

28.40 *Japan* has only small coal fields, but they are readily accessible, and both rail and water transport permit of the movement of fuel to the centers of population. There are also widely distributed and highly developed water powers. Moreover, a large and rapidly increasing population provided cheap and abundant labor and almost enforced modern industrialization in spite of moderate resources in coal and iron. As in nearly all countries, the earlier and larger part of the manufactural development took place in the field of the lighter industries, especially silk and cotton manufactures, food preparation, and small wares of wood, paper, and metal. However, there was a great change in the character of Japanese industry in the last quarter of a century. It expanded into many new fields. Faced with the competition of synthetic fibers against silk, Japanese manufacturers themselves set up such industries. The textile trades were extended also to include wool and other fibers. It was not, however, in the lighter industries alone that expansion took place. Abundant water power, cheap labor, a depreciated currency which made it difficult to buy foreign manufactures, and the desire to become independent of foreign sources of critical military needs combined to promote the heavy industries in spite of deficiencies in the natural equipment of the islands. In order to support

growing steel industries and engineering trades it has been necessary greatly to increase the coal output of Japan's limited deposits and to import additional coking coal. Because the home supply of iron ore• is even more limited than that of coal, it is necessary also to import ore from the United States, Malaya, and the Philippines, and even larger quantities of scrap iron and steel in order to avoid the use of so much coal in the smelting process.

Among the heavy industries were several of large capital and great scope. They included shipbuilding, hydroelectric and other machine equipment, and a variety of chemical industries, which are quite different from the small plants and light manufactures of the earlier period. The districts of manufacture are largely concentrated in the "industrial belt" of southern Japan. It extends westward from Tokyo to the coal fields of northern Kyushu and includes the large cities, Tokyo, Yokohama, Nagoya, Osaka, and Kobe.

28.41 *India and Pakistan,* like other lands of ancient civilization, have a long tradition in the handicrafts. For many years also factory industries have been established, especially in the textile trades, and to some extent also in metalworking. The first to develop on a large scale were the cotton mills of the Bombay district of western India. Subsequently jute mills were set up in the Calcutta region, near the source of the raw fiber. The rise of heavy industry in India is, however, of recent origin. The vast deposits of high-grade iron ore in the district northwest of Calcutta and the nearby coal fields invited the establishment at Jamshedpur of blast furnaces and steel mills of modern type, in spite of limited coking-coal reserves. The large supply of cheap labor makes it possible to produce iron there at very low cost. Until recently, however, it supplied mainly the domestic market for machines and implements. The emergency of the Second World War found in the Indian factories a nucleus capable of rapid expansion, and they quickly became an important source of supply in a variety of goods. Not only textile and leather products were provided for the armed forces, but guns of various types, explosives, vehicles, and small marine craft, and a surplus of crude iron and steel was exported for manufacture elsewhere. The Indian subcontinent may, therefore, be counted as one of the potentially important and growing manufactural regions of the world.

MANUFACTURAL REGIONS OF THE SOUTHERN HEMISPHERE

28.42 The more settled portions of the Southern Hemisphere are mainly producers and exporters of agricultural and mineral raw materials but have not engaged in their manufacture on a large scale. Hence, there are no great industrial centers there. It does not follow, however, that factory industries are entirely undeveloped or incapable of expansion. The South American countries, which have the largest domestic markets, are handicapped by lack of coal, while Australia, New Zealand, and South Africa, which have some coal, have only limited markets because of small populations. In all these areas, however, manufacture has made beginnings, and in some it has advanced considerably.

28.43 *In Argentina and Brazil* the principal factories are those concerned with the preparation of foodstuffs and with textile manufacture. It would be expected that the forms of manufacture that could succeed there would be (*a*) those using raw materials produced in the region, (*b*) those using a comparatively small amount of coal-driven machinery, (*c*) those demanding a relatively small force of technically skilled employees, or (*d*) those producing articles that require local manufacture in order to fill immediate needs or to fit the exact nature of the local markets. In Argentina, where there is little water power and all the coal must be imported, the principal industries are meat packing, flour milling, textile mills, and manufactories of vehicles and farm implements to fit local needs. They are located mainly in the great city and port of Buenos Aires. Brazil has the advantage of large water-power resources and of a larger domestic market, and it has somewhat more diversified manufactures, which include cotton and jute textiles, clothing, chemicals, and some metalwares. Through lack of coal, however, there has been only a little progress in the utilization of the large domestic resources of iron ore. One modern blast furnace and steel rolling mill has been built at Volta Redonda in the eastern highland not far from Rio de Janeiro, but its operation must depend in part on imported coal.

28.44 *In Australia and New Zealand,* as in South America, the settlement and development of a large area of land by a small population has only recently permitted much attention to be given to manufacture. However, conditions there have favored manufacture somewhat more than in South America. In addition to supplies of coal there is the factor of greater distance and higher freight rates from the European and American manufacturing regions. Australians and New Zealanders are dominantly of British stock and have somewhat greater interest in and familiarity with industrial management than those who control the capital and governmental policies of Latin America. The greater number of factories of Australia and New Zealand are concerned with the preparation of foods: flour and sugar milling, fruit preserving, meat packing, and butter and cheese manufacture. Others of long standing are the ore-reduction plants associated with the mining of gold, zinc, and other valuable minerals, also sawmills and plants turning out bulky wood products, such as furniture. During the First World War the shortage of shipping made it profitable to set up a variety of other manufactories, many of which languished in the postwar period because of their high production costs. Some have persisted, however, and Australia, particularly, entered the second great war of the century with several types of manufacture already in operation on a fairly large scale. These include blast furnaces and steel mills, near the coal fields of the east coast, textile mills in Victoria, clothing manufacture, and various types of machine and armament plants.

28.45 *The Union of South Africa,* of all the Southern Hemisphere centers of population, has developed least in manufacture. However, the recent need of equipping military forces has led to industrial expansion there also. Small and local industries have enlarged their capacities and widened their manufactural scope. South African coal and mineral ores make this possible.

References for Chapter 28

Alderfer, E. B., and H. E. Michl. "Economics of American Industry." 2d ed. McGraw-Hill Book Company, Inc., New York, 1950.

Alexander, John W. Industrial Expansion in the United States, 1939–1947, *Econ. Geog.,* Vol. 28, pp. 128–142, 1952.

Balzak, S. S., V. F. Vasyutin, and Ya. G. Feigin (editors). "Economic Geography of the U.S.S.R." English translation by R. M. Hankin and O. A. Titlebaum. American ed. by Chauncy D. Harris (editor), The Macmillan Company, New York, 1949.

Bengtson, Nels A., and William Van Royen. "Fundamentals of Economic Geography." Prentice-Hall, Inc., New York, 1950.

Brush, John E. The Iron and Steel Industry in India. *Geog. Rev.,* Vol. 42, pp. 37–55, 1952.

Cressey, George B. "Asia's Lands and Peoples." 2d ed. McGraw-Hill Book Company, Inc., New York, 1951.

Dicken, Samuel N. "Economic Geography," D. C. Heath and Company, Boston, 1955.

McCarty, H. H. "Geographic Basis of American Economic Life." Harper & Brothers, New York, 1940.

Pounds, N. J. G. "The Ruhr: A Study in Historical and Economic Geography." Indiana University Press, Bloomington, Ind., 1952.

Rodgers, Allan. The Manchurian Iron and Steel Industry and Its Resource Base. *Geog. Rev.,* Vol. 38, pp. 41–54, 1948.

Schumpeter, E. B., *et al.* "The Industrialization of Japan and Manchukuo, 1930–1940." The Macmillan Company, New York, 1940.

Shabad, Theodore. "China's Changing Map." Frederick A. Praeger, Inc., New York, 1956.

Shimkin, Demitri B. Economic Regionalization in the Soviet Union, *Geog. Rev.,* Vol. 42, pp. 591–614, 1952.

Smith, J. Russell, M. Ogden Phillips, and Thomas R. Smith. "Industrial and Commercial Geography." Henry Holt and Company, Inc., New York, 1955.

Thompson, John H. A New Method for Measuring Manufacturing. *Ann. Assoc. Amer. Geog.,* Vol. 45, pp. 416–436, 1955.

Trewartha, Glenn T. "Japan: A Physical, Cultural and Regional Geography." University of Wisconsin Press, Madison, Wis., 1945.

Wright, Alfred J. Recent Changes in the Concentration of Manufacturing. *Ann. Assoc. Amer. Geog.,* Vol. 35, pp. 144–166, 1945.

Zierer, Clifford M. The Australian Iron and Steel Industry as a Functional Unit. *Geog. Rev.,* Vol. 30, pp. 649–659, 1940.

Zimmerman, E. W. "World Resources and Industries." Rev. ed. Harper & Brothers, New York, 1951.

29

Transport and Trade

29.1 Function and Significance of Transport.

All forms of transportation are for the purpose of facilitating the movement of man or his goods from one place to another. When a raw material has been converted by manufacturing processes into a finished product, it has been made more useful or more valuable through a change in *form*. When a commodity is moved from a place where it is not wanted to a place where it is needed, it has been made more useful or more valuable through a change in *place*. Just as manufacturing creates *form utility* in commodities, so transportation creates *place utility*. When raw cotton is converted into a useful and valuable garment, form utility has been added. However there may be little demand for the garments at the place where they are manufactured but, on the other hand, a very active demand for them in other regions. By transporting the garments to the places where they are needed, there has been an increase in their value to society, an increased value that is every bit as real as that added by the manufacturing processes.

It has been said that the dominant economic fact of our modern industrial and scientific age is the development of cheap, fast, and efficient transportation. The economic structure of the nineteenth and twentieth centuries has been built upon cheap transportation. The road, used here as including all lines of transportation, is one of the most fundamental institutions of mankind. It is so necessary and so natural a part of human existence that we take it for granted.

29.2 Effects of Efficient Transportation.

The most obvious effect of efficient transportation is to make available to a community goods which are produced elsewhere. It is this creation of place utility in goods by means of transportation that permits the development of regional specialization in production. Unless goods could be readily moved from places of excess to regions of deficiency, each region would be compelled to produce all the kinds of things needed in just the right quantities—no more and no less than could be consumed at home. Where communications are adequately developed, however, there is no such inhibiting influence, and regions are permitted to specialize, to a greater degree, in those types of production for which they are best fitted by natural endowment or cultural heritage and at the same time neglect those for which they are less well equipped. Without the development of adequate means of transport for facilitating the movement of goods, advanced stages of economic development are impossible. Indeed, there is a direct relationship between the adequacy of the transport facilities of a region and its stage of economic development.

The development of large cities is dependent upon cheap and efficient transportation. In the prerailroad era large cities were located along navigable waterways. The development of inland metropolises waited upon the railroad. The concentration of large numbers of people in a restricted area, such as a city, makes necessary the deriving of a food supply, especially perishable foods, from beyond the immediate locality. The processing of goods, which is one of the primary functions of cities, requires the concentration of large amounts of raw materials and power and the distribution of the finished products to markets beyond. Urbanization, which epitomizes regional specialization and subdivision of labor, is dependent upon a flow of goods.

Cheap and efficient transportation tends to reduce the cost of goods to the consumer. This may be done through the encouragement it gives to large-scale production. It likewise gives purchasers the benefit of increased competition and so tends to hold prices down. The better diffusion of goods through transportation reduces waste from overproduction and stabilizes and equalizes prices.

Apart from the economic effects of improved transportation there are others which are social and political in character. To a considerable degree it determines the distribution pattern of population. Early settlements in this country were usually along navigable waterways. Highways and railways have made wider dispersion possible. Better transportation results in improved housing, food, and clothing, so that the whole standard of living is lifted. Leisure is increased, social contacts are broadened, and incentive to progress is strengthened. National unity is promoted through drawing the different parts of a large and diverse country closer together. By promoting regional specialization an efficient transportation system creates a greater need for national unity. By no means of least importance are the effects of transportation upon national defense.

29.3   The Urge to Trade. Commerce exists because of the desire of individuals and countries having different goods to exchange their surplus for the surplus of some other people. We live in an era of regional specialization and in a society so organized that such an exchange is an absolute necessity. Some regions are dominantly pastoral, others agricultural or manufactural. Some agricultural regions specialize in a limited group of crops, and some manufactural regions in a restricted range of products.

Such differences in production, which are the bases of trade and therefore the prime reason for transportation systems, arise from several causes among which are (*a*) differences in the people themselves, (*b*) differences in the physical characteristics of the various parts of the earth including the unequal distribution of natural resources, and (*c*) differences in the economic development of peoples or in their stage of civilization. Of these the first is perhaps the least important, for with the better development of communications and trade there is a tendency for racial differences and their commercial results to disappear. Native culture finds it difficult to persist in the face of competition offered by the imitations produced by machine manufacture. Still, the blankets and basketry of American Indians, the Oriental rugs of the peoples of western Asia, and the lacquer, porcelains, and tapestries of the Chinese and Japanese are examples of kinds of surpluses entering into trade that have their origins, at least in part, in the characteristics and cultures of the peoples themselves.

More fundamental, however, as a basis of trade are the differences in the characteristics of the physical earth, including its natural resources. Between the tropics and the middle latitudes there is a large exchange of products based primarily, although indirectly, upon differences in climate. Two of the top-ranking imports of the United States (crude rubber, cane sugar) are from the tropics. Manila hemp, coffee, jute, henequen, coconut products, palm oil, bananas, cacao, and tea are other items in the import list arriving from the frostless lands to the south. In our Latin American trade relations we have much closer ties with the tropical parts of that region, whose products are noncompetitive and therefore complementary to ours, than with the middle-latitude countries of southern South America, whose products are similar. California's large export of horticultural products to northern and eastern United States has a basis which is fundamentally climatic. There are some who predict that this north-south trade based upon climatic contrasts is destined to be the trade of the future. Between humid lands and dry lands likewise there are natural bases for trade. Beyond the bounds of cultivation in many dry regions are the sheep and cattle ranches which send their animal products into the markets of the more populous humid lands.

Differences in relief or surface irregularity likewise give rise to contrasts in production, which result in trade. On the steep and rock-strewn slopes of mountains the tilling of crops is difficult so that such regions are more characteristically used for grazing, forestry, or mining. Between the agricultural plain and the less agricultural mountain there are fundamental reasons for an exchange of surpluses. Soil contrasts have a similar effect. Between regions well endowed with basic minerals and those either lacking or having a deficiency in those resources, there is the basis for a flow of goods. This may take the form of actual shipment of minerals in raw or semiprocessed state, such as the movement of Swedish iron ore to Germany and England, the shipment of British coal to the coal-poor Mediterranean lands, or the export of American petroleum to Japan. Or on the other hand, the presence of these basic minerals may lead to specialization in certain kinds of manufacturing and a consequent exchange of commodities between a nonmineralized nonmanufacturing region and one possessing the mineral resources and the manufacturing based upon them. The basic exchange between mineral-poor Argentina and Uruguay, highly specialized in agricultural production, and the industrialized mineral-producing countries of western Europe, is between two regions fundamentally in contrast as regards basic minerals, which contrast is reflected to a degree in the kinds of surpluses of the two regions.

At the present time at least, contrasts in the kinds and stages of economic development of nations and regions seem to be the single most important basis for trade. This is reflected in the preponderance of east-west trade over that moving north-south. It should be recognized, however, that the basis of trade between two regions is more often than not the result of several causes rather than one. Thus the exchange between the United States and tropical Latin America results both from contrasts in climate and from differences in stage of economic development, and perhaps also from differences in the people themselves. The trade between Great Britain and India appears to involve all three reasons as well. The greatest trade is between regions and countries of most advanced economic development and where standards of living are highest.

29.4 Four Classes of Features Associated with Transportation. Transportation involves at least four fairly obvious classes or groups of features that are of geographic significance: (*a*) the things or commodities exchanged, (*b*) the vehicles or conveyances transporting the commodities (ships, trains, motor trucks, airplanes, beasts of burden, men), (*c*) the routes followed by these vehicles (sea lanes, railroad lines, land roads, air lanes, paths), and (*d*) the terminal facilities along the routes. In addition there are numerous auxiliary features and services such as banks, insurance firms, warehousing establishments, and the like which also expedite the trading enterprise.

The Commodities of Trade: Kinds and Magnitude

29.5 It should never be lost sight of that routes of trade, the carriers that move over these routes, and the terminals of these carriers all exist for the sake of the commodities that are in process of being exchanged. Not infrequently it is the trade routes and the trade centers that are given chief attention, but to do so neglects the basic fact that the goods that flow over the routes and pass through the terminals are of primary importance.

Unfortunately it is impossible to give a concise picture of the magnitude and kinds of goods comprising the trade of the world and its various parts. For the trade that crosses international boundary lines, or foreign trade, there are fairly adequate statistics, but for that larger movement that takes place within countries, domestic trade, information is difficult to obtain. In magnitude the foreign trade of the United States is only a fraction of its internal commerce.

29.6 World Trade. In 1952 the foreign trade of the world was valued at about 152 billion dollars. Although hundreds of commodities comprised this trade, the bulk of it was made up of items of general consumption, for food, shelter, clothing, and means of production are the most important requisites of modern society. Foods, textile fibers, minerals, and manufactured goods comprise the four principal classes of commodities entering into trade. Among foods the cereals are most important, with wheat the outstanding single item in the Occident and rice in the Orient. Compared with the trade in these two cereals that involving rye, corn, oats, and barley is small. Another of the important food groups is meats and animal fats. Roughly 2,500,000,000 lb. of beef and its products and 2,000,000,000 lb. of pork and its products annually find their way into world trade. There are additional large quantities of mutton, canned meat, butter, cheese, fish, poultry, and eggs. Vegetable oils make up a third group, and fruits, nuts, vegetables, condiments, and beverages (tea, coffee, cacao) a fourth.

Among the textile fibers, used chiefly as raw materials in the manufacture of cloth, rope, twine, and bagging, are included cotton, wool, silk, jute, hemp, and sisal, together with many less important ones. Outstanding in the mineral group are such bulky ones as coal, petroleum, iron ore, lead, and zinc. In tonnage this group takes first rank. A large group designated as

External or Foreign Trade in 1952, Excluding the Communist Countries
(In millions of dollars)

	Imports	Exports
World	78,900	72,600
Africa	6,270	4,840
Latin America	8,610	8,040
North America	16,430	19,510
Asia	11,820	9,980
Europe	33,100	27,770
Oceania	2,710	2,430

miscellaneous includes a host of items, among them such outstanding ones as rubber and timber.

The striking feature of the preceding table showing amount of foreign trade by continents, and of Fig. 29.1 showing distribution of foreign trade by countries, is the unusual concentration in Europe. In part, this reflects a similar concentration of population and of industrial development. However, the fact that the continent is divided into a large number of relatively small but important countries naturally leads to much trade crossing international land boundary lines, which thereby becomes foreign commerce. On the other hand, the immense trade between different regions within a large political unit like the United States is domestic in character and consequently does not appear in the preceding table.

What becomes clear is that there is a concentration of the external trade of the world in the regions surrounding the North Atlantic Basin, Europe and North America together accounting for two-thirds of the total. First among the nations was the United States with approximately 17 per cent of the total, followed by the United Kingdom, Canada, France, and western Germany.

Foreign Trade of Some Important Trading Countries
(In millions of dollars)

	Imports	Exports
United States	10811.9	15042.3
United Kingdom	9345.5	7227.5
Canada	4120.3	4452.7
France	4435.6	3890.9
Western Germany	3814.1	4001.6
Belgium and Luxemburg	2443.8	2444.8
Netherlands	2221.5	2107.5
Brazil	2009.7	1408.9
Australia	1720.9	1688.9
Japan	2028.2	1272.9
Sweden	1729.6	1571.6

29.7 American Foreign Trade. Although the exports of the United States constitute only a small fraction of its total national production (less than 5 per cent in 1952), external trade is, nevertheless, a vital element in the prosperity of this nation. In the postwar period the United States has become the ranking foreign

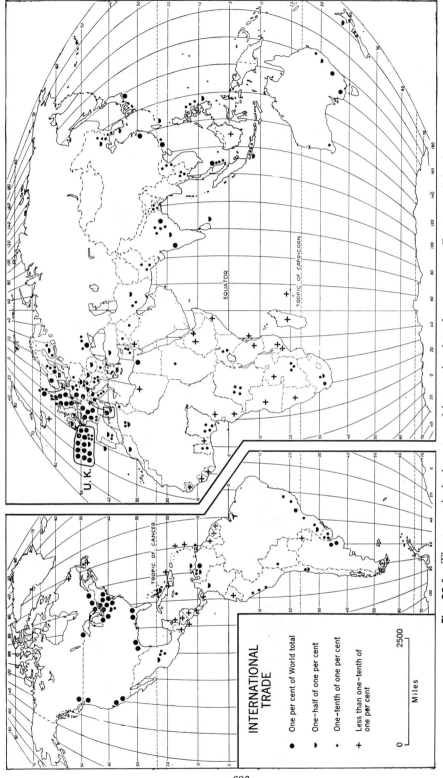

Fig. 29.1 The two principal centers of international trade are western Europe and Anglo-America (United States and Canada) both of which front upon the North Atlantic Ocean. (*Modified from map in Jones and Darkenwald, "Economic Geography," 2d ed.*)

INTERNATIONAL
TRADE

• One per cent of World total

◗ One-half of one per cent

· One-tenth of one per cent

+ Less than one-tenth of
one per cent

0   2500
Miles

trade nation of the world. Unfortunately our external trade has been a very unbalanced one, for we have consistently sold abroad much more than we have purchased and this has been made possible only through the tens of billions of dollars in foreign aid. In the years 1946 to 1952 the United States exported 91 billion dollars' worth of goods while at the same time importing merchandise valued at 55 billion. The difference between exports and imports, amounting to 36 billion dollars, is just about equal to the total foreign aid which was given to other countries during that seven-year period. Since the prosperity of the American domestic economy depends upon a large export trade, and because our exports are sorely needed abroad, it is unthinkable that external sales should be reduced. But it is equally essential that the large gap between the value of our exports and imports should be reduced. The only alternative to continuing aid to other countries is a willingness to open the American market wider to foreign goods so that our imports shall more closely equal our exports. Actually, the gap is gradually being closed and in 1953 the excess of exports over imports was only 1.4 billion dollars if military exports are excluded. Considering the country as a whole and not special groups of producers, the net effect of high protective tariffs upon all groups in this country is adverse. Tariffs imposed primarily for raising revenue, or those necessary to maintain industries essential for defense, are in a different class.

The diversity of the foreign trade of the United States is indicated by the following tables showing the leading exports and imports in 1952. Exports are heavily weighted in favor of manufactured goods, 78 per cent being a combination of finished manufactures, semi-manufactures, and processed foodstuffs. Imports, on the other hand, are less heavily weighted in favor of any one class of goods, crude materials and crude foodstuffs together comprising 47 per cent of the total, and manufactured goods 53 per cent. The single most important class of imports is crude materials for use in American factories, amounting to 27 per

Major Items in American Foreign Trade, 1952
(Ranked according to value)

Exports	Imports
1. Machinery	1. Coffee
2. Automobiles and parts	2. Petroleum and products
3. Wheat and wheat flour	3. Rubber
4. Petroleum and products	4. Paper and manufactures
5. Raw cotton	5. Sugar
6. Iron- and steel-mill products	6. Copper
7. Coal and coke	7. Wool and mohair
8. Cotton textiles	8. Tin
	9. Wood pulp

cent of the total. It appears therefore, that although American foreign trade is highly diversified, there is a high preponderance of processed goods in our sales, but only a very slight preponderance of processed goods in our purchases. All this is evidence of a highly industrialized country but at the same time one which, while it has large surpluses of certain foods and raw materials, must at the same time import heavily in other types of industrial raw materials and foodstuffs.

29.8 Trade Regions of the United States. The three factors of supply, demand and price, if permitted to function freely, will produce trade patterns based upon those factors described in Art. 29.3. Seldom are these factors allowed to function independently, for nations tend to erect artificial barriers which block or modify the normal flow of trade. These man-made controls are not universally injurious, for many of them are designed to benefit a particular country or group of people. Usually, therefore, they are associated with questions of national policy. Unfortunately what may benefit one nation or group is likely to react adversely on another, so that considering the entire earth

The Nature of the Foreign Trade of the United States in 1952
(In millions of dollars)

	Exports	Imports
Crude materials	1,981	2,935
Crude foodstuffs	1,368	2,068
Manufactured foodstuffs	727	1,081
Semimanufactures	1,623	2,567
Finished manufactures	9,326	2,093
Total	15,026	10,745

Foreign Trade of the United States, 1952, by
Continents, and Selected Countries
(In millions of dollars)

	Exports	Imports
North America	4,486	3,739
Canada	2,785	2,385
Mexico	666	411
Central America	281	220
The Caribbean and Bermuda	753	719
South America	1,832	2,283
Argentina	147	159
Brazil	564	808
Chile	130	286
Venezuela	500	396
Colombia	230	384
Europe	3,342	2,028
United Kingdom	676	485
Belgium and Luxemburg	291	189
France	365	167
Germany	444	219
Italy	412	157
Sweden	128	90
Netherlands	276	159
Switzerland	151	142
Asia	2,113	1,813
Japan	622	229
Indonesia	132	276
India	381	272
Philippines	283	236
Malaya	36	38
Australia and Oceania	224	24
Africa	568	60
Total	15,164	10,745

and all its people a commerce free from artificial controls is probably to be preferred.

The foreign trade of the United States is spread widely over the earth (see the tables on this page). Two areas, North America north of the United States and Europe, are almost on a par as trading areas for this country. Since northern North America is largely Canada, the remarkable fact is that our trade with a single country, Canada (20 per cent), is almost equal

Trading Areas of the United States in 1952

	Per Cent of U.S. Exports*	Per Cent of U.S. Imports
Northern North America	18.4	22.3
Southern North America	11.2	12.6
South America	12.1	21.3
Europe	22.0	18.9
Asia	13.9	16.9
Australia and Oceania	1.5	2.3
Africa	3.7	5.7

* Incomplete. Exports of special strategic commodities excluded for security reasons.

to that with all the countries of Europe combined (21 per cent). Next in importance come Asia and South America which are almost on a par, with 15 to 16 per cent each. Tropical North America, including Mexico, Central America, and the islands of the Caribbean, follows next in order with Africa and Oceania much lower in the scale.

By individual countries Canada's trade with the United States far outranks that of any other nation's. After Canada in order of importance are Brazil, the United Kingdom, Mexico, Cuba, Venezuela, Japan, Italy, and West Germany.

Routes of Transport and Their Carriers

29.9 Types of Trade Routes. The world's transportation routes may be classified into three general types: land, water, and air. At least one fundamental difference distinguishes most land routes from those in the air and on the water, *viz.*, in the two latter no trace is left by the vehicle after it passes. A ship slips through the water, and in a few moments all record of its passage has been obliterated. The same is true of air transport. On the other hand, the land almost invariably preserves traces of routes followed. As a consequence of this difference, it is to be expected that air and water routes are not nearly so definite in location as are those of the land. The direction and course of any route are determined, first of all, by the points that are to be connected and, second, by the obstacles that interpose themselves between these points.

But although routes may, for convenience of discussion, be divided into the three classes named above, it should not be lost sight of that they are integrally related. In modern trade a water route may be a continuation of a land route and vice versa, and the coastline is simply a point of transshipment along the route, made necessary by a change in mode of transportation. Thus wheat moving to New York City reaches Duluth by rail, is there shifted to lake steamer, which may carry it to Buffalo, from which terminal it is again transshipped to rail or canal barge, which sets it down in New York.

The foremost factor in establishing transportation routes is the traffic potential, and the general location of lines of transport is determined by the location of surplus and deficiency areas. At the convergence of routes and at their terminals trade centers tend to originate.

LAND ROUTES AND THEIR CARRIERS

29.10 The human body is the most universal as well as the most primitive means of land transport, and human portage still prevails in many parts of the world. Animals, too, such as the horse, camel, donkey, and ox, serve in the same capacity and, because of their greater strength, are able to carry heavier loads and often with greater speed than can man. But it is easier to pull a heavy burden than to carry it, and this fact very early led to such mechanical inventions as the rollers of the

Fig. 29.2 A common form of transportation in many parts of the world, in this case Japan. The roads of Japan are narrow and winding, but on the other hand they are surfaced and all-weather in character. (*Three Lions.*)

Assyrians, and later the wheel, upon the axle of which was built the cart. The exact place and time of origin of the wheeled vehicle are not known, but it goes back into prehistoric times. Its invention marks one of the greatest forward strides in the evolution of transport. Most of our modern means of land transport, the automobile and the train, are but modifications of the original wheeled cart, mechanically powered so as to provide greater speed and pulling strength as compared with the human- or animal-drawn vehicle.

Land routes and their carriers changed more rapidly during the nineteenth century than during the entire period of world history up to that time. Until the development of the portable steam engine, land travel the world over had been by human carriers on foot, pack animals, ox- or horse-drawn wagon, or by river and canal. All these were slow, and the amount of goods that could be carried was relatively small. With the development of the railroad after about 1840, land transportation was revolutionized in some parts of the earth. However the earlier primitive means of travel have by no means disappeared. Over large areas of the earth, particularly those less advanced in material civilization, these forms still are the standard ones (Fig. 29.2). Even in the most advanced countries their least accessible and thinly populated parts are still served by the more primitive transportation facilities.

Highways and Motor Vehicles

29.11 The Road. Of all land routes, the *road*, including everything from the humblest path to the modern concrete highway, is the most ancient as well as the most universal. Ancient Rome recognized the strategic value of roads in facilitating the quick shifting of troops to any part of the Empire, and as a result highways were constructed, not only in Italy, but over the Alps into the basins of the Danube and the Rhine, to the center of Spain, and even in England. Other ancient peoples such as the Chinese and the Incas built paved roads, but it remained for the Romans first to organize separate roads into a system or network, all

Fig. 29.3 Aerial view of the Pennsylvania Turnpike, one of the country's most modern highways. (*Courtesy of Pennsylvania Turnpike Commission.*)

parts of which fed into one another. Not all peoples construct such permanent highways. Among the dunes of the Sahara are paths worn by camel trains of caravans, while porters' feet have left imprints upon the jungle soils and vegetation of the Congo. Every human establishment, no matter how insignificant, becomes a focus of roads, and the greater its attraction, the greater the multiplication of trails leading to it.

29.12 Functions of Roads. Most of the roads of the earth grew out of the needs for local transportation. Only to a limited extent were the public roads expected to function in long-distance movement of people or goods. In the United States the early public roads were for the purpose of providing connections between farmsteads and the market towns where the farmers traded. Only a few, such as the eastern post roads and the Cumberland Road, were planned with long-distance transportation in mind. And, although the development of the motorcar within the past four decades has accelerated the growth of trunk-line highways, it

is still true that of the 3 million miles of public roads in this country, roughly 1.3 million miles are ordinary unsurfaced dirt roads serving chiefly the rural population. Surfaced roads of all kinds reach a total of 1,700,000 miles, of which only 263,000 miles have a hard surface of a high type resting upon a rigid base. The latter are chiefly the trunk-line routes (Fig. 29.3). To a large degree the highway "fills with a finer weave the coarse meshes of the railway net."

29.13 Motorcars and Their Services. The rapid expansion of surfaced highways during the past few decades has been a by-product of the phenomenal increase in the use of motor vehicles. In the preautomobile era it was Europe that set the world standards for good roads. But when Americans began to purchase automobiles in numbers they shortly demanded good roads, for now they had a vehicle that was meant for speed and that could travel long distances. The effect upon road building and improvement in America was startling. At the present time 7 to 9 billion dollars are invested each year in the construction and maintenance and policing of roads in the United States. Other parts of the world also have felt the effect of the automobile upon road building. The costs of rolling stock and right-of-way maintenance are much less for bus and truck than for railroads, and at the same time there is a far greater flexibility of usage. Countries with little capital therefore have elected to improve their transportation by providing themselves with better roads and motorbusses and trucks rather than by investing in railroads. Such a development has been striking in regions like Poland, Finland, the Baltic States, and China.

In 1910 it is estimated there were only 600,000 motor vehicles in existence. By 1920 this had increased to 11 million, in 1930 to 35 million, in 1941 to over 45 million, and in 1953 to 83 million. Nearly 70 per cent of the world's motor vehicles are concentrated in the United States. Northwestern Europe is the region of next highest concentration, with 18 per cent for the continent as a whole. Motor transport has won its present position partly by displacing horse-drawn vehicles, partly by capturing rail traffic, and partly by increasing the total amount of traffic.

Highway motor transport is very diversified in form, for it is conspicuous in both passenger and freight service, in local and intercity movements, and in private and public service. Counting all these different forms, more traffic moves by highway than by all other means of transportation combined. It is in the passenger field that the motor vehicle has contributed most. Largely the passenger miles accumulated are by private passenger cars used for pleasure and not for business. Revenue passenger motor service takes the form of taxicabs and busses operating both within and between cities. To a considerable degree city busses supplement surface trams and subways and in many cities have resulted in the abandonment of surface street cars. Intercity motor bus routes in the United States exceed the line mileage of railroads, and intercity busses carry upwards of the number of passengers carried by the railroads.

Because of the longer hauls, however, the railroad passenger mileage is about three times as great. The advantage of the motorbus over the railroad is associated with two factors: (*a*) the carrying unit is small and less expensive, and (*b*) it is not confined to a fixed roadway. The first permits of service in small loads over public highways with numerous and convenient stops for pickup and discharge of passengers. The bus serves best where traffic is light and where speed is not so important. Where traffic is heavy and speed is essential, it must yield to the railway.

Motor trucking is predominantly short-haul freight transportation, although the length of the haul has been increasing. The average length of freight haul by motor truck in the United States is only 17.4 miles. Over two-fifths of the truck miles on rural roads do not cross county lines. On trunk highways the intercity trucking is largely intrastate in character, only one-fifth of the total ton miles representing interstate freight movement. Intercity trucking also is concerned chiefly with high-class freight, often of the miscellaneous package class. The advantages of motor trucking over rail are related to such items as faster service, store-door pickup and delivery, cheaper total cost, cheaper packing, and less damage to freight. In the long-distance movement of bulk freight, railroads have a decided advantage. Railroads are making an increasing use of trucks for pickup and delivery service, for interline transfers, for reaching off-track stations, and for handling less than carload lots between cities.

29.14   Road Mileage, Density of Road Net, and Pattern of Road Distribution. The United States with its 3.3 million miles of roads suitable for motor traffic has 40 per cent more than its nearest rival, Soviet Russia. After Russia there follow in order Japan, Australia, Canada, France, Germany, and the United Kingdom. The density of the road net is highest in Japan, followed by Great Britain, Denmark, France, Ireland, and Belgium. The two *large* centers of high road density are western Europe and eastern United States, regions with large populations and relatively high standards of living. In these regions there is usually over 1 mile of road for each square mile of territory, and in parts it is much denser. Of surfaced roads in the United States there is about 1 mile to each 4 square miles of land area, but the ratio is only 1 to 25 for roads having a high type of hard surfacing (Fig. 29.4). The highest densities are in the northern and eastern region of the country, extending from northern Illinois to southern New England.

29.15 Road Patterns. Road arrangement, or pattern, is related to both physical and historical conditions. In general roads should, as nearly as possible, represent the shortest line between two points, but often they deviate from this straight-line route because of surface features, river crossings, swamps, and the like. In most sections of Europe and North America the easiest routes of travel were discovered by the earliest inhabitants, so that the main thoroughfares have been the principal arteries of travel since the regions were first inhabited. In the early settled eastern and southern parts of this country, roads tend to radiate from early settlements and follow relatively direct routes to other settlements except as they are deflected by surface features or drainage conditions. In those parts of the country settled after the Ordinance of 1785, which imposed the rectangular square-mile system of sections, townships, and ranges oriented north-south and east-west, the road pattern is distinctive (Fig. 29.5 and Appendix C). The layout is predominantly rectangular, in the form of a checkerboard with roads at 1-mile intervals. Some roads that antedate the survey may cut across this pattern; others deviate from it in places because of physical conditions. New paved highways pay less attention to the rectangular land survey and take their courses so as to give the shortest distances.

Railroads and Their Carriers

29.16 Characteristics of Railroads. As the road is very ancient, so the railroad is a relatively modern type of land route, not having

Fig. 29.4 Aerial view of the Blue Mountain Interchange along the Pennsylvania Turnpike. (*Courtesy of Pennsylvania Turnpike Commission.*)

SELECTED AMERICAN ROAD PATTERNS

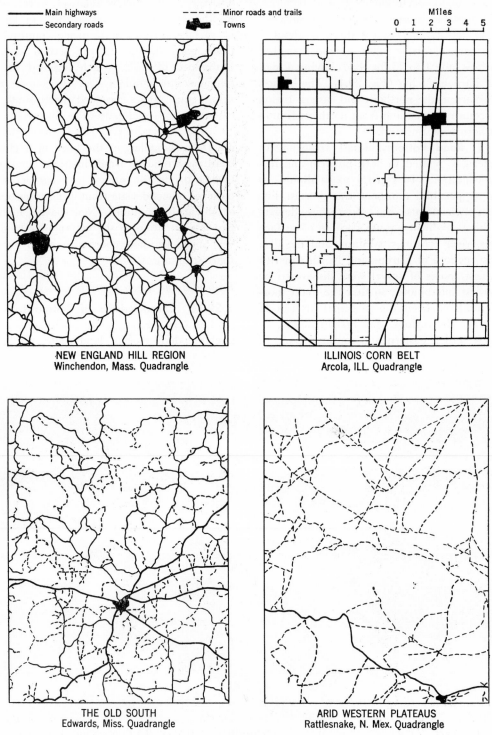

Main highways
Secondary roads
Minor roads and trails
Towns

Miles
0 1 2 3 4 5

NEW ENGLAND HILL REGION
Winchendon, Mass. Quadrangle

ILLINOIS CORN BELT
Arcola, ILL. Quadrangle

THE OLD SOUTH
Edwards, Miss. Quadrangle

ARID WESTERN PLATEAUS
Rattlesnake, N. Mex. Quadrangle

Fig. 29.5

been in use much more than a century. The first railroad was built in England in 1825, and it has followed the expansion of occidental civilization into the far corners of the earth. It is a product of the Industrial Revolution, while at the same time it has made a complex industrial-commercial type of civilization possible. The course taken by a rail line may be quite different from that of a road. A train cannot negotiate steep grades as can a motor vehicle, so that rail lines are obliged to follow rather closely the major relief features. On the other hand, in the construction of a railroad bed use is made of cuts, fills, tunnels, and bridges in order to keep grades low, so that the rail line is less influenced by minor features of the terrain. Because of the high cost of roadbed construction and of the rolling stock, the railway is a paying investment only when distance and length of haul can compensate for these handicaps. Its capacity for hauling large loads long distances at a relatively high rate of speed is

the principal point of advantage which urged the rapid expansion of the world's railway mileage. Unlike waterways, collections and deliveries are not restricted to main lines, for by means of secondary lines and spur tracks small towns off main lines, and even individual factories, may have connections with the markets of the country and the world.

29.17 Expansion of Railroads and Their Present Distribution. Rail building followed closely the spread of western civilization, and the present-day pattern of world distribution closely coincides with that of machine civilization (Figs. 29.6, 29.9). For the entire earth there are in the neighborhood of 750,000 miles of railroad of which nearly 320,000 miles are in North America, 67,000 in South America, including Central America and the West Indies, 250,000 in Europe, 84,000 in Asia, 31,000 in Oceania, and 21,500 in Africa. Western Europe and eastern North America are the two conspicuous centers with a large railroad mile-

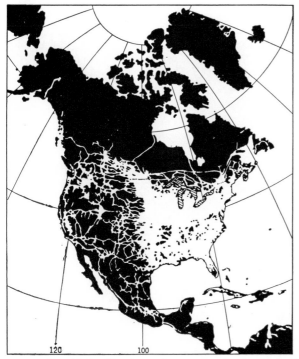

Fig. 29.6 Density and patterns of rail nets in North and South America. Strips shown in white are not more than 10 miles from a railroad. (*Slightly modified from maps by Mark Jefferson.*)

age and closely spaced rail net. In both regions there are few areas that are more than 10 miles from a line. In England, Belgium, northern France, southwestern Germany, and portions of the American Atlantic Seaboard states, most areas are even within a mile or two of rail lines. The railroad is a distinguishing feature of Euro-American culture, and its distribution is a good indicator of the spread and intensity of that culture.

29.18 *North American Railroads.* Only rail transportation could have made the resources of the immense spaces westward from the Appalachian barrier quickly available, and so it was that the rails marched westward with the American frontier. There was a close paralleling of railway building with the settlement and development of the land. The first lines were built to supplement waterways, but eventually they came to dominate transportation back from the seaboards. At present there are

about 225,000 miles of rail in all of the United States, which is approximately one-third of the trackage of the entire world. This immense length of rail line, like America's great length of highways, pipe lines, telephone lines, and her number of automobiles, reflects not only the country's prosperity, but also a disadvantage associated with large area. Coal lies 1,000 miles from the ore, lumber is produced 2,500 miles from the principal markets, food is grown 1,000 miles and more away from the center of consumption. Our magnificent transportation facilities reflect the means by which the handicap of distance is overcome.

29.19 *Density of Rail Net and Patterns of Distribution.* For different sections of the United States and Canada the *density* of the rail net varies greatly. In the poorly populated grazing regions of the western high plains and the intermontane plateaus there is only 1 mile of railroad for each 45 square miles of land. In

Fig. 29.7 Railroad map of the United States. There are about 225,000 miles of road. Note that the greatest density of track is in the north central and northeastern part of the country. It is less dense in the South, while the least density is in the dry West. (*Courtesy of Association of American Railroads.*)

the highly industrialized northeastern part of the country from southern New England to Illinois the comparable figure is 1 mile for each 4.6 square miles, or ten times that density. Over the Middle West and the "old" South the ratio is 1 to 10. There is a remarkable thinning out of the rail net west of the 20-in. rainfall line, where agriculture is relatively unimportant and industries little developed (Fig. 29.7).

Over eastern United States the *pattern* of rail lines is that of a closely woven net. Within the general net there are a number of focal points toward which there is a general convergence of lines. Chief among these are Chicago and Winnipeg. In both cases natural barriers or unproductive land tend to direct rail lines toward these cities. The Great Lakes and the unproductive cutover land around the Upper Lakes prevent American rail lines from taking the shortest route eastward and force them southward through Chicago at the southern end of the barrier. Winnipeg likewise has a lake barrier and unproductive land on the north, which tend to direct rail traffic through that center. Atlanta at the southern end of the Blue Ridge barrier shows a similar pattern. Great ports such as Montreal, New York, and San Francisco are important focal points for local rail nets. Such a natural gateway as the Mohawk Valley across the eastern highlands is a convergence point for several rail lines.

West of the 20-in. rainfall line the rail net disappears, and from there westward to the Pacific Coast states the single strands of the 10 great transcontinental lines with their few feeders are conspicuous. In this section passenger traffic is relatively more important than in eastern United States, and freight less so, for the bulk of the intercoastal freight goes by boat via the Panama Canal. Canadian rail lines are crowded close to the southern margins of the country by the unproductive nature of much of northern Canada.

29.20 *European Railroads.* Whereas in North America railroad building was contemporaneous with the settlement of the country, in Europe it followed the settlement. This con-

trast is reflected in the rail patterns of the two regions, that of Europe being much more perfectly radial with respect to major trade centers (Fig. 29.8). Such great cities as London, Vienna, Paris, Berlin, Munich, and Moscow were already in existence at the beginning of the railroad era so that the rail lines were built with respect to these centers and the resulting patterns were definitely shaped by them.

This radial pattern in Europe has been fostered by another consideration, *viz.*, that of military effectiveness. Europe, made up of numerous independent countries of small size with the problem of national defense a major item, has a series of national railway systems, each system being a unit by itself. Less attention has been paid to the development of a unit system for the continent as a whole, involving international connections and transcontinental lines. Every effort was made to link the capital city and other strategic centers with the international boundaries so that troop movements to the borders could be facilitated in times of national danger. Many of Europe's railroads have been built with military rather than commercial use as the chief consideration.

The major transcontinental rail lines in Europe are the Paris-Berlin-Moscow route, the Paris-Milan-Brindisi route, and the Berlin-Vienna-Istanbul route. All these can be thought of as including London, although there is an obvious break at the English Channel. Relief characteristics of Europe are on the whole favorable to the development of rail lines, in spite of its numerous highlands. Through the highland rim of Bohemia the Elbe River has cut a famous gateway, the Saxon or Elbe Gate, that allows easy access from northwestern Europe to the Danube countries. At the western end of the Transylvanian Alps the Danube has cut the equally famous Iron Gate, which is an easy pass between central and southeastern Europe. By way of the Rhône-Saône depression western Europe finds easy access to the Mediterranean, while the lofty Alps are crossed by a series of low passes with easy approaches. Railroad ferries provide continuous rail routes between the Scandinavian countries and the German and Danish ports.

There are marked contrasts in the densities of the rail net in different parts of Europe. The highest densities per unit area for the entire world are found in western Europe. Belgium leads with 1 mile for each 3.9 square miles, but 11 other countries have densities greater than that of the United States. In southern and east-ern Europe and in Scandinavia, regions of fewer people and less industrialization, the density is much lower than in western Europe.

29.21 *Railroads on the Other Continents.* The life of Asia is concentrated along its eastern and southern margins, and its chief railroad mileage is there as well. India has by far the largest amount of track, followed in turn by Japan and China. The rail net however is

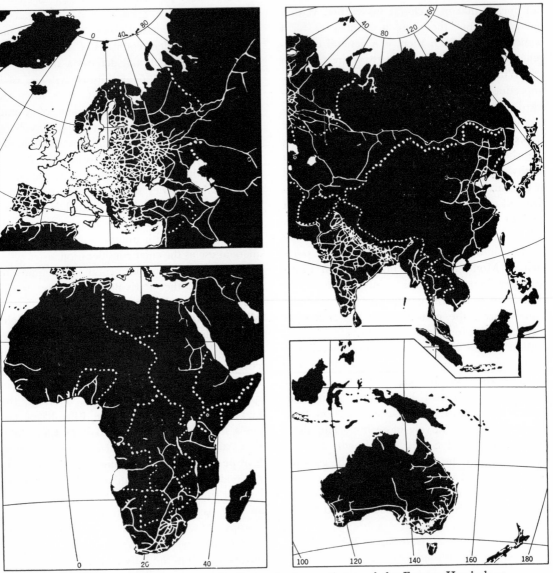

Fig. 29.8 Density and pattern of rail nets in the continents of the Eastern Hemisphere. (*Slightly modified from maps by Mark Jefferson.*)

densest in Japan, which has a length of line per 1,000 square miles just slightly higher than that for the United States. Each of the national railway systems in Asia is something of a unit within itself and has few connections with the others. Dry and high Central Asia is largely without rail lines, the most significant ones being those built by the Russians into Russian Turkistan and by the Chinese into Outer Mongolia and westward from Lanchow. Across Siberia reaches the long thin lines of the Trans-Siberian connecting the Pacific coast with European Russia.

African railroads are for the most part single short lines extending back at right angles from the coast for a greater or shorter distance into the interior. Between these isolated lines there are no connections, for the sea is the highway. Only in French Mediterranean Africa and the Union of South Africa are there any semblances of what could be called rail nets. The most notable route of the continent is that designated as the Cape-to-Cairo route, with railroads providing the means of transport over two-thirds of the length and boats and motorcars the remainder.

In Australia, the railroads follow the concentration of population and economic life along the eastern and southern margins. Genuine rail nets occur only in the southeast and the southwest. The dry deep interior is without through railroads. A number of short lines extend back at right angles from the east and south coasts into the inland semiarid sheep, cattle, and wheat country. These end abruptly on the edge of the desert where the grazing industry is limited by drought. A long, thin transcontinental southern line with few feeders connects the humid regions of the southeast and southwest.

Throughout most of tropical South America railroads are largely absent, the few that do exist being short isolated lines at right angles to the seacoast. In this part of South America the sea is almost the only highway connecting the principal centers of development, which are along the margins of the continent. The intervening lands are barrier areas rather than connections. Around the estuary of the La Plata River in Argentina and Uruguay and in the coffee region of Brazil are the greatest areas of rail development. On the flat Argentine Pampa a fanlike pattern of rail lines, with its principal focus at Buenos Aires, is very conspicuous. West of the Andes a single longitudinal rail line extends from southern Chile to Peru and is connected by numerous laterals with the seaboard. Connection is made between the Argentine rail net and the Pacific Coast in Chile and Peru by three trans-Andean lines.

29.22 Pipe Lines. Fluid commodities, almost solely water, gas, crude oil, and gasoline, are the only ones moving by pipe-line transportation (Fig. 29.9). Nearly three-quarters of the crude oil received at refineries is transported by pipe lines. Because of the very widespread character of gasoline consumption, the percentage of that freight moving by pipe is much less. Pipe-line transport of crude oil is more economical than any other overland type, being only one-quarter to one-half the rail rate. It is more expensive than movement by tanker, however. The operation of a pipe line is simple, and maintenance costs are low. The right-of-way expense is also low for the pipes are buried and the route is in rural areas for the most part.

WATER TRANSPORTATION AND THE MERCHANT MARINE

29.23 Advantages and Disadvantages of Water Transportation. The outstanding advantage of water transportation is the relatively small amount of power necessary to move bulky, heavy loads, provided that the speed of movement required is low. The capital and maintenance costs are also lower on waterways and their carriers. The net result is to make transportation by water unusually cheap. Thus, the cost of shipping iron ore nearly 1,000 miles from the western end of Lake Superior to the Lake Erie ports is less than the charge on rail shipment of this freight from Cleveland to the smelters in western Pennsylvania, a distance somewhat more than one-tenth as great. More freight can be moved by a single tow of barges propelled by one ordinary tug than can be moved by several freight trains. The cost of

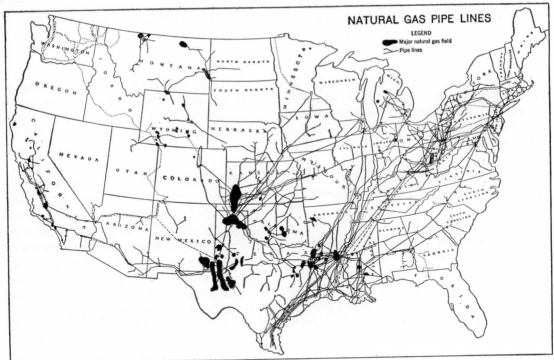

Fig. 29.9 (*Redrawn from map in Oil and Gas Journal.*)

Fig. 29.10

transportation on rivers and canals is higher than on oceans or on the American Great Lakes, but considerably lower than railroad charges. It should be borne in mind, however, that on numerous waterways improved and maintained by the government at public expense, the apparent low costs of water transport are not real costs.

The disadvantages of water transport are associated with the slower speeds maintained by boats and the inability of waterways to reach most parts of any trade region. At high speeds the friction of the water is excessive, and fuel costs rise exorbitantly. Rivers are usually winding, and on canals the locks greatly slow up the movement of boats. In the higher latitudes with severe winters, inland waterways are closed by ice during several months of the year.

29.24 Inland Navigation. The principal handicap of rivers as routes of transport is that their courses are fixed and therefore the river trade route lacks the flexibility of a land or ocean route (Fig. 29.10). The course of a river can be altered only to a minor degree. It has often been pointed out that the Mississippi would be much more useful as a trade route if its course were east-west, which is the direction of our principal trade movement, rather than north-south. In densely populated industrial regions such as western Europe, rivers and canals are used to a much greater degree than they are in the United States. This probably reflects the need for every possible trade route that can be developed.

The relative merits of rail versus river-canal transport have been vigorously debated by students of transportation. Some assert that, if the costs of river improvement and canal construction were paid for by the traffic using these routes, instead of by the government, water rates would be as high as rail. Canals are distinctly best suited to short hauls and therefore to regions of dense population. They are not profitable on long hauls. Where waterways parallel rail lines, their very presence has the ben-

Fig. 29.11 Barge transport on the Ohio River. A single tugboat is shown moving several barges loaded mainly with steel products. (*Courtesy of U.S. Army Engineers.*)

efit of holding rail rates to a lower level than they would be if the competing water route did not exist. It is significant that, as the rail net in eastern and central United States was expanded and the efficiency of the railroads increased, practically all American waterways except the Great Lakes fell into disuse. Only in recent years have such major interior waterways as the Ohio and Mississippi Rivers and the New York Barge Canal shown evidences of a trade revival (Fig. 29.11).

29.25 *The American Great Lakes* form the greatest interior water route of the world. The great urge to build the Erie Canal was the prospect of connecting the Atlantic Coast by an all-water route with the Great Lakes and therefore the heart of the continent. The particular advantage of the Great Lakes is their depth, which permits the use of relatively deep-draft ships with great carrying capacity. The fact

that the lakes are aligned in an east-west direction paralleling the flow of trade is likewise of major significance. Moreover, close to their shores are some of the largest wheat-, iron-ore-, and coal-producing areas of the continent, which provide ideal bulk cargo for lake shipment (Fig. 29.12). They connect the grain- and iron-producing regions of the Middle West with the industrial coal-producing East. Unfortunately falls and rapids in the St. Marys River connecting Lakes Superior and Huron, Niagara Falls between Lakes Erie and Ontario, and a series of rapids and falls in the upper St. Lawrence early handicapped the use of the lakes as a through route. By canals at the St. Marys River and dredging of the connections between Lakes Huron and Erie a 20-ft. channel is provided as far as Buffalo at the eastern end of Lake Erie. The Welland Canal connecting Lakes Erie and Ontario around Niag-

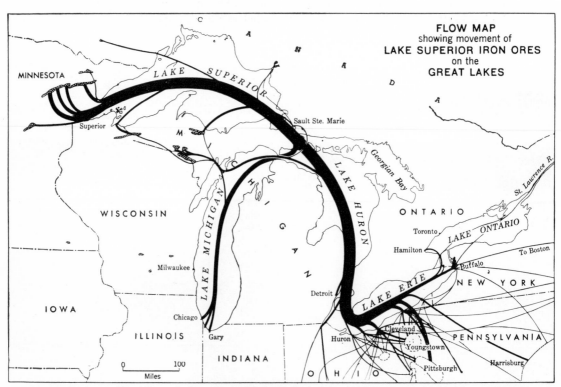

Fig. 29.12 The Great Lakes carry chiefly bulk freight, with iron ore and grain moving eastward and coal furnishing much of the return cargo. (*From map by Lake Superior Iron Ore Association.*)

Fig. 29.13 A bulk-cargo carrier on the Great Lakes. In the above photograph the freighter is loading iron ore. Its capacity is about 14,000 tons and it can be loaded by this inexpensive gravity method in approximately 3 hr. (*Courtesy of Duluth Chamber of Commerce.*)

ara Falls is 30 ft. deep, but the canals on the St. Lawrence are only 14 ft. deep so that only seagoing vessels having less than that draft can enter the Great Lakes. The new St. Lawrence Waterway will provide canals that are 27 ft. deep on the St. Lawrence, which will permit relatively large ocean freighters to enter the lake ports.

The principal cargo carried on the Great Lakes is grain, iron ore, and lumber on the eastward trip and coal from the Pennsylvania field loaded at Lake Erie ports moving westward (Fig. 29.13). These are all bulk cargoes particularly suited to shipment by boat. Unfortunately, because of ice, this greatest of all interior waterways is practically useless during the colder months of the year. During this season the rail lines must carry all the freight. But in spite of that handicap the tons of traffic through the St. Clair River leading into Lake Erie is in many years greater than the combined freight passing through the Panama and Suez Canals. Along the shores of the Great Lakes are the greatest populations, the greatest concentration of rail lines, and the principal manufacturing centers of interior North America. The route is like a great magnet drawing to it population, railroads, and industry.

Ocean Trade and Its Carriers

29.26 The Ocean Highway. It has been said that the nation that does not front upon an ocean is like a house that is not upon a street. This is because the oceans form a world highway that belongs exclusively to no one, reaches everywhere, and can be used by each and all that possess a bit of its shore. Here nature furnishes the roadway and there are no construction costs, no taxes, no upkeep. Costly improvements in the right of way in the form of surveying, dredging, and marking are necessary only in restricted bays, rivers, and the harbors of some of the terminal trade centers. Port cities are so eager to engage in world trade that they provide facilities for docking, loading and unloading, and for taking on fuel at comparatively small expense to the ship. This, together with free use of the ocean highway, helps account for the cheapness of ocean transportation.

"Freedom of the Seas" has been one of the historic principles of the American nation. Of recent years the right to navigate on open ocean has not been challenged, except in time of war, but this right accomplishes little unless a ship may reach a port and there transact business. And since a nation may restrict terminal areas by enforcing restrictions over that part of the ocean within 3 miles of its coasts, and by preventing foreign nations from engaging in coastwise trade, something less than actual freedom of the seas really exists.

Ocean Trade Routes

29.27 The Nature of Ocean Routes. There was a time, and not so long ago, when oceans were looked upon as barriers separating continents. At the present time they are thought of as the highways *connecting* the continents. The ocean route in general is much less rigid than a land route, for there is no fixed track over

which a ship must travel. The route belongs to no one; it is the common property of all men in times of peace. A ship with a cargo of wheat for Antwerp may be directed by radio in mid-ocean to land instead at Marseille without the captain's needing to ask permission of anyone to use the new right of way.

But, although the oceans are open highways to be traversed by ships in any and all directions, in reality most ocean trade is in ships that follow certain general avenues which approach definite routes. The seafaring nations have plotted on navigation charts the best routes between certain trade regions or centers. These routes are established after taking into consideration such items as sailing distances, wind and storm conditions, ocean currents, cargo possibilities, fog, ice, and fueling stations. An ocean trade route, therefore, is an avenue along which, because of one or more of the foregoing reasons, the tracks of numerous ships converge or coincide for a part of their ways. Such a trade route usually consists of (*a*) a central belt or trunk, and (*b*) the several branches that feed into this trunk from numerous trade centers at either end (see Fig. 29.14). Other things being equal the best or cheapest route

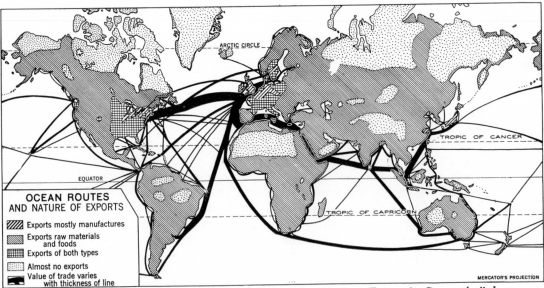

Fig. 29.14 (*From Klimm, Starkey, and Hall, "Introductory Economic Geography," by permission of Harcourt, Brace and Company, Inc.*)

is the shortest route, which on a spherical earth is a great circle. Other factors, however, usually cause some deviation from the true great-circle course.

29.28 *The North Atlantic route* connecting eastern North America and western Europe is the most used of any. This top rank is not unusual when one considers that the regions connected are two of the most populous and highly developed regions of the earth. Passengers and freight traffic originate where people are located, more especially where there are relatively large populations with high standards of living. In North America and western Europe are to be found the world's greatest producers of surpluses of goods of great diversity which are the basis for trade.

The trunk of this route is in the form of a broad northward-curving band running in a northeast-southwest direction roughly between latitudes 40 and 50°. Owing chiefly to the hazard of icebergs at certain seasons, the route is farther north in winter than in summer. Its feeders reach from Labrador to Panama on the west and from Norway to Spain on the east. An unusually high proportion of the world's great ports serve the route as terminals. In both volume and variety of cargo this route far exceeds any other, one-fifth of the shipping of the world being required to serve it.

29.29 *The Mediterranean-Asiatic route* connects the whole North Atlantic region with southeastern Asia and Australia by way of the Mediterranean Sea, Suez Canal, and the Red Sea. Its importance dates from 1869, with the opening of the Suez Canal. Unlike the North Atlantic route this one throughout much of its course follows relatively constricted waterways which jeopardizes its utility in time of war. It is of principal importance to the European countries, particularly Great Britain, for it is the short route connecting them with former colonies and members of the Commonwealth in the Far East and the Pacific. In the Second World War one of the chief objectives of the Axis powers was the Suez Canal and the halting of the flow of goods and men through it to and from England. The fre-

quency of ports along this route provides excellent opportunities for trade of the short-haul type.

29.30 Other Routes. *The South African route* connects the same regions as the Mediterranean route so that it in reality is an alternate to the latter. It is 4,000 miles farther from Liverpool to Calcutta by way of South Africa than by Suez, but many ships take the longer route to avoid the canal tolls.

29.31 *The South American east coast route* connects both sides of the North Atlantic with eastern South America. Because Brazil projects so far eastward into the Atlantic, American ships traveling to eastern South America are forced to make nearly as long a trip as those from western Europe. Under normal conditions the exchange of eastern South America is heavier with Europe than with the United States, with the products of farm, plantation, and range moving north to Europe and manufactured goods south to South America.

At the *Panama Canal* are focused routes (*a*) between the east and west coasts of the United States, (*b*) between either side of the North Atlantic and the west coast of South America, and (*c*) between eastern United States and eastern Asia and Australia. The opening of the canal has eliminated the long trip around Cape Horn together with the dangers associated with navigating those waters. Greatest benefits have accrued to American intercoastal trade and to that of North Atlantic countries with the west coast of South America. From a military standpoint the canal is of utmost importance to the United States since it allows a rapid transfer of the fleet to that ocean where the greatest threat lies. It may be pointed out how fortunate for ocean navigation it is that the land barriers were so narrow at two points on the earth, Suez and Panama, that canals could be cut through, thereby permitting a continuous water route in easily navigable latitudes.

29.32 *The North Pacific trade routes* connect chiefly western North America with eastern Asia. Two principal routes are recognized: (*a*) a shorter northern great-circle route which swings northward almost to the Aleutian Islands and (*b*) a longer southern route which connects the two continents by way of the Hawaiian Islands. This group of islands, the "crossroads of the Pacific," is a converging point for a number of routes including those between Australia and Pacific North America, and Panama Canal and Asia. The amount of trade moving along the Pacific routes is far less than that in the Atlantic, for the former routes connect a region of small population with one in which, although the population is large, the demands for foreign goods are small.

Ocean Carriers

29.33   An additional reason, other than that the right of way is furnished by nature, why ocean transportation is cheaper than land transportation is that the capital invested in the ocean freighter per ton of freight carried is less than in any form of land carrier. Other costs such as insurance, labor, terminal charges, and power per unit of freight volume and weight are also less.

29.34   Ship Service: Liner and Tramp. Ocean carriers are of two kinds, line ships and tramp ships. Liners ply back and forth across oceans on a regular time schedule and between specified ports. Generally they carry both passengers and freight, but the latter is usually of small bulk and composed of numerous packages which have a high unit value and can stand a high freight rate. Some liners, particularly the larger and finer ones, specialize in passenger traffic. These ships emphasize speed and promptness of arrival. They sail on schedule no matter what load is available. Other liners put greater emphasis on freight and the passenger service is auxiliary.

Most of the world's freight, however, is carried, not on sleek line ships, but on slower, blockier little "tramps," which go where cargo is available and are unrestricted by time schedules. Their movements are uncertain, and as they leave the home port they may not return for a year or several years. They go to the far corners of the earth, picking up and discharging cargo as they can find it. Less beautiful, slower, and many times ungraceful, the tramp steamer does the heavy and dirty work in ocean transport, yet its earnings are often more substantial than the liner's.

29.35   Merchant Fleets of the World. The Second World War had the effect of reshuffling the rankings of the merchant fleets of the maritime countries. As of about 1939 Britain's merchant tonnage far exceeded that of any other nation, with that of the United States second, followed in turn by Japan, Norway, Germany, Italy, and the Netherlands. Military requirements compelled a rapid expansion of the American merchant fleet during the Second World War so that throughout the postwar period the United States has continued to hold first rank by a wide margin. Britain is in second position and well below her are Norway, Italy, France, Japan, and the Netherlands in that order (Fig. 29.15).

AIR TRANSPORTATION

29.36   Possibilities and Limitations. Air transport is a development of the past few decades and is still so recent that it has some aspects of the novel about it. The particular asset of air transport is its speed; the handicap, its inability to carry heavy loads of bulk cargo. Thus, at the present time, air transport is chiefly employed in carrying passengers. In addition to mail, only a modest amount of miscellaneous light package express freight is carried. Nevertheless, American airline companies for the first time in 1946 began to pay serious attention to improving air-freight service. Rates

LEADING MERCHANT FLEETS
JAN. 1955

0 2 4 6 8 10 12 14 16 18 20 22 24 26
Millions of gross tons

Fig. 29.15

were reduced, simplified rate structures were put into effect, and specially equipped all-cargo planes were put into operation. Measured in ton-miles the world's air traffic in 1953 was divided as follows: 76 per cent passengers, 19 per cent cargo, and 5 per cent mail.

As in the case of ocean routes, air routes are not rigidly confined and restricted. Yet for the sake of safety and ease of navigation air routes do follow rather closely certain ground marks such as rivers or cities and, at night, lighted beacons. Unlike early rail, motor, and water transport, air transport specializes not in local, but in long-distance carrying. This means that even in those parts of the world where air transport is best developed, such as western Europe and the United States, many trade centers are not served by an air service. On the other hand, air service connects some of the most out-of-the-way places of the earth, preceding rail and motor services into such regions as interior tropical South America and Africa, and subarctic Canada. There are now few substantial centers of population on the earth that cannot be reached by the present air service. On the other hand, there are many pairs of

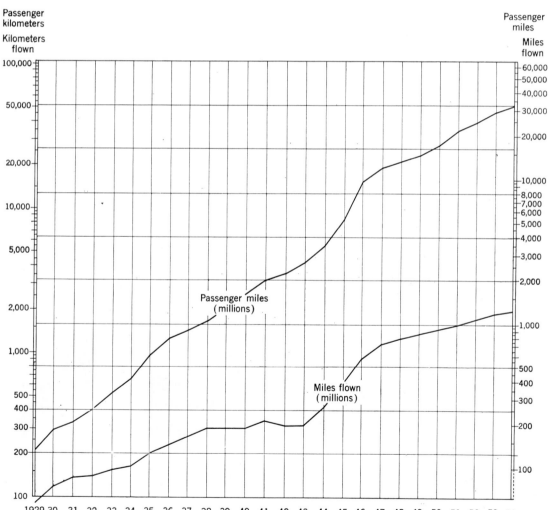

Fig. 29.16 Illustrating the very rapid growth of the earth's air transportation during the past few decades. (*Courtesy of International Civil Aviation Organization.*)

cities between which direct air service is still lacking.

Almost immediately following the Second World War international and overseas commercial air service was reestablished, and by late 1946 the world's international routes exceeded 300,000 miles, more than twice the prewar mileage.

World Air Traffic (Exclusive of U.S.S.R. and China)
(In thousands)

	International and Domestic		International	
Year	Miles Flown	Passenger Miles	Miles Flown	Passenger Miles
1953	1,179,000	28,580,000	397,000	9,719,000
1950	890,000	16,960,000	321,000	6,107,000
1946	585,000	9,601,000	147,000	2,592,000

Since 1946 there has been a steady increase in passenger traffic amounting to about 16 per cent a year up to 1954 (Fig. 29.16). The annual rate of air-freight and air-mail increase was two to five times that of passenger traffic between 1947 and 1950 but from 1950 to 1953 the increase was only half as great. Some 52,-000,000 passengers were transported by plane in 1953, a figure the magnitude of which suggests that both railroads and ships are feeling the competition. For example, 510,000 passengers crossed the Atlantic by air in 1953 as compared with an estimated 900,000 by sea. In the United States domestic air lines flew more than 14.5 billion passenger miles as against 8 billion for rail-pullman travel.

Among the commercial air services of the several nations that of the United States provides the most complete and extensive service. About three-fifths of all air passengers were carried by United States lines in 1953. In 1954 American commercial air carriers had 1,400 planes flying over 184,000 miles of air ways providing a lift capacity greater than that of the rest of the world combined.

Terminals

29.37 *Nature of Terminals.* A terminal is a focal point where freight and passengers are collected and distributed. It usually marks a change in means of conveyance requiring tran-

shipment, rather than a cessation of movement. If people or commodities are to be transported by carriers over routes, it becomes clear that the items to be moved must be concentrated at certain focal points. If this concentration did not take place, a separate branch line of the route would have to connect each producer with his market. Such a system of transportation is unthinkable. As it is, trunk lines of transportation usually connect important terminal sites where goods and people are collected and distributed. Branch lines have terminals of lesser importance. In such terminal centers facilities for loading, unloading, storage, and many other kinds of activities and services are provided. As pointed out in an earlier chapter, these terminal functions are the most common reason for the origin and growth of cities.

The location, organization, and operation of terminals have a very direct bearing on the

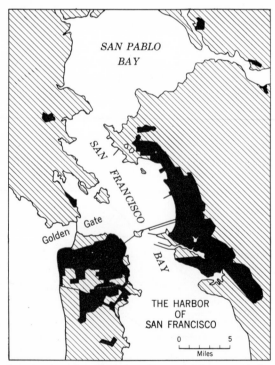

Fig. 29.17 San Francisco Bay provides one of the world's finest natural harbors. The entrance is narrow so that the harbor is a sheltered one, and the waters of the Bay are both extensive and deep.

Fig. 29.18 The Hudson River piers from the New Jersey side of the river. Skyline of New York City in the background. (*Courtesy of Port of New York Authority.*)

efficiency with which freight and passengers can be moved. Since local traffic moving to and from the terminal must use the city streets, it is obvious that the urban location of a terminal greatly affects its efficiency. Terminals should be a part of the integrated plan of city development, but unfortunately in many cities they have grown without plan. Of the several elements comprising the transportation complex, terminal facilities are the most neglected part. Many are badly located. Others are antiquated or they function inefficiently because of lack of unification or coordination. One of the major problems of transportation today is the modernization of terminal facilities.

29.38 Water-route Terminals—Ports and Their Facilities. Ports do not grow and prosper merely because they are on the coast, but because they are important gateways of trade where transfer of freight and passengers is made between water and land carriers. This ability to attract trade reflects certain physical and economic advantages. Among them are (*a*) a good natural harbor, (*b*) a large productive and consuming hinterland, (*c*) easy access to the hinterland, (*d*) location on or close to one or more of the main world trade routes,

and (*e*) efficient terminal facilities for handling freight and passengers. An ideal harbor is a coastal indentation safe for navigation where a ship is protected against storm waves. The term harbor has nothing to do with trade; it is simply a place of refuge. The ideal harbor is bottle shaped with an entrance wide and deep enough to accommodate traffic but narrow enough so that storm waves cannot enter (Fig. 29.17). A good harbor likewise requires ample depth of water, spaciousness, an extensive water front for pier space, freedom from ice, and small tidal range.

There are hundreds of good harbors that have no trade, and this is due either to the lack of a producing or consuming hinterland, or the absence of easy access to it. The number of high-grade harbors along such indented coasts as those of western Canada and Alaska, southern Chile, or Norway illustrates the point in question. In all these regions the hinterlands are relatively unproductive and meagerly populated so that there is little surplus to export, and import requirements are meager.

The effect of relative ease of access to a hinterland is well illustrated in the case of our Atlantic Seaboard ports. By way of the water-level route of the Hudson and Mowhawk val- leys New York has an easier natural route to the Middle West than Boston, Philadelphia, or Baltimore. By means of the Erie Canal, which followed the Mohawk Valley, New York was early provided with a water route to its hinter- land which did much to establish the early pre- eminence of that port. The gap formed by the Columbia River through the Cascades provides Portland with easier access to the interior than its rival Seattle.

A port located on a main route of trade has a far greater chance for growth than one not so located. Ships are not attracted to isolated ports well removed from the main lines of traffic, whereas, on the other hand, trade cen- ters with fewer advantages may become impor- tant ports of call when they are so located that numerous ships pass their doors.

Terminal facilities for ships include a great variety of structures and services. In the larger ports with deep harbors, ships are able to anchor alongside piers most of which are roofed so that they resemble long sheds (Figs. 29.18 and 29.19). In ports where the water is shallower, ships may be obliged to anchor in the harbor and discharge and load cargo from small boats called lighters. Anchor buoys, lighters, tugs, and pilot service are all elements of the terminal facilities. On the pier (quay or wharf) there is machinery in the form of cranes for loading and unloading, storage facil- ities for freight, trackage space for railroad cars, accommodations for trucks, and facilities for taking on fuel. Bulk cargo such as iron ore and coal requires more specialized equipment and facilities. The last few decades have seen marked competition on the part of ports for providing modern and efficient equipment for handling cargo and the quick dispatch of ships. Realizing the part that mechanical facilities play in attracting commerce, trade centers have given this feature much publicity in their ad- vertising.

29.39 *Types of Ocean Ports and Their Services.* Most ports lie at the ends of trans-

Fig. 29.19 The port of Mobile, Ala. (*Courtesy of Alabama State Department of Docks and Terminals.*)

Fig. 29.20 Railroad freight terminal at St. Louis, Mo. (*Photograph by Lloyd Spainhower, St. Louis Post Dispatch.*)

oceanic trade routes, and they function therefore as *terminal ports*. Ships enter them to discharge cargoes that are definitely assigned to that particular port and the hinterland that it serves. New York, for example, is primarily a terminal port. There are other ports, however, whose function is more largely that of a middleman between other ports. These are called *entrepôt ports*, or, as the name suggests, "between ports"—ports for other ports. At the entrepôt, warehousing and processing may occur before reshipment. Singapore is an important entrepôt port in southeastern Asia, acting as the middleman for the world's most important source of tropical raw materials. Hongkong serves in a similar capacity. Before the last war London received cargoes from the far corners of the earth, and from there these

cargoes were distributed in smaller amounts to other ports in northwestern Europe and beyond. Somewhat different is the function of the *free port*, which permits ships to unload their cargoes within a fenced-off "free zone," where they are sorted, perhaps processed, or warehoused without payment of duty. Here the goods may be sold and reloaded on other ships. Payment of duty occurs only when the goods pass from the "free zone" into the city. The advantage of this free-port function is that the middleman transaction involves no customs charge and that fee is paid only once, *viz.*, when the goods enter the country of their final destination.

29.40 Terminals for Land Carriers. Railroad terminals are conspicuous features of most occidental cities. Passenger stations, freight warehouses, switching and storage tracks, classification yards, loading and unloading equipment, and facilities for servicing and repairing locomotives and cars are some of the elements which in combination characterize a railroad terminal (Fig. 29.20). The Chicago railroad terminal area, the largest in the world, shows the following data:

7,869 miles of track in the terminal district
5,183 miles of track in the switching district
4,000 industries and side tracks served by the switching district
700 engine crews
58,000 full-time employees
1,700 passenger trains handled daily
45,000 freight cars handled daily by switching district
125,000,000 passengers handled in a recent year

Motor vehicle terminals are of two kinds: (*a*) those serving motor trucks whose loads are chiefly freight and (*b*) those serving passengers busses. The latter are usually inadequate but they are improving. The function of the motor-truck terminal is to concentrate merchandise freight into truck-load lots going to the same destination. Here small lots are concentrated by local trucks and transferred to line-haul vehicles. Air-line terminals handle chiefly passengers, mail, and luggage. All air fields have terminals and these of necessity are well removed from the heart of the city. Some larger cities also have downtown terminals where plane passengers assemble for transfer to the air field by motorbus.

References for Chapter 29

Berglund, Abraham. "Ocean Transportation." Longmans, Green & Co., Inc., New York, 1931.

Bigham, Truman C., and Merrill T. Roberts. "Transportation." 2d ed. McGraw-Hill Book Company, Inc., New York, 1952.

Clowes, Ernest S. "Shipways to the Sea." The Williams & Wilkins Company, Baltimore, 1929.

Condliffe, J. B. "The Commerce of Nations." W. W. Norton & Company, New York, 1950.

Daggett, Stuart. "Principles of Inland Transportation." 4th ed. Harper & Brothers, New York, 1955.

"Foreign Commerce Yearbook." Bureau of Foreign and Domestic Commerce (annual).

Frederick, John H. "Commercial Air Transportation." Rev. ed. Richard D. Irwin, Inc., Homewood, Ill., 1946.

Jefferson, Mark. The Civilizing Rails. *Econ. Geog.*, Vol. 4, pp. 217–231, 1928.

Johnson, Emory R., Grover G. Huebner, and G. Lloyd Wilson. "Transportation: Economic Principles and Practices." Appleton-Century-Crofts, Inc., New York, 1940.

Killough, Hugh B., and Lucy W. Killough. "Economics of International Trade." 2d ed. McGraw-Hill Book Company, Inc., New York, 1948.

Landon, Charles E. "Transportation; Principles, Practices, Problems." William Sloane Associates, New York, 1951.

Locklin, D. Philip. "Economics of Transportation." 3d ed. Richard D. Irwin, Inc., Homewood, Ill., 1947.

Long, W. R. "Railway and Highway Transportation Abroad: A Study of Existing Relationships, Recent Competitive Measures and Coordination Policies." U.S. Department of Commerce, Trade Promotion Series, 155, 1935.

Sargent, A. J. "Seaports and Hinterlands." A. & C. Black, Ltd., London, 1938.

Stamp, L. Dudley. "Chisholm's Handbook of Commercial Geography." Longmans, Green & Co., Inc., New York, 1937.

Ullman, Edward L. The Railroad Pattern of the United States. *Geog. Rev.*, Vol. 39, pp. 242–256, 1949.

Van Cleef, Eugene. "Trade Centers and Trade Routes." Appleton-Century-Crofts, Inc., New York, 1937.

PART FOUR

Appendices

Supplementary Climatic Data for Selected Stations

(T., temperature in degrees Fahrenheit; Rf., rainfall in inches)

Tropical Wet (Rainforest)

	Jan.	Feb.	Mar.	Apr.	May	June	July	Aug.	Sept.	Oct.	Nov.	Dec.	Year
1. T.	81	81	81	79	79	78	77	78	78	79	80	81	79.3
Rf.	5.6	4.5	5.4	10.9	20.5	23.9	23.2	16.0	9.1	6.9	4.1	5.7	135.8
2. T.	79	80	79	80	80	79	79	79	79	79	79	79	79
Rf.	13.5	9.9	11.9	14.0	12.6	13.0	11.8	13.7	16.1	20.0	20.7	19.4	177.6
3. T.	81	81	81	80	80	80	80	80	80	81	81	81	81
Rf.	11.5	11.9	17.9	14.0	19.8	15.8	15.5	13.8	13.6	11.4	14.0	17.3	176.5
4. T.	78	79	80	80	79	77	76	76	76	77	78	79	78
Rf.	2.6	6.5	10.0	8.6	17.0	18.6	10.1	9.3	19.3	24.7	10.6	6.5	143.8
5. T.	78	78	76	77	76	74	74	76	76	77	78	78	77
Rf.	10.2	9.8	12.2	6.5	10.0	7.4	6.6	4.6	8.7	7.2	8.4	11.5	103.1
6. T.	75	75	76	78	79	78	78	78	78	78	78	76	77.3
Rf.	2.7	1.5	1.8	1.8	3.6	7.9	8.8	9.6	7.4	6.6	7.0	4.7	63.4
7. T.	80	80	82	83	83	82	81	81	81	81	80	80	81.0
Rf.	3.2	1.9	4.3	9.7	10.9	7.3	4.4	3.2	4.8	13.4	11.8	5.1	80.0
8. T.	80	80	80	81	81	80	80	80	80	80	80	79	80
Rf.	3.7	1.6	1.6	4.3	12.4	13.3	16.0	14.8	12.5	15.1	20.7	11.4	127.4
9. T.	80	80	80	80	80	80	81	82	83	83	82	81	81
Rf.	8.3	8.0	8.1	8.4	6.6	3.9	1.8	1.3	1.4	4.6	4.5	8.2	65.1
10. T.	77	79	84	87	84	81	80	80	81	82	80	77	81
Rf.	0.2	0.2	0.3	1.4	12.1	18.4	21.5	19.7	15.4	7.3	2.8	0.3	99.6
11. T.	78	78	79	80	80	79	79	79	80	80	79	79	79
Rf.	13.0	12.8	7.8	5.1	4.0	3.7	2.6	1.7	2.9	4.5	5.5	8.5	72.1
12. T.	81	82	82	82	82	80	79	78	79	80	81	81	80.7
Rf.	0.4	0.3	1.2	4.1	11.5	20.0	35.6	36.6	28.5	12.6	5.1	1.4	157.3

Tropical Wet-and-Dry (Savanna)

	Jan.	Feb.	Mar.	Apr.	May	June	July	Aug.	Sept.	Oct.	Nov.	Dec.	Year
13. T.	79	81	84	86	84	82	82	82	82	81	80	79	81.7
Rf.	0.9	0.1	0.3	1.7	8.3	12.6	11.1	11.0	13.3	11.1	3.7	3.1	77.2
14. T.	76	78	81	85	90	90	88	86	85	82	79	77	83.1
Rf.	1.1	0.3	0.3	0.6	1.8	2.0	3.8	4.5	4.8	11.1	13.6	5.3	49.2
15. T.	71	71	71	73	75	77	78	78	78	77	75	72	75
Rf.	3.7	4.3	3.8	2.3	1.9	1.1	1.3	1.5	1.5	1.9	4.2	4.1	31.6
16. T.	77	77	77	78	80	81	82	82	82	81	79	78	79
Rf.	1.0	0.6	1.0	1.2	4.3	4.1	1.7	3.7	4.1	7.5	3.1	1.0	33.9
17. T.	80	82	83	81	79	77	76	76	77	78	79	79	79
Rf.	0.1	0.8	1.5	4.2	5.4	4.6	5.2	5.8	4.9	4.3	1.8	0.3	38.9
18. T.	70	75	83	90	89	87	87	86	85	83	76	71	82
Rf.	0.1	0.1	0.2	1.1	5.8	5.5	3.3	4.6	5.7	4.7	1.6	0.4	35.1
19. T.	76	76	80	83	86	84	81	81	81	82	81	77	81
Rf.	0.1	0.1			0.7	19.9	24.0	14.5	10.6	1.9	0.4		72.4
20. T.	84	83	84	84	82	79	77	79	83	85	86	85	83
Rf.	15.9	12.9	10.1	4.1	0.7	0.1	0.1	0.1	0.5	2.2	4.8	10.3	61.8

Steppe

	Jan.	Feb.	Mar.	Apr.	May	June	July	Aug.	Sept.	Oct.	Nov.	Dec.	Year
21. T.	54	55	57	58	61	64	67	68	67	63	59	56	61
Rf.	1.8	1.9	1.5	0.6	0.3	0.1	0.1	0.1	0.1	0.4	0.9	1.8	9.6
22. T.	53	57	69	81	89	93	89	87	85	76	63	55	75
Rf.	0.9	1.0	0.8	0.5	0.7	1.4	5.1	4.7	2.3	0.3	0.1	0.4	18.1
23. T.	86	85	85	83	76	71	70	73	77	81	85	86	80
Rf.	6.2	6.1	3.8	1.4	0.6	1.0	0.2	0.2	0.1		0.9	3.7	24.2
24. T.	34	42	48	61	71	80	85	83	77	66	51	42	62
Rf.	1.6	1.0	1.9	1.4	0.5	0.1	0.2		0.1	0.3	1.0	1.3	9.3
25. T.	58	62	68	73	79	82	82	83	78	71	64	57	71.4
Rf.	0.5	0.5	0.7	1.1	1.2	2.3	2.1	2.0	4.4	2.4	1.3	1.0	19.5
26. T.	23	26	38	50	58	64	70	68	58	48	35	28	47
Rf.	1.0	0.8	0.3	0.4	0.9	1.2	1.1	1.1	0.8	0.6	1.0	0.9	10.1
27. T.	30	32	39	47	57	67	72	71	62	51	39	32	50
Rf.	0.4	0.5	1.0	2.1	2.4	1.4	1.8	1.4	1.0	1.0	0.6	0.7	14.3
28. T.	81	83	87	88	85	81	80	80	81	82	82	79	82
Rf.	0.0	0.2	0.2	1.1	3.1	5.4	5.9	7.1	4.3	2.8	0.6	0.0	30.6
29. T.	76	74	70	63	55	49	49	54	61	67	71	75	63.6
Rf.	2.8	3.1	3.0	1.3	0.9	0.3	0.4	0.4	0.7	1.0	1.7	2.4	18

Desert

	Jan.	Feb.	Mar.	Apr.	May	June	July	Aug.	Sept.	Oct.	Nov.	Dec.	Year
30. T.	52	55	59	67	69	77	82	85	76	70	62	54	67
Rf.	1.3	1.2	1.4	1.1	0.7	0.3	0.2		0.3	0.5	1.5	0.9	9.4
31. T.	61	61	63	64	65	67	68	68	69	68	65	62	65
Rf.	0.5	0.5	0.5					0.5	0.5	0.5	0.5	1.0	4.5
32. T.	55	57	63	70	76	80	82	82	78	74	65	58	70
Rf.	0.4	0.2	0.2	0.2							0.1	0.2	1.3
33. T.	49	54	61	71	81	90	95	94	88	80	63	53	73
Rf.	1.2	1.3	1.3	0.9	0.2					0.1	0.8	1.2	7.0
34. T.	65	68	75	81	85	87	84	82	82	80	74	67	78
Rf.	0.5	0.5	0.4	0.2	0.1	0.9	2.9	1.5	0.5		0.1	0.1	7.6
35. T.	60	60	59	58	57	55	55	54	55	58	59	60	58
Rf.		0.1	0.2	0.2	0.4	0.3	0.2	0.4	0.3		0.2	0.1	2.3
36. T.	84	82	77	68	60	54	52	58	66	74	80	82	70
Rf.	1.8	1.7	1.3	0.9	0.6	0.6	0.4	0.4	0.4	0.7	0.9	1.3	11.1
37. T.	73	75	81	81	93	93	90	88	89	89	82	75	84.0
Rf.	0	0	0	0	0.1	0.3	1.8	2.6	0.7	0.2	0	0	5.7
38. T.	19	21	32	48	64	73	77	74	63	50	37	26	49
Rf.	0.5	0.3	0.4	0.5	0.7	0.7	0.5	0.5	0.5	0.4	0.4	0.5	5.9

Dry-summer Subtropical (Mediterranean)

	Jan.	Feb.	Mar.	Apr.	May	June	July	Aug.	Sept.	Oct.	Nov.	Dec.	Year
39. T.	44	46	50	55	61	68	72	71	66	59	51	46	57
Rf.	1.7	1.4	1.9	2.2	1.7	1.1	0.7	0.8	2.4	3.8	2.8	2.1	22.6
40. T.	45	47	51	57	64	71	76	76	70	62	53	46	60
Rf.	3.2	2.7	2.9	2.6	2.2	1.6	0.7	1.0	2.5	5.0	4.4	3.9	32.7
41. T.	48	49	52	59	66	74	80	80	73	66	57	52	63
Rf.	2.0	1.7	1.2	0.9	0.8	0.7	0.3	0.5	0.6	1.6	2.6	2.6	15.5
42. T.	44	48	51	59	66	70	73	73	71	67	56	49	61
Rf.	6.2	4.6	3.5	1.5	0.3					0.4	2.5	5.7	24.7
43. T.	74	74	70	64	58	54	52	54	57	62	67	71	63
Rf.	0.7	0.7	1.0	1.8	2.8	3.1	2.7	2.5	2.0	1.7	1.2	1.0	21.2
44. T.	49	51	53	54	56	57	57	58	60	59	56	51	55
Rf.	4.8	3.6	3.1	1.0	0.7	0.1			0.3	1.0	2.4	4.6	22.2
45. T.	51	52	54	58	60	67	70	71	68	52	57	52	60
Rf.	3.6	3.5	3.4	2.6	2.0	0.8	0.2	0.2	1.4	3.3	4.3	4.1	29.4
46. T.	67	66	62	56	51	46	46	48	52	56	61	66	56
Rf.		0.1	0.2	0.6	2.6	3.2	3.2	2.1	1.2	0.5	0.3	0.2	14.2
47. T.	70	70	68	63	59	56	55	56	58	61	64	68	62
Rf.	0.7	0.6	0.9	1.9	3.8	4.5	3.7	3.4	2.3	1.6	1.1	0.8	25.3

Humid Subtropical

	Jan.	Feb.	Mar.	Apr.	May	June	July	Aug.	Sept.	Oct.	Nov.	Dec.	Year
48. T.	35	34	40	51	59	67	74	78	70	59	49	39	55
Rf.	7.7	4.9	4.1	4.2	3.7	5.2	6.2	5.2	7.4	5.7	7.2	9.1	70.6
49. T.	81	80	78	72	67	63	64	66	70	73	76	80	72
Rf.	5.5	5.1	4.3	5.2	4.6	2.7	2.2	1.6	3.1	5.5	5.9	6.2	50.9
50. T.	39	41	50	59	68	76	79	78	72	69	49	41	59
Rf.	4.8	4.2	5.1	4.4	3.8	4.2	4.1	3.5	3.5	2.4	3.5	3.9	47.4
51. T.	34	35	43	54	64	72	77	74	68	57	46	36	55
Rf.	3.2	3.0	3.5	3.3	3.6	3.9	4.4	4.0	3.1	3.1	2.5	3.1	40.7
52. T.	53	51	62	67	73	78	86	86	81	72	66	57	69
Rf.	3.1	2.5	4.8	5.3	4.6	6.0	4.3	8.7	3.0	1.3	0.8	1.3	45.7
53. T.	48	50	58	68	74	80	83	86	77	68	59	50	67
Rf.	0.7	0.9	1.3	4.0	5.3	6.7	5.3	4.4	5.8	4.6	2.0	0.9	41.9
54. T.	45	45	51	60	65	71	78	80	75	66	57	48	62
Rf.	3.5	3.3	6.1	9.1	9.6	13.9	11.2	7.4	8.7	5.1	3.7	3.5	85.1
55. T.	77	76	70	62	56	49	51	52	57	62	69	75	63
Rf.	3.7	3.2	5.3	3.1	1.8	1.5	1.0	1.5	1.6	3.5	3.4	5.3	34.9
56. T.	74	73	69	61	55	50	49	51	55	60	66	71	61
Rf.	3.1	2.7	4.4	3.5	2.9	2.5	2.2	2.5	3.0	3.5	3.1	3.9	37.3
57. T.	54	56	63	70	76	82	84	83	80	73	63	57	70
Rf.	3.4	3.0	2.9	3.1	3.4	4.2	4.0	4.7	5.7	4.3	3.9	3.7	46.3
58. T.	51	54	60	66	73	79	80	80	77	68	58	52	67
Rf.	4.7	5.2	6.4	4.9	4.4	5.4	7.0	7.1	5.3	3.5	3.7	4.9	62.5
59. T.	60	65	77	87	91	89	84	83	83	78	68	60	77
Rf.	0.7	0.6	0.4	0.2	0.6	4.8	12.1	11.6	7.1	2.1	0.2	0.2	64.3
60. T.	60	59	63	70	77	81	82	82	81	76	69	63	72
Rf.	1.3	1.8	2.7	5.3	12.0	15.8	14.0	14.6	9.7	5.1	1.7	1.1	85.1
61. T.	37	39	44	55	62	69	76	78	71	60	51	41	56.9
Rf.	2.2	2.8	4.4	4.9	5.7	6.5	5.3	5.7	8.7	7.4	4.2	2.1	59.9
62. T.	61	66	77	87	93	93	86	84	84	79	69	62	78.5
Rf.	0.7	0.5	0.4	0.1	0.3	4.7	12.0	11.0	6.3	2.3	0.3	0.2	38.8

Marine

	Jan.	Feb.	Mar.	Apr.	May	June	July	Aug.	Sept.	Oct.	Nov.	Dec.	Year
63. T.	34	34	36	42	49	55	58	57	52	45	39	36	45
Rf.	9.0	6.6	6.2	4.3	4.7	4.1	5.7	7.8	9.2	9.3	8.5	8.9	84.3
64. T.	38	38	40	44	48	54	57	56	53	47	42	39	46
Rf.	2.2	2.1	2.4	1.9	2.3	1.7	2.8	2.7	2.2	3.0	3.0	3.2	29.5
65. T.	45	45	47	50	55	60	65	64	61	56	50	46	54
Rf.	2.6	2.4	2.2	2.1	2.4	1.5	1.3	1.9	2.5	3.4	3.1	3.7	29.1
66. T.	58	58	55	52	47	44	42	44	48	51	53	56	51
Rf.	3.4	2.7	3.0	2.7	3.2	3.2	3.0	3.1	2.8	3.0	3.3	3.5	36.9
67. T.	60	59	57	54	51	49	46	46	49	51	53	57	53
Rf.	2.9	3.2	6.4	9.3	15.3	17.5	15.4	13.5	7.3	5.0	4.4	4.8	105
68. T.	69	70	68	65	62	59	58	58	60	62	65	68	64
Rf.	1.2	1.3	1.8	2.0	2.4	1.7	1.9	2.1	2.2	2.1	2.1	1.7	22.5
69. T.	68	68	65	60	54	51	49	51	54	58	61	65	59
Rf.	1.9	1.7	2.2	2.3	2.2	2.1	1.8	1.8	2.4	2.6	2.2	2.3	25.5
70. T.	36	38	42	47	54	59	63	62	56	49	43	48	48
Rf.	8.6	6.1	5.3	3.3	3.0	2.7	1.3	1.7	4.1	5.9	10.0	7.8	59.8
71. T.	39	42	46	51	57	61	67	66	61	54	46 j	41	53
Rf.	6.7	5.5	4.8	3.1	2.3	1.6	0.6	0.6	1.9	3.3	6.5	6.9	43.8

Humid Continental, Warm Summer

	Jan.	Feb.	Mar.	Apr.	May	June	July	Aug.	Sept.	Oct.	Nov.	Dec.	Year
72. T.	25	28	35	48	59	68	73	71	62	52	41	31	49
Rf.	0.9	0.7	1.1	1.1	1.3	2.3	2.1	1.2	1.4	1.1	1.6	1.3	16
73. T.	32	38	46	55	63	70	75	73	66	56	44	36	55
Rf.	2.4	2.3	2.7	3.4	4.1	3.3	2.8	3.2	3.5	4.7	4.3	3.0	39.8
74. T.	29	34	43	52	62	67	72	71	63	55	43	34	52
Rf.	1.2	1.3	1.6	2.3	2.8	3.2	2.7	1.9	1.7	2.2	1.7	1.7	24.4

		Jan.	Feb.	Mar.	Apr.	May	June	July	Aug.	Sept.	Oct.	Nov.	Dec.	Year
75.	T.	22	25	37	51	63	72	77	75	66	55	39	27	51
	Rf.	0.7	0.9	1.3	2.8	4.1	4.7	4.0	3.2	3.0	2.3	1.1	0.9	29.0
76.	T.	26	27	37	47	58	68	74	73	66	55	42	30	50
	Rf.	2.1	2.1	2.6	2.9	3.6	3.3	3.4	3.0	3.1	2.6	2.4	2.1	33.2
77.	T.	8	14	30	47	60	71	77	75	61	48	29	14	44
	Rf.	0.2	0.3	0.8	1.1	2.2	3.4	6.3	6.1	3.3	1.6	1.0	0.2	26.5
78.	T.	27	28	35	45	57	68	72	69	63	52	41	32	49
	Rf.	3.7	3.5	4.1	3.8	3.7	3.1	3.5	4.2	3.4	3.7	4.1	3.8	44.6
79.	T.	32	34	44	56	66	75	79	77	70	58	45	36	56.0
	Rf.	2.3	2.6	3.5	3.8	4.5	4.6	3.6	3.5	3.2	2.8	2.9	2.5	39.8

Humid Continental, Cool Summer

		Jan.	Feb.	Mar.	Apr.	May	June	July	Aug.	Sept.	Oct.	Nov.	Dec.	Year
80.	T.	12	15	25	40	49	56	61	59	51	42	28	19	38
	Rf.	0.5	0.6	0.7	0.8	2.3	2.9	2.6	2.5	1.3	0.7	0.7	0.5	16.1
81.	T.	16	16	25	38	49	59	65	63	57	46	33	23	41
	Rf.	2.2	1.8	2.1	2.3	3.1	3.5	3.1	2.8	3.2	3.0	3.0	2.5	32.6
82.	T.	22	21	30	42	54	64	69	67	60	49	37	27	45
	Rf.	2.8	2.4	2.4	2.3	2.8	2.7	2.8	2.8	2.7	2.6	2.6	2.5	31.4
83.	T.	7	10	20	38	54	63	68	63	51	39	25	11	37
	Rf.	0.5	0.4	0.6	0.9	1.6	2.2	2.4	2.4	1.6	1.1	1.0	0.7	15.4
84.	T.	0	3	14	34	52	63	68	62	51	35	17	6	33
	Rf.	0.8	0.6	0.6	0.6	1.3	1.7	2.2	1.8	1.1	1.3	1.1	1.1	14.2
85.	T.	23	22	32	37	44	50	58	63	59	50	39	29	42
	Rf.	1.3	1.0	2.2	2.9	3.7	3.7	3.8	4.3	5.6	3.8	3.3	2.3	37.9
86.	T.	24	23	27	38	49	57	62	59	50	41	32	25	41
	Rf.	1.3	1.1	1.2	1.2	1.7	2.0	2.7	2.8	2.0	2.1	1.7	1.6	21.4
87.	T.	18	18	24	36	48	59	63	60	51	41	30	22	39
	Rf.	1.0	0.9	0.9	1.0	1.6	2.0	2.5	2.8	2.1	1.8	1.4	1.2	19.3
88.	T.	30	33	38	48	57	63	66	65	58	49	39	33	48
	Rf.	1.7	1.4	1.6	1.5	1.9	2.3	3.0	2.3	1.7	1.7	1.7	1.9	22.7
89.	T.	29	33	40	50	59	65	68	67	60	50	39	32	49
	Rf.	1.5	1.3	1.8	2.0	2.8	2.7	3.1	2.7	2.0	1.9	1.8	1.8	25.4
90.	T.	26	29	35	46	57	63	66	64	56	46	36	30	46
	Rf.	1.2	1.1	1.3	1.5	1.9	2.6	3.0	2.9	1.9	1.6	1.5	1.5	22.1

Subarctic

		Jan.	Feb.	Mar.	Apr.	May	June	July	Aug.	Sept.	Oct.	Nov.	Dec.	Year
91.	T.	−58	−48	−24	9	36	56	60	52	36	6	−34	−51	3
	Rf.	0.2	0.1	0.1	0.2	0.3	0.9	1.0	1.0	0.5	0.4	0.3	0.1	5.0
92.	T.	26	26	31	39	46	54	57	56	49	41	34	28	41
	Rf.	4.3	3.0	3.4	2.5	2.2	1.9	2.8	3.4	4.4	5.0	3.9	3.4	40.2
93.	T.	−11	−7	7	21	35	45	55	55	46	27	6	−8	22
	Rf.	0.1	0.1	0.1	0.2	0.6	1.1	0.5	1.8	2.1	0.7	0.2	0.2	7.5
94.	T.	8	9	18	30	41	53	60	56	46	34	22	12	33
	Rf.	0.9	0.7	0.8	0.7	1.2	1.8	2.4	2.4	2.2	1.6	1.2	0.9	16.8
95.	T.	−23	−11	4	29	46	57	59	54	42	25	1	−13	23
	Rf.	0.8	0.8	0.5	0.7	0.9	1.3	1.6	1.6	1.7	1.3	1.3	1.1	13.6

Tundra

		Jan.	Feb.	Mar.	Apr.	May	June	July	Aug.	Sept.	Oct.	Nov.	Dec.	Year
96.	T.	−19	−13	−14	−2	21	35	40	39	31	16	0	−15	10
	Rf.	0.3	0.2	0.2	0.3	0.3	0.3	1.1	0.8	0.5	0.8	0.4	0.4	5.6
97.	T.	4	−2	−2	8	23	35	42	40	32	22	11	6	18
	Rf.	1.4	1.3	1.1	0.9	0.5	0.4	0.6	0.9	1.0	1.2	1.0	1.5	11.8
98.	T.	22	21	24	30	35	42	48	48	43	35	28	24	33
	Rf.	2.7	2.6	2.1	1.6	1.4	1.5	1.8	2.0	2.4	2.5	2.5	2.6	25.7
99.	T.	32	33	31	27	19	15	13	15	20	25	28	31	24
	Rf.	1.5	1.5	1.8	1.7	1.3	1.2	1.2	1.4	1.0	1.0	1.4	0.9	15.9
100.	T.	19	19	24	31	40	47	50	47	41	34	26	21	33.1
	Rf.	3.3	2.7	3.4	2.4	3.6	3.0	3.3	3.8	6.0	5.9	4.4	3.1	44.9

Ice Cap

	Jan.	Feb.	Mar.	Apr.	May	June	July	Aug.	Sept.	Oct.	Nov.	Dec.	Year
101. T.	24	16	4	−9	−11	−12	−15	−15	−12	−2	14	25	1
Rf.	No data												
102. T.	22	(9)	(−7)	−24	−27	−29	−34	−34	−29	−14	8.6	24	−13.3
Rf.	No data												

Highland Climates

	Jan.	Feb.	Mar.	Apr.	May	June	July	Aug.	Sept.	Oct.	Nov.	Dec.	Year
103. T.	58	58	59	59	59	58	57	57	57	58	58	58	58
Rf.	3.7	3.5	4.5	9.6	6.5	3.2	2.6	3.3	2.9	8.4	9.6	5.6	63.4
104. T.	40	42	50	56	58	60	62	61	59	55	48	42	53
Rf.	0.6	1.1	1.8	3.8	8.7	24.9	32.3	26.1	18.4	4.5	0.8	0.2	122.7
105. T.	60	62	65	64	66	64	62	61	61	62	59	59	62
Rf.	0.6	1.9	2.8	3.4	3.0	5.7	11.0	12.1	7.6	0.8	0.5	0.2	49.6
106. T.	54	57	61	64	65	64	62	62	61	59	56	54	60
Rf.	0.2	0.2	0.5	0.8	1.9	3.9	4.5	4.6	3.9	1.6	0.5	0.2	22.8
107. T.	16	16	17	24	31	37	41	41	37	30	23	17	27
Rf.	5.7	6.7	6.7	8.1	7.8	11.2	12.3	10.8	8.3	7.2	4.8	6.1	95.7
108. T.	17	19	31	43	50	58	63	61	54	43	32	22	41
Rf.	0.4	0.3	0.3	0.2	0.2	0.2	0.5	0.5	0.3	0.2		0.2	3.2

STATIONS FOR WHICH DATA ARE GIVEN ABOVE

Tropical Wet (Rainforest)

1. Amboina, Moluccas
2. Padang, Sumatra
3. Jaluit, Marshall Islands (6°N., 170°E.)
4. Akassa, Nigeria
5. Iquitos, Peru
6. Port-of-Spain, Trinidad
7. Colombo, Ceylon
8. Colón, Panama
9. Manáos, Brazil
10. Rangoon, Burma
11. Batavia, Java
12. Freetown, Sierra Leone

Tropical Wet-and-Dry (Savanna)

13. Saïgon, Indo-China
14. Madras, India
15. Honolulu, Hawaii
16. Kingston, Jamaica
17. Mongalla, Sudan
18. Mandalay, Burma
19. Bombay, India
20. Darwin, Australia

Steppe

21. San Diego, California
22. Lahore, India

23. Broome, Australia
24. Teheran, Iran
25. Monterrey, Mexico
26. Kamloops, British Columbia
27. Denver, Colorado
28. Hillet Doleib, Sudan
29. Kimberley, South Africa
30. Marrakesh, Morocco

Desert

31. Cape Juby, Africa (28°N., 13°W.)
32. Cairo, Egypt
33. Baghdad, Iraq
34. Karachi, Pakistan
35. Port Nolloth, Cape of Good Hope
36. Alice Springs, Australia
37. Khartoum, Sudan
38. Astrakhan, U.S.S.R. (46°N., 48°E.)

Dry-summer Subtropical (Mediterranean)

39. Marseilles, France
40. Rome, Italy
41. Athens, Greece
42. Jerusalem, Israel-Jordan
43. Adelaide, Australia
44. San Francisco, California

45. Lisbon, Portugal
46. Santiago, Chile
47. Capetown, Cape Province

Humid Subtropical

48. Niigata, Japan
49. Asunción, Paraguay
50. Nashville, Tennessee
51. Washington, D.C.
52. Foochow, China
53. Chungking, China
54. Kagoshima, Japan
55. Rosario, Argentina
56. Buenos Aires, Argentina
57. Galveston, Texas
58. Mobile, Alabama
59. Benares, India
60. Hongkong, China
61. Tokyo, Japan
62. Allahabad, India

Marine

63. Bergen, Norway
64. Aberdeen, Scotland
65. Brest, France
66. Dunedin, New Zealand
67. Valdivia, Chile
68. Port Elizabeth, Cape of Good Hope
69. Melbourne, Australia
70. Vancouver, British Columbia
71. Portland, Oregon

Humid Continental, Warm Summer

72. Odessa, U.S.S.R.
73. Milan, Italy
74. Belgrade, Yugoslavia
75. Omaha, Nebraska
76. Chicago, Illinois
77. Mukden, Manchuria

78. Boston, Massachusetts
79. St. Louis, Missouri

Humid Continental, Cool Summer

80. Calgary, Alberta
81. Marquette, Michigan
82. Toronto, Ontario
83. Kazan, U.S.S.R. (56°N., 49°E.)
84. Barnaul, U.S.S.R. (53°N., 84°E.)
85. Nemuro, Japan (43°N., 146°E.)
86. Uppsala, Sweden
87. Leningrad, U.S.S.R.
88. Berlin, Germany
89. Vienna, Austria
90. Warsaw, Poland

Subarctic

91. Verkhoyansk, U.S.S.R. (68°N., 133°E.)
92. Trondheim, Norway
93. Okhotsk, U.S.S.R. (59°N., 143°E.)
94. Archangel, U.S.S.R. (65°N., 41°E.)
95. **Dawson**, Yukon (64°N., 139°W.)

Tundra

96. Barrow, Alaska (71°N., 150°W.)
97. Spitsbergen (78°N., 14°E.)
98. Vardo, Norway (70°N., 31°E.)
99. South Orkneys (61°S., 45°W.)
100. Ivigtut, Greenland

Ice Cap

101. McMurdo Sound, Antarctica (78°S., 167°E.)
102. Little America, Antarctica

Highland Climates

103. Bogotá, Colombia (8,730 ft.)
104. Darjeeling, India (7,376 ft.)
105. Addis Ababa, Abyssinia (8,000 ft.)
106. Mexico City, Mexico (7,411 ft.)
107. Säntis, Switzerland (8,202 ft.)
108. Leh, Kashmir (11,503 ft.)

APPENDIX B

Map Projections

The Nature of Projections. It is impossible to do more than suggest the significance of map projections and to illustrate a few examples in an Appendix to a book of this sort. If the reader wishes to learn more about this subject, he is referred to the sources suggested at the end of Chap. 1.

Man must reproduce the earth's surface at a reduced size, or scale, in order to extend his comprehension of it, and one way he does so is by making globes. Assuming that they have been correctly prepared, globes are the only "accurate" maps, for the geometry ("earth measure") of the sphere has been changed only in scale; direction and distance relationships remain in strict proportion to those of the earth. A globe, in spite of this obvious advantage, has several, and some serious, disadvantages. Among the more important are (*a*) only a portion (less than half) can be seen at one time; (*b*) if it is big enough to show much detail, it is bulky and unwieldy; (*c*) it is difficult to measure on its curved surface; and (*d*) it is expensive to reproduce. On the other hand most of these mechanical kinds of difficulties are not true of a plane surface, *i.e.*, one can see it all at once; it is relatively easy to handle or store; it is easy to measure on it; and information can easily be printed on its surface. For these reasons "flat" maps on a plane surface are greatly preferred to "curved" maps on the spherical form of globes. Nevertheless, it is *impossible* to transform a curved spherical surface into the flat surface of a plane (or vice versa) without, in the process, changing the distance-direction relationships among similar points on the two surfaces. Even though the flat map has "inaccurate" distance-direction re-lationships, its other advantages far outweigh these disadvantages.

For more than two thousand years man has been devising ways of distributing the distance-direction error, which is inescapable in a flat map, so that the nature of the error may be allowed for by the user. In some instances he has been able to do this in such a way that for particular uses the "distribution of error" becomes a definite advantage, and, as for example, in certain kinds of navigational maps the "inaccurate" map is far superior to the more "accurate" globe. There is an unlimited number of ways by which the distance-direction relationships can be arranged, and the various systems are called *map projections*. Not many are in common use, and the student of geography should become familiar at least with the characteristics of the more useful types of projections. Their useful characteristics, called *properties,* are in many instances some quality of the spherical surface that has been retained on the plane surface. For example, a projection that retains on the map the same relative sizes of areas as on the earth is said to have the property of being *equal-area*. There are several important properties, and some projections can combine several properties; some projections have no useful characteristics.

Most of the properties of map projections are the consequence of scale relationships which are retained or modified by the system of transformation from the spherical to the plane surface. The understanding of properties as based upon scale is somewhat involved for the average geography student. On the other hand, anyone who uses maps should be able to recognize some of the important qualities of projections by a logical analysis of how the projection on the plane differs from the spherical surface; for this purpose the earth grid serves as a useful guide. There are a number of aspects of the arrangement of parallels and meridians on the spherical earth that are easily remembered, and they provide bases for judging what has happened to the spherical surface as a result of transformation.

Characteristics of the Earth Grid. It will be remembered that the earth is almost a sphere (Art. 1.1) and that the ordinary rectangular coordinate system, familiar from its use on graph paper, has been adapted to the spherical surface to form a grid or graticule of parallels and meridians. The parallels, or y values from the equator, are like the horizontal lines on graph paper. The meridians show the x values from some starting place, and are like the vertical lines on graph paper; but, because the earth is spherical, the meridians all converge to a point at each pole rather than being parallel as similar lines are in a rectangular coordinate system. This simple adaptation of the ordinary coordinate system has some complex consequences, for example, it determines the system of directions; but if one studies the grid on a globe even briefly, he will note that it has a number of general characteristics as follows:

1. Parallels are parallel.

2. Parallels are spaced almost equally on meridians.

3. Parallels and meridians intersect at right angles everywhere.

4. Meridians at the equator are spaced almost the same as the parallels.

5. Meridians converge toward the poles.

6. The meridians which intersect with any one parallel are equally spaced.

7. Meridians at 60°Lat. are about half as far apart as they are at the equator; they converge to points at the poles.

Two others are not quite so easy to observe but they are important:

8. The area included between any two parallels, and measuring a given longitude in extent, will be the same anywhere between those two parallels.

9. Any great circle on the globe (all meridians and the equator are included among great circles), which is the shortest course between points over the surface of the earth, appears as a straight line when looked at perpendicularly. This is the way one looks at all points on a map, in theory at least.

It is important also to remember that the scale on the surface of a globe is *everywhere* in every direction the same, and that this *cannot* be the case on any map projection.

The above facts supply the map reader with a kind of check list by which he can analyze the nature of the grid on a map projection. Departures from these facts have necessary consequences which are always important to the map reader, for he must guard against erroneous visual concepts that are the result of the projection system; similarly he can recognize useful attributes.

The most significant attributes of any projection have to do with those elements of distance and direction, and their derivatives, area and angular relationships, which are important in the use to which the map is to be put.

Properties of Map Projections. The only two properties which can exist "all over" a projection are those known as (*a*) *equal-area* or *equivalence* and (*b*) *conformality* or *orthomorphism;* they are mutually exclusive, *i.e.,* they cannot exist together in the same system of projection.

A projection is said to be equal-area when the scale is arranged in such a way that at any point the maximum too-large scale departure in one direction is balanced by a correspondingly too-small departure perpendicular to it. Although this states it in somewhat simple terms the consequence is that the area of any region on the map is shown correctly in relation to the area of any other region. Characteristic 8 in the above list must be maintained if a projection is to be equal-area, and if one (or more) of the others, *e.g.,* 2, 4, or 6, is not maintained there will be some other departure from reality to balance it, so that equality of area is preserved. The quality of being equal-area is extremely useful in many geographic connections, for if proper area relationships are not presented the reader will receive some wrong impressions as to the relative importance or, on some maps, as to the relative density of distributions, as for example on dot maps. Equality of area is also important in many research and governmental connections. For example, areas of the earth surface cannot be measured accurately except from an equivalent projection.[1] In any projection the scale will vary from place to place on the projection, that is, the graphic scale of miles shown or the fractional scale (for example, 1:10,000,000) will be true only for a few places on the map. The difficulty of transforming a spherical surface to a plane surface causes the scale departure from place to place in some instances to be rather large; it is not unusual for the scale to be several times greater at one place compared to the scale at another. Over most of an equal-area projection the scale is *different in different directions* at each point, and this condition causes shapes of areas, even small ones in some instances, to be deformed. Consequently, equivalent projections always deform shapes and in some instances to a very large degree. Equivalent projections concentrate or spread out the scale departures in different places and ways, so that the inescapable deformation of angles (shapes) may be concentrated in the less used portions of the map. The map reader must be alert to make allowance for this, by applying the check list of characteristics.

A projection to be conformal must have the scale arranged in such a way that, whatever the scale may be in any part of the projection, it is the *same in all directions* at each point. Since it is impossible to have the same scale at every point on any flat map, and since, on conformal projections, the scale must be uniform in every direction at each point, it can be concluded that the scale must change from point to point and that the sizes of areas will therefore vary in different parts of the projection. In other words, a conformal projection must

exaggerate or reduce areas relative to one another; this is why conformality and equivalence are mutually exclusive. When the scale is consistent in every direction at a point, earth directions, *i.e.*, the compass rose, will be truly shown. This quality makes conformality useful for maps on which directions at points are important, as, for example, in maps to be used for navigation, surveying, or plotting wind directions. On such maps characteristic 3 will be retained. This is also true of some projections that are not conformal, but it will always be true on conformal projections. Although proper angles will occur at each point and, practically speaking, for a limited distance around each point, the directions (azimuths or bearings) between places distant from one another on conformal projections will usually not be correct.[2] Similarly, shapes of small areas at any place will be good on conformal projections, but shapes of large areas will be deformed, as they are on *all* projections.

Another property of considerable utility is presented by *azimuthal* projections. This is the quality of showing correct azimuths from one particular point to every other point. This can be combined with another property, *equidistance*, which is the quality of showing correct (uniform) scale distance from one point to all other points.[3] Such projections are useful in plotting radii or in figuring distances and directions of travel that follow great-circle routes as, for example, radio beams.

There are many other properties or qualities, but most of them are limited to one projection. Thus there is a projection which shows all great-circle arcs as straight lines (gnomonic); another shows loxodromes, or lines of constant compass heading, as straight lines (Mercator); while several show east-west directions as parallel all over the projection. Properties may

[1] Malcolm J. Proudfoot. "Measurement of Geographic Area." U.S. Bureau of the Census, Washington, D.C., 1940.

[2] An azimuth is the compass bearing at the starting point of the angle between north and the great circle connecting the starting point and some other point. It is usually given in degrees from north reading clockwise.

[3] A projection can be made azimuthal from two points or equidistant from two points, but azimuthal *and* equidistant from only one point.

be combined on projections. Thus there are, for example, projections that are azimuthal and conformal, or azimuthal and equal-area, or conformal with straight loxodromes. Many projections are named after their inventors, and sometimes the primary qualities are not included in the name. Consequently, the frequent user of maps needs to know the commoner projections, and in using them he needs to apply the analytical check list of earth-grid characteristics. A few of the more commonly used projections are illustrated and explained briefly below, with some that are less used but are in striking contrast with them. These are divided into three broad and not necessarily exclusive categories: (*a*) projections used for world maps, (*b*) projections used for maps of hemispheres or similar areas, and (*c*) projections used for smaller areas. Many of the systems of projection especially designed for world maps can be employed for smaller areas, but the reverse is not ordinarily done.

Projections Used For World Maps

Rectangular Projections. Mercator's projection, which is sometimes used for maps of the world, may be understood better by first examining two other contrasting projections between which it seems to effect a compromise. Figures B.1 and B.2 show forms of projection in which the grid of the earth has been projected to a tangent cylinder which has then been developed, *i.e.,* "unrolled" and laid flat. In Fig. B.1 the projection of the grid has been

parallel with the plane of the tangent great circle. The result is the *cylindrical equal-area* projection, but in it the shapes of areas in high latitudes are so stretched out east and west and so shortened north and south that they look very odd—so odd, in fact, that the projection is little used in this form. At the opposite extreme is Fig. B.2. In this one the direction of projection radiates from the center of the earth to the tangent cylinder. In this central-perspective cylindrical projection there is also a great east-west expansion in high latitudes but a still greater north-south expansion. It is neither equal-area nor conformal.

The contrast between these two makes clear the nature and purpose of the Mercator projection (Fig. B.3), first published in 1569, and perhaps the most used of all projections. In it the converging meridians of the globe are represented as parallel lines, spaced as they are on the equator. This obviously creates a rapid east-west scale expansion with increase of latitude, which can be deduced from characteristic 5 in the check list. To balance that distortion, the positions for the parallels of latitude are mathematically computed to produce north-south expansion which increases *at the same rate* as the east-west expansion. The result is a projection having a property that recommends it especially to navigators. *Any loxodrome is a straight line.* This is true of no other projection, and it is most useful for plotting ships' or planes' headings. The shortest distance between any two places follows the arc of the great circle passing through those places, but that is

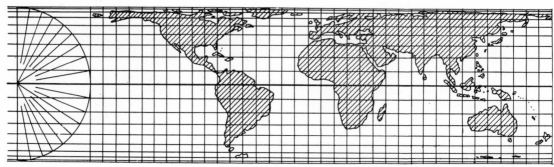

Fig. B.1 A cylindrical equal-area projection.

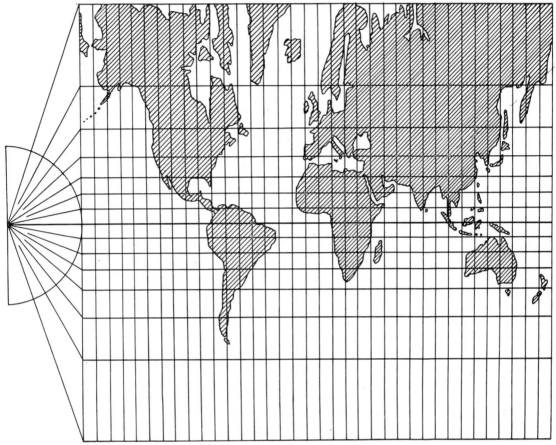

Fig. B.2 A central-perspective cylindrical projection.

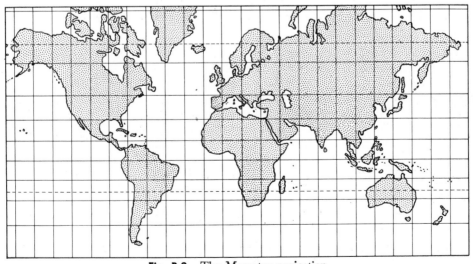

Fig. B.3 The Mercator projection.

a hard course to steer, because in most instances the compass direction at any given point on a great circle is different from that at every other point, and the compass directions of the course must be gradually but continuously changed. In practice, such a course is approximated by plotting on the Mercator projection a series of short straight lines (rhumb lines) which follow the general direction of the great circle but along each of which the compass direction remains constant.

In addition to showing loxodromes as straight lines the Mercator is a conformal projection, and larger areas are distorted both in size and shape by the extreme change of scale from place to place. The expansion of the scale toward the poles in this projection, while of no concern to the navigator, is a serious defect if it is used for educational purposes, since it causes land areas in high latitudes to appear vastly larger than they really are in comparison with those near the equator. For example at 60°Lat. (southern Alaska in the Northern Hemisphere) areas are shown four times larger than they would appear if located at the equator.

There are a number of other projections which have the rectangular-appearing grid associated with projection on a cylinder. Most of them cannot be projected geometrically, but have mathematically derived spacings of the parallels and meridians. They are used either because they are easy to construct and useful for small areas wherein the deformation is not large (*cylindrical equal-area*, and *equirectangular*) or because they effect a sort of compromise in distributing the area and angular deformation (*Miller cylindrical*).

Oval Projections. The projections described above portray the entire earth on one or another form of rectangular grid. There is another group of projections which mainly are oval in form because of having their poles shown as points or as lines not so long as that of the equator. Figures B.4 and B.5 show the plans of two of these. Both are equal-area projections, but they differ slightly in other respects. Both are developed on a polar axis that is one-half the length of the equatorial axis, which is the proper ratio of the length of the equator to the meridian distance from pole to pole. In the *Mollweide* projection (Fig. B.4) and the *sinusoidal* projection (Fig. B.5) the meridians are equally spaced, as they are on a globe, and

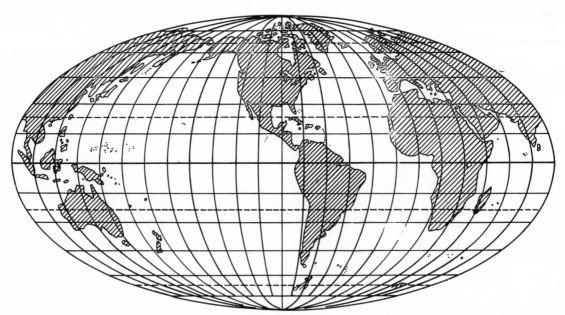

Fig. B.4   The Mollweide equal-area projection.

the parallels are truly parallel, as they also are on a globe. Both of them distort shapes, especially near the margins of the projections and in high latitudes. The differences between the two are in the shapes of the meridians and in the spacings of the parallels, and because of these differences the deformation of shapes is distributed differently. The sinusoidal is best near the equator and central meridian, while the Mollweide is best in the central middle latitudes. There are many other projections of this general type.

In the rectangular group of projections the poles are represented, if they can be shown at all, by lines as long as the equator, which occasions considerable deformation in high latitudes. In the second group described the poles are represented as points, but this causes the polar areas to appear rather crowded. In a third group an attempt has been made to distribute the deformation between the low and high latitudes so that the polar areas will appear less extreme than in either of the first two. In this group the pole is "stretched out" into a line, but one not so long as the equator. The pole line may be any chosen length, and for many of these projections the meridian

curves and parallel spacings are computed so that the resulting grid is equal-area. One of the best known is the *Eckert IV equal-area* projection (Fig. B.6) in which the pole line is half as long as the equator. Another, more recently devised, is the *flat polar quartic equal-area projection* (Fig. B.7) in which the pole is a line one-third the length of the equator.[4] This excellent world projection has been used for many of the larger world maps in this book.

When these projections, and others like them, are to be used for a variety of purposes wherein the interest is concentrated on either the land or, conversely, the water areas, they may be constructed so that there is an interruption to their over-all continuity. This is done for the purpose of having more than one central meridian, so that the better parts of the projection, where there is the least distortion of shape,

[4] F. W. McBryde and Paul D. Thomas. "Equal-area Projections for World Statistical Maps." *Special Publication* 245, Coast and Geodetic Survey, Washington, D.C., 1949. The full name suggested by the inventors for the projection is *flat polar quartic authalic. Quartic* refers to the form of the meridians, and *authalic* is synonymous with equal-area. Several other similar projections are presented in the above reference.

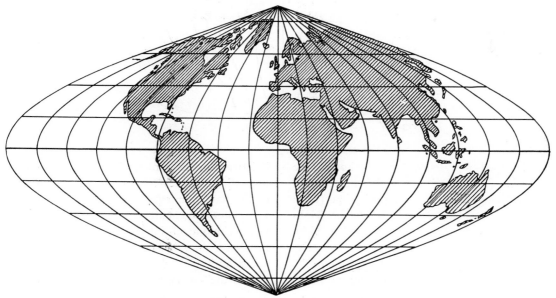

Fig. B.5 The sinusoidal equal-area projection.

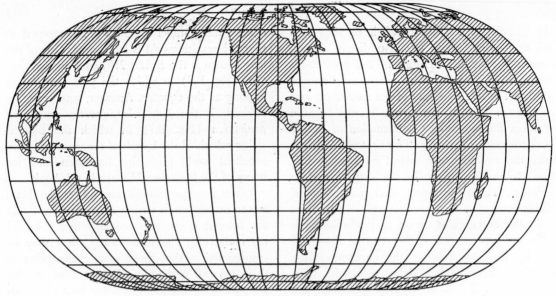

Fig. B.6 The Eckert IV equal-area projection.

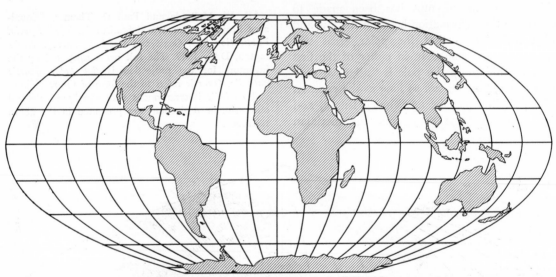

Fig. B.7 The flat polar quartic equal-area projection.

can be used repeatedly. Goode's homolosine projection (Fig. B.8) is one of these. It is made by combining the sinusoidal projection (from the equator to latitude 40°) with the Mollweide projection (from 40° to the pole). Since it is composed of equal-area projections, it also has that quality. In addition, the selection of the meridians to be repeated as principal meridians causes each continent (or ocean) to appear as

if it were in the center of the original projection where shapes are very good. The form of the flat polar equal-area projection used in the plates accompanying this volume employs this technique of interruption also. Offsetting these two desirable qualities (equality of area and a fairly good shape) is the necessity for the eye of the observer to bridge the gaps in the grid caused by the interruptions.

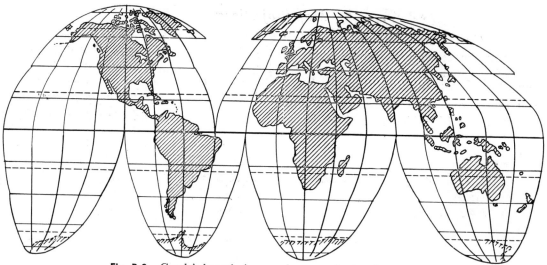

Fig. B.8   Goode's homolosine equal-area projection, interrupted.

Maps of Hemispheres and Similar Areas

Azimuthal Projections. Many books and atlases contain maps of the hemispheres, or of the polar areas, which, when the whole projection is shown, are circular in outline. These have properties of peculiar value. These are *azimuthal* projections which are derived by projecting the earth grid upon tangent *planes,* just as in Figs. B.1 and B.2 it was cast upon tangent *cylinders.* Map grids constructed by these methods may be projected on planes tangent at the poles, at points on the equator, or at any other chosen point. Figures B.9 to B.13 illustrate some of these and show sections of both their polar and equatorial forms. Of great significance in these projections are the following facts: (*a*) the azimuths from the center are correct to any place on the map,

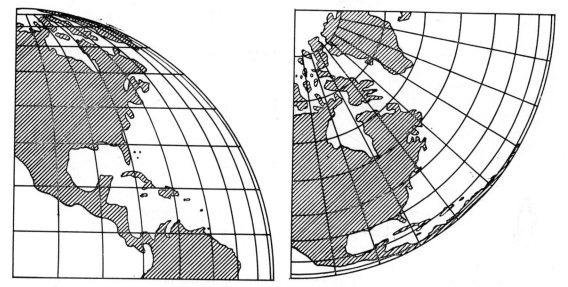

Fig. B.9   The orthographic projection showing hemisphere sections (right) centered on the North Pole, and (left) centered on the Equator.

and (*b*) whatever the deformation may be, it is least at the center and increases outward symmetrically from the center.

The *orthographic projection* (Fig. B.9) shows great compression about its margin and gives the appearance of looking at a globe. It has frequently been used to give some small-scale maps an appearance of rounded perspective, as if the observer were viewing the earth from a point in space.

The *stereographic projection* (Fig. B.10) shows a spacing of lines just the reverse of the

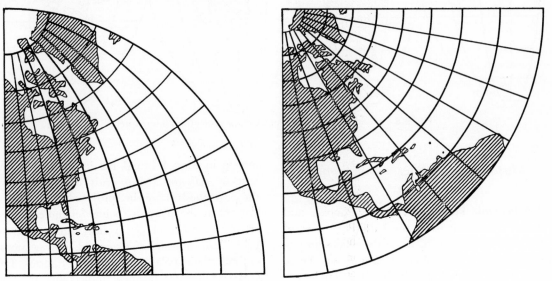

Fig. B.10 The stereographic projection showing hemisphere sections (right) centered on the North Pole, and (left) centered on the Equator.

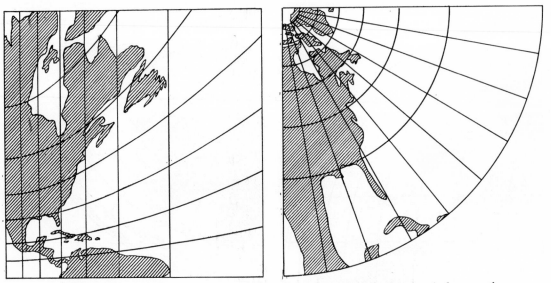

Fig. B.11 The gnomonic projection showing (right) a portion of a hemisphere section centered on the North Pole, and (left) a portion of a hemisphere section centered on the Equator. A complete hemisphere cannot be projected by means of this system.

preceding. It is a conformal projection and renders the shapes of limited areas accurately but greatly distorts the relative areas of different parts of the surface shown. Still more extreme in its marginal expansion is the *gnomonic projection* (Fig. B.11). In fact, the expansion outward is so extreme that no large part of a hemisphere can be shown by it, and on it both shapes and areas are so distorted that it has no value for showing either the shapes or the sizes of regions. It has, however, one unique quality that gives it a place among the valuable projections. On it every arc of a great circle of the earth is rendered as a straight line and, conversely, every straight line drawn on the projection is an arc of a great circle on the globe. This is a most useful device for plotting great-circle (shortest possible) air or ocean routes. Because most lines that would be drawn upon this projection for the purpose of locating sailing courses would cut parallels and meridians at wrong angles, compass steering by it is not easy. For that reason the significant points of latitude and longitude on the course usually are transferred from the gnomonic to a Mercator projection and are connected in a series of short straight lines, as previously indi-

cated. This approximates the great-circle route and makes steering much simpler.

Another azimuthal projection which is commonly used for maps of continents is the Lambert *azimuthal equal-area* (Fig. B.12).

It should be reiterated that the central portions of many projections usable for world maps are frequently employed for smaller areas such as continents and hemispheres.

Projections Used for Smaller Areas

The smaller the area to be represented, the nearer to reality can the earth grid be projected. The detailed and precise requirements called for in maps of smaller areas have given rise to many forms of projections, and one of the most frequently used is the kind derived from projecting the grid upon a *cone*, which like the cylinder, can be unrolled into a plane. The grid may actually be projected geometrically, but the more useful conical projections are derived mathematically.

Conical Projection. To understand the simple form of the conical projection, imagine a large paper cone set down upon a globe with its apex directly above the pole of the globe. The

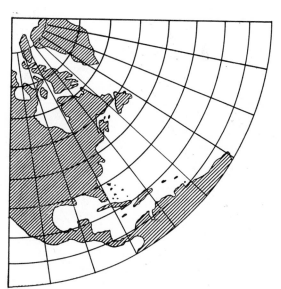

Fig. B.12 The Lambert azimuthal equal-area projection showing hemisphere sections (right) centered on the North Pole, and (left) centered on the Equator.

cone is tangent to the globe along the entire circumference of some selected parallel; it will consequently have the same scale as the globe, and is called the *standard parallel*. Because this parallel is everywhere equally distant from the apex of the cone, it becomes an arc of a circle when the cone is opened out into a plane surface (developed), and all other parallels become arcs of concentric circles (Fig. B.13). Lines drawn on the surface of the cone from the apex through selected points on the standard parallel become the meridians of the map and always are straight lines radiating from the common center. Meridians that are radial straight lines and parallels that are arcs of concentric circles usually indicate immediately one of the several forms of the true conical projection.

In the simple form of the conical projection the scale of the map is true only along the standard parallel. North or south of that parallel the longitudinal or latitudinal distances expand rapidly. Much greater area may be brought within the range of reasonable distortion if the map be constructed on *two standard parallels* instead of one. This is done by making the cone *secant* to the globe rather than tangent to it (Fig. B.14). By careful choice of positions for the standard parallels

an arrangement of lines may be had which, over a wide band of latitude, produces surprisingly little distortion. By mathematical adjustments of the exact positions of the parallels the deformation can be restricted either to the shapes or to the areas of the features shown. Thus both equal-area and conformal types of this projection exist. Such are the *Lambert conformal conic* projection and the *Albers equal-area projection*, each with two standard parallels. The latter is particularly good for showing an area, like the United States, which has a greater east-west than north-south dimension. By proper selection of the standard parallels a map of the United States may be made in which the maximum scale error, which occurs on the northern and southern margins, is only a little more than 1 per cent. The map is, therefore, by construction equal-area and even for so large a region as the United States very nearly conformal. Most of the smaller-scale maps of the United States are now being made on either the Albers equal-area projection or the Lambert conformal conic.

Modified forms of conical and cylindrical projections are particularly useful for survey maps, either the topographic maps of a country, or the individual maps of large series which cover large sections of the earth, such as the

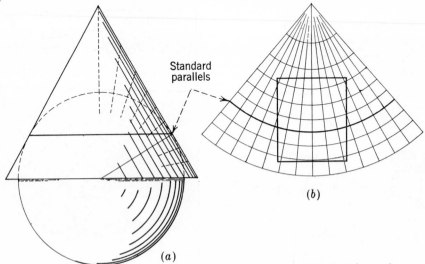

Fig. B.13 A conic projection in which the earth grid is transferred, (*a*), to the cone by projection from the center of the earth. It has one standard parallel at 30° Lat.; in (*b*) a portion of the cone has been developed (i.e., flattened out) into a map grid.

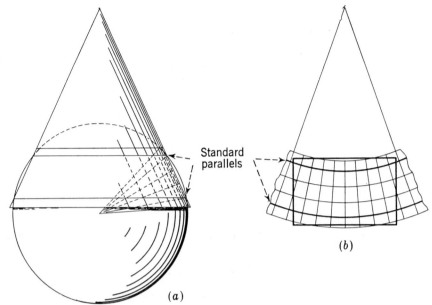

Fig. B.14 A conic projection with two standard parallels because the cone is secant to the globe as shown in (a); in (b) a portion of the cone has been developed into a map grid.

International Map of the World on a scale of 1:1,000,000. One of the earliest forms of modified conical projection used for topographic maps is the *Bonne equal-area,* now only occasionally used for maps of continents. In this projection (Fig. B.15) all parallels are arcs of concentric circles, as they are in the truly conical projections, and they are spaced as they are on the globe. The meridians, however, are not straight lines but curves which converge at the pole and pass through points on the parallels that are spaced in true proportion to their spacing on the globe. Thus every quadrilateral of the grid has its proportional length and breadth as compared with that quadrilateral on a globe, and the projection is equal-area. It gives good shapes near the central meridian, but deformation increases rapidly away from the central meridian. The projection is most appropriately used, therefore, for a land area which has its greater dimension north and south.

Another modified form of conical projection used for the topographic maps of the United States is the *polyconic.* In this projection (Fig.

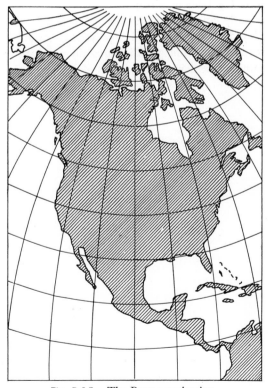

Fig. B.15 The Bonne projection.

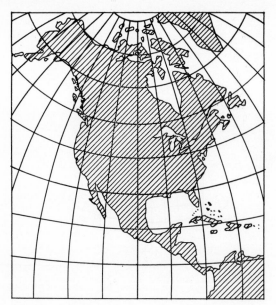

Fig. B.16 The polyconic projection is not much used in this form; instead each topographic sheet has its own straight central meridian.

a different cone, and are thus not concentric. The meridians are curves derived the same way they are in the Bonne projection. The projection is neither equal-area nor conformal, but the error near the central meridian is hardly measurable at large scales. Each map of the United States topographic series is drawn with the central meridian of the projection in the center of the map sheet, and consequently the maps are almost perfect. Each map sheet fits with the maps to the north and to the south of it but not with those to the east or west. A modification of the polyconic having straight-line meridians is employed for the International Map of the World.

A projection much used for topographic maps is the *transverse Mercator*. This is the same as the conventional Mercator but turned 90° so that the area with the least scale change (equatorial area in the conventional projection) runs north and south. This provides a conformal projection which, although cylindrical in concept, looks like a modified conical projection; on it the "best zones" trend north-south instead of east-west as they would on a conventional conformal conic. In areas trending east-west the Lambert conformal conic is commonly employed for topographic maps.

B.16) each parallel is a standard parallel, *i.e.*, it is the tangent circle of a cone, and consequently an infinite number of cones is employed, hence the name polyconic, meaning many cones. The parallel arcs do not have a common center, since each is developed from

APPENDIX C

American Systems of Land Survey[1]

Township and Range System. Over a large part of the United States (and much of Canada) the basic subdivision of the land follows a system of survey originally adopted in the United States in 1785. It was applied especially to the region of the Great Lakes, the Mississippi Valley, and the western states. By this system public and private lands are described in relation to a network of north-south and east-west lines. These include selected meridians, which are called principal meridians, and base lines and correction lines (Fig. C.1). Their use has the effect of dividing the land into essentially rectangular blocks. The location of these blocks is indicated by numbered *townships* and *ranges*. The ranges are north-south strips of land 6 miles wide, and they are numbered east and west from the nearest or most convenient principal meridian. In Wisconsin, for example, the controlling line is the 4th principal meridian and there are 30 ranges east and 20 west of it (Fig. C.2). The ranges are divided into townships by east-west lines at intervals of 6 miles, beginning at a selected southern boundary. In Wisconsin, this is the Illinois-Wisconsin state line. Thus a range consists of a north-south tier of townships each of which is supposed to be 6 miles square. There are 53 townships in the longest range in Wisconsin. By this system any township can be located by reference to its township and range numbers, *e.g.*, township 7 north, range 9 east. This is usually written T. 7 N., R. 9 E. Owing to the fact that the meridians converge toward the north, certain corrections and allowances must be made. Other factors require allowance also, such as a base line which is not true east-west, errors in surveying, and the presence of lakes or streams at critical points. The four correction lines for Wisconsin are shown in Fig. C.2.

The civil, organized, or municipal towns into which counties are divided are units of political administration, and they may or may not coincide with government townships, which exist for purposes of location. In thinly settled districts the civil towns often are much larger and may include two or more government townships or parts of townships. In other areas one government township may be divided into two or more small civil towns. The boundaries of civil towns also are subject to change by appropriate legislation, but the government-survey townships remain.

The usual government township is divided into 36 *sections,* each approximately 1 mile square. The sections are numbered, beginning at the northeastern corner and ending at the southeastern, as is shown in Fig. C.3. The locations of the township and section corners were supposedly marked by a stake, stone, mound, tree, or other device, but too often these were impermanent features and are now difficult to locate. Since each section is supposed to be 1 mile square, its area should be 640 acres. For purposes of more detailed location and description the section is divided into quarters, each containing 160 acres, and the quarter sections are further divided into quarters of 40 acres each (Fig. C.4). These are commonly called "forties." The quarter sections are indicated by the points of the compass, and so also are the forties. To describe and locate a given forty,

[1] Adapted from Appendix F., *Bull.* 36, of the Wisconsin Geological and Natural History Survey. Illustrations by courtesy of E. F. Bean, Director.

671

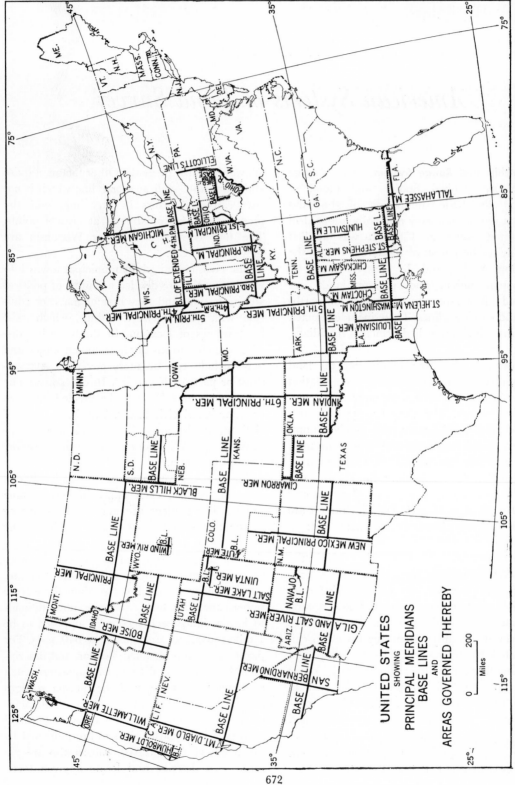

Fig. C.1 The principal meridians and base lines which govern the land-survey systems of most of the United States except Texas and the Atlantic Coast states. The fine-dotted lines surround the areas governed by each principal meridian. Some of these areas are large, some small.

therefore, one might say that it is the NE $\frac{1}{4}$ of the SW $\frac{1}{4}$ of Sec. 31, T. 18 N., R. 9 E. Such a description indicates a precise location, and it tells also the area of the parcel of land in question.

Metes and Bounds. In the Atlantic Coast states and certain others the original land grants and surveys were made prior to the adoption of the township and range system of survey. In those states parcels of land are described by a system known as "metes and bounds." In that system an arbitrary point is taken, such for example as a projecting rock, a tree, or some significant point on the bank of a river or lake. The property is then bounded by lines run in a given compass direction for a certain distance, then in another direction for a specified distance, and so on around to the

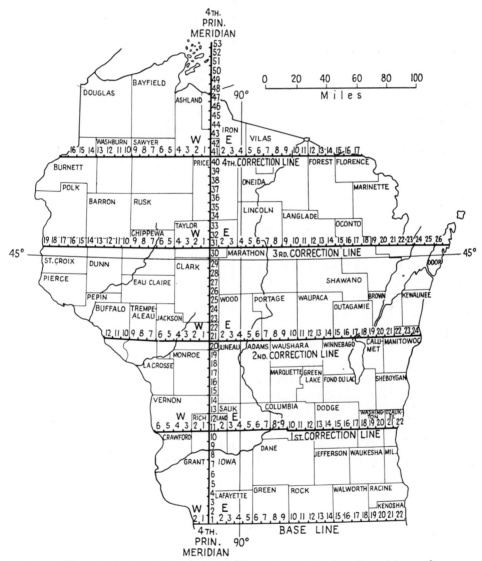

Fig. C.2 The principal meridian (4th) of Wisconsin and the base line of its northern section. The base line is the southern boundary of the state. This map shows correction lines and town and range numbers.

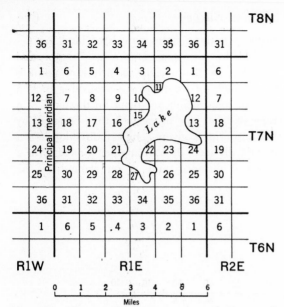

Fig. C.3 The standard system of numbering used for the sections within a township.

point of beginning. This system has often led to conflict over property lines because after a time the tree, stone, or other arbitrary beginning point has been lost or its location has changed. Moreover, the stated distances were sometimes measured inexactly, as in parts of Texas, for example, where some of the early Spanish land grants are said to have been measured in terms of the length of a lariat rope or of how far a horse could walk in a given time. Such lines often did not surround rectangular parcels of land, and seldom did the plots of land have any consistent pattern of shape with respect to the cardinal compass directions.

This lack of coordination is plainly apparent in the road patterns to be seen in detailed maps of New England, Texas, and other states. In some North American localities the present small parcels of land are subdivisions of grants made by the kings of England, France, or Spain to noblemen or to the sponsors of settlement projects. In French Canada or French Louisiana, for example, the present farms often are rectangular but very long and narrow, their narrow frontage being upon a river and their length extending at right angles from the river, regardless of compass direction. Some of the counties of the Province of Quebec may be seen to have the same shape. They were established at a time when river frontage was a most prized possession but the land of the interior had little value. Various systems more or less like that of metes and bounds are prevalent in most of Europe and, in fact, in the larger part of the world.

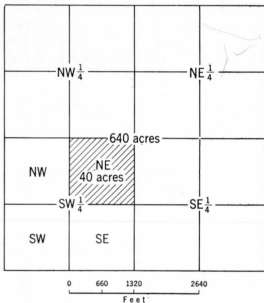

Fig. C.4 The description and location of parts of sections, under the rectangular survey, are by quarter sections, and, within these, by 40-acre tracts, designated by the compass position of each within its quarter section.

APPENDIX D

A Selected List of United States Topographic Quadrangles

The topographic quadrangles indicated below have been selected from those published by the United States Geological Survey because they illustrate in map form certain of the terrain types discussed in the text. Some of the types discussed, ice-scoured plains, for example, are not clearly illustrated in any of the quadrangles now published and are therefore omitted from the list.

Because of the great progress made during the last two decades in accuracy of representation, recently published sheets have been selected wherever possible. To provide uniformity and to afford adequate-sized samples of the terrain, the selection has been largely confined to sheets on the scales of 1:62,500 or 1:63,360. Scales other than those are noted where chosen. In some instances two or three quadrangles are required to show adequately the terrain type in question. Such are listed as a series.

In recent years the Geological Survey has begun issuing a number of sheets in shaded-relief as well as contour editions. Because of the excellence of these maps and their clarity of terrain representation, they are especially valuable for teaching purposes. Quadrangles for which shaded-relief editions are available are marked with an asterisk in the list below.

All the quadrangles listed may be obtained from the United States Geological Survey, Washington 25, D.C.

Plains

PLAINS SCULPTURED BY STREAM EROSION

Youthfully dissected plains:
   Dwight, Ill. (drift; little dissection)
   Binger, Okla. (dendritic dissection)
   Casey, Ill. (dendritic dissection)
   Sandon, Kan. (flat; dissected edge)
   Florence West, S.C. (upland swamps)
Newly emerged coastal plains:
   Limerick, Ga. (low; swampy)
   Lake Drummond, Va.–N.C. (broad swamp)
   Nixonville, S.C. (swampy; low terrace)
   White Lake, N.C. (terrace; upland swamps)
Maturely dissected plains:
   Stanberry, Mo. (late–mid mature)
   Marlow, Okla. (early mature)
   Chatham, La. (low; late–mid mature)
   Wiergate, Tex.–La. (late mature)
   Oxford, N.C. (rolling)
Pediments (on maps, rarely distinguishable from piedmont alluvial plains):
   *Antelope Peak, Ariz. (associated with fans)
   Cuddeback Lake, Calif. (pediment fingers)
   Cotton Center, Ariz. (broad; few peaks)
Cuestaform plains:
   Independence, Kan. (1:125,000) (well-marked scarp)
   Epes, Ala. (ragged scarp)
   Denmark and New Albany, Miss. (eroded and low)

675

Tonawanda, N.Y. (clean scarp)

Fond du Lac, Wis. (clean, glaciated scarp)

PLAINS SHAPED BY STREAM DEPOSITION

Floodplains:

Clarksdale, Miss. (meander scars)

Artonish, Miss.–La. (meanders; bluff)

Mellwood, Ark.–Miss. (meanders, artificial cutoffs)

Fairbanks C-1 and Fairbanks D-1, Alaska (meanders; cutoffs; braided)

Augusta, Mo. (narrow floodplain)

Delta plains:

Dulac, La. (outer; narrow levees)

Empire, La. (outer margin)

East Delta, La. (digitate mouth)

Hahnville, La. (wide levees)

Mt. Vernon, Wash. (small delta)

Bouldin Island and Isleton, Calif. (polders)

Cordova B-3 and Cordova C-3, Alaska (braided channels)

Alluvial fans; piedmont alluvial plains:

*Ennis, Mont. (well-defined fan)

Cucamonga and San Bernardino, Calif. (piedmont alluvial plain)

Santaquin, Utah (several small fans)

Unionville, Nev. (alluvial plain; many fan heads)

Clovis and Selma, Calif. (Kings R. fan)

KARST PLAINS

Karst plains:

*Mammoth Cave, Ky. (karst plains and hills)

Interlachen, Fla. (large sinks; lakes)

Glendale, Fla. (large swampy sinks; surface drainage)

Holt, Fla. (solution valleys; spring sapping)

PLAINS MODIFIED BY GLACIAL DEPOSITION

Till plains:

Gilman, Wis. (low relief; swampy; small moraines)

Perry, Ia. (smooth; well-drained)

Lastrup, Minn. (undulating)

Sun Prairie, Wis. (separated oval drumlins)

Savannah, N.Y. (1:24,000) (elongated drumlins)

Marginal moraines:

St. Croix Dalles, Minn.–Wis. (knob and kettle)

Noonan, N. Dak. (broad knob and kettle)

Vergas and Pelican Rapids, Minn. (broad knob and kettle)

Alma, Mich. (narrow and low; lake plain)

Arrowsmith, Ill. (large, smooth clayey moraine)

Outwash plains:

Three Rivers, Mich. (associated with moraine)

Schoolcraft, Mich. (pitted; with moraine)

Delavan and Manito, Ill. (broad; terraces; sand hills)

Saponac, Me. (esker)

Glaciolacustrine plains:

Grand Forks, N. Dak. (flat)

Wheaton, Minn. (beach ridges)

Merrill, Mich. (slightly dissected)

Perrinton, Mich. (spillway)

PLAINS MODIFIED BY WIND DEPOSITION

Aeolian sand:

*Ashby, Neb. (clumped sand hills)

Crescent Lake, Neb. (low; patternless hills)

Ogilby, Calif. (strip of live dunes)

Holland, Mich. (coastal dunes)

Saltillo Ranch, Tex. (aligned ridges)

Loessial surfaces:

Utica, Neb. (smooth deposition surface; dissected edges)

Endicott, Wash. (Palouse Hills)

St. Francis, Kan. (depos. surface; much dissection)

Broken Bow SW, Neb. (1:24,000) (sharply dissected)

Tablelands

Upland and valleys:

*Portage, Mont. (low; narrow valleys)

The Knoll, Utah (broad upland; canyons)

Mouth of Dark Canyon, Utah (several canyons)

Grand Canyon National Park, Ariz. (2 sheets) (great canyon)

*Grand Coulee Dam, Wash. (broad canyon; dam)

*Thousand Springs, Idaho (broad, benched canyon)

Escarpments and Outliers:
Boot Mesa and Agathla Peak, Ariz. (scarp and outliers)
Promontory Butte, Ariz. (high, dissected scarp)
Chimney Rock, N.M. (two-level scarp)
*Anvil Points, Colo. (1:24,000) (high, dissected scarp)

Plains With Hills and Mountains

Erosional:
*Warm Springs, Ga. (residual ridges; rolling plain)
Greenville, S.C. (residual mtn.; rolling plain)
Saponac, Maine (residual mts.; glaciated)
Cooperton, Okla. (exhumed hills; smooth plain)
Agathla Peak and Dinnehotso, Ariz. (long monoclinal ridge)
Eroded fault blocks:
*Antelope Peak, Ariz. (isolated peaks; pediments)
Sonoma Range, Nev. (1:125,000) (basin and range)
Carrizozo, N.M. (basin and range; lava flow)
Volcanic:
*Bray, Calif. (volcanic cones on plains)
*Menan Buttes, Idaho (1:24,000) (cones on lava plains)
Ship Rock, N.M. (volcanic neck; dikes)

Hills and Mountains

Stream-eroded; no strong structural control:
*Dutchman Butte, Ore. (high relief; mature)
*Renovo West, Pa. (moderate relief; submature)
Cuny Table West, S. Dak. (1:24,000) (badlands)
Sparta, Wis. (moderate relief; late mature)
Round Spring, Mo. (moderate relief; mature)
Wayah Bald, N.C. (high relief; mature)
Structural control; linear ridges:
*Orbisonia, Pa. (smooth monoclinal ridges)
*Strasburg, Va. (synclinal mountain)
*Waldron, Ark. (irregular monoclinal ridges)

*Maverick Spring, Wyo. (1:24,000) (eroded dome)
Dissected fault scarps:
Mount Whitney, Calif. (1:125,000) (huge scarp)
Mount Tom, Calif. (huge scarp)
Logan, Utah (1:125,000) (high straight scarp)
Structural control; miscellaneous:
*Ironton, Mo. (exhumed granite knobs)
Navajo Mountain, Utah-Ariz. (laccolithic dome; jointing)
Volcanic cones:
*Bray, Calif. (large cones)
Mount Rainier, Wash. (1:125,000) (composite cone)
Lassen Volcanic National Park, Calif. (cones; flows)
Mauna Kea, Hawaii (huge shield volcano)
Amboy Crater, Calif. (1:24,000) (cinder cone; flow)
*Menan Buttes, Idaho (1:24,000) (small cones)
*Umnak, Alaska (1:250,000) (huge caldera; glaciated cones)
Mountain glaciers:
Mount Rainier, Wash. (1:125,000) (radial system)
Seldonia D-1 and Seldonia D-2, Alaska (ice field and many tongues)
Cordova C-3 and Cordova C-4, Alaska (large glaciers; medial moraines)
Fremont Peak, Wyo. (largest in Rockies)
*Holden, Wash. (small glaciers)
Mountains affected by mountain glaciers:
Mount Goddard and Mount Tom, Calif. (cirques; horns; troughs; moraines)
*Holden, Wash. (rugged; troughs; small cirques)
*Holy Cross, Colo. (cirques; troughs; moraine loop)
Fremont Peak, Wyo. (1:125,000) (cirques; troughs; lakes)
Glacier National Park, Mont. (1:125,000) (horns; cirques; combs; troughs; lakes)
Mountains affected by continental glaciers:
*Old Speck Mountain, Maine (smoothed slopes)

*Monadnock, N.H. (knobby hills; ponds; swamps; monadnock)

Jay Peak, Vt. (rounded forms)

West Point, N.Y. (aligned forms; lakes; water gap)

*Ithaca West, N.Y. (1:24,000) (smooth slopes; finger lake)

The Continental Margins

Estuaries:

Kilmarnock, Va. (branching; bottom contours)

Chestertown, Md. (branching)

Boothbay, Maine (rias in glaciated area)

Empire and Coos Bay, Ore. (large estuary)

Foley and Ft. Barrancas, Ala.–Fla. (large and branching)

Fiords (all sheets have bottom contours):

Kodiak B-6 and Kodiak C-6, Alaska (basins; sills; moraines)

Seldovia B-2 and Seldovia C-2, Alaska (branching)

Blying Sound D-8, Alaska (large; sill; glaciers)

Sea cliffs:

Pt. Reyes, Calif. (high cliffs; stacks)

Cape San Martin, Calif. (mountainous; cliffs; rocks)

Orick, Calif. (cliffs; bay bars; beach)

Empire, Ore. (cliffs; bay bar)

Redondo Beach, Calif. (cliffs; benches)

Benches and terraces:

Suffolk and Smithfield, Va. (3 levels)

Limerick, Hinesville, and Glennville, Ga. (3 levels)

Encinitas and San Luis Rey, Calif. (1:24,000) (several levels; dissected)

Redondo Beach, Calif. (several levels; sea cliffs)

Kilmarnock, Va. (low terrace and old cliff)

Beaches and spits:

Edgartown, Mass. (1:31,680) (bay bars; hook)

Pt. Reyes, Calif. (bay bar)

Eureka, Calif. (large bay bar; inlet)

Empire, Ore. (broad bay bar)

Provincetown, Mass. (1:31,680) (hook; dunes)

Offshore bars:

Toms River, N.J. (bar; inlets)

Potrero Cortado, Tex. (broad, duned bar)

Back Bay, Va.–N.C. (duned bar; lagoon filling)

Accomac, Va. (low bar; lagoon nearly filled)

Foley, Ala.–Fla. (nearly onshore)

APPENDIX E

Principal Subdivisions of Earth History

PRINCIPAL SUBDIVISIONS OF EARTH HISTORY AND SOME OF ITS EVENTS AS THEY ARE RECORDED IN THE ROCKS OF NORTH AMERICA

ERA			PERIOD		TOPOGRAPHIC DEVELOPMENTS	BIOLOGIC DEVELOPMENTS	
THE SPACES ALLOTTED BELOW TO THE ERAS AND PERIODS ARE NOT IN PROPORTION TO THEIR ESTIMATED DURATION							
CENOZOIC	ERA OF MODERN LIFE	DUR. EST. AT ±70 MILLION YEARS ±4% OF ALL GEOLOGIC TIME	QUARTER-NARY	RECENT ESTIMATED AT ±15,000 YRS.	PRESENT TECTONIC AND GRADATIONAL LAND FORMS	THE DEVELOPMENT AND DOMINANCE OF INTELLIGENT MAN	ALLUVIUMS – OLD & NEW – GLACIAL DRIFT, LOESS
				PLEISTOCENE	CALIF. COAST MTS. APPEAR THE GREAT ICE AGE	NEW SPECIES OF PLANTS AND ANIMALS APPEARANCE OF PRIMITIVE MAN	
			TERTIARY	PLIOCENE	ELEVATION OF ROCKY, SIERRA NEVADA & CASCADE MTS., THE COLORADO & COLUMBIA PLATEAUS, AND THE GREAT BASIN	DEVELOPMENT OF MAMMALS (PRIMITIVE TYPES OF ELEPHANTS, HORSES, DEER, CATS, DOGS, WHALES & MANY OTHERS, INCLUDING FIRST APES) BIRDS & TREES SIMILAR TO MODERN TYPES	
				MIOCENE			
				OLIGOCENE			
				EOCENE			
GENERAL EROSION INTERVAL							
MESOZOIC	ERA OF MEDIEVAL LIFE	DURATION EST. AT ±130 MILLION YEARS ABOUT 8% OF ALL GEOL. TIME		CRETACEOUS ROCKY MT. COAL DEPOSITS	LAST GREAT SUBMERGENCE, GULF OF MEXICO TO ALASKA, FOLLOWED BY UPHEAVAL & BEGINNING OF ROCKY MTS.	RISE OF MAMMALS & BIRDS – DECLINE & EXTINCTION OF DINOSAURS. DEVELOPMENT OF MODERN FLOWERING PLANTS & DECIDUOUS TREES	YOUNGER SEDIMENTARY ROCKS LOCAL IGNEOUS ROCKS
				JURASSIC	APPALACHIAN MTS. BASELEVELED – PACIFIC COAST VULCANISM – SUBMERGENCE FROM COLORADO TO ALASKA.	GIANT REPTILES (DINOSAURS) – FIRST BIRDS – PRIMITIVE MAMMALS – MANY INSECTS SIMILAR TO PRESENT FORMS.	
				TRIASSIC	LARGE LAND AREA – ARIDITY CONTINUED – SOME ROCKS OF LAND-DEPOSITED ORIGIN – VULCANISM	REPTILES (CRAWLING, WALKING, FLYING, SWIMMING) DIVERSE & ABUNDANT. MANY COMPLEX MARINE ANIMALS – FORESTS MAINLY CONIFEROUS	
GENERAL EROSION INTERVAL							
PALEOZOIC ERA	ERA OF ANCIENT LIFE	DURATION VARIOUSLY ESTIMATED AT ±300 MILLION YEARS ABOUT 20 PER CENT OF ALL GEOLOGIC TIME		PERMIAN	GENERAL EMERGENCE – FOLDING OF APPALACHIAN MTS. – WIDESPREAD ARIDITY	DECLINE OF FERN TREES & RISE OF CONIFERS – GREAT VARIETY IN REPTILES & INSECTS – MANY MARINE INVERTEBRATES DISAPPEAR	OLDER AND MORE RESISTANT SEDIMENTARY ROCKS LOCAL INTRUSIVE AND EXTRUSIVE IGNEOUS ROCKS
			CARBONIFEROUS "THE COAL AGE"	PENNSYLVANIAN	FLUCTUATING SEAS IN THE INTERIOR – FORMATION OF EXTENSIVE SWAMPS	VAST FORESTS OF FAST-GROWING TREES AND OTHER PLANTS. COMPLEX MARINE LIFE – RISE OF REPTILES AND INSECTS	
				MISSISSIPPIAN	WIDESPREAD SUBMERGENCE AND DEPOSITION OF SEDIMENTS.	DEVELOPMENT OF SHARKS AND OTHER FISH – NUMEROUS AMPHIBIANS – ABUNDANT FORESTS OF FERNS & PRIMITIVE CONIFERS.	
				DEVONIAN	WIDESPREAD SUBMERGENCE – MOUNTAIN UPLIFT AND VULCANISM IN NEW ENGLAND.	ABUNDANT FISHES WITH VERTEBRAE AND PAIRED FINS, . FIRST AMPHIBIANS, FIRST FORESTS (TREE FERNS)	
				SILURIAN	WIDESPREAD DEVELOPMENT OF PLAINS BY EROSION AND BY EMERGENCE.	DEVELOPMENTS OF FISHES – FIRST LAND ANIMALS (SPIDERLIKE) – FIRST LAND PLANTS – ABUNDANT CORALS	
				ORDOVICIAN	SEDIMENTS DEPOSITED – MOUNTAIN BUILDING IN NEW ENGLAND AND CANADA.	ABUNDANT MOLLUSKS AND TRILOBITES – EARLY FORMS OF FISH – NO EVIDENCE OF LAND ANIMALS OR PLANTS	
				CAMBRIAN	WIDESPREAD SUBMERGENCE AND DEPOSITION OF SEDIMENTARY ROCKS	FIRST ABUNDANT FOSSILS MAINLY OF SHELLED MARINE INVERTEBRATES (MOLLUSKS AND TRILOBITES)	
LONG INTERVAL OF UPLIFT AND EROSION							
PROTEROZOIC					MUCH MOUNTAIN BUILDING, METAMORPHISM OF ROCKS, AND VULCANISM.	PRIMITIVE MARINE LIFE, MAINLY WITHOUT SHELLS, LEAVING ONLY MEAGER FOSSIL REMAINS	ANCIENT CRYSTALLINE ROCKS
LONG INTERVAL OF UPLIFT AND EROSION							
ARCHEOZOIC					MOUNTAIN BUILDING AND VULCANISM Many events obscured by vast lapse of time	PRIMITIVE FORMS OF MARINE LIFE, PERHAPS ALGAE-LIKE NO DIRECT FOSSIL EVIDENCE	
EARTH HISTORY EXTENDS BACK AND MERGES WITH EARTH ORIGIN							

MORE RECENT TIME →

THE ENTIRE SPAN OF EARTH HISTORY IS ESTIMATED TO BE MORE THAN 2,500,000,000 YEARS. PROBABLY FOUR FIFTHS OF IT HAD ELAPSED BEFORE CAMBRIAN TIME.

← EARLIER TIME

PREVAILING CLASSES OF ROCKS IN THE GEOLOGIC REGIONS OF NORTH AMERICA

Index